Sections
7-19
21
27-29

BUILDING CONSTRUCTION HANDBOOK

McGRAW-HILL HANDBOOKS

ABBOTT AND STETKA · National Electrical Code Handbook, 10th ed.
ALJIAN · Purchasing Handbook ·
AMERICAN INSTITUTE OF PHYSICS · American Institute of Physics Handbook
AMERICAN SOCIETY OF MECHANICAL ENGINEERS · ASME Handbooks:
    Engineering Tables   Metals Engineering—Processes
    Metals Engineering—Design   Metals Properties
AMERICAN SOCIETY OF TOOL AND MANUFACTURING ENGINEERS:
    Die Design Handbook   Tool Engineers Handbook, 2d ed.
    Handbook of Fixture Design
BEEMAN · Industrial Power Systems Handbook
BERRY, BOLLAY, AND BEERS · Handbook of Meteorology
BLATZ · Radiation Hygiene Handbook
BRADY · Materials Handbook, 8th ed.
BURINGTON · Handbook of Mathematical Tables and Formulas, 3d ed.
BURINGTON AND MAY · Handbook of Probability and Statistics with Tables
CARROLL · Industrial Instrument Servicing Handbook
COCKRELL · Industrial Electronics Handbook
CONDON AND ODISHAW · Handbook of Physics
CONSIDINE · Process Instruments and Controls Handbook
CROCKER · Piping Handbook, 4th ed.
CROFT AND CARR · American Electricians' Handbook, 8th ed.
DAVIS · Handbook of Applied Hydraulics, 2d ed.
DUDLEY · Gear Handbook
ETHERINGTON · Nuclear Engineering Handbook
FACTORY MUTUAL ENGINEERING DIVISION · Handbook of Industrial Loss
    Prevention
FINK · Television Engineering Handbook
FLÜGGE · Handbook of Engineering Mechanics
FRICK · Petroleum Production Handbook, 2 vols.
GUTHRIE · Petroleum Products Handbook
HARRIS · Handbook of Noise Control
HARRIS AND CREDE · Shock and Vibration Handbook, 3 vols.
HENNEY · Radio Engineering Handbook, 5th ed.
HUNTER · Handbook of Semiconductor Electronics, 2d ed.
HUSKEY AND KORN · Computer Handbook
JASIK · Antenna Engineering Handbook
JURAN · Quality Control Handbook, 2d ed.

BUILDING CONSTRUCTION HANDBOOK

FREDERICK S. MERRITT, Editor

Senior Editor, Engineering News-Record

FIRST EDITION

McGraw-Hill Book Company, Inc.

New York   Toronto   London

1958

BUILDING CONSTRUCTION HANDBOOK

Library of Congress Catalog Card Number: 57-7239

VI

41505

THE MAPLE PRESS CO., YORK, PA.

CONTRIBUTORS

Maurice Barron, Consulting Engineer, Farkas & Barron, New York, N.Y. (*Concrete Construction*)

Reginald S. Brackett, Architectural Superintendent, Voorhees, Walker, Smith & Smith, New York, N.Y. (*Surveying for Building Construction*)

C. S. Cooper, Manager, Eastern Bond and Burglary Department, Fireman's Fund Insurance Group, New York, N.Y. (*Insurance and Bonds*)

M. de la Torre, Consulting Engineer, Miami, Fla. (*Estimating Building Construction Costs*)

Albert G. H. Dietz, Sc. D., Professor of Building Engineering and Construction, Massachusetts Institute of Technology. (*Wood, Metals, and Other Materials*)

F. E. Fahy, Technical Adviser, Research Department, Bethlehem Steel Company, Bethlehem, Pa. (*Lightweight Steel Construction*)

Jacob Feld, Ph.D., Consulting Engineer, New York, N.Y. (*Soil Mechanics and Foundations*)

Cyrus C. Fishburn, Materials Engineer, Building Technology Division, National Bureau of Standards, Washington, D.C. (*Water Permeability of Masonry Structures*)

Arthur J. Fox, Jr., Senior Editor, *Engineering News-Record.* (*Water Supply and Purification; Waste-water Disposal*)

P. M. Grennan, Engineer-Associate, Office of Alfred Easton Poor, Architects, New York, N.Y. (*Windows*)

George W. Handy, General Manager, Acoustical Department, The Myron Cornish Company. (*Acoustics*)

Tyler G. Hicks, Mechanical Engineer. (*Plumbing and Sprinkling Systems*)

Verne Ketchum, Chief Engineer, Timber Structures, Inc., Portland, Ore. (*Wood Construction*)

James McCawley, Editor, *National Roofer.* (*Roof Coverings*)

Robert McLean, Executive Vice-president, Hegeman-Harris Company, Inc., New York, N.Y. (*Construction Management*)

Frederick S. Merritt, Senior Editor, *Engineering News-Record.* (*Stresses in Structures; Walls and Partitions; Doors; Lath and Plaster; Vertical Transportation*)

Raymond V. Miller, Director of Research and Development, George A. Fuller Company, New York, N.Y. (*Builder's Hardware*)

James A. Murray, Associate Professor of Materials, Massachusetts Institute of Technology. (*Masonry Materials*)

E. B. J. Roos, Partner, Seelye, Stevenson, Value & Knecht, New York, N.Y. (*Thermal Insulation*)

Percy A. Sigler, Technologist on Flooring Surfaces, National Bureau of Standards, Washington, D.C. (*Floor Coverings*)

Ben John Small, Architect, Partner, LaPierre, Litchfield & Partners, New York, N.Y. (*Specifications*)

Henry J. Stetina, Regional Engineer, Northeast Area, American Institute of Steel Construction. (*Structural-steel Construction*)

Walter A. Taylor, F.A.I.A., Director, Department of Education and Research, American Institute of Architects, Washington, D.C. (*Professional Services and Business Practices*)

Ralph Torop, Chief Engineer, Forman Air Conditioning Company, Inc., New York, N.Y. (*Heating and Air Conditioning*)

Sol Zuchovitz, Consulting Electrical Engineer, Brooklyn, N.Y. (*Electric Power and Lighting*)

PREFACE

In preparing this handbook, we set out to provide in a single volume information that would be of greatest usefulness to everyone concerned with building design and construction, and especially to those who have to make decisions affecting building materials and construction methods. We wanted it to meet the needs of owners, architects, consulting engineers of various specialties, plant engineers, builders, general contractors, subcontractors of various trades, material and equipment suppliers, manufacturers, financiers, building inspectors, construction labor, and many others, all of whom may have different problems and different interests in building design and construction. Because of their divergent interests and because of the great wealth of material available—each section could readily be expanded into a thick handbook—we were faced with an extremely difficult problem in selecting subject matter.

We believe we have arrived at a satisfactory solution:

● The handbook is comprehensive, but each topic is treated as briefly as clarity permits.

● Information incorporated is of a nature that should be valuable in making decisions—characteristics of building materials and installed equipment, essentials of stress analysis and structural design, recommended construction practices and why they are used, cost estimating and construction management.

● Frequent reference is made to other sources where additional authoritative detailed information can be obtained.

● Each section is written for the nonspecialist in the field, on the theory that the specialist prefers to seek answers to his problems in a more detailed text dealing exclusively with his own field. Emphasis is placed on fundamentals, rather than on tables of design data.

● Tables of design data, building codes, standard specifications, and similar material that may be obtained easily from trade associations, technical societies, and government agencies are referred to but not reprinted in this book.

● The practical approach is stressed throughout. Methods are presented that are as simple and short as possible.

The authors were selected because of extensive experience in each specialty. At the time they were asked to participate, all were busily

occupied in their professions.   As a professional service, they wrote their
sections at substantial personal sacrifice.   The editor and publisher are
deeply grateful, and undoubtedly users of this handbook will be too.

Many of the sections present the author's original work, including
much material that has never been published previously.   In fact,
several of the sections consist almost entirely of material never before
included in a textbook or handbook: Section 7, Lightweight Steel Construction; Section 16, Builders' Hardware; Section 25, Surveying for
Building Construction; and Section 27, Construction Management.

Noteworthy among the original offerings are:

1. The helpful hints for owners in Section 1, Professional Services and
Business Practices, covering the stages from selection of an architect to
the taking of bids and letting of contracts.

2. In Section 3, Stresses in Structures, the treatment of curved beams,
general tools of structural analysis, and single-cycle moment distribution.   This section also presents a single diagram for determining fixed-
end moments for any type of loading and a method for checking moment
distribution that automatically corrects an error.

3. Limit design and methods of correcting defective field work given
in Section 5, Concrete Construction.

4. The multitude of suggestions in Section 6, Structural-steel Construction, for economical construction and the treatment of fasteners, bracing,
connections, and fire protection.

5. Recommended practices for getting the greatest value out of cost
estimates in Section 26, Estimating Building Construction Costs.

It is often pointed out that the building industry is not really a single
industry but a collection of a host of industries.   Taken section by section, the handbook offers the basic working tools of these industries.
Taken as a whole, it gives an accurate up-to-date picture of how the
building industry operates.

FREDERICK S. MERRITT

CONTENTS

SECTION 1

SECTION 3

STRESSES IN STRUCTURES, by Frederick S. Merritt 3–1

STRESS AND STRAIN

STRESSES AT A POINT

STRAIGHT BEAMS

CONTENTS

CONTENTS xvii

ADOBE AND SOIL HOUSES

4-59. Types of Soil Walls 4–39
4-60. Adobe Blocks 4–39
4-61. Materials for Soil Blocks or Walls 4–40

SECTION 5

CONCRETE CONSTRUCTION, by Maurice Barron **5–1**

5-1. Proportioning Concrete Mixes 5–1
5-2. Water-Cement Ratio 5–1
5-3. Consistency of Concrete Mixes 5–2
5-4. Methods of Proportioning Concrete. 5–2
5-5. Properties and Tests of Concrete 5–3
5-6. Concrete-mixing Plants 5–3
5-7. Measuring of Materials for Concrete 5–4
5-8. Concrete Mixing 5–4

CONCRETE PLACEMENT

5-9. Effect of Excess Water on Concrete. 5–5
5-10. Bonding Set and New Concrete 5–5
5-11. Removal of Undesirable Air 5–6
5-12. Spudding, Puddling, Tamping, and Vibrating 5–6
5-13. Vibration of Concrete in Forms 5–6
5-14. Concreting in Cold Weather 5–6
5-15. Curing Concrete 5–7
5-16. Transporting and Placing Concrete Mixes 5–8

REINFORCING STEEL

5-17. Types of Reinforcing 5–9
5-18. Wire-fabric Reinforcement 5–10
5-19. Bending and Placing Reinforcement 5–10
5-20. Supports for Reinforcement 5–11

JOINTS IN CONCRETE

5-21. Construction Joints 5–11
5-22. Expansion and Contraction Joints 5–12

ADMIXTURES FOR CONCRETE

5-23. Accelerators 5–13
5-24. Retarders 5–13
5-25. Air-entraining Agents 5–13
5-26. Gas-forming Agents 5–14
5-27. Cementitious Materials as Admixtures 5–14
5-28. Pozzolanic Materials 5–14
5-29. Alkali-aggregate Expansion Inhibitors 5–14
5-30. Dampproofing and Permeability-reducing Agents 5–15
5-31. Workability Agents 5–15
5-32. Grouting Agents 5–15
5-33. Expanding Cements 5–15

REINFORCED-CONCRETE BEAMS AND SLABS

5-34. Rectangular Beams (Elastic Design) 5–16
5-35. Transformed Section 5–16
5-36. Balanced Design 5–16
5-37. One-way Slab 5–18
5-38. Shear and Bond 5–18
5-39. Bent-up Bars, Cutoff Points, and Other Placing Details . . . 5–19
5-40. Ultimate-strength Design of Beams 5–20

SECTION 7

SECTION 10

SECTION 11

SECTION 12

SECTION 13

SECTION 14

SECTION 15

SECTION 16

SECTION 17

AIR CONDITIONING

SECTION 20

WATER SUPPLY AND PURIFICATION, by Arthur J. Fox, Jr 20–1

DEMAND FOR WATER

SOURCES OF WATER

SECTION 21

CONTENTS

SECTION 24

SECTION 25

SECTION 26

SECTION 27

SECTION 28

SPECIFICATIONS, by Ben John Small **28–1**

SECTION 29

INSURANCE AND BONDS, by C. S. Cooper **29–1**

BUILDING CONSTRUCTION HANDBOOK

All of 7-19
21
27-29 } sections

Section 1

PROFESSIONAL SERVICES AND BUSINESS PRACTICES

WALTER A. TAYLOR, F.A.I.A.

Director, Department of Education and Research
American Institute of Architects
Washington, D.C.

After deciding to create a building, the prospective owner may seek the advice and retain the services of a variety of specialists related to his business, but usually not part of the building industry, who will assist in preparing a statement or program of requirements.

To establish exactly what is to be built to fulfill the program, the owner turns to design professionals of the building industry—architects and engineers, who approach the problem from two viewpoints:

1. *Shelter function.*—The basic function of all buildings is to provide an artificial climate that makes possible the conduct of desired activities. This creation of shelter entails provision of weathertightness, strength, stability, and durability.

2. *Use function*—Of even greater importance to the owner than these general requirements is the requirement that the building provide just the right kinds and amounts of areas and spaces, arranged for access, egress, and circulation, and with optimum conditions of heat, ventilation, light, color, and acoustics, the refinements of the artificial climate. The degree to which the designers solve these particular requirements will largely determine whether the value of the building to the owner equals or exceeds its cost.

The design phase of building requires of the professionals engaged in it several kinds of skills and knowledge:

1. Principles of analysis and planning, ability to visualize fully in three dimensions, principles of composition and esthetics. These are the architects' specialties and unique contribution.

2. The attitude and analytical ability to draw out and understand as fully as possible the owner's problems, needs, and the method of operation of the building to be created.

From experience, the designer may have specialized knowledge of the functions and planning of a particular type of occupancy. This is not essential, particularly if the owner provides it himself or through consultants. In fact this specialization by the designer may prevent a new and creative solution.

3. Knowledge and skill in building technology (the architect in general, the consulting engineers completely in their respective specialties), in order that the owner may have full advantage of the most advanced technical resources, and in order that their choices will be reasonable in relation to both the requirements and the budget.

In some kinds of buildings, such as hospitals or atomic laboratories, for example, the functional requirements change more rapidly than the changes in building construction. Society may at any time require types of buildings that never existed before. Shopping centers are a recent example. Even for less changeable kinds of buildings, there are a hundred variables to be balanced in each case: site, budget, climate, view, codes, etc. So-called "stock plans" are stock only once. For any particular building, the best answer to "what" to build is found by the professional designer focusing his personal attention on the particular client and his requirement.

The procedures, functions, and responsibilities of the architectural profession have an important bearing on the quality of the product and the satisfaction of the consumers—not only the owners, but the general public which is unavoidably exposed to the results.

ROLE OF THE PROFESSIONAL DESIGNER

Architecture is the art and science that seeks to harmonize in a building the requirements of utility and beauty. Architects are a group of professionals who have qualified by education and experience and have developed the requisite abilities to practice architecture.

1-1. Professional Status of Architects. The distinguishing characteristic of a profession such as architecture is that the practitioner is paid for services rendered based on his knowledge, judgment, and skill. The professional man does not derive his livelihood from the sale of goods or products. Thus, according to the principles established by the American Institute of Architects, a national professional organization, a professional architect cannot be engaged in the building business in any relationship such that his remuneration is contingent on profit or loss in the building-construction operation. The reason for this is that, as the owner's agent, his professional judgment must be free from bias caused by financial interest in the building operation or in any particular building material.

Ideally, the professional architect, while of course expecting an income commensurate with his ability and educational investment, is concerned at least equally with the interests of his client whom he is retained to guide and protect in a building enterprise.

1-2. The Role of the Architect. "The function of the architect is to exercise professional leadership in the farflung building industry and to practice the complex art and science of planning and designing structures for human occupancy and use which are functional and efficient, safe and structurally sound, and esthetically satisfying. The position of the architect in building is analogous to that of the 'systems engineer' in other industries that are based on science, research, and technology. He is the generalist; the technologists are the specialists; both are indispensable. The architect's position and function are defined by law in all States." (Walter A. Taylor, "Architectural Education," *Higher Education*, Vol. 10, No. 2, pp. 1–2, October, 1953; also, "Education for the Professions," Chap. 5 in "Architectural Education," Office of Education, U.S. Dept of Health, Education and Welfare, Government Printing Office, Washington 25, D.C., 1955.)

"To a building project the architect brings acquirements and a range of services that cannot be matched by any other factor in the operation. He is not a building contractor, nor is he a structural engineer; neither is he a banker or real estate agent; yet he must have enough experience to advise his client on the respective weight of each element that these individuals bring to his project. He must recognize quality of construction and value of property; he must understand financing and kindred matters that will enable the owner to forecast the value of his investment both at the completion of his building and through the years to come. From start to finish he is the one person in the building industry whose interests are identical with the owner's. He is his client's professional adviser and representative; he plans, he specifies, obtains bids, draws contracts, supervises the progress of the work, oversees construction accounts; he is, in a word, the administrative head of a complex operation carried out by many hands. He must indeed be a man of many talents." ("Architecture: A Profession and a Career," pp. 12–13, The American Institute of Architects, Washington, D.C., 1945.)

The architect's position is one of trust and confidence, and it is fundamental that he should act in absolute and entire good faith throughout.   He has no pecuniary interest other than that arising from his agreement with the owner.

The architect serves in several capacities:

As Adviser.   The architect is primarily the owner's professional adviser.   He advises the owner how best his problem may be solved, informs him of the probable cost of the work, selects methods and materials of construction, and assists in many other ways until the project is completed.

As Agent.   In dealing with other persons on behalf of the owner, the architect, the courts hold, is the agent of the owner.   Where the owner has not exactly defined the authority, it is determined by the general law of agency, by the known customs of architectural practice, by the acts of the owner and architect, and by the circumstances of the case.

A general grant of authority as to all matters connected with the work may be necessary where the owner is to be absent from the country while the work is going on.   The architect's powers are clearly defined and strictly limited in the standard form, "General Conditions of the Contract," of the American Institute of Architects.

As Judge or Arbitrator.   As soon as a contract has been executed between the owner and a contractor by the terms of which the architect becomes the official interpreter of its conditions and the judge of its performance, the architect is thereby given a new status quite different from that of either professional adviser to or agent of the owner. In this status he will favor neither the owner nor the contractor but will use his powers under the contract to enforce its faithful performance by both parties.   Acting under the standard general conditions of the contract, the architect renders most of his decisions as an arbitrator.   The general conditions provide for appeal to other arbitrators, previously unconnected with the matter.

1-3. Architects and Consulting Engineers.   The architect, while responsible for the success of his work as a whole, must know when to consult with a specialist if he would have every detail reflect the best practice in each special field.   As building technology increases in complexity, the necessity of more careful preplanning and integration in advance of construction brings the specialists themselves closer together.

The architect, among the technologists, is not regarded as a specialist, except that he assumes the greatest concern for the human aspects of the problem.   He is usually, during the design phase, the generalist responsible for coordination of all the technologies—structural, mechanical, electrical, acoustics, illumination, etc.

Many of the different types of engineers contribute to building technology in various capacities, such as designers, researchers, and manufacturers of building materials, installed equipment, and construction equipment.   They also play an important role in the field of utilities and services and as officials, inspectors, contractors, superintendents, surveyors, etc.

Many engineers serve as sales representatives of manufacturers of building products. In their contacts with architects and professional consulting engineers, they act as consultants on the application of their particular products.

While professional responsibility for the total design of a complex building generally is shared, there is usually for each project a "prime contractor" for design services, who signs the agreement with the owner and who thereby assumes the legal responsibilities.   He in turn retains the other professionals.

The American Institute of Architects (AIA), in collaboration with the American Society of Civil Engineers, the American Society of Mechanical Engineers, and the National Society of Professional Engineers, has developed a form of agreement between architects and engineers to be used when the architect is the prime contractor.   The engineering societies have developed a complementary form of agreement between engineers and architects, for use on projects where an engineer may be the generalist or prime contractor; for example, for a bridge, an industrial or chemical plant, or a powerhouse.

Association of architects and engineers for professional services is not limited to the relationships covered by these forms.   Many large offices, in existence for many years, have permanent organizations combining architects and several kinds of engineers in partnerships, associateships, and as permanent employees and various combinations of these relationships, offering most or all of the required design services under one agreement with the owner.   This type of organization and combined service has been stimulated by the preference of some Federal agencies for AE (architect-engineer) contracts.   The desired association, however, may be on a temporary basis for each project.   Many consulting engineers prefer to practice independently, being retained in the course of a year by several architects on a number of varied projects.

The standard AIA forms of owner-architect agreement provide variants by which the engineer is paid by the architect out of his total fee, or directly by the owner. Regardless of the variations in the formal arrangements among the architects and engineers, the most important consideration, from the point of view of the owner, is that the designers should all be functioning as professional men.   They should not be beholden to sales commissions or stockpiling of parts or the exigencies of the contracting business.   They should be free to give the owner their best unbiased professional judgment in the solution of his building problem and to exercise objective judgment and authority in the inspection of the work as it is erected.   The latter is a most important consideration in the purchase of a large and costly product, which is only half fabricated in factories, the most critical part being done under conditions of field assembly.

1-4. Contractor-Designers.   Some types of building-contracting organizations offer to prospective building owners to design and build for a guaranteed total cost before the exact design of the structure is begun.   This type of proposal, which may appeal to inexperienced owners, should be carefully examined in terms of a free competitive market.

If a contractor is to absorb all the risk of fluctuations in the economy and the building-construction market, he must, to remain in business, utilize some or all of the following practices, which are not in the best interest of the owner:

1. Adjustment of the quality of the building downward, either in the design phase, particularly when the architects and engineers are engaged by the contractor and are not able to advise the owner in a fully professional manner, or in the construction phase.   The latter is readily possible since the owner does not have the benefit of impartial field inspections by professionals.

2. Quotation of a total cost higher than the prevailing and reasonably anticipated open-market cost for the type and quality of building desired.   The owner is at a disadvantage since he does not have the benefit of competitive bidding by general contractors on a complete and exact set of drawings and specifications.

3. Basing the guaranteed cost on a repetition of a design used for another project for another owner, perhaps for a different functional use.   A variant of this is to use standardized major structural units, possibly stockpiled by the designer-contractor.

In the great majority of such cases, the owner does not get a building designed to meet his particular requirements.

The above considerations are concerned only with initial cost, whereas the concept of value, which should also concern the owner, involves, in addition, the psychological and financial effects of good design for public and labor relations and efficient production, etc.

1-5. Architects' Professional Services.   Architects are professionally retained or employed in several capacities (AIA Document No. 177, AIA Basic Schedule of Architectural Services, 1953):

Executive Architect.   Complete professional services comprising:

1. *Preliminary Services.*   Consultations to determine the requirements and problems of the project.

Development of a written program approved by the owner.

Preparation of schematic drawings showing recommended solutions until an agreement on a solution is reached.

Preparation of preliminary drawings of the approved solution and outline specifications describing materials and structural system to be used.

The furnishing of preliminary estimates of cost.

2. *Working Drawings and Specifications.* Preparation of working drawings and specifications describing in detail the work to be done and the materials and workmanship to be used, including normal structural, plumbing, heating, electrical, and other mechanical work.

Assistance in preparation of forms of proposal and contract documents.

Assistance in securing proposals and in the award of contracts.

3. *During Execution of Work.* Preparation of additional large-scale and full-sized detail drawings, as required.

General supervision of the work including necessary shop inspections and checking of samples and shop drawings submitted and made by contractors and subcontractors.

Issuance of orders for changes in the work approved by the owner.

Checking of contractors' requests for payments and the issuance of certificates for payments, including final inspection of the work prior to issuance of final certificate.

Trends in practice and clients' requirements (particularly government and public agencies) indicate the need for a four-phase breakdown of the architect's services. The AIA offers alternative versions of its standard documents incorporating the following **basic services of the architect:**

1. *Schematic Design Phase.* Consultation with the client and his representatives to determine the requirements of the project; preparation of schematic design studies leading to a recommended solution, with description of the work for acceptance by the client; information regarding the approximate cost of the work.

2. *Basic Design Phase.* Preparation of basic design; preliminary site plan, floor plans, sections and elevation drawings, and outline of specifications based upon the accepted schematic solution—covering, in general, site work, materials, structure, mechanical systems, and special equipment—for written approval of the client; further advice on approximate cost, and if authorized by the client, semidetailed estimate of the cost.

3. *Construction Document Phase.* Preparation of construction documents: working drawings, detailed specifications, bidding information, general conditions, special requirements, and proposal and contract forms, based on approved preliminary documents and setting forth in detail the design, kind, type, extent, location, and method of installation of materials, structure, finishes, specialties, mechanical systems, and special service-connected equipment required; information on any indicated adjustment in previous approximations of cost resulting from known fluctuations in construction costs or changes in scope or requirements of the project; and when authorized by the client, a detailed estimate of cost.

4. *Construction Phase.* No alternative.

Supervising Architect. Where several executive architects may be employed at the same time or successively, a supervising architect is usually employed to coordinate their work, with a view to insuring harmony of purpose, design, and action. Sometimes, the general plan of an institution is prepared by an architect who afterward supervises the work of several others charged with the design and execution of the several units. This secures continuity of policy over a period of years, through possible changes of boards of directors or building committees, avoiding the dangers of opportunism in the choice of sites, materials, and architectural styles.

Consulting Architect. The work of an executive architect may be supplemented by that of a consulting architect, who has specialized knowledge of the problem or of some phase of it. His advice may be confined to a single subject, or he may serve as a general consultant throughout the project. His fee is paid by the client and is not deductible from that of the executive architect.

Associated Architects. It may be desirable, for some projects, to secure the services of two or more architects in a closer relationship than that between the executive and consulting architects. These men associate themselves to act for the time being, as a unit in an executive capacity, the association amounting to a temporary partnership. One reason for such an arrangement is that the owner may desire the services, as designer, of an architect remote from the location of the project, and, for business management and supervision, a local architect. In view of possible increased expense, the associated architects' compensation may be greater than for a single one.

A public bureau sometimes performs the administrative and supervisory services but employs an architect to consult on the design or to take full responsibility for the design and supervision of the preparation of the working drawings.

Occasional Employment.   An architect may be employed as an expert witness; as an arbitrator, to report upon the condition of an existing building or the possible development of a property; as a consultant by a lending institution to guard its interest in a project; as professional adviser on an architectural competition, or as a member of a jury of award in an architectural competition.

SELECTION OF AN ARCHITECT

Two methods of choosing an architect are in use: direct selection and competition.

1-6. Direct Selection of Architect.   The owner appoints an architect after careful inquiry and consideration.   Since the owner commits the expenditure of his money to the architect, and depends for a successful result almost as much on his architect as does a patient on his surgeon, therefore, before reaching a decision, the owner should make careful inquiries about the architect under consideration: his experience, his technical knowledge of the highly complex structure and equipment of a modern building, his ability to secure the best results without waste of space or money, his executive ability to enforce the proper performance of contracts, his successful completion of work of like character or work from which his ability may be inferred, his honesty and incorruptibility.

In brief, the architect must establish to the owner's satisfaction his fitness, above others, to design the work and to control its execution.

As an aid to direct selection, the owner sometimes invites several architects to submit statements of their training and qualifications, with a list and photographs of their more important works, as well as references to those for whom they have erected buildings.

From time to time qualified men who have had long experience as assistants commence practice.   They should not be discriminated against merely because they have had no opportunity to erect buildings in their own names.

1-7. Selection of Architect by Competition.   The AIA recognizes and gives its approval to two types of competitions only:

1. *Primary Type.*   Leading directly to the erection of a definite structure on a definite site.

Selection of an architect by competition requires procedures to assure fair conduct of the competition and establish equitable relations between owner and competitors. The AIA has adopted a competition code, the essential features of which are:

Engagement of a competent architect to serve as professional adviser who will write the program, advise in the choice of competitors, and guide the conduct of the competition under uniform conditions for all competitors.   He will also assist the owner in deciding whether the competition shall be limited to invited architects or be an open competition with few if any restrictions regarding the architects who may compete. He may find that a competition is not desirable in the circumstances.

Designs prepared in accordance with the program will be submitted to a jury of award for selection of the winning design.   The jury will consist of at least three members chosen by agreement between owner and professional adviser.   A majority must be architects.

Strict anonymity must be observed in all stages of the competition so that neither the professional adviser nor the owner nor any member of the jury will be aware of the identity of the author of any design until the jury makes its report.

The owner agrees to employ as architect for the proposed structure the author of the design selected by the jury as the winning design.

The program must contain an agreement and conditions of contract for architectural services in accord with the standards of the AIA.

The professional adviser and the technical members of the jury should be compensated in amounts commensurate with the extent of their duties and responsibilities. Invited competitors in limited competitions and the authors of premiated designs in open competitions should be compensated in fees or prizes consistent with the professional services rendered.

The AIA maintains a standing committee on architectural competitions to give advice and to approve properly drawn programs.

Members of the AIA do not participate as competitors or jurors in any competition the program of which has not received the approval of the AIA, nor does a member continue to act as professional adviser after it has been determined that the program cannot be so drawn as to receive such approval. Competitions for projects sponsored and to be built outside the U.S. may be entered by AIA members if the programs are approved by the Union Internationale des Architects (UIA).

It is important that ample time be allowed for the progressive steps that lead to a satisfactory conclusion.

2. *Secondary Type.* Nonconstructional competitions which do not lead to the erection of any actual structure. Secondary-type competitions are of two kinds: class A-11(a), sponsored by building material or equipment manufacturers, dealers, or trade associations, and class A-11(b), comprising public improvements or artistic developments originating through magazines or from other sources.

1-8. Architect Specialization. Some architects deliberately limit their practice to or give preference to certain building types, as for example, hospitals, churches, or schools, but such specialization or concentration is not officially recognized by the AIA or by law.

Most architects are engaged in general practice, designing all types of buildings. Occasionally, the general-practicing architect and his client may retain another architect of extensive experience and reputation in the problem at hand as consultant or associated architect.

OWNERS' RESPONSIBILITIES AND DUTIES

An owner owes duties to the architect other than sympathetic cooperation and the payment of bills. The owner should clearly state the requirements of his problem and should frankly name the amount that he is willing to spend, indicating if this amount is intended to cover all expenses of the project including equipment and professional services. The owner and architect should have a clear record of these matters.

1-9. Data Owner Should Supply. The owner should furnish the architect with full information, legal and topographical, about the building site; a complete and accurate survey of the building site, giving the grades and lines of streets, pavements, and adjoining properties; the rights, restrictions, easements, boundaries, and contours of the building site; and full information as to sewer, water, gas, and electrical service. The owner should pay for borings or test pits and for chemical, mechanical, and other tests when required. The owner is concerned with the necessity for careful search and extreme accuracy in the legal information to be furnished.

The owner should give thorough consideration to all sketches, drawings, specifications, proposals, contracts, and other documents laid before him by the architect. Inattention to such matters, especially carelessness in studying drawings and specifications, results in failure to understand the work contracted for and in disappointment and expense when the work is in course of execution. Decisions should be rendered as promptly as possible.

1-10. Architect's Role in Owner-Contractor Relations. The owner's duties toward contractors and his rights under his contract are stated in the agreement and in the general conditions of the contract, with which he should make himself conversant.

The owner should provide at his expense all legal advice and services relative to the contracts or other matters pertaining to the project. He should place the advice of his counsel freely at the architect's service, except when the architect is acting as a judge of the performance of a contract or is making a decision between the owner's and the contractor's interests.

The owner should not give orders directly to the contractor or any of his subcontractors or employees. All orders should be given through the architect to avoid misunderstandings and confusion. An order given by the owner, without processing through the architect's office, is likely to be construed as an order for an extra. Even in cases where the contract has stated that no order is valid unless given in writing, courts have held that the giving by the owner to the contractor of a verbal order is a waiver of any special requirement as to the form of an order.

The owner should be informed of important duties relating to insurance against lightning, windstorms, hail, and earthquakes, and liability for necessary fees for architects and engineers employed as a result of loss to the property insured. He should be told to inform his fire insurance company and secure the necessary rider when alterations are begun. He should also be advised to see certificates of the contractor's liability insurance and to check contingent liability.

Applications for permanent electrical, gas, water, and telephone services must usually be made directly by the owner.

1-11. Agreement between Owner and Architect. A clear understanding between owner and architect as to their relations and obligations is of utmost importance. Neither a verbal agreement nor an exchange of letters is an adequate guarantee against misunderstandings, disputes, or litigation.

One form of agreement consists of an offer from the architect to perform services in accordance with the applicable schedule of charges of the local chapter of the AIA. The owner's acceptance of such an offer constitutes a contract. However, it is better to base a contract upon one of the forms of agreement between owner and architect issued by the AIA, which embody many years' experience. Clear and equitable provisions define the relations of owner and architect in many situations not otherwise precisely defined. They represent well-accepted practice and protect public officials or officers of corporations signing them. There are appropriate forms for percentage, fee-plus-cost, lump-sum, and personnel-costs-times-a-factor bases of compensation, with variants for engineers' fees included or reimbursed. Space is provided in the standard forms for additional clauses defining the special conditions and services governing the agreement that vary or add to the standard provisions.

Arbitration provisions in the AIA agreement form are valid under the law of many states. But if they are not valid in the state in which the work is to be done, they should be modified to conform.

The use of a fee-plus-cost system presupposes that the architect maintains an adequate system of accounting, preferably standardized accounting for architects, a system of accounting developed by the AIA.

1-12. Ownership of Drawings. The standard form of agreement states: "Drawings and specifications as instruments of service are the property of the architect whether the work for which they are made be executed or not, and are not to be used on other work except by agreement with the architect."

1-13. Architects' Compensation. There are three principal methods under which architects are ordinarily compensated.

Percentage Method. Most frequently used. The architect is paid a percentage of the final cost of the work executed from his designs and is reimbursed for certain expenses. The various chapters of the AIA issue documents describing the services rendered by the architect and schedules of proper charges based upon a percentage of the cost of the work, varying according to the type of building and its size. Schedules of charges, conforming to Federal law and AIA policy, are not mandatory but are recommended. They vary in some degree because of differences in practice in sections of the country. They conform to a general pattern, and the AIA standard forms of agreement are adaptable for use throughout the country.

The architect's fee, like that of any professional man, must depend upon his skill, experience, and standing, upon the character and location of the work to be done, as well as upon the kind and expense of the services to be rendered.

Reasons for variations in fees according to type of building are obvious. For example, the architect can reasonably charge a lower-percentage fee for a factory building of large volume and cost but of simple plan with many repeated elements. On the other hand, a church building of only a fraction of the size and cost may require as much of the architect's time, study, and drawings as the factory. A larger-percentage fee is therefore necessary and justified.

Fee-plus-cost Method. The architect is reimbursed for all the expense incurred in his work and is paid for his own services a fixed fee or, in some cases, a commission based on the cost of the work.

Salary Method. The architect is paid a salary. All the expense of the office is paid by the employer, which is usually a body politic or corporate, the architect being the executive head of an architectural department or bureau and responsible for design and supervision, cooperating with other executives of the corporation in determining policies and requirements.

Other Methods. Fees for supervising architects and consulting architects and for other types of partial or occasional employment vary according to the importance and extent of the service. They may be lump sums or a stated amount per diem or per hour or on some other agreed-on basis, and they generally provide for the reimbursement of certain out-of-pocket expenditures in addition to the fee.

1-14. "Free Sketches." It is contrary to professional standards for an architect to prepare preliminary designs without formal agreement for services, the architect's compensation to be contingent upon the project going ahead, except possibly for an established client.

The reasons for this are all related to the fact that such practice, commonly called "free sketches," is not in the best interest of the client; the architect cannot afford to devote sufficient time to the study of the problem to produce a good schematic solution; such hastily prepared studies are not a sound basis for the selection of an architect; the best talent of the profession is not available to the owner; the preliminary studies represent only a small fraction of the knowledge and skill required for the entire project—a clever junior draftsman may be able to make an attractive and plausible-looking sketch.

A prospective client who endeavors to secure at the same time several free speculative building designs is conducting an unauthorized competition. Architects who knowingly participate may be suspended or expelled from the professional society.

PHASES OF PROFESSIONAL SERVICES

The first step in the erection of any building or group of buildings is the preparation of a program. This program will determine the elements of the building, its site, the relationship of present to future needs, and most important of all, the relationship of the client's needs to his budget requirements.

Professional services at this stage comprise the following: conferences with owner or owners; inspection of site and of existing construction, if any; and analysis of requirements, local legal restrictions, and financial factors, particularly if the project is to be income-producing.

1-15. Special Consultants. As the functional requirements of buildings become increasingly diversified, complex, and specialized, professional consulting services have been developed to assist owners, architects, and consulting engineers. These special consultants, who have specialized experience and knowledge regarding community relations, internal functioning, and equipment requirements of certain types of buildings, may be classified as architect-consultants and nonarchitect consultants, and by their building-type specialty.

The architect-consultant is usually an architect whose practice has included a large number of buildings of a certain type: e.g., hospitals, and who, in addition to providing complete services in general practice, in his normal geographic area of operation, is available to consult with and advise other owners and their executive architects, on the basis of more extensive experience.

Although usually on call for advice during the entire period of the project, the architect-consultant is most active during the programing phase and especially during the basic-design phase. The architect-consultant may illustrate his recommendations by means of drawings. If he has a more creative role and prepares the basic-design studies, he is more properly designated associated architect.

The nonarchitect consultant, who may be professionally an educator, a physician or hospital administrator, or clergyman, etc., also is usually most active during the programing phase.   Although he may review the architect's drawings at any stage, he does not undertake the architect's professional function of planning and does not provide drawings, except diagrams to illustrate his recommendations.

Relationships and allocation of functions between owner, executive architect, and consultants are defined in AIA Document No. 365, Functions of the Consultant, which is the basis of a formal policy agreement between the AIA and the American Association of Hospital Consultants.

1-16. Survey of an Existing Building.   When a building has to be altered or extended, a survey of it will be needed even before preliminary studies are commenced. The amount and character of the information required vary with the size and type of building surveyed.   General rules to be followed include:

1. Be thorough with measurements.   Better to take more measurements than are needed than too few.

2. Note all types of construction and all materials, including sizes of structural members whenever possible.

3. Record location, type, and size of all mechanical equipment.

4. Provide adequate information about physical condition of the building itself and adjoining property.

1-17. Preliminary Drawings.   Once a program has been determined, the architect composes its elements into a building which will be efficient, workable, and pleasing to the eye.   This most critical operation requires imagination, long training, and well-developed esthetic sense.   During the important basic-design stage, it is advisable to "make haste slowly" to avoid costly mistakes that can never be rectified.

Professional services at this stage include schematics, preliminary drawings, and outline specifications—general small-scale plans and exterior designs of one or more suggested solutions to the problem—these to be revised or modified until a general solution is obtained that meets the approval of the owner.   Then a final preliminary set is prepared of site plan, floor plans, elevations, and sections—drawn to scale—as well as outline specifications, all sufficient to determine an approximate estimate of cost.

For some types of public work, such as school buildings, more fully developed preliminary drawings may be required, to demonstrate approximate conformance with a variety of local and state regulations.

In addition, more complete drawings at the preliminary phase and scale may be required if modular coordination is used (Arts. 1-31 to 1-35).   This method of dimensioning building components and drawings encourages the advance determination of critical and repetitive details, accurately referenced to grid lines, which are shown at the respective scales on the details and the general preliminary drawings.   Thus an earlier precising of the design is permitted in terms of structural system and materials assembly and more reliable preliminary estimates.   It also facilitates the development of working drawings from approved preliminaries (Art. 1-5).

This type of design entails more work by architects and engineers for the preliminary phase and has resulted in a revision of the statement of architects' services and the phases of payment of fees, from three to four phases.   The AIA standard forms of agreement are available in terms of both three and four phases.

1-18. Display Drawings and Models.   Two principal devices for communicating to architecturally untrained owners at least a general idea of the shape, arrangement, and appearance of the proposed building are display drawings and scale models.   Even the trained professional designer, who can readily visualize and communicate by means of two-dimensional drawings, is aided in his analysis by generous use of quickly made perspective sketches and rough small-scale models.

All designers make many sketches at all stages of study of a project, but in the busy architectural office, the making of final display drawings for the client and for publicity and fund raising tends to be the specialty of one man known as a "renderer." Often, however, this work is done by an outside specialist whose entire occupation is making architectural renderings of projects for which he is not the designer or architect.

A model of a proposed building may be useful for various reasons:

1. To facilitate the study of mass, proportion, scale, and the relation of parts before

or during the making of working drawings. Models frequently prove their value by indicating where changes in the design are necessary or profitable.

2. To enable the owner to understand better the design of the building.

3. To interest the public or to stimulate subscriptions to the project.

Models are made at the cost of the owner, but the architect must necessarily furnish all information as to the design and should supervise the construction of the model.

Analogous to professional renderers are skilled modelmakers who specialize in making realistic models from approved designs.

Although special display drawings and models are increasingly used, they are not standard items of professional service and so are not included in services covered by published schedules of professional fees.

1-19. Preliminary Estimates. One of the most prevalent and illogical misconceptions held by the public and prospective building owners is that the professional designer, months in advance of the awarding of contracts, should be able to tell the owner exactly what a proposed building will cost, or even to guarantee that the cost will not exceed a certain amount. Yet it is a common experience that, even with complete working drawings, specifications, and details, with dates and schedules of construction established, the bids from a number of selected reputable contractors may vary 30% or more.

An estimate made before the completion of working drawings and specifications can be regarded only as an approximation and cannot be guaranteed. Nonetheless, such approximation should be as close as can be made. Several methods of arriving at preliminary approximate estimates may be used; they involve selection of a unit of measurement, such as the volume of the building, square feet of floor area, number of beds in a hospital, or number of pupil stations in a school, to which an appropriate unit cost is applied (Art. 26-1).

1-20. Working Drawings. The next step in a building program is to prepare drawings and documents from which the building can be constructed. This means the fitting together of all the things that go to make up a building. Appropriate choices of materials must be made, as well as the correct determination of the structural and mechanical systems. The architect must have a working knowledge of all these things in order that they may be related to each other and to the building as a whole. It is important to realize, however, that in spite of this working knowledge he must rely on men who are specialists in their respective fields to provide technical data. Thus he must retain, or have as partners or associates, structural engineers, mechanical engineers, and other specialists with whom he consults in working out the complete design of a building. These men have spent their lives in study of their own particular subjects. The architect maintains the proper balance and coordination among these special technologies.

Architects and engineers owe to the owner, and to all connected with the work, the duty of making the working drawings and specifications as complete, clear, and thorough as possible. It is in these documents, as much as in supervision and administration, that the professionals must exhibit the "due diligence and reasonable skill" that the law requires. Their careful preparation is the best form of insurance against trouble during the execution of the work. On their quality depend exactness in estimating and effectiveness in competitive bidding.

A good working drawing is one that gives the builder exactly the information he needs in order to build. It must be clear, clean, and simple, arranged in an orderly and readable manner, without unnecessary repetitions, and accurately drawn so that scaled measurements agree with figures.

Drawing titles must be explicit and comprehensive but brief.

All final drawings are sheets of a size that is standard for the job, with provisions for inevitable miscellaneous drawings and details. Each sheet is numbered as early as possible for the convenience of the specification writer; also, the rooms, windows and door openings, stairways, etc., are numbered as soon as possible for the same reason, since schedules and specifications are developed as the drawings progress.

1-21. Authorization for Working Drawings. The owner's formal approval of preliminary drawings and outline specifications and authorization for working drawings and specifications should be in writing. A copy of an authorizing resolution should be obtained in the case of a building committee, corporation, or public body.

If approval or authorization are given only informally or verbally, the architect should formally record the approval and authorization in a letter to the owner.

1-22. Interdependence of Working Drawings and Specifications. Working drawings and specifications are complementary and interdependent, practically and legally. They together constitute the principal basis of the contract between owner and contractor.

So closely are they integrated that the AIA standard documents do not give priority or precedence in authority to one or the other. Court rulings have, in general, treated drawings and specifications as parts of one instrument.

While the working drawings, including notes and schedules, and the specifications must be consistent and must together include all necessary information, there should be no unnecessary duplication, except for correlation and identification. It is not necessary that all items be covered by both documents. Drawings should show all the information that can be most clearly shown by drawing, while the specifications should contain all information that can be more clearly told in words.

Determination of suitable scales for details on working drawings is based on the principle of providing enough information to enable contractors to estimate labor and materials with reasonable accuracy. A more precise determination of shape and assembly, which is important in the over-all design but does not increase the cost, may require drawings at larger scale or full size. To avoid excessive bulk, these larger details are omitted from the numerous sets of blueprints sent out for bidding but are provided only to the successful bidder after the award of contract. They are in many cases translated by the subcontractors into shop drawings and templets.

1-23. Detail Drawings. As working drawings are developed, drawings of parts at large scale or full size are roughly made, wherever necessary, to prove that what is shown at smaller scale on the plans or elevations is possible of execution. These are preserved to aid in the preparation of the details after the contract is signed.

1-24. Schedules. Schedules (tables of materials, quantities, requirements, etc.) may present certain subjects more clearly than do drawings and specifications alone. Schedules may be used for many kinds of items: brick courses; lintels and arches; columns and footings; doors, trims, and frames; room finishes; wall finishes; floor surfaces; hardware; master keys; plumbing fixtures; minor bathroom fittings; lighting fixtures; culinary apparatus and its connections; laboratory equipment and connections.

1-25. Specifications (See also Sec. 29). The many kinds of items that must be described in specifications for the construction of a building may be classified as to the frequency of occurrence in the general range of practice, and as to whether or not they pertain to all aspects of a particular job:

1. Those common to nearly all construction regardless of the type of building. The printed *Standard General Conditions of the Contract* developed by the AIA, for example, cover items that should appear in every contract. They do not pretend, however, to cover all the items that will be required in any individual contract.

2. Those applying to the circumstances of a particular project but of general nature and not limited to certain subcontracts or trades. These are included in Supplementary General Conditions, which are compiled by the architect for each project. They are bound in the specifications following the Standard General Conditions, continuing the numerical sequence.

3. Those pertaining definitely to certain kinds of materials and equipment and the appropriate trades and subcontracts.

1-26. Publicly Financed Buildings. An architect undertaking projects financed by public funds, Federal, state, or county, or by local authorities, such as school districts, must inform himself through legal counsel as to laws to which reference should be made in the documents or to which the procedure of bidding and letting should conform.

Such laws may cover the following: submission of sketches and working drawings to art commissions or similar bodies; advertising for bids; deposit of bond or certified check with bid; letting the work of certain trades separately; award of contract; forms of contract; alien labor; the number of hours constituting a day's work; bonds of suretyship to protect the owner; bonds to protect all those doing work or providing material; mechanics' liens; workmen's compensation, social security, and minimum-wage laws; public officials or employees being financially interested in any firm or corporation contracting with any public body or agency; proper authority of officials executing any contract; the validity of any legislation under which it is executed, etc.

1-27. Development Housing. Architectural services to development builders may include consultation and analysis of market, size and price range for the proposed houses, suitable basic-plan types, and relationship to general community growth and planning.

The architect provides basic-unit plans, usually three, each with two or more variant elevations—all studied and devised for mass-production benefits, or site-prefabricated elements such as roof trusses. He may also do the site planning and landscaping or collaborate with an engineer on this work. His duties also include consultation with utility companies.

Working drawings should show carefully studied construction details at from $\frac{1}{2}$ in. per ft to full size. Specifications are not legal documents as in the usual contract and are therefore in simple outline form, or sufficient for mortgage approval. Specifications and details are subject to revision, after consultation with the architect, for available products or more efficient construction.

The architect may also assist in securing approval or permits from a planning commission, building department, and a financing institution or the Federal Housing Administration.

Supervision of construction is "advisory," not policing and, after a pilot house or the first few units, is usually limited to service at the call of the builder-client.

Types of remuneration for architectural services for development housing include: retainer fee plus royalties on a graduated scale per house; flat fee per basic plan plus royalties on a graduated scale per house; fixed fee per house; drafting cost times a factor to include architect's overhead and fee, with maximum total cost and fee; drafting cost plus fee per house; fixed fee for all services; drafting costs plus per cent for overhead, discounted by royalties; fee per square foot of plan area, original and repeat; percentage on plans plus fee for elevation variants and site planning.

1-28. Competitive Bidding for Construction (See also Sec. 27). Under the competitive-bidding system, contractors submit a proposal to execute the work for a definite sum. The obvious advantages of this simple method are, in many cases, partly offset by difficulties inherent in the system: Bidders are seldom of equal responsibility and competence. Legally for public works, contract award must be made to the "lowest responsible bidder," a term never exactly defined. Striving for the all-important lowest figure, the type of general contractor who is only a purveyor of other's services depends mostly on bids from subcontractors, whose reliability and competence may not be too closely investigated and who may be subjected to negotiation by the successful general contractor bidder, unless controlled by the AIA Instructions to Bidders.

In case of trouble, the management of the job may be left to the architect and the bonding company. Such results of competitive bidding are repugnant to honest and capable builders and to architects.

There are several ways by which the owner, unless compelled to advertise for bids, may avoid the chief evils of the competitive system.

1. Recognizing the importance of a well-chosen list, the owner may limit the list of bidders to the most reputable and competent contractors. The architect protects the interests of the client by advising him in the selection of reliable and competent bidders, to any one of which a contract may safely be awarded.

2. The owner may reserve some of the more important branches of the work to be bid upon separately.

3. The owner may carry on the whole work under the "separate-contract system."

4. The owner may avoid the competitive system altogether and let his contract by the system of "cost-plus-a-fee."

CONTRACTS

Standard contract documents of the AIA are a series of forms reflecting the best practice, and equitable as between owner and contractor. Since first publication in 1915, successive amendments, made in the light of experience and with helpful criticism by contractors and subcontractors, have gradually improved the original form.

1-29. AIA Standard Contract Documents. The series consists of:

Standard form of agreement between contractor and owner when a stipulated sum forms the basis of payment.

General conditions of the contract.

Standard forms of bond.

Standard form of subcontract.

Standard form of acceptance of subcontractor's proposal.

Form of agreement between contractor and owner when the cost of the work plus a fee forms the basis of payment.

Short form for small-construction contracts.

The general conditions include rules affecting nearly all decisions concerning the rights of the owner or contractor. Thorough familiarity with and frequent reference to the general conditions are essential to competent administration of a project. The AIA "Handbook of Architectural Practice" contains extensive explanatory notes, including suggestions regarding items to be included in supplementary general conditions to be drafted for each particular project.

The standard documents are based on the principle that an agreement, drawings, and specifications are the necessary parts of a building contract. Many conditions of a general character related tc the whole, or to a large part of the work, or which should be known in advance to bidders are assembled in a single document. Such conditions have as much bearing on the drawings as on the specifications and even more on the business relations of the contracting parties, and are properly called "general conditions of the contract." The agreement, general conditions, drawings, and specifications are constituent elements of the contract, acknowledged as such in the agreement, and designated the contract documents. Statements made in the general conditions, in the specifications, or in the drawings are just as binding as if made in the agreement.

Since the general conditions, with the drawings and specifications, contain everything necessary to a contract except the agreement, that document may be quite brief, confining itself to matters that are special in each case, such as contract sum, payments on account, and time of completion, to be filled in at appropriate blanks in an otherwise standard form. Since these terms affect a contractor's estimate, the agreement is bound with other contract documents for distribution to bidders.

The forms are suitable for use when all the work is let under a single or general contract. They are equally applicable to any separate contracts.

The general conditions of the contract are primarily intended for use with a stipulated-sum contract. They may be adapted to a cost-plus-a-fee contract, as in the appropriate form of agreement.

1-30. Some Legal Aspects of Contracts. In view of the variation of state laws pertaining to contracts, only general statements can be made. Provisions of the laws of a particular state must be ascertained from legal counsel.

Date of Agreement. Agreements executed on Sunday are generally void by statute.

Names of Contracting Parties. The exact names or legal titles of the parties should be used. Address of the place of business follows the name of an individual or a firm. Note the place of incorporation of a corporation, e.g., "under the laws of the State of Delaware." In case of voluntary association, the names of the officers and some responsible members are inserted, so that all become personally bound unless statute authorizes an association to enter into contracts in its associate name.

Signatures of Contracting Parties. Signatures must agree exactly with names of parties as first written in the agreement. In the case of a firm, the signature of the firm name by one of the partners, in nearly all cases, binds the firm and each of its members. It does not bind special partners, except to the extent of their interest. It does not bind partners if the contract is for something not within the scope of the firm's business.

Best practice is to insert the name of each partner and that of the firm where names of contracting parties first appear in the agreement. If all those mentioned in the agreement as partners are in fact partners at the time of execution of the agreement, the firm's signature signed by one general partner is legally sufficient and affords ample protection.

The name of a corporation should be followed by the signature of the officer authorized to execute a contract. The seal of the corporation should be attached or impressed and attested by the proper officer.

For a voluntary association, signatures are required of its officers and a sufficient number of responsible individual members to insure the carrying out of the financial obligation assumed.

Authority to Execute a Contract

1. Individual: There is ordinarily no legal bar to execution by an individual of a contract for employment of an architect or for erection of a building.

2. Corporation: To be established that:
   a. The corporation has the right to enter into proposed contract.
   b. It has exercised that right by legal action.
   c. The officer executing the contract has been authorized so to act by the corporation.

3. An authority expending public funds. Validity of an agreement between such bodies and an architect or contractor to be determined by competent counsel.

Common practice assumes that the agreement, signed by the president, sealed with corporate seal, and attested by secretary, binds a corporation. A certificate should be attached to the agreement showing that general power to sign is duly vested in the person named or a "true copy" should be secured from minutes attested by the secretary, with corporate seal.

Witnesses. Witnesses at signing are not necessary. Witnesses may be difficult to produce in case of a contest. If there are none, signatures may be proved by any competent evidence.

Seals. Attachment of the seal is a necessary part of legal execution of a contract by a corporation. A firm as such has no seal, but the attachment of a seal binds the partner executing the instrument.

The only significance of a seal in ordinary contracts is to imply a consideration. All AIA forms of agreement name a consideration; use of a seal, therefore, except for a corporation, is unnecessary. A bond must be under seal.

MODULAR MEASURE

Modular measure, formerly officially called modular coordination, is a simplifide dimensional system which coordinates building-layout dimensions with the stock unit sizes of building materials. It is the building industry's counterpart of the production line in industrial manufacturing.

Modular measure provides a disciplined framework for the orderly assembly of building parts. It calls for sizing of different building products on a common basis so that they can be readily fitted together when assembled to form a complete structure.

Modular coordination was proposed in 1936 by Albert Farwell Bemis, an industrialist outside the building industry, who was concerned with ways of reducing housing costs. In 1938, the American Standards Association organized Project A62 with study committees to advance modular coordination. In addition to the original sponsor, the Bemis Foundation, the American Institute of Architects and the Producers' Council became official sponsors in 1939. The findings of A62 study committees were published in 1946 in the "A62 Guide." Following the depletion of the Bemis Foundation funds, the project was for a brief period financed by the U.S. Department of Commerce. In 1950, the AIA and Producers' Council assumed responsibility for financing the technical and educational program. The National

Association of Home Builders and the Associated General Contractors later became additional official sponsors. The program continues under ASA official auspices. In 1957, representatives of the four major sponsors formed The Modular Building Standards Association to promote and support the modular program.

1-31. Basic Module in Modular Design. Modular measure encompasses the interrelated activities of design and production of building parts in sizes established on a uniform system of dimensioning; use of assembly details for determining product sizes and for fitting the uniform-sized parts into building structures; and preparation of working drawings for buildings in accordance with the same uniform system of dimensioning and assembly details.

The basis upon which these activities are integrated is a continuous three-dimensional rectangular grid with 4-in. spacing (Fig. 1-1a).

Standard sizes of mass-produced materials have been determined by study committees of American Standards Association Project A62, using the standard grid for the sizing of products and deciding how they are joined in various combinations. Architects, in turn, use the same grid system for preparing drawings to show combinations of standard products for a specific building structure and for developing assemblies of products not investigated by ASA study committees. The standard grid, used for large-scale details and small-scale plans, permits the interfitting parts to be readily and accurately located and dimensioned in the building structure.

Frequently, it may be desirable to combine nonmodular with modular products. The grid provides a convenient tool for developing these assemblies.

Dimensions on the building layout are "nominal" dimensions between parallel grid lines. They are in multiples of 4 in. and consequently generally avoid fractions of inches on the plans and small-scale drawings. However, under some conditions it is not practical to dimension between grid lines—for example, where the difference between grid and actual dimensions approaches 2 in., and in skeleton-frame structures, where framing members and fireproofing cannot be made economically in grid sizes. These dimensions must be determined and related to the grid. (A62 Guide for Modular Coordination, Modular Service Association, Boston, Mass.)

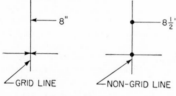

(a) MODULAR GRID

(b) DIMENSION SYMBOLS

FIG. 1-1. Elements of modular measure.

1-32. Modular Measure in Drafting Practice. Preparation of working drawings on a modular basis is essentially the same as that customarily followed in architectural practice, but with the added convenience of the grid (Fig. 1-1a). The 4-in. grid is used in drawing typical details, preferably at a scale of $3''$ or $1\frac{1}{2}'' = 1'0''$. At scales less than $\frac{3}{4}'' = 1'0''$, however, it is not practical to show grid lines at 4-in. spacing. If a larger planning module is used for laying out plans and elevations, it should be a multiple of 4 in.; e.g., 2 ft 8 in., 4 ft, 5 ft, 6 ft 4 in., etc.

The grid is a basis of coordination and not necessarily a dimension of materials. Materials are shown actual size and located either on or related to a grid line by a reference dimension. Dimensions on grid lines are shown by arrows, those not on grid lines by dots (Fig. 1-1b).

1-33. Modular Masonry. Since sizes of modular masonry units determine dimensions of walls and sizes of openings for windows, doors, and other items, they influence the coordination of many other building products. "Modular masonry" includes all masonry products made in coordinated sizes adopted by the producing industries, such as concrete block, brick, structural tile, and structural facing tile.

All modular masonry units are based on standard nominal sizes. *Nominal masonry-unit dimensions are equal to the actual unit dimensions plus the thickness of one mortar joint.*

Masonry coordination is to a considerable extent conditioned by the fact that units are laid up with mortar joints of appreciable thickness.

Standard Joint Thickness:
Concrete masonry, ⅜ in.
Clay backup units, ½ in.
Clay structural units, ½ in.
Clay facing units (brick), ⅜ in., ½ in.
Salt-glazed facing units, ¼ in.
Clear-glazed facing units, ¼ in.
Ceramic-glazed facing units, ¼ in.

Since all masonry-unit sizes are based on standard nominal units, which include the thickness of the mortar joint, various types of masonry units using different thicknesses of mortar joints can be combined in the same wall. The joints between dissimilar units are the average of the joints used with each.

1-34. Modular Wood-frame Construction. Application of modular measure to wood-frame structures follows the same procedure as for masonry structures. American standard yard lumber sizes are convenient for coordination with modular products. Sectional sizes are expressed in nominal dimensions, 2 × 2's, 2 × 3's, 2 × 4's, 2 × 6's, etc., which differ from actual dimensions by amounts almost exactly equal to the mortar joints of modular masonry. This difference provides a reasonable tolerance for the installation of sheet-board materials which traditionally have been modular, i.e., sized in multiples of 4 in.

1-35. Advantages of Modular Design. Modular measure encourages economical use of standardized building elements but does not entail standardization of design. The 4-in. module is small enough to give the designer ample freedom. For special parts of the building, it is always possible to order special-sized elements or to use the traditional cut-and-fit method with either modular or nonmodular units.

Other important factors of freedom and flexibility inherent in the system: The building can be built, if necessary, of nonmodular materials from modular drawings or vice versa, with no penalty, but with only partial economies. It is not necessary that all materials and units in a particular job be modular, nor is it necessary to wait until the whole industry is modular; economies can be made on elements that are modular, and the nonmodular materials will require no more wasteful cutting and fitting than on a nonmodular job.

Experience with modular measure indicates that substantial reductions in the cost of new buildings result from its adoption. Lowered costs result from fewer building-product sizes needed to be carried in stock; quicker drafting of working drawings; simplicity and economy in estimating and in inventory, ordering, delivery, and site storage; less time wasted in cutting and fitting materials at the construction site; and fewer pieces of new material cut off and thrown away.

BUILDING CODES

Municipal building codes are ordinances essentially for the provision of reasonable minimum construction requirements to protect public health, safety, and welfare, under state police power delegated by legislation.

Ideally, state enabling legislation contains several major provisions:

1. Requirement that municipal codes permit use of any material or method meeting minimum performance standards.

2. Permission to adopt by reference building codes and other standards nationally recognized, without customary ordinance publication procedures (now authorized in 18 states).

3. Right of appeal and legal remedies to persons aggrieved by the code or its administration.

4. Requirement of periodic review for updating.

No state has yet enacted legislation including all the above provisions.

1-36. Significance of Building Codes.   While there is growing acceptance of recognized standards, there are many instances of codes containing inconsistent, outmoded, and unnecessarily restrictive provisions that prevent economical and efficient building.

The essential and proper purpose of a building code, an exercise of state police power, is to protect public health, safety, and welfare, not to perpetuate or safeguard financial interests, trade-union prerogatives, or traditional building materials.

In order that the art and science of building may be advanced, building codes should permit individual initiative to improve design, materials, assembly, and equipment by any means that comply with basic principles and standards.   In an age of rapidly advancing technology, it is most important that there be legal provision for performance-type codes, properly safeguarded approvals or revisions by boards of standards, separate boards of appeals, and adoption of current versions of nationally recognized standards by reference—all without the necessity of tedious and costly legislative procedures at frequent intervals.

1-37. Code Standardization.   Some local code-writing commissions, even though comprised of the proper assortment of professional and technical talent, are not, and cannot take the time to become, fully informed on all aspects, principles, and safety criteria.   Many parts of their code are copied from other codes, with well-intentioned but inept minor revisions, resulting in essential omissions, grammatical and legal errors, inconsistencies, and antiquated requirements.   Many of these defects are perpetuated when the patchwork code is later used as a source for writing a new code by other amateur code writers.

The variety and profusion of existing building-code requirements add an incalculably vast amount to the nation's building costs in the form of high overhead cost to producers and distributors of building materials and installed equipment.   These added costs result from the need for demonstrating new products and methods to hundreds of local building officials.   Added expense is also due to the necessity for carrying large inventories with attendant costs for the storing, cataloging, and billing of several models or types of each product needed to meet the assortment of code requirements.

Standardization of building codes can do much to eliminate unnecessary expense in building construction.

Officials appointed to administer building ordinances in municipalities and other units of government have formed in several major areas and several states voluntary extra-legal associations.   These organizations provide means of interchange of information and experience in administration, enforcement, and technical advances, and most notably, they publish model codes, which have been a major force in improving code quality and eliminating differences in code requirements.

Four model codes have been widely adopted nationally or regionally.   They are under constant study and periodic revision, by or with advice of top-level specialists. The codes and the organizations that sponsor them are:

1. National Code—National Board of Fire Underwriters.
2. Uniform Building Code—International Conference of Building Officials.
3. Southern Standard Building Code—Southern Building Code Conference.
4. Basic Building Code—Building Officials Conference of America, Inc.

NBFU, ICBO, and BOCA also publish abbreviated codes suitable for use by small communities.

The basic advantages of model codes are that their use materially reduces the cost to any municipality of writing its own code, and their use promotes nationwide uniformity based upon sound standards developed by competent and impartial experts.

Electrical and plumbing installations and other building service equipment are subject to regulation for which recognized codes are available:

1. The National Electrical Code—sponsored by National Fire Protection Association.

2. The National Plumbing Code—prepared by Coordinating Committee for National Plumbing Code, jointly supported by U.S. Department of Commerce and the Housing and Home Finance Agency.

A good example of state-wide activity is that of the New York State Building Code Commission. The State Building Construction Code is applicable throughout the state, but any municipality may adopt a code of its own that may be more restrictive than the state code, but not less. So far as practicable, the code is of the performance type. An important feature is the "Code Manual," prepared by the same commission, which indicates and illustrates acceptable methods of compliance with the performance requirements of the code but does not exclude other possible methods. The code is the law; the "Code Manual" is not.

In general, the commission is an agency for service, not law enforcement, providing facilities for code drafting, technical research and investigation, and procedures for acceptance of new materials and methods.

ZONING

Although zoning regulates the construction of buildings in a positive but general way, it is generally regarded as a separate matter from building codes. Zoning, like building codes, is based on the legal concept of a police-power function of the state in the interest of public health, safety, and welfare. However, zoning is primarily a regulation of land use, in terms of types of occupancy, height, and density.

1-38. Zoning in the United States. An early example was the enactment, early in the nineteenth century, of an ordinance controlling the height and architectural character of buildings facing on the Boston Common, introduced by architect Charles Bulfinch, serving as a selectman.

In 1910, the Congress applied height restrictions to the District of Columbia. At about the same time, Los Angeles adopted controls on commercial uses. In general, the courts were reluctant to uphold attempts to regulate isolated features of land development, especially when enacted without state authorization.

New York City enacted the first comprehensive zoning ordinance in 1916. In 1926, the Supreme Court of the United States affirmed the right of Euclid Village, Ohio, to zone land exclusively for residence purposes, as being in the public interest. On this decision rest many subsequent state and Federal court zoning decisions.

1-39. Basic Zoning Principles Validated. Decisions from state and Federal courts have established rather definitely certain fundamental principles of zoning law that are universally accepted, including the following:

1. The power to regulate is limited by both constitutional provisions and legislative delegation of authority.

2. There must be specific delegation of police-power authority by the state to the local government, either by charter or by general enabling legislation.

3. Zoning must serve a public purpose related to health, safety, morals, convenience, or general welfare.

4. The regulations must be comprehensive and reasonable, rather than arbitrary or capricious.

5. Zoning conveys no vested rights to the individual property owner, since, under the police power, the interests of the community are paramount.

6. The police power is a flexible instrument, which, through due legislative action, and to some extent, judicial determination, can be adjusted and expanded to meet the new and changing conditions of society at any given time; always, however, within the limitation of reasonableness.

The last point is important, permitting adjustment and improvement of zoning regulations as required by increasingly complex urban life. Otherwise, zoning might become a block to progress rather than a public benefit.

1-40. Errors and Deficiencies in Zoning. In a new field as complex as zoning, mistakes were inevitable, such as:

Minimum-cost restrictions on buildings—nullified by courts as excessive public regulation of private land and having little relation to public health, safety, and welfare.

Zoning of excessive amounts of land for commercial use beyond possible demand but often wrongly located.

Copying of ordinances prepared for other cities. In contrast to building codes, the factors in zoning are geographic and economic and not susceptible of standardization.

Zoning limited to municipal boundaries is ineffectual since it cannot correlate with uncontrolled adjoining and related developments. In many communities, zoning must be extended to township, county, or entire metropolitan area.

Zoning often fails to deal with excessive density of population, which is a basic health-safety-and-welfare concept in long-range comprehensive planning.

Separate regulations for special areas or purposes such as highway strips and airport environs do not recognize the interrelations inherent in comprehensive land-use zoning.

Other revisions or new developments in zoning are indicated as necessary to cope with some of the far-reaching changes in our way of life that have taken place since the beginning of zoning, such as changes in transportation, industrial location, merchandising, and population distribution.

Among the deficiencies that exist in many local ordinances and some state legislation today, the following appear to need the most attention:

1. Absence of a close relationship between zoning and the general planning function.
2. Failure to relate zoning to existing and future land-use needs.
3. Emphasis on negative language that prohibits, rather than on positive language that permits.
4. Undue emphasis on the restrictive, rather than the protective, features of zoning.
5. Failure to control open space and population density directly and adequately.
6. Lack of flexibility to meet the needs of the modern city, including provision for large-scale development and redevelopment.
7. Failure to extend zoning controls to cover the entire urban area.
8. Lack of provision for off-street parking and loading.
9. Lack of provision for the ultimate elimination of nonconforming uses.
10. Regulations that invite the practice of spot zoning.
11. Lack of effective administration.

1-41. Zoning and Master Planning. Zoning is essentially a legal tool and administrative method of putting into current effect certain features of a comprehensive or master plan. The future land-use plan, which is the basic and most important single part of a master plan, must not be confused with the zoning map, which is the current legal and immediately practicable version. The latter is subject to change in the course of years, in the direction of the future land-use plan.

A current zoning map that is not based on a sound concept of the future needs and development of the area is indefensible.

In the apparent conflict between protection vs. restriction, zoning should be considered primarily as a device for the protection and conservation of urban and rural land, to assure its most appropriate use.

1-42. Modern Zoning Requisites

1. Provision for zoning districts based on present conditions and directed at guiding growth in accordance with the future land-use plan.
2. Flexibility to adjust to changing conditions, retaining at the same time the essential quality of stabilizing land uses.
3. The positive statement of objectives sought rather than merely a statement of prohibitions to be imposed.
4. The recognition that all the various uses outlined and arranged on the zoning map have a vital place in the economy of the community. Each has its own particular characteristics and requirements. Zoning has heretofore been considered in terms of "higher" and "lower" uses. A change of direction to thinking in terms of the mutual compatibility and incompatibility of land uses is desirable.

SIGNIFICANCE OF CONTEMPORARY ARCHITECTURAL DESIGN

All great modes of the historic past, such as the Gothic and the Renaissance, have had their beginnings in radically new principles or ideas in technology or other cultural phenomena. These dominant style phases have each gone through a characteristic evolution or cycle of phases: primitive, archaic, development, climax or "golden age," florid or overelaboration, decline and decadence.

The settlement of North America corresponded in time to the later phases of the Renaissance. The Colonial architectures of Central America and Southwest United States, of the St. Lawrence and lower Mississippi Valleys, and of the Eastern Seaboard were true, normal manifestations in the continuity of a genuine and living tradition, the Renaissance, of Spain, France, and England, respectively.

1-43. Eclecticism in Architecture. With the decline of the Renaissance, major new factors arose, providing the occasion and incentive for a new mode. These are summed up in the Industrial Revolution and the unprecedented and rapid evolution of the physical sciences and their application in technology. Characteristically, there was a period of uncertainty and cultural confusion in the overlapping of the last phase of the Renaissance and the crude beginnings of the new. In this period of cultural confusion—the last three-quarters of the nineteenth century and the early twentieth century—other factors, such as the modern science of archeology, extensive travel, and publication of historical books on architecture, gave rise to a strange phenomenon known as eclecticism; that is, the deliberate picking and choosing of modes and styles of architecture from here and there in geography and past history, to be consciously imitated and reproduced. This took the form of a series of revivals: the Greek revival, the Gothic revival, the Romanesque revival, etc.

The architecture produced under this motivation was not part of any genuine tradition; it was induced by devices of literary propaganda, fads, and fashions. This stylistic copyism delayed the true and normal evolution of an architecture suitable for the twentieth century. This approach to architecture has been so completely accepted by the nonprofessional and nontechnical public that it is not surprising that there is a tendency to regard genuinely contemporary architecture as just one more "style" to be used in the manner of cake icing, at the pleasure of the owner.

Under eclecticism, the new technological resources were used furtively, concealed by or forcibly adapted to the forms of a historic and outmoded manner of building. In some utilitarian structures they were used fully and frankly. Altogether great progress was made in a behind-the-scenes evolution.

1-44. "Modern" Architecture. The significance of contemporary or "modern" architecture is that the archeological trappings of the nineteenth century and the habit of trying to make things look like something else have been discarded. Architecture is free to develop naturally.

Modern architecture is the normal and natural evolutionary result of the new demands and resources of the twentieth century. It is not a "style" in the sense that that term has been used during the past century, but a new major mode that is analogous to the Gothic and the Renaissance. It is being worked through its evolutionary stages with, naturally, a great deal of trial and error, and with some very successful and significant examples already recognized as monuments and milestones in the history of architecture.

EFFICIENCY IN SPACE AND PLANNING

The plan plays an important part in determining quantity of materials used, cost of building, and efficiency. However, heights as well as areas are factors in space usage.

1-45. Premises and Principles in Planning. Conservation in space and planning is directly related to long-term conservation and reflected in the efficiency and economy of a building over its lifetime. Long-term conservation must be measured from the original programing of the requirements for a building to its final abandonment or demolition. Investment in competent design is a major factor for conservation.

Definite criteria for efficiency in use of space, as expressed in a recommended "formula for plan efficiency," are needed and useful as a guide to planners and building owners. Such criteria must not be used as absolute measures because many other factors of design and cost must also be evaluated.

1-46. Plan Efficiency. Unit floor areas and a formula for plan efficiency, used *together*, will determine whether various components of a plan are wasteful or out of balance with attainable standards for a building type.

Formula for plan efficiency ratio:

$$\text{Efficiency} = \frac{\text{usable floor area}}{\text{gross area}}$$

(*Note:* For hospitals use net floor area instead of gross.)

When making comparisons of efficiencies of unit areas of individual buildings of the same type (hospitals, office buildings, etc.), it is sometimes desirable to deduct areas of supporting or accessory facilities that are variable or unusual, such as teaching facilities, living quarters, or parking garages.

Recommendations. (1) All plans for proposed buildings submitted to the owner for approval should be accompanied by accurate plan-efficiency analyses (not the sole criteria for judgment, however). (2) Efficiency-ratio guides should be established by research studies for various building types and sizes (especially Federal).

1-47. Building Areas—Definitions

Ground Area. Area at ground level.

Gross Area. Sum of areas at each story level included within the principal outside face of exterior walls [*include* all stories or areas that have floor surfaces with standing headroom (6 ft 6 in. minimum) regardless of use—exclude all unroofed areas and unenclosed roofed-over spaces].

Exception 1: Include roof area of unenclosed roofed-over spaces when principal means of circulation between various elements of a single-purpose building that would ordinarily be enclosed is in a zone with heating-design temperature below 20°F.

Exception 2: For three-story or higher buildings when ground level or an intermediate story, or part thereof, is not enclosed, consider *gross area* of the unenclosed story as the projected area of the story above.

Total Floor Area. *Gross area* excluding exterior walls.

Usable Floor Area. Area required for fixed program requirements, or rentable or direct revenue-producing areas of a building.

Therefore, *usable floor area* is *gross area* excluding the following:

Construction. Exterior walls, permanent interior walls required for fire separation or structural support, permanent partitions.

Circulation. Required and permanent corridors, stairways, elevators, escalators, entrance lobbies.

Mechanical. Fuel and fixed equipment rooms, shafts, stacks, tunnels, and closets used for heating, ventilating, air conditioning, piping, communication, hoisting, conveying, and electrical services.

Public. Public conveniences and other nonrentable spaces, public toilets, rest rooms.

Custodial. Rooms, closets, storage, toilets, locker rooms assigned to building service and custodial personnel employed to protect, supply, operate, maintain, and manage the building structure and its services.

(*Note:* For uniformity and convenience in calculating floor areas, treat the interior walls and partitions enclosing *circulation, mechanical, public,* and *custodial* as part of these respective areas rather than as *construction.*)

Net Floor Areas. *Gross area* excluding only *construction, circulation,* and *mechanical* as defined under *usable floor area.*

Unit Floor Area. Definitions for gross area per unit, net and usable floor areas per unit are corresponding areas above divided by number of units (occupants, desks, vehicles, pallets, beds).

Recommendation. Criteria for unit space allowances should be stated in terms of both minimum usable area and maximum gross area, representing, respectively, health or operating minimum and budgetary maximum.

1-48. Unit Areas for Office, Administrative, and Headquarters Buildings. Wide variations exist among government and private agencies for office-planning standards,

Table 1-1. Unit Areas for Office Space and Planning*

Use of space	Usable floor area, sq ft	Remarks
Over-all space..............	80 per person	Over-all space includes all usable area assigned to a given unit or agency and thus includes all types of space, enclosed and open, plus necessary circulation. 80 sq ft per person assumes a reasonable number of private offices, open spaces with an average amount of furniture and miscellaneous areas. Private offices are assumed to be for not more than 10% of the total personnel
Enclosed offices, average (single occupancy)	175	Average 175 sq ft approximately based on assortment of 3 smaller-sized offices—use only when actual requirements are unknown. Most private offices of 3 smaller sizes, larger ones reserved for highest echelon or for combination private office/conference room or other multiple occupancy. Where secretary is in same room with principal, use next highest category
Working positions: 1-8.....................	375	5 modules wide × 4 modules deep (each module 4 ft 4 in. square)
1-6.....................	300	4 modules wide × 4 modules deep
1-4.....................	225	4 modules wide × 3 modules deep
1-3.....................	170	3 modules wide × 3 modules deep
1-2.....................	115	2 modules wide × 3 modules deep Figures given for multiple occupancy indicate the maximum concentration—use less if possible
Conference rooms: Up to 30 persons.........	20 per person	Conference rooms for less than 30 are assumed with tables—over 30 with seat rows and rostrum. Conference rooms should be justified
30-200.................	8 per person	on the basis of 25% potential use (based on 30 man-hr per week. A room designed for 18 would have a weekly potential of 540 hr, 25% of which would be 135 hr
Open office space, general clerical, etc.	50 per WP	WP (working position) means about 30 sq ft of floor area (60 × 34 in. desk with chair). A person with desk and table behind him equals 1½ WPs—with desk and chair with an additional table and chair beside him for his exclusive use equals 2 WPs. Above-normal requirements: For section heads with extra space for visitors—bookkeeping units with file tubs, etc., use the rate for average space in terms of WPs. The figure of 50 sq ft per WP for general clerical assumes all desks in end-to-end pairs with minimum aisles and allows 1½ lin ft per WP for files
Steno pools...............	40 per WP	WP 21 sq ft (45 × 30 in. single-pedestal typing desk) assumes no supplementary files, etc.
Drafting rooms.............	70 per WP	Standard 60 × 36 in. boards spaced 6 ft back to back with a few reference tables and plan files. Use the standard WP (30 sq ft) when reference tables are provided for each board

Table 1-1. Unit Areas for Office Space and Planning* (*Continued*)

Use of space	Usable floor area, sq ft	Remarks
Central files (minimum of 30 cabinets):		Cabinets in batteries facing each other with 3 ft 8 in. work space. Where files are placed around walls of large area with desks in the center, make a greater allowance
Letter size.............	8 per file	
Legal size.............	9 per file	
Coatrooms..............	1 per person	Assumes 2 rows of racks facing each other with aisle (3 in. of rack per person). If wardrobe shelves are parallel with an aisle used for normal circulation, use ½ sq ft per person
Telephone switchboard.....	40 per position	Assumed in enclosed rooms. Allowance is the normal minimum for basic equipment without desks
Miscellaneous: Stock and supply rooms Libraries Mail and mimeo Business machines Vaults and records Reception and writing		No standards—each space must be analyzed for actual requirements
Circulation.............	10% of total of all areas	Circulation must not be overlooked since figures are minimum and "usable space" does not include corridors and aisles beyond the core. An allowance of 10% will cover an efficiently laid out building assigned to organizational units of reasonable size. If wide corridors are used as primary circulation connecting large number of small units, increase the percentage proportionately

* Based on Conservation Study by Building Research Advisory Board.

as to both space allowance for each component and the average applying to the whole job. Nevertheless, experience justifies the following planning recommendations:

Plan Efficiency. For walk-ups, not exceeding three stories, 85 to 90%; elevator buildings of limited height, not exceeding 12 stories, 80%; multistory office buildings exceeding 12 stories in height, 75 to 80%.

Ceiling height: 9 ft optimum, with 8 ft minimum in limited portions.

Minimum regular partition spacing—optimum module width of 4 ft 4 in. permitting assignment of office space of 2, 3, 4, or more modules. The module may be varied up or down to meet requirements of planned occupancy using 4-in. increments in accordance with modular coordinated planning.

Depth from window to typical corridor or aisle—25 ft optimum for nonventilated buildings.

1-49. Unit Areas for Hospitals. The general acute hospital is an "elaborate" building type in complexity of functions.

Conservation in hospital planning should be approached from two points of view: cost of initial construction and efficiency of future operation. Extreme conservation of space and material in construction can produce extravagant waste in operation. Proper space arrangements, finish materials, and mechanical facilities can effect future conservation. In hospitals, conservation of operating manpower is more important than conservation of materials.

The ratio of net floor area to gross area of a 200-bed, or larger, acute general hospital should be at least 60%. Plan efficiencies of 67% can be achieved, especially where large, open, nursing wards are used since circulation is included in the net area of ward.

Definitions of gross area, net floor area, and plan efficiency for other building types may be adopted with the following comments: Areas are satisfactory criteria provided ceiling heights are controlled. The area of elevator shafts at each floor level should be included in the gross area. Corridor walls are not part of the net area. Passageways, as well as main corridors, should be part of circulation and thus excluded from the net floor area. Unenclosed elements of a building, such as balconies used by patients, should possibly be excluded from gross and net area.

Bed capacities of hospitals should be in terms of normal capacity, followed by parenthetical figures representing maximum capacity and number of bassinets for newborn.

Normal bed capacity is the designated number of beds in spaces for patient care that a hospital accommodates while providing efficient medical and nursing care without strain. Maximum bed capacity is the greatest number of beds in spaces for patient care that a hospital can accommodate by adding beds in an amount which will maintain a minimum center-to-center bed spacing of 6 ft.

Distinguish maximum bed capacity from disaster capacity, which depends upon ingenuity of hospital administrator and involves use of solariums, day rooms, offices, corridors, and other spaces not designed for patient care.

In bed count, include all beds available to patients, regardless of age. Exclude beds used only for maternity labor, receiving, and recovery. List bassinets for newborn separately from bed count.

Criteria for Typical Nursing Unit:

Ceiling heights—9 ft (floor finish to ceiling finish) for all patients' rooms including wards. As a conservation measure, 9 ft should serve as the maximum ceiling height.

Corridor locations—As a conservation measure, use center or offset corridors.

Corridor width—8-ft-wide corridor is universally accepted as optimum.

Table 1-2. Areas in Square Feet for Acute General Hospitals of Capacities Shown

	25-bed*		50-bed		100-bed		150-bed		200-bed	
	Total	Per bed	Total	Per bed	Total	Per bed	Total	Per bed	Total	Per bed
Administration department....	1,175	47.0	1,970	39.4	2,975	29.8	3,575	23.8	4,775	23.8
Adjunct diagnostic and treatment facilities:										
Pathology................	150	6.0	560	11.2	1,140	11.4	1,440	9.6	1,615	8.1
Radiology:										
Diagnostic.............	400	16.0	565	11.3	565	5.7	1,080	7.2	1,285	6.4
Therapy...............	....	....	....	....	....	....	....	....	1,775	8.8
Physical therapy..........	....	....	520	10.2	820	8.2	1,020	6.8	1,215	6.1
Occupational therapy.......	....	....	....	....	....	....	400	2.6	495	2.5
Pharmacy................	50	2.0	205	4.1	445	4.5	855	5.7	1,180	5.9
Nursing department..........	4,340	173.6	8,805	176.0	17,995	179.9	26,995	179.9	35,995	179.9
Nursery...................	380	15.2	500	10.0	835	8.4	1,205	8.0	1,640	8.2
Surgical department..........	1,075	43.0	1,980	39.6	3,235	32.3	4,210	28.1	5,030	25.1
Obstetrics department........	735	29.4	1,175	23.5	1,505	15.1	1,905	12.7	2,110	10.6
Emergency department.......	320	12.8	370	7.4	370	3.7	515	3.4	775	3.9
Service department:										
Dietary facilities............	1,025	41.8	2,025	40.5	3,540	35.4	4,325	28.8	5,165	25.8
Central storage.............	625	25.0	1,175	23.5	2,240	22.4	3,330	22.2	4,390	21.9
Employees' facilities........	500	20.0	765	15.3	1,215	12.2	1,595	10.6	1,895	9.9
Laundry and housekeeping...	300	12.0	1,365	27.3	1,805	18.1	2,325	15.5	2,715	13.6
Mechanical facilities........	725	29.0	1,220	24.4	1,860	18.6	2,250	15.0	2,575	12.8
Circulation spaces............	2,780	111.2	8,010	160.2	13,895	138.9	20,285	135.2	26,875	134.4
Total...................	14,580	583.2	31,210	624.2	54,440	544.4	77,310	515.4	101,505	507.5

* Areas listed for 25-bed hospital are not directly comparable with those shown for larger hospitals because of more limited services and facilities customarily supplied.

Table 1-3. Nursing Department Areas in Square Feet

	25-bed	50-bed	100-bed	150-bed	200-bed
Patient areas:					
Nursing units*	1 nursing unit	2 nursing units	4 nursing units	6 nursing units	8 nursing units
Bed area (includes room clothes lockers and private room toilets and baths	2,980	5,955 (50)	11,915 (100)	17,870 (150)	23,830 (200)
Treatment rooms	....	....	380 (2)	570 (3)	760 (4)
Solariums	485	965 (2)	1,930 (4)	2,900 (6)	3,865 (8)
Visitors	....	130 (1)	260 (2)	390 (3)	520 (4)
Nurses' stations	180	365 (2)	730 (4)	1,095 (6)	1,460 (8)
Toilets, baths, bedpans	150 (2T) (1B) (2BP)	300 (4T) (2B) (4BP)	600 (8T) (4B) (8BP)	900 (12T) (6B) (12BP)	1,200 (16T) (8B) (16BP)
Utility rooms	190 (1)	380 (2)	760 (4)	1,140 (6)	1,520 (8)
Subutility rooms	60 (1)	120 (2)	240 (4)	360 (6)	480 (8)
Floor pantries (central tray service, used)	125 (1)	250 (2)	500 (4)	750 (6)	1,000 (8)
Closets (stretcher, linen, storage, janitor)	120	240	480	720	960
Flower rooms	50 (1)	100 (2)	200 (4)	300 (6)	400 (8)
Total	4,340	8,805	17,995	26,995	35,995

* Each nursing unit to comprise about 25 patient beds, distributed about $\frac{1}{3}$ private room beds, $\frac{1}{3}$ semiprivate room beds, and $\frac{1}{3}$ ward beds.

Table 1-4. Surgical Department Areas in Square Feet

	25-bed	50-bed	100-bed	150-bed	200-bed
Major operating rooms	320	320 (1)	610 (2)	880 (3)	1,305 (4)
Minor operating room	.....	320	190	225	265
Cystoscopic room	.....	....	190	215	230
Scrub-up alcove	30	60 (1)	105 (2)	185 (2)	185 (2)
Substerilizing room(s)	50	120 (1)	165 (2)	260 (2)	245 (2)
Central sterilizing and supply	255	435	520	720	890
Unsterile supply room	75	90	115	140	160
Instruments	.....	....	....	100	145
Clean-up room	90	120	120	140	140
Storage closet	.....	....	165	140	145
Stretcher space	.....	30	30	45	60
Janitor's closet	20	20	20	20	20
Surgical supervisor	.....	50	60	75	90
Recorder	.....	....	45	45	45
Doctor's locker room	185	185	250	310	340
Nurses' locker room	.....	130	180	230	250
Fracture room	.....	....	255	220	220
Plaster closet	.....	....	30	35	35
Splint closet	.....	....	55	55	85
Darkroom (X-ray)	.....	....	30	30	30
Anesthesia storage	50	100	100	140	145
Total	1,075	1,980	3,235	4,210	5,030

Table 1-5. Obstetrics Department Areas in Square Feet

	25-bed	50-bed	100-bed	150-bed	200-bed
Delivery room(s)	290 (1)	290 (1)	290 (1)	580 (2)	610 (2)
Labor room(s)	255 (1)	255 (1)	420 (2)	500 (3)	600 (3)
Scrub-up alcove	30	50	50	60	60
Substerilizing	50	95	95	115	115
Clean-up room	90	125	125	125	130
Doctor's lounge	....	165	265	265	285
Nurses' lockers	....	75	115	115	150
Nurses' station	....	45	45	45	55
Nonsterile storage	....	10	10	10	15
Sterile storage	....	25	40	40	40
Stretcher storage	....	20	30	30	30
Janitor's closet	20	20	20	20	20
Total	735	1,175	1,505	1,905	2,110

Table 1-6. Nursery Areas in Square Feet

	25-bed	50-bed	100-bed	150-bed	200-bed
Nursery*	255 (8B)	255 (8B)	510 (12B)	510 (16B)	765 (24B)
Premature nursery†	255 (8B)	255 (8B)	(4B)	125 (4B)	260 (8B)
Work and examining space	125	25 (1)	160 (1)	320 (2)	320 (2)
Suspect nursery‡	....	80 (2B)	125 (3B)	210 (5B)	250 (6B)
Suspect anteroom	....	40 (1)	40 (1)	40 (1)	45 (1)
Total	380	500	835	1,205	1,640

Formula room included in dietary area.
* Maximum of 10 bassinets in any nursery.
† Maximum of 4 bassinets in any one premature nursery.
‡ Maximum of 3 bassinets in any one suspect nursery.

Table 1-7. Areas in Square Feet For Adjunct Diagnostic and Treatment Facilities

	20-bed	50-bed	100-bed	150-bed	200-bed
Pathology:					
Laboratory	150	280	455	620	745
BMR, EKG, and specimen room	...	.....	190	190	207
Office	...	.....	.....	135	170
Morgue	...	280	495	495	495
Total	150	560	1,140	1,440	1,617
Radiology	400	565	565	1,080	1,285
X-ray therapy	...	.....	.....	.....	1,775
Physical therapy	...	520	820	1,020	1,215
Occupational therapy	...	.....	.....	400	495
Pharmacy (bulk stores included in central stores area):					
Compounding and dispensing laboratory	50	205	320	400	495
Parenteral solution laboratory	...	.....	.....	185	200
Active storeroom	...	.....	125	150	200
Manufacturing laboratory	...	.....	.....	120	120
Office and library	...	.....	.....	.....	105
Circulation	...	.....	.....	.....	60
Total	50	205	445	855	1,180
Grand total	600	1,850	2,970	4,795	7,565

Table 1-8. Emergency Department Areas in Square Feet

	25-bed	50-bed	100-bed	150-bed	200-bed
Emergency operating room.............	255	280	280	280	280
Office and waiting room................	...	...	...	80	80
Bath................................	...	...	...	50	50
Toilet...............................	20	20	20	20	20
Utility room..........................	...	...	...	...	45
Storage and supply closet.............	45	45	45	45	45
Stretcher and wheelchair closet.........	...	25	25	40	50
Observation beds......................	...	...	...	...	205 (2)
Total.............................	320	370	370	515	775

Table 1-9. Administration Department Areas in Square Feet

	25-bed	50-bed	100-bed	150-bed	200-bed
Main lobby and waiting room..........	310	465	520	675	865
Retiring room........................	....	....	110	110	110
Public toilets.........................	130(2)	130(2)	130(2)	130(2)	210(2)
Public telephone(s)...................	10	10(1)	20(2)	20(2)	20(2)
Admitting office......................	....	..115	175	175	175
Social service........................	....	....	180	200	285
Information and telephone.............	*	45	80	80	90
Administrator.......................	125	180	240	240	285
Secretary............................	....	115	115	115	140
Business office(s).....................	400	285	450	625	805
Personnel toilets......................	....	90(2)	130(2)	175(2)	215(2)
Record room.........................	*	180	240	400	510
Director of nursing...................	....	130	130	130	215
Assistant director of nursing...........	....	....	....	....	215
Staff lounge library and conference room.	200	225	455	500	635
Total.............................	1,175	1,970	2,975	3,575	4,775

* Included in business office.

Number of beds in a typical nursing unit—A determination is needed of the largest possible size of nursing unit considering recent advances in hospital techniques and medical practices, such as early ambulation, shorter patient stay, individual toilet facilities, audio-visual nurse's call system, use of personnel other than registered or student nurses, integration of central supply system, and introduction of central piped oxygen and suction systems.

The same size room is recommended for major and minor operating, fracture, and delivery rooms in order to give greater flexibility of use in emergencies.

Because one-half or two-thirds of patients in military hospitals are ambulatory it is suggested that patients in military hospitals be divided into two major groups: (1) those requiring intensive medical and nursing care, and (2) those needing little medical and nursing care.   Design structures as separate but connected facilities for intensive medical and nursing care and little care.

Tables 1-2 to 1-11 of unit areas for hospital facilities were excerpted from reports by the Building Research Advisory Board to the United States Defense Production Administration (June, 1952).

Table 1-10. Service Department Areas in Square Feet

	25-bed	50-bed	100-bed	150-bed	200-bed
Dietary facilities (designed for central tray service):					
Main kitchen and bakery........	600	1,065	1,605	2,000	2,405
Dietitian's office...............	....	50	125	140	165
Formula room...................	70	....	255	255	255
Dishwashing and truck washing..	105	175	175	200	255
Refrigeration (walk-in):					
Meat......................	*	*	35	50	60
Dairy products..............	*	*	35	35	35
Fruit and vegetable...........	*	*	35	65	95
Garbage and can washing........	45				
Receiving area.................	....	60	60	60	50
Janitor's closet.................	....	25	25	25	40
Day storage....................	50	130	115	135	150
Dining space, including serving space:					
Staff supervisory, employees and nurses (two sittings)....	125	310	675	900	1,125
Employees (two sittings)......	125	210	390	460	580
Total.....................	1,025	2,025	3,540	4,325	5,165
Housekeeping facilities:					
Central linen room, sewing room, and housekeeper's office.......	125	300	390	400	435
Soiled linen....................	60	130	195	225	260
Laundry.......................	115†	935	1,220	1,700	2,020
Total.....................	300	1,365	1,805	2,325	2,715
Mechanical facilities (no fuel-storage space included):					
Boiler and pump room..........	600	900	1,200	1,400	1,500
Engineer's office...............	....	....	125	125	125
Maintenance and electrical shop.	125	285	320	320	345
Gear closet....................	....	15	25	25	35
Carpenter shop.................	....	....	....	165	290
Paint storage..................	....	20	50	75	115
Refinish shop..................	....	....	140	140	165
Total.....................	725	1,220	1,860	2,250	2,575
Employee's facilities:					
Nurses' locker room‡ (including lockers, toilets, showers, and rest room)¶	190 (12 L., 1 T., 1 Sh.)	330 (24 L., 1 T., 1 Sh.)	540 (48 L., 2 T., 2 Sh.)	755 (72 L., 3 T., 3 Sh.)	900 (96 L., 4 T., 4 Sh.)
Male help's locker room (including lockers, toilets, shower, and rest space)¶	155 (6 L., 1 T., 1 Sh.)	180 (13 L., 1 T., 1 Sh.)	270 (25 L., 1 T., 1 U., 2 Sh.)	370 (38 L., 2 T., 1 U., 3 Sh.)	410 (50 L., 3 T., 1 U., 4 Sh.)
Female help's locker room (including lockers, toilets, shower, and rest room)¶	155 (6 L., 1 T., 1 Sh.)	255 (13 L., 1 T., 1 Sh.)	405 (25 L., 2 T., 2 Sh.)	470 (38 L., 3 T., 3 Sh.)	385 (50 L., 4 T., 4 Sh.)
Total.....................	500	765	1,215	1,595	1,895
Storage:					
Record........................	....	175	240	330	390
Central stores§................	625	1,000	2,000	3,000	4,000
Total.....................	625	1,175	2,240	3,330	4,390

* Included in kitchen area.
† For domestic type only.
‡ Includes provision for special nurses.
¶ L., Lockers; T, toilets; Sh, showers; U, urinals.
§ Minimum. Based on 20 sq ft per bed. Many authorities recommend storage areas up to 40 sq ft per bed.

Table 1-11. Minimum Net Floor Areas in Square Feet

Room description	Recommended practice	Comment
Isolation or quiet room (single occupancy)..	130	Not including toilet
Single-bed room (max capacity 1)..........	130	
Single-bed room (emergency 2 beds).......	144	
2-bed room............................	190	
4-bed room............................	320	Usually must be larger unless large number are grouped in a controlled-clientele hospital
Larger than 4-bed room (area per bed).....	72	Max capacity
	90	Normal capacity including ward aisle and provision for more beds in emergency
Utility room—nursing unit................	180–200	
Nurse's station........................	136	Nurses' chart station only
Day room or visitor's space..............	180	
Major and minor operating room (nonteaching).................................	288	
Fracture room..........................	288	Portable X-ray
		Surgical operating room for orthopedic conditions
Delivery room..........................	288	
Labor room............................	120	
Autopsy room..........................	280	
Radiography and fluoroscopy room........	225	
Oral-surgery room......................	75	

1-50. Unit Areas for Hotels.   Area requirements for hotel facilities are given in Tables 1-12 to 1-15.

Table 1-12. Areas for 300- to 400-room Commercial Hotel

Space	Area, sq ft		Desirable avg
	Min	Max	
Lobby............................	2,400	8,000	5,000
Front office.......................	100	600	400
Typical guest......................	125	225	150
Typical guest bath.................	30	50	40
Executive and accounting...........	320	700	600
Dining............................	2,400	4,800	3,500
Coffee shop.......................	800	3,200	2,000
Private dining rooms...............	800	2,400	1,200
Serving room......................	200	500	400
Ballrooms.........................	2,400	5,600	4,500
Kitchen...........................	2,000	6,000	3,000
Help dining.......................	400	1,300	800
Help locker.......................	300	800	400
Help toilet........................	200	600	300
Steward office.....................	125	300	150
Steward stores....................	400	800	500
Valet.............................	600	1,204	750
Writing room......................	600	2,000	1,800
2 public lavatories.................	700	1,600	900
Women's rest room.................	300	700	400
Laundry..........................	1,200	3,000	1,800
Linen storeroom...................	500	1,000	700

Table 1-13. Service Areas

	Area, Sq Ft
Coal	500
Boiler	900
Refrigeration and ice	1,400
Pump—water heaters	350
Fan	400
Boiler and engine room	2,800
Repairs	50
Electricians	50
Carpenter	400
Paint shop	175
Upholstery	400
Receiving	500

Table 1-14. Dining Space

Space Requirements Per Seat and Turnover Factor

Type of service	Sq ft dining-room area per seat	No. patrons per seat			
		Per hr	2 hr	2½ hr	3 hr
Cafeteria	16–18	2¾–3	5½–6	6¾–7½	8¼–9
Counter	18–20	3–3½	6–7	7–8¾	9–10½
Table service:					
De luxe	15–18	1–1¼	2–2½	2½–3½	3–3¾
Popular	11–14	1½–1¾	2⅔–3⅓	3⅓–4¼	4–5
Banquet	8½–10				

Table 1-15. Kitchen-planning Recommendations

1. Compact working areas
2. Step-saving arrangement
3. Comfortable working heights
4. Direct-food-service transportation
5. Adequate communication
6. Adequate storage space
7. Proper garbage disposal
8. Plenty of hot water and steam
9. Adequate lighting
10. Scientific ventilation
11. Sanitary (easily cleaned) surfaces
12. Harmonious decorative treatment
13. Modern kitchen equipment
14. Laborsaving machines

1-51. Unit Areas for Residence Halls. Tables 1-16 to 1-19 give useful design data for residence halls.

Table 1-16. Social and Recreational Facilities

Lounges:
  Main Floor—for teas, card parties, discussion, guests, leisure reading, music listening
  Secondary—in "houses" or units for 40–60
  Ladies powder room in men's hall
  Guest rest rooms
Recreation room
Reception room or parlor, family visiting
  Date parlors
Hobby room or workshop
Library and reading room
Dining hall for larger formal social function (flooring, acoustics, furniture storage)
Photographic darkroom
Kitchenette or serving kitchen
  1 main lounge
  1 "house" lounge

Music practice room
Snack room, tap room
Counseling offices
Sun deck
Billiard room
Laundry and ironing
Public telephones
Discussion and meeting rooms
Master's or matron's living room
Women's guest room in suite of master and wife
Radio station
General-purpose social room in married students' apartment group or village
Guest suite
Music listening room
TV Room

Table 1-17. Dining Halls and Food Services

Capacity:
  Min.................. 35
  Max................. 200
Area per person, sq ft:
  Min.................. 10
  Avg................. 12
  Good............... 15

Table 1-18. Administrative Offices and Services

Employees' lounges—separate provisions for kitchen and dormitory help
Offices:
  Head resident
  Unit supervisor
  Dietitian
  Waiting room
  Student organizations and committees
Storage:
  Trunks and luggage—each floor 30 cu ft per student
  Out-of-season sports equipment
  Bicycles
  Linen
  Janitor's supplies

Services—women:
  Laundry—for groups of 40–60 women students
    Washing machine—automatic
    Dryer
    Hanger racks or rods
    Ironing board
  Hair washing and drying
  Sewing room
Services—men:
  Laundry facility for men, automatic washer in men's toilet room or central basement laundry space

Table 1-19. Unit Areas for Residence Hall for 800 Women
(4 units served by central kitchen, each unit including complete dining, lounge, recreation, and office facilities for 200 residents)

I. Central administration and service
  A. Administration area

	Sq Ft
1. Main office—staff or manager	600
2. Private office for manager	120
3. Private office for dietitian	120
4. Private toilet and washroom for office staff (women)	100
5. Private toilet and washroom for office staff (men)	100
6. Guests' toilet and washroom for women	100
7. Guests' toilet and washroom for men	100
8. Communication center for systems to control office at receiving entrance, kitchen, office, engineers, housekeeper, and control office in each of the 4 housing units	100

Table 1-19. Unit Areas for Residence Hall for 800 Women (*Continued*)

Sq Ft

B. Living quarters
1. Manager
   a. Living room...180
   b. Bedroom...120
   c. Bathroom...60
   d. Kitchenette*...80
   e. Closet...21
2. Two assistant dietitians
   a. Bed-sitting rooms...180
   b. Bathrooms..60
   c. Closets..21
3. One housekeeper
   a. Bed-sitting room..180
   b. Bathroom...60
   c. Closet...21
4. Six food interns
   a. Three double rooms...................................160 each
   b. Six closets..10 each
   c. One bathroom...80 each
5. Cooks (four)
   a. One sitting room..180
   b. Four bedrooms..120 each
   c. Four closets..21 each
   d. Two bathrooms...60 each
C. Service area
1. Control office at service entrance for delivery of food, equipment, supplies, student trunks, laundry and dry cleaning—employees' time clock—receiving clerk, area manager, etc.....................................200
2. Halls—corridors connecting to receiving platform, storage rooms, refrigerators, dry storage, etc., 8 ft wide, receiving area—16 × 16 ft = 256, halls—160 × 8 ft = 1,280.......................................1,536
3. Overhead track moving through weighing unit for meats, etc.
4. Floor-level scales for weighing hand trucks with foods, etc.
5. General storage near control office (not foods).....................2,500
6. Machine room, vent systems, boilers, vacuum plant, transformers, ice plant...1,000
7. Machine and carpenter shop...500
8. Trunk storage (800) (women)..3,500
9. Incinerator room 8 × 10 ft...80
10. Mending room (housekeeper)...150
11. Facilities for building personnel not kitchen help (men)............700
    a. Washroom and toilets..250
    b. Locker room...200
    c. Rest room...250
12. Facilities for building personnel not kitchen help (women)..........700
    a. Washroom and toilets..250
    b. Locker room...200
    c. Rest room...250
13. Housekeeper's supply room...200
14. Telephone booth for employees...9
15. Linen room (soiled) 800 students from dining rooms and bedrooms......200
16. Corridors in living areas—5 ft wide...................................?
17. Stairways 10 ft wide (5 ft each flight allowing for rail)............?
18. Elevators (service use only)—four—one for each unit of 200 girls 6 × 7 ft = 42 × 4 ft...168
19. Fire-alarm systems connected with city fire department headquarters

* Should contain a sink, electric plate, small refrigerator, cupboards, and adequate drainboards.

Table 1-19. Unit Areas for Residence Hall for 800 Women (*Continued*)

Sq Ft

II. Central food service for 800
  A. Accommodations for staff
    1. Managerial staff
      a. Private offices assistant dietitians
        (1) Main-kitchen assistant adjacent to or within main-kitchen area..80
        (2) Snack-bar assistant
      b. Food-service interns..200
      c. Food-service director...200
      d. Private toilet and washroom...100
    2. Kitchen staff
      a. Locker, wash, and toilet rooms for 40 women employees..............300
      b. Locker, wash, and toilet rooms for 10 men employees................150
      c. Locker, wash, and toilet rooms for 60 women students...............400
      d. Locker, wash, and toilet rooms for 20 men students.................200
      e. Rest room—women..200
      f. Rest room—men..200
  B. Storage of food
    1. General storage
      a. Dry storage for staples and canned foods
      b. Cooled storage for potatoes, root vegetables, and fruits...............200
      c. Refrigerated storage—walk-in boxes
        (1) Meats..70
        (2) Dairy products...50
        (3) Fresh fruits and vegetables..80
        (4) Fish..9
      d. Freezing storage
  C. Food-preparation areas
    (1) Vegetable-preparation unit...150
    (2) Butcher shops..100
  D. Kitchen...2,400
  E. Bakery...600
  F. Four service units
    a. Between kitchen and dining rooms for serving tables, dish, etc., storage,
    beverage and ice-cream equipment...................................600 each
    Salad unit, refrigeration, sinks...................................150 each
    b. Garbage rooms—two...120 each
    (1) One for wet garbage..120
    (2) One for dry garbage..120
  G. Dishwashing..600
  H. Dining room for employees (kitchen and house)...........................400
  I. Furniture storage for dining-room furniture when rooms are used for dancing..200
  J. Snack bar...800
III. Individual residence-hall units housing 200 students
  A. Main office
    1. Built-in safe for student valuables.....................................600
    2. Private office—head resident...120
    3. Staff office...120
    4. Call board to front office or telephone.................................100
    5. Post office with lock boxes for 200 students............................200
    6. Private toilet and washroom for office staff............................100
    7. Flower-preparation room...60
  B. Entrance hall, about 20 × 30 ft..600
    1. Powder room and toilet—washroom and cloak room.........................250
    2. Men's toilet and cloak room..250
  C. Lounge, 40 × 60 ft...2,400
  D. Dining room, 4 dining rooms, 200 each.........................2,400–2,800
  E. Five or six date alcoves, 150 sq ft..............................750–900
  F. Game room...250
  G. Library, 20 × 30 ft..600
  H. Music or radio room...150
  I. Kitchenette..150

Table 1-19. Unit Areas for Residence Hall for 800 Women (*Continued*)

Sq Ft

J. Telephone booths
  1. 2 booths (closed)..18
  2. 2 booths (open)..8
K. Recreation room, in basement, 40 × 60 ft..............................2,400
L. Laundry
  1. Washing room..300
  2. Drying room...300
  3. Ironing room..300
M. Sewing room...120
N. Head resident's suite
  1. Living room...180
  2. Bedroom..144
  3. Closet..21
  4. Bath..60
  5. Kitchenette...80
O. Assistant head resident's room
  1. Bed-living room...180
  2. Bathroom..60
  3. Closet..21
P. Two graduate resident's rooms
  1. 2 rooms..160–320
  2. Closets...10–20
Q. Student bedrooms
  1. 98 double bedrooms per 200 students—each 160 sq ft exclusive of closet
     space, 160 × 98..15,680
     One closet per occupant, 10 × 196.................................1,960
  2. Four single rooms per 200 students—each 100 sq ft exclusive of closet space. 400
     Closet, 10 × 4..40
  3. Buzzer system, call and answer from office to rooms, or ideal, telephone in
     each room connected with central switchboard
R. Common rooms (for each 100 students)
  1. Small lounges, 340 × 2..680
  2. Small kitchenette, 80 × 2...160
  3. Linen room, 60 × 2...120
  4. Janitor closet, 60 × 2..120
  5. Pressing room, 60 × 2...120
  6. Shower, bath, toilet, 2 units on each floor..........................245
     a. Shower (1 for 6 students)
     b. Wash basins (1 for 6 students)
     c. Toilets (1 for 5 students)
  7. Four telephone booths (2 house, 2 pay)

1-52. School-design Check List

Site:

Accessibility—travel distances, vehicular transport, traffic hazards, travel conditions.
Environment—type of district, atmospheric conditions, noise, light obstructions, proximity, vista.
Size. Shape and orientation, topography and soil.

General Planning:

Facilities for community use, meetings, food service, handcrafts, library, audio-visual recreation, demonstration.
For age group(s), as required.
For instructional program.
Related services—physical examination, lunchroom, recreational.

Design for:

Physical comfort and well-being.
Esthetic and emotional values.
Orientation on site.
Expansibility.
Flexibility.
Multiple use of space—proportioning of kinds of space: instruction, administration, circulation, services, accessories.

One-story vs. Multistory:

Land cost vs. minimum safety standards for multistory—enclosed stairs and fire doors, adequate fire escapes well maintained, and oversize halls for maximum, safe, emergency capacity.

Space for Various Arrangements:

	Sq Ft per Pupil
Formal desk and chair	10
Closed-circle desk and chair	16
Open-circle desk and chair	25
Chairs in rows	5
Small groupings of tables	10
Large chair circle	8
Small chair circles	8
Sleeping	18

Building Services: water, gas, electricity, heating and ventilating, cleaning, waste disposal, supplies, storage, maintenance and repair, warning system, clocks, telephones, intercommunication.

Technical:

Lighting—natural, orientation, fenestration, bilateral, trilateral, artificial.
Heating.
Ventilation.
Acoustics—airborne sound, sound transmission.
Windows.
Plumbing.
Drinking fountain.
Sinks.
Corridors.
Exits.

1-53. Factory-design Check List.   Processes, in general, may be classified as continuous, repetitive, intermittent (by purpose), extractive, preparatory, conditioning or forming, transforming, synthetic, analytic, by-product, and waste utilization and disposal.

Factors to be considered include purpose of plant; location—terrain, climate, hurricanes, earthquakes, air pollution; products—floor loadings, vibration; adaptability—short-range and long-range rearrangement, extensions, change of occupancy or process, materials handling—clearances, spacing of columns, dynamic loading on roof construction vs. cranes, etc.

Criteria for types of partitions—separation and privacy, noise reduction, confining of hazardous processes, odors, and heat.

Plant Layout—General Procedure:

1. Select equipment on basis of product design and volume of output to be attained.
2. Accumulate layout data: machine data cards, machine load charts, and templets of equipment.

3. Develop process charts.
4. Develop an over-all flow plan of operations (a tentative area-allocation floor plan for plant activities) for efficient processing and materials handling, based on product-layout and process-layout principles.
5. Selection of plant site.
6. Determination of type of buildings and number of floors in each.
7. Arrangement of producing departments within the buildings.
8. Selection of method of departmentalization.
9. Lay out templets or models of individual production machines according to flow plan of operation, achieving balanced capacity.
10. Lay out templets and space for service activities, materials handling, receiving and shipping, inspection, storage, maintenance, power-plant and building services.
11. Location and arrangement of personnel facilities.
12. Develop building specifications to house layout; and modify floor plan to accommodate limitations of building detail.
13. Provision for factory services (steam, heat, air, power, gas, etc.).
14. Make detailed layout drawing, plot-plan drawing, and a layout model (when required).
15. Make flow-process chart and flow diagram to verify attainment of objectives of an efficient layout.
16. Submit layout drawings and charts to specialists in various fields for review and suggestions, and make modifications when necessary.
17. Submit final layout drawing to management for approval.
18. Construct plant and install equipment.
19. Make test run and adjust layout where required.

Space Utilization and Disposition:

Sufficient space for operator to perform all his tasks at machine.
Sufficient space around machine for easy maintenance.
Avoid machines locked in by other machines, so that they cannot be moved without first moving other machines.
Space for tools, auxiliary equipment, jigs, fixtures, tables, tool cabinets, etc., required for proper functioning of machine.
Sufficient space for worked and unworked materials.
Machine accessible, so that worker can get to and from work station without danger of injury.
Avoid machine location too close to aisle or conveyors for safety of operator.
Avoid too much space allowance, so that operator becomes inefficient.

Machine-location Factors:

Best position or angle for effective supply and removal of materials and for effective use of floor space.
Best location for both natural and artificial lighting.
Avoid location which subjects operator to excessive amounts of heat.
Avoid subjecting operator to excessive noise.
Best position for safety and to prevent hazards due to fire, explosions, flying particles, moving trucks and cranes, overhead conveyors, etc.
In relation to the sequence of operations.

Services:

Machine location such that special services, steam, power, compressed air, gas, etc., are available without excessive additional installations.
Protective devices, hoods, shields, baffles, insulators, etc., to protect operator and adjoining personnel and equipment.
Avoid too much space for aisles.
Avoid a large number of turns and obstructions in aisles.
Each aisle to serve a maximum number of machines.

Avoid too many aisles.

Aisles clearly marked.

Aisles wide enough to provide for volume of traffic expected.

Aisles wide enough to provide for proper manipulation of trucks carrying contemplated loads.

Optimum Aisle Widths:

Truck traffic	Frequency, trips per hr	Max width of load, ft	Safety clearance, ft	Pedestrian traffic	Aisle width, ft
One-way fork-lift trucks......	15–20	4	2	Infrequent	6
Two-way fork-lift trucks......	15–20	4	4	Frequent; worker carries light load	12
Tractor, and one to four 8-ft trailers, one-way...........	8–12	4	3	Infrequent	7
Tractor, and one to four 8-ft trailers, two-way...........	8–12	4	4	Infrequent	12
Two-way, manually operated, warehouse two-wheeled trucks	20–30	2½	1	Frequent	7

Storage Areas:

Tool cribs and storage areas at convenient locations.

Avoid excessive distances from work stations to storage areas frequented by employees.

Storage areas protected from theft or loss of materials of high value.

Special storage facilities for paints, oils, acids, gas, cylinders, chemicals, flammable and explosive substances, and other special materials.

Location of storage areas convenient for receiving and checking of incoming materials.

Location of the storage areas to avoid long hauls of large volumes of materials.

Arrangement of the storage areas to permit use of mechanical handling facilities.

Provisions for inspection of incoming materials.

Personnel Facilities and Services:

Employment, interviews, testing, physical examinations, assignment to jobs, training, and upgrading.

Medical service, dispensary, first aid located conveniently to work areas.

Lockers, washroom, toilets within 200 ft of employees' work stations.

Food service.

Special services.

1. Loans and banking.
2. Commissary or purchase service.
3. Union activities.
4. Insurance programs.
5. Legal, income tax, and similar services.

Recreation programs.

Worker comfort, heat, light, noise.

Avoid too great distances from employee entrances to work stations.

Water fountains at frequent intervals.

Single vs. Multistory Buildings:

Advantages of single-story factories—low first cost, ease of materials handling, reduced foundation problems, reduced obstruction by columns, ease of plant expansion, better natural lighting, better natural ventilation, reduced liability through fire damage, absence of floor-loading design problems.

Disadvantages of single-story factories—high land costs, increased heating costs, high transportation (if horizontal distances are too great), increased installation cost of utility supplies.

Multistory buildings are advantageous when the process involves gravity-flow or other vertical relationship or high land values preclude single-story construction. Possible economies include better layout of utilities (electric, steam, gas, air, water) and less costly heating, because of lower ratio of heat-loss exposure areas to total volume.

In general, the disadvantages of a single-story building are the advantages of a multistory building, and vice versa.

Section 2

BUILDING MATERIALS

PART 1. MASONRY MATERIALS

PROFESSOR JAMES A. MURRAY

Massachusetts Institute of Technology

Masonry materials, in the widest sense of the term, include all the inorganic, non-metallic materials of construction.   These encompass a wide range of materials, from insulating blocks of lightweight concrete to slate tile roofs.   Only the most important of these will be presented in this section, and attention will be focused as far as possible on those characteristics of the materials which affect their utilization, strength, durability, volume change, etc.

2-1. Cementitious Materials. Cementitious materials include the many and varied products that may be mixed with water or another liquid to form a paste that may or may not have aggregate added to it.   The paste (mortar or concrete if aggregate is used) is temporarily plastic and may be molded or deformed.   But later, it hardens or sets to a rigid mass.

There are many varieties of cements and numerous ways of classification.   One of the simplest classifications is by the chemical constituent that is responsible for the setting or hardening of the cement.   On this basis, the silicate and aluminate cements, wherein the setting agents are calcium silicates and aluminates, constitute the most important group of modern cements.   Included in this group are the portland, aluminous, and natural cements.

Limes, wherein the hardening is due to the conversion of hydroxides to carbonates, were formerly widely used as the sole cementitious material, but their slow setting and hardening are not too compatible with modern requirements.   Hence, their principal function today is to plasticize the otherwise harsh cements and add resilience to mortars and stuccoes.

Another class of cements is comprised of calcined gypsum and its related products.   The gypsum cements are widely used in interior plaster and for fabrication of boards and blocks; but the solubility of gypsum prevents its use in construction exposed to any but extremely dry climates.

Oxychloride cements constitute a class of specialty cements of unusual properties.   Their cost prohibits their general use in competition with the cheaper cements; but for special uses, such as the production of sparkproof floors, they cannot be equaled.

Masonry cements or mortar cements are widely used because of their convenience.   While they are, in general, mixtures of one or more of the above-mentioned cements with some admixes, they deserve special consideration because of their economies.

THE SILICATE AND ALUMINATE CEMENTS

2-2. Portland Cements. Portland cements are the most common of the modern hydraulic cements. They are made by blending a carefully proportioned mixture of calcareous and argillaceous materials. The mixture is burned in a rotary kiln at a temperature of about 2700°F to form hard nodulized pellets, called clinker. The clinker is ground with a retarder (usually rock gypsum) to a fine powder, which constitutes the portland cement.

Since cements are rarely used in construction without addition of aggregates to form mortars or concretes, properties of the end products are of much greater importance to the engineer than the properties of the cement from which they are made. Properties of mortars and concretes are determined to a large extent by the amount and grading of aggregate, amount of mixing water, and use of admixtures.

One property of mortars and concretes—durability—is greatly affected by the chemical composition of the cement used. It is therefore pertinent to consider the composition of the several types of cement and the effect of composition on the use of the cement.

The composition of portland cement is now usually expressed in terms of the potential phase compounds present, the tricalcium silicate (C_3S), dicalcium silicate (C_2S), tricalcium aluminate (C_3A), and tetracalcium aluminum ferrite (C_4AF). Portland cements are made in five types, distinction between the types being based upon both physical and chemical requirements. Some of the current requirements of the American Society for Testing Materials Specification for Portland Cement (C150) are given in Table 2-1. Other requirements of the specification, such as autoclave expansion, time of set, and magnesia content, which are constant for all types of cement, are omitted from the table.

Table 2-1. Chemical and Physical Requirements for Portland Cement

Type Name	I General-purpose	II Modi-fied	III High early	IV Low-heat	V Sulfate-resisting
C_3S, max, %	....	50	....	35	50
C_2S, min, %	....	....	....	40	
C_3A, max, %	....	8	15	7	5
Fineness, specific surface, sq cm per g, avg, min	1,600	1,700	....	1,800	1,800
Compressive strength, psi, mortar cubes of 1 part cement and 2.75 parts graded standard sand after:					
1 day in moist air	....	....	1,250		
1 day in moist air, 2 days in water	900	750	2,500		
1 day in moist air, 6 days in water	1,800	1,500	....	800	1,500
1 day in moist air, 27 days in water	3,000	3,000	....	2,000	3,000
Tensile strength, psi, mortar briquets of 1 part cement and 3 parts standard sand after:					
1 day in moist air	....	....	275		
1 day in moist air, 2 days in water	150	125	375		
1 day in moist air, 6 days in water	275	250	....	175	250
1 day in moist air, 27 days in water	350	325	....	300	325

Type I, general-purpose cement, is the one commonly used for many structural purposes. Chemical requirements for this type of cement are limited to magnesia and sulfur trioxide contents and loss on ignition, since the cement is adequately defined by its physical characteristics.

Type II is a modified cement for use in general concrete where a moderate exposure to sulfate attack may be anticipated or where a moderate heat of hydration is required. These characteristics are attained by placing limitations on the C_3S and C_3A content of the cement. Type II cement gains strength a little more slowly than Type I but ultimately will achieve equal strength. It is generally available in most sections of the country and is preferred by some engineers over Type I for general construction.

Type III cement attains high early strength. In 3 days, strength of concrete made with it is practically equal to that made with Type I or Type II cement at 28 days. This high early strength is attained by finer grinding (although no minimum is placed upon the fineness by specification) and by increasing the C_3S and C_3A content of the cement. Type III cement, however, has high heat evolution and therefore should not be used in large masses. It also has poor sulfate resistance. Type III cement is not always available out of building materials dealers' stocks but may be obtained by them from the cement manufacturer on short notice.

Type IV is a low-heat cement, which has been developed for mass concrete construction. Normal Type I cement, if used in large masses that cannot lose heat by radiation, will liberate enough heat during the hydration of the cement to raise the temperature of the concrete as much as 50 or 60°F. This results in a relatively large increase in dimensions while the concrete is still soft and plastic. Later, as the concrete cools after hardening, shrinkage causes cracks to develop, weakening the concrete and affording points of attack for aggressive solutions. The potential-phase compounds which make the largest contribution to the heat of hydration are C_3S and C_3A; so the amounts of these that are permitted to be present are limited. Since these compounds also produce the early strength of cement, the limitation results in a cement that gains strength relatively slowly. This is of little importance, however, in the mass concrete for which this type of cement is designed.

Type V is a special portland cement intended for use when high sulfate resistance is required. Its resistance to sulfate attack is attained through the limitation on the C_3A content. It is particularly suitable for structures subject to attack by liquors containing sulfates, such as sea water and some other natural waters.

Both Type IV and Type V cements are specialty cements; they are not normally available from dealer's stocks but are usually obtainable for use on a large job if arrangements are made with the cement manufacturer in advance.

For use in the manufacture of air-entraining concrete, agents may be added to the cement by the manufacturer, thereby producing "Air-Entraining Portland Cements." These cements are available in Types I, II, and III, but not in Types IV and V.

Most cements will exceed the requirements of the specification as shown in Table 2-1 by a comfortable margin. Table 2-2 presents data taken from Chap. 3 of the "Long Time Study of Cement Performance in Concrete" by W. Lerch and C. L. Ford (*Journal of the American Concrete Institute*, April, 1948, p. 745). The range in values for the several cements of each type is shown, together with the average values for the tensile and compressive tests of those cements which did not contain air. These data may be considered as fairly representative of current cement production.

2-3. Aluminous Cements. Aluminous cements are prepared by fusing a mixture of aluminous and calcareous materials (usually bauxite and limestone) and grinding the resultant product to a fine powder. They are composed primarily of calcium aluminates with a small proportion of dicalcium silicate or of dicalcium alumina silicate (C_2AS).

Aluminous cements are characterized by their rapid-hardening properties and the high strength developed at early ages. Table 2-3 (adapted from F. M. Lea "Chemistry of Cement and Concrete," St. Martin's Press, Inc., New York, 1956) shows the relative strengths of 4-in. cubes of 1:2:4 concrete made with normal portland, high-early-strength portland, and aluminous cements.

Since a large amount of heat is liberated with rapidity by aluminous cement during hydration, care must be taken not to use the cement in places where this heat cannot be dissipated. It is usually not desirable to place aluminous-cement concretes in lifts of over 12 in., otherwise the temperature rise may cause serious weakening of the concrete.

Aluminous cements are much more resistant to the action of sulfate waters than are portland cements. They also appear to be much more resistant to attack by water containing aggressive carbon dioxide or weak mineral acids than the silicate cements. Their principal use is in concretes where advantage may be taken of their very high

Table 2-2. Physical and Chemical Tests of Cements Used in Long-time Study of Cement Performance in Concrete

Cement type	I	II	III	IV	V
No. of samples	12	6	4	4	1
C_3S, %	42.5–64.5	34.0–51.0	56.0–64.0	20.0–29.0	41.0
C_2S, %	10.0–32.0	24.0–41.0	10.5–17.0	48.0–55.0	39.0
C_3A, %	7.5–13.2	3.7–6.6	5.7–10.8	3.5–6.2	3.7
Sp. gravity	3.113–3.181	3.174–3.246	3.102–3.156	3.221–3.224	3.210
Sp. surface	1,665–2,010	1,630–1,925	2,465–2,795	1,915–1,965	2,025
Time of set, Gillmore:					
Initial, hr	3:05–4:45	4:05–5:20	2:20–3:25	4:45–6:30	6:20
Final, hr	4:35–6:30	6:10–7:05	3:50–5:20	7:05–8:20	8:20
Tensile strength, 1:3 mortar briquets, psi:					
1 day	20–215	85–215	310–390	75–110	120
3 days	230–495	240–355	460–535	185–215	300
7 days	390–565	345–485	520–580	270–310	400
28 days	475–600	465–565	565–630	425–475	485
3 months	505–585	515–580	505–600	540–580	605
1 year	465–535	505–580	490–545	545–585	590
5 years	390–515	460–555	425–535	470–575	535
No. of samples	8	5	3	4	1
Tensile strengths, 1:3 mortar briquets, avg for non-air-entraining cements only, psi:					
1 day	172	146	362	98	120
3 days	364	303	515	206	300
7 days	476	411	553	288	400
28 days	535	524	603	445	485
3 months	539	543	585	564	605
1 year	514	546	535	569	590
5 years	479	513	532	520	535
Compressive strengths, 1:2.77 mortar cubes, avg for non-air-entraining cements only, psi:					
1 day	528	412	1,457	288	400
3 days	1,689	1,180	3,457	688	1,240
7 days	2,944	2,034	5,103	1,000	1,780
28 days	4,789	3,728	6,250	2,510	3,010
3 months	5,279	5,094	6,367	5,110	5,550
1 year	5,325	5,520	6,300	5,980	6,460
5 years	5,076	5,692	5,923	6,110	6,880

early strength or of their sulfate resistance, and where the extra cost of the cement is not an important factor.

2-4. Natural Cements. Natural cements are formed by calcining a naturally occurring mixture of calcareous and argillaceous substances at a temperature below that at which sintering takes place. The American Society for Testing Materials

Specification for Natural Cement (C10) requires that the temperature shall be no higher than is necessary to drive off the carbonic acid gas. Since natural cements are derived from naturally occurring materials and no particular effort is made to adjust the composition, both the composition and properties vary rather widely. Some

Table 2-3. Relative Strengths of Concretes Made from Portland and Aluminous Cements

Days	Compressive strength, psi		
	Normal portland	High-early portland	Aluminous
1	460	790	5,710
3	1,640	2,260	7,330
7	2,680	3,300	7,670
28	4,150	4,920	8,520
56	4,570	5,410	8,950

Table 2-4. Range of Properties of Natural Cements

SiO_2, %...	20.6–24.7
Fe_2O_3, %...	1.2– 3.5
Al_2O_3, %...	5.1– 9.7
CaO, %..	34.5–49.8
MgO, %...	6.3–23.9
SO_3, %...	1.6– 3.0
Lb per cu ft, loose.................................	47.5–55.8

Compressive strength on water storage, 1:3 standard sand cubes, psi:

7 days....................	0–100 group to 100– 300 group
28 days..................	100–300 group to 500–1,000 group
3 months.................	300–500 group to 1,500–2,000 group
1 year...................	300–500 group to over 2,000 group

Table 2-5. Properties of Two Brands of Hydraulic Hydrated Lime

SiO_2, %....................................	17.3	7.6
Fe_2O_3, %..................................	1.6	1.0
Al_2O_3, %..................................	6.7	2.5
CaO, %.....................................	58.9	70.9
MgO, %....................................	1.8	0.5
SO_3, %....................................	0.5	0.5
Lb per cu ft, loose........................	42.1	32.5
Compressive strength on water storage, 1:3 standard sand cubes, psi:		
7 days...............................	100– 300 group	100–300 group
28 days..............................	300– 500 group	100–300 group
3 months.............................	500–1,000 group	100–300 group
1 year...............................	1,000–1,500 group	100–300 group

natural cements may be almost the equivalent of portland cement in properties; others are much weaker.

Rogers and Blaine in their study of masonry cements included four which were classified as natural cements ("Investigation of Commercial Masonry Cements," *Journal of Research of the National Bureau of Standards*, Vol. 13, No. 6, p. 811). The range of properties is indicated in Table 2-4. Their data on strength are not given exactly but are presented as falling within certain groups as indicated.

The wide range in properties is indicated by the 1-year strength test where one cement had a strength of less than 500 psi while another had a strength of over 2,000 psi. The large content of magnesia is of interest since portland cements are restricted to less than 5%. Natural cements are principally used now in masonry mortars and as an admixture in portland-cement concretes.

2-5. Hydraulic Limes. Hydraulic lime is made by calcining a limestone containing silica and alumina to a temperature short of incipient fusion so as to form sufficient free lime (CaO) to permit hydration and at the same time leaving unhydrated sufficient calcium silicates to give the dry powder its hydraulic properties (see American Society for Testing Materials Specification C141). Analyses and strength data on two samples are given by Rogers and Blaine ("Investigation of Commercial Masonry Cements," *Journal of Research of the National Bureau of Standards*, Vol. 13, No. 6, p. 811) and are partly summarized in Table 2-5.

Because of the low silicate and high lime contents, hydraulic limes are relatively weak. They find their principal use in masonry mortars.

LIMES

2-6. Quicklimes. When limestone is heated to a temperature in excess of 1700°F, the carbon dioxide content is driven off and the remaining solid product is quicklime. It consists essentially of calcium and magnesium oxides plus impurities such as silica, iron, and aluminum oxides. The impurities are usually limited to less than 5%. If they exceed 10%, the product may be a hydraulic lime.

Two classes of quicklime are recognized, high-calcium and dolomitic. A high-calcium quicklime usually is considered as one containing less than 5% magnesium oxide. A dolomitic quicklime usually contains from 35 to 40% magnesium oxide. A few quicklimes are found that contain from 5 to 35% magnesium oxide and are called magnesian limes.

The outstanding characteristic of quicklime is its ability to slake with water. When quicklime is mixed with from two to three times its weight of water, a chemical reaction takes place: The calcium oxide combines with water to form calcium hydroxide, and sufficient heat is evolved to bring the entire mass to a boil. The resulting product is a suspension of finely divided calcium hydroxide (and magnesium hydroxide or oxide if dolomitic lime is used) in water. On cooling, the semifluid mass stiffens to a putty of such consistency that it may be shoveled or carried in a hod. This slaked quicklime putty is the form in which the material is used in construction. Quicklime should never be used without thorough slaking.

The yield of putty will vary, depending upon the type of quicklime, its degree of burning, slaking conditions, etc., and will usually be from 70 to 100 cu ft of putty per ton of quicklime. The principal use of the putty is in masonry mortars, where it is particularly valuable because of the high degree of plasticity or workability it imparts to the mortar. It is used at times as an admixture in concrete for the purpose of improving workability. It also is used in some localities as finish-coat plaster where full advantage may be taken of its high plasticity.

2-7. Mason's Hydrated Lime. Hydrated limes are prepared from quicklimes by addition of a limited amount of water. After hydration ceases to evolve heat, the resulting product is a fine, dry powder. It is then classified by air-classification methods to remove undesirable oversize particles and packaged in 50-lb sacks. It is always a factory-made product, whereas quicklime putty is almost always a job-slaked product.

Mason's hydrated limes are those hydrates suitable for use in mortars, base-coat plasters, and concrete. They necessarily follow the composition of the quicklime. High-calcium hydrates are composed primarily of calcium hydroxide. Normal dolomitic hydrates are composed of calcium hydroxide plus magnesium oxide.

Plasticity of mortars made from normal mason's hydrated limes (Type N) is fair. It is better than that attained with most cements but not nearly so high as that of mortars made with an equivalent amount of slaked quicklime putty.

The normal process of hydration of a dolomitic quicklime at atmospheric pressure results in the hydration of the calcium fraction only, leaving the magnesium oxide portion substantially unchanged chemically. When dolomitic quicklime is hydrated under pressure, the magnesium oxide is converted to magnesium hydroxide. This results in the so-called "special" hydrates (Type S), which not only have their magnesia contents substantially completely hydrated but also have a high degree of plasticity immediately on wetting with water. Mortars made from Type S hydrates are more workable than those made from Type N hydrates. In fact, Type S hydrates are nearly as workable as those made from slaked quicklime putties. The user of this type of hydrate may therefore have the convenience of a bagged product and a high degree of workability without having the trouble and possible hazard of slaking quicklime.

2-8. Finishing Hydrated Limes. Finishing hydrated limes are particularly suitable for use in the finishing coat of plaster. They are characterized by a high degree of whiteness and of plasticity. Practically all finishing hydrated limes are produced in the Toledo district of Ohio from dolomitic limestone. The normal hydrate is composed of calcium hydroxide and magnesium oxide. When first wetted, it is no more plastic than Type N mason's hydrates. It differs from the latter, however, in that, on soaking overnight, the finishing hydrated lime develops a very high degree of plasticity, whereas the mason's hydrate shows relatively little improvement in plasticity on soaking.

Finishing hydrated lime is also made by the pressure method, which forms a Type S hydrate. This material, similar in characteristics (except color) to the Type S mason's hydrate, is also used for finish-coat plaster but does not have quite as satisfactory characteristics for plastering as does Type N finishing hydrate.

GYPSUM CEMENTS

2-9. Low-temperature Gypsum Derivatives. When gypsum rock ($CaSO_4 \cdot 2H_2O$) is heated to a relatively low temperature, about 130°C, three-fourths of the water of crystallization is driven off. The resulting product is known by various names such as hemihydrate, calcined gypsum, and first-settle stucco. Its common name, however, is plaster of paris. It is a fine powder, usually white. When mixed with water, it sets rapidly and attains its strength on drying. While it will set under water, it does not gain strength and ultimately, on continued water exposure, will disintegrate.

Plaster of paris, either retarded or unretarded, is used as a molding plaster for preparing ornamental plaster objects or as gaging plaster, which is used with finishing hydrated lime to form the smooth white-coat finish on plaster walls. The unretarded plaster of paris is used by manufacturers to make gypsum block, tile, wallboard, and plaster board.

When plaster of paris is retarded and mixed with fiber such as sisal, it is marketed under the name of hardwall plaster or cement plaster. (The latter name is misleading, since it does not contain any portland cement.) Hardwall plaster, mixed with water and with from 2 to 3 parts of sand by weight, is widely used for base-coat plastering. In some cases wood fiber is used in place of sand, making a "wood-fibered" plaster.

Special effects are obtained by combining hardwall plaster with the correct type of aggregate. With perlite aggregate, a lightweight plaster is obtained; with pumice or some other aggregates, acoustical plasters are produced.

Gypsum plasters, in general, have a strong set, gain their full strength when dry, do not have abnormal volume changes, and have excellent fire-resistance characteristics. They are not well adapted for use under continued damp conditions or intermittent wet conditions.

2-10. High-temperature Gypsum Derivatives. When gypsum rock is heated to a high temperature, all the water is driven off and anhydrous calcium sulfate results. This material will not set. But addition of a small amount of alum to the rock before calcination acts as an accelerator, and the resulting product, known as Keene's cement, sets hard. It forms a more durable plastering material than hardwall plaster and is much more resistant to water. Hence it is extensively used as a plastering material in bathrooms and kitchens. It also has good fire-retarding properties. Cost of Keene's cement, however, is appreciably higher than that of hardwall plaster; consequently, its use has been somewhat limited except for special finishes.

MISCELLANEOUS CEMENTS

2-11. Oxychloride Cements. Lightly calcined magnesium oxide mixed with a solution of magnesium chloride forms a cement known as magnesium oxychloride cement, or Sorel cement. It is particularly useful in making flooring compositions in which it is mixed with colored aggregates. Floors made of oxychloride cement are sparkproof and are more resilient than floors of concrete.

Oxychloride cement has very strong bonding power and may be used with greater quantities of aggregate than are possible with portland cement because of its higher bonding power. It also bonds well with wood and is used in making partition block or tile with wood shavings or sawdust as aggregate. It is moderately resistant to water but should not be used under continually wet conditions.

2-12. Masonry Cements. Masonry cements, or—as they are sometimes called—mortar cements, are intended to be mixed with sand and used for setting brick, tile, stone, etc. They may be any one of the hydraulic cements already discussed or mixtures of them in any proportion. Rogers and Blaine in their study of commercial masonry cements obtained 41 brands then available (Investigation of Commercial Masonry Cements, *Journal of Research of the National Bureau of Standards*, vol. 13, No. 6, p. 811). On the basis of their chemical and physical properties, the researchers divided them into the following classes: Largely portland cement; portland cement and hydrated lime mixtures; portland cement mixed with unidentified material; portland cement and natural cement mixtures; natural cement; hydraulic lime; large amounts of clay; and unidentified.

Many present masonry cements are mixtures of portland cement and pulverized limestone, frequently containing as much as 50 or 60% limestone. They are sold in bags containing from 70 to 80 lb, each bag nominally containing a cubic foot. Price per bag is commonly about 10 cents less than that of portland cement, but because of the use of the lighter bag, cost per ton is higher than that of portland cement.

Since there is no specification as to chemical content and physical requirements of masonry cement, specifications are quite liberal; some manufacturers vary the composition widely, depending upon competition, weather conditions, or availability of materials. Resulting mortars may vary widely in properties.

AGGREGATES

2-13. Desirable Characteristics of Aggregates. Aggregate is defined as "inert material which when bound together into a conglomerated mass by a matrix, forms concrete, mastic, mortar, plaster, etc." [American Society for Testing Materials (ASTM) designation C58.]

As such, the term aggregate includes the normal sands, gravels, and crushed stone used for making mortar, plaster, and concrete. It also includes the lightweight materials, such as slag, vermiculite, and pumice, used to prepare lightweight plasters and concretes. It does not include finely divided or pulverized stone or sand sometimes used with cement that is more properly termed an admixture or filler.

As in the case of cements, properties of aggregates are of less importance than properties of mortars or concretes made from aggregates. The most important property of an aggregate is its soundness, or its dimensional stability. Concrete may be unsound if made with a sound aggregate if not properly proportioned, handled, and placed; but no amount of precaution will enable sound concrete to be made with unsound aggregate.

Cleanliness, strength, and gradation are important in any aggregate. For most purposes, an aggregate should be free of clay, silt, organic matter, and salts. Such cleanliness is usually readily obtainable if facilities are available for washing the aggregate; but bank sands and gravels may contain clay and loam unless special precautions are taken. Strength is important but is infrequently measured, reliance being placed to a large extent upon the performance of existing structures as being evidence of adequate strength. Grading, while important, is under the control of the producer, who can usually adjust his operation to meet the grading requirements of any normal pecification.

2-14. Coarse Aggregates. Coarse aggregates comprise that portion of the aggregate retained on a No. 4 sieve ($\frac{3}{16}$-in.). Normal coarse aggregate is composed of gravel or crushed stone and for structural concrete is usually required to be fairly uniformly graded from a maximum size of about 2 in. down to $\frac{3}{16}$ in. It should, of course, be clean and strong as well as sound.

Gravel is "the coarse granular material, larger than sand, resulting from the erosion of rock by natural agencies." (See ASTM Standard C125.) It is normally composed

Table 2-6. Properties of Lightweight Aggregates

Aggregate	Unit weight, lb per cu ft rodded	Max size	Bulk sp. gravity	Absorption		Crushing strength, psi	
				Weight %	Volume, lb of water per cu ft	1-in. compaction	2-in. compaction
Perlite....................	9.4	No.8	0.86	153.2	14.3	30	91
Exfoliated vermiculite........	10.0	No. 8	1.35	128.5	18.5	11	38
Sintered diatomite............	31.0	$\frac{3}{8}$ in.	1.44	75.2	23.8	615	3,840
Expanded slag No. 3—coarse..	31.0	$\frac{1}{2}$ in.	1.13	21.3	7.1	360	1,290
Expanded slate—coarse.......	39.0	$\frac{3}{8}$ in.	1.29	15.0	6.1	635	2,120
Sintered fly ash—coarse.......	42.0	$\frac{1}{2}$ in.	1.75	15.2	6.3	325	1,160
Pumice—coarse..............	44.0	$\frac{3}{4}$ in.	1.46	42.8	16.9	485	1,710
Expanded slag No. 2—coarse..	48.0	$\frac{1}{2}$ in.	1.96	22.8	10.4	250	1,040
Pumice—fine.................	49.0	$\frac{3}{8}$ in.	1.66	29.1	14.9	485	1,710
Expanded clay—coarse........	53.0	$\frac{1}{2}$ in.	1.65	21.2	11.6	935	6,930
Sintered fly ash—fine........	58.0	$\frac{3}{8}$ in.	2.10	8.2	1.4	325	1,160
Expanded slag No. 3—fine....	59.0	No. 4	2.08	5.2	2.9	360	1,290
Expanded shale—coarse.......	60.0	$\frac{1}{2}$ in.	1.74	6.9	4.6	2,120	16,500
Expanded slag No. 2—fine....	61.0	No. 4	2.26	8.0	5.6	240	1,040
Expanded clay—fine..........	66.0	No. 4	1.98	15.8	11.1	935	6,930
Expanded slag No. 1..........	67.0	$\frac{3}{8}$ in.	2.36	9.3	6.7	395	1,360
Expanded slate—fine..........	73.0	No. 4	2.20	8.2	7.1	635	2,120
Expanded shale—fine........	76.0	No. 8	2.09	7.5	5.7	2,120	16,500

of well-rounded particles and requires less sand and less water to make concrete equivalent in strength to crushed-stone concrete. Because of its origin, it is composed of heterogeneous minerals and rocks and may contain some unsound particles. Particles of shale or slate are objectionable because of their laminar structure; water may enter the laminations and on freezing may cause local unsoundness. Particles containing pyrite may oxidize and expand. Some gravels contain particles of flint, chert, or opaline silica, which when sound may be used with many cements to give very excellent concrete. But if used with a cement high in alkalies, these particles may cause unsoundness and disruption of the concrete.

Crushed stone is "the product resulting from the artificial crushing of rocks, boulders or large cobblestones, substantially all faces of which have resulted from the crushing operation." (See ASTM Standard C125.) As a result of its processing, it is angular in contour. It should be roughly cubical in shape for use in concrete but frequently contains flat or needle-shaped particles that may be a source of weakness in the concrete. Crushed stone is usually of a single rock species and is not so heterogeneous as gravel. It may contain unsound impurities of the same characteristics as found in gravel.

Blast-furnace slag is used as a coarse aggregate in some localities where it is economically available. It is lighter in weight than gravel and crushed stone but normally is not considered a lightweight aggregate.

2-15. Fine Aggregates. Fine aggregate is that portion of aggregate finer than a No. 4 sieve. It is usually graded fairly uniformly from No. 4 to No. 100 in size. Unless otherwise mentioned, fine aggregate is usually considered to be sand, the product of the natural disintegration of a siliceous or calcareous rock. The fine product obtained from crushing of stone is known as "stone sand," while that from crushing of slag is known as "slag sand." Sand for use in concrete must contain negligible amounts of clay, coal, and lignite, material finer than a No. 200 sieve, shale, alkali, mica, coated grains, soft and flaky particles, and organic impurities.

2-16. Lightweight Aggregates. Lightweight aggregates include perlite, exfoliated vermiculite, pumice, lava, tufa, cinders, expanded clay products, etc. When mixed with cement, the resulting concrete also is light in weight and has low thermal conductivity. Strength of the concrete will be almost inversely proportional to the weight of the aggregate, although comparisons are not always easily made because of the difficulty of making concrete mixes that have the type of aggregate as the sole variable. Table 2-6 presents data on some typical lightweight aggregates as reported by Kluge, Sparks, and Tuma ("Lightweight Aggregate Concrete," *Journal of the American Concrete Institute*, May, 1949, p. 625). The data have been arranged in order of increasing unit weights.

MORTARS AND CONCRETES

2-17. Mortars. Mortars are composed of a cementitious material, fine aggregate, sand, and water. They are used for bedding unit masonry, for plasters and stuccoes, and with the addition of coarse aggregate, for concrete. In this article, consideration will be given primarily to those mortars used for unit masonry and plasters.

Properties of mortars vary greatly, being dependent on the properties of the cementitious material used, ratio of cementitious material to sand, characteristics and grading of the sand, and ratio of water to solids.

Mortars are usually proportioned by volume. A common specification is that not more than 3 cu ft of sand shall be used with 1 cu ft of cementitious material. Difficulty is sometimes encountered, however, in determining just how much material constitutes a cubic foot: A bag of cement (94 lb) by agreement is called a cubic foot in proportioning mortars or concretes, but an actual cubic foot of lime putty may be used in proportioning mortars. Since hydrated limes are sold in 50-lb bags, each of which makes somewhat more than a cubic foot of putty, weights of 40, 42, and 45 lb of hydrated lime have been used as a cubic foot in laboratory studies; but on the job, a bag is frequently used as a cubic foot. Masonry cements are sold in bags containing 70 to 80 lb, and again a bag is considered a cubic foot.

Workability is an important property of mortars, particularly of those used in conjunction with unit masonry of high absorption. Workability is controlled by the character of the cement and amount of sand. For example, a mortar made from 3 parts sand and 1 part slaked lime putty will be more workable than one made from 2 parts sand and 1 part portland cement. But it will also have much less strength when tested by the conventional cube test. By proper selection or mixing of cementitious materials, a satisfactory compromise may usually be obtained, producing a mortar of adequate strength and workability.

Water retention—the ratio of flow after one minute standard suction to the flow before suction—is used as an index of the workability of mortars. A high value of water retention is considered desirable for most purposes. Table 2-7, adapted from the data of Wells, Bishop, and Watstein ("Differences in Limes as Reflected in Certain Properties of Masonry Mortars," *Journal of Research of the National Bureau of Standards*, Vol. 17, p. 895), illustrates the wide variation in water retention of mortars made with varying proportions of cement and lime and with varying limes.

The water retention of commercial masonry cements as measured by Rogers and Blaine ("Investigation of Commercial Masonry Cements," *Journal of Research of the National Bureau of Standards*, Vol. 13, No. 6, p. 811) varied from 50 to 98%. Fink and Trattner found the water retention of six brands of Type S hydrated dolomitic lime to be from 94 to 97% ("Properties of Highly Hydrated Dolomitic Masonry Limes

Table 2-7. Water Retention of Cement-Lime Mortars, %

Proportion by volume*.	1C:OL:3S	1C:¼L:3S	1C:1L:6S	1C:2L:9S	OC:1L:3S
Cement only............	35				
Cement plus lime A....	...	67	80	84	89
Cement plus lime B....	...	...	60	...	80
Cement plus lime C (soaked).............	...	...	49	...	66
Cement plus lime C (not soaked).............	...	...	38	39	49

* C = cement; L = lime; S = sand.

and Certain of Their Cement-Lime Mortars," *Proceedings of the ASTM*, Vol. 45, p. 723).

The strength of mortar is frequently used as a specification requirement, even though it has little relation to the strength of masonry. The strength of mortar is affected primarily by the amount of cement in the matrix. Other factors of importance are the ratio of sand to cementing material, curing conditions, and age when tested. Staley studied the strength of mortars as a function of the cement-lime ratio under 14 different curing conditions ("Curing of Masonry Mortars," *Proceedings of the ASTM*, Vol. 42, p. 762). The maximum and minimum compressive strengths that he obtained at 28 days are shown in Table 2-8.

Table 2-8. 28-day Strengths of Cement-Lime Mortars

Proportions by volume, cement:lime:sand	Compressive strengths, psi	
	Min	Max
1:0.25: 3	3,200	5,500
1: 1 : 5	1,480	2,290
1:1.25:6.25	635	1,370
1: 2 :7.5	545	1,085
1: 3 : 10	165	525

Rogers and Blaine found the compressive strength of mortars made from masonry cements to vary from less than 100 psi to over 4,800 psi at 28 days.

Volume change of mortars constitutes another important property. Normal volume change (as distinguished from unsoundness) may be considered as the shrinkage during early hardening, shrinkage on drying, expansion on wetting, and changes due to temperature. Palmer and Parsons reported the shrinkage of mortars during the initial 48 hr ("A Study of the Properties of Mortars and Bricks and Their Relation to Bond," *Journal of Research of the National Bureau of Standards*, Vol. 12, p. 609). They tested the mortars at three consistencies—dry, intermediate, and wet. Their results for the intermediate consistency are summarized in Table 2-9.

Rogers and Blaine, using a somewhat different technique, reported shrinkages of 41 masonry cements at 24 hr varying from 0.087 to 0.585% and averaging 0.335%.

Davis and Troxell found that all mortars shrank on drying ("Volumetric Changes in Portland Cement Mortars and Concretes," *Proceedings of the American Concrete Institute*, Vol. 25, p. 210). Their results on cement-lime mortars after drying for 1 year showed a shrinkage of 0.14 to 0.16%. Rogers and Blaine found shrinkages during drying of masonry-cement mortars ranging from 0.055 to 0.195% and averaging 0.099%.

After drying, mortars expand again when wetted. Cement-lime mortars tested by Davis and Troxell showed wetting expansions of 0.06 to 0.085%. Alternate wetting and drying produces alternate expansion and contraction, which apparently continues indefinitely with portland-cement mortars.

Palmer measured the coefficient of thermal expansion of several mortars ("Volume Changes in Brick Masonry Materials," *Journal of Research of the National Bureau of Standards,* Vol. 6, p. 1003). The coefficients ranged from 0.38×10^{-5} to 0.60×10^{-5} for masonry-cement mortars; from 0.41×10^{-5} to 0.53×10^{-5} for lime mortars, and from 0.42×10^{-5} to 0.61×10^{-5} for cement mortars. Composition of the cementitious material apparently has little effect upon the coefficient of thermal expansion of a mortar.

Table 2-9. Linear Shrinkage During Early Hardening of Mortars

Mortar composition, parts by volume	Linear shrinkage at 48 hr, %		
	Min	Max	Avg
1 portland cement:0 lime:3 sand	0.21	0.24	0.22
1P.C.:0.15L:3S	0.18	0.30	0.24
1P.C.: 1L :6S	0.26	0.35	0.30
1P.C.: 2L :9S	0.41	0.61	0.48
1P.C.: 3L :12S	0.52	0.77	0.62
1 lime:3 sand	0.66	1.11	0.83
1 masonry cement:3 sand	0.24	0.58	0.37

2-18. Normal Concrete. Concrete is a mixture of portland cement, fine aggregate, coarse aggregate, and water, which is temporarily fluid and capable of being poured, cast, or molded, but which later sets and hardens to form a solid mass. Normal concrete is here considered to be concrete made with sand as fine aggregate and with conventional aggregates, such as gravel or crushed stone, and to which no air-entrainment admixture has been added. It is to be distinguished from air-entrained concrete, which has some air deliberately added and from lightweight concretes made with special lightweight aggregates or with a large air content.

The ultimate consumer of concrete is interested in three major properties of concrete—adequate strength, adequate durability, and minimum cost. In the attainment of these three objectives, the concrete designer may wish to vary the proportions of ingredients widely. The principal variations which may be imposed are:

1. The water-cement ratio.
2. The cement-aggregate ratio.
3. The size of coarse aggregate.
4. The ratio of fine aggregate to coarse aggregate.
5. The type of cement.

With varying ingredients, concretes may be made with strengths as low as 1,500 psi or as high as 8,000 psi at 28 days. Durability may vary from almost complete durability under the most severe exposure to none at all unless the concrete is protected from weather. Material costs may vary from very expensive to very cheap.

The property of fluid concrete that is of greatest importance is workability. Workability is much talked about but is poorly defined and poorly measured. It involves the concepts of fluidity, cohesiveness, adhesiveness, plasticity, and probably others. A definition sometimes used is "ability to flow without segregation." Workability is enhanced by high cement factors and high sand-to-coarse-aggregate ratios; but these factors also involve high cost and may involve undesirable, high-volume change. The concrete designer must strike a balance between all factors involved and must frequently allow less workability than he wants in order to obtain concrete that is satisfactory from some other aspect.

The density of fluid concrete made with conventional aggregates will approximate 150 lb per cu ft. This value may be used in calculating strength of formwork and density of set concrete.

Setting and hardening of concrete are caused by a chemical reaction between the constituents of the cement and the water. This reaction is accompanied by the evolution of considerable heat. Normally, in structural concrete, this heat is removed by conduction, radiation, or convection about as rapidly as it is generated; but in large masses, the heat cannot be dissipated rapidly and may be sufficient to raise the temperature of the mass by 50 to 60°F. In such cases, Type IV cement may be used to keep the temperature rise as low as possible and thereby prevent delayed cracking.

Table 2-10. Relation between W/C* Ratio and Compressive Strength

Net W/C by Weight	28-day Strength, Psi
0.40	5,500
0.42	5,200
0.44	5,000
0.46	4,800
0.49	4,400
0.53	4,000
0.58	3,600
0.62	3,300
0.67	2,900
0.71	2,600
0.75	2,400

* Water-cement.

Table 2-11. Relation between Age and Compressive Strength, Psi

Age	Type I cement	Type II cement	Type III cement
3 days...........	2,100	2,100	3,400
7 days...........	3,200	3,000	4,400
28 days...........	4,500	4,500	5,500
90 days...........	5,000	5,400	6,100
1 year...........	5,600	5,800	6,700

Table 2-12. Relation between Cement Content and Strength of Concrete

Cement Content, Lb per Cu Yd	Avg 28-day Strength, Psi
350	2,000
400	2,700
450	3,300
500	3,800
550	4,300
600	4,800
650	5,200

Strength of concrete is conventionally measured by testing in compression cylinders 6 in. in diameter and 12 in. high.

The prime factor affecting strength is the water-cement (W/C) ratio. This is commonly expressed as a ratio by weight but may be expressed as gallons of water per sack of cement. Table 2-10 shows the relation between the W/C ratio and 28-day compressive strength of normal concrete as used by the Bureau of Reclamation ("Concrete Manual," Government Printing Office, Washington, D.C.).

The strength is affected by the age of the concrete when tested, as shown in Table 2-11.

Strength of concrete is affected by the cement content, as shown in Table 2-12.

Strength of concrete is diminished by curing at low temperatures, as is shown in Table 2-13.

Other factors have a bearing on the strength of a particular concrete but may usually be compensated for in mix design.　Strength of a concrete made from one aggregate may be somewhat less than that made from a second aggregate, but a slight decrease in water-cement ratio of the former concrete may make the two identical.　Similarly, variations in strength due to grading of aggregate and to the type or brand of cement may be compensated in the mix design.

Table 2-13. Effect of Curing Temperature on Relative Strength of Concrete

Curing Temp, °F	Relative 28-day Strength 70°F = 100
40	78
55	98
70	100
85	101
100	103
115	105

A property of importance equal to that of strength is volume change.　Volume changes that occur while concrete is in a plastic state are normally not of great importance in mass concrete, but in reinforced concrete they may be.　The result of settlement, sedimentation, or bleeding may be to cause the concrete to settle away from the underside of the reinforcement, thereby impairing bond of the concrete to the reinforcing steel.　This may be avoided by using a workable nonbleeding concrete, obtainable by using less water, finer cement, pozzolanic admixtures, or air entrainment.

Volume changes that occur after hardening are apt to result in cracking, which weakens the concrete and makes it susceptible to early disintegration by attack by frost or by aggressive solutions.

The thermal coefficient of expansion of concrete varies with the cement content, water content, type of aggregate, and other factors, but averages 0.000005 in. per in. per degree Fahrenheit ("Concrete Manual," Bureau of Reclamation, Government Printing Office, Washington, D.C.).

Concrete is subject to expansion and contraction with wetting and drying.　The drying shrinkage of concrete is slightly more than $\frac{1}{2}$ in. per 100 ft.　This, in magnitude, is equivalent to a thermal change of about 83°F.

The stress-strain curve for concrete appears to be slightly curved over its entire length.　The portion from zero load to about 40% of the ultimate load is sufficiently straight that a secant modulus of elasticity may be determined on this portion.　The modulus of elasticity, calculated in this manner, is about 1,000 times the compressive strength in pounds per square inch.

When concrete is subjected to a sustained load, it first undergoes an elastic deformation, the magnitude of which is proportional to the load and the elasticity of the concrete.　As the load is continued, however, deformation continues to increase with time.　This deformation under load is termed creep or plastic flow.　The creep continues for an indefinite time, measurements having been made for periods in excess of 10 years.　It proceeds at a continuously diminishing rate and approaches some limiting value.　The amount of creep at this limiting value appears to be from one to three times the amount of the elastic deformation.　Usually, more than 50% of the ultimate creep takes place within the first 3 months after loading.　Upon unloading, an immediate elastic recovery takes place, followed by a plastic recovery of lesser amount than the creep on first loading.

2-19. Air-entraining Concretes.　All normal concrete contains some air, usually between 0.5 and 1.0%.　By the addition of a small amount of an air-entraining agent, the amount of air contained in the concrete may be materially increased to 10% or more (by volume) if desired.　This extra air is present in the form of small, discrete air bubbles, which have a marked effect upon the workability, durability, and strength of the concrete.

Since addition of air decreases strength of concrete, it is necessary to compensate for this decrease by decreasing the water-cement ratio or decreasing unit water content, or both.　Even with compensating adjustments of this nature, it is usually impossible to maintain the design strength of the concrete if more than 6% air is present. Consequently, air contents are usually specified to be about 4%, with 6% air as a maximum.

Air-entrained concrete has a lower unit weight than normal concrete. A concrete that would weigh 150 lb per cu ft without air will weigh only 144 with 4% entrained air.

Addition of air to concrete makes a great improvement in workability. If air is added to a normal concrete of 2-in. slump without compensating adjustments, an air-entrained concrete with a slump of 6 to 8 in. will result. By removal of some of the water, thereby increasing the water-cement ratio, the slump may be brought back to 2 in., but the resulting air-entrained concrete is still much more workable and more cohesive and has less bleeding and segregation than the normal concrete of equivalent slump. This improvement in workability persists, even if some of the sand is withdrawn, as is common practice.

Durability of air-entrained concrete exposed to severe weathering is much superior to that of normal concrete. This has been adequately demonstrated by many laboratory and field studies which have been reported in recent years. Table 2-14 presents some generalized data on durability and relative strength, which have been adapted from a more extensive presentation given in the "Concrete Manual" (Bureau of Reclamation, Government Printing Office, Washington, D.C.).

Table 2-14. Effect of Air-Entrainment on Strength and Durability of Concrete

Water-cement ratio	Normal concrete		Concrete with 4% air	
	Probable strength, psi	Durability factor	Probable strength, psi	Durability factor
0.40	5,500	4.4	4,500	15.1
0.50	4,300	2.6	3,500	10.0
0.60	3,400	1.7	2,800	5.7
0.70	2,600	1.3	2,200	2.9

The other properties of air-entrained concrete such as rate of development of strength, volume change, and elasticity appear to be identical with those of normal concrete, if allowance is made for the weakening effect of the air and the additional workability attained through its incorporation.

2-20. Lightweight Concretes. Appreciable savings in weight and accompanying savings in steel costs and other costs are often obtainable through the use of lightweight concretes. These are concretes wherein the normal heavy aggregates have been replaced with lightweight aggregates (see Art. 2-16). Kluge, Sparks, and Tuma made an extensive study of concretes made from lightweight aggregates, and a small portion of their data is given in Table 2-15 ("Lightweight Aggregate Concrete," *Journal of the American Concrete Institute*, May, 1949, p. 625).

As will be seen from the table, there are certain general trends. The lighter concretes, in general, have higher absorptions, lower strengths, lower elastic moduli, lower thermal conductivity, and higher shrinkage. The data must be used with caution, however. For example, the difference in weight between expanded slate and expanded slag No. 3 is negligible, but the differences in absorption, strength, and thermal conductivity are appreciable. The variability in any one type of material is indicated by the three brands of expanded slag used in this study.

Extensive data covering these and some other types of aggregates are given by Price and Cordon ("Tests of Lightweight Aggregate Concrete Designed for Monolithic Construction," *Journal of the American Concrete Institute*, Vol. 20, p. 581). Their data indicate the same trends and further emphasize the fact that the designer of lightweight concrete must base his design on specific tests of the particular aggregate under consideration rather than upon average data obtainable from tables and charts.

Table 2.15. Properties of Concretes Made with Lightweight Aggregates

Property	Normal sand and gravel	Ex-panded shale	Ex-panded slag No. 2	Ex-panded slag No. 1	Sintered fly ash	Ex-panded clay	Ex-panded slate	Ex-panded slag No. 3	Pumice	Sintered dia-tomite	Ex-panded vermic-ulite	Perlite
Sacks of cement per cu yd	5.5	4.9	4.8	4.9	5.1	4.4	5.0	5.2	4.7	4.4	4.7	4.4
Slump, in.	4	5	3	4	5	3	7	4	4	4	7	7
Water, gal per cu yd	42	58	67	78	61	46	59	61	73	121	99	74
Unit weight, lb per cu ft:												
Fresh	146	106	98	99	92	89	81	81	81	77	54	44
Room-dry	144	104	97	96	87	85	79	79	70	58	34	33
Oven-dry	137	95	89	86	82	78	74	72	63	48	29	28
Absorption:												
% by weight	4.8	10.6	14.5	17.6	15.2	10.3	7.5	16.5	25.5	60.1	85.2	54.4
% by volume	11.3	17.5	23.3	26.4	21.2	13.9	9.5	20.8	28.6	52.3	44.2	27.3
Compressive strength, psi:												
7-day	4,040	2,380	530	610	1,170	1,746	1,680	1,200	1,540	400	185	250
28-day	4,810	4,000	1,400	705	1,800	2,596	2,300	1,725	1,765	654	290	270
Oven-dry	4,710	4,250	1,280	915	1,736	2,975	2,165	1,480	1,782	500	325	267
Transverse strength, psi:												
28-day	611	470	278	177	298	334	371	244	106	70	76	53
Oven-dry	488	666	286	227	255	351	305	241	119	44	72	50
Elastic modulus:												
Static × 10⁻³	3,680	2,479	1,560	1,285	1,453	1,060	1,255	1,317	385	282	158	120
Sonic × 10⁻³	4,376	2,748	1,706	1,372	1,519	1,460	1,365	1,315	588	360	161	157
Thermal conductivity, K, Btu/hr/sq ft/deg F/in.	9.57	4.03	2.49	2.42	2.80	3.15	2.80	1.81	1.89	1.27	1.02	0.92
Durability factor	86	79	69	76	100	76	100	75	92	2	10	78
Shrinkage at 100 days, in. per ft.	0.0060	0.0115	0.0100	0.0110	0.0100	0.0123	0.0103	0.0120	0.0170	0.0315	0.0565	0.0235

Aggregate

Other lightweight concretes are produced by various methods.   One of these methods is to mix a concrete or mortar with a treated aluminum powder.   The reaction of the aluminum with calcium hydroxide liberated by the cement evolves hydrogen, which causes the plastic concrete to expand.   The expansion may be as much as 100% of the unexpanded volume.   The cement sets at about the time the expansion is completed.   Hence the set concrete remains in the expanded form.   Concretes weighing

Table 2-16. Summary of ASTM Specification Requirements for Concrete Masonry Units

	Compressive strength, min, psi		Water absorption, max, lb per cu ft	Moisture content, max, %	Modulus of rupture, min, psi	
	Avg of 5 specimens	Individual min			Avg of 5 specimens	Individual min
Concrete building brick—ASTM C55-37:						
Grade A...................	2,500	2,000	...	...	450	300
Grade B...................	1,250	1,000	...	...	300	200
Hollow non-load-bearing masonry units—ASTM C129-39..........	350	300	...	40		
Hollow load-bearing masonry units —ASTM C90-44						
Face shell thickness 1¼ in. or more:						
Grade A...................	1,000	800	15	40		
Grade B...................	700	600	...	40		
Face shell thickness—over ¾ in., under 1¼ in...............	1,000	800	15	40		
Solid load-bearing concrete masonry units—ASTM C145-40:						
Grade A...................	1,800	1,600	15	40		
Grade B...................	1,200	1,000	15	40		

from 75 to 100 lb per cu ft are produced in this manner.   The upper surface of the concrete may be irregular if there has been irregularity in distribution of the aluminum powder.

Another method of producing very lightweight concrete is to mix cement and fine filler, such as pulverized stone, silica flour, or fly ash, with a stabilized foam.   By proper proportioning of the volumes of foam and solids, concretes weighing as little as 10 lb per cu ft have been produced.   These materials have very low strength but are well adapted for production of insulated and fire-resistant roof slabs and other members where strength is of little importance.

A lightweight concrete into which nails can be readily driven and which will hold the nails firmly is produced by mixing equal volumes of cement, sand, and pine sawdust with enough water to give a slump of 1 to 2 in.   This concrete, after moist curing for 2 days and drying for 1 day, has excellent holding power for nails.

2-21. Concrete Masonry Units.   A wide variety of manufactured products are produced from concrete and used in building construction.   These include such items as concrete brick, concrete block or tile, concrete floor and roof slabs, precast lintels, and cast stone.   These items are made both from normal dense concrete mixes and from mixes with lightweight aggregates.

Properties of the units vary tremendously—from strong, dense load-bearing units used under exposed conditions to light, relatively weak, insulating units used for roof and fire-resistant construction.

Many types of concrete units have not been covered by adequate standard specifications. For these units, reliance must be placed upon the manufacturer's specifications. Requirements for strength and absorption of concrete brick and block have been established by the American Society for Testing Materials. A summary of these requirements is presented in Table 2-16.

Manufactured concrete units are subject to the advantage (or sometimes disadvantage) that curing is under the control of the manufacturer. Many methods of curing are used, from simply stacking the units in a more or less exposed location to curing under high-pressure steam. The latter method appears to have considerable merit in reducing ultimate shrinkage of the block. Easterly found shrinkages ranging from $\frac{1}{4}$ to $\frac{3}{8}$ in. per 100 ft for concretes cured with high-pressure steam ("Shrinkage and Curing in Masonry Units," *Journal of the American Concrete Institute*, Vol. 23, p. 393). These values are about one-half as great as those obtained with normal atmospheric curing. Easterly also obtained values for the moisture movement in test blocks that had been cured with high-pressure and high-temperature steam. He found expansions of from $\frac{1}{4}$ to $\frac{1}{2}$ in. per 100 ft on saturating previously dried specimens.

BURNED-CLAY UNITS

Use of burned-clay structural units dates from prehistoric times. Hence durability of well-burned units has been adequately established through centuries of exposure in all types of climate.

Modern burned-clay units are made in a wide variety of size, shape, color, and texture to suit the requirements of modern architecture. They include such widely diverse units as common and face brick; hollow clay tile in numerous shapes, sizes, and

Table 2-17. Physical Requirements for Clay or Shale Brick

Grade	Compressive strength, flat, min, psi		Water absorption, 5-hr boil, max—%		Saturation* coefficient, max—%	
	Avg of 5	Indi-vidual	Avg of 5	Indi-vidual	Avg of 5	Indi-vidual
SW—Severe weathering.	3,000	2,500	17.0	20.0	0.78	0.80
MW—Moderate weather-ing.............. ..	2,500	2,200	22.0	25.0	0.88	0.90
NW—No exposure......	1,500	1,250	No limit	No limit	No limit	No limit

* Ratio of 24-hr cold absorption to 5-hr boil absorption.

designs for special purposes; ceramic tile for decorative and sanitary finishes, and architectural terra cotta for ornamentation.

Properties of burned-clay units vary with the type of clay or shale used as raw material, method of fabrication of the units, and temperature of burning. As a consequence, some units, such as salmon brick, are underburned, highly porous, and of poor strength. But others are almost glass hard, have been pressed and burned to almost eliminate porosity, and are very strong. Between these extremes lie most of the units used for construction.

2-22. Brick. Brick have been made in a wide range of sizes and shapes, from the old Greek brick, which was practically a 23-in. cube of 12,650 cu in. volume, to the small Belgian brick, approximately $1\frac{3}{4} \times 3\frac{3}{8} \times 4\frac{1}{2}$ in. with a total volume of only 27 cu in. The present common size in the United States is $2\frac{1}{4} \times 3\frac{3}{4} \times 8$ in., with a volume of $67\frac{1}{2}$ cu in., and a weight between $4\frac{1}{2}$ and 5 lb. Current specification requirements for strength and absorption of building brick are given in Table 2-17 (see ASTM Specification C62).

A study of the strength distribution of brick classified as "hard" by manufacturers from all sections of the United States was reported by McBurney and Lovewell ("Strength, Water Absorption and Weather Resistance of Building Brick Produced in the U.S.," *Proceedings of the ASTM*, Vol. 33, Part II, p. 636). Table 2-18 briefly summarizes some of their findings.

Table 2-18. Distribution of Strength Properties of Brick

Compressive strength, flatwise		Modulus of rupture	
Range, psi	Percentage within range	Range, psi	Percentage within range
0– 1,500	0.36	0– 150	0.37
1,501– 3,000	7.46	151– 300	0.37
3,001– 6,000	34.78	301– 600	11.87
6,001– 9,000	27.39	601– 900	25.34
9,001–12,000	16.39	901–1,200	20.99
12,001–15,000	8.47	1,201–1,500	12.46
15,001–18,000	3.53	1,501–1,800	15.91
18,001–22,500	1.59	1,801–3,450	12.69

Table 2-19. Distribution of Water Absorption and *C/B* Ratio for Brick

Range, %	Water absorption		Ratio, 48-hr cold to 4-hr boil absorption	
	% within range			
	48-hr cold	5-hr boil	Range	% within range
0– 4.00	7.61	3.30	0.16–0.35	0.82
4.01– 8.00	27.22	13.21	0.36–0.45	0.85
8.01–12.00	27.59	24.96	0.46–0.55	2.45
12.01–16.00	23.53	26.97	0.56–0.65	11.94
16.01–20.00	10.29	20.16	0.66–0.75	29.17
20.01–24.00	2.95	7.86	0.76–0.85	35.06
24.01–28.00	0.68	2.70	0.86–0.95	19.21
28.01–34.00	0.11	0.75	0.96–1.00	0.51

McBurney and Lovewell also studied the absorptive properties of brick. Their results are partly summarized in Table 2-19.

Thermal expansion of brick has been measured by Ross ("Thermal Expansion of Clay Building Brick," *Journal of Research of the National Bureau of Standards*, Vol. 27, p. 197). He obtained values ranging from 0.0000017 per °F for a sample of fire-clay brick to 0.0000069 per °F for a surface-clay brick. The average coefficient for 80 specimens of surface-clay brick was 0.0000033; that for 41 specimens of shale brick was 0.0000034. These results are of the same order of magnitude as those obtained by Palmer, who found a variation of from 0.0000036 to 0.0000085 ("Volume Changes in Brick Masonry Materials," *Journal of Research of the National Bureau of Standards* Vol. 6, p. 1003).

Palmer studied the expansion of brick due to wetting and obtained wetting expansions varying from 0.0005 to 0.025%.

The thermal conductivity of dry brick as measured by several investigators ranges from 1.29 to 3.79 Btu/hr/sq ft/°F/in. The values are increased by wetting.

Table 2-20. Physical Requirement Specifications for Structural Clay Tile

Type and grade	Absorption, %			Compressive strength, psi (based on gross area)			
				End-construction tile		Side-construction tile	
	Avg of 5 tests	Individual max	Individual min	Min avg of 5 tests	Individual min	Min avg of 5 tests	Individual min
Load-bearing (ASTM C34):							
LBX..................	5–16	19	4	1,400	1,000	700	500
LB....................	0–25	28	4	1,000	700	700	500
Non-load-bearing (ASTM C56):							
NB....................	5–15	28	4				
Floor tile (ASTM C57):							
FT 1.................	5–25	25	4	3,200	2,250	1,600	1,100
FT 2.................	5–25	25	4	2,000	1,400	1,200	850
Facing tile (ASTM C212):							
FTX..................	7 (max)	9					
FTS..................	13 (max)	16					
Standard..............	....	. . .	. . .	1,400	1,000	700	500
Special duty...........	....	. . .	. . .	2,500	2,000	1,200	1,000
Glazed units (ASTM C126)	5 (max)	7	. . .	3,000	2,500	2,000	1,500

LBX. Tile suitable for general use in masonry construction and adapted for use in masonry exposed to weathering. They may also be considered suitable for direct application of stucco.

LB. Tile suitable for general use in masonry where not exposed to frost action, or in exposed masonry where protected with a facing of 3 in. or more of stone, brick, terra cotta, or other masonry.

NB. Non-load-bearing tile made from surface clay, shale, or fire clay.

FT 1 and FT 2. Tile suitable for use in flat or segmental arches or in combination tile and concrete ribbed-slab construction.

FTX. Smooth-face tile suitable for general use in exposed exterior and interior masonry walls and partitions, and adapted for use where tile low in absorption, easily cleaned, and resistant to staining are required and where a high degree of mechanical perfection, narrow color range, and minimum variation in face dimensions are required.

FTS. Smooth or rough-texture face tile suitable for general use in exposed exterior and interior masonry walls and partitions and adapted for use where tile of moderate absorption, moderate variation in face dimensions, and medium color range may be used, and where minor defects in surface finish, including small handling chips, are not objectionable.

Standard. Tile suitable for general use in exterior or interior masonry walls and partitions.

Special duty. Tile suitable for general use in exterior or interior masonry walls and partitions and designed to have superior resistance to impact and moisture transmission, and to support greater lateral and compressive loads than standard tile construction.

Glazed units. Ceramic-glazed structural clay tile with a glossy or satin-mat finish of either an opaque or clear glaze, produced by the application of a coating prior to firing and subsequently made vitreous by firing.

2-23. Structural Clay Tile. Structural clay tile are hollow burned-clay masonry units with parallel cells. Such units have a multitude of uses: as a facing tile for interior and exterior unplastered walls, partitions, or columns; as load-bearing tile in masonry constructions designed to carry superimposed loads; as partition tile for interior partitions carrying no superimposed load; as fireproofing tile for protection of structural members against fire; as furring tile for lining the inside of exterior walls; as floor tile in floor and roof construction; and as header tile, which are designed to provide recesses for header units in brick or stone-faced walls.

Two general types of tile are available—side-construction tile, designed to receive its principal stress at right angles to the axis of the cells, and end-construction tile, designed to receive its principal stress parallel to the axis of the cells.

Table 2-21. Strength and Absorption of Hollow Clay Tile

Kind of clay	Average compressive strength, psi			Avg absorption		
	Test on end	Test on edge	Test on side			
Shale.........................	1,509	490	721	8.44	7.52	11.92
	1,362	361	914	8.99	9.71	10.50
	2,826	1,557	1,376	8.47	8.56	10.09
	3,150	2,630	690	6.89	8.87	13.39
	5,304	.....	.....	7.02		
Surface clay..................	1,510	355	767	15.07	13.57	25.11
	1,900	516	1,000	16.20	16.74	14.40
	2,639	493	.....	9.79	16.88	
	1,473	710	.....	19.02	19.43	
	1,050	596	.....	21.39	25.64	
	1,921	807	.....	26.11	24.77	
	1,654	.....	.....	24.53		
Dense-burning fire clay..........	2,546	989	1,365	11.92	11.89	7.77
	2,897	978	731	11.47	11.69	8.74
	2,681	776	1,182	8.65	8.12	11.55
Open-burning fire clay............	2,250	581	.....	12.29	11.14	
	1,675	544	.....	12.85	13.62	
	1,408	336	.....	15.61	15.81	
50% fire clay, 50% shale.........	1,606	975	.....	8.91	9.36	
85% fire clay, 15% shale.........	1,520	314	.....	12.39	12.48	
Dense-burning clay..............	4,060	1,861	.....	9.42	9.01	
50% shale, 50% surface clay......	.....	.....	1,273	10.83		

Tile are also available in a number of surface finishes, such as opaque glazed tile, clear ceramic-glazed tile, nonlustrous glazed tile, and scored, combed, or roughened finishes designed to receive mortar, plaster, or stucco.

Requirements of the appropriate ASTM specifications for absorption and strength of several types of tile are given in Table 2-20 (see ASTM Specifications C34, C56, C57, C212, and C126 for details pertaining to size, color, texture, defects, etc.).

Committee C-10 of ASTM developed a large amount of data pertaining to strength and absorption of structural clay tile (Report of ASTM Committee C-10, *Proceedings of the ASTM*, Vol. 24, Part I, p. 411). A portion of their data is summarized in Table 2-21. Each figure represents the average of from three to five individual tests of tile from the same source. The wide variation in strength and absorption of tile made from similar clays but from different sources and manufacturers is obvious.

Foster presents data on the modulus of elasticity of tile showing a range in modulus from 1,620,000 to 6,059,000 psi for tile from 18 different sources ("Strength, Absorption and Freezing Resistance of Hollow Building Tile," *Journal of the American Ceramic Society*, Vol. 7, No. 3, p. 189).

Data for thermal expansion and for wetting expansion of tile apparently are not available, but since tile are made from the same clays as brick, the values previously cited for brick should be applicable to tile (see Art. 2-22). Some data are available on thermal conductivity of individual tile; but since the conductivity of the whole wall is more important than that of the units, these data will be considered under the properties of assemblages (Sec. 18).

2-24. Ceramic Tile. Ceramic tile is a burned-clay product used primarily for decorative and sanitary effects. It is composed of a clay body on which is superimposed a decorative glaze.

The tile are usually flat but vary in size from about ½ in. square up to about 6 in. or even larger. Their shape is also widely variable—squares, rectangles, and hexagons are the predominating forms, to which must be added coved moldings and other decorative forms. They are not dependent upon the color of the clay for their final color since they are usually glazed. Hence they are available in a complete color gradation from pure whites through pastels of varying hue to deep solid colors and jet blacks.

Properties of the base vary somewhat, particularly absorption, which ranges from almost zero up to about 15%. The glaze is required to be impervious to liquids and should not stain, crack, or craze.

Ceramic tile are applied on a solid backing, either masonry or plaster, by means of a mortar or adhesive. They are usually applied with the thinnest possible mortar joint: consequently accuracy of dimensions is of greatest importance. Since color, size, and shape of tile are the important features in these tile, reliance must be placed upon the current literature of the manufacturer for information on these characteristics; general summaries are of little value.

2-25. Architectural Terra Cotta. The term "terra cotta" has been applied for centuries to decorative molded-clay objects whose properties are similar to brick. The shapes are molded either by hand or by machine and fired in a manner similar to brick. Terra cotta is frequently glazed to produce a desired color or finish. This introduces the problem of cracking or crazing of the glaze, particularly over large areas. Structural properties of terra cotta are similar to those of brick.

BUILDING STONES

Principal building stones generally used in the United States are limestones, marbles, granites, and sandstones. Other stones such as serpentine and quartzite are used locally but to a much lesser extent. Stone, in general, makes an excellent building material, if properly selected on the basis of experience; but the cost may be relatively high.

Properties of stone are not under the control of the manufacturer. He must take what nature has provided, and therefore, he cannot provide the choice of properties and color available in some of the manufactured building units. The most the stone producer can do is to avoid quarrying certain stone beds that have been proved by experience to have poor strength or poor durability.

2-26. Strength of Stone. Data on the strength of building stones are presented in Table 2-22, summarized from the extensive work of D. W. Kessler and his associates (*National Bureau of Standards (U.S.) Technical Papers*, No. 123, B. S. Vol. 12; No. 305, vol. 20, p. 191; No. 349, Vol. 21, p. 497; *Journal of Research of the National Bureau of Standards*, Vol. 11, p. 635; Vol. 25, p. 161). The data in Table 2-22 pertain to dried specimens. Strength of saturated specimens may be either greater or less than that of completely dry specimens. In a comparison of 90 specimens of marble tested in compression both dry and saturated, it was found that the strength of 69 saturated marbles was less than that of the same marbles when dry by amounts ranging from 0.3 to 46.0% and averaging 9.7%. On the other hand, 21 marbles showed an increase in strength on soaking; the increase ranged from 0.04 to 35.4% and averaged 7.6%.

The modulus of rupture of dry slate is given in Table 2-22 as ranging from 6,000 to

Table 2-22. Strength Characteristics of Commercial Building Stones

Stone	Compressive strength, psi, range	Modulus of rupture, psi, range	Shear strength, psi, range	Tensile strength, psi, range	Elastic modulus, psi, range	Toughness		Wear resistance	
						Range	Avg	Range	Avg
Granite	7,700–60,000	1,430–5,190	2,000–4,800	600–1,000	5,700,000–8,200,000	8–27	13	43.9–87.9	60.8
Marble	8,000–50,000	600–4,900	1,300–6,500	150–2,300	7,200,000–14,500,000	2–23	6	6.7–41.7	18.9
Limestone	2,600–28,000	500–2,000	800–4,580	280–890	1,500,000–12,400,000	5–20	7	1.3–24.1	8.4
Sandstone	5,000–20,000	700–2,300	300–3,000	280–500	1,900,000–7,700,000	2–35	10	1.6–29.0	13.3
Quartzite	16,000–45,000	.....	.....	.....	.....	5–30	15	.....	.....
Serpentine	11,000–28,000	1,300–11,000	.....	800–1,600	4,800,000–9,600,000	.....	.....	13.3–111.4	46.9
Basalt	28,000–67,000	.....	.....	.....	.....	5–40	20	.....	.....
Diorite	16,000–35,000	.....	.....	.....	.....	6–38	23	.....	.....
Syenite	14,000–28,000	.....	.....	.....	.....	.....	.....	.....	.....
Slate	.....	6,000–15,000	2,000–3,600	3,000–4,300	9,800,000–18,000,000	10–56	.....	5.6–11.7	7.7
Diabase	.....	.....	.....	.....	.....	6–50	19	.....	.....
Building limestone	.....	.....	.....	.....	.....	3–8	4.4	.....	.....

15,000 psi. Similar slates, tested wet, gave moduli ranging from 4,700 to 12,300 psi. The ratio of wet modulus to dry modulus varied from 0.42 to 1.12 and averaged 0.73.

2-27. Specific Gravity, Porosity, and Absorption of Stone. Data on the true specific gravity, bulk specific gravity, unit weights, porosity, and absorption of various stones have been obtained by Kessler and his associates. Some of these data are given in Table 2-23.

2-28. Permeability of Stone. Permeability of stone varies with type of stone, thickness, and driving pressure that forces water through the stone. Table 2-24 presents data by Kessler for the more common stones at three different pressures ("Permeability of Stone," *National Bureau of Standards (U.S.) Technical Papers*, No. 305, Vol. 20, p. 191). The units of measurement of permeability are cubic inches of water which will flow through a square foot of a specimen ½ in. thick in 1 hr.

Table 2-23. Specific Gravity and Porosity of Commercial Building Stones

Stone	Specific gravity		Unit weight, lb per cu ft	Porosity, %	Absorption, %	
	True	Bulk			By weight	By volume
Granite.....	2.599–3.080	2.60–3.04	157–187	0.4–3.8	0.02–0.58	0.4–1.8
Marble......	2.718–2.879	2.64–2.86	165–179	0.4–2.1	0.01–0.45	0.04–1.2
Limestone...	2.700–2.860	1.87–2.69	117–175	1.1–31.0	....	6–15
Slate........	2.771–2.898	2.74–2.89	168–180	0.1–1.7	0.00–1.63	0.3–2.0
Basalt.......	....	2.9–3.2				
Soapstone...	....	2.8–3.0				
Gneiss.......	....	2.7–3.0				
Serpentine...	....	2.5–2.8	158–183			
Sandstone...	....	2.2–2.7	119–168	1.9–27.3	....	6–18
Quartzite....	....	....	165–170	1.5–2.9		

Table 2-24. Permeability of Commercial Building Stones
(cu in. per sq ft per hr for ½-in. thickness)

Pressure, psi..........	1.2	50	100
Granite..............	0.6–0.8	0.11	0.28
Slate................	0.006–0.008	0.08–0.11	0.11
Marble..............	0.06–0.35	1.3–16.8	0.9–28.0
Limestone............	0.36–2.24	4.2–44.8	0.9–109
Sandstone............	4.2–174.0	51.2	221

2-29. Thermal Expansion of Stone. Thermal expansion of building stones as measured by Kessler and his associates is given in Table 2-25. It shows that limestones have a wide range of expansion as compared with granites and slates.

Table 2-25. Coefficient of Thermal Expansion of Commercial Building Stones

Stone	Range of Coefficient
Limestone............	$(4.2–22) \times 10^{-6}$
Marble..............	$(3.6–16) \times 10^{-6}$
Sandstone...........	$(5.0–12) \times 10^{-6}$
Slate................	$(9.4–12) \times 10^{-6}$
Granite.............	$(6.3–9) \times 10^{-6}$

The effect of repeated heating and cooling on marble has been studied. A marble that had an original strength of 9,174 psi, after 50 heatings to 150°C had a strength of 8,998 psi—a loss of 1.9%. After 100 heatings to 150°C, the strength was only 8,507 psi, or a loss of 7.3%. The latter loss in strength was identical with that obtained on freezing and thawing the same marble for 30 cycles.

Wheeler measured the permanent expansion that occurs on repeatedly heating marble ("Thermal Expansion of Rock at High Temperatures," *Transactions of the Royal Society of Canada*, Vol. 4, sec. 3, p. 19). Using specimens 20 cm in length, he obtained total expansions of over 2 mm and permanent expansions of over 1 mm, as shown in Table 2-26.

Table 2-26. Permanent Expansion of Marble on Heating

Heating cycle	Temp, °C	Expansion, mm per 20-cm specimen	
		Total	Permanent
First...............	448	1.611	
	19.5	.....	0.732
Second.............	464	1.810	
	16	.....	0.897
Third..............	463	1.852	
	19	.....	0.952
Fourth.............	504	2.119	
	18	.....	1.048
Fifth..............	478	1.998	
	25	.....	1.074
Sixth..............	478	2.129	
	18	.....	1.095

2-30. Freezing and Thawing Tests of Stone. Kessler made freezing and thawing tests of 89 different marbles ("Physical and Chemical Tests of Commercial Marbles of U.S.," *National Bureau of Standards (U.S.) Technical Papers*, No. 123, vol. 12). After 30 cycles, 66 marbles showed loss of strength ranging from 1.2 to 62.1% and averaging 12.3% loss. The other 23 marbles showed increases in strength ranging from 0.5 to 43.9% and averaging 11.2% increase.

Weight change was also determined in this same investigation to afford another index of durability. Of 86 possible comparisons after 30 cycles of freezing and thawing, 16 showed no change in weight, 64 showed decreases in weight ranging from 0.01 to 0.28% and averaging 0.04% loss, while 6 showed increases in weight ranging from 0.01 to 0.08% and averaging 0.04%.

GYPSUM PRODUCTS

2-31. Gypsum Wallboard. Gypsum wallboard consists of a core of set gypsum surfaced with paper or other fibrous material firmly bonded to the core. It is designed to be used without addition of plaster for walls, ceilings, or partitions and provides a surface suitable to receive either paint or paper (see also Section 12, Part 2).

Wallboards are extensively used in "dry-wall" construction, where plaster is eliminated. They are available with one surface covered with aluminum or other heat-reflecting type of foil. Other wallboards have imitation wood-grain patterns on the exposed surface so that no additional decoration is required.

2-32. Gypsum Lath. Gypsum lath, or as it was formerly called, gypsum plaster-board, is similar to gypsum wallboard in that it consists of a core of set gypsum surfaced with paper. The paper for wallboard, however, is treated so that it is ready to receive paint or paper, while that for gypsum lath is specially designed or treated so that plaster will bond tightly to the paper. In addition, some lath provides perforations or other mechanical key devices to assist in holding the plaster firmly on the lath. It is also available with reflective foil backing (see also Section 12, part 1).

2-33. Gypsum Sheathing Board. Gypsum sheathing boards are similar in construction to wallboards, except that they are provided with a water-repellent paper surface. They are commonly made in only ½-in. thickness, and with a nominal width of 24 in. Length is either 6 ft 8 in. or 8 ft. They are made with either square edges or with V tongue-and-groove edges.

2-34. Gypsum Partition Tile or Block. Gypsum tile or block are used for non-load-bearing partition walls and for protection of columns, elevator shafts, etc., against fire. They are made from set gypsum in the form of blocks that are 12 in. in height, 30 in. in length, and in thicknesses varying from 1½ to 6 in. The 1½- and 2-in. thicknesses are commonly used as furring block and are solid. The 3-, 4-, 5-, and 6-in. thicknesses are provided with round, elliptical, or rectangular cores parallel to the long dimension of the block to reduce weight.

2-35. Gypsum Plank. A precast gypsum product used particularly for roof construction is composed of a core of gypsum cast in the form of a plank and usually with tongue-and-groove metal edges and ends. The planks are available in two thicknesses —a 2-in. plank, which is 15 in. wide and either 8 or 10 ft long, and a 2½-in. plank which is 10 in. wide and 6 ft long. Some reinforcing is used, particularly in the 2½-in. plank.

GLASS AND GLASS BLOCK

2-36. Glass for General Use. Glass is so widely used for decorative and utilitarian purposes in modern construction that it would require an encyclopedia to list all the varieties available. Clear glass for windows and doors is made in varying thicknesses or strengths, also in double layers to obtain additional thermal insulation. Safety glass, laminated from sheets of glass and plastic, or made with embedded wire reinforcement, is available for locations where breakage might be hazardous. For ornamental work, glass is available in a wide range of textures, colors, finishes, and shapes.

For many of its uses, glass presents no problem to the materials engineer. It is used in relatively small sheets or sections, which are frequently free-floating in their supports; therefore, expansion is not a problem. Most kinds of glass are highly resistant to weathering so that durability of the glass itself is not a problem, although the weathertightness of the frame may be a serious problem. Much glass is used in interiors for esthetic reasons where it is not subject to the stresses imposed upon many of the other masonry materials. An exception to this general condition is found in the case of glass block.

2-37. Glass Block. Glass block are made by first pressing or shaping half blocks to the desired form, then fusing the half blocks together to form a complete block. It is usually 3⅞ in. thick and 5¾, 7¾, or 11¾ in. square. The center of the block is hollow and is under a partial vacuum, which adds to the insulating properties of the block. Corner and radial block are also available to produce desired architectural effects.

Glass block are commonly laid up in a cement or a cement-lime mortar. Since there is no absorption by the block to facilitate bond of mortar, various devices are employed to obtain a mechanical bond. One such device is to coat the sides of the block with a plastic and embed therein particles of sand. The difficulty in obtaining permanent and complete bond sometimes leads to the opening up of mortar joints; a wall of glass block, exposed to the weather, may leak badly in a rainstorm unless unusual precautions have been taken during the setting of the block to obtain full and complete bond.

Glass block have a coefficient of thermal expansion which is from 1½ to 2 times that of other masonry. For this reason, large areas of block may expand against solid masonry and develop sufficient stress so that the block will crack. Manufacturers usually recommend an expansion joint every 10 ft or so, to prevent building up of pressure sufficient to crack the block. With adequate protection against expansion and with good workmanship, or with walls built in protected locations, glass-block walls are ornamental, sanitary, excellent light transmitters, and have rather low thermal conductivity.

ASBESTOS-CEMENT PRODUCTS

Asbestos-cement products are formed from a mixture of portland cement and asbestos fiber that has been wetted and then pressed into a board or sheet form. Organic fiber is added in some cases to promote resiliency and ease of machining. Curing agents, water-repellent admixtures, pigments, mineral granules, and mineral fillers may or may not be added, depending upon the particular end use of the product and its desired appearance.

2-38. Properties of Asbestos-Cement. Since these materials are used in sheet form and frequently under exposed weather conditions, the properties of most importance are flexural strength, deflection under load while wet, and absorption. The requirements of ASTM Specifications C220, C221, C222, and C223 for asbestos-cement products are given in Table 2-27.

Table 2-27. Specification Requirements for Asbestos-Cement Products

Material	Thickness, in.	Size of test specimen, in.	Length of test span, in.	Min flexural strength, lb	Min deflection at max load, in.	Max water absorption, % by weight
Flat sheets, type I	1/8	6 × 12	10	9	.....	30
	3/16	6 × 12	10	21	.....	30
	1/4	6 × 12	10	38	.....	30
	3/8	6 × 12	10	84	.....	30
Flat sheets, type II	1/8	6 × 12	10	13	.....	25
	3/16	6 × 12	10	30	.....	25
	1/4	6 × 12	10	52	.....	25
	3/8	6 × 12	10	120	.....	25
	1/2	6 × 12	10	210	.....	25
Flat sheets, type III	1/8	6 × 12	10	17	.....	20
	1/8	Parallel with length		....	0.55	
	1/8	Parallel with width		....	0.45	
	3/16	6 × 12	10	38	.....	20
	3/16	Parallel with length		....	0.40	
	3/16	Parallel with width		....	0.30	
Corrugated sheets	5/16	12.6 × 36	30	180 per ft	.....	20
Roofing shingles	>0.150	6 × 12	10	17	0.125	22.5
Siding shingles and clapboards	>0.150	6 × 12	10	15	0.125	25

Type I, or general-utility flat sheets, are "suitable for exterior and interior use, having sufficient strength for general utility and construction purposes and suitable where high density, glossy finish and lowest absorption are not essential. Sheets of this type are easy to cut and work, are bendable, and need not be drilled for nailing" (ASTM Specification C220).

Type II, or rigid, high-strength flat sheets, are "suitable for exterior and interior use where higher strength, greater rigidity and resistance to abrasion, low absorption and smoother finish than Type I are essential. These sheets are harder to cut than Type I sheets, are relatively rigid, and should be drilled for fasteners" (ASTM Specification C220).

Type III, or flexible, high-strength flat sheets, are "suitable for exterior and interior use where a combination of strength and density, flexibility, smooth surface, resistance to abrasion and low absorption are desired.   Sheets of this type are readily cutable and workable and need not be drilled for fastening" (ASTM Specification C220).

Corrugated sheets are designed "to provide structural weather-exposed surfaces of roofs and building walls on industrial, residential, agricultural, commercial and institutional buildings" (ASTM Specification C221).

Roofing shingles are designed "to provide the weather-exposed surface on roofs. . . " (ASTM Specification C222).   They are available in a number of shapes and patterns.

Siding shingles and clapboards are designed "to provide the weather-exposed sidewall surfaces of buildings. . . " (ASTM Specification C223).

PART 2. WOOD, METALS, AND OTHER MATERIALS

PROFESSOR ALBERT G. H. DIETZ

Massachusetts Institute of Technology

WOOD

2-39. Mechanical Properties of Wood. Because of its structure, wood has different strength properties parallel and perpendicular to the grain. Tensile, bending, and compressive strengths are greatest parallel to the grain and least across the grain, whereas shear strength is least parallel to the grain and greatest across the grain. Except in plywood, the shearing strength of wood is usually governed by the parallel-to-grain direction.

The compressive strength of wood at an angle other than parallel or perpendicular to the grain is given by the following formula:

$$C_\theta = \frac{C_1 C_2}{C_1 \sin^2 \theta + C_2 \cos^2 \theta} \tag{2-1}$$

in which C_θ is the strength at the desired angle θ with the grain, C_1 is the compressive strength parallel to grain, and C_2 is the compressive strength perpendicular to the grain.

Increasing moisture content reduces all strength properties except impact bending, in which green wood is stronger than dry wood. The differences are brought out in Table 2-28. In practice, no differentiation is made between the strength of green wood in engineering timbers because of seasoning defects that may occur in timbers as they dry and because large timbers normally are put into service without having been dried. This is not true of laminated timber, in which dry wood must be employed to obtain good glued joints. For laminated timber, higher stresses can be employed than for ordinary lumber. In general, compression and bending parallel to the grain are affected most severely by moisture, whereas modulus of elasticity, shear, and tensile strength are affected less. In practice, tensile strength is taken equal to the bending strength of wood.

In Table 2-28 are summarized also the principal mechanical properties of the most important American commercial species.

Values given in the table are average ultimate strengths. To obtain working stresses from these, the following must be considered: (1) Individual pieces may vary 25% above and below the average. (2) Values given are for standard tests that are completed in a few minutes. Over a period of years, however, wood may fail under a continuous load about $\%_6$ that sustained in a standard test. (3) The modulus of rupture of a standard 2-in.-deep flexural-test specimen is greater than that of a deep beam. In deriving working stresses, therefore, factors of 75%, $\%_6$, 0.9 (for an average-depth factor), and $\%$ (for a safety factor) are applied to the average ultimate strengths to provide basic stresses, or working stresses, for blemishless lumber. These are still further reduced on the basis of knots, wane, slope of grain, shakes, and checks to provide

Table 2.28. Strength of Some Commercially Important Woods Grown in the U.S.*
(Results of tests on small, clear specimens in the green and air-dry condition)

| Commercial and botanical name of species | Moisture content, % | Specific gravity | Static bending | | | Compression parallel to grain | | Compression perpendicular to grain fiber stress at proportional limit, psi | Shear parallel to grain max shearing strength, psi | Hardness Load required to embed a 0.444 in. ball to ½ its diameter, lb | |
			Fiber stress at proportional limit, psi	Modulus of Rupture, psi	Modulus of Elasticity, psi	Fiber stress at proportional limit, psi	Max crushing strength, psi			End	Side
Ash, commercial white (*Fraxinus* sp.)	43	0.54	5,300	9,500	1,400	3,360	4,060	860	1,350	1,010	940
	12	0.58	8,900	14,600	1,680	5,580	7,280	1,510	1,920	1,680	1,260
Beech (*Fagus grandifolia*)	54	0.56	4,300	8,600	1,380	2,550	3,550	670	1,290	970	850
	12	0.64	8,700	14,900	1,720	4,880	7,300	1,250	2,010	1,590	1,300
Birch (*Betula* sp.)	62	0.57	4,400	8,700	1,560	2,640	3,510	550	1,160	910	850
	12	0.63	10,100	16,700	2,070	6,200	8,310	1,250	2,020	1,660	1,340
Chestnut (*Castanea dentata*)	122	0.40	3,100	5,600	930	2,080	2,470	380	800	530	420
	12	0.43	6,100	8,600	1,230	3,780	5,320	760	1,080	720	540
Cypress, southern (*Taxodium distichum*)	91	0.42	4,200	6,600	1,180	3,100	3,580	500	810	440	390
	12	0.46	7,200	10,600	1,440	4,740	6,360	900	1,000	660	510
Douglas fir (coast region) (*Pseudotsuga taxifolia*)	36	0.45	4,800	7,600	1,550	3,410	3,890	510	930	510	480
	12	0.48	8,100	11,700	1,920	6,450	7,420	910	1,140	760	670
Douglas fir ("Inland Empire" region) (*Pseudotsuga taxifolia*)	42	0.41	3,600	6,800	1,340	2,460	3,240	500	870	530	470
	12	0.44	7,400	11,300	1,610	5,520	6,700	950	1,190	720	630
Elm, American (*Ulmus americana*)	89	0.46	3,900	7,200	1,110	1,920	2,910	440	1,000	680	
	12	0.50	7,600	11,800	1,340	4,030	5,520	850	1,510	1,110	
Elm, rock (*Ulmus racemosa*)	48	0.57	4,600	9,500	1,190	2,970	3,780	750	1,270	980	
	12	0.63	8,000	14,800	1,540	4,700	7,050	1,520	1,920	1,510	
Gum, black (*Nyssa sylvatica*)	55	0.46	4,000	7,000	1,030	2,490	3,040	600	1,100	790	640
	12	0.50	7,300	9,600	1,200	3,470	5,520	1,150	1,340	1,240	810

Species	Moisture, %	Sp. gr.									
Gum, red (*Liquidambar styraciflua*)	81	0.44	3,700	6,800	1,150	2,230	2,840	460	1,070	630	520
	12	0.49	8,100	11,900	1,490	4,700	5,800	860	1,610	950	690
Gum, tupelo (*Nyssa aquatica*)	97	0.46	4,200	7,300	1,050	2,690	3,370	590	1,190	800	710
	12	0.50	7,200	9,600	1,260		5,920	1,070	1,590	1,200	880
Hemlock, eastern (*Tsuga canadensis*)	111	0.38	3,800	6,400	1,070	2,600	3,080	440	850	500	400
	12	0.40	6,100	8,900	1,200	4,020	5,410	800	1,060	810	500
Hemlock, western (*Tsuga heterophylla*)	74	0.38	3,400	6,100	1,220	2,480	2,990	390	810	520	430
	12	0.42	6,800	10,100	1,490	5,340	6,210	680	1,170	940	580
Hickory, pecan (*Hicoria* sp.)	68	0.59	5,300	9,900	1,380	3,810	4,320	980	1,260	1,274	1,308
	12	0.65	9,100	16,300	1,780	6,360	8,280	2,040	1,770	1,930	1,820
Hickory, true (*Hicoria* sp.)	57	0.65	6,100	11,300	1,570	3,650	4,570	1,080	1,360		
	12	0.73	10,900	19,700	2,180		8,970	2,310	2,140		
Honey locust (*Gleditsia triacanthos*)	63	0.60	5,600	10,200	1,290	3,320	4,420	1,420	1,660	1,440	1,390
	12		8,800	14,700	1,630		7,500	2,280	2,250	1,860	1,580
Larch, western (*Larix occidentalis*)	58	0.48	4,600	7,500	1,350	3,250	3,800	560	920	470	450
	12	0.52	7,900	11,900	1,710	5,950	7,490	1,080	1,360	1,110	760
Maple, sugar (*Acer saccharum*)	58	0.56	5,100	9,400	1,550	2,850	4,020	800	1,460	1,070	970
	12	0.63	9,500	15,800	1,830	5,390	7,830	1,810	2,330	1,840	1,450
Oak, red (*Quercus* sp.)	80	0.57	4,400	8,500	1,360	2,590	3,520	800	1,220	1,050	1,030
	12	0.63	8,400	14,400	1,810	4,610	6,920	1,260	1,830	1,490	1,300
Oak, white (*Quercus* sp.)	70	0.59	4,700	8,100	1,200	2,940	3,520	850	1,270	1,110	1,070
	12	0.67	7,900	13,900	1,620	4,350	7,040	1,410	1,890	1,420	1,330
Pines, southern yellow:											
Longleaf (*Pinus palustris*)	63	0.54	5,200	8,700	1,600	3,430	4,300	590	1,040	550	590
	12	0.58	9,300	14,700	1,990	6,150	8,440	1,190	1,500	920	870
Shortleaf (*Pinus echinata*)	81	0.46	3,900	7,300	1,390	2,500	3,430	440	850	410	440
	12	0.51	7,700	12,800	1,760	5,090	7,070	1,000	1,310	750	690
Poplar, yellow (*Liriodendron tulipifera*)	64	0.38	3,400	5,400	1,090	1,930	2,420	330	740	390	340
	12	0.40	6,100	9,200	1,500	3,550	5,290	580	1,100	560	450
Redwood (virgin) (*Sequoia sempervirens*)	112	0.38	4,800	7,500	1,180	3,700	4,200	520	800	570	410
	12	0.40	6,900	10,000	1,340	4,560	6,150	860	940	790	480
Spruce, eastern (*Picea* sp.)	46	0.38	3,300	5,600	1,110	2,120	2,600	290	710	390	340
	12	0.40	6,500	10,100	1,440	4,160	5,590	590	1,070	630	490

* From U.S. Forest Products Laboratory.

Table 2-29. Shrinkage Values for Commercially Important Woods Grown in the United States*

Species	Shrinkage (% of dimension when green) from green to oven-dried to 0% moisture (test values)		
	Radial	Tangential	Volumetric
Ash, commercial white	4.6	7.5	12.8
Basswood	6.6	9.3	15.8
Beech	5.1	11.0	16.3
Birch	6.9	8.9	16.3
Cedar:			
Eastern red	3.1	4.7	7.8
Northern white	2.1	4.7	7.0
Port Orford	4.6	6.9	10.1
Southern white	2.8	5.2	8.4
Western red	2.4	5.0	7.7
Cherry, black	3.7	7.1	11.5
Chestnut	3.4	6.7	11.6
Cypress, southern	3.8	6.2	10.5
Douglas fir:			
Coast region	5.0	7.8	11.8
"Inland Empire" region	4.1	7.6	10.9
Rocky Mountain region	3.6	6.2	10.6
Elm:			
American	4.2	9.5	14.6
Rock	4.8	8.1	14.1
Gum:			
Black	4.4	7.7	13.9
Red	5.2	9.9	15.0
Hemlock:			
Eastern	3.0	6.8	9.7
Western	4.3	7.9	11.9
Hickory:			
Pecan	4.9	8.9	13.6
True	7.3	11.4	17.9
Larch, western	4.2	8.1	13.2
Maple:			
Red	4.0	8.2	13.1
Sugar	4.9	9.5	14.9
Oak:			
Red	4.3	9.0	14.8
White	5.4	9.3	16.0
Pine:			
Loblolly	4.8	7.4	12.3
Longleaf	5.1	7.5	12.2
Northern white	2.3	6.0	8.2
Ponderosa	3.9	6.3	9.6
Shortleaf	4.4	7.7	12.3
Sugar	2.9	5.6	7.9
Western white	4.1	7.4	11.8
Poplar, yellow	4.0	7.1	12.3
Redwood	2.6	4.4	6.8
Spruce:			
Eastern	4.3	7.7	12.6
Engelmann	3.4	6.6	10.4
Walnut, black	5.2	7.1	11.3

* From U.S. Forest Products Laboratory.

working stresses for classes of commercial engineering timbers. (See Sec. 8 for engineering design in timber.)

2-40. Hygroscopic Properties of Wood. Because of its nature, wood tends to absorb moisture from the air when the relative humidity is high, and to lose it when the relative humidity is low. Moisture imbibed into the cell walls causes the wood to shrink and swell as the moisture content changes with the relative humidity of the surrounding air. The maximum amount of imbibed moisture the cell walls can hold is known as the fiber-saturation point, and for most species is in the vicinity of 25 to 30% of the oven-dry weight of the wood. Free water held in the cell cavities above the fiber-saturation point has no effect upon shrinkage or other properties of the wood. Changes in moisture content below the fiber-saturation point cause negligible shrinkage or swelling along the grain, and such shrinkage and swelling are normally ignored; but

Table 2-30. Measured Moisture-content Values for Various Wood Items*

Use of lumber	Moisture content (% of weight of oven-dry wood) for					
	Dry Southwestern states		Damp Southern coastal states		Remainder of the United States	
	Avg	Individual pieces	Avg	Individual pieces	Avg	Individual pieces
Interior finish woodwork and softwood flooring.............................	6	4–9	11	8–13	8	5–10
Hardwood flooring....................	6	5–8	10	9–12	7	6–9
Siding, exterior trim, sheathing, and framing.............................	9	7–12	12	9–14	12	9–14

* From U.S. Forest Products Laboratory.

across the grain, considerable shrinkage and swelling occur in both the radial and tangential directions. Tangential shrinkage (as in flat-cut material) is normally approximately 50% greater than radial shrinkage (as in edge-grain material).

Table 2-29 gives average-shrinkage values in the radial and tangential directions for a number of commercial species as they dry from the fiber-saturation point (or green condition) to oven-dry. For intermediate changes in moisture content, shrinkage is proportional; e.g., if the fiber-saturation point is assumed to be 28% (average), a change in moisture content from 21 to 14% would cause shrinkage one-quarter as great as the shrinkage from 28% to zero.

Table 2-30 gives measured average moisture contents of wood in buildings in various parts of the United States.

2-41. Commercial Grades of Wood. Lumber is graded by the various associations of lumber manufacturers having jurisdiction over various species. Two principal sets of grading rules are employed: (1) for softwoods, and (2) for hardwoods.

Softwoods. Manufacturers of softwood lumber conform, in general, to American Lumber Standards drawn up by the various lumber associations in cooperation with the National Bureau of Standards. The principal classifications of lumber under American Lumber Standards are structural, yard, and factory and shop. Yard lumber is general construction lumber expected to be used largely in the construction industry for framing of houses and other general construction purposes. Structural lumber is engineering timber that has been graded according to the presence of defects that affect strength. The structural grades carry permissible working stresses based on the size and distribution of knots, presence or absence of checks or shakes, presence or absence of wane, degree of cross grain, and to a limited extent, whether the lumber is green or dry. Factory and shop lumber is expected to be used in the factory for the manufacture of sash, doors, and other items of finish.

Yard lumber is subclassified as finish, boards, and dimension, according to the intended use and according to size. It is further classified as select or common,

Table 2-31. Softwood Lumber Classification*

Softwood lumber applies to rough or dressed lumber; sizes given are nominal)

Yard lumber (lumber less than 5 in. thick, intended for general building purposes; grading based on use of the entire piece)

Type	Detail	Grades
Finish (less than 3 in. thick and 12 in. and under in width)		A select, B select, C select, D select
Boards (less than 2 in. thick and 8 in. or over in width). Strips (under 8 in. in width)		Construction, Standard, Utility, Economy
Dimension (2 in. and under 5 in. thick and of any width)	Planks (2 in. and under 4 in. thick and 8 in. and over wide)	Construction, Standard, Utility
	Scantling (2 in. and under 5 in. thick and under 8 in. wide)	Construction, Standard, Utility
	Heavy joists (4 in. thick and 8 in. or over wide)	Construction, Standard, Utility

Structural material (lumber 5 in. or over in thickness and width, except joist and plank; grading based on strength and on use of entire piece)

- Joist and plank (2 in. to 4 in. thick and 4 in. and over wide)
- Beams and stringers (5 in. and over thick and 8 in. and over wide)
- Posts and timbers (6 by 6 in. and larger)

Factory and shop (grading based on area of piece suitable for cuttings of certain size and quality)

Type	Detail	Grades
Factory plank graded for door, sash, and other cuttings 1 in. to 4 in. thick and 5 in. and over wide	Factory clears upper grades	Nos. 1 and 2 clear factory, No. 3 clear factory
	Shop lower grades	No. 1 shop, No. 2 shop, No. 3 shop
Shop lumber graded for general cut-up purposes	1 in. thick (northern and western pine, and Pacific coast woods)	Select Shop
	All thicknesses (cypress, redwood, and North Carolina pine)	Tank and boat stock, firsts and seconds, selects; No. 1 shop; No. 2 shop, box

* Adapted from American Lumber Standards.

depending on whether it is intended for finish (visible) applications, or for general construction that will be covered. Select A and B are suitable for transparent finishes; select C and D are suitable for painted or other opaque finishes.

Structural lumber is classified as joist and plank, beams and stringers, posts and timbers, depending on the dimensions of the cross section and the expected final use. Sizes and grades are summarized in Tables 2-31 and 2-32.

Hardwoods. Because of the great diversity of applications for hardwood both in and outside the construction industry, hardwood grading rules are based upon the proportion of a given piece that can be cut into smaller pieces of material clear on one or both sides and not less than a specified size. Grade classifications are therefore based on the amount of clear usable lumber in a piece.

Standard hardwood grades are firsts, seconds, selects, number 1 common, number 2 common, sound wormy, number 3-A common, and number 3-B common. Firsts and seconds, selects and number 1 common, and numbers 3-A and 3-B common are often combined.

Special grading rules of interest in the construction industry cover hardwood interior trim and moldings, in which one face must be practically free of imperfections and in which Grade A may further limit the amount of sapwood as well as stain. Hardwood dimension rules, in addition, cover clears, which must be clear both faces; clear one

Table 2-32. Yard Lumber Grades*

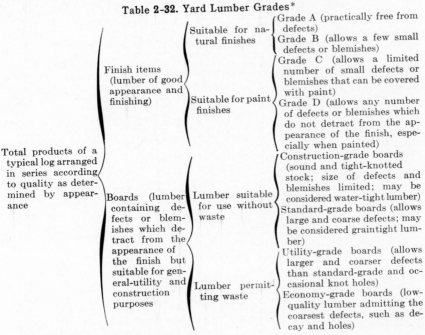

Total products of a typical log arranged in series according to quality as determined by appearance	Finish items (lumber of good appearance and finishing)	Suitable for natural finishes	Grade A (practically free from defects)
			Grade B (allows a few small defects or blemishes)
		Suitable for paint finishes	Grade C (allows a limited number of small defects or blemishes that can be covered with paint)
			Grade D (allows any number of defects or blemishes which do not detract from the appearance of the finish, especially when painted)
	Boards (lumber containing defects or blemishes which detract from the appearance of the finish but suitable for general-utility and construction purposes	Lumber suitable for use without waste	Construction-grade boards (sound and tight-knotted stock; size of defects and blemishes limited; may be considered water-tight lumber)
			Standard-grade boards (allows large and coarse defects; may be considered graintight lumber)
		Lumber permitting waste	Utility-grade boards (allows larger and coarser defects than standard-grade and occasional knot holes)
			Economy-grade boards (low-quality lumber admitting the coarsest defects, such as decay and holes)

* Adapted from American Lumber Standards.

face; paint quality, which can be covered with paint; core, which must be sound on both faces and suitable for cores of glued-up panels; and sound, which is a general-utility grade.

Hardwood flooring is graded under two separate sets of rules: (1) for maple, birch, beech, and pecan; and (2) for red and white oak. In both sets of rules, color and quality classifications range from top-quality to the lower utility grades. Oak may be further subclassified as quarter-sawed and plain-sawed. In all grades, top-quality material must be uniform in color, whereas other grades place no limitation on color.

Shingles are graded under special rules, usually into three classes: numbers 1, 2, and 3. Number 1 must be all edge grain and strictly clear, containing no sapwood. Numbers 2 and 3 must be clear to a distance far enough away from the butt to be well covered by the next course of shingles.

2-42. Destroyers and Preservatives. The principal destroyers of wood are decay, caused by fungus, and attack by a number of animal organisms of which termites, carpenter ants, and grubs of a variety of beetles, teredo, and limnoria are the principal offenders. In addition, fire annually causes widespread destruction of wood structures.

Decay will not occur if wood is kept well ventilated and air-dry or, conversely, if it is kept continuously submerged so that air is excluded. Most termites in the United

States are subterranean and require contact with the soil. Termite shields, therefore, are generally effective in combating termites. The drywood and dampwood termites found along the southern fringes of the country and along the west coast do not require direct soil contact and are more difficult to control. Teredo, limnoria, and other water-borne wood destroyers are found only in salt or brackish waters.

Various species vary in their natural durability and resistance to decay and insect attack. The sapwood of all species is relatively vulnerable; only the heartwood can be considered to be resistant. Table 2-33 lists the common species in descending order of resistance. Such a list is only approximate, and individual pieces deviate considerably.

Table 2-33. Resistance of Various Heartwoods to Decay

Heartwood durable even when used under conditions that favor decay:	Cedar, Alaska Cedar, eastern red Cedar, northern white Cedar, Port Orford Cedar, southern white Cedar, western red Chestnut Cypress, southern Locust, black Osage-orange Redwood Walnut, black Yew, Pacific
Heartwood of intermediate durability but nearly as durable as some of the species named in the high-durability group	Douglas fir (dense) Honey locust Oak, white Pine, southern yellow (dense)
Heartwood of intermediate durability:	Douglas fir (unselected) Gum, red Larch, western Pine, southern yellow (unselected) Tamarack
Heartwood between the intermediate and the nondurable group:	Ash, commercial white Beech Birch, sweet Birch, yellow Hemlock, eastern Hemlock, western Hickory Maple, sugar Oak, red Spruce, black Spruce, Engelmann Spruce, red Spruce, Sitka Spruce, white
Heartwood low in durability when used under conditions that favor decay	Aspen Basswood Cottonwood Fir, commercial white Willow, black

Preservatives employed to combat the various destructive agencies may be subdivided into oily, water-soluble salts, and solvent-soluble organic materials. The principal oily preservatives are coal-tar creosote and creosote mixed with petroleum. The most commonly employed water-soluble salts are zinc chloride, chromated zinc chloride, sodium fluoride, copper salts, mercuric salts, and a variety of other materials that are often sold under various proprietary names. The principal solvent-soluble organic materials are chlorinated phenols, such as pentachlorphenol.

Preservatives may be applied in a variety of ways, including brushing and dipping, but for maximum treatment, pressure is required to provide deep side-grain penetration.   Butts of poles and other parts are sometimes placed in a hot boiling creosote or salt solution, and after the water in the wood has been converted to steam, they are quickly transferred to a cold vat of the same preservative.   As the steam condenses, it produces a partial vacuum, which draws the preservative fairly deeply into the surface.

Pressure treatments may be classified as full-cell and empty-cell.   In the full-cell treatment, a partial vacuum is first drawn in the pressure-treating tank to withdraw most of the air in the cells of the wood.   The preservative is then let in without breaking the vacuum, after which pressure is applied to the hot solution.   After treatment is completed, the individual cells are presumably filled with preservative.   In the empty-cell method, no initial vacuum is drawn, but the preservative is pumped in under pressure against the back pressure of the compressed air in the wood.   When the pressure is released, the air in the wood expands and forces out excess preservative, leaving only a coating of preservative on the cell walls.

Retentions of preservative depend on the application.   For teredo-infested harbors, full-cell treatment to refusal may be specified, with a range from 16 to 20 lb per cu ft of wood.   For ordinary decay conditions and resistance to termites and other destroyers of a similar nature, the empty-cell method may be employed with retentions in the vicinity of 6 to 8 lb of creosote per cu ft of wood.   Salt retentions generally range in the vicinity of $1\frac{1}{2}$ to 3 lb of dry salt retained per cu ft of wood.

Solvent-soluble organic materials, such as pentachlorphenol, are commonly employed for the treatment of sash and door parts to impart greater resistance to decay.   This is commonly done by simply dipping the parts in the solution and then allowing them to dry.   As the organic solvent evaporates, it leaves the water-insoluble preservative behind in the wood.

These organic materials are also employed for general preservative treatment, including fence posts and structural lumber.   The water-soluble salts and solvent-soluble organic materials leave the wood clean and paintable.   Creosote in general cannot be painted over, although partial success can be achieved with top-quality aluminum-flake pigment paints.

Treatment against fire consists generally of salts containing ammonium and phosphates, of which mono-ammonium phosphate and di-ammonium phosphate are widely employed.   At retentions of 3 to 5 lb of dry salt per cu ft, the wood does not support its own combustion, and the afterglow when fire is removed is short.   A variety of surface treatments is also available, most of which depends on the formation of a blanket of inert-gas bubbles over the surface of the wood in the presence of flame or other sources of heat.   The blanket of bubbles insulates the wood beneath and retards combustion.

2-43. Glues and Adhesives.   A variety of adhesives is now available for use with wood, depending on the final application.   The older adhesives include animal glue, casein glue, and a variety of vegetable glues, of which soybean is today the most important.   Animal glues provide strong, tough, easily made joints, which, however, are not moisture-resistant.   Casein mixed with cold water, when properly formulated, provides highly moisture-resistant glue joints, although they cannot be called waterproof.   The vegetable glues have good dry strength but are not moisture-resistant.

The principal high-strength glues today are synthetic resins, of which phenol formaldehyde, urea formaldehyde, resorcinol formaldehyde, and melamine formaldehyde are the most important.   Phenol, resorcinol, and melamine provide glue joints that are completely waterproof and will not separate when properly made even on boiling.   Urea formaldehyde provides a glue joint of high moisture resistance, although not quite so good as the other three.   Phenol and melamine require application of heat, as well as pressure, to cure the adhesive, whereas urea and resorcinol can both be formulated to be mixed with water at ordinary temperatures and hardened without application of heat above room temperature.   Waterproof plywood is commonly made in hot-plate presses with phenolic or melamine adhesive.   Resorcinol is employed where heat cannot be applied, as in a variety of assembly operations and the manufacture of laminated parts like ships' keels, which must have the maximum in waterproof qualities.

An emulsion of polyvinyl acetate serves as a general-purpose adhesive, for general assembly operations where maximum strength and heat or moisture resistance are not required. This emulsion is merely applied to the surfaces to be bonded, after which they are pressed together and the adhesive is allowed to harden.

2-44. Plywood. As ordinarily made, plywood consists of thin sheets, or veneers, of wood glued together. The grain is oriented at right angles in adjacent plies. To obtain plywood with balance—that is, which will not warp, shrink, or twist unduly— the plies must be carefully selected and arranged to be mirror images of each other with respect to the central plane. All plies are at the same moisture content at the time of manufacture. The outside plies or faces are parallel to each other and are of species that have the same shrinkage characteristics. The same holds true of the cross bands or inner plies, and finally of the core or central ply itself. As a consequence, plywood, as ordinarily made, has an odd number of plies, the minimum being three. Matching the plies involves thickness, the species of wood with particular reference to shrinkage, equal moisture content, and making certain that the grain in corresponding plies is parallel.

Principal advantages of plywood over lumber are its more nearly equal strength properties in length and width, greater resistance to checking, greatly reduced shrinkage and swelling, and resistance to splitting.

The approach to equalization of strength of plywood in the various directions is obtained at the expense of strength in the parallel-to-grain direction; i.e., plywood is not so strong in the direction parallel to its face plies as lumber is parallel to the grain. But plywood is considerably stronger in the direction perpendicular to its face plies than wood is perpendicular to the grain. Furthermore, the shearing strength of plywood in a plane perpendicular to the plane of the plywood is very much greater than that of ordinary wood parallel to the grain. In a direction parallel to the plane of the plywood, however, the shearing strength of plywood is less than that of ordinary wood parallel to the grain, because in this direction rolling shear occurs in the plywood; i.e., the fibers in one ply tend to roll rather than to slide.

Depending on whether plywood is to be used for general utility or for decorative purposes, the veneers employed may be cut by peeling from the log, by slicing, or today very rarely, by sawing. Sawing and slicing give the greatest freedom and versatility in the selection of grain. Peeling provides the greatest volume and the most rapid production, because the logs are merely rotated against a flat knife and the veneer is peeled off in a long continuous sheet.

Plywood is classified as interior or exterior, depending on the type of adhesive employed. Interior-grade plywood must have a reasonable degree of moisture resistance but is not considered to be waterproof. Exterior-grade plywood must be completely waterproof and capable of withstanding immersion in water or prolonged exposure to outdoor conditions.

In addition to these classifications, plywood is further subclassified in a variety of ways depending on the quality of the surface ply. Top-quality is clear on one or both faces, except for occasional patches. Lower qualities permit sound defects, such as knots and similar blemishes, which do not detract from the general utility of the plywood but detract from its finished appearance.

A recent development is plywood faced with a resin-impregnated paper, which provides a smooth, hard, uniform face either for finish purposes or for concrete forms. The paper employed is a tough, strong, kraft paper, and the resin is normally a phenol-formaldehyde impregnating varnish. The surface is cured under heat and pressure in a hot-plate press and, when properly made, is impervious to moisture.

2-45. Wood Bibliography

Dietz, A. G. H.: "Materials of Construction: Wood, Plastics, Fabrics," D. Van Nostrand Company, Inc., Princeton, N.J., 1949.

Forest Products Laboratory, Forest Service, U.S. Department of Agriculture: "Wood Handbook," Government Printing Office, Washington, D.C.

Hunt, G. M., and G. A. Garratt: "Wood Preservation," 2d ed., McGraw-Hill Book Company, Inc., New York, 1953.

Markwardt, L. J., and T. R. C. Wilson: Strength and Related Properties of Woods Grown in the United States, *U.S. Department of Agriculture Technical Bulletin* 479, Superintendent of Documents, Washington, D.C.

National Hardwood Lumber Association, Chicago, Ill.: "Rules for the Measurement and Inspection of Hardwood Lumber, Cypress, Veneer, and Thin Lumber."

National Lumber Manufacturers Association, Washington, D.C.: "National Design Specifications for Stress-grade Lumber and Its Fastenings," 1952.

U.S. Department of Commerce, National Bureau of Standards, Washington, D.C.: American Lumber Standards for Softwood Lumber, Simplified Practice Recommendation R 16; Douglas Fir Plywood, Commercial Standard CS 45; Hardwood Plywood, Commercial Standard CS 35.

FERROUS METALS

The iron-carbon equilibrium diagram in Fig. 2-1 shows that, under equilibrium conditions (slow cooling) if not more than 2.0% carbon is present, a solid solution of car-

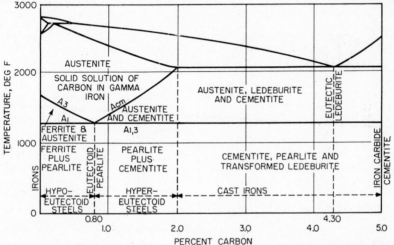

FIG. 2-1. Iron-carbon diagram.

bon in gamma iron exists at elevated temperatures. This is called austenite. If the carbon content is less than 0.8%, cooling below the A_3 temperature line causes transformation of some of the austenite to ferrite, which is substantially pure alpha iron (containing less than 0.01% carbon in solution). Still further cooling to below the A_1 line causes the remaining austenite to transform to pearlite—the eutectoid mixture of fine plates, or lamellas, of ferrite-and cementite (iron carbide) whose iridescent appearance under the microscope gives it its name.

If the carbon content is 0.8%, no transformation on cooling the austenite occurs until the A_1 temperature is reached. At that point, all the austenite transforms to pearlite, with its typical "thumbprint" microstructure.

At carbon contents between 0.80 and 2.0%, cooling below the A_{cm} temperature line causes iron carbide, or cementite, to form in the temperature range between A_{cm} and $A_{1,3}$. Below $A_{1,3}$, the remaining austenite transforms to pearlite.

2-46. Steels. The plain iron-carbon metals with less than 0.8% carbon content consist of ferrite and pearlite and provide the low (0.06 to 0.30%), medium (0.30 to 0.50%), and high carbon (0.50 to 0.80%) steels called hypoeutectoid steels. The higher-carbon or hypereutectoid tool steels contain 0.8 to 2.0% carbon and consist of pearlite and cementite. The eutectoid steels occurring in the vicinity of 0.8% carbon are essentially all pearlite.

2-47. Irons. Metals containing substantially no carbon (several hundredths of 1%) are called irons, of which wrought iron, electrolytic iron, and "ingot" iron are examples.

Wrought iron, whether made by the traditional puddling method or by mixing very low carbon iron and slag, contains a substantial amount of slag. Because it contains very little carbon, it is soft, ductile, and tough, and like low-carbon ferrous metals generally, is relatively resistant to corrosion. It is easily worked. When broken, it shows a fibrous fracture because of the slag inclusions. "Ingot" iron is a very low carbon iron containing no slag, which is also soft, ductile, and tough.

Above 2.0% carbon content is the region of the cast irons. Above the $A_{1,3}$ temperature, austenite, the eutectic ledeburite and cementite occur; below the $A_{1,3}$ temperature, the austenite transforms to pearlite, and a similar transformation of the ledeburite occurs.

Table 2-34. Standard Steels for Hot-rolled Bars
(Basic open-hearth and acid bessemer carbon steels)

AISI No.	Chemical composition limits, %				Corresponding SAE No.
	Carbon	Manganese	max Phosphorus	max Sulfur	
C1006	0.08 max	0.25/0.40	0.040	0.050	1006
C1010	0.09/0.13	0.30/0.60	0.040	0.050	1010
C1015	0.13/0.18	0.30/0.60	0.040	0.050	1015
C1020	0.18/0.23	0.30/0.60	0.040	0.050	1020
C1025	0.22/0.28	0.30/0.60	0.040	0.050	1025
C1030	0.28/0.34	0.60/0.90	0.040	0.050	1030
C1040	0.37/0.44	0.60/0.90	0.040	0.050	1040
C1050	0.48/0.55	0.60/0.90	0.040	0.050	1050
C1070	0.65/0.75	0.60/0.90	0.040	0.050	1070
C1085	0.80/0.93	0.70/1.00	0.040	0.050	1085
C1095	0.90/1.03	0.30/0.50	0.040	0.050	1095

When the silicon content is kept low, and the metal is cooled rapidly, *white cast iron* results. It is hard and brittle because of the high cementite content. White cast iron as such has little use; but when it is reheated and held a long time in the vicinity of the transformation temperature, then cooled slowly, the cementite decomposes to ferrite and nodular or temper carbon. The result is black-heart *malleable iron*. If the carbon is removed during malleabilization, white-heart malleable iron results.

If the silicon content is raised, and the metal is cooled relatively slowly, *gray cast iron* results. It contains cementite, pearlite, ferrite, and some free carbon, which gives it its gray color. Gray iron is considerably softer and tougher than white cast iron and is generally used for castings of all kinds. Often, it is alloyed with elements like nickel, chromium, copper, and molybdenum.

At 5.0% carbon, the end product is hard, brittle iron carbide or cementite.

2-48. Standard Steels. The American Iron and Steel Institute and the Society of Automotive Engineers have designated standard compositions for various steels including plain carbon steels and alloy steels. AISI and SAE numbers and compositions for several representative hot-rolled carbon-steel bars are given in Table 2-34.

Most of the steel used for construction is low- to medium-carbon, relatively mild, tough, and strong, fairly easy to work by cutting, punching, riveting, and welding. Table 2-35 summarizes the most important carbon steels, cast irons, wrought iron, and low-alloy steels used in construction as specified by the ASTM. This includes structural steels, rivet and bolt steels, various cast metals, and reinforcing steels.

Prestressed concrete imposes special requirements for reinforcing steel. Standard specifications are still to be adopted for wire and cable. It must be of high strength

Table 2-35. ASTM Requirements for Structural Steel and Iron

Material	ASTM specification No.	Tensile strength, 1,000 psi	Yield point min 1,000 psi	Elongation in 8 in., min %	Elongation in 2 in., min %	Reduction area, min %	Bend test, ratio of bend diam to thickness of specimen
Structural steel	A7	60–72	33	21	24	.....	0–¾ in.; ½ | ¾–1 in.; 1 | 1–1½ in.; 1½ | 1½–2 in.; 2½ | Over 2 in.; 3
Structural nickel steel	A8	90–115	55	14	30	.....	0–¾ in.; 1½ | ¾–1¼ in.; 2
Structural silicon steel	A94	80–95	45	16	19	30	0–¾ in.; 1 | ¾–1 in.; 1½ | Over 1¼ in.; 2½
Structural rivet steel	A141	52–62	28	24			
High-strength structural rivet steel	A195	68–82	38	20		34–36	
Carbon-steel forgings, C1	A235	66	33		22–23		
Low-alloy structural steel	A242	63–70	40–50	18–19			
Heavy-gaze hot-rolled sheets, C							3/16–¾ in.; 1 | ¾–1 in.; 1½ | 1–1½ in.; 2 | 1½–2 in.; 2½
Carbon-steel plates	A245	55	33	15.5–17.5	18.5–23.5		Depends on grade
Silicon-carbon-steel plates	A283	45–72	24–33	27–21	30–24		Depends on grade
Carbon-steel strip, C	A284	50–60	25–33	25–21	28–24		
Bolts and nuts, machine	A303	55	33	15.5–17.5	17.0–23.5		
	A307	55–90*					
Sheet piling	A328	70	38.5				
Cast steel, 65–35, annealed	A27	65	35	17	24	35	
Malleable iron 35018	A47	53	35		18		
Cast iron, class 25	A48	25					
Wrought-iron bars	A41	48	25	22			

Material	ASTM specification No.	Tensile strength, 1,000 psi	Yield point min 1,000 psi	Elongation in 8 in., min %	Reduction area, min %	Bending test, d = diam of pin, t = diam of specimen
Concrete reinforcing steel: Billet steel bars	A15					
Plain, structural		55–75	33	1,400,000 / tens. str., 20 min		Under ¾; 180°, $d = t$ | ¾ and over, 180°, $d = t$
Intermediate		70–90	40	1,300,000 / tens. str., 16 min		Under ¾; 180°, $d = 2t$ | ¾ and over; 90°, $d = 2t$
Hard		80 min	50	1,100,000 / tens. str.		Under ¾; 180°, $d = 4t$ | ¾ and over; 90°, $d = 4t$
Deformed, structural		55–75	33	1,200,000 / tens. str., 16 min		Under No. 6; 180°, $d = 2t$ | No. 6 and over; 180°, $d = 4t$
Intermediate		70–90	40	1,000,000 / tens. str., 12 min		Under No. 6; 180°, $d = 6t$ | No. 6 and over; 90°, $d = 6t$
Hard		80 min	50	1,000,000 / tens. str.		Under No. 6; 90°, $d = 6t$ | No. 6 and over; 90°, $d = 6t$
Rail steel bars	A16					
Plain		80	50	1,100,000 / tens. str.		Under ¾; 180°, $d = 4t$ | ¾ and over; 90°, $d = 4t$
Deformed		80	50	1,000,000 / tens. str.		Under No. 6; 90°, $d = 6t$ | No. 6 and over; 90°, $d = 6t$
Axle steel bars	A160	Same as billet steel 0.8 tens. str.				
Cold-drawn wire	A82	80 min			30	0.3 in. or under, bend around $d = t$ | Over 0.3 in., bend around $d = 2t$

* Stripping load of nuts must equal larger value.

with a high yield point and minimum creep in the working range.　One proposed specification calls for the following (for linear prestressed members):

Wire diam, in.	Stress at 0.7 % elongation, psi, min	Tensile strength, psi, min
0–0.100	195,000	280,000
0.100–0.200	190,000	
Above 0.200	180,000	235,000

2-49. Heat-treatment and Hardening of Steels.　Heat-treated and hardened steels are sometimes required in building operations.　The most familiar heat-treatment is annealing, a reheating operation in which the metal is usually heated to the austenitic range and cooled slowly to obtain the softest, most ductile state.　Cold working is often preceded by annealing.　Annealing may be only partial, just sufficient to relieve internal stresses that might cause deformation or cracking, but not enough to reduce markedly the increased strength and yield point brought about by the cold working, for example.

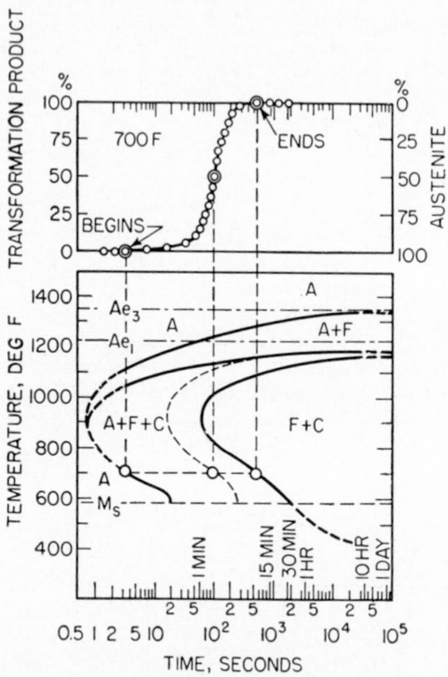

Heat-treatments are best exemplified by isothermal transformation curves, also called S curves and TTT (transformation-temperature-time) curves.　Figure 2-2 is typical.　It shows that above A_{e3} austenite is stable, between A_{e1} and A_{e3} some austenite transforms to ferrite, but below A_{e1} various transformations occur at various rates depending on temperature.　A specimen cooled to above the "knee" at 900°F shows proeutectoid transformation to ferrite (between the first two curves) followed by transformation to pearlite (ferrite plus carbide) in the second zone, until transformation is complete.　At the knee, transformation is extremely rapid, and the proeutectoid formation of ferrite disappears.　A specimen cooled rapidly to below the knee and held at a lower temperature transforms completely to ferrite plus carbide in a strong, hard form called bainite.　If cooled quickly to below the M_S temperature and held, the transformation product is the very hard, strong, but relatively brittle form, known as martensite.

In plain carbon steels, the knee of the curve is extremely critical because of the short transformation time.　It may be impossible to cool the centers of heavy parts fast enough to get below the knee,

Fig. 2-2. Typical isothermal transformation curve at a single temperature (top) and complete isothermal transformation diagram (bottom), showing effects of heat-treatment. ("*Metals Handbook,*" 1948, American Society for Metals.)

and hardenability is therefore limited.　The addition of alloying elements almost always shifts the knee to the right, that is, makes transformation more sluggish and therefore increases the hardenability of the metal.　Many alloys, such as several stainless steels, remain austenitic at ordinary temperatures; others can easily be made martensitic throughout, but still others merely become ferritic and cannot be hardened.

Often, a hard surface is required on a soft, tough core.　Two principal casehardening methods are employed.　For *case carburizing*, the low- to medium-carbon steel is packed in carbonaceous materials and heated to the austenite range. Carbon diffuses into the surface, providing a hard, high-carbon case when the part is cooled. For *nitriding*, the part is exposed to ammonia gas or a cyanide at moderately elevated temperatures. Extremely hard nitrides are formed in the case and provide a hard surface. Cast iron is frequently cast against metal inserts in the molds. The cast metal is chilled by the inserts and forms white cast iron, whereas the rest of the more slowly cooled metal becomes gray cast iron.

2–50. Steel Alloys. Plain carbon steels can be given a great range of properties by heat-treatment and by working; but addition of alloying elements greatly extends those properties or makes the heat-treating operations easier and simpler. For example, combined high tensile strength and toughness, corrosion resistance, high-speed cutting, and many other specialized purposes require alloy steels. However, the most important effect of alloying is the influence on hardenability. The most important alloying elements from the standpoint of building, and their principal effects, are summarized below:

Aluminum restricts grain growth during heat-treatment and promotes surface hardening by nitriding.

Chromium is a hardener, promotes corrosion resistance (see stainless steels, below), and promotes wear resistance.

Copper promotes resistance to atmospheric corrosion and is sometimes combined with molybdenum for this purpose in low-carbon steels and irons. It strengthens steel and increases the yield point without unduly changing elongation or reduction of area.

Manganese in low concentrations promotes hardenability and nondeforming, nonshrinking characteristics for tool steels. In high concentrations, the steel is austenitic under ordinary conditions, is extremely tough, and work-hardens readily. It is therefore used for teeth of power-shovel dippers, railroad frogs, rock crushers, and similar applications.

Molybdenum is usually associated with other elements, especially chromium and nickel. It increases corrosion resistance, raises tensile strength and elastic limit without reducing ductility, promotes casehardening and improves impact resistance.

Nickel boosts tensile strength and yield point without reducing ductility; increases low-temperature toughness, whereas ordinary carbon steels become brittle; promotes casehardening; and in high concentrations improves corrosion resistance under severe conditions. It is commonly associated with chromium (see stainless steels, below). *Invar* contains 36% nickel.

Silicon strengthens low-alloy steels; improves oxidation resistance; with low carbon yields transformer steel, because of low hysteresis loss and high permeability; in high concentrations provides hard, brittle castings, resistant to corrosive chemicals, useful in plumbing lines for chemical laboratories.

Sulfur promotes free machining, especially in mild steels.

Titanium prevents intergranular corrosion of stainless steels by preventing grain-boundary depletion of chromium during such operations as welding and heat-treatment.

Tungsten, vanadium, and *cobalt* are all used in high-speed tool steels, because they promote hardness and abrasion resistance. Tungsten and cobalt also increase high-temperature hardness.

The principal effects of alloying elements are summarized in Table 2–36.

2–51. Stainless Steels. Stainless steels of primary interest in building are the wrought stainless steels of the austenitic type. The austenitic stainless steels contain both chromium and nickel. Total content of alloy metals is not less than 23%, with chromium not less than 16% and nickel not less than 7%. Table 2–37 summarizes the composition and principal properties of these metals.

Austenitic stainless steels are tough, strong, and shock-resistant, but work-harden readily; so some difficulty on this score may be experienced with cold working and machining. These steels can be welded readily but may have to be stabilized (e.g., AISI types 321 and 347) against carbide precipitation and intergranular corrosion due to welding unless special precautions are taken. These steels have the best high-temperature strength and resistance to scaling of all the stainless steels.

Table 2-36. Effects of Alloying Elements in Steel*

Element	Solid solubility		Influence on ferrite	Influence on austenite (hardenability)	Influence exerted through carbide		Principal functions
	In gamma iron	In alpha iron			Carbide-forming tendency	Action during tempering	
Aluminum (Al)	1.1 % (increased by C)	36 %	Hardens considerably by solid solution	Increases hardenability mildly, if dissolved in austenite	Negative (graphitizes)	....	1. Deoxides efficiently 2. Restricts grain growth (by forming dispersed oxides or nitrides) 3. Alloying element in nitriding steel
Chromium (Cr)	12.8 % (20 % with 0.5 % C)	Unlimited	Hardens slightly; increases corrosion resistance	Increases hardenability moderately	Greater than Mn; less than W	Mildly resists softening	1. Increases resistance to corrosion and oxidation 2. Increases hardenability 3. Adds some strength at high temperatures 4. Resists abrasion and wear (with high carbon)
Cobalt (Co)	Unlimited	75 %	Hardens considerably by solid solution	Decreases hardenability as dissolved	Similar to Fe	Sustains hardness by solid solution	1. Contributes to red hardness by hardening ferrite
Manganese (Mn)	Unlimited	3 %	Hardens markedly; reduces plasticity somewhat	Increases hardenability moderately	Greater than Fe; less than Cr	Very little, in usual percentages	1. Counteracts brittleness from the sulfur 2. Increases hardenability inexpensively
Molybdenum (Mo)	3 % ± (8 % with 0.3 % C)	37.5 % (less with lowered temp)	Provides age-hardening system in high Mo-Fe alloys	Increases hardenability strongly (Mo > Cr)	Strong; greater than Cr	Opposes softening by secondary hardening	1. Raises grain-coarsening temperature of austenite 2. Deepens hardening 3. Counteracts tendency toward temper brittleness 4. Raises hot and creep strength, red hardness 5. Enhances corrosion resistance in stainless steel 6. Forms abrasion-resisting particles
Nickel (Ni)	Unlimited	10 % (irrespective of carbon content)	Strengthens and toughens by solid solution	Increases hardenability mildly, but tends to retain austenite with higher carbon	Negative (graphitizes)	Very little in small percentages	1. Strengthens unquenched or annealed steels 2. Toughens pearlitic-ferritic steels (especially at low temperature) 3. Renders high-chromium iron alloys austenitic

Table 2-36. Effects of Alloying Elements in Steel (Continued)

Element	Solid solubility		Influence on ferrite	Influence on austenite (hardenability)	Influence exerted through carbide		Principal functions
	In gamma iron	In alpha iron			Carbide-forming tendency	Action during tempering	
Phosphorus, (P)....	0.5 %	2.8 % (irrespective of carbon content)	Hardens strongly by solid solution	Increases hardenability	Nil	....	1. Strengthens low-carbon steel 2. Increases resistance to corrosion 3. Improves machinability in free-cutting steels
Silicon (Si)........	2 % ± (9 % with 0.35 % C)	18.5 % (not much changed by carbon)	Hardens with loss in plasticity (Mn < Si < P)	Increases hardenability moderately	Negative (graphitizes)	Sustains hardness by solid solution	1. Used as general-purpose deoxidizer 2. Alloying element for electrical and magnetic sheet 3. Improves oxidation resistance 4. Increases hardenability of steel carrying nongraphitizing elements 5. Strengthens low-alloy steels
Titanium (Ti)......	0.75 % (1 % ± with 0.20 % C)	6 % ± (less with lowered temp)	Provides age-hardening system in high Ti-Fe alloys	Probably increases hardenability very strongly as dissolved. The carbide effects reduce hardenability	Greatest known (2 % Ti renders 0.50 % carbon steel unhardenable)	Persistent carbides probably unaffected. Some secondary hardening	1. Fixes carbon in inert particles a. Reduces martensitic hardness and hardenability in medium-chromium steels b. Prevents formation of austenite in high-chromium steels c. Prevents localized depletion of chromium in stainless steel during long heating
Tungsten (W)......	6 % (11 % with 0.25 % C)	33 % (less with lowered temp)	Provides age-hardening system in high W-Fe alloys	Increases hardenability strongly in small amounts	Strong	Opposes softening by secondary hardening	1. Forms hard, abrasion-resistant particles in tool steels 2. Promotes hardness and strength at elevated temperature
Vanadium (V)......	1 % (4 % with 0.20 % C)	Unlimited	Hardens moderately by solid solution	Increases hardenability very strongly, as dissolved	Very strong (V < Ti or Cb)	Max for secondary hardening	1. Elevates coarsening temperature of austenite (promotes fine grain) 2. Increases hardenability (when dissolved) 3. Resists tempering and causes marked secondary hardening

* Metals Handbook," American Society for Metals, 1948.

Table 2-37. Austenitic Stainless Steels*

AISI No.	Carbon, max %	Chromium, %	Nickel, %	Other elements, max %	Modulus of elasticity, 10^6 psi	Tensile strength, 1,000 psi		Yield point, 1,000 psi		Elongation % in 2 in.		Reduction area, %	Izod impact, ft-lb	Drawing or stamping	Remarks — General properties	Welding properties
						A†	CR‡	A†	CR‡	A†	CR‡	A†	A†			
301	0.08–0.20	16–18	6–8	Mn 2											A general-utility stainless steel, easily worked; for trim household utensils, structural purposes	Very good; tough welds
302	0.08–0.20	17–19	8–10	Mn 2	29	80–90	100–180	35–45	50–150	60–55	50–10	65–55	110–70	Very good	A readily fabricated stainless steel for decorative or corrosion-resistant use	Very good; tough welds
302B	0.08–0.20	17–19	8–10	Si 2–3, Mn 2											Silicon added to increase resistance to scaling at high temperatures	Fairly good. May crack; not recommended
303	0.15	17–19	8–10	D, S, Se 0.07 min, Zr, Mo 0.60	29	80–90		35–45		60–50		70–55	110–70	Fairly good	A free-machining grade 18-8 stainless steel	
304	0.08	18–20	8–11	Mn 2											A low-carbon 18-8 steel, weldable with less danger of intercrystalline corrosion	
308	0.08	19–21	10–12	Mn 2											For use when corrosion resistance greater than that of 18-8 is needed	
309	0.20	22–24	12–15	Mn 2	30	90–110		40–60		65–50		65–50		Good	For use at elevated temperature, combining high scaling resistance and good strength	Good
309S	0.08	22–24	12–15	Mn 2											Low carbon permits welded fabrication with a minimum of carbide precipitation	
310	0.25	24–26	19–22	Mn 2	30.5	90–110		40–60		55–45		60–50		Good	Similar to 25-12 stainless, with higher nickel content for greater stability at welding temperatures	Good
316	0.10	16–18	10–14	Mo 2–3	28.5	80–90	100–150	35–55	50–125	70–60	50–15	75–60	120–70	Good	Superior resistance to chemical corrosion	Very good
317	0.10	18–20	11–14	Mo 3–4											Higher alloy content than 316 for increased corrosion resistance	Very good
321	0.08	17–19	8–11	Ti 5 × C min	29	80–90	100–180	35–45	50–150	60–55	50–10	65–55		Good	An 18-8 type, stabilized against intercrystalline corrosion at elevated temperatures	Very good
347	0.08	17–19	9–12	Cb 10 × C										Good	A stabilized 18-8 steel for service at elevated temperatures	Very good

* "Metals Handbook," American Society for Metals, 1948.
† A, annealed.
‡ CR, cold-rolled.

Types 303 and 304 are the familiar 18-8 stainless steels widely used for building applications. These, and Types 302 and 316 are the most commonly employed stainless steels. Where maximum resistance to corrosion is required, such as resistance to pitting by sea water and chemicals, the molybdenum-containing types 316 and 317 are best.

For resistance to ordinary atmospheric corrosion, some of the martensitic and ferritic stainless steels, containing 15 to 20% chromium and no nickel, are employed. The martensitic steels, in general, range from about 12 to 18% chromium and from 0.08 to 1.10% carbon. Their response to heat-treatment is similar to the plain carbon steels. When chromium content ranges from 15 to 30% and carbon content is below 0.35%, the steels are ferritic and nonhardenable. The high-chromium steels are resistant to oxidizing corrosion and are useful in chemical plants.

2-52. Welding Ferrous Metals. Table 2-38 summarizes the welding characteristics of the various types of ferrous metals. The following observations are pertinent:

Wrought iron is ideally forged but may be welded by other methods if the base metal is thoroughly fused. Slag melts first and may confuse unwary operators.

Low-carbon iron and steels (0.30%C or less) are readily welded and require no preheating or subsequent annealing unless residual stresses are to be removed.

Medium-carbon steels (0.30 to 0.50%C) can be welded by the various fusion processes. In some cases, especially in steel with more than 0.40% carbon, preheating and subsequent heat-treatment may be necessary.

High-carbon steels (0.50 to 0.90%C) are more difficult to weld and, especially in arc welding, may have to be preheated to at least 500°F and subsequently heated between 1200 and 1450°F. For gas welding, a carburizing flame is often used. Care must be taken not to destroy the heat-treatment to which high-carbon steels may have been subjected.

Tool steels (0.80 to 1.50%C) are difficult to weld. Preheating, postannealing, heat-treatment, special welding rods, and great care are necessary for successful welding.

2-53. Corrosion of Iron and Steel. Corrosion of ferrous metals is caused by the tendency of iron (anode) to go into solution in water as ferrous hydroxide and displace hydrogen, which in turn combines with dissolved oxygen to form more water. At the same time, the dissolved ferrous hydroxide is converted by more oxygen to the insoluble ferric hydroxide, thereby allowing more iron to go into solution. Corrosion, therefore, requires liquid water (as in damp air) and oxygen (which is normally present dissolved in the water).

Protection against corrosion takes a variety of forms:

Deaeration. If oxygen is removed from water, corrosion stops. In hot-water heating systems, therefore, no fresh water should be added. Boiler feedwater is sometimes deaerated to retard corrosion.

Coatings

1. *Paints.* Most paints are based on linseed oil and a variety of pigments, of which red lead, oxides of iron, lead sulfate, zinc sulfate, graphite, aluminum, and various hydrocarbons are a few. No one paint is best for all applications. Other paints are coatings of asphalt and tar.

2. *Metallic.* Zinc applied by hot dipping (galvanizing) or hot powder (sherardizing), hot tin dip, hot aluminum dip, and electrolytic plates of tin, copper, nickel, chromium, cadmium, and zinc. A mixture of lead and tin is called terneplate. Zinc is anodic to iron and protects, even after the coating is broken, by sacrificial protection. Tin and copper are cathodic and protect as long as the coating is unbroken but may hasten corrosion by pitting and other localized action once the coating is pierced.

3. *Chemical.* Insoluble phosphates, such as iron or zinc phosphate, are formed on the surface of the metal by treatment with phosphate solutions. These have some protective action and also form good bases for paints. Black oxide coatings are formed by treating the surface with various strong salt solutions. This coating is good for indoor use but has limited life outdoors. It provides a good base for rust-inhibiting oils.

Cathodic Protection. As corrosion proceeds, electric currents are produced as the metal at the anode goes into solution. If a sufficient countercurrent is produced, the metal at the anode will not dissolve. This is accomplished in various ways, such as

Table 2-38. Welding Characteristics of Ferrous Metals*

Metals and alloys	Forge	Resistance	Thermit	Thermit pressure	Oxyacetylene pressure	Gas	Bronze	Inert-gas-shielded arc	Arc	Submerged melt
Iron:										
1. Wrought iron	A	A	A	A	A	A	A	..	A	A
2. Low-carbon iron	A	A	A	A	A	A	A	..	A	A
Carbon steels:										
1. Low-carbon	A	A	A	A	A	A	A	B	A	A
2. Medium-carbon	A	B	A	A	A	A	A	B	A	A
3. High-carbon	..	B	B	A	A	B	B	B	B	B
4. Tool steel	..	A	B	B	A	B	B	B	A	B
5. Copper-bearing steel	..	..	B	A	A	A	B	..	A	A
Cast steel:										
1. Plain carbon	..	B	A	A	B	A	A	..	A–B	A
2. High-manganese	..	..	B	B	No	A–B	A–B	..	A–B	B
3. Other alloys	..	B	A	A	B	A–B	A–B	..	A–B	A–B
Cast iron:										
1. Gray iron	..	..	B	No	No	A	A	B	B	No
2. Malleable iron	..	..	B	B	No	B	A	B	B	No
3. Alloy cast irons	..	..	A	B	No	A	A	..	B	No
Low-alloy steels:										
1. Plain nickel	..	A	B	B	A	A	..	B	A	A
2. Nickel-copper	..	A	B	B	A	A	..	..	A	A
3. Manganese-molybdenum	..	A	B	B	B	A	..	..	A	A
4. Carbon-molybdenum	..	No	B	B	B	A	..	..	A	A
5. Nickel-chromium	..	No	B	B	A	A	..	B	A	A
6. Chromium-molybdenum	..	No	B	B	A	A	..	..	A	A
7. Nickel-chromium-molybdenum	..	No	B	B	B	B	..	..	B	B
8. Nickel-molybdenum	..	No	B	B	A	B	..	..	B	B
9. Chromium	..	No	B	B	A	A	..	..	A	A
10. Chromium-vanadium	..	No	B	B	A	A	..	..	A	A
11. Manganese	..	No	B	B	B	A	..	..	A	A
Stainless steels:										
1. Chromium	A	A	No	No	B	B	..	B	A	A
2. Chromium-nickel	A	A	No	No	A	A	..	A	A	A

Code: A, commonly used.   B, used occasionally, under favorable conditions.   No, not used.   (..) no information available.

* "Metals Handbook," American Society for Metals, 1948.

connecting the iron to a more active metal like magnesium (rods suspended in domestic water heaters) or connecting the part to be protected to buried scrap iron and providing an external current source such as a battery or rectified current from a power line (protection of buried pipe lines).

2-54. Ferrous Metals Bibliography

American Iron and Steel Institute, New York, N.Y.: "Carbon Steels, Chemical Composition Limits," "Constructional Alloys, Chemical Composition Limits;" "Steel Products Manuals," secs. 4, 6, 7, 16, 18, 21, 28.

American Society for Testing Materials, Philadelphia, Pa.: "Standards," Part 1.

American Society for Metals, Cleveland, Ohio: "Metals Handbook," 1948.

Proceedings of the First United States Conference on Prestressed Concrete, Massachusetts Institute of Technology, Cambridge, Mass., August, 1951.

Williams, R. S., and V. O. Homerberg: "Principles of Metallography," 5th ed., McGraw-Hill Book Company, Inc., New York, 1948.

ALUMINUM AND ALUMINUM-BASED ALLOYS

Pure aluminum and aluminum alloys are used in building in various forms. High-purity aluminum (at least 99% pure) is soft and ductile but weak. It has excellent corrosion resistance and is used in building for such applications as bright foil for heat insulation, roofing, flashing, gutters and downspouts, exterior and interior architectural trim, and as pigment in aluminum-based paints. Its high heat conductivity recommends it for cooking utensils. The electrical conductivity of the electrical grade is 61% of that of pure copper on an equal-volume basis and 201% on an equal-weight basis.

Aluminum alloys are generally harder and stronger than the pure metal. Furthermore, pure aluminum is difficult to cast satisfactorily, whereas many of the alloys are readily cast.

2-55. Aluminum-alloy Designations. The alloys may be classified: (1) as cast and wrought, and (2) as heat-treatable and non-heat-treatable. Alloys are heat-treatable if the dissolved constituents are less soluble in the solid state at ordinary temperatures than at elevated temperatures, thereby making age-hardening possible. When heat-treated to obtain complete solution, the product may be unstable and tend to age spontaneously. It may also be treated to produce stable tempers of varying degree. Cold working or strain hardening is also possible, and combinations of tempering and strain hardening can also be obtained.

Because of these various possible combinations, a system of letter and number designations has been worked out by the producers of aluminum and aluminum alloys to indicate the compositions and the tempers of the various metals. The nominal chemical compositions and commercial designations of the important wrought and casting alloys are given in Table 2-39.

Wrought alloys are designated by a four-digit index system. 1xxx is for 99.00% aluminum minimum. The last two digits indicate the minimum aluminum percentage. The second digit represents impurity limits. (EC is a special designation for electrical conductors.) 2xxx to 8xxx represent alloy groups in which the first number indicates the principal alloying constituent, and the last two digits are identifying numbers in the group. The second digit indicates modification of the basic alloy. The alloy groups are

Copper	2xxx
Manganese	3xxx
Silicon	4xxx
Magnesium	5xxx
Magnesium and silicon	6xxx
Zinc	7xxx
Other elements	8xxx
Unused series	9xxx

Cast alloys have not been brought into the same digit system, and are designated by numbers, which may have letter prefixes to indicate modifications, e.g., 113 and C113.

Casting alloys may be sand, permanent-mold, or die-casting alloys. Some casting alloys may be used for all three.

Among the wrought alloys, the letters F, O, H, W, and T following the letter S indicate various basic temper designations. These letters in turn may be followed by

Table 2-39. Nominal Compositions, Selected Aluminum Alloys*
(% of alloying elements—aluminum and normal impurities constitute remainder)

Alloy	Copper	Silicon	Manganese	Magnesium	Zinc	Nickel	Chromium	Lead	Bismuth
A. Wrought alloys									
EC	....	....	99.45% min aluminum		(Electrical conductors)				
1100	....	....	99% min aluminum						
2001	5.5	....	...	....	...	...	....	0.5	0.5
2014	4.4	0.8	0.8	0.4					
2024	4.5	....	0.6	1.5					
3003	....	....	1.2						
3004	....	....	1.2	1.0					
5052	....	....	...	2.5	...	...	0.25		
6061	0.25	0.6	...	1.0	...	...	0.25		
6063	....	0.4	...	0.7					
6151	....	1.0	...	0.6	...	...	0.25		
7075	1.6	....	...	2.5	5.6	...	0.3		
B. Casting alloys									
13	....	12.0							
43	....	5.0							
85	4.0	5.0							
113	7.0	2.0							
C113	7.0	3.5							
195	4.5	0.8							
212	8.0	1.5							
214	....	....	...	3.8					
220	....	....	...	10.0					
319	3.5	6.3							
356	....	7.0	...	0.3					
380	3.5	9.0							

* Heat-treatment symbols have been omitted since composition does not vary for different heat-treatment practices.

numerals to indicate various degrees of treatment. Temper designations are summarized in Table 2-40.

The American Society for Testing Materials (ASTM) and the Society of Automotive Engineers (SAE) have also established number and letter designations, which differ from the commercial designations. For comparison, the commercial, ASTM, and SAE designations are given in Table 2-41, which also summarizes the important properties of a number of commercially important alloys.

The alloys commonly used for structural purposes are:

Wrought........... 2014, 2024, 3003, 3004, 5052, 6061, 6063, 6151
Cast............... 43, 195, 214, 220, 356

The structural alloys generally employed in building are 2014-T6, 6061-T6, and 6063-T6.

2-56. Clad Aluminum. Pure aluminum is generally more corrosion-resistant than its alloys. Furthermore, its various forms—pure and alloy—have different solution potentials; that is, they are anodic or cathodic to each other, depending on their rela-

Table 2-40. Basic Temper Designations*

-F   As fabricated.   This designation applies to products which acquire some temper qualities in the shaping processes but are not subsequently thermally treated or intentionally strain-hardened.

-O   Annealed, recrystallized.   This designation applies to the softest temper of wrought alloy products.

-H   Strain-hardened.   This designation applies to those products which have their strength increased by strain hardening with or without supplementary thermal treatments to produce partial softening.   The -H is always followed by two or more digits.   The first digit indicates the specific combination of basic operations and the following digit or digits the final degree of strain hardening.

Subdivision of the -H temper:

-H1   Strain-hardened only.   The number following this designation indicates the degree of strain hardening.

-H2   Strain-hardened and then partial annealed.   The number following this designation indicates the degree of strain hardening remaining after the product has been partial annealed.

-H3   Strain-hardened and then stabilized.   The number following this designation indicates the degree of strain hardening remaining after the product has been strain-hardened a specific amount and then stabilized.   Numerals 2, 4, 6, 8, and 9 correspond to the former designations $\frac{1}{4}$H, $\frac{1}{2}$H, $\frac{3}{4}$H, H, and extra hard and are employed as a second digit after H.

-W   The unstable condition following solution heat-treatment.   This designation, because of natural aging, is specific only when the period of aging is indicated, e.g., 24S-W ($\frac{1}{2}$ hr)

-T   Treated to produce stable tempers other than -F, -O, or -H.   This designation applies to products thermally treated to produce stable tempers with or without supplementary strain hardening.   The -T followed by the numerals 2 to 19, inclusive, designates one specific combination of basic operations.   Should some other variation of the same basic operations be applied to the same alloy, resulting in different characteristics, then other digits are added to the basic designation.   It should be understood that a period of natural aging at room temperature may occur between or after the operations listed.   Control of this period is exercised when it is metallurgically important.

Subdivision of the -T temper:

-T2   Annealed.   (Cast products only.)   This designation is applied to castings only, for such purposes as improving ductility and increasing dimensional stability.

-T3   Solution heat-treated and then cold-worked.   This designation applies to those products where cold work is performed for the primary purpose of improving the strength and also applies to those products in which the effect of cold work, such as flattening or straightening, is recognized in applicable specifications.

-T4   Solution heat-treated and naturally aged to a substantially stable condition.   This designation applies when the product is not cold-worked after heat-treatment and also when applicable specifications do not recognize the effect of cold work in flattening and straightening operations.

-T5   Artificially aged only.   This designation applies to products which are artificially aged without prior solution heat-treatment.   The artificially aging of these products improves mechanical properties and dimensional stability.

-T6   Solution heat-treated and then artificially aged.   This designation applies to products which are not cold-worked after solution heat-treatment and in which the effect, if any, of flattening or straightening is not recognized in applicable specifications.

-T7   Solution heat-treated and then stabilized.   This designation applies to products in which the temperature and time conditions for stabilizing are such that the alloy is carried beyond the point of maximum hardness, providing control of growth and/or residual stress.

-T8   Solution heat-treated, cold-worked, and then artificially aged.   This designation applies when the cold working is done for the purpose of improving strength and also when the cold-working effect of flattening or straightening is recognized in applicable specifications.

-T9   Solution heat-treated, artificially aged, and then cold-worked.   This designation applies when the cold working is done for the purpose of improving strength.

-T10   Artificially aged and then cold-worked.

* Reynolds Metals Co.

Table 2-41. Properties of Selected Structural Aluminum Alloys[a]

Spec. No. (ASTM)[b]	Alloy	S.A.E. alloy No.	Commercial alloy No.	Condition	Approx. weight, lb per cu in.	Relative resistance to corrosion[c]	Relative suitability for being cold worked[d]	Relative machinability[d]	Relative suitability for being brazed[d]	Gas	Arc	Resistance (spot and seam)	Ultimate tensile strength, 1,000 psi	Yield strength, tension, 1,000 psi[f]	Elongation, Sheet specimen (1/16 in. thick)	Elongation, Round specimen (1/2 in. diam, 1/4 in. die cast)	Yield strength, compression, 1,000 psi	Shear strength, 1,000 psi[g]	Fatigue endurance limit, 1,000 psi[g]	Brinell hardness (500-kg load, 10-mm ball)[h]
													Wrought alloys							
B178, B209, B211, B221, B247, B273	990A	25	1100-0	Annealed	0.098	A	A+	B	A	A	A	A	13	5	35	45	5	9.5	5.0	23
			1100-H18	Hard	0.098	A	B-	B	A	A	A	A	24	22	5	15	22	13.0	8.5	44
B178, B209, B221, B241, B247, B273, B274	M1A	29	3003-O	Annealed	0.099	A	A+	B	A	A	A	A	16	6	30	40	6	11.0	7.0	28
			3003-H18	Hard	0.099	A	C+	B	A	A	A	A	29	26	4	10	26	16.0	10.0	55
B234, B274	Clad M1A		Clad 3003	Annealed	0.099	A	A+	B	…	A	A	A	16	6	30	40	6	11.0	7.0	
			Clad 3003-H18	Hard	0.099	A	C+	B	…	A	A	A	29	26	4	10	26	16.0	10.0	
B178, B209, B210, B211, B221, B273, B274	MG11A	20	3004	Annealed	0.098	A	C-	B	…	B	A	A	26	10	20	25	10	16.0	14.0	45
			3004-H38	Hard	0.098	A	C-	B	…	B	A	A	40	34	5	6	34	21.0	16.0	77
B211, B221	CS41A	260	2014-T4	Heat-treated	0.101	C[k]	C-	A	X	D	C	D	62	44		20	40	38.0	20.0	105
			2014-T6	H.T. and aged	0.101	C[k]	C-	A	X	D	C	D	70	60		13	60	42.0	18.0	135
B209	Clad CS41A		Clad 2014-T3[i]	Heat-treated	0.101	A	C-	A	X	D	C	D	63	40	20	…	40	37.0		
			Clad 2014-T6[i]	H.T. and aged	0.101	A	C-	A	X	D	C	D	68	60	11	…	60	41.0		
B209, B210, B211, B221, B235, B273, B274	CG42A	24	2024-T3	Heat-treated	0.100	C[k]	C-	A	X	D	C	D	70	50	18	…	50	41.0	20.0	120
			2024-T36	H.T. and cold-worked	0.100	C[k]	D+	A	X	D	C	D	72	57	14	…	57	42.0	18.0	130
B209	Clad CG42A		Clad 2024-T3[i]	Heat-treated	0.099	A	C-	B	X	D	C	A	64	44	18	…	44	40.0		
			Clad 2024-T36[i]	H.T. and cold-worked	0.099	A	C-	B	X	D	C	A	67	53	11	…	53	41.0		
B247	SG11A	240	6151-T6	H.T. and aged	0.098	B		B	C	C	A	A	48	43		17	43	32.0	11.0	100
B178, B209, B210, B211, B221, B274	GR20A	280	5052-O	Annealed	0.097	A	A+	B	C	B	A	A	27	12	25	30	12	18.0	17.0	45
			5052-H38	Hard	0.097	A	C+	B	C	B	A	A	41	36	7	8	36	24.0	19.0	85
B211	GS11B	201	5053-T4	Heat-treated	0.097	A	B-	B	A	A	A	A	30	20		21	20	18.0	13.0	62
			5053-T6	H.T. and aged	0.097	A	C+	B	A	A	A	A	37	32		13	32	23.0	13.0	80
B178, B209, B210, B211, B221, B235, B273, B274	GS11A	282	6061-T4	Heat-treated	0.098	A	B-	B	A	A	A	A	35	21	22	25	21	24.0	13.5	65
			6061-T6	H.T. and aged	0.098	A	B-	B	A	A	A	A	45	40	12	17	40	30.0	13.5	95
B221, B235, B241, B274	GS10A	281	6063-T5	Extruded and aged	0.098	A	B	B	B	A	A	A	27	21	12	…	21	17.0	9.5	60
B209, B211	ZG62A		6063-T6	H.T. and aged	0.098	A	B-	B	B	A	A	A	35	31	12	…	31	22.0	9.5	73
B221, B235			7075-T6[i]	H.T. and aged	0.101	C	D	A	X	D	C	D	82	72	11	11	72	49.0	24.0	150
B209	Clad ZG62A		Clad 7075-T6[i]	H.T. and aged	0.101	A	D+	A	X	D	C	A	76	67	11	…	67	46.0		

Note: this table is printed rotated 90°; the column headings are not printed on this page. The values below are transcribed in their original left-to-right order; the property labels for the numeric and letter-rating columns are inferred.

Sand-casting alloys

ASTM	No.	Alloy	Form/Temper	Condition	Weight (lb/in³)	Corrosion[c]	Workability[d]	Weldability[d]	Brazeability[d]	Machinability[d]	Tensile	Yield[f]	Elong. %	Comp. yield	Shear[g]	Fatigue[h]	Brinell
B26	35	S5A	43	As cast	0.097	B	A	A	B	B	19	8	8.0	9	14.0	8.0	40
B26	38	C4A	195-T4	Heat-treated	0.102	C	B	B	X	C	32	16	8.5	17	26.0	7.0	60
B26	38	C4A	195-T6	H. T. and aged	0.102	C	B	B	X	C	36	24	5.0	25	30.0	7.5	75
B26	320	G4A	214	As cast	0.096	A	A	A	X	A	25	12	9.0	12	20.0	7.0	75
B26		GS42A	B214	As cast	0.093	A	A	A	X	D	20	13	2.0	14	17.0	…	50
B26	324	G10A	220-T4	Heat-treated	0.093	A	B	C	X	B	46	25	14.0	26	33.0	8.0	50
B26	329	SC64C	319	As cast	0.102	C	B	B	X	C	27	18	2.0	19	22.0	10.0	70
B26	329	SC64C	319-T6	H. T. and aged	0.102	C	B	C	X	B	36	24	2.0	25	29.0	10.0	70
B26	323	SG70A	356-T6	H. T. and aged	0.097	B	A	A	X	A	33	24	3.5	25	26.0	8.5	80
B26	323	SG70A	356-T51	Aged only	0.097	B	A	A	B	A	25	20	2.0	21	20.0	7.5	60

Permanent-mold casting alloys

ASTM	No.	Alloy	Form/Temper	Condition	Weight (lb/in³)	Corrosion[c]	Workability[d]	Weldability[d]	Brazeability[d]	Machinability[d]	Tensile	Yield[f]	Elong. %	Comp. yield	Shear[g]	Fatigue[h]	Brinell
B108	35	S5A	43	As cast	0.097	B	A	A	B	B	23	9	10.0	9	16.0	…	45
B108	380	CS42A	B195-T4	Heat-treated	0.101	C	B	C	X	B	37	19	9.0	20	30.0	9.5	75
B108	380	CS42A	B195-T6	H. T. and aged	0.101	C	B	C	X	B	40	26	5.0	26	32.0	10.0	90
B108		G242A	A214	As cast	0.097	A	A	B	X	A	27	16	7.0	17	22.0	…	60
B108	323	SG70A	356-T6	H. T. and aged	0.097	A	A	A	X	A	40	27	5.0	27	32.0	13.0	90

Die-casting alloys

ASTM	No.	Alloy	Form/Temper	Condition	Weight (lb/in³)	Corrosion[c]	Workability[d]	Weldability[d]	Brazeability[d]	Machinability[d]	Tensile	Yield[f]	Elong. %	Shear[g]	Fatigue[h]
B85	305	S5	13	As cast	0.096	C	B	D	X	B	39	21	2.0	25.0	19.0
B85	304	S4	43	As cast	0.096	D	D	D	X	B	30	16	9.0	19.0	17.0
B85	307	SC2	85	As cast	0.099	B	C	D	X	C	40	24	5.0	26.0	22.0

[a] Aluminum Company of America.

[b] For all alloys wrought and cast, the following data apply: (a) Young's modulus of elasticity may be taken as 10,300,000 psi; (b) modulus of rigidity may be taken as 3,800,000 psi; (c) Poisson's ratio is 0.33; (d) bearing strength is equal to 1.8 times the tensile strength, provided the edge distance, in the direction of stressing, is not less than twice the diameter of the hole.

[c] An A rating is highest. However, under many conditions, alloys rated D are used with entirely satisfactory results; on the other hand, alloys rated A require protection in some exposures. Ratings are based on aluminum-base alloys as a group and are not to be used in comparison with other metals.

[d] Relative hot and cold workability, weldability, brazeability and machinability are indicated as follows: A = excellent, B = good, C = fair, D = poor; and X = cannot be brazed.

[e] Mechanical properties are obtained on ASTM specimens. Since minimum guaranteed values vary with the commodity, they are not given in this table.

[f] Yield strength is the stress at which the material exhibits a permanent set of 0.2%.

[g] Shearing strengths are single-shear values obtained from double-shear tests.

[h] Fatigue endurance values are based on withstanding 500 million cycles of completely reversed stress using the R.R. Moore type of machine and specimen.

[i] Sheet over 0.064 in. thick will have slightly higher tensile and yield strengths.

[j] For extrusions the strengths will be higher.

[k] In thicknesses of about 1/8 in. and over, these alloys in the -T3, -T4, and -T36 tempers have a D rating.

tive solution potentials. A number of alloys are therefore made with centers or "cores" of aluminum alloy, overlaid with layers of metal, either pure aluminum or alloys, which are anodic to the core.   If galvanic corrosion conditions are encountered, the cladding metal protects the core sacrificially.   Such clad metals are given commercial names, such as alclad (Alcoa) and pure clad (Reynolds).   Clad metal is generally available only as sheet, wire, and tube.

2-57. Corrosion Resistance and Corrosion Protection of Aluminum. Although aluminum ranks high in the electromotive series of the metals, it is highly corrosion-resistant because of the tough, transparent, tenacious film of aluminum oxide which rapidly forms on any exposed surface.   It is this corrosion resistance that recommends aluminum for building applications.   For most exposures, including industrial and seacoast atmospheres, the alloys normally recommended are adequate, particularly if used in usual thicknesses and if mild pitting is not objectionable.

Pure aluminum is the most corrosion-resistant of all and is used alone or as cladding on strong-alloy cores where maximum resistance is wanted.   Of the alloys, those containing magnesium, manganese, chromium or magnesium, and silicon in the form of $MgSi_2$ are highly resistant to corrosion.   The alloys containing substantial proportions of copper are more susceptible to corrosion, depending markedly on the heat-treatment.

Certain precautions should be taken in building.   Aluminum is subject to attack by alkalies, and it should therefore be protected from contact with wet concrete, mortar, and plaster.   Clear methacrylate lacquers or strippable plastic coatings are recommended for interiors, and methacrylate lacquer for exterior protection during construction.   Strong alkaline and acid cleaners should be avoided and muriatic acid should not be used on masonry surfaces adjacent to aluminum.   If aluminum must be contiguous to concrete and mortar outdoors, or where it will be wet, it should be insulated from direct contact by asphalts, bitumens, felts, or other means.   As is true of other metals, atmospheric-deposited dirt must be removed to maintain good appearance.

Electrolytic action between aluminum and less active metals should be avoided, because the aluminum then becomes anodic.   If aluminum must be in touch with other metals, the faying surfaces should be insulated by painting with asphaltic or similar paints, or by gasketing.   Steel rivets and bolts, for example, should be insulated.   Drainage from copper-alloy surfaces onto aluminum must be avoided.   Frequently, steel surfaces can be galvanized or cadmium-coated where contact is expected with aluminum.   The zinc or cadmium coating is anodic to the aluminum and helps to protect it.

2-58. Finishes for Aluminum. Finishes for aluminum and its alloys may be classified as electrochemical, organic and ceramic, mechanical, and chemical.

Most of the electrochemical treatments provide a thicker aluminum oxide coating than would normally be found, thereby increasing resistance to corrosion.   Colors can be incorporated at the same time, or the surface may be readily color-coated later. Other metals may be plated onto the aluminum by electrochemical means.

Organic and ceramic finishes include lacquer, varnish, builders' enamel, specialties such as wrinkle and crackle, and vitreous enamel.

Mechanical finishes include grinding, buffing, oiling, and similar treatments.

Chemical finishes include bright dips, frosted finishes, and phosphate treatments for subsequent painting.

The principal finishes are summarized in Table 2-42.

2-59. Welding and Brazing of Aluminum. The most weldable materials are 1100 and 3003; i.e., the commercially pure metal and the low-manganese alloy.   Both are widely used for resistance and fusion welding.

For higher strengths, 5052 is used but it is more difficult to handle by fusion welding. Any of the wrought products can be welded, as can the sand and permanent-mold castings; but die castings are difficult to handle by resistance or fusion welding.   The strength of some alloys, such as 6061, depends on heat-treatment after welding.   It should be remembered that any alloy solution, heat-treated and artificially aged, is susceptible to loss of strength at the weld because the weld metal is essentially cast.

Table 2-42. Finishes for Aluminum and Aluminum Alloys*

Type of finish	How produced	Application and use
A. Electrochemical		
Anodic finishes...	In electrolytes of dilute sulfuric, chromic, anodic, or boric acids aluminum parts made anodic—tank and cooling coils may be cathodes	Sulfuric and anodic used for plain and colored coatings; gives combination of hardness, resistance to corrosion, and attractive appearance Chromic acid anodic used where max resistance to corrosion and paint adhesion is prime requisite Oxalic acid anodic used to produce hard coatings where appearance is not a factor Boric acid anodic used to produce rectifying films
Bright anodic....	Anodic treatment in electrolyte containing high percentage of phosphoric acid	To polish a surface and remove a thin film of metal together with any contaminating substance such as oxide buffing compound, or alloy constituent. Used mostly for consumer products and specialty items
High-reflectivity anodic	A modified electrobrightening process consisting of an anodic treatment in a fluoboric acid electrolyte	Used exclusively for finishing aluminum lighting reflectors to obtain high reflectivity
Electroplated....	Brass may be applied directly over zinc film. Cadmium may be applied after an initial strike from a cadmium-cyanide bath. Nickel can be applied directly but copper strike first is recommended. Chromium is usually applied over a copper-nickel undercoat when maximum adherence and best appearance is required. Hard chromium for wear resistance usually is directly over a copper underlayer. For silver, treatment in low-concentration silver cyanide baths is recommended prior to plating in the standard cyanide bath	To improve both appearance and protection. Die castings particularly are representative of the types of products that are plated. In many instances aluminum is chromium-plated to match the appearance of mating parts. Zinc is used to prevent seizing of threaded parts; brass, to obtain a surface suitable for rubber bonding; hard chrome, to reduce friction and wear; copper, to permit soft soldering to the surface; and silver to obtain better electrical characteristics
B. Organic and Ceramic		
Lacquer, enamel, or varnish finishes	An organic finish is applied in the same manner as on other metals—by dipping or spraying. Either enamel, lacquer, varnish, or black japan finish used, depending on requirements. Synthetic resin enamels highly satisfactory, as also are colored lacquers. When a clear coating is desired, either clear cellulosic or acrylic lacquers, or clear varnishes formulated with alkyd or urea-formaldehyde resins, form hard protective coatings that do not turn yellow in service	On all types of aluminum and aluminum alloy products (1) to match finishes on other components; (2) to obtain inexpensive finish; (3) to get better protection under certain atmospheric conditions; (4) to obtain special effects, such as natural metal, and protecting surface against oxidation; or (5) to desired appearance or characteristics, as, for example, brilliant colors that are difficult to get with other types of finishes

Table 2-42. Finishes for Aluminum and Aluminum Alloys (*Continued*)

Type of finish	How produced	Application and use
	B. Organic and Ceramic (*Continued*)	
Specialty finishes.	Wrinkle, single-tone and two-tone hammer, veiled lacquer, crystal, crackle, or flock finishes applied by special techniques	Particularly on business machines and office equipment, laboratory equipment, and industrial machinery. Not too widely used on household equipment.
Vitreous enamel..	Prefired at 970 to 1000°F for 5 min Ground coats sprayed, dried, and fired at 940 to 1000°F. Application weight, 15 to 20 g per sq ft Cover coats sprayed and fired at 940 to 1000°F. Application weight, 25 to 50 g per sq ft	Sanitary ware, washing-machine tubs, and agitators and architectural trim
	C. Mechanical	
Grinding........	With wheels consisting of 80 to 120 emery applied to face-glued sections of muslin, canvas, or solid felt wheels. Tallow, mineral grease, or lard oil should be used as a lubricant to prevent burning	To remove metal from sand and permanent-mold castings, fins from die castings, or burrs or edges from fabricated parts that are unusually rough
Oiling..........	Refinement of grinding operation using finer abrasives and softer wheels. Abrasives range from 120 to 200 mesh. Wheels are usually constructed of soft felt, and speeds of about 6,000 fpm are generally satisfactory	Usually is the initial step in polishing, since rough grinding is required only in special instances. Is being replaced by abrasive-coated belts operated in conjunction with contact wheels. Speeds up to 7,000 fpm with suitable lubricants produce excellent results
Buffing..........	With stitched rag wheel and tripoli compound in a grease binder. Fine-grain tripoli and high wheel speeds—7,000 to 7,500 fpm— give surface with highest luster. Pitting and cloudiness may result from using too hard a wheel or too much pressure	To bring out high luster on the metal and remove surface scratches. Usually necessary for any part that is to be electroplated, anodized, or finished by other chemical are electrochemical processes for appearance
Coloring........	With loose or unsewed buffs operated at speeds of 7,500 to 8,000 fpm. Coloring compounds are usually a soft silica and lime composition abrasive with a grease base	To impart a highly reflective, lustrous surface on such products as trim, refrigerator evaporator doors, giftware, cooking utensils, and reflectors
Satin finish......	With a fine wire wheel, scratch brush, tampico brush, greaseless satin compounds, an air-abrasive blast, or a liquid-abrasive blast	To obtain a soft, smooth sheen on a surface by scratching fine parallel lines with it. Widely used for decorative effect on consumer products or architectural trim
Sand and vapor blasting	With sand and a high-pressure air stream or with a mixture of fine-grain abrasives and water. Alumina and silicon carbide abrasives used to obtain certain colorations	To get a uniform mat surface finish on parts for home appliances or on decorative trim. Vapor blasting also used to remove dirt and oxide films from a surface
Hammered or peened finish	Manually or by shot peening. Can be done after covering surface with soot to obtain wrought-iron effect	To obtain an irregular pattern on the surface of a part. Mainly used for giftware and architectural trim

Table 2-42. Finishes for Aluminum and Aluminum Alloys (*Continued*)

Type of finish	How produced	Application and use
	D. Chemical	
Bright dip.......	Immersion in an acid solution held at a temperature of about 180 to 200°F	For most wrought alloys and some cast alloys having a low silicon content. Gives a bright finish that is similar to a buffed finish at a much lower cost
Frosted and etched finish	Frosted usually produced by an etch in hot caustic soda; smoother etch, in soda ash and trisodium phosphate. Acid treatments also used to obtain less drastic etch	To get uniform mat effect for decoration on consumer products, diffusing surface on light reflectors, to clean the surface prior to anodizing, or to obtain contrasts and design in nameplates
Oxide...........	A series of finishes produced by forming an oxide coat by means of chemical solutions, such as hot sodium carbonate and sodium dichromate	As a base coat for organic finishes; gives fairly good protection to abrasion and corrosion. Suitable for small bulk parts where higher cost of electrochemical finishes is not justified
Bonderite 170, Alodine, Iridite 14, and Lyfanite	Immersion or spray	Almost exclusively as base for paint. See organic finishes

* Aluminum Company of America.

For this reason, the high-strength structural alloys are commonly fabricated by riveting or bolting, rather than welding.

Brazing is done by furnace, torch, or dip methods. Successful brazing is accomplished with special fluxes which permit the filler to wet the surface completely.

Table 2-41 summarizes the relative welding and brazing characteristics of aluminum alloys.

2-60. Aluminum Bibliography

Dix, E. H., Jr., and R. B. Mears: "The Resistance of Aluminum-base Alloys to Atmosphere Exposure," Symposium on Atmospheric Exposure Tests on Non-ferrous Metals, American Society for Testing Materials, Philadelphia, Pa., 1946.

Aluminum Company of America, Pittsburgh, Pa.: "Alcoa Aluminum and Its Alloys;" "Welding and Brazing Alcoa Aluminum."

American Society of Civil Engineers, New York: Specifications for Heavy Duty Structures of High-strength Aluminum Alloy, Paper 2532, *Transactions*, Vol. 117, 1952.

Reynolds Metals Co., Louisville, Ky.: "The Aluminum Data Book."

Van den Berg, R. V.: "Finishes for Aluminum Products," *Product Engineering*, October, 1951.

COPPER AND COPPER-BASED ALLOYS

Copper and its alloys are widely used in the building industry for a large variety of purposes, particularly applications requiring corrosion resistance, high electrical conductivity, strength, ductility, impact resistance, fatigue resistance, or other special characteristics possessed by copper or its alloys. Some of the special characteristics of importance to building are ability to be formed into complex shapes, appearance, and high thermal conductivity, although many of the alloys have low thermal conductivity and low electrical conductivity as compared with the pure metal.

Table 2-43. Copper and Copper Alloys*

Alloy name	Electrolytic tough pitch Hard	Soft	Deoxidized Hard	Soft	Commercial bronze, 90% Hard	Soft	Red brass, 85% Hard	Soft	Cartridge brass, 70% Hard	Soft	Muntz metal Hard	Soft	High-leaded brass Hard	Soft	Forging brass Hard	Soft*	Architectural bronze Hard	Soft¶
Working properties:																		
1. Cold-working	Excellent		Excellent		Excellent		Excellent		Excellent		Fair		Poor		Fair		Very poor	
2. Hot-working	Excellent		Excellent		Excellent		Good		Good		Excellent		Poor		Excellent		Excellent	
3. Machining	Fair		Poor		Poor		Poor		Fair		Good		Excellent		Good		Good	
4. Welding†	deoxidized copper preferred		Gas, carbon arc, metal arc		Gas, carbon arc, metal arc		‡		‡		‡		Non-leaded brass preferred		Non-leaded brass preferred		Poor	
5. Soldering	Excellent		Excellent		Excellent		Excellent		Excellent		Excellent		Excellent		Good		Excellent	
6. Polishing	Excellent		Excellent		Excellent		Excellent		Excellent		Excellent		Excellent		Excellent		Excellent	
Young's modulus of elasticity, psi (000,000 omitted)	17		17		17		17		16		15		15		15		14	
Avg coefficient of thermal expansion, per °F (68 to 570°F)	0.0000098		0.0000098		0.0000102		0.0000104		0.0000111		0.0000116		0.0000116		0.0000115		0.0000116	
Electrical conductivity, % IACS at 68°F	100 min		85 annealed		44		37		28		28		26		27		28	
Thermal conductivity, Btu, per sq ft, per ft, per hr, per °F, at 68°F	226		196		109		92		70		71		67		69		71	
Tensile strength, 1,000 psi:																		
Sheet	50	32	50	32	61	37	70	40	82	47	80	54	74	49	...	...	...	...
Rod	48	32	...	...	55	40	57	40	70	48	75	54	...	...	...	52	...	60
Tube	55	32	55	32	...	38	70	40	78	47	74	56	...	...	...	...	...	...
Elongation, % in 2 in.:																		
Sheet	6	45	5	45	5	45	5	47	8	62	10	45	7	52	...	...	...	...
Rod	16	55	...	...	20	50	23	55	30	65	20	50	...	...	...	45	...	30
Tube	8	45	8	45	...	50	8	55	8	65	10	50	...	...	...	...	...	...
Yield strength, 1000 psi:																		
0.5% extension under load:																		
Sheet	47	8	45	8	54	10	58	12	65	15	60	21	51	17	...	...	...	...
Rod	45	8	...	...	48	10	52	10	52	16	55	21	...	...	...	20	...	20
Tube	52	8	50	8	...	12	58	12	64	15	55	23	...	...	...	...	...	...
0.2% offset																		
Sheet	47	8	45	8	56	10	61	12	74	15	66	21	66	17	...	...	...	...
Rod	45	8	...	...	48	10	54	10	53	16	59	21	...	...	...	20	...	20
Tube	52	8	50	8	...	12	61	12	70	15	60	23	...	...	...	...	...	...
Rockwell hardness:																		
Sheet	50B	40F	50B	40F	70B	53F	77B	59F	82B	64F	85B	80F	80B	68F	...	...	...	...
Rod	47B	40F	60B	...	60B	55F	75B	55F	80B	65F	80B	80F	...	...	...	78F	...	65B
Tube	60B	40F	...	40F	...	57F	77B	60F	82B	64F	80B	82F	...	...	...	...	...	...

Table 2-43. Copper and Copper Alloys* (Continued)

Alloy name	Admiralty		Manganese bronze (A)		Nickel silver 18% (A), deep drawing		Nickel silver, 12% leaded		Cupronickel, 30%		Silicon bronze (high-silicon bronze, A)		Aluminum silicon bronze		Phosphor bronze, 5% (A)		Phosphor bronze, 8% (C)	
Working properties:																		
1. Cold-working	Good		Poor		Excellent		Poor		Excellent		Good		Poor		Excellent		Excellent	
2. Hot-working	Poor		Excellent		Fair		Fair		Fair		Excellent		Excellent		Poor		Poor	
3. Machining	Fair		Good		Fair		Excellent		Fair		Fair		Excellent		Fair		Fair	
4. Welding†	Gas, carbon arc		‡		‡		Non-leaded preferred		Gas, metal arc, resistance		Gas, carbon arc, metal arc—spot and seam for thin gage		Gas, carbon arc, metal arc		Gas, carbon arc, metal arc—spot and seam for thin gage		Gas, carbon arc, metal arc—spot and seam for thin gage	
5. Soldering	Good		Excellent		Excellent		Excellent		Excellent		Excellent		Fair		Excellent		Excellent	
6. Polishing	Good		Excellent		Excellent		Excellent		Good		Good		Excellent		Excellent		Excellent	
Young's modulus of elasticity, psi (000,000 omitted)	16		15		18		17		22		17		14		16		16	
Avg coefficient of thermal expansion, per °F (68 to 570°F)	0.0000112		0.0000118		0.0000090		0.0000083		0.0000090		0.0000100		0.0000092		0.0000099		0.0000101	
Electrical conductivity, % IACS at 68°F	25		24		6		7		4.6		7		7		18		13	
Thermal conductivity, Btu, per sq ft, per hr, per °F, at 68°F	64		61		19		23		17		21		22		47		36	
	Hard	Soft	Hard	Soft	Hard	Soft	Hard	Soft	Hard	Soft	Hard§	Soft	Hard§	Soft	Hard	Soft	Hard	Soft
Tensile strength, 1,000 psi:																		
Sheet	90	50			85	58	78	55	82	54	94	60		80	81	47	93	55
Rod	100	53	75	65					80	60	92	58			70	64		
Tube																		
Elongation, % in 2 in.:																		
Sheet	5	55			3	49	5	40	4	35	10	55		20	10	64	10	70
Rod	3	65	25	33					5	45	22	60			25			
Tube																		
Yield strength, 1000 psi:																		
0.5% extension under load:																		
Sheet	70	18			74	25	69	18	76	10	69	21		43	71	22	73	22
Rod	80	22	41	30					75	25	55	22			64			
Tube																		
0.2% offset:																		
Sheet	76	18			80	25	74	18	78	10	83	21		43	79	22	79	22
Rod	90	22	50	30					77	25		22			64			
Tube																		
Rockwell hardness:																		
Sheet	90B	25B			87B	85F	82B	35B	85B	40B	93B	82F		80B	87B	73F	93B	75F
Rod	95B	75F	74B	65B					82B	80F	90B	60B			78B			
Tube																		

* Revere Copper and Brass, Inc.

† By fusion methods; conductivity of the coppers makes resistance welding (spot and seam) impractical. Coppers, however, may be resistance-brazed by a patented method.

Basis of rating: sheet, hard—0.040 in. stock, previously rolled 4 B & S numbers hard (37.5 % area reduction).

Basis of rating: rod, hard—1 in. and under diameter, previously drawn through 25 to 35 % area reduction.

‡ For welding—gas, carbon arc, metal arc, spot and seam welding for thin gage.

§ As extruded.

§ Hard, for rod, bolt temper, extra hard.

In the following paragraphs, brief comments will be made respecting the properties and uses of the principal copper and copper-based alloys of interest in building.   The principal properties are summarized in Table 2-43.

2-61. Copper.   The excellent corrosion resistance of copper makes it suitable for such applications as roofing, flashing, cornices, gutters, downspouts, leaders, fly screens, and similar applications.   For roofing and flashing, soft-annealed copper is employed, because it is ductile and can easily be bent into various shapes.   For gutters, leaders, downspouts, and similar applications, cold-rolled hard copper is employed, because its greater hardness and stiffness permit it to stand without large numbers of intermediate supports.

Copper and copper-based alloys, particularly the brasses, are employed for water pipe in buildings, because of their corrosion resistance.   Electrolytic tough-pitch copper is usually employed, but for maximum electrical conductivity and weldability, oxygen-free high-conductivity copper is used.

When arsenic is added to copper, it appears to form a tenacious adherent film, which is particularly resistant to pitting corrosion.   Phosphorus is a powerful deoxidizer and is particularly useful for copper to be used for refrigerator tubing and other applications where flaring, flanging, and spinning are required.   Arsenic and phosphorus both reduce the electrical conductivity of the copper.

For flashing, copper is frequently coated with lead to avoid the green patina formed on copper that is sometimes objectionable when it is washed down over adjacent surfaces, such as ornamental stone.   The patina is formed particularly in industrial atmospheres.   In rural atmospheres, where industrial gases are absent, the copper normally turns to a deep brown color.

Principal types of copper and typical uses are (see also Table 2-43):

Electrolytic tough pitch (99.90% copper) is used for electrical conductors—bus bars, commutators, etc.; building products—roofing, gutters, etc.; process equipment—kettles, vats, distillery equipment; forgings.   General properties are high electrical conductivity, high thermal conductivity, and excellent working ability.

Deoxidized (99.90% copper and 0.025% phosphorus) is used, in tube form, for water and refrigeration service, oil burners, etc.; in sheet and plate form, for welded construction.   General properties include higher forming and bending qualities than electrolytic copper.   They are preferred for coppersmithing and welding (because of resistance to embrittlement at high temperatures).

2-62. Plain Brass.   A considerable range of brasses is obtainable for a large variety of end uses.   The high ductility and malleability of the copper-zinc alloys, or brasses, make them suitable for operations like deep drawing, bending, and swaging.   They have a wide range of colors.   They are generally less expensive than the high-copper alloys.

Grain size of the metal has a marked effect upon its mechanical properties.   For deep drawing and other heavy working operations, a large grain size is required, but for highly finished polished surfaces, the grain size must be small.

Like copper, brass is hardened by cold working.   Hardnesses are sometimes expressed as quarter hard, half hard, hard, extra hard, spring, and extra spring, corresponding to reductions in cross section during cold working ranging from approximately 11 to 69%.   Hardness is strongly influenced by alloy composition, original grain size, and form (strip, rod, tube, wire).

Brass compositions range from high copper content to zinc contents as high as 40% or more.   Brasses with less than 36% zinc are plain alpha solid solutions; but Muntz metal, with 40% zinc, contains both alpha and beta phases.

The principal plain brasses of interest in building, and their properties are (see also Table 2-43):

Commercial bronze, 90% (90.0% copper, 10.0% zinc).   Typical uses are forgings, screws, weatherstripping, and stamped hardware.   General properties include excellent cold working and high ductility.

Red brass, 85% (85.0% copper, 15.0% zinc).   Typical uses are dials, hardware, etched parts, automobile radiators, and tube and pipe for plumbing.   General properties are higher strength and ductility than copper, and excellent corrosion resistance.

Cartridge brass, 70% (70.0% copper, 30.0% zinc). Typical uses are deep drawing, stamping, spinning, etching, rolling—for practically all fabricating processes—cartridge cases, pins, rivets, eyelets, heating units, lamp bodies and reflectors, electrical sockets, drawn shapes, etc. General properties are best combination of ductility and strength of any brass, and excellent cold-working properties.

Muntz metal (60.0% copper, 40.0% zinc). Typical uses are sheet form, perforated metal, architectural work, condenser tubes, valve stems, and brazing rods. General properties are high strength combined with low ductility.

2-63. Leaded Brass. Lead is added to brass to improve its machinability, particularly in such applications as automatic screw machines where a freely chipping metal is required. Leaded brasses cannot easily be cold-worked by such operations as flaring, upsetting, or cold heading. Several leaded brasses of importance in the building field are the following (see also Table 2-43):

High-leaded brass (64.0% copper, 34.0% zinc, 2.0% lead). Typical uses are engraving plates, machined parts, instruments (professional and scientific), nameplates, keys, lock parts, and tumblers. General properties are free machining and good blanking.

Forging brass (60.0% copper, 38.0% zinc, 2.0% lead). Typical uses are hot forgings, hardware, and plumbing goods. General properties are extremely plastic when hot and a combination of good corrosion resistance with excellent mechanical properties.

Architectural bronze (56.5% copper, 41.25% zinc, 2.25% lead). Typical uses are handrails, decorative moldings, grilles, revolving door parts, miscellaneous architectural trim, industrial extruded shapes (hinges, lock bodies, automotive parts). General properties are excellent forging and free-machining properties.

2-64. Tin Brass. Tin is added to a variety of basic brasses to obtain hardness, strength, and other properties which would otherwise not be available. Two important alloys are (see also Table 2-43):

Admiralty (71.0% copper, 28.0% zinc, 1.0% tin, 0.05% arsenic). Typical uses are condenser and heat-exchanger plates and tubes, steam-power-plant equipment, chemical and process equipment, and marine uses. General properties are excellent corrosion resistance, combined with strength and ductility.

Manganese bronze (58.5% copper, 39.2% zinc, 1.0% iron, 1.0% tin, 0.3% manganese). Typical uses are forgings, condenser plates, valve stems, and coal screens. General properties are high strength combined with excellent wear resistance.

2-65. Nickel Silvers. These are alloys of copper, nickel, and zinc. Depending on the composition, they range in color from a definite to slight pink cast through yellow, green, whitish green, whitish blue, to blue. A wide range of nickel silvers is made, of which only two typical compositions will be described (see also Table 2-43). Those that fall in the combined alpha-beta phase of metals are readily hot-worked and therefore are fabricated without difficulty into such intricate shapes as plumbing fixtures, stair rails, architectural shapes, and escalator parts. Lead may be added to improve machining.

Nickel silver, 18% (A), (65.0% copper, 17.0% zinc, 18.0% nickel). Typical uses are hardware, architectural panels, lighting, electrical and plumbing fixtures. General properties are high resistance to corrosion and tarnish, malleable, and ductile. Color: silver-blue-white.

Nickel silver, 12% leaded (65.0% copper, 20.7% zinc, 2.0% lead, 12.0% nickel, 0.3% manganese). Typical uses are keys, products requiring machinability, lock washers, cotter pins, and fuse clips. It has good machinability but is preferred nonleaded for bending and drawing.

2-66. Cupronickel. Copper and nickel are alloyed in a variety of compositions of which the high-copper alloys are called the cupronickels. A typical commercial type of cupronickel contains 30% nickel (Table 2-43):

Cupronickel, 30% (70.0% copper, 30.0% nickel). Typical uses are condenser tubes and plates, tanks, vats, vessels, process equipment, automotive parts, meters, refrigerator pump valves. General properties are high strength and ductility, resistance to corrosion and erosion. Color: white-silver.

2-67. Silicon Bronze. These are high-copper alloys containing percentages of silicon ranging from about 1% to slightly more than 3%. In addition, they generally contain one or more of the four elements, tin, manganese, zinc, and iron. A typical one is high-silicon bronze, type A (see also Table 2-43):

High-silicon bronze, A (96.0% copper, 3.0% silicon, 1.0% manganese). Typical uses are tanks—pressure vessels, vats; weatherstrips, forgings. General properties are corrosion resistance of copper and mechanical properties of mild steel.

2-68. Aluminum Bronze. Like aluminum, these bronzes form an aluminum oxide skin on the surface, which materially improves resistance to corrosion, particularly under acid conditions. Since the color of the 5% aluminum bronze is similar to that of 18-carat gold, it is used for costume jewelry and other decorative purposes. Aluminum-silicon bronzes (Table 2-43) are used in applications requiring high tensile properties in combination with good corrosion resistance in such parts as valves, stems, air pumps, condenser bolts, and similar applications. Their wear-resisting properties are good; consequently, they are used in slide liners and bushings.

2-69. Tin Bronze. Originally and historically, the bronzes were all alloys of copper and tin. Today, the term bronze is generally applied to engineering metals having high mechanical properties and the term brass to other metals. The commercial wrought bronzes do not usually contain more than 10% tin because the metal becomes extremely hard and brittle. When phosphorus is added as a deoxidizer, to obtain sound dense castings, the alloys are known as phosphor bronzes. The two most commonly used tin bronzes contain 5 and 8% tin. Both have excellent cold-working properties (Table 2-43).

2-70. Copper Bibliography

American Society for Testing Materials, Philadelphia, Pa.: "Standards," Part 2.

Revere Copper and Brass, Inc., New York: "Revere Copper and Copper Alloys."

Wilkins, R. A., and E. S. Bunn: "Copper and Copper-base Alloys," McGraw-Hill Book Company, Inc., New York, 1943.

Williams, R. S., and V. O. Homerberg: "Principles of Metallography," 5th ed., McGraw-Hill Book Company, Inc., New York, 1948.

LEAD AND LEAD-BASED ALLOYS

Lead is used primarily for its corrosion resistance. Lead roofs 2,000 years old are still intact. Exposure tests indicate corrosion penetrations ranging from less than 0.0001 in. to less than 0.0003 in. in 10 years in atmospheres ranging from mild rural to severe industrial and seacoast locations. Sheet lead is therefore used for roofing, flashing, spandrels, gutters, and downspouts.

2-71. Applications of Lead. Because the green patina found on copper may wash away sufficiently to stain the surrounding structure, lead-coated copper is frequently employed. Three classes are recognized by the ASTM:

Class	Weight of lead coating, lb per 100 sq ft, total, coated both sides	
	Min	Max
Class A standard (general utility).............	12	15
Class B heavy............................	20	30
Class C extra heavy.......................	40	50

Lead pipe for the transport of drinking water should be used with care. Distilled and very soft waters slowly dissolve lead and may cause cumulative lead poisoning.

Hard waters apparently deposit a protective coating on the wall of the pipe and little or no lead is subsequently dissolved in the water.

Principal alloying elements used with building leads are antimony (for hardness and strength) and tin. But copper, arsenic, bismuth, nickel, zinc, silver, iron, and manganese are also added in varying proportions.

Soft solders consist of varying percentages of lead and tin. For greater hardness, antimony is added, and for higher-temperature solders, silver is added in small amounts. A few solder compositions and their uses are given in Table 2-44.

Table 2-44. Properties of Soft-Solder Alloys (ASTM B32)

Nominal composition, %			Melting ranges		Uses
Tin	Lead	Antimony	Solidus, °F	Liquidus, °F	
Tin-lead Alloys					
60	40	. . .	361	374	"Fine solder." For general purposes, but particularly where the temperature requirements are critical
50	50	. . .	361	421	For general purposes. Most popular of all
45	55	. . .	361	441	For automobile radiator cores and roofing seams
35	65	. . .	361	477	General-purpose and wiping solder
20	80	. . .	361	531	For coating and joining metals
					For filling dents or seams in automobile bodies
10	90	. . .	514	570	For coating and joining metals
Tin-lead-antimony Alloys					
40	58	2	365	448	Same uses as 50-50 tin-lead, but not recommended for use on galvanized iron
30	68.4	1.6	364	482	For torch soldering or machine soldering, except on galvanized iron
20	79	1	363	517	For machine soldering and coating of metals, tipping, and like uses, but not recommended for use on galvanized iron
Silver-lead Alloys					
Tin	Lead	Silver			
1	97.5	1.5	588	588	For use on copper, brass, and similar metals with torch heating

Low-melting alloys and many bearing metals are alloys of lead, bismuth, tin, cadmium, and other metals including silver, zinc, indium, and antimony. The fusible links used in sprinkler heads and fire-door closures, made of such alloys, have a low melting point, usually lower than the boiling point of water. Yield (softening) temperatures range from 73 to 160°F and melting points from about 80 to 480°F, depending on the composition.

2-72. Lead Bibliography

American Society for Metals, Cleveland, Ohio: "Metals Handbook," 1948.
American Society for Testing Materials, Philadelphia, Pa.: "Standards," Part 2.

NICKEL AND NICKEL-BASED ALLOYS

Nickel is used mostly as an alloying element with other metals, but it finds use in its own right, largely as electroplate or as cladding metal. Among the principal high-nickel alloys are Monel and Inconel. The nominal compositions of these three metals are given in Table 2-45.

Table 2-45. Composition of Nickel Alloys

	Nickel, %	Copper, %	Chromium %	Iron, %	Manganese, %	Silicon, %	Carbon, %
Nickel........	99.4	0.1	....	0.15	0.2	0.05	0.1
Monel........	67.0	30.0	....	1.4	1.0	0.1	0.15
Inconel.......	78.5	0.2	14.0	6.5	0.25	0.25	0.08

2-73. Properties of Nickel and Its Alloys. Nickel is resistant to alkaline corrosion under nonoxidizing conditions but is corroded by oxidizing acids and oxidizing salts. It is resistant to fatty acids, other mildly acid conditions, such as food processing and beverages, and resists oxidation at temperatures as high as 1600°F.

Monel is widely used in kitchen equipment. It is better than nickel in reducing conditions like warm unaerated acids, and better than copper under oxidizing conditions, such as aerated acids, alkalies, and salt solutions. It is widely used for handling chlorides of many kinds.

Inconel is almost completely resistant to corrosion by food products, pharmaceuticals, biologicals, and dilute organic acids. It is superior to nickel and Monel in resisting oxidizing acid salts like chromates and nitrates but is not resistant to ferric, cupric, or mercuric chlorides. It resists scaling and oxidation in air and furnace atmospheres at temperatures up to 2000°F.

Some of the important mechanical properties are listed in Table 2-46.

Table 2-46. Properties of Nickel Alloys

Property	Nickel	Monel	Inconel
Density, lb per cu in..........................	0.321	0.319	0.307
Specific gravity...............................	8.89	8.84	8.51
Melting point, °C.............................	1435–1445	1300–1350	1395–1425
°F...	2615–2635	2370–2460	2540–2600
Expansion, thermal, in. per in. per °F (77–212°F).	0.0000072	0.0000078	0.0000064
Moduli of elasticity:			
Tension....................................	30,000,000	26,000,000	31,000,000
Torsion....................................	11,000,000	9,500,000	11,000,000
Poisson's ratio...............................	0.31	0.32	0.29
Avg mechanical properties, hot-rolled plate:			
Yield strength, 0.20% offset, 1,000 psi........	25	50	60
Tensile strength, 1,000 psi...................	75	90	100
Elongation in 2 in., %.........................	40	35	35
Brinell hardness, 3,000 kg....................	110	150	180
Impact Charpy room temp, ft-lb..............	195	219	236
Impact Charpy temp −112°F, ft-lb...........	236	213	206

2-74. Nickel Bibliography

International Nickel Co., New York: "Nickel and Nickel Alloys."
Theisinger, W. G.: Nickel-clad, Monel-clad, and Inconel-clad Steel, Chap. 11 in A. G. H. Dietz, ed., "Engineering Laminates," John Wiley & Sons, Inc., New York, 1949.

PLASTICS

The synonymous terms plastics and synthetic resins denote synthetic organic high polymers, all of which are plastic at some stage in their manufacture. Plastics fall into two large categories—thermoplastic and thermosetting materials.

Thermoplastics may be softened by heating and hardened by cooling any number of times. Thermosetting materials are either originally soft or liquid, or they soften once upon heating; but upon further heating, they harden permanently. Some thermosetting materials harden by an interlinking mechanism in which water or other by-product is given off, by a process called condensation; but others, like the unsaturated polyesters, harden by a direct interlinking of the basic molecules without any by-product's being given off.

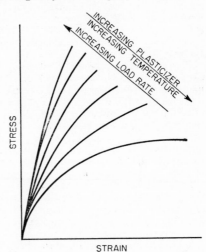

FIG. 2-3. Stress-strain diagram shows the influence of temperature, plasticizer, and rate of loading on behavior of plastics.

Most plastics are modified with plasticizers, fillers, or other ingredients. Consequently, each base material forms the nucleus for a large number of products having a wide variety of properties. This section can only indicate generally the range of properties to be expected.

Because plastics are quite different in their composition and structure from other materials, such as metals, their behavior under stress and under other conditions is likely to be different from other materials. Just as steel and lead are markedly different and are used for different applications, so the various plastics materials— some hard and brittle, others soft and extensible—must be designed on different bases and used in different ways. Some plastics show no yield point, because they fail before a yield point can be reached. Others have a moderately high elastic range, followed by a highly plastic range. Still others are highly extensible and are employed at stresses far beyond the yield point.

More than many other materials, plastics are sensitive to temperature and to the rate and time of application of load. How these parameters influence the properties is indicated in a general way in Fig. 2-3, which shows that for many plastics an increase in temperature, increase in plasticizer content, and decrease in rate of load application mean an increase in strain to fracture, accompanied by a decrease in maximum stress. This viscoelastic behavior, combining elastic and viscous or plastic reaction to stress, is unlike the behavior of materials which are traditionally considered to behave only elastically.

2-75. Fillers and Plasticizers. Fillers are commonly added, particularly to the thermosetting plastics, to alter their basic characteristics. For example, wood flour converts a hard, brittle resin, difficult to handle, into a cheaper, more easily molded material for general purposes. Asbestos fibers provide better heat resistance; mica gives better electrical properties; and a variety of fibrous materials, such as chopped fibers, chopped fabric, and chopped tire cords, increase the strength and impact properties.

Plasticizers are added to many thermoplastics, primarily to transform hard and rigid materials into a variety of forms having varying degrees of softness, flexibility, and strength.   In addition, dyes or pigments, stabilizers, and other products may be added.

2-76. Molding and Fabricating Methods for Plastics.   Both thermosetting and thermoplastic molding materials are formed into final shape by a variety of molding and fabricating methods:

Thermosetting materials are commonly formed by placing molding powder or molded preform in heated dies and compressing under heat and pressure into the final infusible shape.   Or they are formed by forcing heat-softened material into a heated die for final forming into the hard infusible shape.

Thermoplastics are commonly formed by injection molding; that is, by forcing soft, hot plastic into a cold die, where it hardens by cooling.   Continuous profiles of thermoplastic materials are made by extrusion.   Thermoplastic sheets, especially transparent acrylics, are frequently formed into final shape by heating and then blowing to final form under compressed air or by drawing a partial vacuum against the softened sheet.

All the plastics can be machined, if proper allowance is made for the properties of the materials.

Plastics are often combined with sheet or mat stocks, such as paper, cotton muslin, glass fabric, glass filament mats, nylon fabric, and other fabrics, to provide laminated materials in which the properties of the combined plastic and sheet stock are quite different from the properties of either constituent by itself.   Two principal varieties of laminates are commonly made: (1) High-pressure laminates employing condensation-type thermosetting materials, which are formed at elevated temperatures and pressures.   (2) Reinforced plastics, also called low-pressure laminates, employing unsaturated polyesters and epoxides, from which no by-products are given off, and consequently, either low pressures or none at all may be required to form combinations of these materials with a variety of reinforcing agents, like glass fabric or mat.

In the following articles, the principal varieties of plastics are briefly described and their principal fields of application indicated.   In Table 2-47, ranges of values to be expected of specimens made and tested under specific conditions, usually those of the American Society for Testing Materials, are given.   The method of fabrication and specific application of a particular plastic may severely modify these properties.

2-77. Thermosetting Plastics.   *Phenol Formaldehyde.*   These materials provide the greatest variety of thermosetting molded plastic articles.   They are used for chemical, decorative, electrical, mechanical, and thermal applications of all kinds. Hard and rigid, they change slightly, if at all, on aging indoors but, on outdoor exposure, lose their bright surface gloss.   However, the outdoor-exposure characteristics of the more durable formulations are otherwise generally good.   Phenol formaldehydes have good electrical properties, do not burn readily, and do not support combustion.   They are strong, light in weight, and generally pleasant to the eye and touch, although light colors by and large are not obtainable because of the fairly dark-brown basic color of the resin.   They have low water absorption and good resistance to attack by most commonly found chemicals.

Cast Phenolics.   Unlike the phenolic molding materials, the unfilled cast phenolics have an unlimited range of deep rich colors.   Therefore, they find wide use as decorative accessory fitments, including costume and ornamental jewelry, furniture, hardware, instrument and clock casings, radio housings, and similar applications.   On ordinary exposure, their color stability is reasonably good, especially in indoor locations.   Special formulations are used for special applications.

Epoxy and Polyester Casting Resins.   These are used for a large variety of purposes. For example, electronic parts with delicate components are sometimes cast completely in these materials to give them complete and continuous support, and resistance to thermal and mechanical shock.   Some varieties must be cured at elevated temperatures; others can be formulated to be cured at room temperatures.   One of the outstanding attributes of the epoxies is their excellent adhesion to a variety of materials, including such metals as copper, brass, steel, and aluminum.

Polyester Molding Materials.   When compounded with fibers, particularly glass fibers, or with various mineral fillers, including clay, the polyesters can be formulated

Table 2-47. Properties of Plastics*

Properties	ASTM test method	Phenol-formaldehyde and phenol-furfural compounds — Molding				Phenol-formaldehyde and phenol-furfural compounds — Cast		Urea-formaldehyde molding compound, alpha-cellulose filler	Melamine-formaldehyde molding compounds, alpha-cellulose filler
		Wood flour and cotton flock filler	Asbestos filler	Mica filler	Macerated fabric and cord filler	No filler	Casting resin, mechanical grade		
Specific gravity	D792	1.32–1.55	1.52–2.0	1.75–1.92	1.36–1.43	1.30–1.32	1.25–1.30	1.47–1.52	1.47–1.52
Specific volume, cu in. per lb	D792	20.9–17.8	18.2–13.8	15.8–14.3	20.4–19.4	21.3–20.9	22.2–21.3	18.8–18.2	18.8–18.2
Refractive index, n_D	D542					1.58–1.66		1.54–1.56	
Tensile strength, psi	D638, D651	6,500–8,500	4,000–6,500	5,000–7,000	3,300–9,000	6,000–9,000	4,000–7,000	6,000–13,000	7,000–13,000
Modulus of elasticity in tension, 10^5 psi	D638	0.4–0.8	0.18–0.50	0.13–0.5	0.37–0.57	1.5–2.0		0.5–1.0	0.6–0.9
Elongation, %	D638	8–12	10–25	30–50	9–13	4–5	5–7	15	13
Compressive strength, psi	D695	22,700–36,000	15,000–35,000	15,000–30,000	15,000–30,000	12,000–15,000	15,000–20,000	25,000–35,000	25,000–43,000
Flexural strength, psi	D650, D790	8,500–12,000	7,000–15,000	8,000–12,000	8,500–15,000	11,000–17,000	9,000–14,000	10,000–16,000	10,000–16,000
Impact strength, ft-lb per in. of notch ($\frac{1}{2} \times \frac{1}{2}$ in. notched bar, Izod test)	D256	0.24–0.60	0.35–3.5	0.30–0.38	0.75–8.0	0.25–0.40	0.3–0.4	0.25–0.35	0.24–0.35
Hardness, Rockwell	D785	M100–M120	M95–M115	M100–M110	M95–M120	M93–M120	M70–M110	M115–M120	M110–M125
Thermal conductivity, 10^{-4} cal per sec per sq cm per 1°C per cm	D325	4–7	8–16	10–14	4–7	3–5	3–5	7–10	7–10
Thermal expansion, 10^{-5} per °C	D696	3.0–4.5	1.5–2.12	1.9	1–4	6–8	8–11	2.7	4.0
Resistance to heat, °F (continuous)		300–350	350–450	250–300	250	160	250	170	210
Heat-distortion temp, °F	D648	260–340	290–350	230–350	250–300	165–175	240–260	270–280	400
Burning rate	D635	Very low	Nil	Nil	Approx nil	Very low	Very low	Very low	Nil
Effect of sunlight		General darkening				Colors may fade	Darkens	None	Slight color change
Effect of weak acids	D543	None to slight depending on acid				Slight to marked depending on acid	None to slight	None to slight depending on acid	None
Effect of strong acids	D543	Decomposed by oxidizing acids; reducing and organic acids none to slight effect					Attacked by oxidizing acids	Decomposed or surface attacked depending on acid	Decomposes
Effect of weak alkalies	D543	Slight to marked depending on alkalinity				Slight to marked depending on alkalinity	Slight to marked	Slight to marked depending on alkalinity	None
Effect of strong alkalies	D543	Attacked by strong alkalies unless a special alkali-resistant resin is used				Decomposes	Decomposes	Decomposes	Attacked
Effect of organic solvents	D543	None on bleedproof materials				Attacked by some	None	None to slight	None
Clarity		Opaque	Opaque	Opaque	Opaque	Transparent, translucent, opaque	Opaque	Translucent opaque	Translucent
Color possibilities		Limited	Limited	Limited	Limited	Unlimited	Limited	Unlimited; pastel shades	Unlimited

* "Modern Plastics Encyclopedia," 1952, and "Technical Data on Plastics," 1953, Manufacturing Chemists' Association.

Table 2-47. Properties of Plastics*—(Continued)

Properties	ASTM test method	Melamine-formaldehyde molding compounds, macerated fabric filler	Epoxy cast resin, no filler	Silicone molding compound, glass-fiber filler	Cellulosic molding compounds				
					Ethyl cellulose	Cellulose acetate		Cellulose acetate butyrate	Cellulose nitrate (pyroxylin)
						Sheet	Molding		
Specific gravity	D792	1.5	1.11–1.23	1.70	1.09–1.17	1.28–1.32	1.27–1.34	1.15–1.25	1.35–1.40
Specific volume, cu in. per lb	D792	18.5	24.9–22.5	16.3	25.5–23.6	21.6–20.9	21.8–20.6	24.0–22.2	20.5–19.8
Refractive index, n_D	D542				1.47	1.49–1.50	1.46–1.50	1.46–1.49	1.49–1.51
Tensile strength, psi	D638, D651	9,500–10,500	12,000	2,800–3,200	2,000–8,000	4,500–7,500	1,900–8,500	1,900–6,800	7,000–8,000
Elongation, %	D638	0.6–0.8	4.5		5–40	20–50	6–50	38–75	40–45
Modulus of elasticity in tension, 10^5 psi	D638	16			1.0–3.0	2.5–3	0.86–4.0	0.7–2.0	1.9–2.2
Compressive strength, psi	D695	30,000–35,000	16,000	11,200	10,000–35,000	18,000–25,000	13,000–36,000	7,500–22,000	22,000–35,000
Flexural strength, psi	D650, D790	12,000–15,000	18,800	9,800	4,000–12,000	6,000–10,000	2,000–16,000	1,500–9,300	9,000–11,000
Impact strength, ft-lb per in. of notch (½ × ½ in. notched bar, Izod test)	D256	0.6–0.8	0.5–1.7	4.0–4.5	2.0–80	1.0–3.0	0.4–5.2	0.6–5.4	5.0–70
Hardness, Rockwell	D785	M120	M100	M45	R50–R115	R95–R120	R50–R125	R60–R115	R95–R115
Thermal conductivity, 10^{-4} cal per sec per sq cm per 1°C per cm	D325	10.6			3.8–7	4–8	4–8	4–8	5.5
Thermal expansion, 10^{-5} per °C	D696	2.8	6		10–20	10–15	8–16	11–17	8–12
Resistance to heat, °F (continuous)		250	300	480	115–185	140–185	140–220	140–220	ca. 140
Heat-distortion temp, °F	D648	310		>570	115–190	130–160	115–235	120–210	140–160
Burning rate	D635	None	Slow	Nil	Slow when properly stabilized	Slow to self-extinguishing	Slow	Slow	Very high
Effect of sunlight		Slight discoloration	None	None to slight	Slight	Slight	Slight	Slight	Discolors and becomes brittle
Effect of weak acids	D543	None	None	None to slight	Slight	Slight	Slight	Slight	Slight
Effect of strong acids	D543	Decomposes	Attacked by some	Slight	Decomposes	Decomposes	Decomposes	Decomposes	Decomposes
Effect of weak alkalies	D543	None	None	None to slight	None	Slight	Slight	Slight	Slight
Effect of strong alkalies	D543	Attacked	Slight	None to marked	Slight	Decomposes	Decomposes	Decomposes	Decomposes
Effect of organic solvents	D543	None on bleedproof colors	Generally resistant	Attacked by some	Widely soluble	Soluble in ketones and esters; softened or slightly soluble in alcohol; little affected by hydrocarbons			
Clarity		Opaque	Translucent	Opaque	Transparent, translucent, opaque	Transparent, translucent, opaque	Transparent, translucent, opaque	Transparent, translucent, opaque	Transparent, translucent, opaque
Color possibilities		Limited	Wide choice		Unlimited	Unlimited	Unlimited	Unlimited	Unlimited

Table 2-47. Properties of Plastics*—(Continued)

Properties	ASTM test method	Nylon molding compound, injection molding	Vinyl chloride-acetate molding compounds — Rigid	Vinyl chloride-acetate molding compounds — Flexible unfilled	Vinyl chloride molding compounds — Rigid	Vinyl chloride molding compounds — Flexible unfilled	Vinylidene chloride molding compound	Vinyl butyral molding compounds, flexible unfilled	Polyester cast resins, rigid
Specific gravity	D792	1.14	1.34–1.45	1.2–1.3	1.35–1.55	1.25–1.35	1.65–1.72	1.05	1.10–1.46
Specific volume, cu in. per lb	D792	24.2	20.7–19.1	23.0–21.3	20.5–17.8	22.2–20.5	16.8–16.1	26.4	25.2–19.0
Refractive index, n_D	D542	1.53	1.52–1.53				1.60–1.63	1.47–1.49	1.53–1.57
Tensile strength, psi	D638, D651	10,900	7,200–9,000	1,500–3,500	8,000–9,000	1,500–3,500	3,000–5,000	500–3,000	3,500–10,000
Elongation, %	D638	90		Up to 350	5	200–450	Up to 250	150–450	<5
Modulus of elasticity in tension, 10^5 psi	D638	4.0	3.5–4.1				0.5–0.8		3.0–6.4
Compressive strength, psi	D695	13,000	9,900–11,300	900–1,700	14,000				13,000–27,000
Flexural strength, psi	D650, D790	13,800	12,600–14,500	Varies depending on type and amount of plasticizer				Varies depending on type and amount of plasticizer	8,500–17,000
Impact strength, ft-lb per in. of notch (½ × ½ in. notched bar, Izod test)	D256	1.0	0.4–0.75		0.4–0.75		0.3–1.0		0.2–0.4
Hardness, Rockwell	D785	R118					M50–M65	10–100(Shore)	M70–M115
Thermal conductivity, 10^{-4} cal per sec per sq cm per 1°C per cm	D325	5.8	3.7	3.0–4.0	3.5–4.0	3.0–4.0	3.0		4
Thermal expansion, 10^{-5} per °C	D696	10	6.9–18.5	7–25			19		8–10
Resistance to heat, °F (continuous)	D648	300	130	150	130–160	150–175	160–200		250
Heat-distortion temp, °F	D635	360(66 psi)	140–155		140–185		130–150		140–400
Burning rate		Self-extinguishing	Self-extinguishing	Dependent on type and amount of plasticizer	Self-extinguishing	Slow to self-extinguishing	Self-extinguishing	Slow	1.1 to self-extinguishing
Effect of sunlight		Discolors slightly	Darkens on prolonged intense exposure	Darkens on prolonged intense exposure	Darkens on prolonged intense exposure	Darkens on prolonged intense exposure	Slight	Slight	None to slight
Effect of weak acids	D543	None	None	None to slight	None	None	None	Slight	Nil
Effect of strong acids	D543	Attacked	None	None to slight	None	None to slight	Highly resistant	Slight	None to considerable
Effect of weak alkalies	D543	None	None	None	None		Resistant	Slight	None to slight
Effect of strong alkalies	D543	None	None	None to slight	None		Resistant	Slight	Attacked
Effect of organic solvents	D543	Resistant to common solvents	Resists alcohols, and oils. Soluble in ketones and esters; swells in aromatic hydrocarbons	Soluble in ketones and esters; swells in aromatic hydrocarbons	Resists alcohols, carbons, and oils. Soluble in ketones and esters; swells in aromatic hydrocarbons	Soluble in ketones and esters; swells in aromatic hydrocarbons	Resistant	Resists aliphatic hydrocarbons and most oils. Swells in ketones, esters, and aromatic hydrocarbons; dissolves in alcohols	Attacked by ketones and chlorinated solvents
Clarity		Translucent to opaque	Transparent to opaque	Transparent to opaque	Transparent to opaque	Transparent to opaque	Translucent to opaque	Transparent to opaque	Transparent to opaque
Color possibilities		Unlimited	Unlimited	Unlimited	Unlimited	Unlimited	Extensive	Unlimited	Unlimited

Table 2-47. Properties of Plastics*—(Continued)

Properties	ASTM test method	Polyester molding compounds, glass-fiber filler	Methyl methacrylate resin — Cast	Methyl methacrylate resin — Molding	Polystyrene molding compounds	Styrene copolymer molding compounds, heat- and chemical-resistant type	Polyethylene molding compounds	Polymonochlorotrifluoroethylene	Polytetrafluoroethylene molding compound
Specific gravity	D792	1.90	1.18–1.19	1.18–1.19	1.05–1.065	1.05–1.11	0.92	2.1	2.1–2.3
Specific volume, cu in. per lb	D792	14.6	23.4–23.2	23.4–23.2	26.3–26.0	26.2–24.8	30.1	13.2	13.2–12.1
Refractive index, n_D	D542		1.485–1.50	1.49	1.59–1.60	1.57–1.60	1.51	1.43	1.35
Tensile strength, psi	D638, D651	5,000–9,000	6,100–10,000	7,500–10,000	5,000–9,000	7,000–12,000	1,500–1,800	5,700	1,800
Elongation, %	D638		2–7	2–10	1.0–3.6	1.5–2.5	50–400	28–36	110
Modulus of elasticity in tension, 10^6 psi	D638	16–20	3.5–5.0	4.5	4–6	4–6	0.19	1.9	0.58
Compressive strength, psi	D695	20,000–25,000	11,000–19,000	12,000–18,000	11,500–16,000	11,500–16,000		32,000–80,000	1,700
Flexural strength, psi	D650, D790	14,000–17,000	12,000–17,000	13,000–17,000	8,000–16,000	10,000–17,000		8,250	1,600
Impact strength, ft-lb per in. of notch (½ × ½ in. notched bar, Izod test)	D256	12–24	0.4–0.5	0.4–0.5	0.25–0.50	0.25–0.50	>16	3.5	2.5–4.5
Hardness, Rockwell	D785		M90–M100	M85–M105	M65–M90	M65–M90	R11	R110–R115	D55 (Shore)
Thermal conductivity, 10^{-4} cal per sec per sq cm per 1°C per cm	D325	8–12	4–6	4–6	2.4–3.3	1.9–3.0	8.0	1.4	6
Thermal expansion, 10^{-5} per °C	D696	1.0–3.0	9	9	6–8	6–8	16–18	4.5–7.0	10
Resistance to heat, °F (continuous)		300	140–200	155–190	150–205	170–220	212	390	500
Heat-distortion temp, °F	D648	400	150–210	160–195	160–215	190–235	(66 psi)		270 (66 psi)
Burning rate	D635	Self-extinguishing	Slow	Slow	Slow	Slow	Slow	Nil	Nil
Effect of sunlight		Nil	Very slight	Very slight	Yellows slightly	Yellows slightly	Colors may fade	None	None
Effect of weak acids	D543	Slight effect	Practically nil	Practically nil	None	None	Resistant	None	None
Effect of strong acids	D543	Attacked	Affected only by oxidizing acids	Practically nil	Attacked by oxidizing acids	Attacked by oxidizing acids	Attacked by oxidizing acids	None	None
Effect of weak alkalies	D543	Attacked	Practically nil	Practically nil	None	None	Resistant	None	None
Effect of strong alkalies	D543	Attacked	Practically nil	Practically nil	None	None	Resistant	None	None
Effect of organic solvents	D543	No effect	Soluble in ketones, esters, and aromatic hydrocarbon		Soluble in aromatic and chlorinated hydrocarbons	Soluble in aromatic and chlorinated hydrocarbons	Soluble in aromatic solvents above 60°C	Halogenated compounds cause slight swelling	None
Clarity		Opaque	Transparent (90–92% light transmission)		Transparent (88–92% light transmission)	Transparent (90% light transmission)	Translucent to opaque	Transparent to translucent	Opaque
Color possibilities		Limited	Unlimited	Unlimited	Unlimited	Essentially unlimited	Unlimited	Unlimited	Limited

into putties or premixes that are easily compression- or transfer-molded into parts having high impact resistance.

Melamine Formaldehyde. These materials are unaffected by common organic solvents, greases, and oils, as well as most weak acids and alkalies. Their water absorption is low. They are insensitive to heat and are highly flame-resistant, depending on the filler. Electrical properties are particularly good, especially resistance to arcing. Unfilled materials are highly translucent and have unlimited color possibilities. Principal fillers are alpha cellulose for general-purpose compounding; minerals to improve electrical properties, particularly at elevated temperatures; chopped fabric to afford high shock resistance and flexural strength; and cellulose, mainly for electrical purposes.

Alkyd. These are customarily combined with mineral or glass fillers, the latter for high impact strength. Extreme rapidity and completeness of cure permit rapid production of large numbers of parts from relatively few molds. Because electrical properties, especially resistance to arcing, are good, many of the applications for alkyd molding materials are in electrical applications.

Urea Formaldehyde. Like the melamines, these offer unlimited translucent to opaque color possibilities, light-fastness, good mechanical and electrical properties, and resistance to organic solvents as well as mild acids and alkalies. Although there is no swelling or change in appearance, the water absorption of urea formaldehyde is relatively high, and it is therefore not recommended for applications involving long exposure to water. Occasional exposure to water is without deleterious affect. Strength properties are good, although special shock-resistant grades are not made.

Silicones. Unlike other plastics, silicones are based on silicon rather than carbon. As a consequence, their inertness and durability under a wide variety of conditions are outstanding. As compared with the phenolics, their mechanical properties are poor, and consequently, glass fibers are added. Molding is more difficult than with other thermosetting materials. Unlike most other resins, they may be used in continuous operations at 400°F; they have very low water absorption; their dielectric properties are excellent over an extremely wide variety of chemical attack; and under outdoor conditions their durability is particularly outstanding. In liquid solutions silicones are used to impart moisture resistance to masonry walls and to fabrics. They also form the basis for a variety of paints and other coatings capable of maintaining flexibility and inertness to attack at high temperatures in the presence of ultraviolet sunlight and ozone. Silicone rubbers maintain their flexibility at much lower temperatures than other rubbers.

2-78. Thermoplastic Resins. Materials under this heading in general can be softened by heating and hardened by cooling. There are some exceptions such as polytetrafluoroethylene, and the polyvinyl butyral thermosetting plastics.

Acrylics. In the form of large transparent sheets these are used in aircraft enclosures and building construction. Although not so hard as glass, they have perfect clarity and transparency. They are the most resistant of the transparent plastics to sunlight and outdoor weathering, and they have an optimum combination of flexibility and sufficient rigidity with resistance to shattering. A wide variety of transparent, translucent, and opaque colors can be produced. The sheets are readily formed to complex shapes. They are used for such applications as transparent windows, outdoor and indoor signs, parts of lighting equipment, decorative and functional automotive parts, reflectors, household-appliance parts, and similar applications. They can be used as large sheets, molded from molding powders, or cast from the liquid monomer.

Polyethylene. In its unmodified form, this is a flexible, waxy, translucent plastic maintaining flexibility at very low temperatures, in contrast to many other thermoplastic materials. The heat-distortion point of the low-density polyethylenes is low; these plastics are not recommended for uses above 150°F. Newer, high-density materials have higher heat-distortion temperatures. Some may be heated to temperatures above 212°F. The heat-distortion point may rise well above 250°F for plastics irradiated with high-energy beams. Unlike most plastics, this material is partly crystalline. It is highly inert to solvents and corrosive chemicals of all kinds at ordinary temperatures. Unusually low moisture permeability and absorption are combined with excellent electrical properties. Its density is lower than that of any other commercially available nonporous plastic. When compounded with black pigment, its weathering properties are good. It is widely used as a primary insulating material on wire and cable and has been used as a replacement for the lead jacket in communication cables and other cables. It is widely used also as thin flexible film for packaging, particularly of food, and as corrosionproof lining for tanks and other chemical equipment.

Polytetrafluoroethylene. When fluorine replaces hydrogen, the resulting plastic is a highly crystalline linear-type polymer, unique among organic compounds in its chemical inertness and resistance to change at high and low temperatures. It has an extremely low dielectric-loss factor. In addition, its other electrical properties are excellent. Its outstanding property is extreme resistance to attack by corrosive agents and solvents of all kinds. No substance has been found that will dissolve or even swell this material, with the exception of molten alkali metals. Under some conditions, it is subject to attack by fluorine. At temperatures well above 500°F, it can be held for long periods with practically no change in properties, except loss in tensile strength. Service temperatures are generally maintained below 480°F. It is not embrittled at low temperatures, and its films remain flexible at temperatures below −100°F. It is difficult to mold because it has no true softening temperature. Because of this, a modified form in which one chlorine is substituted for fluorine is employed. This is *polymonochlorotrifluoroethylene.* Like the silicones, these fluorocarbons are difficult to wet; consequently, they have high moisture repellence and are often used as parting agents, or where sticky materials, such as candy, must be handled.

Polyvinyl Formal and Polyvinyl Butyral. Polyvinyl formal resins are principally used as a base for tough, water-resistant insulating enamel for electric wire. Polyvinyl butyral is the tough interlayer in safety glass. In its cross-linked and plasticized form, polyvinyl butyral is extensively used in coating fabrics for raincoats, upholstery and other heavy-duty moisture-resistant applications.

Vinyl Chloride Polymers and Copolymers. These materials vary from hard and rigid to highly flexible. Polyvinyl chloride is naturally hard and rigid but can be plasticized to any required degree of flexibility as in raincoats and shower curtains. Copolymers, including vinyl chloride plus vinyl acetate, are naturally flexible without plasticizers. Nonrigid vinyl plastics are widely used as insulation and jacketing for electric wire and cable because of their electrical properties and their resistance to oil and water. Thin films are used for rainwear and similar applications, whereas heavy-gage films and sheets are widely used for upholstery. Vinyl chlorides are used for floor coverings in the form of tile and sheet because of their abrasion resistance and relatively low water absorption. The rigid materials are used for tubing, pipe, and many other applications where their resistance to corrosion and action of many chemicals, especially acids and alkalies, recommends them. They are attacked by a variety of organic solvents, however. Like all thermoplastics, they soften at elevated temperatures, and their maximum recommended temperature is therefore about 140°F, although at low loads they may be used at temperatures as high as 180°F.

Vinylidene Chloride. This material is highly resistant to most inorganic chemicals and to organic solvents generally. It is impervious to water on prolonged immersion, and its films are highly resistant to moisture-vapor transmission. It can be sterilized, if not under load, in boiling water. Mechanical properties are good. It is not recommended for uses involving high-speed impact, shock resistance, or flexibility at subfreezing temperatures. It should not be used for continuous exposures to temperatures in excess of 170°F.

Polystyrene. Polystyrene formulations constitute a large and important segment of the entire field of thermoplastic materials. Numerous modified polystyrenes provide a relatively wide range of properties. Polystyrene is one of the lightest of the presently available commercial plastics. It is relatively inexpensive, easily molded, has good dimensional stability, and good stability at low temperatures; it is brilliantly clear when transparent and has an infinite range of colors. Water absorption is negligible even after long immersion. Electrical characteristics are excellent. It is resistant to most corrosive chemicals, such as acids, and to a variety of organic solvents, although it is attacked by others.   Polystyrenes as a class are considerably more brittle and less extensible than many other thermoplastic materials, but these properties are markedly improved in copolymers.   Under some conditions, they have a tendency to develop fine cracks, known as craze marks, on exposure, particularly outdoors.   This is true of many other thermoplastics, especially when highly stressed.

Nylon.   Molded nylon is used in increasing quantities for impact and high resistance to abrasion.   It is employed in small gears, cams, and other machine parts, because even when unlubricated they are highly resistant to wear.   Its chemical resistance, except to phenols and mineral acids, is excellent.   Extruded nylon is coated onto electric wire, cable, and rope for abrasion resistance.   Applications like hammerheads indicate its impact resistance.

2-79. Cellulose Derivatives.   Cellulose is a naturally occurring high polymer found in all woody plant tissue and in such materials as cotton.   It can be modified by chemical processes into a variety of thermoplastic materials, which, in turn, may be still further modified with plasticizers, fillers, and other additives to provide a wide variety of properties.   The oldest of all plastics is cellulose nitrate.

Cellulose Acetate.   This is the basis of safety film developed to overcome the highly flammable nature of cellulose nitrate.   Starting as film, sheet, or molding powder, it is made into a variety of items such as transparent packages and a large variety of general-purpose items.   Depending on the plasticizer content, it may be hard and rigid or soft and flexible.   Moisture absorption of this and all other cellulosics is relatively high, and they are therefore not recommended for long-continued outdoor exposure.   But cellulose acetate film, reinforced with metal mesh, is widely used for temporary enclosures of buildings during construction.

Cellulose Acetate Butyrate.   The butyrate copolymer is inherently softer and more flexible than cellulose acetate and consequently requires less plasticizer to achieve a given degree of softness and flexibility.   It is made in the form of clear transparent sheet and film, or in the form of molding powders, which can be molded by standard injection-molding procedures into a wide variety of applications.   Like the other cellulosics, this material is inherently tough and has good impact resistance.   It has infinite colorability, like the other cellulosics.   Cellulose acetate butyrate tubing is used for such applications as irrigation and gas lines.

Ethyl Cellulose.   This is similar to cellulose acetate and acetate butyrate in its general properties.   Two varieties, general-purpose and high-impact, are common, the high-impact being made for better-than-average toughness at normal and low temperatures.

Cellulose Nitrate.   One of the toughest of the plastics, cellulose nitrate is widely used for tool handles and similar applications requiring high impact strength.   The high flammability requires great caution, particularly in the form of film.   Most commercial photographic film is cellulose nitrate as opposed to safety film.   Cellulose nitrate is the basis of most of the widely used commercial lacquers for furniture and similar items.

LAMINATES CONTAINING PLASTICS

2-80. High-pressure Laminates.   Laminated thermosetting products consist of fibrous sheet materials combined with a thermosetting resin, usually phenol formaldehyde or melamine formaldehyde.   The commonly used sheet materials are paper, cotton fabric, asbestos paper or fabric, nylon fabric, and glass fabric.   The usual form is flat sheet, but a variety of rolled tubes and rods is made.   Table 2-48 presents some engineering properties of high-pressure laminated thermosetting sheet.   Values are averages for a large number of tests on materials made by various manufacturers and are subject to variation.   Modulus of elasticity values are subject to variation with magnitude of load and temperature.

Standard grades as developed by the National Electrical Manufacturers Association, Division on High-pressure Laminated Materials, are the following:

Paper-based Grades.   Grade X primarily for mechanical applications; Grade P for punching while hot; Grade PC for cold punching and shearing; Grade XX for the usual electrical applications (not so good for mechanical applications as Grade X);

Table 2-48. Engineering Properties of Laminated Thermosetting Sheets*

Property	NEMA and ASTM grades											
	X	P	PC	XX	XXP	XXX	XXXP	ES-1	ES-2	ES-3	C	CE
Tensile strength, psi:												
Lengthwise	20,000	12,000	10,500	16,000	11,000	15,000	12,400	12,000	13,000	15,000	11,200	12,000
Crosswise	16,000	9,000	8,500	13,000	8,500	12,000	9,500	8,500	9,000	12,000	9,500	9,000
Modulus of elasticity in tension:												
Lengthwise	1,900,000	1,200,000	1,000,000	1,500,000	900,000	1,300,000	1,000,000				1,000,000	900,000
Crosswise	1,400,000	900,000	800,000	1,200,000	700,000	1,000,000	800,000				900,000	800,000
Modulus of elasticity in flexure:												
Lengthwise	1,800,000	1,200,000	1,000,000	1,400,000	900,000	1,300,000	1,000,000				1,000,000	900,000
Crosswise	1,300,000	900,000	800,000	1,100,000	700,000	1,000,000	700,000				900,000	800,000
Compressive strength, psi:												
Flatwise	36,000	25,000	22,000	34,000	25,000	32,000	25,000				37,000	39,000
Edgewise	19,000			23,000		25,500					23,500	24,500
Rockwell hardness (M)	M110	M95	M75	M105	M100	M110	M105	M118	M118	M120	M103	M105
Deformation and shrinkage (cold flow at 4,000 psi for ⅛-in. thickness, % change)				0.90		0.80	0.80					
Insulation resistance, condition C-96/35/90, megohms				60	500	1,000	20,000					
Specific volume, cu in. per lb	20.4	20.8	20.6	20.6	21.0	21.0	21.3	19.1	19.8	20.1	20.4	20.8
Thermal expansion, cm per cm per °C						2.0×10^{-5}						
Max operating temp, continuous, °F	225	250	200	250	250	250	250	250	250	250	225	250
AIEE insulation class	A	A	A	A	A	A	A	A	A	A	A	A

Table 2-48. Engineering Properties of Laminated Thermosetting Sheets* (Continued)

Property	NEMA and ASTM grades										
	L	LE	A	AA	G-1	G-2	G-3	G-5	G-6	G-7	N-1
Tensile strength, psi:											
Lengthwise	14,000	13,500	10,000	12,000	12,500	16,000	23,000	37,000		23,000	8,500
Crosswise	10,000	9,500	8,000	10,000	9,500	11,000	20,000	30,000		18,500	8,000
Modulus of elasticity in tension:											
Lengthwise	1,200,000	1,000,000	2,500,000	1,700,000	1,900,000	1,800,000	2,000,000	2,300,000		1,800,000	400,000
Crosswise	900,000	850,000	1,600,000	1,500,000	1,100,000	1,200,000	1,700,000	2,000,000		1,800,000	400,000
Modulus of elasticity in flexure:											
Lengthwise	1,100,000	1,000,000	2,300,000	1,600,000	1,800,000	1,300,000	1,500,000	1,700,000		1,400,000	600,000
Crosswise	850,000	850,000	1,400,000	1,400,000	1,000,000	1,000,000	1,200,000	1,500,000		1,200,000	500,000
Compressive strength, psi:											
Flatwise	35,000	37,000	40,000	38,000	50,000	38,000	50,000	70,000	40,000	45,000	
Edgewise	23,500	25,000	17,000	21,000		15,000	17,500	25,000	9,000	14,000	
Rockwell hardness (M)	M105	M105	M111	M103	M110	M105	M100	M120	M95	M100	M105
Deformation and shrinkage (cold flow at 4,000 psi for $\frac{1}{8}$-in. thickness, % change)		30				0.40	0.30	0.30		0.30	
Insulation resistance, condition C-96/35/90, megohms						5,000		100		2,500	50,000
Specific volume, cu in. per lb	20.5	20.8	16.1	16.3	17.3	18.5	16.8	14.6	16.8	16.5	24.1
Thermal expansion, linear, cm per cm per °C	2.0×10^{-5}		1.5×10^{-5}			1.8×10^{-5}			1.0×10^{-5}		
Max operating temp, continuous, °F	225	250	275	275	290	275	290	300	400	400	165
AIEE insulation class	A	A	B	B	B	B	B	B	H	H	A

* National Electrical Manufacturers Association.

Grade XXP better than Grade XX in electrical applications and good for punching; Grade XXX suitable for radio-frequency and high-humidity applications; Grade XXXP better electrical properties than Grade XXX and more suitable for hot punching. Three Grades, ES-1, ES-2, and ES-3 are for engraving, as for nameplates.

Fabric-based Grades. Grade C made from fairly heavy cotton fabric is strong and tough, suitable for gears and other high-impact applications. Grade CE made from same weight and thread count as Grade C is suitable for electrical applications. Grade L made from finer cotton fabric than Grades C and CE is especially suitable for small gears and other fine machining applications. Grade LE, similar to Grade L, is especially useful for electrical applications.

Asbestos Grades. Grade A is made of asbestos paper, Grade AA of asbestos fabric. Both are recommended for heat resistance.

Glass-based Grades. Grade G1, made of staple fiber-type glass cloth, is for general-purpose heat-resistant applications and high impact strength. Grade G2 is similar to Grade G1, except that it is especially useful for combined electrical and heat resistance at high humidities. Grade G3, made of continuous-filament-type glass cloth, is a general-purpose grade with especially high impact and flexural strength. Grade G5, made with continuous-filament glass fabric with a melamine resin binder, is the strongest and hardest of the laminates. Grade G6, staple-fiber-type glass cloth with a silicone resin binder, has extremely low dielectric loss and good insulation resistance when dry, and good electrical properties under humid conditions. Grade G7, continuous-filament glass cloth with silicone resin binder, has exceptionally high strength and impact properties combined with extremely good dielectric properties and insulation resistance. H is second only to Grade G5 in flame resistance.

Nylon-based Grades. Grade N1, made of nylon cloth with phenolic resin binder, has excellent electrical properties under high humidity conditions and good impact strength.

Decorative Laminates. These high-pressure laminates consist of a base of phenolic resin-impregnated kraft paper over which an overlay of printed paper or wood veneer is applied. Over all this is laid a thin sheet of melamine resin. When the entire assemblage is pressed in a hot-plate press at elevated temperatures and pressures, the various layers are fused together and the melamine provides a completely transparent finish, resistant to alcohol, water, and common solvents. This material is widely used for tabletops, counter fronts, wainscots, and similar building applications. It is customarily bonded to a core of plywood to develop the necessary thickness and strength. In this case, a backup sheet consisting of phenolic resin and paper alone, without the decorative surface, is employed to provide balance to the entire sandwich. When a thin sheet of aluminum is placed directly under the decorative sheet, it carries heat rapidly away from heat sources like burning cigarettes and prevents scorching.

2-81. Reinforced Plastics. These are commonly made with allyl, polyester and epoxide resins combined with various types of reinforcing agents, of which glass fibers in the form of mats or fabrics are the most common. Because little or no pressure is required to form large complex parts, rather simple molds can be employed for the manufacture of such things as boat hulls and similar large parts. In buildings, these reinforced plastics have been rather widely used in the form of corrugated sheet for skylights, side lighting of buildings, and similar applications.

These materials may be formulated to cure at ordinary temperatures, or they may require moderate temperatures to cure the resins. Customarily, parts are made by laying up successive layers of the glass fabric or the glass mat and applying the liquid resin to them. The entire combination is allowed to harden at ordinary temperatures, or it is placed in a heated chamber for final hardening. It may be placed inside a rubber bag and a vacuum drawn to apply moderate pressure, or it may be placed between a pair of matching molds and cured under moderate pressure in the molds.

The high impact resistance of these materials combined with good strength properties and good durability recommends them for building applications. When the quantity of reinforcing agent is kept relatively low, a high degree of translucence may be achieved, although it is less than that of the acrylics and the other transparent thermoplastic materials.

Table 2-49 presents some engineering properties of reinforced plastics employing allyl and rigid styrene alkyd-type resins in combination with chopped glass strand or woven glass fabric.

Table 2-49. Glass-fiber Reinforced Allyl and Polyester Plastics*

Property	ASTM test method	Allyl resins, reinforced		Polyester resins, reinforced rigid styrene alkyd type	
		Chopped glass strand	Woven glass fabric†	Chopped glass strand	Woven glass fabric‡
Values from mechanical tests:					
Impact strength, Izod, notched, 73.4°F, ft-lb per in.	D256	13.3	15.0	Over 7	13–19 (edge)
Compression:					
Stress at yield (upper), psi........	.....	....	20,200		
Stress at fracture, psi............	D695	22,300	30,200	20,000–35,000	20,000–45,000
Flexure:					
Stress at yield (upper), psi........	.....	....	51,300		
Stress at fracture, psi............	D790	28,200	62,350	30,000–50,000	36,000–70,000¶
Tension					
Stress at yield (upper), psi........	.....	....	30,400		
Stress at fracture:					
73.4°F.......................	D638	20,000	40,800	10,000–20,000	30,000–46,000
158°F.......................		2.0			
Modulus of elasticity (apparent):					
Compression, psi................	D695	....	38×10^5	....	20–34×10^5
Flexure, psi...................	D790	....	28×10^5	10–20×10^5	20–35×10^5
Tension, psi...................	D638	13×10^5	25×10^5	5–15×10^5	18–30×10^5
Rockwell hardness................	D785	M113	....	M90–M100	M105–M120§
Experience regarding durability:					
Effect of light..................	D620	....	....	....	Slight
Heat resistance, °F (max recommended continuous service temp)..	.....	350	350	250	
Chemical resistance...............	.....				Good. Weak acid and alkali —good; strong acid and alkali —poor; hydrocarbons, alcohols esters —good; ketones, chlorinated solvents —poor

* "Technical Data on Plastics," Manufacturing Chemists' Association Inc., 1953.
† Data reported are those obtained on laminates prepared in accordance with Air Force Specification 12049 using type 181-114 glass fabric.
‡ Data reported are those obtained on laminates prepared in accordance with Air Force Specification 12049 using type 181-114 glass fabric.
¶ Run by method 1031 of Federal Specification LP406a.
§ Run by method 1081 of Federal Specification LP406a.

2-82. Plastics Bibliography

Manufacturing Chemists' Association, Inc., Washington, D.C.: "Technical Data on Plastics," 1953.
"Modern Plastics Encyclopedia and Engineers' Handbook," Plastics Catalog Corporation, New York, 1952.
National Electrical Manufacturers Association, New York: Standards for Laminated Thermosetting Products, LP1-1951.

PORCELAIN-ENAMELED PRODUCTS

Porcelain-enameled metal is used for indoor and outdoor applications because of its hardness, durability, washability, and color possibilities. For building purposes, porcelain enamel is applied to sheet metal and cast iron, the former for a variety of purposes including trim, plumbing, and kitchen fixtures, and the latter almost entirely for plumbing fixtures.   Most sheet metal used for porcelain enameling is steel—low in carbon, manganese, and other elements.   Aluminum is also used for vitreous enamel.

2-83. Porcelain Enamel on Metal.   Low-temperature softening glasses must be employed, especially with sheet metal, to avoid the warping and distortion that would occur at high temperatures.   To obtain lower softening temperatures than would be attainable with high-silica glasses, boron is commonly added.   Fluorine may replace some of the oxygen, and lead may also be added to produce easy-flowing brilliant enamels; but lead presents an occupational health hazard.

Composition of the enamel is carefully controlled to provide a coefficient of thermal expansion as near that of the base metal as possible.   If the coefficient of the enamel is greater than that of the metal, cracking and crazing are likely to occur, but if the coefficient of the enamel is slightly less, it is lightly compressed upon cooling, a desirable condition because glass is strong in compression.

To obtain good adhesion between enamel and metal, one of the so-called transition elements used in glass formulation must be employed.   Cobalt is favored.   Apparently, the transition elements promote growth of iron crystals from base metal into the enamel, encourage formation of an adherent oxide coating on the iron, which fuses to the enamel, or develop polar chemical bonds between metal and glass.

Usually white or colored opaque enamels are desired.   Opacity is promoted by mixing in, but not dissolving, finely divided materials possessing refractive indexes widely different from the glass.   Tin oxide, formerly widely used, is now largely displaced by less expensive and more effective titanium and zirconium compounds.   Clay adds to opacity.   Various oxides are included to impart color.

Most enameling consists of a ground coat and one or two cover coats fired on at slightly lower temperatures; but one-coat enameling of somewhat inferior quality can be accomplished by first treating the iron surface with soluble nickel salts.

The usual high-soda glasses used to obtain low-temperature softening enamels are not highly acid-resistant and therefore stain readily and deeply when iron-containing water drips on them.   Enamels highly resistant to severe staining conditions must be considerably harder; i.e., have higher softening temperatures and therefore require special techniques to avoid warping and distorting of the metal base.

Interiors of refrigerators are often made of porcelain-enameled steel sheets for resistance to staining by spilled foods, whereas the exteriors are commonly baked-on synthetic-resin finishes, such as those incorporating melamine and urea formaldehyde.

2-84. Porcelain Bibliography

Andrews, A. I.: "Enamels," 2d ed., The Twin City Ptg. Co., Champaign, Ill., 1945.
Norton, F. H.: "Elements of Ceramics," pp. 183–189, Addison-Wesley Publishing Company, Cambridge, Mass., 1952.
White, A. H.: "Engineering Materials," 2d ed., McGraw-Hill Book Company, Inc., New York, 1948.

RUBBER

Rubber for construction purposes is both natural and synthetic.   Natural rubber, often called crude rubber in its unvulcanized form, is composed of large complex molecules of isoprene.

2-85. Synthetic Rubbers.   The principal synthetic rubbers are the following:

GR-S is the one most nearly like crude rubber and is the product of styrene and butadiene copolymerization.   It is the most widely used of the synthetic rubbers and comprised about five-sixths of the synthetics produced during World War II.   It is not oil-resistant but is widely used for tires and similar applications.

Nitril was known as GR-A when it was made in government plants.   This is a copolymer of acrylonitrile and butadiene.   Its excellent resistance to oils and solvents makes it useful for fuel and solvent hoses, hydraulic-equipment parts, and similar applications.

Butyl is made by the copolymerization of isobutylene with a small proportion of isoprene or butadiene.   It has the lowest gas permeability of all the rubbers and consequently is widely used for making inner tubes for tires and other applications in which gases must be held with a minimum of diffusion.

Neoprene is made by the polymerization of chloroprene. It has very good mechanical properties and is particularly resistant to sunlight, heat, aging, and oil; it is therefore used for making machine belts, gaskets, oil hose, insulation on wire cable, and other electrical applications to be used for outdoor exposure.

Sulfide rubbers, or thiokols—the polysulfides of high molecular weight—have rubbery properties, and articles made from them, such as hose and tank linings, exhibit good resistance to solvents, oils, ozone, low temperature, and outdoor exposure.

Silicone rubber, which is discussed also in the section on plastics, when made in rubbery consistency forms a material exhibiting exceptional inertness and temperature resistance. It is therefore used in making gaskets, electrical insulation, and similar products that maintain their properties at both high and low temperatures.

2-86. Properties of Rubber. Principal properties of the synthetic rubbers are summarized in Table 2-50.

Additional elastomers, which are sometimes grouped with the rubbers, include polyethylene, cyclized rubber, plasticized polyvinyl chloride, and polybutene.

In the raw state, rubbers are generally quite plastic, especially when warm, have relatively low strength, are attacked by various solvents, and often can be dissolved to form cements. These characteristics are necessary for processing, assembling, and forming but are not consistent with the strength, heat stability, and elasticity required in a finished product. The latter desirable properties are obtained by vulcanization, a chemical change involving the interlinking of the rubber molecules and requiring incorporation of sulfur, zinc oxide, organic accelerators, and other ingredients in the raw rubber prior to heat-treatment.

Other compounding ingredients do not enter into the chemical reaction but add considerably to the mechanical properties of finished rubber. This is particularly true of carbon black. Antioxidants retard the rate of deterioration of rubber on exposure to light and oxygen. The great variety of materials entering into various rubber compounds therefore provides a wide range of properties. In addition, many rubber products are laminated structures of rubber compounds combined with materials like fabric and metals.

The two principal categories of rubber are hard and soft. Hard rubber has a high degree of hardness and rigidity produced by vulcanization with high proportions of sulfur (ranging as high as 30 to 50% of the rubber). In soft rubber, however, sulfur may range as low as 1 to 5% and usually not more than 10%.

Principal properties of rubber compounds of interest in building are the following:

Age Resistance. Rubber normally oxidizes slowly on exposure to air at ordinary temperatures. Oxidation is accelerated by heat and ozone. Hard rubber ages less rapidly than soft, and most of the synthetics age at somewhat the same or greatly retarded rates compared with natural rubber.

Compressibility. With the exception of sponge rubber, completely confined rubber, as in a tight container, is virtually impossible to compress.

Elongation. Soft vulcanized compounds may stretch as much as 1,000% of the original length, whereas the elongation of hard rubber ranges usually between 1 and 50%. Even after these great elongations, rubber will return practically to its original length.

Energy Absorption. The energy-storing ability of rubber is about 150 times that of spring-tempered steel. The resilient energy-storing capacity of rubber is 14,600 ft-lb per lb as compared with 95.3 for spring steel.

Expansion and Contraction. The volumetric changes caused by temperature are generally greater for rubber than for metals. Soft vulcanized-rubber compounds, for example, have thermal coefficients of expansion ranging from 0.00011 to 0.00005, whereas hard vulcanized-rubber compounds range from 0.00004 to 0.000015, as compared with coefficients of aluminum of 0.000012, glass of 0.000005, and steel of 0.000007.

Friction. The coefficient of friction between soft rubber and dry steel may exceed unity. But when the surfaces are wet, the friction coefficient drops radically and may become as low as 0.02 in water-lubricated rubber bearings.

Heat Resistance. Vulcanized-natural-rubber compounds are normally limited in use to temperatures of 150 to 200°F, whereas some of the synthetic-rubber compounds like the silicones may be used at temperatures as high as 450°F.

Table 2-50. Properties of Synthetic and Natural Rubber[a]

Property	Crude (natural) rubber	Neoprene GR-M[b]	Thiokol	Nitril type	GR-S type[c]	Butyl GR-I[d]
Workability[e]	Excellent	Good	Fair	Good	Good	Good
Vulcanizing properties	Excellent	Excellent	Fair	Excellent	Excellent	Good
Adhesion to metals	Excellent	Excellent	Poor	Excellent	Excellent	Good
Adhesion to fabrics	Excellent	Excellent	Fair	Good	Good	Good
Resistance to swelling in lubricating oil	Poor	Good	Excellent	Excellent	Poor	Poor
Resistance to deterioration in oil	Poor	Excellent	Fair	Excellent	Poor	Good
Resistance to aromatic hydrocarbons (benzol, toluene, xylene, etc.)	Poor	Poor	Good	Fair	Poor	Fair
Resistance to chlorinated hydrocarbons	Poor	Poor	Good	Good	Poor	Poor
Resistance to lacquer solvents	Poor	Poor	Good	Fair	Poor	Poor
Gas diffusion	Fair	Good	Excellent	Good	Fair	Excellent
Resistance to diffusion of petroleum products	Poor	Fair	Excellent	Excellent	Poor	Poor
Adaptability for contact with food[f]	Excellent	Fair	Poor	Fair	Fair	Good
Dielectric strength[f]	Excellent	Fair	Fair	Fair	Excellent	
Electrical conductivity[f]	Fair	Fair[g]	Fair	Fair[g]	Fair	Fair
Resistance to water absorption[f]	Fair	Good	Fair	Good	Good	Fair
Resistance to strong oxidizing agents	Poor	Poor	Poor	Poor	Poor	Good
Resistance to other corrosives	Good	Good	Good	Good	Good	Good
Tensile strength[f]	Excellent	Good	Fair	Excellent	Good	Fair
Elongation	Excellent	Excellent	Fair	Excellent	Good	Excellent
Resistance to cold flow[f]	Excellent	Good	Poor	Excellent	Excellent	Fair
Resistance to sunlight[f]	Fair	Excellent	Excellent	Good	Fair	Excellent
Resistance to ozone[f]	Fair	Excellent	Excellent	Good	Fair	Excellent
Resistance to aging	Good	Excellent	Excellent	Excellent	Excellent	Excellent
Approx specific gravity basic material	0.93	1.23	1.34	1.00	0.94	0.92
Heat resistance[f]	Good	Excellent	Poor	Excellent	Excellent	Excellent
Flame resistance	Poor	Good	Poor	Poor	Poor	Poor
Cold resistance[f]	Excellent	Good	Fair	Good	Excellent	Good
Rebound elasticity (snap)	Excellent	Good	Good	Fair	Good	Poor
Abrasion[f]	Excellent	Good	Poor	Excellent	Excellent	Fair
Tear resistance[f]	Excellent	Good	Poor	Good	Fair	Good
Abrasion resistance—soaked in oil	Poor	Fair	Poor	Excellent	Poor	Poor
Hardness durometer A tests (100 is bone-hard)	20–100	20–90	35–80	20–100	35–100	15–90
Color range	Good	Good	Poor	Good	Good	Good
Freedom from odor[f]	Excellent	Fair	Poor	Fair	Good	Good
Resistance to paint and ink dryers	Poor	Excellent	Excellent	Excellent	Excellent	Excellent

[a] A. G. H. Dietz, ed., "Engineering Laminates," John Wiley & Sons, Inc., New York, 1949.
[b] GR-M is an abbreviation for "Government Rubber—Monovinylacetylene."
[c] GR-S is an abbreviation for "Government Rubber—Styrene."
[d] GR-I is an abbreviation for "Government Rubber—Isobutylene."
[e] All synthetic rubbers can be worked on rubber machinery, but in some products they are more difficult and expensive to fabricate than crude rubber owing to lack of tack.
[f] These properties available only in specific compounds.
[g] Electrically conductive compounds having more "rubbery" characteristics can be made of these synthetic rubbers than with crude rubber, which has to be very heavily "loaded" to attain the same degree of conductivity.

Light Resistance. The natural, GR-S, and nitryl rubber compounds under tension are likely to crack when exposed to sunlight. Other rubbers are highly resistant to similar attack. Sunlight discolors hard rubber somewhat and reduces its surface electrical resistivity.

Gas Permeability. The thiokol and butyl compounds have very low rates of permeation by air, hydrogen, helium, and carbon dioxide, in contrast with the natural and

GR-S compounds, whose gas permeability is relatively high. A butyl inner tube loses air only about 10% as rapidly as a natural rubber tube.

Strength. The tensile strength based on original cross section ranges from 300 to 4,500 psi for soft-rubber stocks, and from about 1,000 to 10,000 psi for hard rubber. Under compression, soft rubber merely distorts, whereas true hard rubber can be subjected to 10,000 to 15,000 psi before distorting markedly.

2-87. Laminated Rubber. Rubber is often combined with various textiles, fabrics, filaments, and metal wire to obtain strength, stability, abrasion resistance, and flexibility. Among the laminated materials are the following:

V Belts. These consist of a combination of fabric and rubber, frequently combined with reinforcing grommets of cotton, rayon, steel, or other high-strength material extending around the central portion.

Flat Rubber Belting. This laminate is a combination of several plies of cotton fabric or cord, all bonded together by a soft-rubber compound.

Conveyor Belts. These, in effect, are moving highways used for transporting such material as crushed rock, dirt, sand, gravel, slag, and similar materials. When the belt operates at a steep angle, it is equipped with buckets or similar devices and becomes an elevator belt. A typical conveyor belt consists of cotton duck plies alternated with thin rubber plies; the assembly is wrapped in a rubber cover, and all elements are united into a single structure by vulcanization. A conveyor belt to withstand extreme conditions is made with some textile or metal cords instead of the woven fabric. Some conveyor belts are especially arranged to assume a trough form and made to stretch less than similar all-fabric belts.

Rubber-lined Pipes, Tanks, and Similar Equipment. The lining materials include all the natural and synthetic rubbers in various degrees of hardness, depending on the application. Frequently, latex rubber is deposited directly from the latex solution onto the metal surface to be covered. The deposited layer is subsequently vulcanized. Rubber linings can be bonded to ordinary steel, stainless steel, brass, aluminum, concrete, and wood. Adhesion to aluminum is inferior to adhesion to steel. Covering for brass must be compounded according to the composition of the metal.

Rubber Hose. Nearly all rubber hose is laminated and composed of layers of rubber combined with reinforcing materials like cotton duck, textile cords, and metal wire. The modern laminated rubber hose can be made with a large variety of structures. Typical hose consists of an inner rubber lining, a number of intermediate layers consisting of braided cord or cotton duck impregnated with rubber, and outside that, several more layers of fabric, spirally wound cord, spirally wound metal, or in some cases, spirally wound flat steel ribbon. Outside of all this is another layer of rubber to provide resistance to abrasion. Hose for transporting oil, water, wet concrete under pressure, and for dredging purposes is made of heavy-duty laminated rubber.

Vibration Insulators. These usually consist of a layer of soft rubber bonded between two layers of metal. Another type of insulator consists of a rubber tube or cylinder vulcanized to two concentric metal tubes, the rubber being deflected in shear. A variant of this consists of a cylinder of soft rubber vulcanized to a tubular or solid steel core and a steel outer shell, the entire combination being placed in torsion to act as a spring. Heavy-duty mounts of this type are employed on trucks, buses, and other applications calling for rugged construction.

2-88. Rubber Bibliography

American Society for Testing Materials, Philadelphia, Pa.: "Standards," Part 6.

Burton, W. E.: Rubber Laminates, Chap. 21 in A. G. H. Dietz, ed., "Engineering Laminates," John Wiley & Sons, Inc., New York, 1949.

Fisher, H. L.: "Rubber and Its Use," Chemical Publishing Company, Inc., New York, 1941.

ASPHALT AND BITUMINOUS PRODUCTS

Asphalt, because of its water-resistant qualities and good durability, is used for many building applications to exclude water, to provide a cushion against vibration and expansion, and in similar applications.

2-89. Dampproofing and Waterproofing Asphalts. For dampproofing (mopped-on coating only), and waterproofing (built-up coating of one or more plies) three types of asphalt are recognized (ASTM Specification D449):

Type A, an easily flowing, soft, adhesive, "self-healing" material for use underground or wherever similar moderate temperatures are found.

Type B, a less susceptible asphalt for use aboveground where temperatures do not exceed 125°F.

Type C, for use aboveground where exposed on vertical surfaces to direct sunlight or other areas where temperatures exceed 125°F. Softening ranges are, respectively, 115 to 145°F, 145 to 170°F, and 180 to 200°F.

2-90. Roofing Asphalts and Pitches. For constructing built-up roofing, three grades of asphalt are recognized (ASTM D312): (1) For slag or gravel-surfaced roofings on inclines up to 3 in. per ft; (2) for inclines up to 3 in. per ft, not surfaced with slag or gravel; (3) for use on inclines between 3 and 6 in. per ft. Softening ranges are, respectively, 135 to 150°F, 135 to 170°F, and 170 to 200°F.

Coal-tar pitches for roofing, dampproofing, and waterproofing are of two types (ASTM D450): Type A, for gravel or slag-surfaced roofing on inclines up to 3 in. per ft (nailed) or 1 in. per ft (not nailed), and for dampproofing and waterproofing above ground; Type B, for dampproofing and waterproofing under moderate temperature conditions. Softening ranges are, respectively, 140 to 155°F, and 120 to 140°F. One type of coal-tar pitch is designated for steep roofs, with inclines up to 6 in. per ft (ASTM D654). Its softening range is 150 to 170°F. A creosote primer (ASTM D43) may be applied first.

2-91. Roofing Felts. For built-up waterproofing and roofing, three types of membranes are employed: felt (ASTM D226, D227), asbestos felt (ASTM D250, D655), and cotton fabrics (ASTM D173). Felts are felted sheets of vegetable or animal fibers or mixtures of both, saturated with asphalt or with coal tar from which the highly volatile constituents have been removed.

Standard asphalt felts weigh 15 or 30 lb per square (100 sq ft), and standard coal-tar felts are 15 lb per square.

Asbestos felts, weighing 15, 20, 30, or 50 lb per square, are asphalt-saturated felts containing at least 85% asbestos fiber. In these four weights, the felt itself weighs at least 9.0, 8.5, 17.5, and 17.5 lb per square, respectively.

Cotton fabrics are open-weave materials weighing at least 3½ oz per sq yd before saturating, with thread counts of 24 to 32 per in. The saturants are either asphalts or coal tars. The saturated fabric must weigh at least 10 oz per sq yd.

2-92. Roll Roofing. Asphalt roll roofing, shingles, and siding consist basically of roofing felt first uniformly impregnated with hot asphaltic saturant and then coated on each side with at least one layer of a hot asphaltic coating compounded with a water-insoluble mineral filler. The bottom or reverse side, in each instance, is covered with some suitable material, like powdered mica, to prevent sticking in the package or roll.

Granule-surfaced roll roofing (ASTM D249) is covered uniformly on the weather side with crushed mineral granules, such as slate. Minimum weight of the finished roofing must be 80 to 83 lb per square (100 sq ft), and the granular coating must weigh between 16 and 35 lb per square.

Roll roofing (ASTM 224), surfaced with powdered talc or mica, is made in two grades, 65 and 55 lb per square, of which at least 18 lb must be the surfacing material.

2-93. Asphalt Shingles and Siding. There are three standard types of granule-surfaced asphalt shingles (ASTM D225), whose minimum weights per 108 sq ft of exposed areas must be, respectively, 83, 94, and 108 lb (see also Art. 2-92). The material of which these shingles is made is similar to granule-surfaced roll roofing. Granule-surfaced asphalt siding is similar to asphalt shingles, except for the weight requirement, which is a minimum of 75 lb per square for the regular weight.

2-94. Asphalt Mastics and Grouts. Asphalt mastics used for waterproofing floors and similar structures, but not intended for pavement, consist of mixtures of asphalt cement, mineral filler, and mineral aggregate, which can be heated at about 400°F to a sufficiently soft condition to be poured and troweled into place. The raw ingredients may be mixed on the job or may be premixed, formed into cakes, and merely heated on the job (ASTM D491).

Bituminous grouts are suitable for waterproofing above or below ground level as protective coatings. They also can be used for membrane waterproofing or for bedding and filling the joints of brickwork. Either asphaltic or coal-tar pitch materials of dampproofing and waterproofing grade are used, together with siliceous sands (ASTM D170, D171).

2-95. Bituminous Pavements. Asphalts for pavement are of two principal types (ASTM D946): (1) petroleum asphalt cement, derived by the distillation of asphaltic petroleum; and (2) filled or native asphalt cement, prepared by fluxing native asphalt with a petroleum flux, or by mixing petroleum asphalt with a suitable filler. Various grades are designated as 40-50, 50-60, 60-70, 70-85, 85-100, 100-120, 120-150, 150-200, and 200-300 depending upon the depth of penetration of a standard needle in a standard test (ASTM D5).

Asphalts are modified in various ways, including:

Emulsions ranging from low to high viscosity and quick- to slow-setting (ASTM D977).

Cutbacks, consisting of asphalts fluxed with distillates (medium-curing) or light volatile solvents (rapid-curing), to be used primarily in treating road surfaces (ASTM D598, D597).

Asphalt pavements are classified as asphaltic concrete binder and sheet asphalt (ASTM D978).

Asphaltic concrete binder pavement consists of either petroleum or filled or native asphalt (penetrations 50-60, 60-70, 70-85, or 85-100) combined with fine and coarse aggregates ranging in size from 200 mesh to $1\frac{1}{2}$ in. Binder courses have from 4.0 to 9.0% and surface courses from 7.0 to 12.0% bitumen.

Sheet asphalts consist of asphaltic binder, plus fine aggregate (200 mesh to $\frac{3}{8}$ in.) and a mineral filler such as limestone dust and portland cement.

2-96. Asphalt Bibliography

American Society for Testing Materials, Philadelphia, Pa.: "Standards," Part 3.

MASTIC SEALERS

Mastic sealers or calking compounds are employed to seal the points of contact between similar and dissimilar building materials that cannot otherwise be made completely tight. Such points include glazing, the joints between windows and walls, the many joints occurring in the increasing use of panelized construction, the copings of parapets, and similar spots.

The requirements of a good mastic sealer or calking compound are: (1) good adhesion to the surrounding materials, (2) good cohesive strength, (3) elasticity to allow for shrinkage and expansion as the surrounding materials retract or approach each other because of changes in moisture content or temperature, (4) good durability or the ability to maintain their properties over a long period of time without marked deterioration, and (5) no staining of surrounding materials such as stone.

2-97. Calking Compounds. Most calking compounds have been composed of a variety of drying oils combined with fillers such as ground limestone, asbestos fiber, chalk, silica, and similar materials. Within the past few years rubber-based elastomeric compounds, including those based on polysulfide rubbers, have been introduced which promise superior performance on the basis of past records of use in other applications involving long-time outdoor exposure.

In the oil-based compounds, the oils are given a variety of treatments depending upon their ultimate uses. Standard procedure is to treat the oils by either or both of the following procedures:

1. *Polymerization.* The oil is raised to a temperature of 500 to 600°F to promote an increase in molecular size, which at the same time changes the viscosity of the oil. Oils so treated have good package stability and increased resistance to absorption into the capillaries of masonry materials.

2. *Oxidation.* The oil is raised to a temperature of 200 to 300°F, and air is blown through the hot oil. Oxygen is absorbed and increases the molecular size and the viscosity of the oil. Oxidized oils have a tendency to continue to oxidize or "body" even while in storage in sealed drums. Oxidized oils resist the tendency to be drawn into the capillaries of masonry and other porous surfaces even more than the polymerized oils and are therefore chosen for calking compounds to be applied directly to porous unprimed masonry. Their package stability is not so good as that of the polymerized oils. Oxidized oils are rapid film formers and tend to skin over quickly either in the package or after being applied on the building.

In addition to the foregoing treatments, it is possible to separate the slow-drying and fast-drying portions of linseed, fish, and other oils, and thereby to obtain faster- or slower-hardening mastics. Materials based on synthetic resins such as the polybutenes of various molecular weights have opened new possibilities in the formulation of mastics. Some of these remain flexible at temperatures as low as −65°F.

Four basic types of consistencies are required for the various types of building applications:

1. Knife-consistency glazing compounds are used to glaze lights of glass in window frames. Whereas standard putties consist of about 10% raw linseed oil and 90% ground calcium carbonate, the newer glazing compounds employ about 14 to 15% mixed raw and bodied oils with oil-absorbing pigments such as asbestos fiber and other fibrous silicates in addition to ground calcium carbonate or marble dust. Reactive pigments such as lead carbonate are used to promote flexible skin formation.

2. Hand- or tool-consistency compounds are formulated to be highly cohesive and more adhesive than the knife glazing compounds. Their consistency is something like that of modeling clay and they are formulated with bodied oils only. Asbestos fiber, amorphous calcium carbonate whiting, and some crystalline whiting in the form of ground calcium carbonate are the usual pigments.

3. Gun-consistency calking compounds are formulated entirely from bodied oil much of which is oxidized. Pigmentation consists of asbestos fibers, silicate fibers of shorter sizes, ground clays, and sometimes ground calcium carbonate in crystalline form.

4. Paddle or spray mastics are thin consistencies like extremely heavy paints and are specifically designed for use in narrow joints.

Because mastic sealers are based on drying oils that eventually harden in contact with the air, the best joints are generally thick and deep, with a relatively small portion exposed to the air. The exposed surface is expected to form a tough protective skin for the soft mass underneath which in turn provides the cohesiveness, adhesiveness and elasticity required. Thin shallow beads cannot be expected to have the durability of thick joints with small exposed surface areas.

The rubber-based compounds are composed of two components, the base material and the catalyst. These two are mixed when they are to be used and, once mixed, proceed to harden by intermolecular linking and must therefore be put in place before they stiffen too much. At ordinary temperatures the "pot life," or period during which they are workable, is approximately 6 to 7 hr. Heating shortens the pot life; cooling lengthens it.

Various consistencies and hardnesses are possible. The soft formulations (Shore A hardness 10 to 20) show elongations of about 300 to 350%, whereas the heavier gum consistencies may show elongations of 90 to 150%.

The best of the rubber-based formulations show little change in hardness, elongation, and adhesiveness with age. Manufacturers recommend them particularly for uses involving large differential movements where maximum adhesion must at the same time be maintained, as in large double-glass units set in metal frames, curtain walls in which metal sheets undergo marked changes in dimension with changes in temperature, and similar applications.

For setting large sheets of glass and similar units, setting or supporting spacer blocks of rubber are often combined with gaskets of materials such as vulcanized chlorine-based rubber and are finally sealed with the elastomeric rubber-based mastics or glazing compounds.

2-98. Mastic Sealers Bibliography

Hann, Gordon, Tremco Manufacturing Co., Cleveland, Ohio: private communication.

COATINGS

Protective and decorative coatings generally employed in building are the following:

Oil Paint. Drying-oil vehicles or binders plus opaque and extender pigments.

Water Paint. Pigments plus vehicles based on water, casein, protein, oil emulsions, and rubber or resin latexes, separately or in combination.

Calcimine. Water and glue, with or without casein, plus powdered calcium carbonate and any desired colored pigments.

Varnish. Transparent combination of drying oil and natural or synthetic resins.

Enamel. Varnish vehicle plus pigments.

Lacquer. Synthetic-resin film former, usually nitrocellulose, plus plasticizers, volatile solvents, and other resins.

Shellac. Exudations of the lac insect, dissolved in alcohol.

Japan. Solutions of metallic salts in drying oils, or varnishes containing asphalt and opaque pigments.

Aluminum Paint. Fine metallic aluminum flakes suspended in drying oil plus resin, or in nitrocellulose.

2-99. Drying-oil Vehicles or Binders. Most vehicles contain drying oils. These are vegetable and animal oils that harden or "dry" by absorbing oxygen. The most important drying oils are:

Linseed oil derived from flaxseed by crushing, cooking, and pressing. Like other drying oils, this raw oil hardens slowly and is therefore usually treated by "boiling" or blowing. Boiling consists of heating at elevated temperatures to promote polymerization, which is accompanied by increased body and viscosity and increased readiness to react with oxygen. Blowing consists of heating to moderate temperature and blowing air through the oil to cause bodying and increased viscosity by oxidation.

Dehydrated castor oil, made by heating under vacuum with catalysts to remove water. Natural castor oil is not a drying oil; but dehydrated castor oil is excellent, with good flexibility, adhesion, and rapid-drying characteristics.

Fish oil, used mostly in cheap paints where softness and aftertack are not undesirable. The oil must be refined, as by refrigeration, to remove nonhardening constituents.

Soybean oil, obtained from the seeds of the soya plant, has excellent flexibility and is nonyellowing but dries slowly and is usually combined with tung, perilla, or linseed oil.

Tung or chinawood oil, derived from the tung tree nut, is especially waterproof, fast-drying, and durable. It is usually used with less reactive oils, such as linseed or soya. In the raw state, it tends to wrinkle on hardening and is used for wrinkle finishes; otherwise it is treated or combined with other oils.

Other oils include oiticica, perilla, chia, hempseed, peanut, corn, poppyseed, safflower, sunflower, and walnut.

An important class of vehicles consists of **alkyd resins** combined with drying oils. A considerable number of alkyds can be reacted with a wide variety of drying oils in combinations ranging from mostly alkyd to mostly oil, to provide a large choice of alkyd-oil combinations useful for numerous air-drying and heat-hardening finishes.

Dryers are catalysts that hasten the hardening of drying oils. Most dryers are salts of heavy metals, especially cobalt, manganese, and lead, to which salts of zinc and calcium may be added. Iron salts, usable only in dark coatings, accelerate hardening at high temperatures. Dryers are normally added to paints to hasten hardening, but they must not be used too liberally or they cause rapid deterioration of the oil by overoxidation.

Thinners are volatile constituents added to coatings to promote their spreading qualities by reducing viscosity. They should not react with the other constituents and should evaporate completely. Commonly used thinners are turpentine and mineral spirits; i.e., derivatives of petroleum and coal tar.

2-100. Pigments for Paints. Pigments may be classified as white and colored, or as opaque and extender pigments. The hiding power of pigments depends on the difference in index of refraction of the pigment and the surrounding medium—usually the vehicle of a protective coating. In opaque pigments, these indexes are markedly different from those of the drying-oil vehicles; in extender pigments, they are nearly the same. The comparative hiding efficiences of various pigments must be evaluated on the basis of hiding power per pound and cost per pound. The relative hiding power per pound of various important white pigments, in descending order, is approximately as follows: rutile titanium dioxide, anatase titanium dioxide, zinc sulfide, lead titanate, titanium calcium, titanium barium, zinc sulfide barium, titanated lithopone, lithopone, antimony oxide, zinc oxide, white lead.

Principal white pigments are white lead (basic carbonate and basic sulfate), lead titanate, zinc oxide, leaded zinc oxide, lithopone, titanated lithopone, zinc sulfide, titanated zinc sulfide, zinc sulfide–barium, zinc sulfide–calcium, zinc sulfide–magnesium, antimony oxide, titanium dioxide (anatase and rutile), titanium-barium, titanium-calcium, and titanium-magnesium.

White lead is the oldest white pigment. Basic lead carbonate imparts adhesion, toughness, elasticity, durability, and chalking properties, and is widely used, especially in exterior paints. It is the only pigment that by itself will produce a durable exterior paint. Basic lead sulfate is widely used as a replacement for lead carbonate in mixed-pigment paints.

Zinc oxide is widely used by itself or in combination with other pigments. Its color is unaffected by many industrial and chemical atmospheres. It imparts gloss and reduces chalking but tends to crack and alligator instead.

Zinc sulfide is a highly opaque pigment widely used in combination with other pigments.

Titanium dioxide and extended titanium pigments are relative newcomers but have forged into the forefront because of their high opacity and generally excellent properties. Various forms of the pigments have different properties. For example, anatase titanium dioxide promotes chalking, whereas rutile inhibits it.

Colored pigments for building use are largely inorganic materials, especially for outdoor use, where the brilliant but fugitive organic pigments soon fade. The principal inorganic colored pigments are:

Metallic. Aluminum flake or ground particle, copper bronze, gold leaf, zinc dust.

Black. Carbon black, lampblack, graphite, blue basic lead sulfate (gray), vegetable black, and animal blacks.

Earth colors. Yellow ocher, raw and burnt umber, raw and burnt sienna, reds, and maroons.

Blue. Ultramarine, iron (Prussian, Chinese, Milori).

Brown. Mixed ferrous and ferric oxide.

Green. Chromium oxide, hydrated chromium oxide, chrome greens.

Maroon. Iron oxide, cadmium.

Orange. Basic lead chromate, molybdated chrome orange.

Red. Iron oxide, cadmium red, red lead, vermilion.

Yellow. Chrome yellow (lead chromate), zinc chromate, cadmium yellows, hydrated iron oxide.

Extender pigments are added to extend the opaque pigments, increase durability, provide better spreading characteristics, and reduce cost. The principal extender pigments are silica, china clay, talc, mica, barium sulfate, calcium sulfate, calcium carbonate, and such materials as magnesium oxide, magnesium carbonate, barium carbonate, and others used for specific purposes.

2-101. Resins for Paints. Natural and synthetic resins are used in a large variety of air-drying and baked finishes. The natural resins include both fossil resins, which are harder and usually superior in quality, and recent resins tapped from a variety of resin-exuding trees. The most important fossil resins are amber (semiprecious jewelry) Kauri, Congo, Boea Manila, and Pontianak. Recent resins include Damar, East India, Batu, Manila, and rosin. Shellac, the product of the lac insect, may be considered to be in this class of resins.

The synthetic resins, in addition to the alkyds already considered under drying oils (Art. 2-99), are increasing in importance, especially for applications requiring maximum durability. Among them are phenol formaldehyde, melamine formaldehyde, urea formaldehyde, epoxides, and the silicones.

Phenolics in varnishes are used for outdoor and other severe applications on wood and metals. They are especially durable when baked.

Melamine and urea find their way into a large variety of industrial finishes like automobile and refrigerator finishes.

Epoxides bond well to a variety of surfaces, including metals, and are used for tough, durable, and transparent or pigmented coatings.

Silicones are used when higher temperatures are encountered than can be borne by the other finishes.

2-102. Coatings Bibliography

Dietz, A. G. H.: "Dwelling House Construction," D. Van Nostrand Company, Inc., Princeton, N.J., 1946.

Mattiello, J. J.: "Protective and Decorative Coatings," John Wiley & Sons, Inc., New York, 1946.

Von Fischer, W.: "Paint and Varnish Technology," Reinhold Publishing Corporation, New York, 1948.

Section 3

STRESSES IN STRUCTURES

Frederick S. Merritt

Senior Editor, Engineering News-Record

STRESS AND STRAIN

Loads are the external forces acting on a structure. Stresses are the internal forces that resist them. Depending on the manner in which the loads are applied, they tend to deform the structure and its components—tensile forces tend to stretch, compressive forces to squeeze together, torsional forces to twist, and shearing forces to slide parts of the structure past each other.

If the structure and its components are so supported that, after a very small deformation occurs, no further motion is possible, they are said to be in equilibrium. Under such circumstances, internal forces, or stresses, exactly counteract the loads.

3-1. Static Equilibrium. Several useful conclusions may be drawn from this state of static equilibrium: Since there is no translatory motion, the sum of the external forces must be zero; and since there is no rotation, the sum of the moments of the external forces about any point must be zero.

For the same reason, if we consider any portion of the structure and the loads on it, the sum of the external and internal forces on the boundaries of that section must be zero. Also, the sum of the moments of these forces must be zero.

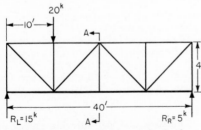 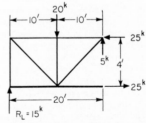

Fig. 3-1. Truss in equilibrium under load. Upward-acting forces equal downward.

Fig. 3-2. Section of truss kept in equilibrium by stresses in its components.

In Fig. 3-1, for example, the sum of the forces R_L and R_R needed to support the roof truss is equal to the 20-kip load on the truss (1 kip = 1 kilopound = 1,000 lb = 0.5 ton). Also, the sum of the moments of the external forces is zero about any point; about the right end, for instance, it is $40 \times 15 - 30 \times 20 = 600 - 600$.

In Fig. 3-2 is shown the portion of the truss to the left of section AA. The internal forces at the cut members balance the external load and hold this piece of the truss in equilibrium.

3–1

Generally, it is convenient to decompose the forces acting on a structure into components parallel to a set of perpendicular axes that will simplify computations. For example, for forces in a single plane—a condition commonly encountered in building design—the most useful technique is to resolve all forces into horizontal and vertical components. Then, for a structure in equilibrium, if H represents the horizontal components, V the vertical components, and M the moments of the components about any point in the plane,

$$\Sigma H = 0 \qquad \Sigma V = 0 \qquad \text{and} \qquad \Sigma M = 0 \qquad\qquad (3\text{-}1)$$

These three equations may be used to evaluate three unknowns in any nonconcurrent coplanar force system, such as the roof truss in Figs. 3-1 and 3-2. They may determine the magnitude of three forces for which the direction and point of application already are known, or the magnitude, direction, and point of application of a single force.

Suppose, for the truss in Fig. 3-1, the reactions at the supports are to be computed. Taking moments about the right end and equating to zero yields $40\,R_L - 30 \times 20 = 0$, from which the left reaction $R_L = 600/40 = 15k$. Equating the sum of the vertical forces to zero gives $20 - 15 - R_R = 0$, from which the right reaction $R_R = 5k$.

3-2. Types of Load. External loads on a structure may be classified in several different ways. In one classification, they may be considered as static, repeated, and impact loads.

Static loads are forces that are applied slowly and then remain nearly constant. One example is the weight, or dead load, of a floor or roof system.

Repeated loads are forces that are applied a number of times, causing a variation in the magnitude, and sometimes also in the sense, of the internal forces. A good example is a bridge crane.

Impact loads are forces that require a structure or its components to absorb energy in a short interval of time. An example is the dropping of a heavy weight on a floor slab, or the shock wave from an explosion striking the walls and roof of a building.

External forces may also be classified as distributed and concentrated.

Uniformly distributed loads are forces that are, or for practical purposes may be considered, constant over a surface of the supporting member. Dead weight of a rolled-steel I beam is a good example.

Concentrated loads are forces that have such a small contact area as to be negligible compared with the entire surface area of the supporting member. A beam supported on a girder, for example, may be considered, for all practical purposes, a concentrated load on the girder.

Another common classification for external forces labels them axial, eccentric, and torsional.

An axial load is a force whose resultant passes through the centroid of a section under consideration and is perpendicular to the plane of the section.

An eccentric load is a force perpendicular to the plane of the section under consideration but not passing through the centroid of the section, thus bending the supporting member (see Arts. 3-33, 3-35, and 3-78).

Torsional loads are forces that are offset from the shear center of the section under consideration and are inclined to or in the plane of the section, thus twisting the supporting member (see Art. 3-78).

For design loads, see Tables 3-1 and 3-2.

3-3. Unit Stress. For convenience in evaluating the load-carrying ability of a member of a structure, it is customary to express its strength in terms of the maximum unit stress, or internal force per unit of area, that it can sustain without suffering structural damage. Then, application of a safety factor to the maximum unit stress determines a unit stress that should not be exceeded when design loads are applied to the member. That unit stress is known as the allowable stress or working stress.

To ascertain whether a structural member has adequate load-carrying capacity, the designer generally has to compute the maximum unit stress produced by design loads in the member for each type of internal force—tensile, compressive, or shearing—and compare it with the corresponding allowable unit stress.

Table 3-1. Minimum Design Live Loads*
Usual Uniformly Distributed Loads

Occupancy or use	Live load, psf	Occupancy or use	Live load, psf
Apartments (see Residential)		Corridors.....................	100
Armories and drill rooms..........	150	Residential:	
Assembly halls and other places of		Multifamily houses:	
assembly:		Private apartments..........	40
Fixed seats....................	60	Public rooms...............	100
Movable seats................	100	Corridors....................	60
Balcony (exterior)...............	100	Dwellings:	
Bowling alleys, poolrooms, and		First floor...................	40
similar recreational areas.......	75	Second floor and habitable	
Corridors:		attics.....................	30
First floor....................	100	Uninhabitable attics..........	20
Other floors, same as occupancy		Hotels:	
served except as indicated		Guest rooms..................	40
Dance halls....................	100	Public rooms...............	100
Dining rooms and restaurants.....	100	Corridors serving public rooms.	100
Dwellings (see Residential)		Public corridors..............	60
Garages (passenger cars)..........	100	Private corridors.............	40
Floors shall be designed to carry		Reviewing stands and bleachers[a]...	100
150% of the max wheel load		Schools:	
anywhere on the floor.		Classrooms....................	40
Grandstands (see Reviewing stands)		Corridors....................	100
Gymnasiums, main floors, and bal-		Sidewalks, vehicular driveways, and	
conies......................	100	yards, subject to trucking.......	250
Hospitals:		Skating rinks...................	100
Operating rooms..............	60	Stairs, fire escapes, and exitways...	100
Private rooms.................	40	Storage warehouse, light..........	125
Wards.......................	40	Storage warehouse, heavy.........	250
Hotels (see Residential)		Stores:	
Libraries:		Retail:	
Reading rooms.................	60	First-floor rooms.............	100
Stack rooms....................	150	Upper floors.................	75
Manufacturing..................	125	Wholesale....................	125
Marquees......................	75	Theaters:	
Office buildings:		Aisles, corridors, and lobbies....	100
Offices.......................	80	Orchestra floors................	60
Lobbies.......................	100	Balconies.....................	60
Penal institutions:		Stage floors...................	150
Cell blocks....................	40	Yards and terraces, pedestrians....	100

* As recommended in American Standard A58.1-1955.

[a] For detailed recommendations, see American Standard for Places of Outdoor Assembly, Grandstands and Tents, Z20.3-1950, or the latest revision thereof approved by the American Standards Association, Incorporated.

Table 3-1. Minimum Design Live Loads* *(Continued)*
Other Uniformly Distributed Loads

Occupancy or use	Live load, psf	Occupancy or use	Live load, psf
Air-conditioning (machine space)...	200[b]	Incinerator charging floor.........	100
Amphitheater:		Kitchens, other than domestic.....	150[b]
Fixed seats..................	60	Laboratories, scientific............	100
Movable seats...............	100	Laundries......................	150[b]
Amusement-park structure........	100[b]	Libraries, corridors...............	100[c]
Attic:		Manufacturing, ice...............	300
Nonstorage..................	25	Morgue......................	125
Storage.....................	80[c]	Office buildings:	
Bakery.........................	150	Files (see File room)	
Balcony:		Business-machine equipment....	100[b]
Exterior.....................	100	Printing plants:	
Interior (fixed seats)............	60	Composing rooms.............	100
Interior (movable seats)	100	Linotype rooms...............	100
Boathouse, floors................	100[c]	Press rooms..................	150[b]
Boiler room, framed..............	300[b]	Paper storage.................	f
Broadcasting studio..............	100	Public rooms...................	100
Catwalks.......................	25	Railroad tracks.................	g
Ceiling, accessible furred.........	10	Ramps, driveway (see Garages)	
Cold storage:		Ramps, pedestrian (see Sidewalk,	
No overhead system...........	250[d]	also Corridors)	
Overhead system:		Ramps, seaplane (see Hangars)	
Floor	150	Rest rooms....................	60
Roof.....................	250	Rink, ice skating................	250
Dormitories:		Storage, hay or grain.............	300[c]
Partitioned..................	40	Telephone exchange.............	150[b]
Nonpartitioned...............	80	Theaters:	
Driveways (see Garages)		Dressing rooms...............	40
Elevator machine room..........	150[b]	Grid-iron floor or fly gallery:	
Fan room......................	150[b]	Grating....................	60
File room:		Well beams, 250 lb per lin ft per	
Letter......................	80[c]	pair	
Card........................	125[c]	Header beams, 1,000 lb per lin	
Addressograph................	150[c]	ft	
Foundries......................	600[b]	Pin rail, 250 lb per lin ft	
Fuel rooms, framed..............	400	Projection room...............	100
Garages:		Toilet rooms...................	60
Trucks, with load, 3 to 10 tons..	150[e]	Transformer rooms..............	200[b]
Trucks, with load, above 10 tons.	200[e]	Vaults, in offices................	250[c]
Greenhouses....................	150		
Hangars........................	150[e]		

[b] Use weight of actual equipment when greater.
[c] Increase when occupancy exceeds this amount.
[d] Plus 150 lb for trucks.
[e] Also subject to not less than 125 % maximum axle load.
[f] Paper storage 50 lb per ft of clear story height.
[g] As required by railroad company.

Concentrated Loads[h]

Location	Load, Lb
Elevator machine room grating (on area of 4 sq in.)...............	300
Finish light floor plate construction (on area of 1 sq in.)...............	200
Office floors......................	2,000
Scuttles, skylight ribs, and accessible ceilings........................	200
Sidewalks........................	8,000
Stair treads (on center of tread)......	300

[h] Considered to act on an area 2.5 ft square, except as noted.

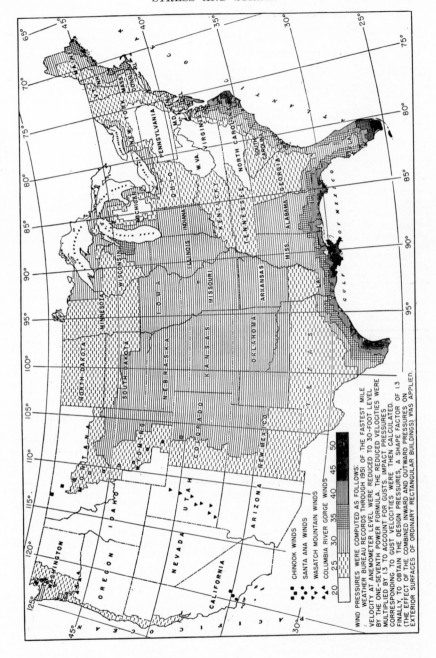

WIND PRESSURES WERE COMPUTED AS FOLLOWS:
WEATHER BUREAU RECORDS THROUGH 1951 OF THE FASTEST MILE
VELOCITY AT ANEMOMETER LEVEL WERE REDUCED TO 30-FOOT LEVEL
BY THE ONE-SEVENTH POWER FORMULA. THE REDUCED VELOCITIES WERE
MULTIPLIED BY 1.3 TO ACCOUNT FOR GUSTS. IMPACT PRESSURES
CORRESPONDING TO GUST VELOCITIES WERE THEN CALCULATED.
FINALLY, TO OBTAIN THE DESIGN PRESSURES, A SHAPE FACTOR OF 1.3
(THE EFFECT OF THE COMBINED INWARD AND OUTWARD PRESSURES ON
EXTERIOR SURFACES OF ORDINARY RECTANGULAR BUILDINGS) WAS APPLIED.

■ CHINOOK WINDS
● SANTA ANA WINDS
▼ WASATCH MOUNTAIN WINDS
▲ COLUMBIA RIVER GORGE WINDS

20 25 30 35 40 45 50

Table 3-1. Minimum Design Live Loads* (Continued)

Wind Pressures on Roofs for Various Height
Zones Above Ground[i]

Height zone, ft	Wind-pressure-map areas, psf						
	20	25	30	35	40	45	50
Less than 30....	15	20	25	25	30	35	40
30–49.........	20	25	30	35	40	45	50
50–99.........	25	30	40	45	50	55	60
100–499.......	30	40	45	55	60	70	75
500–1,199......	35	45	55	60	70	80	90
1,200 and over..	40	50	60	70	80	90	100

[i] Reference should be made to map on p. 3-5 and that column in the table above should be selected which is headed by a value corresponding to the minimum permissible resultant wind pressure indicated for the particular locality on the map.

The figures given are recommended as minimum. These requirements do not provide for tornadoes. Height of roof is measured from average level of ground.

Design for outward pressures normal to surface equal to 1¼ times those specified. Surfaces with slopes greater than 30° should be designed for normal inward pressures as specified in the table.

For chimneys, tanks, and solid towers, with round or elliptical horizontal cross section, multiply pressures by 0.6; for hexagonal or octagonal, multiply by 0.8.

Minimum Design Loads for Materials

Material	Load, lb per cu ft	Material	Load, lb per cu ft
Bituminous products:		Earth (submerged):	
Asphaltum....................	81	Clay.........................	80
Graphite.....................	135	Soil.........................	70
Paraffin.....................	56	River mud....................	90
Petroleum, crude..............	55	Sand or gravel...............	60
Petroleum, refined............	50	Sand or gravel, and clay........	65
Petroleum, benzine............	46	Gold, solid....................	1,205
Petroleum, gasoline............	42	Gold, bars, stacked..............	1,133
Pitch........................	69	Gold coin in bags..............	1,084
Tar.........................	75	Gravel, dry...................	104
Brass........................	526	Gypsum, loose.................	70
Bronze.......................	552	Ice...........................	57.2
Cement, portland, loose..........	90	Iron, cast.....................	450
Cinders, dry, in bulk...........	45	Iron, wrought..................	480
Coal, anthracite, piled...........	52	Lead..........................	710
Coal, bituminous, piled..........	47	Lime, hydrated, loose.............	32
Coal, lignite, piled	47	Lime, hydrated, compacted........	45
Coal, peat, dry, piled............	23	Mortar, hardened:	
Charcoal......................	12	Cement....................	130
Copper.......................	556	Lime.......................	110
Cork, compressed...............	14.4	Riprap (not submerged):	
Earth (not submerged):		Limestone....................	83
Clay, dry....................	63	Sandstone....................	90
Clay, damp..................	110	Sand, clean and dry.............	90
Clay and gravel, dry...........	100	Sand, river, dry.................	106
Silt, moist, loose..............	78	Slag, bank.....................	70
Silt, moist, packed.............	96	Slag, bank screenings.............	108
Silt, flowing..................	108	Slag, machine..................	96
Sand and gravel, dry, loose......	100	Slag, sand.....................	52
Sand and gravel, dry, packed....	110	Silver, solid...................	656
Sand and gravel, wet...........	120	Silver bars, stacked..............	590

Table 3-2. Minimum Design Dead Loads*

Walls†	Psf
4-in. clay brick, high absorption	34
4-in. clay brick, medium absorption	39
4-in. clay brick, low absorption	46
8-in. clay brick, low absorption	89
12½-in. clay brick, low absorption	130
4-in. sand-lime brick	38
4-in. concrete brick, heavy aggregate	46
4-in. concrete brick, light aggregate	33
8-in. concrete block, heavy aggregate	55
8-in. concrete block, light aggregate	35
12-in. concrete block, heavy aggregate	85
12-in. concrete block, light aggregate	55
4-in. brick, 4-in. tile backup	60
4-in. brick, 8-in. tile backup	75
8-in. load-bearing structural clay tile	42
12-in. load-bearing structural clay tile	58
4-in. glass block	18

Partitions	Psf
4-in. clay tile	18
6-in. clay tile	28
8-in. clay tile	34
2-in. gypsum block	9.5
4-in. gypsum block	12.5
6-in. gypsum block	18.5
2-in. solid plaster	20
4-in. concrete block, heavy aggregate	30
4-in. concrete block, light aggregate	20
Wood studs, 2 × 4, unplastered	4
Wood studs, 2 × 4, plastered one side	12
Wood studs, 2 × 4, plastered two sides	20

Concrete Slabs	Psf
Stone aggregate, reinforced, per in	12.5
Cinder, reinforced, per in	9.25
Lightweight aggregate, reinforced, per in	9

Floor finish and fill	Thickness, in.	Psf
Double ⅞ wood on sleepers, light-concrete fill	4	19
Single ⅞ wood on sleepers, light-concrete fill	4	23
3-in. wood block on mastic	3	10
1½-in. asphalt mastic flooring	1½	18
Solid flat tile on 1-in. mortar	2	23

Waterproofing	Thickness, in.	Psf
5-ply membrane	½	5
5-ply membrane, mortar, stone concrete	5	55
2-in. split tile, 3-in. stone concrete	5	45

Table 3-2. Minimum Design Dead Loads* (Continued)

Wood joists, double wood floor, joist size	Psf	
	12-in. spacing	16-in. spacing
2 × 6	6	5
2 × 8	6	6
2 × 10	7	6
2 × 12	8	7

Ceilings   *Psf*
Plaster (on tile or concrete)..................................... 5
Suspended metal lath and gypsum plaster.................... 10
Suspended metal lath and cement plaster.................... 15
Roof Coverings   *Psf*
Asbestos-cement corrugated or shingles........................ 4
Asphalt shingles... 2
Copper or tin... 1
Corrugated iron... 2
Clay tile (add 10 lb for mortar):
     2-in. book tile.. 12
     3-in. book tile.. 20
     Roman.. 12
     Spanish... 19
     Ludowici.. 10
Cement tile... 16
Composition:
     3-ply ready roofing...................................... 1
     4-ply felt and gravel.................................... 5.5
     5-ply felt and gravel.................................... 6
Sheathing (gypsum), $\frac{1}{2}$ in............................ 2
Sheathing (wood), per in. thickness........................... 3
Slate, $\frac{3}{16}$-in....................................... 7
Wood shingles... 3
Materials   *Psf*
Cast-stone masonry... 144
Cinder fill... 57
Concrete, stone aggregate, reinforced......................... 150
Concrete, cinder, reinforced.................................. 111
Masonry, ashlar:
     Granite... 165
     Limestone, crystalline................................... 165
     Limestone, oölitic...................................... 135
     Marble.. 173
     Sandstone... 144
Timber, seasoned:
     Ash, commercial white.................................... 41
     Cypress, southern.. 32
     Fir, Douglas, coast region............................... 34
     Oak, commercial reds and white........................... 45
     Pine, southern yellow.................................... 39
     Redwood... 28
     Spruce, red, white, and Sitka............................ 28
Plate glass... 161

* As recommended in American Standard A58.1-1955.
† For plaster add 5 psf for each face plastered.

When the loading is such that the unit stress is constant over a section under consideration, the stress may be obtained by dividing the force by the area of the section. But in general, the unit stress varies from point to point. In that case, the unit stress at any point in the section is the limiting value of the ratio of the internal force on any small area to that area, as the area is taken smaller and smaller.

3-4. Unit Strain. Sometimes in the design of a structure, unit stress may not be the prime consideration. The designer may be more interested in limiting the deformation or strain.

Deformation in any direction is the total change in the dimension of a member in that direction.

Unit strain in any direction is the deformation per unit of length in that direction. When the loading is such that the unit strain is constant over a portion of a member, it may be obtained by dividing the deformation by the original length of that portion. In general, however, the unit strain varies from point to point in a member. Like a varying unit stress, it represents the limiting value of a ratio (Art. 3-3).

3-5. Hooke's Law. For many materials, unit strain is proportional to unit stress, until a certain stress, the **proportional limit,** is exceeded. Known as Hooke's law, this relationship may be written as

$$f = E\epsilon \qquad \text{or} \qquad \epsilon = \frac{f}{E} \tag{3-2}$$

where f = unit stress
ϵ = unit strain
E = modulus of elasticity
Hence, when the unit stress and modulus of elasticity of a material are known, the unit strain can be computed. Conversely, when the unit strain has been found, the unit stress can be calculated.

3-6. Constant Unit Stress. The simplest cases of stress and strain are those in which the unit stress and strain are constant. Stresses due to an axial tension or compression load or a centrally applied shearing force are examples; also an evenly applied bearing load. These loading conditions are illustrated in Figs. 3-3 to 3-6.

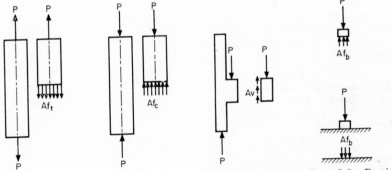

FIG. 3-3. Tension member. FIG. 3-4. Compression member. FIG. 3-5. Bracket in shear. FIG. 3-6. Bearing load.

For the axial tension and compression loadings, we take a section normal to the centroidal axis (and to the applied forces). For the shearing load, the section is taken along a plane of sliding. And for the bearing load, it is chosen through the plane of contact between the two members.

Since for these loading conditions, the unit stress is constant across the section, the equation of equilibrium may be written

$$P = Af \tag{3-3}$$

where P = load

    f = a tensile, compressive, shearing, or bearing unit stress

    A = cross-sectional area for tensile or compressive forces, or area on which sliding may occur for shearing forces, or contact area for bearing loads

For torsional stresses, see Art. 3-78.

The unit strain for the axial tensile and compressive loads is given by the equation

$$\epsilon = \frac{e}{L} \tag{3-4}$$

where ϵ = unit strain

    e = total lengthening or shortening of the member

    L = original length of the member

Applying Hooke's law and Eq. (3-4) to Eq. (3-3) yields a convenient formula for the deformation:

$$e = \frac{PL}{AE} \tag{3-5}$$

where P = load on the member

    A = its cross-sectional area

    E = modulus of elasticity of the material

[Since long compression members tend to buckle, Eqs. (3-3) to (3-5) are applicable only to short members.]

While tension and compression strains represent a simple stretching or shortening of a member, shearing strain represents a distortion due to a small rotation. The load on the small rectangular portion of the member in Fig. 3-5 tends to distort it into a rhombus. The unit shearing strain is the change in the right angle, measured in radians.

Modulus of rigidity, or shearing modulus of elasticity, is defined by

$$G = \frac{v}{\gamma} \tag{3-6}$$

where G = modulus of rigidity

    v = unit shearing stress

    γ = unit shearing strain

It is related to the modulus of elasticity in tension and compression E by the equation

$$G = \frac{E}{2(1 + \mu)} \tag{3-7}$$

where μ is a constant known as Poisson's ratio.

3-7. Poisson's Ratio. Within the elastic limit, when a material is subjected to axial loads, it deforms not only longitudinally but also laterally. Under tension, the cross section of a member decreases, and under compression, it increases. The ratio of the unit lateral strain to the unit longitudinal strain is called Poisson's ratio.

For many materials, this ratio can be taken equal to 0.25. For structural steel, it is usually assumed to be 0.3.

Assume, for example, that a steel hanger with an area of 2 sq in. carries a 40-kip (40,000-lb) load. The unit stress is 40,000/2, or 20,000 psi. The unit tensile strain, taking the modulus of elasticity of the steel as 30,000,000 psi, is 20,000/30,000,000, or 0.00067 in. per in. With Poisson's ratio as 0.3, the unit lateral strain is -0.3×0.00067, or a shortening of 0.00020 in. per in.

3-8. Thermal Stresses. When the temperature of a body changes, its dimensions also change. Forces are required to prevent such dimensional changes, and stresses are set up in the body by these forces.

If α is the coefficient of expansion of the material and T the change in temperature, the unit strain in a bar restrained by external forces from expanding or contracting is

$$\epsilon = \alpha T \tag{3-8}$$

According to Hooke's law, the stress f in the bar is

$$f = E\alpha T \tag{3-9}$$

where E = modulus of elasticity

3-9. Strain Energy. When a bar is stressed, energy is stored in it. If a bar supporting a load P undergoes a deformation e the energy stored in it is

$$U = \tfrac{1}{2}Pe \tag{3-10}$$

This equation assumes the load was applied gradually and the bar is not stressed beyond the proportional limit. It represents the area under the load-deformation curve up to the load P. Applying Eqs. (3-2) and (3-3) to Eq. (3-10) gives another useful equation for energy:

$$U = \frac{f^2}{2E}\, AL \tag{3-11}$$

where f = unit stress

E = modulus of elasticity of the material

A = cross-sectional area

L = length of the bar

Since AL is the volume of the bar, the term $f^2/2E$ indicates the energy stored per unit of volume. It represents the area under the stress-strain curve up to the stress f. Its value when the bar is stressed to the proportional limit is called the **modulus of resilience.** This modulus is a measure of the capacity of the material to absorb energy without danger of being permanently deformed and is of importance in designing members to resist energy loads.

Equation (3-10) is a general equation that holds true when the principle of superposition applies (the total deformation produced by a system of forces is equal to the sum of the elongations produced by each force). In the general sense, P in Eq. (3-10) represents any group of statically interdependent forces that can be completely defined by one symbol, and e is the corresponding deformation.

The strain-energy equation can be written as a function of either the load or the deformation.

For axial tension or compression:

$$U = \frac{P^2L}{2AE} \qquad U = \frac{AEe^2}{2L} \tag{3-10a}$$

where P = axial load

e = total elongation or shortening

L = length of the member

A = cross-sectional area

E = modulus of elasticity

For pure shear:

$$U = \frac{V^2L}{2AG} \qquad U = \frac{AGe^2}{2L} \tag{3-10b}$$

where V = shearing load

e = shearing deformation

L = length over which deformation takes place

A = shearing area

G = shearing modulus

For torsion:

$$U = \frac{T^2L}{2JG} \qquad U = \frac{JG\phi^2}{2L} \tag{3-10c}$$

where T = torque

ϕ = angle of twist

L = length of shaft

J = polar moment of inertia of the cross section

G = shearing modulus

For pure bending (constant moment):

$$U = \frac{M^2 L}{2EI} \qquad U = \frac{EI\theta^2}{2L} \qquad (3\text{-}10d)$$

where M = bending moment
$\quad\quad \theta$ = angle of rotation of one end of the beam with respect to the other
$\quad\quad L$ = length of beam
$\quad\quad I$ = moment of inertia of the cross section
$\quad\quad E$ = modulus of elasticity (see also Art. 3-55)

For beams carrying transverse loads, the strain energy is the sum of the energy for bending and that for shear.

STRESSES AT A POINT

Tensile and compressive stresses are sometimes referred to also as normal stresses, because they act normal to the cross section. Under this concept, tensile stresses are considered as positive normal stresses and compressive stresses as negative.

3-10. Stress Notation. Suppose a member of a structure is acted upon by forces in all directions. For convenience, let us establish a reference set of perpendicular coordinate x, y, and z axes. Now let us take at some point in the member a small cube with sides parallel to the coordinate axes. The notations commonly used for the components of stress acting on the sides of this element and the directions assumed as positive are shown in Fig. 3-7.

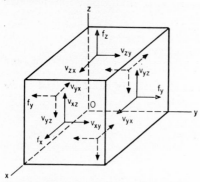
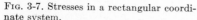
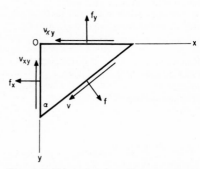

FIG. 3-7. Stresses in a rectangular coordinate system.

FIG. 3-8. Stresses at a point on a plane inclined to the axes.

For example, for the sides of the element perpendicular to the z axis, the normal component of stress is denoted by f_z. The shearing stress v is resolved into two components and requires two subscript letters for a complete description. The first letter indicates the direction of the normal to the plane under consideration. The second letter indicates the direction of the component of the stress. Considering the sides perpendicular to the z axis, the shear component in the x direction is labeled v_{zx} and that in the y direction v_{zy}.

3-11. Stress Components. If, for the small cube in Fig. 3-7, moments of the forces acting on it are taken about the x axis, considering the cube's dimensions as dx, dy, and dz, the equation of equilibrium requires that

$$v_{zy}\, dx\, dy\, dz = v_{yz}\, dx\, dy\, dz$$

(Forces are taken equal to the product of the area of the face and the stress at the center.) Two similar equations can be written for moments taken about the y axis and the z axis. These equations show that

$$v_{xy} = v_{yx} \qquad v_{zx} = v_{xz} \qquad \text{and} \qquad v_{zy} = v_{yz} \qquad (3\text{-}12)$$

In words, the components of shearing stress on two perpendicular faces and acting normal to the intersection of the faces are equal.

Consequently, to describe the stresses acting on the coordinate planes through a point, only six quantities need be known. These stress components are f_x, f_y, f_z, $v_{xy} = v_{yx}$, $v_{yz} = v_{zy}$, and $v_{zx} = v_{xz}$.

If the cube in Fig. 3-7 is acted on only by normal stresses f_x, f_y, and f_z, from Hooke's law and the application of Poisson's ratio, the unit strains in the x, y, and z directions, in accordance with Arts. 3-5 and 3-6, are, respectively,

$$\epsilon_x = \frac{1}{E}[f_x - \mu(f_y + f_z)]$$

$$\epsilon_y = \frac{1}{E}[f_y - \mu(f_x + f_z)] \tag{3-13}$$

$$\epsilon_z = \frac{1}{E}[f_z - \mu(f_x + f_y)]$$

If only shearing stresses act on the cube in Fig. 3-7, the distortion of the angle between edges parallel to any two coordinate axes depends only on shearing-stress components parallel to those axes. Thus, the unit shearing strains are (see Art. 3-6)

$$\gamma_{xy} = \frac{1}{G}v_{xy} \qquad \gamma_{yz} = \frac{1}{G}v_{yz} \qquad \text{and} \qquad \gamma_{zx} = \frac{1}{G}v_{zx} \tag{3-14}$$

3-12. Two-dimensional Stress. When the six components of stress necessary to describe the stresses at a point are known (Art. 3-11), the stress on any inclined plane through the same point can be determined. For the case of two-dimensional stress, only three stress components need be known.

Assume, for example, that at a point O in a stressed plate, the components f_x, f_y, and v_{xy} are known (Fig. 3-8). To find the stresses for any plane through the z axis, take a plane parallel to it close to O. This plane and the coordinate planes form a triangular prism. Then, if α is the angle the normal to the plane makes with the x axis, the normal and shearing stresses on the inclined plane, obtained by application of the equations of equilibrium, are

$$f = f_x \cos^2 \alpha + f_y \sin^2 \alpha + 2v_{xy} \sin \alpha \cos \alpha \tag{3-15}$$
$$v = v_{xy}(\cos^2 \alpha - \sin^2 \alpha) + (f_y - f_x)\sin \alpha \cos \alpha \tag{3-16}$$

3-13. Principal Stresses. If the inclined plane is rotated, it will reach a position for which the normal stress on it is a maximum or a minimum. There are two such positions, perpendicular to each other. And on those planes, there are no shearing stresses.

The directions in which the normal stresses become maximum or minimum are called principal directions and the corresponding normal stresses principal stresses.

To find the principal directions, set the value of v given by Eq. (3-16) equal to zero. The resulting equation is

$$\tan 2\alpha = \frac{2v_{xy}}{f_x - f_y} \tag{3-17}$$

If the x and y axes are taken in the principal directions, v_{xy} is zero. Consequently, Eqs. (3-15) and (3-16) may be simplified to

$$f = f_x \cos^2 \alpha + f_y \sin^2 \alpha \tag{3-18}$$
$$v = \tfrac{1}{2} \sin^2 \alpha (f_y - f_x) \tag{3-19}$$

where f and v are, respectively, the normal and shearing stress on a plane at an angle α with the principal planes and f_x and f_y are the principal stresses.

If on any two perpendicular planes only shearing stresses act, the state of stress at the point is said to be one of pure shear or simple shear. Under such conditions, the principal directions bisect the angles between the planes on which these shearing stresses occur. The principal stresses are equal in magnitude to the unit shearing stresses.

3-14. Maximum Shearing Stress. The maximum unit shearing stress occurs on each of two planes that bisect the angles between the planes on which the principal stresses act. The maximum shear is equal to one-half the algebraic difference of the principal stresses:

$$\max v = \frac{f_1 - f_2}{2} \tag{3-20}$$

where f_1 is the maximum principal stress and f_2 the minimum.

3-15. Mohr's Circle. The relationship between stresses at a point may be represented conveniently on Mohr's circle (Fig. 3-9). In this diagram, normal stress f and shear stress v are taken as coordinates. Then, for each plane through the point, there

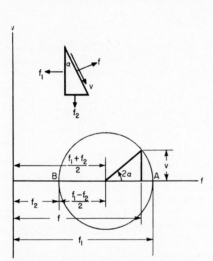
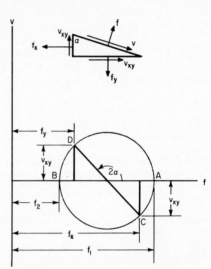

FIG. 3-9. Mohr's circle for stresses at a point—constructed from known principal stresses.

FIG. 3-10. Stress circle constructed from two known normal positive stresses, f_x and f_y, and a known shear, v_{xy}.

will correspond a point on the circle, whose coordinates are the values of f and v for the plane.

To construct the circle given the principal stresses, mark off the principal stresses f_1 and f_2 on the f axis (points A and B in Fig. 3-9). Tensile stresses are measured to the right of the v axis and compressive stresses to the left. Construct a circle with its center on the f axis and passing through the two points representing the principal stresses. This is the Mohr's circle for the given stresses at the point under consideration.

Suppose now, we wish to find the stresses on a plane at an angle α to the plane of f_1. If a radius is drawn making an angle 2α with the f axis, the coordinates of its intersection with the circle represent the normal and shearing stresses acting on the plane.

Mohr's circle can also be plotted when the principal stresses are not known but the stresses f_x, f_y, and v_{xy}, on any two perpendicular planes, are. The procedure is to plot the two points representing these known stresses with respect to the f and v axes (points C and D in Fig. 3-10). The line joining these points is a diameter of Mohr's circle. Constructing the circle on this diameter, we find the principal stresses at the intersection with the f axis (points A and B in Fig. 3-10).

For more details on the relationship of stresses and strains at a point, see Timoshenko and Goodier, "Theory of Elasticity," 2d ed., McGraw-Hill Book Company, New York, 1951.

STRAIGHT BEAMS

Beams are the horizontal members used to support vertically applied loads across an opening. In a more general sense, they are structural members that external loads tend to bend, or curve.

3-16. Types of Beams. There are many ways in which beams may be supported. Some of the more common methods are shown in Figs. 3-11 to 3-16.

FIG. 3-11. Simple beam.

FIG. 3-12. Cantilever beam.

FIG. 3-13. Beam with one end fixed.

FIG. 3-14. Fixed-end beam.

FIG. 3-15. Beam with overhangs.

FIG. 3-16. Continuous beam.

The beam in Fig. 3-11 is called a simply supported, or **simple beam.** It has supports near its ends, which restrain it only against vertical movement. The ends of the beam are free to rotate. When the loads have a horizontal component, or when change in length of the beam due to temperature may be important, the supports may also have to prevent horizontal motion. In that case, horizontal restraint at one support is generally sufficient.

The distance between the supports is called the **span.** The load carried by each support is called a **reaction.**

The beam in Fig. 3-12 is a **cantilever.** It has only one support, which restrains it from rotating or moving horizontally or vertically at that end. Such a support is called a **fixed end.**

If a simple support is placed under the free end of the cantilever, the beam in Fig. 3-13 results. It has one end fixed, one end simply supported.

The beam in Fig. 3-14 has both ends fixed. No rotation or vertical movement can occur at either end. In actual practice, a fully fixed end can seldom be obtained. Some rotation of the beam ends generally is permitted. Most support conditions are intermediate between those for a simple beam and those for a fixed-end beam.

In Fig. 3-15 is shown a beam that overhangs both its simple supports. The overhangs have a free end, like a cantilever, but the supports permit rotation.

When a beam extends over several supports, it is called a **continuous beam** (Fig. 3-16).

Reactions for the beams in Figs. 3-11, 3-12, and 3-15 may be found from the equations of equilibrium. They are classified as **statically determinate beams** for that reason.

The equations of equilibrium, however, are not sufficient to determine the reactions of the beams in Figs. 3-13, 3-14, and 3-16. For those beams, there are more unknowns than equations. Additional equations must be obtained based on the deformations permitted; on the knowledge, for example, that a fixed end permits no rotation. Such beams are classified as **statically indeterminate.** Methods for finding the stresses in that type of beam are given in Arts. 3-55, 3-57, and 3-58 to 3-69.

3-17. Reactions. As an example of the application of the equations of equilibrium (Art. 3-1) to the determination of the reactions of a statically determinate beam, we shall compute the reactions of the 60-ft-long beam with overhangs in Fig. 3-17. This beam carries a uniform load of 200 lb per lin ft over its entire length and several concentrated loads. The supports are 36 ft apart.

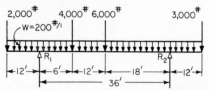

FIG. 3-17. Beam with overhangs loaded both uniformly and with concentrated loads.

To find reaction R_1, we take moments about R_2 and equate the sum of the moments to zero (clockwise rotation is considered positive, counterclockwise, negative):

$$-2{,}000 \times 48 + 36R_1 - 4{,}000 \times 30 - 6{,}000 \times 18 + 3{,}000 \times 12 - 200 \times 60 \times 18 = 0$$
$$R_1 = 14{,}000 \text{ lb}$$

In this calculation, the moment of the uniform load was found by taking the moment of its resultant, which acts at the center of the beam.

To find R_2, we can either take moments about R_1 or use the equation $\Sigma V = 0$. It is generally preferable to apply the moment equation and use the other equation as a check.

$$3{,}000 \times 48 - 36R_2 + 6{,}000 \times 18 + 4{,}000 \times 6 - 2{,}000 \times 12 + 200 \times 60 \times 18 = 0$$
$$R_2 = 13{,}000 \text{ lb}$$

As a check, we note that the sum of the reactions must equal the total applied load:

$$14{,}000 + 13{,}000 = 2{,}000 + 4{,}000 + 6{,}000 + 3{,}000 + 12{,}000$$
$$27{,}000 = 27{,}000$$

3-18. Internal Forces. Since a beam is in equilibrium under the forces applied to it, it is evident that at every section internal forces are acting to prevent motion. For example, suppose we cut the beam in Fig. 3-17 vertically just to the right of its center.

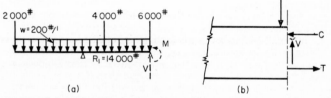

(a) (b)

FIG. 3-18. Sections of beam kept in equilibrium by internal stresses.

If we total the external forces, including the reaction, to the left of this cut (see Fig. 3-18a), we find there is an unbalanced downward load of 4,000 lb. Evidently, at the cut section, an upward-acting internal force of 4,000 lb must be present to maintain equilibrium. Again, if we take moments of the external forces about the section, we find an unbalanced moment of 54,000 ft-lb. So there must be an internal moment of 54,000 ft-lb acting to maintain equilibrium.

This internal, or resisting, moment is produced by a couple consisting of a force C acting on the top part of the beam and an equal but opposite force T acting on the bottom part (Fig. 3-18b). The top force is the resultant of compressive stresses acting over the upper portion of the beam, and the bottom force is the resultant of tensile stresses acting over the bottom part. The surface at which the stresses change from compression to tension—where the stress is zero—is called the **neutral surface.**

3-19. Shear Diagrams. The unbalanced external vertical force at a section is called the shear. It is equal to the algebraic sum of the forces that lie on either side of the section. Upward-acting forces on the left of the section are considered positive, downward forces negative; signs are reversed for forces on the right.

A diagram in which the shear at every point along the length of a beam is plotted as an ordinate is called a shear diagram. The shear diagram for the beam in Fig. 3-17 is shown in Fig. 3-19b.

The diagram was plotted starting from the left end. The 2,000-lb load was plotted downward to a convenient scale. Then, the shear at the next concentrated load—the left support—was determined. This equals −2,000 − 200 × 12, or −4,400 lb. In

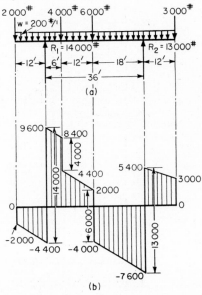

FIG. 3-19. Shear diagram for beam of Fig. 3-17.

passing from just to the left of the support to a point just to the right, however, the shear changes by the magnitude of the reaction. Hence, on the right-hand side of the left support the shear is −4, 400 + 14,000, or 9,600 lb. At the next concentrated load, the shear is 9,600 − 200 × 6, or 8,400 lb. In passing the 4,000-lb load, however, the shear changes to 8,400 − 4,000, or 4,400 lb. Proceeding in this manner to the right end of the beam, we terminate with a shear of 3,000 lb, equal to the load on the free end there.

It should be noted that the shear diagram for a uniform load is a straight line sloping downward to the right (see Fig. 3-21). Therefore, the shear diagram was completed by connecting the plotted points with straight lines.

Shear diagrams for commonly encountered loading conditions are given in Figs. 3-30 to 3-41.

3-20. Bending-moment Diagrams. The unbalanced moment of the external forces about a vertical section through a beam is called the bending moment. It is equal to the algebraic sum of the moments about the section of the external forces that lie on one side of the section. Clockwise moments are considered positive, counterclockwise moments negative, when the forces considered lie on the left of the section. Thus, when the bending moment is positive, the bottom of the beam is in tension.

A diagram in which the bending moment at every point along the length of a beam is plotted as an ordinate is called a bending-moment diagram.

Figure 3-20c is the bending-moment diagram for the beam loaded with concentrated loads only in Fig. 3-20a. The bending moment at the supports for this simply supported beam obviously is zero. Between the supports and the first load, the bending moment is proportional to the distance from the support, since it is equal to the reaction times the distance from the support. Hence the bending-moment diagram for this portion of the beam is a sloping straight line.

The bending moment under the 6,000-lb load in Fig. 3-20a considering only the force to the left is 7,000 × 10, or 70,000 ft-lb. The bending-moment diagram, then, between the left support and the first concentrated load is a straight line rising from zero at the left end of the beam to 70,000, plotted to a convenient scale, under the 6,000-lb load.

The bending moment under the 9,000-lb load, considering the forces on the left of it, is 7,000 × 20 − 6,000 × 10, or 80,000 ft-lb. (It could have been more easily obtained by considering only the force on the right, reversing the sign convention: $8,000 \times 10 = 80,000$ ft-lb.) Since there are no loads between the two concentrated loads, the bending-moment diagram between the two sections is a straight line.

If the bending moment and shear are known at any section of a beam, the bending

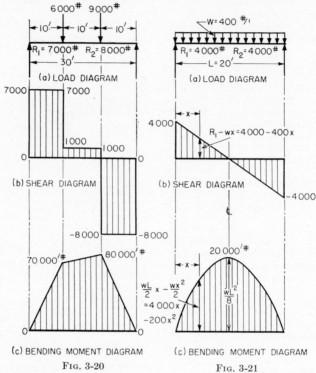

(c) BENDING MOMENT DIAGRAM   (c) BENDING MOMENT DIAGRAM

FIG. 3-20   FIG. 3-21

FIG. 3-20. Shear and moment diagram for beam with concentrated loads.
FIG. 3-21. Shear and moment diagram for uniformly loaded beam.

moment at any other section may be computed, providing there are no unknown forces between the two sections. The rule is:

The bending moment at any section of a beam is equal to the bending moment at any section to the left, plus the shear at that section times the distance between sections, minus the moments of intervening loads. If the section with known moment and shear is on the right, the sign convention must be reversed.

For example, the bending moment under the 9,000-lb load in Fig. 3-20*a* could also have been obtained from the moment under the 6,000-lb load and the shear to the right of the 6,000-lb load given in the shear diagram (Fig. 3-20*b*). Thus, $80,000 = 70,000 + 1,000 \times 10$. If there had been any other loads between the two concentrated loads, the moment of these loads about the section under the 9,000-lb load would have been subtracted.

Bending-moment diagrams for commonly encountered loading conditions are given in Figs. 3-30 to 3-41. These may be combined to obtain bending moments for other loads.

3-21. Moments in Uniformly Loaded Beams. When a beam carries a uniform load, the bending-moment diagram does not consist of straight lines. Consider, for example, the beam in Fig. 3-21a, which carries a uniform load over its entire length. As shown in Fig. 3-21c, the bending-moment diagram for this beam is a parabola.

The reactions at both ends of a simply supported uniformly loaded beam are both equal to $wL/2 = W/2$, where w is the uniform load in pounds per linear foot, $W = wL$ is the total load on the beam, and L is the span.

The shear at any distance x from the left support is $R_1 - wx = wL/2 - wx$ (see Fig. 3-21b). Equating this expression to zero, we find that there is no shear at the center of the beam.

The bending moment at any distance x from the left support is

$$R_1x - wx\left(\frac{x}{2}\right) = \frac{wLx}{2} - \frac{wx^2}{2} = \frac{w}{2}x(L - x)$$

Hence:

The bending moment at any section of a simply supported, uniformly loaded beam is equal to one-half the product of the load per linear foot and the distances to the section from both supports.

The maximum value of the bending moment occurs at the center of the beam. It is equal to $wL^2/8 = WL/8$.

3-22. Shear-Moment Relationship. The slope of the bending-moment curve for any point on a beam is equal to the shear at that point; i.e.,

$$V = \frac{dM}{dx} \tag{3-21}$$

Since maximum bending moment occurs when the slope changes sign, or passes through zero, maximum moment (positive or negative) occurs at the point of zero shear.

After integration, Eq. (3-21) may also be written

$$M_2 - M_1 = \int_{x_2}^{x_1} V \, dx \tag{3-22}$$

This equation indicates that the change in bending moment between any two sections of a beam is equal to the area of the shear diagram between ordinates at the two sections.

3-23. Moving Loads and Influence Lines. One of the most helpful devices for solving problems involving moving loads is an influence line. Whereas shear and moment diagrams evaluate the effect of loads at all sections of a structure, an influence line indicates the effect at a given section of a unit load placed at any point on the structure.

For example, to plot the influence line for bending moment at some point A on a beam, a unit load is applied at some point B. The bending moment at A due to the unit load at B is plotted as an ordinate to a convenient scale at B. The same procedure is followed at every point along the beam and a curve is drawn through the points thus obtained.

Actually, the unit load need not be placed at every point. The equation of the influence line can be determined by placing the load at an arbitrary point and computing the bending moment in general terms (see also Art. 3-57).

Suppose we wish to draw the influence line for reaction at A for a simple beam AB (Fig. 3-22a). We place a unit load at an arbitrary distance of xL from B. The reaction at A due to this load is $1 \, xL/L = x$. Then, $R_A = x$ is the equation of the influence line. It represents a straight line sloping upward from zero at B to unity at A (Fig. 3-22a). In other words, as the unit load moves across the beam, the reaction at A increases from zero to unity in proportion to the distance of the load from B.

Figure 3-22b shows the influence line for bending moment at the center of a beam. It resembles in appearance the bending-moment diagram for a load at the center of the beam, but its significance is entirely different. Each ordinate gives the moment at mid-span for a load at the corresponding location. It indicates that, if a unit load is placed at a distance xL from one end, it produces a bending moment of $\frac{1}{2} xL$ at the center of the span.

Figure 3-22c shows the influence line for shear at the quarter point of a beam. When the load is to the right of the quarter point, the shear is positive and equal to the left reaction. When the load is to the left, the shear is negative and equal to the right reaction.

The diagram indicates that, to produce maximum shear at the quarter point, loads should be placed only to the right of the quarter point, with the largest load at the quarter point, if possible. For a uniform load, maximum shear results when the load extends from the right end of the beam to the quarter point.

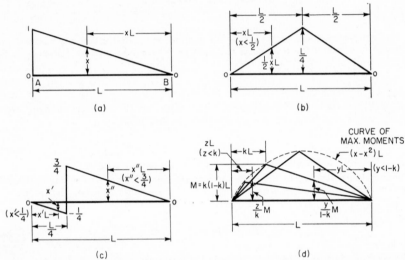

FIG. 3-22. Influence lines—(a) for reaction at A; (b) for mid-span bending moment; (c) for quarter-point shear; and (d) for bending moments at several points in a beam.

Suppose, for example, that the beam is a crane girder with a span of 60 ft. The wheel loads are 20 and 10 kips, respectively, and are spaced 5 ft apart. For maximum shear at the quarter point, the wheels should be placed with the 20-kip wheel at that point and the 10-kip wheel to the right of it. The corresponding ordinates of the influence line (Fig. 3-22c) are $\frac{3}{4}$ and $\frac{40}{45} \times \frac{3}{4}$. Hence, the maximum shear is $20 \times \frac{3}{4} + 10 \times \frac{40}{45} \times \frac{3}{4} = 51.7$ kips.

Figure 3-22d shows influence lines for bending moment at several points on a beam. It is noteworthy that the apexes of the diagrams fall on a parabola, as shown by the dashed line. This indicates that the maximum moment produced at any given section by a single concentrated load moving across a beam occurs when the load is at that section. The magnitude of the maximum moment increases when the section is moved toward mid-span, in accordance with the equation shown in Fig. 3-22d for the parabola.

3-24. Maximum Bending Moment. When there is more than one load on the span, the influence line is useful in developing a criterion for determining the position of the loads for which the bending moment is a maximum at a given section.

Maximum bending moment will occur at a section C of a simple beam as loads move across it when one of the loads is at C. The proper load to place at C is the one for which the expression $W_a/a - W_b/b$ (Fig. 3-23) changes sign as that load passes from one side of C to the other.

When several loads move across a simple beam, the maximum bending moment produced in the beam may be near but not necessarily at mid-span. To find the maximum moment, first determine the position of the loads for maximum moment at mid-span. Then shift the loads until the load P_2 (Fig. 3-24) that was at the center of the beam is as far from mid-span as the resultant of all the loads on the span is on the other side of mid-span. Maximum moment will occur under P_2.

When other loads move on or off the span during the shift of P_2 away from mid-span, it may be necessary to investigate the moment under one of the other loads when it and the resultant are equidistant from mid-span.

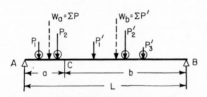

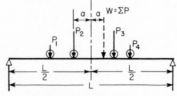

FIG. 3-23. Moving loads on simple beam AB placed for maximum moment at C.

FIG. 3-24. Moving loads placed for maximum moment in a simple beam.

3-25. Bending Stresses in a Beam. To derive the commonly used flexure formula for computing the bending stresses in a beam, we have to make the following assumptions:

1. The unit stress on any fiber of a beam is proportional to the unit strain of the fiber.

2. The modulus of elasticity in tension is the same as that in compression.

3. The total and unit axial strain of any fiber are both proportional to the distance of that fiber from the neutral surface. (Cross sections that are plane before bending remain plane after bending. This requires that all fibers have the same length before bending; thus, that the beam be straight.)

4. The loads act in a plane containing the centroidal axis of the beam and are perpendicular to that axis. Furthermore, the neutral surface is perpendicular to the plane of the loads. Thus, the plane of the loads must contain an axis of symmetry of each cross section of the beam. (The flexure formula does not apply to a beam loaded unsymmetrically.)

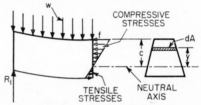

FIG. 3-25. Unit stresses due to bending on a beam section.

5. The beam is proportioned to preclude prior failure or serious deformation by torsion, local buckling, shear, or any cause other than bending.

Equating the bending moment to the resisting moment due to the internal stresses at any section of a beam yields

$$M = \frac{fI}{c} \qquad (3\text{-}23)$$

M is the bending moment at the section, f is the normal unit stress on a fiber at a distance c from the neutral axis (Fig. 3-25), and I is the moment of inertia of the cross section with respect to the neutral axis. If f is given in pounds per square inch (psi), I in in.⁴, and c in inches, then M will be in inch-pounds. Generally, c is taken as the distance to the outermost fiber.

3-26. Moment of Inertia. The neutral axis in a symmetrical beam is coincidental with the centroidal axis; i.e., at any section the neutral axis is so located that

$$\int y\, dA = 0 \qquad (3\text{-}24)$$

where dA is a differential area parallel to the axis (Fig. 3-25), y is its distance from the axis, and the summation is taken over the entire cross section.

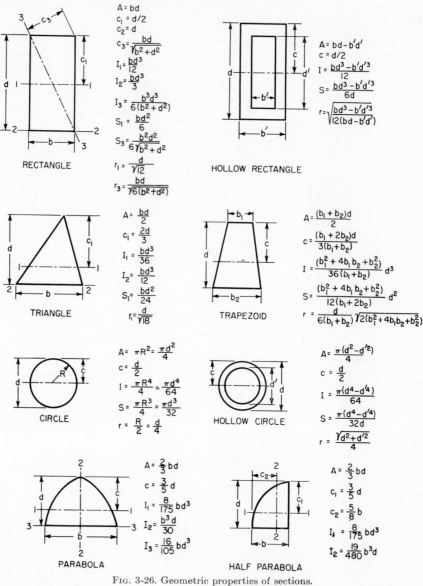

$$A = bd$$
$$c_1 = d/2$$
$$c_2 = d$$
$$c_3 = \frac{bd}{\sqrt{b^2 + d^2}}$$
$$I_1 = \frac{bd^3}{12}$$
$$I_2 = \frac{bd^3}{3}$$
$$I_3 = \frac{b^3 d^3}{6(b^2 + d^2)}$$
$$S_1 = \frac{bd^2}{6}$$
$$S_3 = \frac{b^2 d^2}{6\sqrt{b^2 + d^2}}$$
$$r_1 = \frac{d}{\sqrt{12}}$$
$$r_3 = \frac{bd}{\sqrt{6(b^2 + d^2)}}$$

RECTANGLE

$$A = bd - b'd'$$
$$c = d/2$$
$$I = \frac{bd^3 - b'd'^3}{12}$$
$$S = \frac{bd^3 - b'd'^3}{6d}$$
$$r = \sqrt{\frac{bd^3 - b'd'^3}{12(bd - b'd')}}$$

HOLLOW RECTANGLE

$$A = \frac{bd}{2}$$
$$c_1 = \frac{2d}{3}$$
$$I_1 = \frac{bd^3}{36}$$
$$I_2 = \frac{bd^3}{12}$$
$$S_1 = \frac{bd^2}{24}$$
$$r_1 = \frac{d}{\sqrt{18}}$$

TRIANGLE

$$A = \frac{(b_1 + b_2)d}{2}$$
$$c = \frac{(b_1 + 2b_2)d}{3(b_1 + b_2)}$$
$$I = \frac{(b_1^2 + 4b_1 b_2 + b_2^2)}{36(b_1 + b_2)} d^3$$
$$S = \frac{(b_1^2 + 4b_1 b_2 + b_2^2)}{12(b_1 + 2b_2)} d^2$$
$$r = \frac{d}{6(b_1 + b_2)} \sqrt{2(2b_1^2 + 4b_1 b_2 + b_2^2)}$$

TRAPEZOID

$$A = \pi R^2 = \frac{\pi d^2}{4}$$
$$c = \frac{d}{2}$$
$$I = \frac{\pi R^4}{4} = \frac{\pi d^4}{64}$$
$$S = \frac{\pi R^3}{4} = \frac{\pi d^3}{32}$$
$$r = \frac{R}{2} = \frac{d}{4}$$

CIRCLE

$$A = \frac{\pi(d^2 - d'^2)}{4}$$
$$c = \frac{d}{2}$$
$$I = \frac{\pi(d^4 - d'^4)}{64}$$
$$S = \frac{\pi(d^4 - d'^4)}{32d}$$
$$r = \frac{\sqrt{d^2 + d'^2}}{4}$$

HOLLOW CIRCLE

$$A = \frac{2}{3} bd$$
$$c = \frac{3}{5} d$$
$$I_1 = \frac{8}{175} bd^3$$
$$I_2 = \frac{b^3 d}{30}$$
$$I_3 = \frac{16}{105} bd^3$$

PARABOLA

$$A = \frac{2}{3} bd$$
$$c_1 = \frac{3}{5} d$$
$$c_2 = \frac{5}{8} b$$
$$I_1 = \frac{8}{175} bd^3$$
$$I_2 = \frac{19}{480} b^3 d$$

HALF PARABOLA

Fɪɢ. 3-26. Geometric properties of sections.

Moment of inertia with respect to the neutral axis is given by

$$I = \int y^2 \, dA \tag{3-25}$$

Values of I for several common types of cross section are given in Fig. 3-26. Values for standard structural-steel sections are presented in "Steel Construction," American Institute of Steel Construction, New York. When the moments of inertia of other types of sections are needed, they can be computed directly by application of Eq. (3-25) or by breaking the section up into components for which the moment of inertia is known.

If I is the moment of inertia about the neutral axis, A the cross-sectional area, and d the distance between that axis and a parallel axis in the plane of the cross section, then the moment of inertia about the parallel axis is

$$I' = I + Ad^2 \qquad (3\text{-}26)$$

With this equation, the known moment of inertia of a component of a section about the neutral axis of the component can be transferred to the neutral axis of the complete section. Then, summing up the transferred moments of inertia for all the components yields the moment of inertia of the complete section.

When the moments of inertia of an area with respect to any two rectangular axes are known, the moment of inertia with respect to any other axis passing through the point of intersection of the two axes may be obtained through the use of Mohr's circle as for stresses (Fig. 3-10). In this analog, I_x corresponds with f_x, I_y with f_y, and the product of inertia I_{xy} with v_{xy} (Art. 3-15).

$$I_{xy} = \int xy \, dA \qquad (3\text{-}27)$$

The two perpendicular axes through a point about which the moments of inertia are a maximum and a minimum are called the principal axes. The products of inertia are zero for the principal axes.

3-27. Section Modulus. The ratio $S = I/c$ is called the section modulus. I is the moment of inertia of the cross section about the neutral axis and c the distance from the neutral axis to the outermost fiber. Values of S for common types of sections are given in Fig. 3-26.

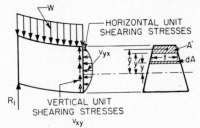

Fig. 3-27. Unit shearing stresses on a beam section.

3-28. Shearing Stresses in a Beam. The vertical shear at any section of a beam is resisted by nonuniformly distributed, vertical unit stresses (Fig. 3-27). At every point in the section, there is also a horizontal unit stress, which is equal in magnitude to the vertical unit shearing stress there [see Eq. (3-12)].

At any distance y' from the neutral axis, both the horizontal and vertical shearing unit stresses are equal to

$$v = \frac{V}{It} A'\bar{y} \qquad (3\text{-}28)$$

where V = vertical shear at the cross section
t = thickness of beam at distance y' from neutral axis
I = moment of inertia about neutral axis
A' = area between the outermost fiber and the fiber for which the shearing stress is being computed
$\bar{y}$ = distance of center of gravity of this area from the neutral axis (Fig. 3-27)

For a rectangular beam, the maximum shearing stress occurs at mid-depth. Its magnitude is

$$v = \frac{12V}{bd^3b} \frac{bd^2}{8} = \frac{3}{2} \frac{V}{bd}$$

That is, the maximum shear stress is 50% greater than the average shear stress on the section. Similarly, for a circular beam, the maximum is one-third greater than the average. For an I beam, however, the maximum shearing stress in the web is not appreciably greater than the average for the web section alone, assuming the flanges to take no shear.

3-29. Combined Shear and Bending Stress. For deep beams on short spans and beams made of low-tensile-strength materials, it is sometimes necessary to determine the maximum stress f' on an inclined plane due to a combination of shear and bending stress—v and f, respectively. This stress f', which may be either tension or compression, is greater than the normal stress. Its value may be obtained by application of Mohr's circle (Art. 3-15), as indicated in Fig. 3-10, but with $f_y = 0$, and is

$$f' = \frac{f}{2} + \sqrt{v^2 + \left(\frac{f}{2}\right)^2} \tag{3-29}$$

3-30. Stresses in the Plastic Range. When the bending stresses exceed the proportional limit and stress no longer is proportional to strain, the distribution of bending stresses over the cross section ceases to be linear. The outer fibers deform with little change in stress, while the fibers not stressed beyond the proportional limit continue to take more stress as the load on the beam increases. (A. Nádai, "Theory of Flow and Fracture of Solids," 2d ed., McGraw-Hill Book Company, Inc., New York, 1950. A. Freudenthal, "The Inelastic Behavior of Engineering Materials and Structures," John Wiley & Sons, Inc., New York.)

Modulus of rupture is defined as the stress computed from the flexure formula [Eq. (3-23)] for the maximum bending moment a beam sustains at failure. It is not the actual maximum unit stress in the beam but is sometimes used to compare the strength of beams.

3-31. Beam Deflections. When a beam is loaded, it deflects. The new position of its longitudinal centroidal axis is called the **elastic curve.**

At any point of the elastic curve, the radius of curvature is given by

$$R = \frac{EI}{M} \tag{3-30}$$

where M = bending moment at the point

E = modulus of elasticity

I = moment of inertia of the cross section about the neutral axis

Since the slope dy/dx of the curve is small, its square may be neglected, so that, for all practical purposes, $1/R$ may be taken equal to d^2y/dx^2, where y is the deflection of a point on the curve at a distance x from the origin of coordinates. Hence, Eq. (3-30) may be rewritten

$$M = EI \frac{d^2y}{dx^2} \tag{3-31}$$

To obtain the slope and deflection of a beam, this equation may be integrated, with M expressed as a function of x. Constants introduced during the integration must be evaluated in terms of known points and slopes of the elastic curve.

Equation (3-31), in turn, may be rewritten after one integration as

$$\theta_B - \theta_A = \int_A^B \frac{M}{EI} \, dx \tag{3-32}$$

in which θ_A and θ_B are the slopes of the elastic curve at any two points A and B. If the slope is zero at one of the points, the integral in Eq. (3-32) gives the slope of the elastic curve at the other. It should be noted that the integral represents the area of the bending-moment diagram between A and B with each ordinate divided by EI.

The **tangential deviation** t of a point on the elastic curve is the distance of this point, measured in a direction perpendicular to the original position of the beam, from a tangent drawn at some other point on the elastic curve.

$$t_B - t_A = \int_A^B \frac{Mx}{EI} \, dx \tag{3-33}$$

Equation (3-33) indicates that the tangential deviation of any point with respect to a second point on the elastic curve equals the moment about the first point of the M/EI diagram between the two points. The **moment-area method** for determining the deflection of beams is a technique in which Eqs. (3-32) and (3-33) are utilized.

Suppose, for example, the deflection at mid-span is to be computed for a beam of uniform cross section with a concentrated load at the center (Fig. 3-28).

Since the deflection at mid-span for this loading is the maximum for the span, the slope of the elastic curve at the center of the beam is zero; i.e., the tangent is parallel to the undeflected position of the beam. Hence, the deviation of either support from the mid-span tangent is equal to the deflection at the center of the beam. Then, by the moment-area theorem [Eq. (3-33)], the deflection y_c is given by the moment about either support of the area of the M/EI diagram included between an ordinate at the center of the beam and that support.

$$y_c = \frac{1}{2}\frac{PL}{4EI}\frac{L}{2}\frac{2}{3}\frac{L}{2} = \frac{PL^3}{48EI}$$

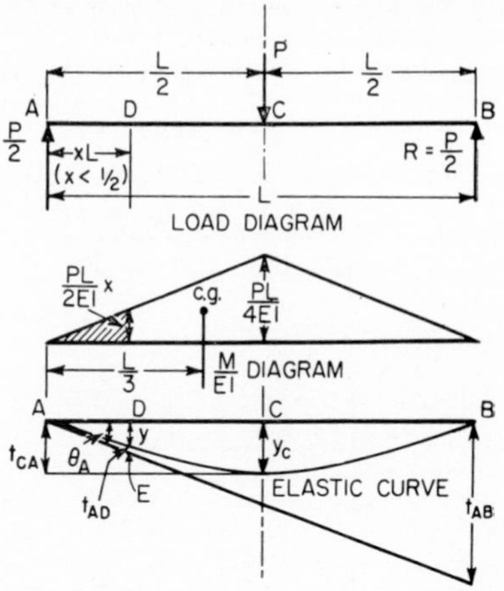

FIG. 3-28. Elastic curve for a simple beam.

Suppose, now, the deflection y at any point D at a distance xL from the left support (Fig. 3-28) is to be determined. Referring to the sketch, we note that the distance DE from the undeflected position of D to the tangent to the elastic curve at support A is given by

$$y + t_{AD} = xt_{AB}$$

where t_{AD} is the tangential deviation of D from the tangent at A and t_{AB} is the tangential deviation of B from that tangent. This equation, which is perfectly general for the deflection of any point of a simple beam, no matter how loaded, may be rewritten to give the deflection directly:

$$y = xt_{AB} - t_{AD} \tag{3-34}$$

But t_{AB} is the moment of the area of the M/EI diagram for the whole beam about support B. And t_{AD} is the moment about D of the area of the M/EI diagram included between ordinates at A and D. Hence.

$$y = x\frac{1}{2}\frac{PL}{4EI}\frac{L}{2}\left(\frac{2}{3}+\frac{1}{3}\right)L - \frac{1}{2}\frac{PLx}{2EI}xL\frac{xL}{3} = \frac{PL^3}{48EI}x(3 - 4x^2)$$

It is also noteworthy that, since the tangential deviations are very small distances, the slope of the elastic curve at A is given by

$$\theta_A = \frac{t_{AB}}{L} \tag{3-35}$$

This holds, in general, for all simple beams regardless of the type of loading.

The procedure followed in applying Eq. (3-34) to the deflection of the loaded beam in Fig. 3-28 is equivalent to finding the bending moment at D with the M/EI diagram serving as the load diagram. The technique of applying the M/EI diagram as a load and determining the deflection as a bending moment is known as the **conjugate-beam method.**

The conjugate beam must have the same length as the given beam; it must be in equilibrium with the M/EI load and the reactions produced by the load; and the bending moment at any section must be equal to the deflection of the given beam at the corresponding section.   The last requirement is equivalent to requiring that the shear at any section of the conjugate beam with the M/EI load be equal to the slope of the elastic curve at the corresponding section of the given beam.   Figure 3-29 shows the conjugates for various types of beams.

Deflections for several types of loading on simple beams are given in Figs. 3-30 to 3-35 and for overhanging beams and cantilevers in Figs. 3-36 to 3-41.

ACTUAL BEAM   CONJUGATE BEAM

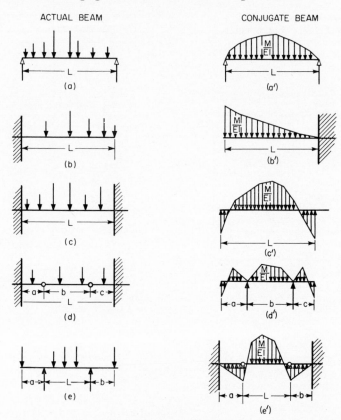

Fig. 3-29. Conjugate beams.

When a beam carries a number of loads of different types, the most convenient method of computing its deflection generally is to find the deflections separately for the uniform and concentrated loads and add them up.

For several concentrated loads, the easiest solution is to apply the reciprocal theorem (Art. 3-57).   According to this theorem, if a concentrated load is applied to a beam at a point A, the deflection it produces at point B is equal to the deflection at A for the same load applied at $B(d_{AB} = d_{BA})$.

Suppose, for example, the mid-span deflection is to be computed.   Then, assume each load in turn applied at the center of the beam and compute the deflection at the point where it originally was applied from the equation of the elastic curve given in Fig. 3-33.   The sum of these deflections is the total mid-span deflection.

Another method for computing deflections of beams is presented in Art. 3-55.   This method may also be applied to determining the deflection of a beam due to shear.

3-32. Combined Axial and Bending Loads. For short beams, subjected to both transverse and axial loading, the stresses are given by the principle of superposition if the deflection due to bending may be neglected without serious error. That is, the

SHEAR, BENDING MOMENTS AND DEFLECTIONS
SIMPLE BEAMS OF UNIFORM CROSS SECTION

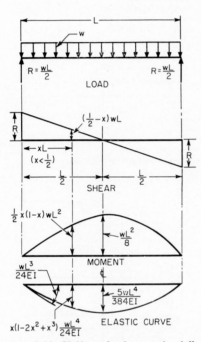

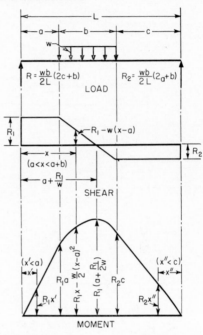

Fig. 3-30. Uniform load over the full span of a simple beam.

Fig. 3-31. Uniform load over part of a simple beam.

total stress is given with sufficient accuracy at any section by the sum of the axial stress and the bending stresses. The maximum stress equals

$$f = \frac{P}{A} + \frac{Mc}{I} \qquad (3\text{-}36)$$

where P = axial load

A = cross-sectional area

M = maximum bending moment

c = distance from neutral axis to outermost fiber at the section where maximum moment occurs

I = moment of inertia of cross section about neutral axis at that section

When the deflection due to bending is large and the axial load produces bending stresses that cannot be neglected, the maximum stress is given by

$$f = \frac{P}{A} + (M + Pd)\frac{c}{I} \qquad (3\text{-}37)$$

where d is the deflection of the beam. For axial compression, the moment Pd should be given the same sign as M, and for tension, the opposite sign, but the minimum value of $M + Pd$ is zero. The deflection d for axial compression and bending can be obtained by applying Eq. (3-31).   (S. Timoshenko, "Theory of Elastic Stability," McGraw-Hill Book Company, Inc., New York, 1936.   Friedrich Bleich, "Buckling Strength of Metal Structures," McGraw-Hill Book Company Inc., New York, 1952).   However, it may be closely approximated by

$$d = \frac{d_o}{1 - (P/P_c)} \tag{3-38}$$

where d_o = deflection for the transverse loading alone
P_c = the critical buckling load $\pi^2 EI/L^2$ (see Art. 3-71)

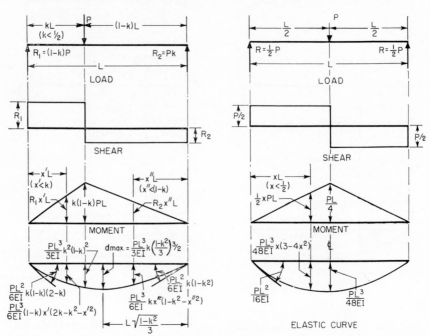

FIG. 3-32. Concentrated load at any point of a simple beam.

FIG. 3-33. Concentrated load at mid-span of a simple beam.

3-33. Eccentric Loading.   An eccentric longitudinal load in the plane of symmetry produces a bending moment Pe where e is the distance of the load from the centroidal axis.   The total unit stress is the sum of this moment and the stress due to P applied as an axial load:

$$f = \frac{P}{A} \pm \frac{Pec}{I} = \frac{P}{A}\left(1 \pm \frac{ec}{r^2}\right) \tag{3-39}$$

where A = cross-sectional area
c = distance from neutral axis to outermost fiber
I = moment of inertia of cross section about neutral axis
r = **radius of gyration**, which is equal to $\sqrt{I/A}$

Figure 3-26 gives values of the radius of gyration for some commonly used cross sections.

If there is to be no tension on the cross section, e should not exceed r^2/c.   For a rectangular section with width b and depth d the eccentricity, therefore, should be less than $b/6$ and $d/6$; i.e., the load should not be applied outside the middle third. For a circular cross section with diameter D the eccentricity should not exceed $D/8$.

When the eccentric longitudinal load produces a deflection too large to be neglected in computing the bending stress, account must be taken of the additional bending

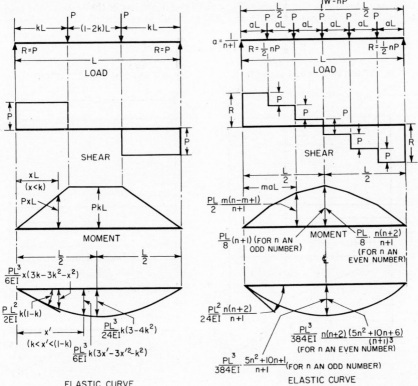

FIG. 3-34. Two equal concentrated loads on a simple beam.

FIG. 3-35. Several equal concentrated loads on a simple beam.

moment Pd, where d is the deflection. This deflection may be computed by employing Eq. (3-31) or closely approximated by

$$d = \frac{4eP/P_c}{\pi(1 - P/P_c)} \qquad (3\text{-}40)$$

P_c is the critical buckling load, $\pi^2 EI/L^2$ (see Art. 3-71).

If the load P does not lie in a plane containing an axis of symmetry, it produces bending about the two principal axes through the centroid of the cross section. The stresses are given by

$$f = \frac{P}{A} \pm \frac{Pe_x c_x}{I_y} \pm \frac{Pe_y c_y}{I_x} \qquad (3\text{-}41)$$

where A = cross-sectional area
e_x = eccentricity with respect to principal axis YY
e_y = eccentricity with respect to principal axis XX
c_x = distance from YY to outermost fiber
c_y = distance from XX to outermost fiber
I_x = moment of inertia about YY
I_y = moment of inertia about XX

The principal axes are the two perpendicular axes through the centroid for which the moments of inertia are a maximum or a minimum and for which the products of inertia are zero.

3-34. Unsymmetrical Bending. Bending caused by loads that do not lie in a plane containing a principal axis of each cross section of a beam is called unsymmetrical bending. Assuming that the bending axis of the beam lies in the plane of the loads, to preclude torsion (see Art. 3-35), and that the loads are perpendicular to the bending

SHEAR, BENDING MOMENTS AND DEFLECTIONS

OVERHANGING BEAMS OF UNIFORM CROSS SECTION   CANTILEVER BEAMS OF UNIFORM CROSS SECTION

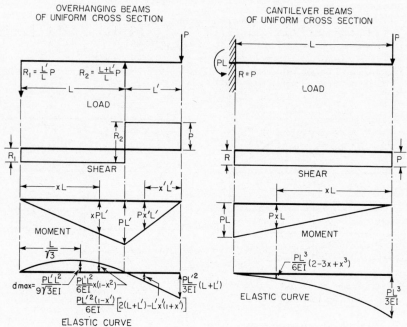

FIG. 3-36. Concentrated load on a beam overhang.   FIG. 3-37. Concentrated load on the end of a cantilever.

axis, to preclude axial components, the stress at any point in a cross section is given by

$$f = \frac{M_x y}{I_x} \pm \frac{M_y x}{I_y} \tag{3-42}$$

where M_x = bending moment about principal axis XX
     M_y = bending moment about principal axis YY
     x = distance from point for which stress is to be computed to YY axis
     y = distance from point to XX axis
     I_x = moment of inertia of the cross section about XX
     I_y = moment of inertia about YY.

If the plane of the loads makes an angle θ with a principal plane, the neutral surface will form an angle α with the other principal plane such that

$$\tan \alpha = \frac{I_x}{I_y} \tan \theta \tag{3-43}$$

3-35. Beams with Unsymmetrical Sections. In the derivation of the flexure formula $f = Mc/I$ (Art. 3-25), the assumption is made that the beam bends, without twisting, in the plane of the loads and that the neutral surface is perpendicular to the plane of the loads. These assumptions are correct for beams with cross sections symmetrical about two axes when the plane of the loads contains one of these axes. They are not necessarily true for beams that are not doubly symmetrical. The reason is that in beams that are doubly symmetrical the bending axis coincides with the centroidal axis, whereas in unsymmetrical sections the two axes may be separate. In the

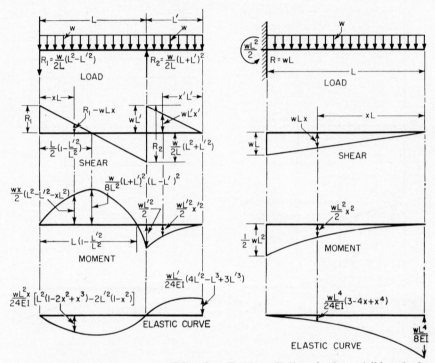

FIG. 3-38. Uniform load over the full length of a beam with overhang.

FIG. 3-39. Uniform load over full length of a cantilever.

latter case, if the plane of the loads contains the centroidal axis but not the bending axis, the beam will be subjected to both bending and torsion.

The **bending axis** may be defined as the longitudinal line in a beam through which transverse loads must pass to preclude the beam's twisting as it bends. The point in each section through which the bending axis passes is called the **shear center**, or center of twist (Fred B. Seely, "Resistance of Materials," John Wiley & Sons, Inc., New York). The shear center is also the center of rotation of the section in pure torsion (Art. 3-77). Its location depends on the dimensions of the section.

If a beam has an axis of symmetry, the shear center lies on it. In doubly symmetrical beams, the shear center lies at the intersection of the two axes of symmetry and hence coincides with the centroid.

For any section composed of two narrow rectangles, such as a T beam or an angle, the shear center may be taken as the intersection of the longitudinal center lines of the rectangles.

For a channel section with one axis of symmetry, the shear center is outside the section at a distance from the centroid equal to $e(1 + h^2A/4I)$, where e is the distance from the centroid to the center of the web, h is the depth of the channel, A the cross-sectional area, and I the moment of inertia about the axis of symmetry. (The web lies between the shear center and the centroid.)

Locations of shear centers for several other sections are given in Friedrich Bleich, "Buckling Strength of Metal Structures," chap. III, McGraw-Hill Book Company, Inc., New York, 1952.

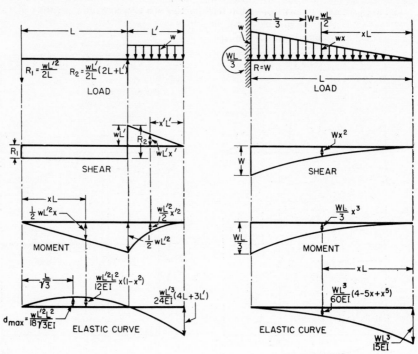

FIG. 3-40. Uniform load on a beam over-hang.

FIG. 3-41. Triangular loading on a canti-lever.

CURVED BEAMS

Structural members, such as arches, crane hooks, chain links, and frames of some machines, that have considerable initial curvature in the plane of loading are called curved beams. The flexure formula of Art. 3-25, $f = Mc/I$, cannot be applied to them with any reasonable degree of accuracy unless the depth of the beam is small compared with the radius of curvature.

Unlike the condition in straight beams, unit strains in curved beams are not proportional to the distance from the neutral surface, and the centroidal axis does not coincide with the neutral axis. Hence the stress distribution on a section is not linear but more like the distribution shown in Fig. 3-42c.

3-36. Stresses in Curved Beams. Just as for straight beams, the assumption that plane sections before bending remain plane after bending generally holds for curved beams. So the total strains are proportional to the distance from the neutral axis. But since the fibers are initially of unequal length, the unit strains are a more complex function of this distance. In Fig. 3-42a, for example, the bending couples have rotated section AB of the curved beam into section $A'B'$ through an angle $\Delta\,d\theta$. If ϵ_o is the unit strain at the centroidal axis and ω is the angular unit strain $\Delta\,d\theta/d\theta$, then the unit strain at a distance y from the centroidal axis (measured positive in the direction of the center of curvature) is

$$\epsilon = \frac{DD'}{DD_o} = \frac{\epsilon_o R \, d\theta - y\Delta \, d\theta}{(R - y) \, d\theta} = \epsilon_o - (\omega - \epsilon_o) \frac{y}{R - y} \tag{3-44}$$

where R = radius of curvature of centroidal axis

Equation (3-44) can be expressed in terms of the bending moment if we take advantage of the fact that the sum of the tensile and compressive forces on the section must be zero and the moment of these forces must be equal to the bending moment M.

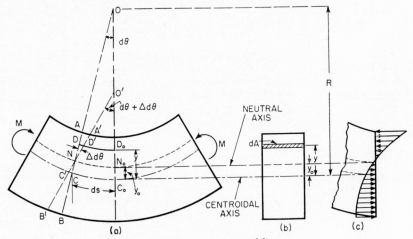

FIG. 3-42. Stresses in a curved beam.

These two equations yield

$$\epsilon_o = \frac{M}{ARE} \qquad \text{and} \qquad \omega = \frac{M}{ARE} \left(1 + \frac{AR^2}{I'}\right) \tag{3-45}$$

where A is the cross-sectional area, E the modulus of elasticity, and

$$I' = \int \frac{y^2 \, dA}{1 - y/R} = \int y^2 \left(1 + \frac{y}{R} + \frac{y^2}{R^2} + \cdots\right) dA \tag{3-46}$$

It should be noted that I' is very nearly equal to the moment of inertia I about the centroidal axis when the depth of the section is small compared with R, so that the maximum ratio of y to R is small compared with unity. M is positive when it decreases the radius of curvature.

Since the stress $f = E\epsilon$, we obtain the stresses in the curved beam from Eq. (3-44) by multiplying it by E and substituting ϵ_o and ω from Eq. (3-45):

$$f = \frac{M}{AR} - \frac{My}{I'} \frac{1}{1 - y/R} \tag{3-47}$$

The distance y_o of the neutral axis from the centroidal axis (Fig. 3-42) may be obtained from Eq. (3-47) by setting $f = 0$:

$$y_o = \frac{I'R}{I' + AR^2} \tag{3-48}$$

Since y is positive, the neutral axis shifts toward the center of curvature.

3-37. Curved Beams with Rectangular Sections. Taking the first three terms of the series in Eq. (3-46) and integrating, we obtain for a rectangular cross section

$$I' = I \left(1 + \frac{3}{5} \frac{c^2}{R^2} \right) \tag{3-49}$$

where I is the moment of inertia about the centroidal axis and c is one-half the depth of the beam. The stresses in the outer fibers are given by

$$f_{max} = -\frac{Mc}{I} \left(\frac{I}{I'} \frac{R}{R - c} - \frac{c}{3R} \right)$$
$$f_{min} = +\frac{Mc}{I} \left(\frac{I}{I'} \frac{R}{R + c} + \frac{c}{3R} \right) \tag{3-50}$$

It is noteworthy that the factor by which Mc/I is multiplied in Eq. (3-50) is a function of c/R and independent of the other dimensions of the beam.

3-38. Curved Beams with Circular Section. Integrating the series in Eq. (3-46) for a circle and taking the first three terms of the result, we obtain

$$I' = I \left(1 + \frac{1}{2} \frac{c^2}{R^2} \right) \tag{3-51}$$

where I = moment of inertia about centroidal axis
       c = one-half depth of beam.

The stresses in the outer fibers are given by

$$f_{max} = -\frac{Mc}{I} \left(\frac{I}{I'} \frac{R}{R - c} - \frac{c}{4R} \right)$$
$$f_{min} = +\frac{Mc}{I} \left(\frac{I}{I'} \frac{R}{R + c} + \frac{c}{4R} \right) \tag{3-52}$$

For this section, too, the factor by which Mc/I is multiplied is a function of c/R and independent of the other dimensions of the beam.

3-39. Curved I or T Beams. If Eq. (3-47) is applied to I or T beams or tubular members, it may indicate circumferential flange stresses that are much lower than will actually occur. The error is due to the fact that the outer edges of the flanges deflect radially. The effect is equivalent to having only part of the flanges active in resisting bending stresses. Also, accompanying the flange deflections, there are transverse bending stresses in the flanges. At the junction with the web, these reach a maximum, which may be greater than the maximum circumferential stress. Furthermore, there are radial stresses (normal stresses acting in the direction of the radius of curvature) in the web that also may have maximum values greater than the maximum circumferential stress.

A good approximation to the stresses in I or T beams is presented in Seely and Smith, "Advanced Mechanics of Materials," 2d ed., John Wiley & Sons, Inc., New York. In brief, the authors contend that, for circumferential stresses, Eq. (3-47) may be used with a modified cross section, which is obtained by using a reduced flange width. The reduction is calculated from $b' = \alpha b$, where b is the length of the portion of the flange projecting on either side from the web, b' is the corrected length, and α is a correction factor determined from equations developed by H. Bleich. α is a function of b^2/rt, where t is the flange thickness and r the radius of the center of the flange:

$b^2/rt =$	0.5	0.7	1.0	1.5	2	3	4	5
$\alpha =$	0.9	0.6	0.7	0.6	0.5	0.4	0.37	0.33

When the parameter b^2/rt is greater than 1.0, the maximum transverse bending stress is approximately equal to 1.7 times the stress obtained at the center of the flange from Eq. (3-47) applied to the modified section. When the parameter equals 0.7, that stress should be multiplied by 1.5, and when it equals 0.4, the factor is 1.0. In Eq. (3-47), I' for I beams may be taken for this calculation approximately equal to

$$I' = I\left(1 + \frac{c^2}{R^2}\right) \tag{3-53}$$

where I = moment of inertia of modified section about its centroidal axis
$\quad R$ = radius of curvature of centroidal axis
$\quad c$ = distance from centroidal axis to center of the more sharply curved flange.
Because of the high stress factor, it is advisable to stiffen or brace curved I-beam flanges.

The maximum radial stress will occur at the junction of web and flange of I beams. If the moment is negative; that is, if the loads tend to flatten out the beam, the radial stress is tensile, and there is a tendency for the more sharply curved flange to pull away from the web. An approximate value of this maximum stress is

$$f_r = -\frac{A_f}{A}\frac{M}{t_w c_g r'} \tag{3-54}$$

where f_r = radial stress at junction of flange and web of a symmetrical I beam
$\quad A_f$ = area of one flange
$\quad A$ = total cross-sectional area
$\quad M$ = bending moment
$\quad t_w$ = thickness of web
$\quad c_g$ = distance from centroidal axis to center of flange
$\quad r'$ = radius of curvature of inner face of more sharply curved flange

3-40. Axial and Bending Loads on Curved Beams. If a curved beam carries an axial load P as well as bending loads, the maximum unit stress is

$$f = \frac{P}{A} \pm \frac{Mc}{I}K \tag{3-55}$$

where K is a correction factor for the curvature [see Eqs. (3-50) and (3-52)]. The sign of M is taken positive in this equation when it increases the curvature, and P is positive when it is a tensile force, negative when compressive.

3-41. Slope and Deflection of Curved Beams. If we consider two sections of a curved beam separated by a differential distance ds (Fig. 3-42), the change in angle $\Delta\,d\theta$ between the sections due to a bending moment M and an axial load P may be obtained from Eq. (3-45), noting that $d\theta = ds/R$.

$$\Delta\,d\theta = \frac{M\,ds}{EI'}\left(1 + \frac{I'}{AR^2}\right) + \frac{P\,ds}{ARE} \tag{3-56}$$

where E is the modulus of elasticity, A the cross-sectional area, R the radius of curvature of the centroidal axis, and I' is defined by Eq. (3-46) [see also Eqs. (3-49), (3-51), and (3-53)].

If P is a tensile force, the length of the centroidal axis increases by

$$\Delta\,ds = \frac{P\,ds}{AE} + \frac{M\,ds}{ARE} \tag{3-57}$$

The effect of curvature on shearing deformations for most practical applications is negligible.

For shallow sections (depth of section less than about one-tenth the span), the effect of axial forces on deformations may be neglected. Also, unless the radius of curvature is very small compared with the depth, the effect of curvature may be ignored. Hence, for most practical applications, Eq. (3-56) may be used in the simplified form:

$$\Delta\, d\theta = \frac{M\, ds}{EI} \tag{3-58}$$

For thicker beams, the action of axial forces, as well as bending moments, should be taken into account; but unless the curvature is sharp, its effect on deformations may be neglected. So only Eq. (3-58) and the first term in Eq. (3-57) need be used. (S. Timoshenko and D. H. Young, "Theory of Structures," McGraw-Hill Book Company, Inc., New York, 1945.) See also Arts. 3-82 to 3-86.

GRAPHIC-STATICS FUNDAMENTALS

A force may be represented by a straight line of fixed length. The length of line to a given scale represents the magnitude of the force. The position of the line parallels the line of action of the force. And an arrowhead on the line indicates the direction in which the force acts.

Forces are concurrent when their lines of action meet. If they lie in the same plane, they are coplanar.

3-42. Parallelogram of Forces. The resultant of several forces is a single force that would produce the same effect on a rigid body. The resultant of two concurrent forces is determined by the parallelogram law:

If a parallelogram is constructed with two forces as sides, the diagonal represents the resultant of the forces (Fig. 3-43a).

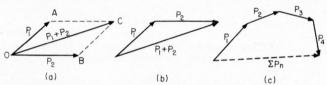

(a)   (b)   (c)

FIG. 3-43. Addition of forces—(a) by parallelogram law; (b) by triangle construction; and (c) by polygon construction.

The **resultant** is said to be equal to the sum of the forces, sum here meaning, of course, addition by the parallelogram law. Subtraction is carried out in the same manner as addition, but the direction of the force to be subtracted is reversed.

If the direction of the resultant is reversed, it becomes the **equilibrant,** a single force that will hold the two given forces in equilibrium.

3-43. Resolution of Forces. To resolve a force into two components, a parallelogram is drawn with the force as a diagonal. The sides of the parallelogram represent the components. The procedure is: (1) Draw the given force. (2) From both ends of the force draw lines parallel to the directions in which the components act. (3) Draw the components along the parallels through the origin of the given force to the intersections with the parallels through the other end. Thus, in Fig. 3-43a, P_1 and P_2 are the components in directions OA and OB of the force represented by OC.

3-44. Force Polygons. Examination of Fig. 3-43a indicates that a step can be saved in adding the two forces. The same resultant could be obtained by drawing only the upper half of the parallelogram. Hence, to add two forces, draw the first force; then draw the second force beginning at the end of the first one. The resultant is the force drawn from the origin of the first force to the end of the second force, as shown in Fig. 3-43b. Again, the equilibrant is the resultant with direction reversed.

From this diagram, an important conclusion can be drawn: **If three forces meeting at a point are in equilibrium, they will form a closed force triangle.**

The conclusions reached for addition of two forces can be generalized for several concurrent forces: To add several forces, $P_1, P_2, P_3, \ldots, P_n$, draw P_2 from the end of P_1, P_3 from the end of P_2, etc. The force required to close the force polygon is the resultant (Fig. 3-43c).

If a group of concurrent forces are in equilibrium, they will form a closed force polygon.

3-45. Equilibrium Polygons. When the forces are coplanar but not concurrent, the force polygon will yield the magnitude and direction of the resultant but not its point of application. To complete the solution, the easiest method generally is to employ an auxiliary force polygon, called an equilibrium, or funicular (string), polygon. Sides of this polygon represent the lines of action of certain components of the given forces; more specifically, they take the configuration of a weightless string holding the forces in equilibrium.

In Fig. 3-44a are shown three forces P_1, P_2, and P_3. The magnitude and direction of their resultant R are determined from the force polygon in Fig. 3-44b. To construct the equilibrium polygon for determining the position of the resultant, select a point O in or near the force polygon. From O, which is called a **pole**, draw rays OA, OB, OC, and OD to the extremities of the forces (Fig. 3-44b). Note that consecutive pairs of rays form closed triangles with the given forces, and therefore, they are components of the forces in the directions of the rays. Furthermore, each of the rays OB and OC, drawn to a vertex of the polygon formed by two given forces, represents, in turn, two forces with the same line of action but act-

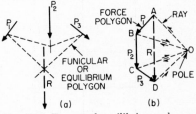

FIG. 3-44. Force and equilibrium polygons for a system of forces.

ing in opposite directions to help hold the given forces in equilibrium. Ray OA is a component not only of P_1 but also of R; similarly, OD is a component of both P_3 and R, and with OA holds R in equilibrium.

If in Fig. 3-44a, where the given forces are shown in their relative positions, lines are drawn from each force in the direction of the rays forming their components, they will form a funicular polygon. For example, starting with a convenient point on P_1 (Fig. 3-44a), draw a line parallel to OB until it intersects P_2. This represents the line of action of both force BO, which helps hold P_1 in equilibrium, and OB, which helps hold P_2 in equilibrium. Through the intersection with P_2, draw a line parallel to OC until it intersects P_3. Through this last intersection, draw a line parallel to DO, one component of R, and through the starting point on P_1, draw a line parallel to OA, the second component of R, completing the funicular polygon. These two lines intersect on the line of action of R.

3-46. Beam and Truss Reactions by Graphics. The equilibrium polygon can also be used to find the reactions of simple beams and trusses supporting vertical loads. First, a force polygon is constructed to obtain the magnitude and direction of the resultant of the loads, which is equal in magnitude but opposite in direction to the sum of the reactions. Second, rays are drawn to the vertexes of the polygon from a conveniently located pole. These rays are used to construct all but one side of an equilibrium polygon. The closing side is the common line of action of two equal but opposite forces that act with a pair of rays already drawn to hold the reactions in equilibrium. Therefore, draw a line through the pole parallel to the closing side. The intersection with the resultant separates it into two forces, which are equal to the reactions sought.

For example, suppose the reactions were to be obtained graphically for the beam (or truss) in Fig. 3-45a. As a first step, the force polygon $ABCD$ is constructed, a pole selected, and rays drawn to the extremities of the forces (Fig. 3-45b). Since the loads are parallel, the force polygon is a straight line. The sum of the reactions, in this case, is equal to the length of the line AD.

Next, the equilibrium polygon is constructed. Starting with a convenient point on the line of action of R_1, draw a line oa parallel to ray OA in Fig. 3-45b and locate its intersection with the line of action of P_1 (Fig. 3-45d). Through this intersection, draw ob, a line parallel to OB to the intersection with P_2, then a line oc parallel to OC, and finally a line od parallel to OD, which terminates on the line of action of R_2. Draw the closing line oe of the polygon between this last intersection and the starting point of the polygon. The last step is to draw through the pole (Fig. 3-45b) OE, a line parallel to oe, the closing line of the equilibrium polygon, cutting the force-polygon resultant at E. Then, $DE = R_2$, and $EA = R_1$. (See Art. 3-17 for an analytical method of computing reactions.)

3-47. Shear and Moment Diagrams by Graphics. The shear at any section of a beam is equal to the algebraic sum of the loads and reactions on the left of the section,

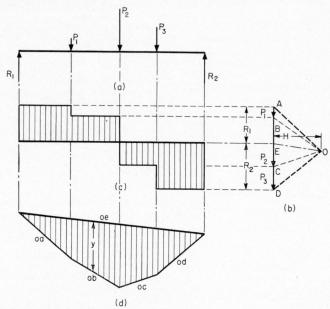

Fig. 3-45. Shear and moment diagrams obtained by graphic statics—(a) loaded beam; (b) force polygon; (c) shear diagram; and (d) equilibrium polygon and bending-moment diagram.

upward-acting forces being considered positive, downward forces negative. If the forces are arranged in the proper order, the shear diagram may be obtained directly from the force polygon after the reactions have been determined.

For example, the shear diagram for the beam in Fig. 3-45a can be easily obtained from the force polygon $ABCDE$ in Fig. 3-45b. The zero axis is a line parallel to the beam through E. As indicated in Fig. 3-45c, the ordinates of the shear diagram are laid off, starting with R_1 along the line of action of the left reaction, by drawing lines parallel to the zero axis through the extremities of the forces in the force polygon. (See Art. 3-19 for an analytical method of determining shears.)

The moment of a force about a point can be obtained from the equilibrium and force polygons. In the equilibrium diagram, draw a line parallel to the force through the given point. Measure the intercept of this line between the two adjacent funicular-polygon sides (extended if necessary) that originate at the given force. The moment is the product of this intercept by the distance of the force-polygon pole from the force. The intercept should be measured to the same linear scale as the beam and load positions, and the pole distance to the same scale as the forces in the force polygon.

As a consequence of this relationship between the sides of the funicular polygon, each ordinate (parallel to the forces) multiplied by the pole distance is equal to the bending moment at the corresponding section of the beam or truss. In Fig. 3-45d, for example, the equilibrium polygon, to scale, is the bending-moment diagram for the beam in Fig. 3-45a. At any section, the moment equals the ordinate y multiplied by the pole distance H. (See Art. 3-20 for an analytical method.)

ROOF TRUSSES

A truss is a coplanar system of structural members joined together at their ends to form a stable framework. Neglecting small changes in the lengths of the members due to loads, the relative positions of the joints cannot change.

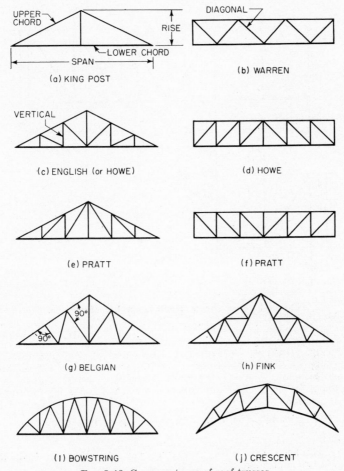

FIG. 3-46. Common types of roof trusses.

Three bars pinned together to form a triangle represent the simplest type of truss. Some of the more common types of roof trusses are shown in Fig. 3-46.

The top members are called the upper chord; the bottom members, the lower chord; and the verticals and diagonals, web members.

The purpose of roof trusses is to act like big beams, to support the roof covering over long spans. They not only have to carry their own weight and the weight of the roofing and roof beams, or purlins, but cranes, wind loads, snow loads, suspended ceilings, and equipment, and a live load to take care of construction, maintenance, and repair loading. These loads are applied at the intersection of the members, or panel points, so that the members will be subjected principally to direct stresses.

3-48. Method of Sections. A convenient method of determining the stresses in truss members is to isolate a portion of the truss by a section so chosen as to cut only as many members with unknown stresses as can be evaluated by the laws of equilibrium applied to that portion of the truss. The stresses in the cut members are treated as external forces. Compressive forces act toward the panel point and tensile forces away from the joint.

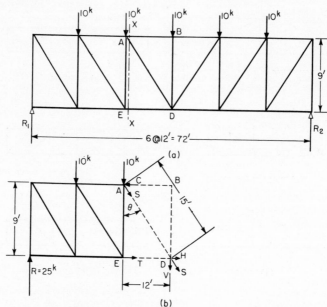

Fig. 3-47. Truss stresses found by method of sections.

Suppose, for example, we wish to find the stress in chord AB of the truss in Fig. 3-47a. We can take a vertical section XX close to panel point A. This cuts not only AB but AD and ED as well. The external 10-kip (10,000-lb) loading and 25-kip reaction at the left are held in equilibrium by the compressive force C in AB, tensile force T in ED, and tensile force S in AD (Fig. 3-47b). The simplest way to find C is to take moments about D, the point of intersection of S and T, eliminating these unknowns from the calculation.

$$-9C + 36 \times 25 - 24 \times 10 - 12 \times 10 = 0$$

from which C is found to be 60 kips.

Similarly, to find the stress in ED, the simplest way is to take moments about A, the point of intersection of S and C:

$$-9T + 24 \times 25 - 12 \times 10 = 0$$

from which T is found to be 53.3 kips.

On the other hand, the stress in AD can be easily determined by two methods. One takes advantage of the fact that AB and ED are horizontal members, requiring AD to carry the full vertical shear at section XX. Hence we know that the vertical component V of $S = 25 - 10 - 10 = 5$ kips. Multiplying V by sec θ (Fig. 3-47b), which is equal to the ratio of the length of AD to the rise of the truss ($15\!\!\frac{}{9}$), S is found to be

8.3 kips. The second method—presented because it is useful when the chords are not horizontal—is to resolve S into horizontal and vertical components at D and take moments about E. Since both T and the horizontal component of S pass through E, they do not appear in the computations, and C already has been computed. Equating the sum of the moments to zero gives $V = 5$, as before.

3-49. Method of Joints. Another useful method for determining the stresses in truss members is to select sections that isolate the joints one at a time and then apply the laws of equilibrium to each. Considering the stresses in the cut members as external forces, the sum of the horizontal components of the forces acting at a joint must be zero, and so must be the sum of the vertical components. Since the lines of action of all the forces are known, we can therefore compute two unknown magnitudes at each joint by this method. The procedure is to start at a joint that has only two unknowns (generally at the support) and then, as stresses in members are determined, analyze successive joints.

Let us, for illustration, apply the method to joint 1 of the truss in Fig. 3-48a. Equating the sum of the vertical components to zero, we find that the vertical component of the top chord must be equal and opposite to the reaction, 12 kips (12,000 lb). The stress in the top chord at this joint, then, must be a compression equal to $12 \times {}^{30}\!/_{18} = 20$ kips. From the fact that the sum of the horizontal components must be zero, we find that the stress in the bottom chord at the joint must be equal and opposite to the horizontal component of the top chord. Hence the stress in the bottom chord must be a tension equal to $20 \times {}^{24}\!/_{30} = 16$ kips.

Moving to joint 2, we note that, with no vertical loads at the joint, the stress in the vertical is zero. Also, the stress is the same in both bottom chord members at the joint, since the sum of the horizontal components must be zero.

Joint 3 now contains only two unknown stresses. Denoting the truss members and the loads by the letters placed on opposite sides of them, as indicated in Fig. 3-48a, the unknown stresses are S_{BH} and S_{HG}. The laws of equilibrium enable us to write the following two equations, one for the vertical components and the second for the horizontal components:

$$\Sigma V = 0.6S_{FA} - 8 - 0.6S_{BH} + 0.6S_{HG} = 0$$
$$\Sigma H = 0.8S_{FA} - 0.8S_{BH} - 0.8S_{HG} = 0$$

Both unknown stresses are assumed to be compressive; i.e., acting toward the joint. The stress in the vertical does not appear in these equations, because it was already determined to be zero. The stress in FA, S_{FA}, was found from analysis of joint 1 to be 20 kips. Simultaneous solution of the two equations yields $S_{HG} = 6.7$ kips and $S_{BH} = 13.3$ kips. (If these stresses had come out with a negative sign, it would have indicated that the original assumption of their directions was incorrect; they would, in that case, be tensile forces instead of compressive forces.)

3-50. Bow's Notation. The method of designating the loads and stresses used in the previous paragraph is the basis of Bow's notation. Capital letters are placed in the spaces between truss members and between forces. Each member and load is then designated by the letters on opposite sides of it. For example, in Fig. 3-48a, the upper chord members are AF, BH, CJ, and DL. The loads are AB, BC, and CD, and the reactions are EA and DE. Stresses in the members generally are designated by the same letters but in lower case.

3-51. Graphical Analysis of Trusses. The method of joints may also be used with graphical techniques. Figure 3-48b, c, d, and e shows how the polygon of force may be applied at each joint to determine the two unknown stresses. Since each joint is in equilibrium, the loads and the stresses in each member must form a closed polygon. The known forces are constructed first. Then, from the origin and the end point, respectively, a line is drawn parallel to the line of action of each of the two unknown stresses. Their intersection determines the magnitude of the unknown stresses.

This solution, as well as the preceding ones, presumes that the reactions are known. They may be computed analytically or graphically, with load and funicular polygons, as explained in Arts. 3-17 and 3-46.

Examination of Fig. 3-48b, c, d, and e indicates that each stress occurs in two force polygons. Hence the graphical solution can be shortened by combining the polygons. The combination of the various polygons for all the joints into one stress diagram is known as a **Maxwell diagram**.

The procedure consists of first constructing the force polygon for the loads and reactions and then applying the method of joints, employing each stress as it is found for finding the stresses in the next joint. To make it easy to determine whether the stresses are compression or tension, loads and reactions should be plotted in the force polygon in the order in which they are passed in going clockwise around the truss.

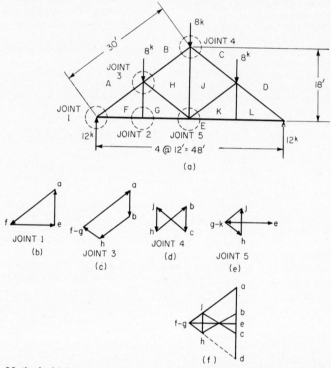

FIG. 3-48. Method of joints applied to a roof truss, leading to a graphical solution with a Maxwell diagram (f).

Similarly, in drawing the force polygon for each joint, the forces should be plotted in a clockwise direction around the joint. If these rules are followed, the order of the space letters indicates the direction of the forces—compressive stresses act toward the joint, tensile stresses away from the joint. Going around joint 1 clockwise, for example, we find the reaction EA as an upward-acting vertical force ea (e to a) in Fig. 3-48b; the top-chord stress af acting toward the joint (a to f), and the bottom-chord stress fe acting away from the joint (f to e). Hence af is compressive, fe tensile.

To construct a Maxwell diagram for the truss in Fig. 3-48a, we lay off all the loads and reactions in clockwise order (Fig. 3-48f). The force polygon abcde is a straight line because all the forces are vertical. To solve joint 1, a line is drawn through point a in Fig. 3-48f parallel to AF and a second line through point e parallel to FE. Their intersection is point f. Going around this triangle in the same order as the loads and members are encountered in traveling clockwise around joint 1, we find ea, the reaction, as an upward force; going from a to f, we move toward the joint, indicating that af is a compressive stress; and going from f to e, we move away from the joint, indicating that fe is a tensile stress.

At joint 2, the stress in the vertical is zero. Hence point g coincides with point f. To solve joint 3, we start with the known stress af and proceed clockwise around the joint. To complete the force polygon, we draw a line through point b parallel to BH and a line through g parallel to GH. Their intersection locates point h. Similarly, the force polygon for joint 4 is completed by drawing a line through c parallel to CJ and a line through h parallel to JH.

Wind loads on a truss with a sloping top chord are assumed to act normal to the roof. In that case, the load polygon will be an inclined line or a true polygon. The reactions are computed generally on the assumption either that both are parallel to the resultant of the wind loads or that one end of the truss is free to move horizontally and therefore will not resist the horizontal components of the loads. The stress diagram is plotted in the same manner as for vertical loads after the reactions are found.

Some trusses are complex and require special methods of analysis. For methods of solving these, see Timoshenko and Young, "Theory of Structures," McGraw-Hill Book Company, Inc., New York, 1945; or Urquhart and O'Rourke, "Stresses in Simple Structures," McGraw-Hill Book Company, Inc., New York. These references also present a graphical method for obtaining the deflections of a truss. An analytical method is given in Art. 3-56.

GENERAL TOOLS FOR STRUCTURAL ANALYSIS

For some types of structures, the equilibrium equations are not sufficient to determine the reactions or the internal stresses. These structures are called **statically indeterminate.**

For the analysis of such structures, additional equations must be written based on a knowledge of the elastic deformations. Hence methods of analysis that enable deformations to be evaluated in terms of unknown forces or stresses are important for the solution of problems involving statically indeterminate structures. Some of these methods, like the method of virtual work, are also useful in solving complicated problems involving statically determinate systems.

3-52. Virtual Work. A virtual displacement is an imaginary small displacement of a particle consistent with the constraints upon it. Thus, at one support of a simply supported beam, the virtual displacement could be an infinitesimal rotation $d\theta$ of that end but not a vertical movement. However, if the support is replaced by a force, then a vertical virtual displacement may be applied to the beam at that end.

Virtual work is the product of the distance a particle moves during a virtual displacement by the component in the direction of the displacement of a force acting on the particle. If the displacement and the force are in opposite directions, the virtual work is negative. When the displacement is normal to the force, no work is done.

Suppose a rigid body is acted upon by a system of forces with a resultant R. Given a virtual displacement ds at an angle α with R, the body will have virtual work done on it equal to $R \cos \alpha \, ds$. (No work is done by internal forces. They act in pairs of equal magnitude but opposite direction, and the virtual work done by one force of a pair is equal but opposite in sign to the work done by the other force.) If the body is in equilibrium under the action of the forces, then $R = 0$ and the virtual work also is zero.

Thus, the principle of virtual work may be stated: **If a rigid body in equilibrium is given a virtual displacement, the sum of the virtual work of the forces acting on it must be zero.**

As an example of how the principle may be used to find a reaction of a statically determinate beam, consider the simple beam in Fig. 3-49a, for which the reaction R is to be determined. First, replace the support by an unknown force R. Next, move that end of the beam upward a small amount dy as in Fig. 3-49b. The displacement under the load P will be $x \, dy/L$, upward. Then, by the principle of virtual work, $R \, dy - Px \, dy/L = 0$, from which $R = Px/L$.

The principle may also be used to find the reaction R of the more complex beam in Fig. 3-49c. The first step again is to replace the support by an unknown force R. Next, apply a virtual downward displacement dy at hinge A (Fig. 3-49d). The displacement under the load P will be $x\,dy/c$, and at the reaction R will be $a\,dy/(a+b)$. According to the principle of virtual work, $-Ra\,dy/(a+b) + Px\,dy/c = 0$, from which $R = Px(a+b)/ac$. In this type of problem, the method has the advantage that only one reaction need be considered at a time and internal forces are not involved.

When an elastic body is deformed, the virtual work done by the internal forces is equal to the corresponding increment of the strain energy taken with negative sign.

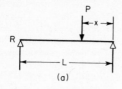

(a)

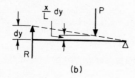

(b)

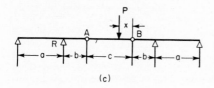

(c)

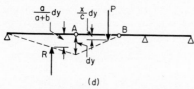

(d)

FIG. 3-49. Virtual work applied to determining a simple-beam reaction (a) and (b) and the reaction of a beam with suspended span (c) and (d).

Utilizing this concept, the principle of virtual work can be adapted for the solution of statically indeterminate structures.

Assume a constrained elastic body acted upon by forces $P_1, P_2, \ldots$, for which the corresponding deformations are $e_1, e_2, \ldots$. Applying the principle of virtual work yields $\Sigma P_n\,de_n + (-dU) = 0$, in which the first term on the left side of the equation gives the work done by the external forces on a virtual displacement and the second term is the work done by the internal forces. The increment of the strain energy due to the increments of the deformations is given by

$$dU = \frac{\partial U}{\partial e_1}\,de_1 + \frac{\partial U}{\partial e_2}\,de_2 + \cdots$$

In solving a specific problem, a virtual displacement that is most convenient in simplifying the solution should be chosen. Suppose, for example, a virtual displacement is selected that affects only the deformation e_n corresponding to the load P_n, other deformations being unchanged. Then, the principle of virtual work requires that

$$P_n\,de_n - \frac{\partial U}{\partial e_n}\,de_n = 0$$

This is equivalent to

$$\frac{\partial U}{\partial e_n} = P_n \qquad (3\text{-}59)$$

which states that the partial derivative of the strain energy with respect to any specific deformation gives the corresponding force.

Suppose, for example, the stress in the vertical bar in Fig. 3-50 is to be determined. All bars are made of the same material and have the same cross section. If the vertical bar stretches an amount e under the load P, the inclined bars will each stretch an amount $e \cos \alpha$. The strain energy in the system is [from Eq. (3-10a)]

$$U = \frac{AE}{2L}\,(e^2 + 2e^2 \cos^3 \alpha)$$

and the partial derivative of this with respect to e must be equal to P; that is

$$P = \frac{AE}{2L}\,(2e + 4e \cos^3 \alpha) = \frac{AEe}{L}\,(1 + 2 \cos^3 \alpha)$$

Noting that the force in the vertical bar equals AEe/L, we find from the above equation that the required stress equals $P/(1 + 2 \cos^3 \alpha)$.

3-53. Castigliano's Theorem. It can also be shown that, if the strain energy is expressed as a function of statically independent forces, the partial derivative of the strain energy with respect to one of the forces gives the deformation corresponding to that force. (See Timoshenko and Young, "Theory of Structures," McGraw-Hill Book Company, Inc., New York, 1945.)

$$\frac{\partial U}{\partial P_n} = e_n \qquad (3\text{-}60)$$

This is known as Castigliano's first theorem. (His second theorem is the principle of least work.)

3-54. Method of Least Work. If deformation of a structure is prevented, as at a support, the partial derivative of the strain energy with respect to that supporting force must be zero, according to Castigliano's first theorem. This establishes his second theorem:

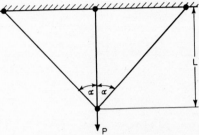

FIG. 3-50. Indeterminate truss.

The strain energy in a statically indeterminate structure is the minimum consistent with equilibrium.

As an example of the use of the method of least work, we shall solve again for the stress in the vertical bar in Fig. 3-50. Calling this stress X, we note that the stress in each of the inclined bars must be $(P - X)/2 \cos \alpha$. With the aid of Eq. (3-10a), we can express the strain energy in the system in terms of X as

$$U = \frac{X^2 L}{2AE} + \frac{(P - X)^2 L}{4AE \cos^3 \alpha}$$

Hence, the internal work in the system will be a minimum when

$$\frac{\partial U}{\partial X} = \frac{XL}{AE} - \frac{(P - X)L}{2AE \cos^3 \alpha} = 0$$

Solving for X gives the stress in the vertical bar as $P/(1 + 2 \cos^3 \alpha)$, as before (Art 3-52).

3-55. Dummy Unit-load Method. In Sec. 1, the strain energy for pure bending was given as $U = M^2 L/2EI$ in Eq. (3-10d). To find the strain energy due to bending stress in a beam, we can apply this equation to a differential length dx of the beam and integrate over the entire span. Thus,

$$U = \int_0^L \frac{M^2 \, dx}{2EI} \qquad (3\text{-}61)$$

If M represents the bending moment due to a generalized force P, the partial derivative of the strain energy with respect to P is the deformation d corresponding to P. Differentiating Eq. (3-61) under the integral sign gives

$$d = \int_0^L \frac{M}{EI} \frac{\partial M}{\partial P} \, dx \qquad (3\text{-}62)$$

The partial derivative in this equation is the rate of change of bending moment with the load P. It is equal to the bending moment m produced by a unit generalized load applied at the point where the deformation is to be measured and in the direction of the deformation. Hence, Eq. (3-62) can also be written

$$d = \int_0^L \frac{Mm}{EI} \, dx \qquad (3\text{-}63)$$

To find the vertical deflection of a beam, we apply a dummy unit vertical load at the point where the deflection is to be measured and substitute the bending moments due to this load and the actual loading in Eq. (3-63). Similarly, to compute a rotation, we apply a dummy unit moment. (See also Art. 3-31.)

As a simple example, let us apply the dummy unit-load method to the determination of the deflection at the center of a simply supported, uniformly loaded beam of constant moment of inertia (Fig. 3-51a). As indicated in Fig. 3-51b, the bending moment

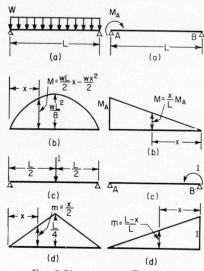

(a)

(b)

(c)

(d)

Fig. 3-51.　　Fig. 3-52.

Fig. 3-51. Dummy unit-load method applied to a uniformly loaded beam (a) to find mid-span deflection; (b) moment diagram for the uniform load; (c) unit load at mid-span; (d) moment diagram for unit load.

Fig. 3-52. End rotation due to end moment (a) by dummy unit-load method; (b) moment diagram for end moment; (c) unit moment applied at beam end; (d) moment diagram for unit moment.

at a distance x from one end is $(wL/2)x - (w/2)x^2$. If we apply a dummy unit load vertically at the center of the beam (Fig. 3-51c), where the vertical deflection is to be determined, the moment at x is $x/2$, as indicated in Fig. 3-51d. Substituting in Eq. (3-63) gives

$$d = 2\int_0^{L/2}\left(\frac{wL}{2}x - \frac{w}{2}x^2\right)\frac{x}{2}\frac{dx}{EI} = \frac{5wL^4}{384EI}$$

As another example, let us apply the method to finding the end rotation at one end of a simply supported, prismatic beam produced by a moment applied at the other end. In other words, the problem is to find the end rotation at B, θ_B, in Fig. 3-52a, due to M_A. As indicated in Fig. 3-52b, the bending moment at a distance x from B due to M_A is $M_A x/L$. If we applied a dummy unit moment at B (Fig. 3-52c), it would produce a moment at x of $(L - x)/L$ (Fig. 3-52d). Substituting in Eq. (3-63) gives

$$\theta_B = \int_0^L M_A\frac{x}{L}\frac{L - x}{L}\frac{dx}{EI} = \frac{M_A L}{6EI}$$

To determine the deflection of a beam due to shear Castigliano's theorems can be applied to the strain energy in shear:

$$V = \iint \frac{v^2}{2G}\,dA\,dx$$

where v = shearing unit stress
　　　　G = modulus of rigidity
　　　　A = cross-sectional area

3-56. Truss Deflections. The dummy unit-load method may also be adapted for the determination of the deformation of trusses. As indicated by Eq. (3-10a), the strain energy in a truss is given by

$$U = \sum \frac{S^2 L}{2AE} \tag{3-64}$$

which represents the sum of the strain energy for all the members of the truss. S is the stress in each member due to the loads. Applying Castigliano's first theorem and differentiating inside the summation sign yield the deformation:

$$d = \sum \frac{SL}{AE}\frac{\partial S}{\partial P} \tag{3-65}$$

The partial derivative in this equation is the rate of change of axial stress with the load P. It is equal to the axial stress in each bar of the truss u produced by a unit load applied at the point where the deformation is to be measured and in the direction of the deformation. Consequently, Eq. (3-65) can also be written

$$ d = \sum \frac{SuL}{AE} \tag{3-66} $$

To find the deflection of a truss, apply a dummy unit vertical load at the panel point where the deflection is to be measured and substitute in Eq. (3-66) the stresses in each member of the truss due to this load and the actual loading. Similarly, to find the

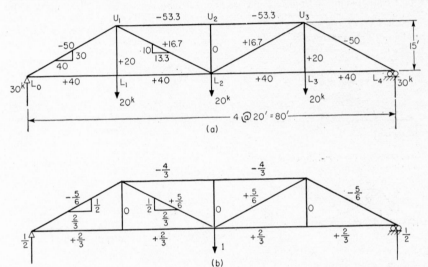

Fig. 3-53. Dummy unit-load method applied to a loaded truss (a) to find mid-span deflection; (b) unit load applied at mid-span.

rotation of any joint, apply a dummy unit moment at the joint, compute the stresses in each member of the truss, and substitute in Eq. (3-66). When it is necessary to determine the relative movement of two panel points, apply dummy unit loads in opposite directions at those points.

It is worth noting that members that are not stressed by the actual loads or the dummy loads do not enter into the calculation of a deformation.

As an example of the application of Eq. (3-66), let us compute the deflection of the truss in Fig. 3-53. The stresses due to the 20-kip load at each panel point are shown in Fig. 3-53a, and the ratio of length of members in inches to their cross-sectional area in square inches is given in Table 3-3. We apply a dummy unit vertical load at L_2,

Table **3-3.** Deflection of a Truss

Member	L/A	S	u	SuL/A
L_0L_2	160	$+40$	$+\frac{2}{3}$	4,267
L_0U_1	75	-50	$-\frac{5}{6}$	3,125
U_1U_2	60	-53.3	$-\frac{4}{3}$	4,267
U_1L_2	150	$+16.7$	$+\frac{5}{6}$	2,083
				13,742

$$ d = \frac{SuL}{AE} = \frac{2 \times 13{,}742{,}000}{30{,}000{,}000} = 0.916 \text{ in.} $$

where the deflection is required. Stresses u due to this load are shown in Fig. 3-53b and Table 3-3.

The computations for the deflection are given in Table 3-3. Members not stressed by the 20-kip loads or the dummy unit load are not included. Taking advantage of the symmetry of the truss, we tabulate the values for only half the truss and double the sum. Also, to reduce the amount of calculation, we do not include the modulus of elasticity E, which is equal to 30,000,000, until the very last step, since it is the same for all members.

3-57. Reciprocal Theorem. Consider a structure loaded by a group of independent forces A, and suppose that a second group of forces B are added. The work done by the forces A acting over the displacements due to B will be W_{AB}.

Now, suppose the forces B had been on the structure first, and then load A had been applied. The work done by the forces B acting over the displacements due to A will be W_{BA}.

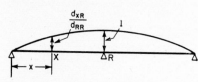

Fig. 3-54. Reaction-influence line for a continuous beam.

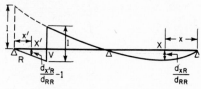

Fig. 3-55. Shear-influence line for a continuous beam.

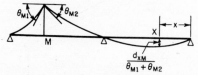

Fig. 3-56. Moment-influence line for a continuous beam.

Fig. 3-57. Deflection-influence line for a continuous beam.

The reciprocal theorem states that $W_{AB} = W_{BA}$.

Some very useful conclusions can be drawn from this equation. For example, there is the reciprocal deflection relationship: **The deflection at a point A due to a load at B is equal to the deflection at B due to the same load applied at A. Also, the rotation at A due to a load (or moment) at B is equal to the rotation at B due to the same load (or moment) applied at A.**

Another consequence is that deflection curves may also be influence lines to some scale for reactions, shears, moments, or deflections (**Muller-Breslau principle**). For example, suppose the influence line for a reaction is to be found; that is, we wish to plot the reaction R as a unit load moves over the structure, which may be statically indeterminate. For the loading condition A, we analyze the structure with a unit load on it at a distance x from some reference point. For loading condition B, we apply a dummy unit vertical load upward at the place where the reaction is to be determined, deflecting the structure off the support. At a distance x from the reference point, the displacement is d_{xR} and over the support the displacement is d_{RR}. Hence $W_{AB} = -1 (d_{xR}) + Rd_{RR}$. On the other hand, W_{BA} is zero, since loading condition A provides no displacement for the dummy unit load at the support in condition B. Consequently, from the reciprocal theorem,

$$R = \frac{d_{xR}}{d_{RR}}$$

Since d_{RR} is a constant, R is proportional to d_{xR}. Hence the influence line for a reaction can be obtained from the deflection curve resulting from a displacement of the support (Fig. 3-54). The magnitude of the reaction is obtained by dividing each ordinate of the deflection curve by the displacement of the support (see also Art. 3-23).

Similarly, the influence line for shear can be obtained from the deflection curve produced by cutting the structure and shifting the cut ends vertically at the point for which the influence line is desired (Fig. 3-55).

The influence line for bending moment can be obtained from the deflection curve produced by cutting the structure and rotating the cut ends at the point for which the influence line is desired (Fig. 3-56).

And finally, it may be noted that the deflection curve for a load of unity at some point of a structure is also the influence line for deflection at that point (Fig. 3-57).

CONTINUOUS BEAMS AND FRAMES

Fixed-end beams, continuous beams, continuous trusses, and rigid frames are statically indeterminate. The equations of equilibrium are not sufficient for the

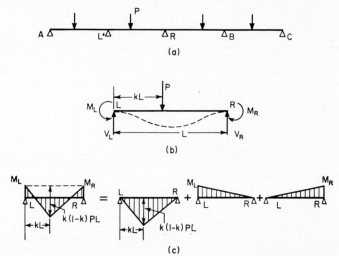

FIG. 3-58. Any span of a continuous beam (a) can be treated as a simple beam, as shown in (b) and (c). In (c) the moment diagram is decomposed into basic components.

determination of all the unknown forces and moments. Additional equations based on a knowledge of the deformations of the member are required.

Hence, while the bending moments in a simply supported beam are determined only by the loads and the span, bending moments in a statically indeterminate member are also a function of the geometry, cross-sectional dimensions, and the modulus of elasticity.

3-58. General Method of Analysis for Continuous Members. Continuous beams and frames consist of members that can be treated as simple beams, the ends of which are prevented by moments from rotating freely. Member LR in the continuous beam $ALRBC$ in Fig. 3-58a, for example, can be isolated, as shown in Fig. 3-58b, and the elastic restraints at the ends replaced by couples M_L and M_R. In this way, LR is converted into a simply supported beam acted upon by transverse loads and end moments.

The bending-moment diagram for LR is shown at the left in Fig. 3-58c. Treating LR as a simple beam, we can break this diagram down into three simple components, as shown at the right of the equal sign in Fig. 3-58c: Thus the bending moment at any section equals the simple-beam moment due to the transverse loads, plus the simple-beam moment due to the end moment at L, plus the simple-beam moment due to the end moment at R,

Obviously, once M_L and M_R have been determined, the shears may be computed by taking moments about any section.   Similarly, if the reactions or shear are known, the bending moments can be calculated.

A general method for determining the elastic forces and moments exerted by redundant supports and members is as follows: Remove as many redundant supports or members as necessary to make the structure statically determinate.   Compute for the actual loads the deflections or rotations of the statically determinate structure in the direction of the forces and couples exerted by the removed supports and members.   Then, in terms of these forces and couples, compute the corresponding deflections or rotations the forces and couples produce in the statically determinate structure (see Arts. 3-55 and 3-31).   Finally, for each redundant support or member write equations that give the known rotations or deflections of the original structure in terms of the deformations of the statically determinate structure.

For example, one method of finding the reactions of the continuous beam $ALRBC$ in Fig. 3-58a is to remove supports L, R, and B temporarily.   The beam is now simply supported between A and C, and the reactions and moments can be computed from the laws of equilibrium.   Beam AC deflects at points L, R, and B, whereas we know that continuous beam $ALRBC$ is prevented from deflecting at these points by the supports there.   This information enables us to write three equations in terms of the three unknown reactions that were eliminated to make the beam statically determinate.

So we first compute the deflections of simple beam AC at L, R, and B due to the loads.   Then, in terms of the unknown reactions, we compute the deflection at L when AC is loaded with only the three reactions.   The first equation is obtained by noting that the sum of this deflection and the deflection at L due to the loads must be zero.   Similarly, equations can be written making the total deflection at R and B, successively, equal to zero.   In this way, three equations with three unknowns are obtained, which can be solved simultaneously to yield the required reactions.

For continuous beams and frames with a large number of redundants, this method becomes unwieldy because of the number of simultaneous equations.   Special methods, like moment distribution, are preferable in such cases.

3-59. Sign Convention.   For moment distribution, the following sign convention is most convenient: A moment acting at an end of a member or at a joint is positive if it tends to rotate the joint clockwise, negative if it tends to rotate the joint counterclockwise.   Hence, in Fig. 3-58, M_R is positive and M_L is negative.

Similarly, the angular rotation at the end of a member is positive if in a clockwise direction, negative if counterclockwise.   Thus, a positive end moment produces a positive end rotation in a simple beam.

For ease in visualizing the shape of the elastic curve under the action of loads and end moments, bending-moment diagrams will be plotted on the tension side of each member.   Hence, if an end moment is represented by a curved arrow, the arrow will point in the direction in which the moment is to be plotted.

3-60. Fixed-end Moments.   A beam so restrained at its ends that no rotation is produced there by the loads is called a fixed-end beam, and the end moments are called fixed-end moments.   Actually, it would be very difficult to construct a beam with ends that are truly fixed.   However, the concept of fixed ends is useful in determining the moments in continuous beams and frames.

Fixed-end moments may be expressed as the product of a coefficient and WL, where W is the total load on the span L.   The coefficient is independent of the properties of other members of the structure.   Thus, any member can be isolated from the rest of the structure and its fixed-end moments computed.   Then, the actual moments in the beam can be found by applying a correction to each fixed-end moment.

Fixed-end moments may be determined conveniently by the moment-area method or the conjugate-beam method (Art. 3-31).   For frames, the **column analogy** is frequently very useful (Cross and Morgan, "Continuous Frames of Reinforced Concrete," John Wiley & Sons, Inc., New York).   This method takes advantage of the mathematical identity between the moments produced by continuity and the fiber stresses in a short column eccentrically loaded.

To find statically indeterminate moments by the column analogy, choose any convenient bending-moment diagram statically consistent with the loads, apply this diagram as the loading on the analogous column, and compute the fiber stresses [see Eqs. (3-36) and (3-41)]. The total moment at any point, thus computed, is the difference between the moments statically determined and the indeterminate moments. The analogous column has the same dimensions as the frame except that at each point of its cross section the width is equal to $1/EI$, where E is the modulus of elasticity and I the moment of inertia of the frame cross section at that point.

Fixed-end moments for several common types of loading on beams of constant moment of inertia (prismatic beams) are given in Figs. 3-59 to 3-62. Also, the curves in Fig. 3-64 enable fixed-end moments to be computed easily for any type of loading on

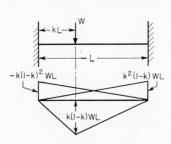

FIG. 3-59. Concentrated load at any point of a fixed-end beam.

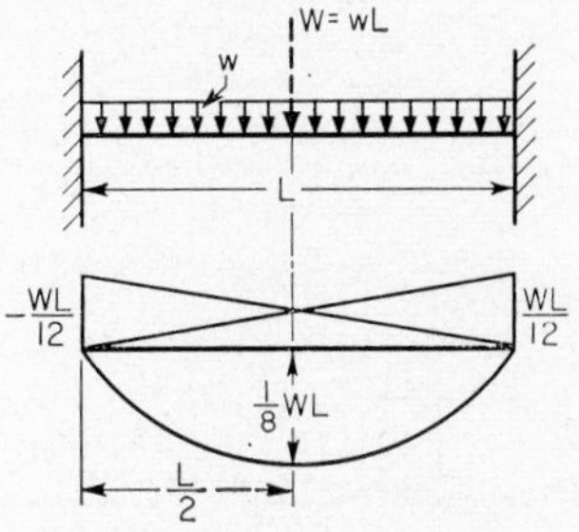

FIG. 3-60. Uniform load on a fixed-end beam.

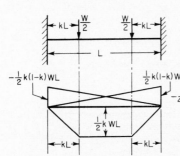

FIG. 3-61. Two equal concentrated loads on a fixed-end beam.

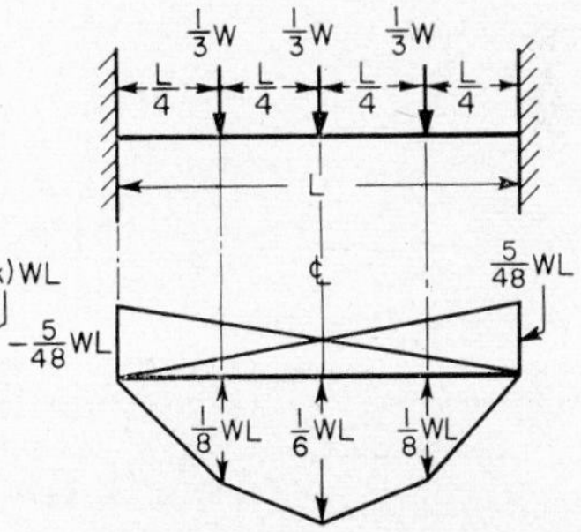

FIG. 3-62. Several equal concentrated loads on a fixed-end beam.

a prismatic beam. Before the curves can be entered, however, certain characteristics of the loading must be calculated. These include $\bar{x}L$, the location of the center of gravity of the loading with respect to one of the loads; $G^2 = \Sigma b_n{}^2 P_n/W$, where b_nL is the distance from each load P_n to the center of gravity of the loading (taken positive to the right); and $S^3 = \Sigma b_n{}^3 P_n/W$. (See case 9, Fig. 3-63.) These values are given in Fig. 3-63 for some common types of loading.

The curves in Fig. 3-64 are entered with the location a of the center of gravity with respect to the left end of the span. At the intersection with the proper G curve, proceed horizontally to the left to the intersection with the proper S line, then vertically to the horizontal scale indicating the coefficient m by which to multiply WL to obtain the fixed-end moment. The curves solve the equations:

$$m_L = \frac{M_L{}^F}{WL} = G^2[1 - 3(1 - a)] + a(1 - a)^2 + S^3 \tag{3-67}$$

$$m_R = \frac{M_R{}^F}{WL} = G^2(1 - 3a) + a^2(1 - a) - S^3 \tag{3-68}$$

where $M_L{}^F$ is the fixed-end moment at the left support and $M_R{}^F$ at the right support.

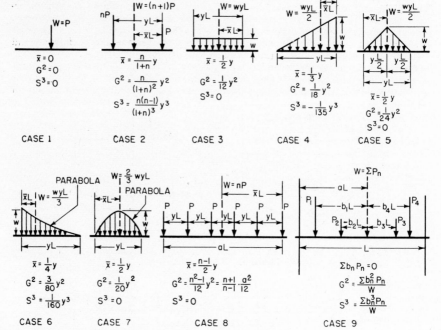

FIG. 3-63. Characteristics of loadings.

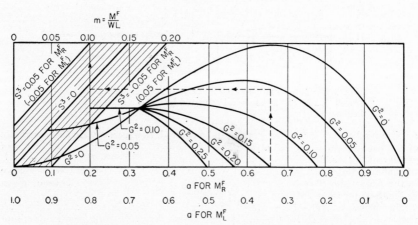

FIG. 3-64. Chart for fixed-end moments due to any type of loading.

As an example of the use of the curves, find the fixed-end moments in a prismatic beam of 20-ft span carrying a triangular loading of 100 kips, similar to the loading shown in case 4, Fig. 3-63, distributed over the entire span, with the maximum intensity at the right support.

Case 4 gives the characteristics of the loading: $y = 1$; the center of gravity is $0.33L$ from the right support, so $a = 0.667$; $G^2 = \frac{1}{18} = 0.056$; and $S^3 = -1/135 = -0.007$. To find M_R^F, we enter Fig. 3-64 with $a = 0.67$ on the upper scale at the bottom of the diagram, and proceed vertically to the estimated location of the intersection of the coordinate with the $G^2 = 0.06$ curve. Then, we move horizontally to the intersection with the line for $S^3 = -0.007$, as indicated by the dash line in Fig. 3-64. Referring to the scale at the top of the diagram, we find the coefficient m_R to be 0.10. Similarly, with $a = 0.67$ on the lowest scale, we find the coefficient m_L to be 0.07. Hence, the fixed-end moment at the right support is $0.10 \times 100 \times 20 = 200$ ft-kips, and at the left support $-0.07 \times 100 \times 20 = -140$ ft-kips.

3-61. Fixed-end Stiffness. To correct a fixed-end moment to obtain the end moment for the actual conditions of end restraint in a continuous structure, the end of the member must be permitted to rotate. The amount it will rotate depends on its stiffness, or resistance to rotation.

The fixed-end stiffness of a beam is defined as the moment required to produce a rotation of unity at the end where it is applied, while the other end is fixed against rotation. It is represented by $K_R{}^F$ in Fig. 3-65.

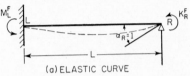

(a) ELASTIC CURVE

For prismatic beams, the fixed-end stiffnesses for both ends are equal to $4EI/L$, where E is the modulus of elasticity, I the moment of inertia of the cross section about the centroidal axis, and L the span (generally taken center to center of supports). When deformations are not required to be calculated, only the relative value of K^F for each member need be known; hence, only the ratio of I to L has to be computed. (For prismatic beams with a hinge at one end, the actual stiffness is $3EI/L$, or three-fourths the fixed-end stiffness.)

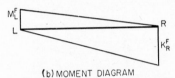

(b) MOMENT DIAGRAM

Fig. 3-65. Fixed-end stiffness.

For beams of variable moment of inertia, the fixed-end stiffness may be calculated by methods presented later in this section or obtained from prepared tables. See Art. 3-62.

3-62. Fixed-end Carry-over Factor. When a moment is applied at one end of a beam, a resisting moment is induced at the far end if that end is restrained against rotation (Fig. 3-65). The ratio of the resisting moment at a fixed end to the applied moment is called the fixed-end carry-over factor C^F.

For prismatic beams, the fixed-end carry-over factor toward either end is 0.5. It should be noted that the applied moment and the resisting moment have the same sign (Fig. 3-65); i.e., if the applied moment acts in a clockwise direction, the carry-over moment also acts clockwise.

For beams of variable moment of inertia, the fixed-end carry-over factor may be calculated by methods presented later in this section or obtained from tables such as those in the "Handbook of Frame Constants," Portland Cement Association, Chicago, Ill. and J. M. Gere, "Moment Distribution Factors for Beams of Tapered I-section," American Institute of Steel Construction, New York, N.Y.

3-63. Moment Distribution by Converging Approximations. The frame in Fig. 3-66 consists of four prismatic members rigidly connected together at O and fixed at ends A, B, C, and D. If an external moment U is applied at O, the sum of the end moments in each member at O must be equal to U. Furthermore, all members must rotate at O through the same angle θ, since they are assumed to be rigidly connected there. Hence, by the definition of fixed-end stiffness, the proportion of U induced in the end of each member at O is equal to the ratio of the stiffness of that member to the sum of the stiffnesses of all the members at the joint.

Suppose a moment of 100 ft-kips is applied at 0, as indicated in Fig. 3-66b. The relative stiffness (or I/L) is assumed as shown in the circle on each member. The distribution factors for the moment at O are computed from the stiffnesses and shown in the boxes. For example, the distribution factor for OA equals its stiffness divided by the sum of the stiffnesses of all the members at the joint: $3/(3 + 2 + 4 + 1) = 0.3$.

Hence, the moment induced in OA at O is $0.3 \times 100 = 30$ ft-kips. Similarly, OB gets 10 ft-kips, OC 40 ft-kips, and OD 20 ft-kips.

Because the far ends of these members are fixed, one-half of these moments are carried over to them. Thus $M_{AO} = 0.5 \times 30 = 15$; $M_{BO} = 0.5 \times 10 = 5$; $M_{CO} = 0.5 \times 40 = 20$; and $M_{DO} = 0.5 \times 20 = 10$.

Most structures consist of frames similar to the one in Fig. 3-66, or even simpler, joined together. Though the ends of the members are not fixed, the technique employed for the frame in Fig. 3-66b can be applied to find end moments in such continuous structures.

Before the general method is presented, one short cut is worth noting. Advantage can be taken when a member has a hinged end to reduce the work of distributing moments. This is done by using the true stiffness of the member instead of the fixed-end stiffness. (For a prismatic beam, the stiffness of a member with one end hinged is three-fourths the fixed-end stiffness; for a beam with variable I, it is equal to the fixed-end stiffness times $1 - C_L{}^F C_R{}^F$.) Naturally, the carry-over factor toward the hinge is zero.

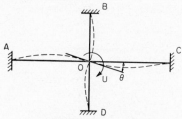

(a) ELASTIC CURVE FOR
UNBALANCED MOMENT AT JOINT O

When a joint is neither fixed nor pinned but is restrained by elastic members connected there, moments can be distributed by a series of converging approximations. All joints are locked against rotation. As a result, the loads will create fixed-end moments at the ends of every loaded member. At each joint, a moment equal to the algebraic sum of the fixed-end moments there is required to hold it fixed. Then, one joint is unlocked at a time by applying a moment equal but opposite in sign to the moment that was needed to prevent rotation. The unlocking moment must be distributed to the members at the joint in proportion to their fixed-end stiffnesses and the distributed moments carried over to the far ends.

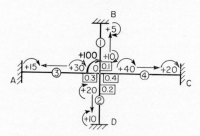

(b) STIFFNESSES AND DISTRIBUTION
FACTORS FOR A FRAME

FIG. 3-66. Moments in a simple frame.

After all joints have been released at least once, it generally will be necessary to repeat the process—sometimes several times—before the corrections to the fixed-end moments become negligible. To reduce the number of cycles, the unlocking of joints should start with those having the greatest unbalanced moments.

Suppose the end moments are to be found for the continuous beam $ABCD$ in Fig. 3-67. The I/L values for all spans are equal; therefore, the relative fixed-end stiffness for all members is unity. However, since A is a hinged end, the computation can be shortened by using the actual relative stiffness, which is $\frac{3}{4}$. Relative stiffnesses for all members are shown in the circle on each member. The distribution factors are shown in boxes at each joint.

The computation starts with determination of fixed-end moments for each member (Art. 3-60). These are assumed to have been found and are given on the first line in Fig. 3-67. The greatest unbalanced moment is found from inspection to be at hinged end A; so this joint is unlocked first. Since there are no other members at the joint, the full unlocking moment of $+400$ is distributed to AB at A and one-half of this is carried over to B. The unbalance at B now is $+400 - 480$ plus the carry-over of $+200$ from A, or a total of $+120$. Hence, a moment of -120 must be applied and distributed to the members at B by multiplying by the distribution factors in the corresponding boxes.

The net moment at B could be found now by adding the entries for each member at the joint. However, it generally is more convenient to delay the summation until the last cycle of distribution has been completed.

The moment distributed to BA need not be carried over to A, because the carry-over factor toward the hinged end is zero. However, half the moment distributed to BC is carried over to C.

Similarly, joint C is unlocked and half the distributed moments carried over to B and D, respectively. Joint D should not be unlocked, since it actually is a fixed end. Thus, the first cycle of moment distribution has been completed.

The second cycle is carried out in the same manner. Joint B is released, and the distributed moment in BC is carried over to C. Finally, C is unlocked, to complete the cycle. Adding the entries for the end of each member yields the final moments.

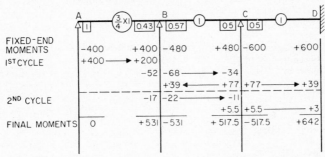

Fig. 3-67. Moment distribution by converging approximations.

	A (AB-L)	(AB mid)	B (AB-R)	B (BC-L)	(BC mid)	C (BC-R)	C (CD-L)	(CD mid)	D (CD-R)	D (DE-L)	(DE mid)	E (DE-R)
1. RELATIVE STIFFNESS			$K^F=1$			$K^F=1$			$K^F=1$			$K^F=1$
2. DISTRIBUTION FACTOR	1/3		1/4	1/4		1/4	1/4		1/4	1/4		1/3
3. F.E.M. DEAD LOAD	–		+91	-37		+37	-70		+70	-59		–
4. F.E.M. TOTAL LOAD	-172	+99	+172	-78	+73	+78	-147	+85	+147	-126	+63	+126
5. CARRY-OVER	-17	+11	+29	-1	+1	-2	-11	+7	+14	-21	+13	+7
6. ADDITION	-189	+18	+201	-79	-1	+76	-158	+9	+161	-147	+5	+133
7. DISTRIBUTION	+63		-30	-30		+21	+21		-4	-4		-44
8. MAX. MOMENTS	-126	+128	+171	-109	+73	+97	-137	+101	+157	-151	+81	+89

Fig. 3-68. Moments in a continuous frame.

3-64. Continuous Frames. In practice, the problem is to find the maximum end moments and interior moments produced by the worst combination of loading. For maximum moment at the end of a beam, live load should be placed on that beam and on the beam adjoining the end for which the moment is to be computed. Spans adjoining these two should be assumed to be carrying only dead load.

For maximum mid-span moments, the beam under consideration should be fully loaded, but adjoining spans should be assumed to be carrying only dead load.

The work involved in distributing moments due to dead and live loads in continuous frames in buildings can be greatly simplified by isolating each floor. The tops of the upper columns and the bottoms of the lower columns can be assumed fixed. Furthermore, the computations can be condensed considerably by following the procedure recommended in "Continuity in Concrete Building Frames," Portland Cement Association, Chicago, Ill., and indicated in Fig. 3-68.

Figure 3-68 presents the complete calculation for maximum end and mid-span moments in four floor beams AB, BC, CD, and DE. Building columns are assumed to be fixed at the story above and below. None of the beam or column sections is known to begin with; so as a start, all members will be assumed to have a fixed-end stiffness of unity, as indicated on the first line of the calculation.

On the second line, the distribution factors for each end of the beams are shown, calculated from the stiffnesses (Arts. 3-61 and 3-63). Column stiffnesses are not shown, because column moments will not be computed until moment distribution to the beams has been completed. Then the sum of the column moments at each joint may be easily computed, since they are the moments needed to make the sum of the end moments at the joint equal to zero. The sum of the column moments at each joint can then be distributed to each column there in proportion to its stiffness. In this problem, each column will get one-half the sum of the column moments.

Fixed-end moments at each beam end for dead load are shown on the third line, just above the heavy line, and fixed-end moments for live plus dead load on the fourth line. Corresponding mid-span moments for the fixed-end condition also are shown on the fourth line, and like the end moments will be corrected to yield actual mid-span moments.

For maximum end moment at A, beam AB must be fully loaded, but BC should carry dead load only. Holding A fixed, we first unlock joint B, which has a total-load fixed-end moment of $+172$ in BA and a dead-load fixed-end moment of -37 in BC. The releasing moment required, therefore, is $-(172 - 37)$, or -135. When B is released, a moment of $-135 \times \frac{1}{4}$ is distributed to BA. One-half of this is carried over to A, or $-135 \times \frac{1}{4} \times \frac{1}{2} = -17$. This value is entered as the carry-over at A on the fifth line in Fig. 3-68. Joint B is then relocked.

At A, for which we are computing the maximum moment, we have a total-load fixed-end moment of -172 and a carry-over of -17, making the total -189, shown on the sixth line. To release A, a moment of $+189$ must be applied to the joint. Of this, $189 \times \frac{1}{3}$, or 63, is distributed to AB, as indicated on the seventh line of the calculation. Finally, the maximum moment at A is found by adding lines 6 and 7: $-189 + 63 = -126$.

For maximum moment at B, both AB and BC must be fully loaded, but CD should carry only dead load. We begin the determination of the moment at B by first releasing joints A and C, for which the corresponding carry-over moments at BA and BC are $+29$ and $-(+78 - 70) \times \frac{1}{4} \times \frac{1}{2} = -1$, shown on the fifth line in Fig. 3-68. These bring the total fixed-end moments in BA and BC to $+201$ and -79, respectively. The releasing moment required is $-(201 - 79) = -122$. Multiplying this by the distribution factors for BA and BC when joint B is released, we find the distributed moments, -30, entered on line 7. The maximum end moments finally are obtained by adding lines 6 and 7: $+171$ at BA and -109 at BC. Maximum moments at C, D, and E are computed and entered in Fig. 3-68 in a similar manner. This procedure is equivalent to two cycles of moment distribution.

The computation of maximum mid-span moments in Fig. 3-68 is based on the assumption that in each beam the mid-span moment is the sum of the simple-beam mid-span moment and one-half the algebraic difference of the final end moments (the span carries full load but adjacent spans only dead load). Instead of starting with the simple-beam moment, however, we begin with the mid-span moment for the fixed-end condition and apply two corrections. In each span, these corrections are equal to the carry-over moments entered on line 5 for the two ends of the beam multiplied by a factor.

For beams with variable moment of inertia, the factor is $\pm\frac{1}{2}[(1/C^F) + D - 1]$ where C^F is the fixed-end carry-over factor toward the end for which the correction factor is being computed and D the distribution factor for that end. The plus sign is used for correcting the carry-over at the right end of a beam, and the minus sign for the carry-over at the left end. For prismatic beams, the correction factor becomes $\pm\frac{1}{2}(1 + D)$.

For example, to find the corrections to the mid-span moment in AB, we first multiply the carry-over at A on line 5, -17, by $-\frac{1}{2}(1 + \frac{1}{3})$. The correction, $+11$, is also entered on the fifth line. Then, we multiply the carry-over at B, $+29$, by $+\frac{1}{2}(1 + \frac{1}{4})$ and enter the correction, $+18$, on line 6. The final mid-span moment is the sum of lines 4, 5, and 6: $+99 + 11 + 18 = +128$. Other mid-span moments in Fig. 3-68 are obtained in a similar manner.

3-65. Moment-influence Factors.   In certain types of problems, particularly those in which different types of loading conditions must be investigated, it may be convenient to find maximum end moments from a table of moment-influence factors. This table is made up by listing for the end of each member in the structure the moment induced in that end when a moment (for convenience, $+1,000$) is applied to every joint successively.   Once this table has been prepared no additional moment distribution is necessary for computing the end moments due to any loading condition.

For a specific loading pattern, the moment at any beam end M_{AB} may be obtained from the moment-influence table by multiplying the entries under AB for the various joints by the actual unbalanced moments at those joints divided by 1,000, and summing (see also Art. 3-67 and Table 3-4).

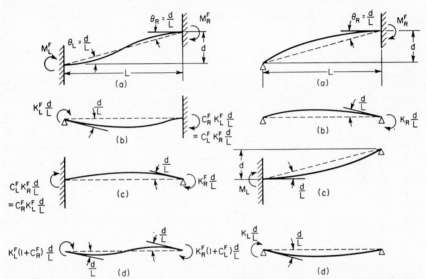

FIG. 3-69. Moments due to deflection of a fixed-end beam.

FIG. 3-70. Moments due to deflection of a beam with one end fixed, one end hinged.

3-66. Deflection of Supports.   For some problems, it is convenient to know the effect of a deflection of a support normal to the original position of a continuous beam. But the moment-distribution method is based on the assumption that such movement of a support does not occur.   However, the method can be modified to evaluate the end moments resulting from a support movement.

The procedure is to distribute moments, as usual, assuming no deflection at the supports.   This implies that additional external forces are exerted at the supports. These forces can be computed.   Then, equal and opposite forces are applied to the structure to produce the final configuration, and the moments that they produce are distributed as usual.   These moments added to those obtained with undeflected supports yield the final moments.

To apply this procedure, it is first necessary to know the fixed-end moments for a beam with supports at different levels.   In Fig. 3-69a, the right end of a beam with span L is at a height d above the left end.   To find the fixed-end moments, we first consider the left end hinged, as in Fig. 3-69b.   Noting that a line connecting the two supports makes an angle approximately equal to d/L (its tangent) with the original position of the beam, we apply a moment at the hinged end to produce an end rotation there equal to d/L.   By the definition of stiffness, this moment equals $K_L^F d/L$.   The carry-over to the right end is C_R^F times this.

By the law of reciprocal deflections (Art. 3-57), the fixed-end moment at the right end of a beam due to a rotation of the other end is equal to the fixed-end moment at the left end of the beam due to the same rotation at the right end. Therefore, the carry-over moment for the right end in Fig. 3-69b is also equal to $C_L{}^F K_R{}^F d/L$ (see Fig. 3-69c). By adding the end moments for the loading conditions in Fig. 3-69b and c, we obtain the end moments in Fig. 3-69d, which is equivalent to the deflected beam in Fig. 3-69a:

$$M_L{}^F = K_L{}^F(1 + C_R{}^F) \frac{d}{L} \tag{3-69}$$

$$M_R{}^F = K_R{}^F(1 + C_L{}^F) \frac{d}{L} \tag{3-70}$$

In a similar manner, the fixed-end moment can be found for a beam with one end hinged and the supports at different levels (Fig. 3-70):

$$M^F = K \frac{d}{L} \tag{3-71}$$

where K is the actual stiffness for the end of the beam that is fixed. For prismatic beams, this value is three-fourths that for fixed-end stiffness; for beams of variable moment of inertia, it is equal to the fixed-end stiffness times $(1 - C_L{}^F C_R{}^F)$.

3-67. Procedure for Sidesway. The problem of computing sidesway moments in rigid frames is conveniently solved by the following method:

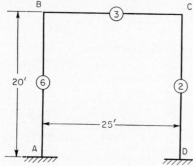

FIG. 3-71. Rigid frame.

1. Apply forces to the structure to prevent sidesway while the fixed-end moments due to loads are distributed.

2. Compute the moments due to these forces.

3. Combine the moments obtained in steps 1 and 2 to eliminate the effect of the forces that prevented sidesway.

Suppose the rigid frame in Fig. 3-71 is subjected to a 2,000-lb horizontal load acting to the right at the level of beam BC. The first step is to compute the moment-influence factors (Table 3-4) by applying moments of $+1,000$ at joints B and C, assuming sidesway prevented. Since there are no intermediate loads on the beams and columns, the only fixed-end moments that need be considered are those in the columns due to lateral deflection of the frame caused by the horizontal load.

Table 3-4. Moment-influence Factors for Fig. 3-71

Member	+1,000 at B	+1,000 at C
AB	351	-105
BA	702	-210
BC	298	210
CB	70	579
CD	-70	421
DC	-35	210

This deflection, however, is not known initially. So we assume an arbitrary deflection, which produces a fixed-end moment of $-1,000M$ at the top of column CD. M is an unknown constant to be determined from the fact that the sum of the shears in the deflected columns must be equal to the 2,000-lb load.   The same deflection also produces a moment of $-1,000M$ at the bottom of CD [see Eqs. (3-69) and (3-70)].

From the geometry of the structure, we furthermore note that the deflection of B relative to A is equal to the deflection of C relative to D.   Then, according to Eqs. (3-69) and (3-70), the fixed-end moments in the columns are proportional to the stiffnesses of the columns and hence are equal in AB to $-1,000M \times \frac{6}{2} = -3,000M$. The column fixed-end moments are entered in the first line of Table 3-5, which is called a moment-collection table.

Table 3-5. Moment-collection Table for Fig. 3-71

Remarks	AB		BA		BC		CB		CD		DC	
	+	−	+	−	+	−	+	−	+	−	+	−
Sidesway, FEM.......	....	3,000M	....	3,000M	......					1,000M	.....	1,000M
B moments.........	1,053M	....	2,106M	......	894M	......		210M		210M	.....	105M
C moments.........		105M	......	210M	210M	......	579M	....	421M	......	210M	
Partial sum.........	1,053M	3,105M	2,106M	3,210M	1,104M	......	789M	....	421M	1,210M	210M	1,105M
Totals..............	....	2,052M	......	1,104M	1,104M	......	789M	....		789M	.....	895M
For 2,000-lb load........	....	17,000	....	9,100	9,100	......	6,500	....		6,500	.....	7,400
4,000-lb load, FEM.....	....		......		......	12,800	3,200					
B moments.........	4,490	......	8,980	....	3,820	......	897	....		897	.....	448
C moments.........	336	......	672	....		672	......	1,853	....	1,347	.....	672
Partial sum.........	4,826	......	9,652	....	3,820	13,472	4,097	1,853	....	2,244	.....	1,120
No-sidesway sum...	4,826	......	9,652	•		9,652	2,244	....		2,244	.....	1,120
Sidesway M.........	....	4,710	......	2,540	2,540	......	1,810	....		1,810	.....	2,060
Totals.............	120	......	7,110	....	7,110	4,050	....		4,050	.....	3,180

In the deflected position of the frame, joints B and C are unlocked.   First, we apply a releasing moment of $+3,000M$ at B and distribute it by multiplying by 3 the entries in the column marked " $+1,000$ at B " in Table 3-4.   Similarly, a releasing moment of $+1,000M$ is applied at C and distributed with the aid of Table 3-4.   The distributed moments are entered in the second and third lines of Table 3-5.   The final moments are the sum of the fixed-end moments and the distributed moments and are given in the fifth line.

Isolating each column and taking moments about one end, we find that the overturning moment due to the shear is equal to the sum of the end moments.   We have one such equation for each column.   Adding these equations, noting that the sum of the shears equals 2,000 lb, we obtain

$$-M(2,052 + 1,104 + 789 + 895) = -2,000 \times 20$$

from which we find $M = 8.26$.   This value is substituted in the sidesway totals in Table 3-5 to yield the end moments for the 2,000-lb horizontal load.

Suppose now a vertical load of 4,000 lb is applied to BC of the rigid frame in Fig. 3-71, 5 ft from B.   Tables 3-4 and 3-5 can again be used to determine the end moments with a minimum of labor:

The fixed-end moment at B, with sidesway prevented, is $-12,800$, and at $C + 3,200$. With the joints still locked, the frame is permitted to move laterally an arbitrary amount, so that in addition to the fixed-end moments due to the 4,000-lb load, column fixed-end moments of $-3,000M$ at B and $-1,000M$ at C are induced.   Table 3-5 already indicates the effect of relieving these column moments by unlocking joints B and C.   We now have to superimpose the effect of releasing joints B and C to relieve the fixed-end moments for the vertical load.   This we can do with the aid of Table 3-4. The distribution is shown in the lower part of Table 3-5.   The sums of the fixed-end moments and distributed moments for the 4,000-lb load are shown on the line, "No-sideway sum."

The unknown M can be evaluated from the fact that the sum of the horizontal forces acting on the columns must be zero. This is equivalent to requiring that the sum of the column end moments equals zero:

$$-M(2{,}052 + 1{,}104 + 789 + 895) + 4{,}826 + 9{,}652 - 2{,}244 - 1{,}120 = 0$$

from which $M = 2.30$. This value is substituted in the sideway totals in Table 3-5 to yield the sideway moments for the 4,000-lb load. The addition of these moments to the totals for no sideway yields the final moments.

This procedure enables one-story bents with straight beams to be analyzed with the necessity of solving only one equation with one unknown regardless of the number of bays. If the frame is several stories high, the procedure can be applied to each story. Since an arbitrary horizontal deflection is introduced at each floor or roof level, there are as many unknowns and equations as there are stories.

The procedure is more difficult to apply to bents with curved or polygonal members between the columns. The effect of the change in the horizontal projection of the curved or polygonal portion of the bent must be included in the calculations (Cross and Morgan, "Continuous Frames of Reinforced Concrete," John Wiley & Sons, Inc., New York; "Gabled Concrete Roof Frames Analyzed by Moment Distribution," Portland Cement Association, Chicago, Ill.). In many cases, it may be easier to analyze the bent as a curved beam (arch) or by the column analogy.

3-68. Single-cycle Moment Distribution. In the method of moment distribution by converging approximations, all joints but the one being unlocked are considered fixed. In distributing moments, the stiffnesses and carry-over factors used are based on this assumption. However, if actual stiffnesses and carry-over factors are employed, moments can be distributed throughout continuous frames in a single cycle.

Formulas for actual stiffnesses and carry-over factors can be written in several simple forms. The equations given in the following text were chosen to permit the use of existing tables for beams of variable moment of inertia that are based on fixed-end stiffnesses and fixed-end carry-over factors, such as the "Handbook of Frame Constants," Portland Cement Association, Chicago, Ill.

Considerable simplification of the formulas results if they are based on the simple-beam stiffness of members of continuous frames. This value can always be obtained from tables of fixed-end properties by multiplying the fixed-end stiffness given in the tables by $(1 - C_L{}^F C_R{}^F)$, in which $C_L{}^F$ is the fixed-end carry-over factor to the left and $C_R{}^F$ is the fixed-end carry-over factor to the right.

To derive the basic constants needed, we apply a unit moment to one end of a member, considering it simply supported (Fig. 3-72a). The end rotation at the support where the moment is applied is α, and at the far end, the rotation is β. By the dummy-load method (Art. 3-55), if x is measured from the β end,

$$\alpha = \int_0^L \frac{x^2}{EI_x}\, dx \tag{3-72}$$

$$\beta = \int_0^L \frac{x(L - x)}{EI_x}\, dx \tag{3-73}$$

in which I_x = moment of inertia at a section a distance of x from the β end
        E = modulus of elasticity

The simple-beam stiffness K of the member is the moment required to produce a rotation of unity at the end where it is applied (Fig. 3-72b). Hence, at each end of a member, $K = 1/\alpha$.

For prismatic beams, K has the same value for both ends and is equal to $3EI/L$. For haunched beams, K for each end can be obtained from tables for fixed-end stiffnesses, as mentioned previously, or by numerical integration of Eq. (3-72).

While the value of α, and consequently of K, is different at opposite ends of an unsymmetrical beam, the value of β is the same for both ends, in accordance with the law of reciprocal deflections (compare Fig. 3-72a and c). This is also evident from Eq. (3-73), where $L - x$ can be substituted for x without changing the value of the integral.

Now, if we apply a moment J at one end of a simple beam to produce a rotation of unity at the other end (Fig. 3-72d), this moment will be equal to $1/\beta$ and will have the same value regardless of the end at which it is applied. As can be shown, K/J is equal to the fixed-end carry-over factor.

J is equal to $6EI/L$ for prismatic beams. For haunched beams, it can be computed by numerical integration of Eq. (3-73).

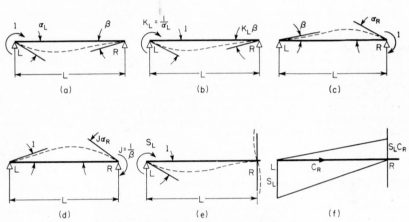

Fig. 3-72. End rotations of simple beams.

The actual stiffness S of the end of an unloaded span is the moment producing a rotation of unity at the end where it is applied when the other end of the beam is restrained against rotation by other members of the structure (Fig. 3-72e).

The bending-moment diagram for a moment S_L applied at the left end of a member of a continuous frame is shown in Fig. 3-72f. As indicated, the moment carried over to the far end is $S_L C_R$, where C_R is the carry-over factor to the right. At L, the rotation produced by S_L alone is S_L/K_L, and by $S_L C_R$ alone is $-S_L C_R/J$. The sum of these angles must equal unity by definition of stiffness:

$$\frac{S_L}{K_L} - \frac{S_L C_R}{J} = 1$$

Solving for S_L and noting that $K_L/J = C_L{}^F$, the fixed-end carry-over factor to the left, we find the formula for the stiffness of the left end of a member:

$$S_L = \frac{K_L}{1 - C_L{}^F C_R} \tag{3-74}$$

For the right end:

$$S_R = \frac{K_R}{1 - C_R{}^F C_L} \tag{3-75}$$

For prismatic beams, the stiffness formulas reduce to

$$S_L = \frac{K}{1 - C_R/2} \qquad S_R = \frac{K}{1 - C_L/2} \tag{3-76}$$

where $K = 3EI/L$

When the far end of a prismatic beam is fully fixed against rotation, the carry-over factor equals $\frac{1}{2}$. Hence, the fixed-end stiffness equals $4K/3$. This indicates that the effect of partial restraint on prismatic beams is to vary the stiffness between K for no restraint and $1.33K$ for full restraint. Because of this small variation, an estimate of the actual stiffness of a beam may be sufficiently accurate in many cases.

The restraint R at the end of an unloaded beam in a continuous frame is the moment applied at that end to produce a unit rotation in all the members of the joint. Since the sum of the moments at the joint must be zero, R must be equal to the sum of the stiffnesses of the adjacent ends of the members connected to the given beam at that joint.

Furthermore, the moment induced in any of these other members bears the same ratio to the applied moment as the stiffness of the member does to the restraint. Consequently, *end moments are distributed at a joint in proportion to the stiffnesses of the members.*

Actual carry-over factors can be computed by modifying the fixed-end carry-over factors. In Fig. 3-72e and f, by definition of restraint, the rotation at joint R is $-S_L C_R / R_R$, which must be equal to the rotation of the beam at R due to the moments at L and R. The rotation due to $S_L C_R$ alone is equal to $S_L C_R / K_R$, and the rotation due to S_L alone is $-S_L / J$. Hence $-S_L C_R / R_R = S_L C_R / K_R - S_L / J$. Solving for C_R and noting that $K_R / J = C_R{}^F$, the fixed-end carry-over factor to the right, we find the actual carry-over factor to the right:

$$C_R = \frac{C_R{}^F}{1 + K_R/R_R} \tag{3-77}$$

Similarly, the actual carry-over factor to the left is

$$C_L = \frac{C_L{}^F}{1 + K_L/R_L} \tag{3-78}$$

In analyzing a continuous beam, we generally know the carry-over factors toward the ends of the first and last spans. Starting with these values, we can calculate the rest of the carry-over factors and the stiffnesses of the members. However, in many frames, there are no end conditions known in advance. To analyze these structures, we must assume several carry-over factors.

This will not complicate the analysis, because in many cases it will be found unnecessary to correct the values of C based on assumed carry-over factors of preceding spans. The reason is that C is not very sensitive to the restraint at far ends of adjacent members. When carry-over factors are estimated, the greatest accuracy will be attained if the choice of assumed values is restricted to members subject to the greatest restraint.

A very good approximation to the carry-over factor for prismatic beams may be obtained from the following formula, which is based on the assumption that far ends of adjacent members are subject to equal restraint:

$$C = \frac{\Sigma K - K}{2(\Sigma K - \delta K)} \tag{3-79}$$

where ΣK = sum of K values of all members at joint toward which carry-over factor is acting

   K = simple-beam stiffness of member for which carry-over factor is being computed

   δ = a factor that varies from zero for no restraint to $\frac{1}{4}$ for full restraint at far ends of connecting members

Since δ varies within such narrow limits, it affects C very little.

To illustrate the estimation and calculation of carry-over factors, the carry-over factors and stiffnesses in the clockwise direction will be computed for the frame in Fig. 3-73a. Relative I/L, or K values, are given in the circles.

A start will be made by estimating C_{AB}. Taking $\delta = \frac{1}{8}$, we apply Eq. (3-79) at B with $K = 3$ and $\Sigma K = 5$ and find $C_{AB} = 0.216$, as shown in Fig. 3-73a. We can now compute the stiffness S_{AB} employing Eq. (3-76): $S_{AB} = 3/(1 - 0.108) = 3.37$. Noting that $R_{AD} = S_{AB}$, we can use the exact formula [Eq. (3-78)] to obtain the carry-over factor for DA: $C_{DA} = 0.5/(1 + 6/3.37) = 0.180$. Continuing around the frame in this manner, we return to C_{AB} and recalculate it by Eq. (3-78), obtaining 0.221. This differs only slightly from the estimated value. The change in C_{DA} due to the new value of C_{AB} is negligible.

If a bending moment of 1,000 ft-lb were introduced at A in AB, it would induce a moment of 1,000 $C_{AB} = 221$ ft-lb at B; $221 \times 0.321 = 71$ ft-lb at C; 71×0.344 $= 24$ ft-lb at D; $24 \times 0.180 = 4$ ft-lb at A, etc.

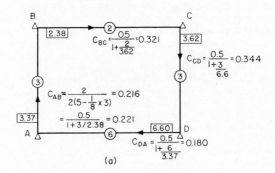

(a)

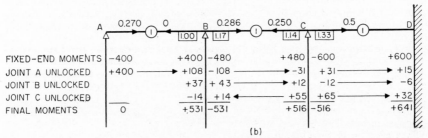

(b)

Fig. 3-73. Moments in a quadrangular frame.

To demonstrate how the moments in a continuous beam would be computed, the end moments will be determined for the beam in Fig. 3-73b, which is identical with the one in Fig. 3-67 for which moments were obtained by converging approximations. Relative I/L, or K values, are shown in the circles on each span. Since A is a hinged end, $C_{BA} = 0$. $S_{BA} = 1/(1 - 0) = 1$. Since there is only one member joined to BC at B, $R_{BC} = S_{BA}$, and $C_{CB} = 0.5/(1 + 1/1) = 0.250$. With this value, we compute $S_{CB} = 1.14$. To obtain the carry-over factors for the opposite direction, we start with $C_{CD} = 0.5$, since we know D is a fixed end. This enables us to compute $S_{CD} = 1.33$ and the remainder of the beam constants.

The fixed-end moments are given on the first line of calculations in Fig. 3-73b. We start the distribution by unlocking A by applying a releasing moment of $+400$. Since A is unrestrained, the full 400 is given to A and $400 \times 0.270 = 108$ is carried over to B. If several members had been connected to AB at B, this moment, with sign changed, would be distributed to them in proportion to their stiffnesses. But since only one member is connected at B, the moment at BC is -108. Next, $-108 \times 0.286 = -31$ is carried over to C. Finally, a moment of $+15$ is carried to D.

Then, joint B is unlocked. The unbalanced moment of $400 - 480 = -80$ is counteracted with a moment of $+80$, which is distributed to BA and BC in proportion to their stiffnesses (shown in the boxes at the joint). BC, for example, gets

$$80 \times \frac{1.17}{(1.17 + 1.00)} = 43$$

The carry-over to C is $43 \times 0.286 = 12$, and to D, -6.

Similarly, the unbalanced moment at C is counteracted and distributed to CB and CD in proportion to the stiffnesses shown in the boxes at C, then carried over to B and D. The final moments are the sum of the fixed-end and distributed moments.

On occasion, advantage can be taken of certain properties of loads and structures to save work in distribution by using carry-over factors as the ratio of end moments in loaded members. For example, suppose it is obvious, from symmetry of loading and structure, that there will be no end rotation at an interior support. The part of the structure on one side of this support can be isolated and the moments distributed only in this part, with the carry-over factor toward the support taken as C^F.

Again, suppose it is evident that the final end moments at opposite ends of a span must be equal in magnitude and sign. Isolate the structure on each side of this beam and distribute moments only in each part, with the carry-over factor for this span taken as 1.

3-69. Method for Checking Moment Distribution. End moments computed for a continuous structure must be in accordance with both the laws of equilibrium and the requirements of continuity. At each joint, therefore, the sum of the moments must be equal to zero (or to an external moment applied there), and the end of every member connected there must rotate through the same angle. It is a simple matter to determine whether the sum of the moments is zero, but further calculation is needed to prove that the moments yield the same rotation for the end of each member at a joint. The following method not only will indicate that the requirements of continuity are satisfied but also will tend to correct automatically any mistakes that may have been made in computing the end moments.

Consider a joint O made up of several members OA, OB, OC, etc. The members are assumed to be loaded and the calculation of end moments to have started with fixed-end moments. For any one of the members, say OA, the end rotation at O for the fixed-end condition is

$$O = \frac{M_{OA}{}^F}{K_{OA}} - \frac{M_{AO}{}^F}{J_{OA}} - \phi \tag{3-80}$$

where $M_{OA}{}^F$ = fixed-end moment at O
  $M_{AO}{}^F$ = fixed-end moment at A
  K_{OA} = simple-beam stiffness at O
  J_{OA} = moment required at A to produce a unit rotation at O when the span is considered simply supported
  ϕ = simple-beam end rotation at O due to loads
For the final end moments, the rotation at O is

$$\theta = \frac{M_{OA}}{K_{OA}} - \frac{M_{AO}}{J_{OA}} - \phi \tag{3-81}$$

Subtracting Eq. (3-80) from Eq. (3-81) and multiplying by K_{OA} yields

$$K_{OA}\theta = M_{OA} - M_{OA}{}^F - C_{AO}{}^F M'_{OA} \tag{3-82}$$

in which the fixed-end carry-over factor toward O, $C_{AO}{}^F$, has been substituted for K_{OA}/J_{OA}, and M'_{OA} for $M_{AO} - M_{AO}{}^F$. An expression analogous to Eq. (3-82) can be written for each of the other members at O. Adding these to Eq. (3-82), we obtain

$$\theta \Sigma K_O = \Sigma M_O - \Sigma M_O{}^F - \Sigma C_O{}^F M'_O \tag{3-83}$$

Equating the value of θ obtained from Eqs. (3-82) and (3-83) and solving for M_{OA}, we determine the equations that will check the joint for continuity:

$$M_{OA} = M_{OA}{}^F + C_{AO}{}^F M_{OA}' - m_{OA} \tag{3-84}$$

$$m_{OA} = \frac{K_{OA}}{\Sigma K_O} (-\Sigma M_O + \Sigma M_O{}^F + \Sigma C_O{}^F M_O') \tag{3-85}$$

Similar equations can be written for the other members at O by substituting the proper letter for A in the subscripts.

If the calculations based on these equations are carried out in table form, the equations prove to be surprisingly simple (see Tables 3-6 and 3-7).

For prismatic beams, the terms $C^F M'$ become $\frac{1}{2}$ the change in the fixed-end moment at the far end of each member at a joint.

For example, suppose we want to check the beam in Fig. 3-73b. Each joint and the ends of the members connected are listed in Table 3-6, and a column is provided for the summation of the various terms for each joint. K values are given on line 1, the

Table 3-6. Moment-distribution Check
(No deflection at supports)

Line No.	Term	Joint A		Joint B			Joint C			Joint D	
		AB	Sum	BA	BC	Sum	CB	CD	Sum	DC	Sum
1	K	1	1	1	1	2	1	1	2	1	∞
2	M	0	0	+600	−600	0	+450	−450	0	+700	
3	M^F	−400	−400	+400	−480	−80	+480	−600	−120	+600	
						First Cycle					
4	$\frac{1}{2}M'$	+100	+100	+200	−15	+185	−60	+50	−10	+75	
5	$-m$	+300	+300	−53	−52	−105	+65	+65	+130	0	
6	M	0	0	+547	−547	0	+485	−485	0	+675	
						Second Cycle					
7	$\frac{1}{2}M'$	.....	.....	+200	+2	+202	−33	+37	+4	+57	
8	$-m$	.....	.....	−61	−61	−122	+58	+58	+116	0	
9	M	.....	.....	+539	−539	0	+505	−505	0	+657	

end moments to be checked on line 2, and the fixed-end moments on line 3. On line 4 is entered one-half the difference obtained when the fixed-end moment is subtracted from the final moment at the far end of each member. $-m$ is placed on line 5 and the corrected end moment on line 6. The $-m$ values are obtained from the summation columns by adding line 2 to the negative of the sum of lines 3 and 4 and distributing the result to the members of the joint in proportion to the K values. The corrected moment M is the sum of lines 3, 4, and 5.

Assume that a mistake was made in computing the end moments for Fig. 3-73b, giving the results shown on line 2 of Table 3-6 for the fixed-end moments on line 3. The correct moments can be obtained as follows:

At joint B, the sum of the incorrect moments is zero, as shown in the summation column on line 2. The sum of the fixed-end moments at B is −80, as indicated on line 3. For BA, $\frac{1}{2} M'$ is obtained from lines 2 and 3 of the column for AB: $\frac{1}{2} \times (0 + 400) = +200$, which is entered on line 4. The line 4 entry for BC is obtained from CB: $\frac{1}{2} \times (450 - 480) = -15$. The sum of the line 4 values at B is therefore $200 - 15 = +185$. Entered in the summation column, this is then added to the summation value on line 3, the sign is changed and the number on line 2 (in this case zero) added to the sum, giving -105, which is noted in the summation column on line 5. The values for BA and BC on line 5 are obtained by multiplying -105 by the ratio of the K value of each member to the sum of the K values at the joint; that is, for BA, $-m = -105 \times \frac{1}{2} = -53$. The corrected moment for BA, the sum of lines 3, 4, and 5, is $+400 + 200 - 53 = +547$. The other corrected moments are found in the same way and are shown are line 6.

The new end moments differ considerably from the moments on line 2, indicating that those moments were incorrect. A comparison with Fig. 3-73b shows that the new moments are nearer to the correct answer than those on line 2. Even closer results can be obtained by repeating the calculations using the moments on line 6 as demonstrated in the second cycle in Table 3-6.

The procedure is useful also for estimating the effect of changing the stiffness of one or more members.

Equations (3-84) and (3-85) can be generalized to include the effect of the movement d of a support in a direction normal to the initial position of a span of length L:

$$M_{OA} = M_{OA}{}^F + C_{AO}{}^F M'_{OA} - K_{OA}\frac{d}{L} - m_{OA} \tag{3-86}$$

$$m_{OA} = \frac{K_{OA}}{\Sigma K_O}\left(-\Sigma M_O + \Sigma M_O{}^F + \Sigma C_O{}^F M'_O - \Sigma K_O \frac{d}{L}\right) \tag{3-87}$$

For each span with a support movement, the term Kd/L can be obtained from the fixed-end moment due to this deflection alone; for OA, for example, by multiplying moment $M_{OA}{}^F$ by $(1 - C_{AO}{}^F C_{OA}{}^F)/(1 + C_{OA}{}^F)$. For prismatic beams, this factor reduces to $\frac{1}{2}$.

In Table 3-7, the solution for the bent in Fig. 3-71 is checked for the condition in which a 4,000-lb vertical load was placed 5 ft from B on span BC. The computations are similar to those in Table 3-6, except that the terms $-Kd/L$ are included for the columns to account for the sidesway. These values are obtained from the sidesway fixed-end moments in Table 3-5. For BA, for example, $Kd/L = \frac{1}{2} \times 3{,}000M$, with $M = 2.30$, as found in the solution. The check indicates that the original solution was sufficiently accurate for a slide-rule computation. If line 7 had contained a different set of moments, the shears would have had to be investigated again. A second cycle could be carried out by distributing the unbalance to the columns to obtain new Kd/L values.

Table 3-7. Moment-distribution Check
(Frame with sidesway)

Line No.	Term	Joint A		Joint B			Joint C			Joint D	
		AB	Sum	BA	BC	Sum	CB	CD	Sum	DC	Sum
1	K	6	∞	6	3	9	3	2	5	2	∞
2	M	+120	...	+ 7,110	− 7,110	0	+4,050	−4,050	0	−3,180	
3	M^F	0	...	0	−12,800	−12,800	+3,200	0	+3,200	0	
4	$-Kd/L$	−3,450	...	−3,450	0	− 3,450	0	−1,150	−1,150	−1,150	
5	$+\frac{1}{2}M'$	+3,555	...	+60	+425	+485	+2,845	−1,590	+1,255	−2,025	
6	$-m$	0	...	+10,510	+ 5,255	+15,765	−1,983	−1,322	−3,305	0	
7	M	+105	...	+ 7,120	− 7,120	0	+4,062	−4,062	0	−3,175	

BUCKLING OF COLUMNS

Columns are compression members whose cross-sectional dimensions are relatively small compared with their length in the direction of the compressive force. Failure of such members occurs because of instability when a certain load (called the critical, or **Euler load**) is equaled or exceeded. The member may bend, or buckle, suddenly and collapse.

Hence the strength of a column is not determined by the unit stress in Eq. (3-3) ($P = Af$) but by the maximum load it can carry without becoming unstable. The condition of instability is characterized by disproportionately large increases in lateral deformation with slight increase in load. It may occur in slender columns before the unit stress reaches the elastic limit.

3-70. Stable Equilibrium. Consider, for example, an axially loaded column with ends unrestrained against rotation, shown in Fig. 3-74. If the member is initially perfectly straight, it will remain straight as long as the load P is less than the critical load P_c. If a small transverse force is applied, it will deflect, but it will return to the straight position when this force is removed. Thus, when P is less than P_c, internal and external forces are in stable equilibrium.

3-71. Unstable Equilibrium. If $P = P_c$ and a small transverse force is applied, the column again will deflect, but this time, when the force is removed, the column will remain in the bent position (dash line in Fig. 3-74). The equation of this elastic curve can be obtained from Eq. (3-31):

$$EI \frac{d^2y}{dx^2} = -P_c y \qquad (3\text{-}88)$$

in which E = modulus of elasticity

I = least moment of inertia
y = deflection of the bent member from the straight position at a distance x from one end

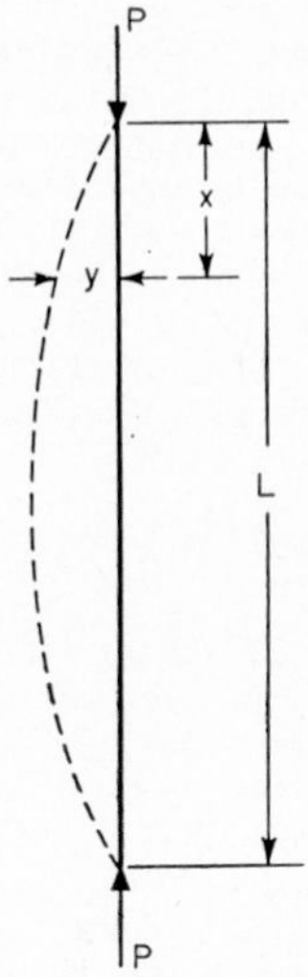

FIG. 3-74. Buckling of a column.

This assumes, of course, that the stresses are within the elastic limit. Solution of Eq. (3-88) gives the smallest value of the Euler load as

$$P_c = \frac{\pi^2 EI}{L^2} \qquad (3\text{-}89)$$

Equation (3-89) indicates that there is a definite finite magnitude of an axial load that will hold a column in equilibrium in the bent position when the stresses are below the elastic limit. Repeated application and removal of small transverse forces or small increases in axial load above this critical load will cause the member to fail by buckling. Internal and external forces are in a state of unstable equilibrium.

It is noteworthy that the Euler load, which determines the load-carrying capacity of a column, depends on the stiffness of the member, as expressed by the modulus of elasticity, rather than on the strength of the material of which it is made.

By dividing both sides of Eq. (3-89) by the cross-sectional area A and substituting r^2 for I/A (r is the radius of gyration of the section), we can write the solution of Eq. (3-88) in terms of the average unit stress on the cross section:

$$\frac{P_c}{A} = \frac{\pi^2 E}{(L/r)^2} \qquad (3\text{-}90)$$

This holds only for the elastic range of buckling; i.e., for values of the slenderness ratio L/r above a certain limiting value that depends on the properties of the material. For inelastic buckling, see Art. 3-73.

3-72. Effect of End Conditions. Equation (3-90) was derived on the assumption that the ends of the column are free to rotate. It can be generalized, however, to take into account the effect of end conditions:

$$\frac{P_c}{A} = \frac{\pi^2 E}{(kL/r)^2} \qquad (3\text{-}91)$$

where k is a factor that depends on the end conditions. For a pin-ended column, $k = 1$; for a column with both ends fixed, $k = \frac{1}{2}$; for a column with one end fixed and one end pinned, k is about 0.7; and for a column with one end fixed and one end free from all restraint, $k = 2$.

3-73. Inelastic Buckling. Equations (3-89) to (3-91), having been derived from Eq. (3-88), the differential equation for the elastic curve, are based on the assumption that the critical average stress is below the elastic limit when the state of unstable equilibrium is reached. In members with slenderness ratio L/r below a certain limiting value, however, the elastic limit is exceeded before the column buckles. As the axial load approaches the critical load, the modulus of elasticity varies with the stress. Hence Eqs. (3-89) to (3-91), based on the assumption that E is a constant, do not hold for these short columns.

After extensive testing and analysis, prevalent engineering opinion favors the Engesser equation for metals in the inelastic range:

$$\frac{P_t}{A} = \frac{\pi^2 E_t}{(kL/r)^2} \tag{3-92}$$

This differs from Eqs. (3-89) to (3-91) only in that the tangent modulus E_t (the actual slope of the stress-strain curve for the stress P_t/A) replaces the modulus of elasticity E in the elastic range. P_t is the smallest axial load for which two equilibrium positions are possible, the straight position and a deflected position.

3-74. Column Curves. Curves obtained by plotting the critical stress for various values of the slenderness ratio are called column curves. For axially loaded, initially straight columns, the column curve consists of two parts: (1) the Euler critical values, and (2) the Engesser, or tangent-modulus critical values.

The latter are greatly affected by the shape of the stress-strain curve for the material of which the column is made, as shown in Fig. 3-75. The stress-strain curve for a material, such as an aluminum alloy or high-strength steel, which does not have a sharply defined yield point, is shown in Fig. 3-75a. The corresponding column curve is drawn in Fig. 3-75b. In contrast, Fig. 3-75c presents the strain-strain curve for structural steel, with a sharply defined yield point, and Fig. 3-75d the related column curve. This curve becomes horizontal as the critical stress approaches the yield strength of the material and the tangent modulus becomes zero, whereas the column curve in Fig. 3-75b continues to rise with decreasing values of the slenderness ratio.

Examination of Fig. 3-75b also indicates that slender columns, which fall in the elastic range, where the column curve has a large slope, are very sensitive to variations in the factor k which represents the effect of end conditions. On the other hand, in the inelastic range, where the column curve is relatively flat, the critical stress is relatively insensitive to changes in k. Hence the effect of end conditions on the stability of a column is of much greater significance for long columns than for short columns.

3-75. Local Buckling. A column may not only fail by buckling of the member as a whole but as an alternative, by buckling of one of its components. Hence, when members like I beams, channels, and angles are used as columns or when sections are built up of plates, the possibility of the critical load on a component (leg, half flange, web, lattice bar) being less than the critical load on the column as a whole should be investigated.

Similarly, the possibility of buckling of the compression flange or the web of a beam should be looked into.

Local buckling, however, does not always result in a reduction in the load-carrying capacity of a column. Sometimes, it results in a redistribution of the stresses enabling the member to carry additional load.

3-76. Behavior of Actual Columns. For many reasons, columns in structures behave differently from the ideal column assumed in deriving Eqs. (3-89) and (3-92). A major consideration is the effect of accidental imperfections, such as nonhomogeneity of materials, initial crookedness, and unintentional eccentricities of the axial load, since neither field nor shopwork can be perfect. These effects can be taken into account by a proper choice of safety factor.

There are other significant conditions, however, that must be considered in any design rule: continuity in framed structures and eccentricity of the axial load. Continuity affects column action in two ways. The restraint at column ends determines the value of k, and bending moments are transmitted to the column by adjoining structural members.

Because of the deviation of the behavior of actual columns from the ideal, columns generally are designed by empirical formulas. Separate equations usually are given for short columns, intermediate columns, and long columns. For specific materials—steel, concrete, timber—these formulas are given in Secs. 5 to 8.

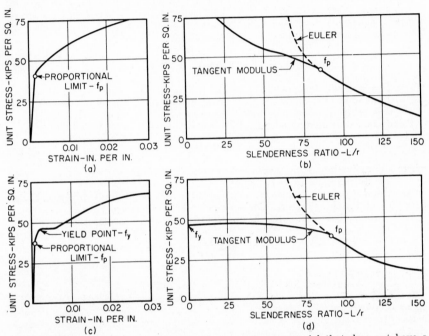

Fig. 3-75. Column curves—(a) stress-strain curve for a material that does not have a sharply defined yield point; (b) column curve for this material; (c) stress-strain curve for material with a sharply defined yield point; (d) column curve for that material.

For more details on column action, see F. Bleich, "Buckling Strength of Metal Structures," McGraw-Hill Book Company, Inc., New York, 1952; and S. Timoshenko, "Theory of Elastic Stability," McGraw-Hill Book Company, Inc., New York, 1936.

TORSION

Forces that cause a member to twist about a longitudinal axis are called torsional loads. Simple torsion is produced only by a couple, or moment, in a plane perpendicular to the axis.

If a couple lies in a nonperpendicular plane, it can be resolved into a torsional moment, in a plane perpendicular to the axis, and bending moments, in planes through the axis.

3-77. Shear Center. The point in each normal section of a member through which the axis passes and about which the section twists is called the shear center. (The location of the shear center in commonly used shapes is given in Art. 3-35.) If the loads on a beam, for example, do not pass through the shear center, they cause the beam to twist.

3-78. Stresses Due to Torsion. Simple torsion is resisted by internal shearing stresses. These can be resolved into radial and tangential shearing stresses, which being normal to each other also are equal (see Art. 3-11). Furthermore, on planes that bisect the angles between the planes on which the shearing stresses act, there also occur compressive and tensile stresses. The magnitude of these normal stresses is equal to that of the shear. Therefore, when torsional loading is combined with other types of loading, the maximum stresses occur on inclined planes and can be computed by the methods explained in Arts. 3-12 and 3-15.

If a circular shaft (hollow or solid) is twisted, a section that is plane before twisting remains plane after twisting. Within the proportional limit, the shearing stress at any point in a transverse section varies with the distance from the center of the section. The maximum shear occurs at the circumference and is given by

$$v = \frac{Tr}{J} \tag{3-93}$$

where T = torsional moment
r = radius of section
J = polar moment of inertia
Polar moment of inertia is defined by

$$J = \int \rho^2 \, dA \tag{3-94}$$

where ρ = radius from shear center to any point in section
dA = differential area at the point
In general, J equals the sum of the moments of inertia about any two perpendicular axes through the shear center. For a solid circular section, $J = \pi r^4/2$.

Within the proportional limit, the angular twist for a circular bar is given by

$$\theta = \frac{TL}{GJ} \tag{3-95}$$

where L = length of bar
G = shearing modulus of elasticity (see Art. 3-6)
If a shaft is not circular, a plane transverse section before twisting does not remain plane after twisting. The resulting warping increases the shearing stresses in some parts of the section and decreases them in others, compared with the shearing stresses that would occur if the section remained plane. Consequently, shearing stresses in a noncircular section are not proportional to distances from the shear center. In elliptical and rectangular sections, for example, maximum shear occurs on the circumference at a point nearest the shear center.

For a solid rectangular section, this maximum may be expressed in the following form:

$$v = \frac{T}{kb^2d} \tag{3-96}$$

where b = short side of the rectangle
d = long side
k = a constant depending on the ratio of these sides:

$b/d =$	1.0	1.5	2.0	2.5	3	4	5	10	∞
$k =$	0.208	0.231	0.246	0.257	0.267	0.282	0.291	0.312	0.333

(S. Timoshenko, "Theory of Elasticity," 2d ed., McGraw-Hill Book Company, Inc., New York, 1951.)

If a thin-shell hollow tube is twisted, the shearing force per unit of length on a cross section (shear flow) is given approximately by

$$H = \frac{T}{2A} \tag{3-97}$$

where T = torsional moment
A = area enclosed by mean perimeter of wall of tube
And the unit shearing stress is given approximately by

$$v = \frac{H}{t} = \frac{T}{2At} \tag{3-98}$$

where t = thickness of tube
For a rectangular tube with sides of unequal thickness, the total shear flow can be computed from Eq. (3-97), and the shearing stress along each side from Eq. (3-98).

For a narrow rectangular section, the maximum shear is very nearly equal to

$$v = \frac{T}{\frac{1}{3}b^2d} \tag{3-99}$$

where b = short dimension of the rectangle
d = long side
This formula can also be used to find the maximum shearing stress due to torsion in members, such as I beams and channels, made up of thin rectangular components. Let $J = \frac{1}{3}\Sigma b^3 d$, where b is the thickness of each rectangular component and d the corresponding length. Then, the maximum shear is given approximately by

$$v = \frac{Tb}{J} \tag{3-100}$$

In this equation, b is the thickness of the web or the flange. The maximum shearing stress is at the center of one of the long sides of the rectangular part that has the greatest thickness (Seely and Smith "Advanced Mechanics of Materials," John Wiley & Sons, Inc., New York).

REPEATED LOADS

Some building members are subjected to forces that vary in magnitude. This variation causes stresses that also vary in intensity. If the stresses are sufficiently large and repeated frequently, the member may fail because of "fatigue" at a stress smaller than the yield point of the material.

Fatigue failure is believed to be initiated at a point of high stress concentration with the formation of a microscopic crack. As the stress is repeated, the crack spreads, and the member ruptures without measurable yielding.

3-79. Endurance Limit. Some materials (generally those with a well-defined yield point) have what is known as an endurance limit. This is the maximum unit stress that can be repeated, through a definite range, an indefinite number of times without causing structural damage. Generally, when no range is specified, the endurance limit is intended for a cycle in which the stress is varied between tension and compression stresses of equal value. For a different range, if f is this endurance limit, f_y the yield point, and r ratio of the minimum stress to the maximum, then the relationship between endurance stresses is given approximately by

$$f_{max} = \frac{2f}{(1 - r) + (f/f_y)(1 + r)} \tag{3-101}$$

A range of stress may be resolved into two components—a steady, or mean, stress and an alternating stress. The endurance limit is sometimes defined as the maximum value of the alternating stress that can be superimposed on the steady stress an indefinitely large number of times without causing fracture. If f is the endurance limit for completely reversed stresses, s the steady unit stress, f_u the ultimate tensile strength—all in pounds per square inch—then the alternating stress may be obtained from a relationship of the type:

$$f_a = f \left(1 - \frac{s^n}{f_u} \right) \qquad (3\text{-}102)$$

where n generally has a value between 1 and 2, depending on the material.

Design of members to resist repeated loading cannot be executed with the certainty with which members can be designed to resist static loading. Stress concentrations may be present for a wide variety of reasons, and it is not practicable to calculate their intensities. But sometimes it is feasible to reduce the value of a stress concentration below the minimum value that will cause fatigue failure or to improve the fatigue strength of the material.

One of the most common causes of fatigue failure is an abrupt change of cross section. High localized stresses occur at sharp corners or notches. Hence, one way to prevent structural damage under repeated loading is to make the change in section less abrupt by inserting a fillet of relatively large radius.

Fatigue strength of a material may be improved by cold-working the material in the region of stress concentration, by thermal processes, or by prestressing it in such a way as to introduce favorable internal stresses. Where fatigue stresses are unusually severe, special materials may have to be selected with high energy absorption and notch toughness. For more detailed information, see W. M. Murray, ed., "Fatigue and Fracture of Metals," John Wiley & Sons, Inc., New York.

ENERGY LOADS

When a load is applied suddenly to a member, the resulting stresses may be several times larger than those caused by a static load. Also, the dimensions of the member and the properties of its material that offer maximum resistance to an energy load may be different from those that give the member maximum resistance to static loading. As might be expected, the factors that improve resistance to energy loads are much the same as those that improve resistance to fatigue failures (see Art. 3-79).

3-80. Stresses Caused by Energy Loads. Generally, the stresses due to an energy load are computed by using an equivalent static load obtained by multiplying the live load by a factor. But when the energy load is large, it may be necessary to compute the stresses and deformations by more exact methods (see F. B. Seely, "Resistance of Materials," John Wiley & Sons, Inc., New York; and S. Timoshenko and J. N. Goodier, "Theory of Elasticity," 2d ed., McGraw-Hill Book Company, Inc., New York, 1951).

If a tensile stress is produced by an axial energy load on a bar, the energy absorbed by the bar per unit of volume is given by the area under the stress-strain curve between the origin, the strain axis, and the ordinate corresponding to the tensile stress. The energy absorbed per unit of volume when the bar is stressed to the proportional limit is called the **modulus of resilience** and is given by $f_y{}^2/2E$. Below the proportional limit, the stress in pounds per square inch due to an axial-energy load U in inch-pounds, is

$$f = \sqrt{\frac{2UE}{AL}} \qquad (3\text{-}103)$$

where E = modulus of elasticity, psi
$\quad A$ = cross sectional area, sq in.
$\quad L$ = length of bar, in.

From Eq. (3-103), it may be concluded that the energy absorption of a member may be improved by increasing its length or area. Sharp changes in cross section should be avoided, however, because of associated high stress concentrations. Also, uneven distribution of stress in a member due to changes in section should be avoided. For example, if part of a member is given twice the diameter of another part, the stress in the larger portion is one-fourth that in the smaller. Since the energy absorbed is proportional to the square of the stress, the energy taken per unit of volume by the larger portion is, therefore, only one-sixteenth that absorbed by the smaller. So despite the increase in volume due to doubling of the diameter the larger portion absorbs less energy than the smaller. Thus, energy absorption would be larger with a uniform stress distribution throughout the length of the member.

If a static axial load W would produce a tensile stress f' and an elongation e' then the axial stress produced in a bar by W falling through a distance h is given by

$$f = f' + f' \sqrt{1 + \frac{2h}{e'}} \qquad (3\text{-}104)$$

provided f is within the proportional limit. The elongation due to this energy load is

$$e = e' + e' \sqrt{1 + \frac{2h}{e'}} \qquad (3\text{-}105)$$

These equations indicate that the stress and deformation due to an energy load may be considerably larger than those produced by the same weight applied gradually. Similar expressions can be written for a weight falling on a beam in terms of the static deflection.

According to these equations, a sudden load ($h = 0$) causes twice the stress and twice the deflection as the same load applied gradually.

VIBRATION

In general, vibrations in a building are objectionable from the viewpoint of physical comfort, noise, protection of delicate apparatus, and danger of fatigue failures (Figs.

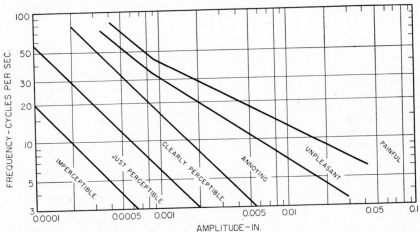

Fig. 3-76. Chart indicating human sensitivity to vibration. (*British Research Station Digest No. 78.*)

3-76 and 3-77). The simplest ways to eliminate them are to isolate vibrating machinery, install supports that transmit a minimum of energy, install shock absorbers, and insert mufflers and screens to absorb noise.

3-81. How to Reduce Vibrations. Sometimes, machines with rotating parts can be made to vibrate less by balancing the rotating parts to reduce the exciting force or the speed can be adjusted to prevent resonance.   Also, the masses of the supports can be adjusted to change the natural frequency so that resonance is avoided.

The surfaces of a foundation subjected to vibration should be shaped to preclude the possibility of the vibrations being reflected from them back into the interior in a direction in which a stress buildup can occur.   Such a foundation should be made of a homogeneous material, since objectionable stresses may occur in the region of an inhomogeneity.   The foundation should be massive—weight comparable with that of

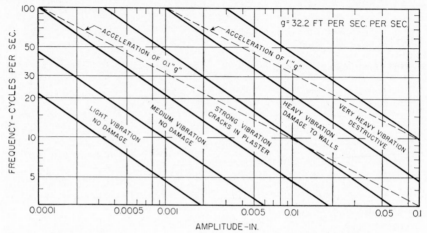

Fig. 3-77. Chart showing possibility of damage from vibrations.   (*British Research Station Digest No. 78.*)

the machine it supports—and should be isolated by an air gap or insulating material from the rest of the building.   ("Vibration in Buildings," Building Research Station Digest No. 78, Her Majesty's Stationery Office, London, June, 1955.)

ARCHES AND RIGID FRAMES

An arch is a curved beam, the radius of curvature of which is very large relative to the depth of the section.   It differs from a straight beam in that: (1) loads induce both bending and direct compressive stresses in an arch; (2) arch reactions have horizontal components even though loads are all vertical; and (3) deflections have horizontal as well as vertical components (see also Arts. 3-36 to 3-41).

The necessity of resisting the horizontal components of the reactions is an important consideration in arch design.   Sometimes these forces are taken by tie rods between the supports, sometimes by heavy abutments or buttresses.

Arches may be built with fixed ends, as can straight beams, or with hinges at the supports.   They may also be built with a hinge at the crown.

3-82. Three-hinged Arches.   An arch with a hinge at the crown as well as at both supports (Fig. 3-78) is statically determinate.   There are four unknowns—two horizontal and two vertical components of the reactions—but four equations based on the laws of equilibrium are available: (1) The sum of the horizontal forces must be zero. (2) The sum of the moments about the left support must be zero.   (3) The sum of the moments about the right support must be zero.   (4) The bending moment at the crown hinge must be zero (not to be confused with the sum of the moments about the crown, which also must be equal to zero but which would not lead to an independent equation for the solution of the reactions).

Stresses and reactions in three-hinged arches can be determined graphically by utilizing the principles presented in Arts. 3-43 to 3-47 and 3-51 and taking advantage of the fact that the bending moment at the crown hinge is zero.   For example, in Fig.

3-78a, a concentrated load P is applied to segment AB of the arch. Then, since the bending moment at B must be zero, the line of action of the reaction at C must pass through the crown hinge. It intersects the line of action of P at X. The line of action of the reaction at A must also pass through X. Since P is equal to the sum of the reactions, and since the directions of the reactions have thus been determined, the magnitude of the reactions can be measured from a parallelogram of forces (Fig. 3-78b). When the reactions have been found, the stresses can be computed from the laws of statics or, in the case of a trussed arch, determined graphically.

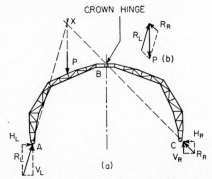

3-83. Two-hinged Arches. When an arch has hinges at the supports only (Fig. 3-79), it is statically indeterminate, and some knowledge of its deformations is required to determine the reactions. One procedure is to assume that one of the supports is on rollers. This makes the arch statically determinate. The reactions and the horizontal movement of

Fig. 3-78. Three-hinged arch.

the support are computed for this condition (Fig. 3-79b). Then, the magnitude of the horizontal force required to return the movable support to its original position is calculated (Fig. 3-79c). The reactions for the two-hinged arch are finally found by superimposing the first set of reactions on the second (Fig. 3-79d).

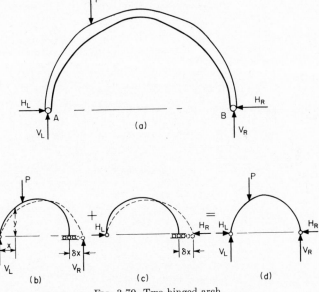

Fig. 3-79. Two-hinged arch.

For example, if δx is the horizontal movement of the support due to the loads, and if $\delta x'$ is the horizontal movement of the support due to a unit horizontal force applied to the support, then

$$\delta x + H\ \delta x' = 0 \qquad H = -\frac{\delta x}{\delta x'}$$

where H is the unknown horizontal reaction. (When a tie rod is used to take the thrust, the right-hand side of the first equation is not zero, but the elongation of the rod HL/AE.) The dummy unit-load method [Eq. (3-63)] can be used to compute δx and $\delta x'$:

$$\delta x = \int_A^B \frac{Mm}{EI} \, ds = \int_A^B \frac{My}{EI} \, ds \qquad (3\text{-}106)$$

where M = moment at any section due to loads
$\quad y$ = ordinate of section measured from A as origin, when B is on rollers
$\quad I$ = moment of inertia of section
$\quad E$ = modulus of elasticity
$\quad ds$ = differential length along axis of arch

$$\delta x' = \int_A^B \frac{y^2}{EI} \, ds \qquad (3\text{-}107)$$

However, when the thrust is very large and would be responsible for large strains in the direction of the arch axis, its effect must be included in Eq. (3-106). The additional term to be incorporated in Eq. (3-106) can be obtained from Eq. (3-65).

In most cases, integration is impracticable. The integrals generally must be evaluated by approximate methods. The arch axis is divided into a convenient number of sections and the functions under the integral sign evaluated for each section. The sum is approximately equal to the integral.

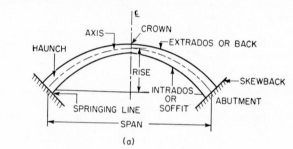

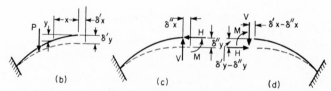

FIG. 3-80. Fixed-end arch.

3-84. Fixed Arches. An arch is considered fixed when rotation is prevented at the supports (Fig. 3-80a). Such an arch is statically indeterminate; there are six reaction components and only three equations are available from conditions of equilibrium. Three more equations must be obtained from a knowledge of the deformations.

One way to determine the reactions is to consider the arch cut at the crown, forming two cantilevers. First, the horizontal and vertical deflections and rotation produced at the end of each half arch by the loads are computed (Fig. 3-80b). Next, the deflection components and rotation at those ends are determined for unit vertical force, unit horizontal force, and unit moment applied separately at the ends (Fig. 3-80c). These deformations, multiplied, respectively, by V, the unknown shear; H, the unknown horizontal thrust at the crown; and M, the unknown moment there, yield the deformations caused by the unknown forces at the crown. Adding these deformations algebraically to the corresponding ones produced by the loads gives the net movement of the free end of each half arch. Since these ends must deflect and rotate the same amount to maintain continuity, three equations can be obtained in this manner for the determination of V, H, and M. The various deflections can be computed by the dummy unit-load method [Eq. (3-63)], as has been demonstrated for two-hinged arches [see Eqs. (3-106) and (3-107)]. For typical solutions by this method, see S. Timoshenko and D. H. Young, "Theory of Structures," McGraw-Hill Book Company, Inc., New York, 1945. For solution by the column analogy, see H. Cross and N. D. Morgan, "Continuous Frames of Reinforced Concrete," John Wiley & Sons, Inc., New York.

3-85. Rigid Frames. The structural frame of a building is considered a rigid frame when the connections between beams and columns are of such a nature that at each joint the ends of the beams and columns rotate the same amount.

A rigid frame consisting only of one beam and two columns behaves in much the same manner as an arch. Reactions and stresses in the members can be computed by applying the arch theory previously described. On the other hand, this simple rigid frame, as well as continuous frames, can be readily analyzed by the methods given in Arts. 3-63 to 3-68 for continuous beams. Care must be taken, however, when the columns are flexible to take sidesway into account (see Art. 3-67).

3-86. Stresses in Arch Ribs. When the reactions have been found for a rigid frame or an arch, the normal and tangential forces and the bending moment at any section can be found by applying the laws of equilibrium. The shearing unit stresses on a section can be computed from the tangential force with the aid of Eq. (3-28). The normal unit stresses can be calculated from the normal force and bending moment with the aid of Eq. (3-36).

In designing an arch, it may be necessary to compute certain secondary stresses, in addition to those caused by live, dead, wind, and snow loads. Among the secondary stresses to be considered are those due to temperature changes, rib shortening due to thrust or shrinkage, deformation of tie rods, and unequal settlement of footings. The procedure is the same as for loads on the arch, with the deformations producing the secondary stresses substituted for or treated the same as the deformations due to loads.

CYLINDRICAL SHELL STRUCTURES

Thin shells forming a circular arc in one vertical plane and a horizontal line in a perpendicular vertical plane are used occasionally for long-span roofs. These barrel arches are generally supported by and are integral with transverse stiffening ribs (Fig. 3-81a). Loads on the shell are resisted primarily by direct stresses. Bending stresses are relatively small.

Shell action is distinguished from arch action by the fact that the load is resisted not only by the thrust, moment, and shear on a radial section but also by tangential shears on a transverse section (Fig. 3-81b).

3-87. Shell Analysis. Stress analysis of shells may involve the solution of differential equations and much tedious calculation. However, the work can be simplified and shortened by the methods and tables presented in "Design of Cylindrical Shell Roofs," Manual of Engineering Practice No. 31, American Society of Civil Engineers (see also "Design of Barrel Shell Roofs," Portland Cement Association).

The procedure employed is to start with the assumption that the shell is statically determinate and the loads are carried by direct stresses only (membrane theory). This condition can be met, however, only when transverse and shearing forces at the boundaries are countered by equal and opposite reactions. When the required reactions are not supplied, radial shearing forces and moments are required to maintain equilibrium. The stresses created by actual edge and end conditions must be added to those obtained by the membrane theory.

The relative importance of the boundary conditions depends on the ratio of the radius r of the shell to the distance between longitudinal supports L. When r/L is less than 0.25, the longitudinal stresses are given fairly accurately by simple-beam theory, treating the barrel as a beam with a curved cross section. In shells of this proportion, stresses due to deformations of the transverse supports, such as stiffeners or end beams, fade out rapidly, whereas stresses due to deflection of the longitudinal edges are felt throughout the shell and influence the stress distribution in the shell substantially. For larger values of r/L, the longitudinal stresses are much larger than those given by simple-beam theory.

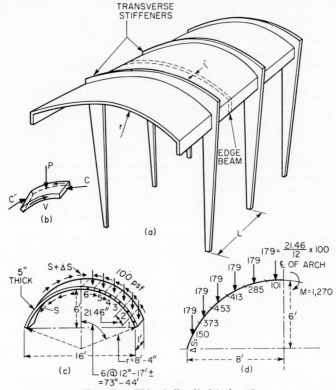

FIG. 3-81. Thin-shell cylindrical roof.

As an example of the application of simple-beam theory to a cylindrical arch, assume a 5-in.-thick roof curved to a radius of 8 ft 4 in. to be designed to support a uniform vertical load of 100 psf, with columns spaced 16 ft on centers transversely and 40 ft longitudinally. Basically, the shell will act as a beam in the long direction and as an arch in the short direction. This arch, however, is not supported at the ends but by internal shearing forces. If a 1-ft-wide strip is cut transversely out of the shell, as in Fig. 3-81c, it will be supported by the algebraic sum of the shearing forces acting on both faces:

$$(S + \Delta S) - S = \Delta S$$

For convenience in computing the stresses in the curved element, it is divided into 12 units, each 21.46 in. long. From the geometric properties of these units, the section moduli of the curved element acting as a beam are found to be

$$\frac{I}{c} \text{ (top)} = 23,860 \text{ cu in.}$$

$$\frac{I}{c} \text{ (bottom)} = 12,934 \text{ cu in.}$$

The total load on the shell is $W = 12 \times 100 \times 21.46/12 = 2,146$ lb, from which the longitudinal bending moment is computed:

$$M = 2,146 \times \frac{40^2}{8} = 429,200 \text{ ft-lb}$$

and the longitudinal stresses in the top and bottom fibers are

Top: $\qquad\qquad\qquad f = 429,200 \times 12/23,860 = 216$ psi

Bottom: $\qquad\qquad\quad f = 429,200 \times 12/12,934 = 398$ psi

For computing the transverse bending moment, the shearing forces ΔS acting on each unit may be calculated from the standard formula for shearing stressses, $S = VQ/It$, where V is the total shear on the section, Q is the moment about the center of gravity of the areas on either side of the fiber for which the shear is to be computed, I is the moment of inertia of the section, and t is the thickness of the section. For the arch element,

$$\Delta S = \frac{(\Delta V)Q}{It}$$

Values of ΔS computed for each element are shown in Fig. 3-81d. Each of these forces acts tangent to the curve. The net moment of the load and these forces about the crown figure out to be 1,270 ft-lb (*Engineering News-Record*, Sept. 2, 1954, p. 40).

Surface loads supported by a shell are transmitted by tangential and radial shears to the stiffeners. Since the shell and each stiffener are continuous, the shell participates in the bending action of the stiffener. As a result, tangential and radial shears determined from the shell analysis are changed. A two-step procedure is required to compute the final stresses:

1. Initially, the stiffeners are assumed to be infinitely rigid. Stresses and reactions of the shell are computed for this condition. Equivalent surface loads are next computed having the same effect as the radial and tangential shears.

2. These loads are applied to the stiffener, which is considered a T beam. The flanges represent the effect of the shell on the bending of the curved stiffener.

As in the case of arches, careful consideration should be given to secondary stresses. Included in these are stresses due to uniform volume change of the rib and shell, rib shortening, unequal settlement of footings, and differential volume change between rib and shell.

3-88. Folded-plate Roofs. When a thin-shell roof is formed by joining two or more flat plates along their edges, the result is a "folded-plate" roof (Fig. 3-82a). Just as a curved roof can be analyzed as a beam with a curved cross section, so can a folded-plate shell. Transverse tie rods or stiffeners are required at the ends of the span or at intermediate points to take the thrust.

In Fig. 3-82b is shown an element 1 ft wide cut out of the folded-plate roof in Fig. 3-82c. (Spans and rise are the same as for the curved roof in Art. 3-87.) The element carries a uniform vertical load of 100 psf of sloping surface. It is supported by the algebraic sum of the shearing forces acting on both faces ΔS.

Since the vertical component of the sum of the ΔS forces must equal the sum of the applied vertical forces,

$$\Sigma \, \Delta S = 100 \times 10 \times 1\%_6 = 1,667 \text{ lb}$$

for each plate.

The transverse bending moment at any section of the element is the moment about the section of the applied load on one side of it, less the moment of the ΔS forces on that side. The moment at the crown, noting that the ΔS forces act at the center of the section and go through the crown, thus producing no moment, is

$$M = \frac{WL}{2} = 100 \times 10 \times \frac{8}{2} = 4,000 \text{ ft-lb}$$

With the folded plate acting as a simple beam on a 40-ft span, the longitudinal bend-

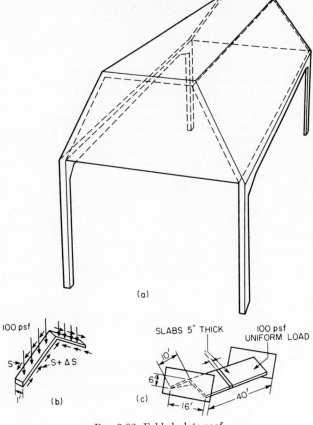

100 psf

S → S + ΔS

(b)

SLABS 5" THICK   100 psf
UNIFORM LOAD

10'

6'

16'   40'

(c)

(a)

Fɪɢ. 3-82. Folded-plate roof.

ing moment in each plate is that due to the shear, $\Sigma \, \Delta S$, acting on a simple beam:

$$M = 1{,}667 \times \frac{40^2}{8} = 333{,}333 \text{ ft-lb}$$

The section modulus of the 120-in.-deep tilted girder is

$$\frac{I}{c} = \frac{bd^2}{6} = 5 \times \frac{120^2}{6} = 12{,}000 \text{ cu in.}$$

Hence the unit stress in the top or bottom fiber is

$$f = 333{,}333 \times \frac{12}{12{,}000} = 333 \text{ psi}$$

(*Engineering News-Record*, Sept. 2, 1954, p. 40). For a more complete analysis, see also George Winter and Minglung Pei, "Hipped Plate Construction," *Journal of the American Concrete Institute*, January, 1947, p. 505).

DOMES AND CATENARIES

Doubly curved thin-shell structures support loads much more efficiently even than singly curved or cylindrical structures, and arches.   They are used when large unobstructed floor areas are desired.

The shells generally are made so thin that it is reasonable to assume that they cannot develop bending moment and yet are thick enough to preclude the possibility of buckling under compressive forces.   An exact solution of the stresses in such shells is very complex; usually approximate methods are used.

When the shell extends above its supports, the major stresses produced by vertical downward-acting loads are compressive.   Such shells are called domes or vaults.

When the shell lies completely below its supports, the major stresses produced by vertical downward-acting loads are tensile.   Such shells are called catenaries.   Obviously, the simplified solution for domes applies also to catenaries, but with the signs

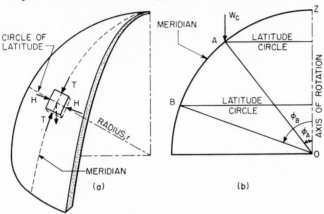

FIG. 3-83. Thin-shell dome.

of the stresses changed; for if the direction of the vertical loads on a dome are reversed, the dome will behave like a catenary.

3-89. Circular Domes.   A spherical surface is often used for domes, with an integral edge member provided at the base to resist hoop tension there.   Such domes are called circular, because the surface is formed by revolving an arc of a circle about a vertical axis.

Theoretically, the shells are assumed to carry only uniformly distributed, symmetrical loading.

In Fig. 3-83b, the surface area of the strip of the dome between points A and B is given by

$$A = 2\pi r^2 (\cos \phi_A - \cos \phi_B) \qquad (3\text{-}108)$$

For a constant load w per square foot of area, the total load is

$$W_u = 2\pi r^2 w (\cos \phi_A - \cos \phi_B) \qquad (3\text{-}109)$$

If the load increases from zero at point Z at a rate of w' per radian (57.3°), the total load on the strip between A and B then is

$$W_v = 2\pi r^2 w' [\sin \phi_B - \sin \phi_A - \cos \phi_B(\phi_B - \phi_A)] \qquad (3\text{-}110)$$

Another type of load sometimes considered to act on a dome is a collar load uniformly distributed around a circle of latitude.   Let W_c be the total load from this source. Then, the total load acting on the strip between A and B is

$$W = W_u + W_v + W_c \qquad (3\text{-}111)$$

As indicated in Fig. 3-83a, the vertical load at any point on the dome is resisted by a meridional thrust T and a hoop force H. Along the circle of latitude through B, the total meridional thrust is

$$T = \frac{W}{2\pi r \sin^2 \phi_B} \tag{3-112}$$

Accompanying it is a hoop force

$$H = -T + [w + w'(\phi_B - \phi_A)]r \cos \phi_B \tag{3-113}$$

If the dome is discontinued along a circle of latitude through point B, the edge member will be subjected to a ring tension equal to

$$S = \frac{W \cos \phi_B}{2\pi \sin \phi_B} \tag{3-114}$$

If the dome is omitted above a circle of latitude through point A, the collar load will produce a ring compression along the edge of the opening:

$$S' = \frac{W_c \cos \phi_A}{2\pi \sin \phi_A} \tag{3-115}$$

At the top of a solid dome:

$$T = H = \tfrac{1}{2}wr \tag{3-116}$$

Similar approximate formulas for the design of conoidal and elliptical domes are given in a pamphlet published by the Portland Cement Association.

3-90. Stresses in Cables.   When a cable is suspended from two points of support, the end reactions have a horizontal as well as a vertical component. If the cable carries only vertical loads, the horizontal component of the tension at any point in the cable is equal to the horizontal component of the end reaction.   The vertical components of the reactions can be computed by taking moments about the supports in the same way as for beams, provided the cable supports are at the same level.   When the supports are not at the same level, another equation, derived from a knowledge of the shape of the cable, is required.

Generally, it is safe to assume that the thickness of the cable is negligible compared with the span.   Hence, bending stresses may be neglected, and the bending moment at any point is equal to zero.   As a consequence, the shape assumed by the cable is similar to that of the bending-moment diagram for a simply supported beam carrying the same loads.   Stresses in the cable are directed along the axis.

At the lowest point of a cable, the vertical shear either is zero or changes sign on either side of the low point.

The horizontal component of the reaction can be computed from the fact that the bending moment is zero at a point on the cable at which the sag is known (usually the low point).

For example, suppose a cable spanning 30 ft between supports at the same level is permitted to sag 2 ft in supporting a 12-kip load at a third point.   Taking moments about the supports, we find the vertical components of the reactions equal to 8 and 4 kips, respectively.   Setting the bending moment at the low point equal to zero, we can write the equation $8 \times 10 - 2H = 0$; from which the horizontal component H of the reaction is found to be 40 kips.   The maximum tension in the cable then is

$$T = \sqrt{8^2 + 40^2} = 40.8 \text{ kips}$$

WIND AND SEISMIC STRESSES IN TALL BUILDINGS

Buildings must be designed to resist horizontal forces as well as vertical loads.   In tall buildings, the lateral forces must be given particular attention, because if they are not properly provided for, they can cause collapse of the structure.

Horizontal forces are generally taken care of with X bracing, shear walls, or wind connections. **X bracing,** usually adopted for low industrial-type buildings, transmits the forces to the ground by truss action. **Shear walls** are vertical slabs capable of transmitting the forces to the ground without shearing or buckling; they generally are so deep in the direction of the lateral loads that bending stresses are easily handled. **Wind connections** are a means of establishing continuity between girders and columns. The structure is restrained against lateral deformation by the resistance to rotation of the members at the connections.

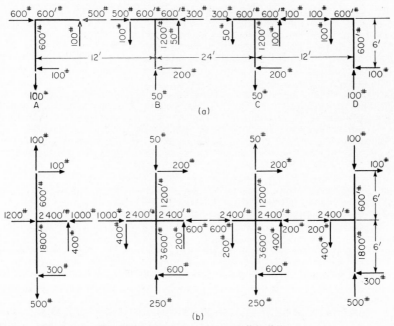

Fig. 3-84. Wind stresses in a tall building.

The continuous rigid frames thus formed can be analyzed by the methods of Arts. 3-63 to 3-68.   Generally, however, approximate methods are used.

It is noteworthy that for most buildings even the "exact" methods are not exact. In the first place, the forces acting are not static loads, but generally dynamic; they are uncertain in intensity, direction, and duration.   Earthquake forces, usually assumed as a percentage of the weight of the building above each level, act at the base of the structure, not at each floor level as is assumed in design, and accelerations at each level vary nearly linearly with distance above the base.   Also, at the beginning of a design, the sizes of members are not known; so the exact resistance to lateral deformation cannot be calculated.   Furthermore, floors, walls, and partitions help resist the lateral forces in a very uncertain way.

3-91. Portal Method.   Since an exact analysis is impossible, most designers prefer a wind-analysis method based on reasonable assumptions and requiring a minimum of calculations.   One such method is the so-called "portal method."

It is based on the assumptions that points of inflection (zero bending moment) occur at the mid-points of all members and that exterior columns take half as much shear as do interior columns.   These assumptions enable all moments and shears throughout the building frame to be computed by the laws of statics.

Consider, for example, the roof level (Fig. 3-84a) of a tall building.   A wind load of 600 lb is assumed to act along the top line of girders.   To apply the portal method, we cut the building along a section through the inflection points of the top-story columns, which are assumed to be at the column mid-points, 6 ft down from the top of the building.   We need now consider only the portion of the structure above this section.

Since the exterior columns take only half as much shear as do the interior columns, they each receive 100 lb, and the two interior columns, 200 lb.   The moments at the tops of the columns equal these shears times the distance to the inflection point.   The wall end of the end girder carries a moment equal to the moment in the column.   (At the floor level below, as indicated in Fig. 3-84b, that end of the end girder carries a moment equal to the sum of the column moments.)   Since the inflection point is at the mid-point of the girder, the moment at the inner end of the girder must be the same as at the outer end.   The moment in the adjoining girder can be found by subtracting this moment from the column moment, because the sum of the moments at the joint must be zero.   (At the floor level below, as shown in Fig. 3-84b, the moment in the interior girder is found by subtracting the moment in the exterior girder from the sum of the column moments.)

Girder shears then can be computed by dividing girder moments by the half span. When these shears have been found, column loads can be easily computed from the fact that the sum of the vertical loads must be zero, by taking a section around each joint through column and girder inflection points.   As a check, it should be noted that the column loads produce a moment that must be equal to the moments of the wind loads above the section for which the column loads were computed.   For the roof level (Fig. 3-84a), for example, $-50 \times 24 + 100 \times 48 = 600 \times 6$.

3-92. Cantilever Method.   Another wind-analysis procedure that is sometimes employed is the cantilever method.   Basic assumptions here are that inflection points are at the mid-points of all members and that direct stresses in the columns vary as the distances of the columns from the center of gravity of the bent.   The assumptions are sufficient to enable shears and moments in the frame to be determined from the laws of statics.

The results obtained from this method generally will be different from those obtained by the portal method.   In general, neither solution is correct, but the answers provide a reasonable estimate of the resistance to be provided against lateral deformation. (See also *Transactions of the ASCE*, Vol. 105, pp. 1713–1739, 1940.)

ULTIMATE STRENGTH OF DUCTILE FLEXURAL MEMBERS

When an elastic material, such as structural steel, is loaded with a gradually increasing load, stresses are proportional to strains up to the yield point.   If the material, like steel, also is ductile, then it continues to carry load beyond the yield point, though strains increase rapidly with little increase in load (Fig. 3-85a).

Similarly, a beam made of an elastic material continues to carry more load after the stresses in the outer fibers reach the yield point.   However, the stresses will no longer vary with distance from the neutral axis; so the flexural formula [Eq. (3-23)] no longer holds.   However, if simplifying assumptions are made, approximating the stress-strain relationship beyond the elastic limit, the load-carrying capacity of the beam can be computed with satisfactory accuracy.

3-93. Theory of Plastic Behavior.   For a ductile material, the idealized stress-strain relationship in Fig. 3-85b may be assumed.   Stress is proportional to strain until the yield-point stress f_y is reached, after which strain increases at a constant stress.

For a beam made of this material, the following assumptions will also be made: plane sections remain plane, strains thus being proportional to distance from the neutral axis; properties of the material in tension are the same as those in compression; its fibers behave the same in flexure as in tension; and deformations remain small.

Strain distribution across the cross section of a rectangular beam, based on these assumptions, is shown in Fig. 3-86a.   At the yield point, the unit strain is ϵ_y and the curvature ϕ_y, as indicated in (1).   In (2), the strain has increased several times, but the section still remains plane. Finally, at failure, (3), the strains are very large and nearly constant across upper and lower halves of the section.

Corresponding stress distributions are shown in Fig. 3-86b. At the yield point, (1), stresses vary linearly and the maximum is f_y. With increase in load, more and more fibers reach the yield point, and the stress distribution becomes nearly constant, as indicated in (2). Finally, at failure, (3), the stresses are constant across the top and bottom parts of the section and equal to the yield-point stress.

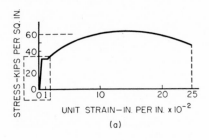

(a)

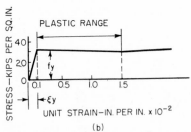

(b)

FIG. 3-85. Stress-strain relationship for a ductile material generally is similar to the curve shown in (a). To simplify plastic analysis, the portion of (a) enclosed by the dash lines is approximated by the curve in (b), which extends to the range where strain hardening begins.

The resisting moment at failure for a rectangular beam can be computed from the stress diagram for stage 3. If b is the width of the member and d its depth, then the ultimate moment for a rectangular beam is

$$M_P = \frac{bd^2}{4} f_y \qquad (3\text{-}117)$$

Since the resisting moment at stage 1 is $M_y = f_y bd^2/6$, the beam carries 50% more moment before failure than when the yield-point stress is first reached in the outer fibers.

A circular section has an M_P/M_y ratio of about 1.7, while a diamond section has a ratio of 2. The average wide-flange rolled-steel beam has a ratio of about 1.14.

The relationship between moment and curvature in a beam can be assumed to be similar to the stress-strain relationship in Fig. 3-85b. Curvature ϕ varies linearly with moment until $M_y = M_P$ is reached, after which ϕ increases indefinitely at constant moment. That is, a plastic hinge forms.

This ability of a ductile beam to form plastic hinges enables a fixed-end or continuous beam to carry more load after M_P occurs at a section, because a redistribution of moments takes place. Consider, for example, a uniformly loaded fixed-end beam. In the elastic range, the end moments are $M_L = M_R = WL/12$, while the mid-span moment M_C is $WL/24$. The load when the yield point is reached in the outer fibers is

$W_y = 12M_y/L$. Under this load, the moment capacity of the ends of the beam is nearly exhausted; plastic hinges form there when the moment equals M_P. As load is increased, the ends then rotate under constant moment and the beam deflects like a simply supported beam. The moment at mid-span increases until the moment capacity at that section is exhausted and a plastic hinge forms. The load causing that condition is the ultimate load W_u since, with three hinges in the span, a link mechanism is formed and the member continues to deform at constant load. At the time the third hinge is formed, the moments at ends and center are all equal to M_P. Therefore, for

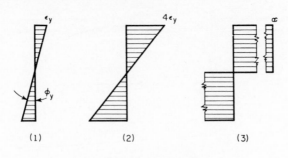

(a) STRAIN DISTRIBUTION

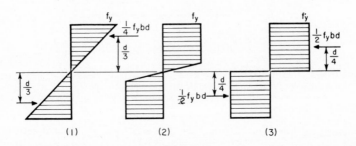

(b) STRESS DISTRIBUTION

FIG. 3-86. Strain distribution is shown in (a) and stress distribution in (b) for a cross section of a beam as it is loaded beyond the yield point, assuming the idealized stress-strain relationship in Fig. 3-85b: stage (1) shows the conditions at the elastic limit of the outer fibers; (2) after yielding starts; and (3) at ultimate load.

equilibrium, $2M_P = W_uL/8$, from which $W_u = 16M_P/L$. Since for the idealized moment-curvature relationship, M_P was assumed equal to M_y, the carrying capacity due to redistribution of moments is 33% greater.

3-94. Upper and Lower Bounds for Ultimate Loads. Methods for computing the ultimate strength of continuous beams and frames may be based on two theorems that fix upper and lower limits for load-carrying capacity.

Upper-bound Theorem. A load computed on the basis of an assumed link mechanism will always be greater than or at best equal to the ultimate load.

Lower-bound Theorem. The load corresponding to an equilibrium condition with arbitrarily assumed values for the redundants is smaller than or at best equal to the ultimate loading—provided that everywhere moments do not exceed M_P.

The equilibrium method, based on the lower-bound theorem, usually is easier for simple cases. The steps involved are: (1) Select redundants that if removed would leave the structure determinate. (2) Draw the moment diagram for the determinate structure. (3) Sketch the moment diagram for an arbitrary value of each redundant. (4) Combine the moment diagrams, forming enough peaks so that the structure will act as a link mechanism if plastic hinges are formed at those points. (5) Compute the value of the redundants from the equations of equilibrium, assuming that at the peaks $M = M_P$. (6) Check to see that there are sufficient plastic hinges to form a mechanism and that M is everywhere less than or equal to M_P.

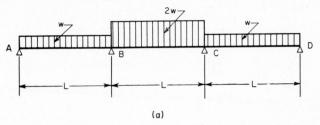

(a)

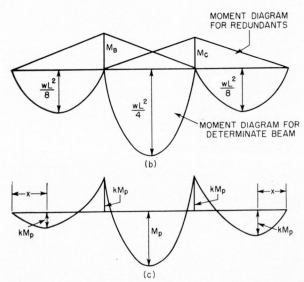

FIG. 3-87. Continuous beam shown in (a) carries twice as much uniform load in the center span as in the side span. In (b) are shown the moment diagrams for this loading condition with redundants removed and for the redundants. The two moment diagrams are combined in (c), producing peaks at which plastic hinges are assumed to form.

Consider, for example, the continuous beam $ABCD$ in Fig. 3-87a with three equal spans, uniformly loaded, the center span carrying double the load of the end spans. Assume that the ratio of the plastic moment for the end spans is k times that for the center span ($k < 1$). For what value of k will the ultimate strength be the same for all spans?

Figure 3-87b shows the moment diagram for the beam made determinate by ignoring the moments at B and C, and the moment diagram for end moments M_B and M_C applied to the determinate beam. Figure 3-87c gives the combined moment diagram. If plastic hinges form at all the peaks, a link mechanism will exist.

Since at B and C the joints can develop only the strength of the weakest beam, a plastic hinge will form when $M_B = M_C = kM_P$. A plastic hinge also will form at the center of span BC when the mid-span moment is M_P. For equilibrium to be maintained, this will occur when $M_P = wL^2/4 - \frac{1}{2}M_B - \frac{1}{2}M_C = wL^2/4 - kM_P$, from which

$$M_P = \frac{wL^2}{4(1 + k)}$$

Maximum moment will occur in the interior of spans AB and CD when

$$x = \frac{L}{2} - \frac{M}{wL} \text{ — or if } M = kM_P, \text{ when } x = \frac{L}{2} - \frac{kM_P}{wL}$$

A plastic hinge will form at this point when the moment equals kM_P. For equilibrium, therefore,

$$kM_P = \frac{w}{2}x(L - x) - \frac{x}{L}kM_P = \frac{w}{2}\left(\frac{L}{2} - \frac{kM_P}{wL}\right)\left(\frac{L}{2} + \frac{kM_P}{wL}\right) - \left(\frac{1}{2} - \frac{kM_P}{wL^2}\right)kM_P$$

This leads to the quadratic equation:

$$\frac{k^2 M_P{}^2}{wL^2} - 3kM_P + \frac{wL^2}{4} = 0$$

When the value of M_P previously computed is substituted in this equation, it becomes

$$7k^2 + 4k = 4 \qquad \text{or} \qquad k(k + \tfrac{4}{7}) = \tfrac{4}{7}$$

from which $k = 0.523$. And the ultimate load is

$$wL = \frac{4M_P(1 + k)}{L} = 6.1\,\frac{M_P}{L}$$

The mechanism method, based on the upper-bound theorem, requires the following steps: (1) Determine the location of possible hinges (points of maximum moment). (2) Pick combinations of hinges to form possible link mechanisms. Certain types are classed as elementary, such as the mechanism formed when hinges are created at the ends and center of a fixed-end or continuous beam, or when hinges form at top and bottom of a column subjected to lateral load, or when hinges are formed at a joint in the members framing into it, permitting the joint to rotate freely. If there are n possible plastic hinges and x redundant forces or moments, then there are $n - x$ independent equilibrium equations and $n - x$ elementary mechanisms. Both elementary mechanisms and possible combinations of them must be investigated. (3) Apply a virtual displacement to each possible mechanism in turn and compute the internal and external work (Art. 3-52). (4) From the equality of internal and external work, compute the critical load for each mechanism. The mechanism with the lowest critical load is the most probable, and its load is the ultimate, or limit, load. (5) Make an equilibrium check to ascertain that moments everywhere are less than or equal to M_P.

As an example of an application of the mechanism method, let us find the ultimate load for the rigid frame of constant section throughout in Fig. 3-88a. Assume that the vertical load at mid-span is equal to 1.5 times the lateral load.

Maximum moments can occur at five points—A, B, C, D, and E—and plastic hinges may form there. Since this structure has three redundants, the number of elementary mechanisms is $5 - 3 = 2$. These are shown in Fig. 3-88b and c. A combination of these mechanisms is shown in Fig. 3-88d.

Let us first investigate the beam alone, with plastic hinges at B, E, and C. As indicated in Fig. 3-88e, apply a virtual rotation θ to BE at B. The center deflection, then, is $\theta L/2$. Since C is at a distance of $L/2$ from E, the rotation at C must be θ and at E, 2θ. The external work, therefore, is $1.5P$ times the mid-span deflection, $\theta L/2$, which equals $\frac{3}{4}\theta PL$. The internal work is the sum of the work at each hinge, or

$M_P\theta + 2M_P\theta + M_P\theta = 4M_P\theta$. Equating internal and external work: $\frac{3}{4}\theta PL = 4M_P\theta$, from which $P = 5.3M_P/L$.

Next, let us investigate the frame mechanism, with plastic hinges at A, B, C, and D. As shown in Fig. 3-88f, apply a virtual rotation θ to AB. The point of application of the lateral load P will then move a distance $\theta L/2$, and the external work will be $\theta PL/2$. The internal work, being the sum of the work at the hinges, will be $4M_P\theta$. Equating internal and external work, $\theta PL/2 = 4M_P\theta$, from which $P = 8M_P/L$.

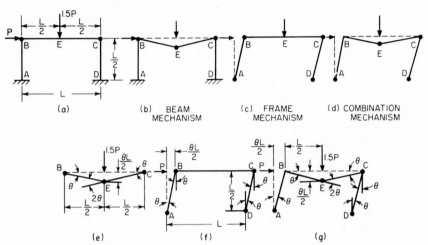

FIG. 3-88. Ultimate-load possibilities for a rigid frame of constant section with fixed bases.

Finally, let us compute the critical load for the combination beam-frame mechanism in Fig. 3-88g. Again, apply a virtual rotation θ to AB, moving B horizontally and E vertically a distance of $\theta L/2$. The external work, therefore, equals

$$\frac{\theta PL}{2} + \frac{3}{4}\,\theta PL = \frac{5\theta PL}{4}$$

The internal work is the sum of the work at hinges A, E, C, and D and is equal to $M_P\theta + 2M_P\theta + 2M_P\theta + M_P\theta = 6M_P\theta$. Equating internal and external work, $5\theta PL/4 = 6M_P\theta$, from which $P = 4.8M_P/L$.

The combination mechanism has the lowest critical load. Now an equilibrium check must be made to insure that the moments everywhere in the frame are less than M_P. If they are, then the combination mechanism is the correct solution.

Consider first the length EC of the beam as a free body. Taking moments about E, noting that the moments at E and C equal M_P, the shear at C is computed to be $4M_P/L$. Therefore, the shear at B is $1.5 \times 4.8M_P/L - 4M_P/L = 3.2M_P/L$. By taking moments about B, with BE considered as a free body, the moment at B is found to be $0.6M_P$. Similar treatment of the columns as free bodies indicates that nowhere is the moment greater than M_P. Therefore, the combination mechanism is the correct solution, and the ultimate load for the frame is $4.8M_P/L$ laterally and $7.2M_P/L$ vertically at mid-span. (Aris Phillips, "Introduction to Plasticity," The Ronald Press Company, New York.)

Section 4

SOIL MECHANICS AND FOUNDATIONS

Jacob Feld, Ph.D.

Consulting Engineer
New York, N.Y.

Two hundred years ago, John Muller wrote in his "Treatise Containing the Practical Part of Fortifications" (A. Muller, London, 1755):

"As the foundations of all buildings, in general, are of utmost importance, in respect to the strength and duration of the work, we shall enter into all the most material particulars, which may happen in different soils, in order to execute works with all the security possible, because many great buildings have been rent to pieces, and some have fallen down, for want of having taken proper care in laying the foundation."

Muller made five recommendations, which are still pertinent:

1. Use proper augers to bore holes from 10 to 15 ft deep to discover the nature of the soil and its hardness.

2. If the soil is gravel or hard stiff clay, no sinking will occur.

3. If the soil is not uniform, or loose sand, lay a grate of timbers crossed two ways, sometimes boarded over with 3-in. wood planks.

4. If the soil is first soft and hard below, then drive piles and lay a grate above them; drive a few piles to determine the proper length before cutting all the piles.

5. Sometimes a bed of gravel or clay has soft mud below, and it is dangerous to drive piles; then build a timber deck and let it sink to bearing, a method used in Russia and Flanders with good results.

TYPES AND NORMAL QUALITIES OF SOILS

The geologist defines a soil as an altered rock. The engineer defines a soil as the material which supports a structure.

The geologist distinguishes among three soil classes:

1. Primitive—formed by the mechanical and chemical decomposition of a rock.

2. Derived—a mixture of primitives with changes resulting from water and air action.

3. Decayed—a mixture of minerals with vegetable- and animal-decay refuse.

4-1. Physical Properties of Soils. The engineer needs to know, for complete identification of a soil: the size of grains, gradation, particle shapes, grain orientation, chemical make-up, and colloidal and dust fractions. Even then, the physical properties can be made to vary over a large range with slight chemical additives or electrochemical controls. The importance of shape in controlling the ratio of surface areas to volume is readily seen from the following example of fractures from a cube:

4-1

Shape	Total volume	Surface area of all pieces
Cube....................................	1	6.0
Cubes cut into two slices................	1	8.0
Cube cut diagonally.....................	1	8.8
Cube cut into three slices...............	1	10.0
Cube cut into three tetrahedrons.........	1	14.5

Where surface properties are important, grain shape becomes at least equal in influence to size gradation.   Normally, an important characteristic is the relative positioning of the grains within the soil body, since this controls the resistance to internal displacement and is at least a qualitative measure of shear and compression strengths.

There have been many attempts to codify all soils into classes of similar and recognizable properties.   As more information is collected on soil properties, the systems of classification become more elaborate and complicated.   One difficulty is the attempt to use similar classifications for different uses; for instance, a system applicable to highway design has little value when the problem is basically that of building foundations.

Structurally, the soil problem can be solved if the physical action can be predicted and deviations therefrom restricted within desired limits.   Most, if not all, subsurface failures occur when a soil, expected to act in accordance with the laws governing solid behavior, actually becomes viscous, plastic, or even liquid.   Such change may be temporary; but the release of internal stresses, while the soil is in the nonsolid phase, causes sufficient displacements to crack the superstructure.

Soils are peculiar in their structural behavior in that, while static equilibrium can be shown to exist along a series of closely proximate points, yet failure may occur along surfaces enclosing such investigated points.   Because of the lack of isotropic structure, surplus strength at one point will seldom transfer to adjacent points that require a little extra strength to prevent failure.   Recognition of these inherent characteristics of soil will take the mystery out of many observed incidents.

4-2. States of Matter Affecting Soil Behavior.   Soils can exhibit solid, viscous, plastic, or liquid action; if the true state can be predicted, the structural design can be prepared accordingly.

Solids are materials having constant density, elasticity, and internal resistance, little affected by normal temperature changes, moisture variations, and vibration below seismic values.   Deformation by shearing takes place along two sets of parallel planes, with the angle between the sets constant for any material and independent of the nature or intensity of the external forces inducing shearing strain.   The harder and more brittle the material, the more this angle differs from a right angle.

If tension is taken as negative compression, Hartmann's law states that the acute angle formed by the shear planes is bisected by the axis of maximum compression, and the obtuse angle by the axis of minimum compression (usually tension).   Shearing planes do not originate simultaneously and are not uniformly distributed.

The angle of shear is related to the ultimate compression and tension stresses by Mohr's formula:

$$\cos \theta = \frac{f_1 - f_2}{f_1 + f_2} \tag{4-1}$$

i.e., the cosine of the angle of shear equals the ratio of the difference of the normal stresses to the sum.   When lateral pressures are applied externally simultaneously with loads, the angle of shear increases; i.e., the material becomes less brittle.

These basic properties of solids can be used in designs affecting soils only if the soils remain solid.   When changes in conditions modify soil structures so that they are not solid, these properties are nonexistent, and a new set of rules governs the actions. Most soils will act like solids, but only up to a certain loading.   This limit loading depends on many external factors, such as flow of moisture, temperature, vibration, age, and sometimes the rate of loading.

No marked subdivision exists between liquid, plastic, and viscous action. These three states have the common property that volume changes are difficult to accomplish, but shape changes occur continuously. They differ in the amount of force necessary to start motion. There is a minimum value necessary for the plastic or viscous states, while a negligible amount will start motion in the liquid state. Upon cessation of the force, a plastic material will stop motion, but liquid and viscous materials will continue indefinitely, or until counteracting forces come into play. Usually, division between solid and plastic states is determined by the percentage of moisture in the soil. This percentage, however, is not a constant but decreases with increase in pressure on the material. Furthermore, the entire relationship between moisture percentage and change of state can be deranged by adding chemicals to the water.

Liquids retained in a vessel are almost incompressible. In water-bearing soils, therefore, if movement or loss of water can be prevented, volume change and settlement will be avoided. Water loss can be prevented by both physical and chemical changes in the nature of the water.

4-3. Soil Moisture. If the water content of soil is chiefly film or adsorbed moisture, the mass will not act as a liquid. All solids tend to adsorb or condense upon their surfaces any liquids (and gases) with which they come into contact.

The kind of ion, or metal element, in the chemical make-up of a solid has a great influence on how much water can be adsorbed. Ion-exchange procedures for soil stabilization and percolation control are therefore an important part of soil mechanics.

The effect of temperature on soil action may be explained by the reduction of film thickness with rise of temperature. This is comparable with the thinning out of glue holding a granular mass together. Soil failures are most common in the spring months after warm rains, when the strong water films are weakened by temperature rise and by accretion of more water.

Water films are tougher than pore water. (Terzaghi, in 1920, stated that water films less than two-millionths of an inch thick are semisolid in action; they will not boil or freeze at normal temperatures.) Consequently, saturated soil freezes much more easily than damp soil, and ice crystals will grow by sucking free moisture out of the pores. A sudden thaw will then release large concentrations of water, often with drastic results.

When liquids evaporate, they first change to films, requiring large thermal increment for the change from film to vapor. The strong binding power of water film is the explanation for the toughness of beaches, for the ebbing tides pull out free moisture.

Compaction of soils artificially or by natural causes is best carried out under fairly definite moisture contents, since redistribution of soil grains to a closely packed volume cannot be accomplished without sufficient moisture to coat each particle. The film acts as a lubricant to permit easier relative movements and by its capillary tension holds the grains in position. Obviously, finer grains require more water for best stabilization than coarser materials.

4.4. Resistance of Soils to Pressure. Before 1640, Galileo distinguished among solids, semifluids, and fluids. He stated that semifluids, unlike fluids, maintain their condition when heaped up, and if a hollow or cavity is made, agitation causes the filling up of the hollow; whereas in solids, the hollow does not fill up. This is an early description of the property known as the natural slope of granular materials—an easily observed condition for clean dry sands, but a variable slope for soils containing clays with varying moisture percentages. The angle of natural slope should not be confused with the angle of internal friction, although many writers have followed Woltmann (1799), who, in translating Coulomb's papers, made that mistake.

The fundamental laws of friction were applied to soils by Coulomb. He recognized that the resistance along a surface of failure within a soil is a function of both the load per unit area and the surface of contact.

One factor determining resistance of a soil is the coefficient of friction; friction is a resistance independent of the area loaded, but directly proportional to the intensity of loading. A second factor is cohesion, which is a characteristic of the material.

Mayniel, in 1808, describes these factors as: "Perfect friction, as in sand, caused by the intercogging of particles; cohesion, a reunion of masses, like a glueing together; imperfect friction, the rubbing or rolling of particles over each other, due entirely to their own individual weights."

4-5. Soil Properties Important in Engineering. The normally important soil properties are:

1. *Weight or Density.* The amount of solid material in a unit volume is called the "dry weight." Usually, it is taken as a measure of solidity or compressive strength. The ratio of actual weight as found in nature or in a prepared soil to the corresponding weight of an artificially compacted sample is the measure of density relative to the standard optimum. Of the various standards used, the technique developed by Proctor was first accepted but has been replaced by a modification known as the AASHO test.

2. *Elastic Modulus.* This is of value only where the soil acts as a solid, with complete rebound on release of load. Most soils do act in this fashion over limited ranges of load application and favorable external conditions. Reliance on elasticity is limited by the possibility of unfavorable change in conditions during the life of a structure.

3. *Internal Resistance.* This is probably the most important soil property. There are many methods for its determination. Unfortunately, results obtained vary with the method. In a perfectly dry, graded sand of similarly shaped grains, shear resistance is a definite value; but in other soils, the value varies, being larger at the beginning of motion than after the first slip has started. Variations in shear value can result from temperature, chemicals in the soil, moisture, direction of moisture flow, vibration, and time of application or release of loading. In practice, it is necessary to estimate the worst possible set of conditions and use the corresponding value. Internal resistance is a combination of frictional and cohesive forces. Both can vary, but usually not in parallel relationships.

4. *Internal Friction.* Coulomb pure friction corresponds to simple shear in the theory of elasticity. It can never exceed the value of internal resistance. Many designers use it as the total shear resistance—an assumption also made in most earth-pressure formulas.

5. *Cohesion.* This is the maximum tensile value of the soil. It is a complicated coordination of many factors, such as gravitational grain attraction, colloidal adhesion of the grain covering, capillary tension of the moisture films, atmospheric pressure where gases in the void space have been dissolved or adsorbed, electrostatic attraction of charged surfaces, and many others.

6. *Dilatancy or volume change* as a result of applied external forces. This, too, is a complicated property, since it is difficult to separate true dilatancy from shrinkage (sometimes expansion) as a result of variation in fluid content. Dilatancy is a reversible phenomenon; unfortunately, so is the effect of fluid change. If either action is disregarded, prediction of movements of structures on volume-changing soils can lead to inaccurate values.

7. *Poisson's Ratio.* This measures the lateral effects produced by a linear strain, in a continuous series of values of reversible sign. With a value of unity, as occurs in a fluid, any force is transferred undiminished in all directions, simultaneously in a pure liquid and with a lag in other fluids.

There are other minor properties sometimes of importance. The vegetable-refuse content of a soil may affect the fixity of any properties induced by treatment. For instance, soils very heavy in rotted vegetation, containing tannic acids, are not suitable for cement stabilization. Soils with large limestone-dust content can be weakened by water flow through the mass, to say nothing of the disintegrating effect from percolating sewage and other waste liquors.

IDENTIFICATION, SAMPLING, AND TESTING OF SOILS

To permit the application of previously collected experience to new problems, a standard system of soil identification is necessary; then classification of a soil follows the determination of physical properties in accordance with standardized testing procedures.   Testing for soil properties or reactions to applied loads involves both laboratory and field procedures.

4-6. Soil Identification.   Field investigations to identify soils can be made by surface surveying, aerial surveying, or geophysical or subsurface exploratory analysis. Complete knowledge of the geological structure of an area permits definite identification from a surface reconnaissance.   Tied together with a mineralogical classification of the surface layers, the reconnaissance can at least recognize structures of some soils. The surveys, however, cannot alone determine soil behavior unless identical conditions have previously been encountered.

Up to recent times, most foundation designs were based on assumed properties deduced from surface observations.   Geological maps and detailed reports, useful for this purpose, are available for most populated areas in the United States.   They are issued by the U.S. Department of Agriculture, U.S. Geological Survey, and corresponding state offices.

Old surveys are of great value in locating original shore lines and stream courses, as well as existence of surface-grade changes.   Correlation between geological names of exposed soils and the engineering terminology is not a difficult matter.

A complete site inspection is a necessary adjunct to the data collected from maps and surveys and will often clarify the question of uniformity.   Furthermore, inspection of neighboring structures will point up some possible difficulties.

Aerial surveying has been developed to the extent where very rapid determination of soil types can be made at low cost over very large areas.   Stereoptic photographic data, correlated with standard charts, identify soil types from color, texture, drainage characteristics, and ground cover.

4-7. Subsoil Exploration.   Geophysical or seismic exploration of subsoils is a carry-over from practice standardized in oil-field surveys to determine discontinuities in soil structure.   The principles involved are the well-known characteristics of sound-wave transmission, reflection, and refraction in passing through materials of different densities.   The method charts time and intensity of sound-wave emergence at various points, induced by the explosion of a submerged charge.

A similar technique uses the variation in electric conductivity of various densities and discontinuities in layer contacts.

These methods can give a good qualitative picture of certain soil properties, depths of layers, and depth to soil rock.   They cannot be expected to give more than an average or statistical picture of conditions or to give definite identification of the kinds of soils.   However, they are an excellent guide to programing a complete exploratory investigation, since the locations of changes and discontinuity in soil layers cannot otherwise be learned.

The most usual exploratory investigation of subsurface soil conditions is by borings. If properly made, these will portray the depth and thickness of each soil layer; its color and texture; resistance to penetration of a fixed area of plunger under standardized impact or static forces; depth of the free-water surface and depth of rock.

Since it is impossible to guarantee that all rock encountered is bedrock, some additional core borings are necessary when subsurface conditions vary.   The minimum depth of a core should be 5 ft, but if the recovery indicates rock nature or seams not consistent with the local geology, the cores should be at least 10 ft long.

Many foundation-construction difficulties, often of very expensive nature, result from either unreliable methods of taking borings or from too much reliance on extrapolation of the results.   After all, except in uniform soil bodies, of which there are practically none, a boring can only be expected to depict truly the condition at the boring location.   Hence, choosing the number and location of borings calls for good judgment.   Many municipal and state codes fix a minimum number for each project.

Unfortunately, except in large projects, discontinuities of layers do not become known until the boring rig has been removed from the site, making the cost of additional borings quite high.   Without exception, however, that cost is a small part of either the wastage in overdesign or the cost of corrective revisions necessary during foundation construction; additional borings should be made wherever a discontinuity is indicated. The usual plan is to spot a boring midway between a pair showing inconsistent results; then if the new boring is not a fair average of the two, placing the next one midway between the two showing the greatest variation, and so on. In this way, the location of changes in condition can be closely fixed and overconservative estimates eliminated.

The New York City Building Code (1948) sets forth minimum requirements for number and depth of borings, as follows: Borings or test pits shall show the nature of the soil in at least one location in every 2,500 sq ft of building area. The borings or test pits shall be carried sufficiently into good bearing material to establish its character and thickness. For structures more than one story in height—except dwellings

Table 4-1. Correlation of Boring-spoon Results

Descriptive term	Number of blows per ft		
	A	B	C
	For sand (medium)		
Loose....................	15	10	25
Medium compact..........	16–30	11–25	25–45
Compact..................	30–50	26–45	45–65
Very compact..............	Over 50	Over 45	Over 65
	For clay		
Very soft..................	To 3	To 2	To 5
Soft......................	4–12	3–10	5–15
Stiff......................	12–35	10–25	15–40
Hard.....................	Over 35	Over 25	Over 45

A. 2-in. spoon, 148-lb hammer, 30-in. fall.
B. 2-in. spoon, 300-lb hammer, 18-in. fall.
C. 2-in. spoon, 150-lb hammer, 18-in. fall.
NOTE: Coarser soil requires more blows; finer material fewer blows. A variation of 10 % in the weight of the hammer will not materially affect values in the table. (Compiled by T. V. Burke).

not more than two stories in height—or for structures having an average area load exceeding 1,000 psf, there shall be at least one boring in every 10,000 sq ft of building area carried down to a depth of 100 ft below the curb or to a depth which shows 25 continuous feet of class 10 (2-ton value) or better below the deepest part of the excavation of the proposed structure, or 5 ft into ledge rock. For structures having an average area load in excess of 2,000 psf, supported on rock, borings shall be made to a depth of at least 5 ft below the surface of the rock, except where ledge rock is completely uncovered. Such structures not bearing on rock shall have at least one boring in each 10,000 sq ft of building area carried down to a depth of 100 ft below curb or 5 ft into ledge rock.

In every built-up community, there should be a central public depository of subsurface boring records. A compilation of boring results plotted on a city street map is invaluable. In areas where consistent soil conditions exist, a map record of previous investigations can well permit one to dispense with any further exploration.

The tendency in recent years is toward more careful, and therefore more expensive, boring methods. Except for the test pit, the older methods (auger and wash borings) are now no longer accepted as true indications of soil conditions. The auger mixes up all the soils; the wash boring deletes the finer fractions and often completely revises the make-up of the soils.

The test pit is a definite method of showing what exists but, of course, is limited as to depth. Test pits are especially useful where boring records are not consistent with predictions from surface and geological records.

The presently accepted test-boring procedure is to drive a pipe into the ground, remove the soil to the lower extremity either by auger or washing methods, then insert a sampling tube, which is pressed into the ground to permit recovery of a true piece of the soil at that depth. (There has been some standardization of equipment dimensions and penetration forces, although outside barrels used vary from $1\frac{1}{2}$ to 4 in. and inside samplers from 1 to $2\frac{1}{2}$ in. ID.) Record is kept of the number of blows with a falling weight required to force the casing down each foot. (It is noteworthy that resistance decreases whenever the inside of the casing is cleared out.) Record is also made of the resistance of the sampling spoon to penetration, usually for a depth of 1 ft. Here, the thickness and shape of the cutting edge are important factors.

Table 4-2. Usual Laboratory Soil Tests*

Test	Soil to which adaptable	General use of results
Specific gravity	All	Void-ratio determination
Grain size	Granular	Estimate permeability, frost action, compaction, shear strength
Grain shape	Fine granular	Estimate shear strength
Liquid and plastic limits	Cohesive	Compressibility, compaction
Water content	Cohesive	Compressibility, compaction
Void ratio	All	Compressibility, strength
Unconfined compression	Cohesive	Estimate shear strength

NOTE: The last two tests must be of undisturbed samples. Mineralogical identification techniques in various clays have been developed by T. W. Lambe and R. T. Martin, Massachusetts Institute of Technology, and are reported excellent for soil description and usually reliable indicators of behavior for clay soils.

* Adapted from Sowers and Sowers, "Introductory Soil Mechanics and Foundations," The Macmillan Company, New York.

Some correlation has been attempted between the resistances of various sized spoon samplers under various impact pressures. The New York City Department of Housing and Buildings has issued a table of such correlation as a guide, together with an indication of the density of the soil as measured by the resistance to penetration (see Table 4-1).

Where laboratory tests are to be made on the samples recovered, both to identify the soil better and to determine its physical properties, special methods are necessary, such as "undisturbed sampling." The soil sample is taken with an ultra-thin, noncorrosive metal shell, which is immediately sealed upon removal from the casing to avoid all changes in moisture or density of the sample.

Rock borings or drillings are made by rotating a hard steel tube with a bit, or lower end, specially treated to cut the rock along an annular ring. Bits are surfaced with some extra-hard, tough alloy, such as tungsten carbide, or with commercial diamond chips known as "borts." High-pressure water jets are always necessary to dissipate the frictional heat. The lower tube section, or recovery barrel, contains part of the rock freed by the annular cutting. In the best of ledge rock, not over 80% of the depth cored will be found in the recovered core. This is reduced by the existence of seams to some 50%. In soft rock, the total of all pieces left in the core may be only 10 to 20% of the drilled length.

4-8. Soil Tests. Laboratory, and to a smaller extent field, testing of soils has developed into a complicated maze of interrelated tests, with many forms of apparatus. A summary of these tests was prepared by the American Society for Testing Materials Committee D-18, and published as "Procedure for Testing Soils," July, 1950. Many of the test techniques are applicable only to certain restricted soil groups and give misleading data if otherwise used. Table 4-2 lists the usual laboratory tests.

Where important structures are founded on rather uncertain soil types and some estimate of long-time settlements is desired, or where more than one soil type is found under a structure, more detailed testing is warranted. Laboratory determinations of unconfined compression, direct or simple shear, triaxial shear, and consolidation rate and extent are also required.

In-place soil tests are more popular in Europe than in the United States. One method is to drive a casing to the desired depth, and after the soil is cleaned out, the exposed bottom is tested by statically loading cone-shaped plungers or tight-fitting bearing plates. In another test, called the *Vane shear test*, a rod is inserted into the ground. The rod has two to four vertical steel plates. The torque necessary to start rotation and to maintain rotation of the rod is determined. These values are measures of the shear resistance and friction and are quite reliable in soft and fine-grained soils. Under the European techniques, resistances measured at various depths are used to determine not only soil-bearing values but also pile-friction resistances, from which are obtained required pile lengths for desired load capacity.

4-9. Load Tests on Soils. The use of field load tests for determining soil-bearing values is as old as the art of foundation design. The techniques described centuries ago in the literature have only been changed by the use of equipment to prepare the test area and to handle the static loads.

Loads may be applied by jacks reacting against a loaded truck or weight of castings set up on a frame. Recently, the trend is toward jacking against a beam held in place by screw anchors. Now available for this purpose is an aluminum truss, which reduces the weights to be handled and expedites the making of load tests in isolated sites.

There is no completely accepted formula for determination of safe bearing value of a soil from the results of a load-bearing test. For equal settlement, average bearing values depend on the shape, size, and rigidity of the footing. Choice of bearing value without relation to settlement is meaningless. Furthermore, bearing capacity as a contact pressure at the footing base is not necessarily proof of safety, since failure by local or general shear within the soil may be the true criterion to be considered. The distribution of contact pressure, usually assumed as uniform over the entire area, is also variously assumed, as shown in Fig. 4-2 (Art. 4-18).

Better correlation between load tests and safe bearing values can be expected in granular soils than in clays and silts.

Under constant unit load on clay soils, settlements will vary almost directly with the diameter of the test loading device. For a desired settlement in clay soils, bearing value will vary with the density. F. L. Plummer has estimated a value of 1 ton per sq ft if the density is 100 lb per cu ft and 5 tons per sq ft if the density is 140 lb per cu ft. The Krey method of plastic equilibrium, based on an assumed circular section of failure below the footing, shows the bearing value as directly proportional to the width of the footing, if cohesion is disregarded.

4-10. Settlement. Settlement of structures must always be expected. Measurement is usually by surveying methods, referring the elevations of fixed points to a bench mark sufficiently remote so as not to be affected by the loaded structure. For differential settlements within a structure, a simpler leveling device consists of water-filled tubes with gage glasses.

For approximate settlements under various loadings at different ages, a soil-loading test made with an undisturbed sample in a triaxial-compression machine—the lateral loads representing restraint within the soil—gives results which should be used as a general guide only. In saturated soils, the load applied will be entirely carried by the water until it has enough time to flow out. The settlement at any given time after load application is

$$S_t = qS \tag{4-2}$$

where q is the percentage of the consolidation with time as shown by the laboratory test and

$$S = \frac{h(e_i - e_f)}{1 + e_i} \tag{4-3}$$

where h = depth of layer
    e_f = final voids ratio
    e_i = initial voids ratio.
A fairly accurate indication of future behavior can be obtained from this type of test and analysis, but quantitive results closely fitting field measurements over long periods of time should not be expected.

SOIL CONSOLIDATION AND IMPROVEMENT

Soil as an engineering material differs from stone, timber, and other natural products in that it can be improved and altered to conform to desired characteristics. Up to recent years, the usual studies were for improvement of bearing capacity.

4-11. Methods for Improving Soil Bearing Capacity. In normal soil conditions, increasing the depth of the footing is the simplest method of increasing bearing capacity, especially if the concrete is poured directly against the soil at the bottom of the pit. The counterbalancing of lateral displacements by the surcharge of the unexcavated soil surrounding a pit markedly improves the capacity of the soil to carry load. There are exceptions to this rule, especially if the pit is carried down to below the free-water level in clay or silt, where the opposite effect will be found.

Drainage is another well-known method to improve physical characteristics. Where soil is possibly moved by subterranean water flow, open-joint tile drains should be placed just above the footing base to lead away free water before it can move or soften the bearing strata.

A compressible soil is improved by covering with a porous granular layer—sand, gravel, or crushed rock—and by impressing or blending it into the natural material, forming a new and much stronger soil stratum. In the Spezia, Italy, docks, built in a tidal marsh of great thicknesses of soft silt, it was found that a cushion layer of sand could be hydraulically deposited to form a base for very heavy masonry docks and quay walls. The interlocking of fine and porous-grained materials, often found in nature as hardpans, can be artificially produced.

Dry density of a soil is a fair measure of its strength. Therefore, to improve a soil, reduce the void volume. This was first accomplished, centuries ago, by driving short wood piles into soft ground—not as piles to carry loads to lower strata but to compress or consolidate the upper layer and make it available for the support of loading. About 1800, it was found that, if the wood piles, usually only 6 to 10 ft in length and driven manually, were retracted and the open space filled with friable material, such as sand or limestone dust, the improvement of bearing value was at least equal to the effect of the wood piles. Further, by ramming the sand in position, additional compaction of the soil was accomplished. Later, when pile-driving machinery became available, the holes were prepared by ramming, and the space was filled with concrete. In this way, there originated the sand pile for soil consolidation and the cast-in-place concrete pile for load transfer by friction along the surfaces in contact.

Extremely weak soils can be used for the support of buildings. On a sanitary fill on marshland, for example, very light consolidation by bulldozers of a 12-in. layer of fine cinders formed a blanket strong enough to support one-story frame dwellings and light-gage metal arch huts, as well as access roads and subsurface utilities. Similarly, a three-story masonry-wall and timber-floor housing project was placed on a 30-ft depth of domestic ashes, filling in an abandoned clay pit. Based upon some extensive load tests, a spread-footing design for a maximum of 750 psf added load was found to be an economical solution. For many structures on similar soils, on the other hand, pile foundations have been found unsatisfactory because of later consolidation of the soft soils and movements of the piles.

S. J. Johnson, at the 1952 Soil Stabilization Conference held at Massachusetts Institute of Technology, differentiated between temporary procedures to permit construction of foundations and permanent improvements of the soil. Among temporary procedures are control of ground-water levels by sumps and pumps, well points, or electro-osmosis and the surrounding of excavations by sheeting.

Sumps to lower water-table levels by pumping, placed not too close to the slopes of an excavation to avoid local slides, are effective only if the soil has a high coefficient of permeability; i.e., greater than 0.1 cm per sec, although in very dense, well-graded soils good results are achieved with medium coefficients.   Glossop and Skempton have reported good results with wells where the soil has 25% finer than 0.05-mm grain size (silt smaller than No. 200 mesh), while Terzaghi and Peck state that the limit is 10% of 0.05-mm grain size.

Electro-osmosis as a control of moisture is feasible only in fine-grained soils and is still in the experimental stage for use where economical methods are necessary.

Sheetpiling as an enclosure to reduce unbalanced pressures is an important procedure for temporary control of soil strength.

4-12. Compaction of Soils.   Permanent soil alteration is accomplished usually by physical means.   Most soils can be compacted or densified by the application of pressure sufficient to reduce the water content.   The effect of water in soils is unimportant if less than 3 to 7% of the soil grains will pass a No. 200 mesh screen.

Compaction by heavy rubber-tired wheels will show change in density to depths as much as 4 ft, especially if large tire pressures (100 psi) are used.

Surface vibration is of value only for local uses.   Deep methods of soil compaction, such as the "Vibrofloat" machinery, can compact loose sands to substantial depths over limited areas but are not suitable for clays, silts, and marls.   Even explosives are restricted to free-draining soils, if proper consolidation is desired.

Since 1941, the use of artificially stabilized fills for building foundations has become fairly common.   Such fills must be made under careful moisture control with due regard to the local rainy season.   Densities should be 100% of optimum for sandy soils and about 97% for cohesive soils.   Since usually the settlements will be less than for the local soils, special care must be taken at the limits of the fills, and proper slip joints must be provided in the buildings.

4-13. Densification of Soils.   Loose soils can be grouted for densification by adding cement (often mixed with fly ash or bentonite to provide better mobility) into the pores, or with silt intrusion, chemical or asphalt emulsion.   These procedures replace the void content, which is partly or wholly filled with moisture, with some more solid filler.

Prestressing of soil by temporary overloading, usually simultaneously with sand drains or wicks to lower the water table, has been used in road and airport designs and is also applicable to large building projects.

The opposite problem is the control of heaving from frost entering the soil or from the expansion of dried-out clay when water seepage is available.   These conditions are serious; the frost difficulty can be eliminated only by carrying the footings below the deepest frost penetration; the solution of the heaving-soil problem is not so simple and is still not completely solved.

Freezing of soils to unexpected depths below cold-storage rooms, as well as the complete drying out of soils under boiler settings and similar hot-process equipment, result in serious foundation displacements.   These locations require special insulation blankets with free-drainage qualities, so that soil volumes will remain constant.

Many of the troubles with soil behavior can be eliminated if proper densification is obtained.   The cost of obtaining density by mechanical means is roughly proportional to the compactive effort employed.   However, different compaction methods must be used with different soils, and only the proper methods are of value.   For instance, vibration can be very helpful with sands but may be useless or harmful with clays.   It is therefore necessary to identify the soils being operated on, and after determination of the possibilities of property change by different construction procedures has been made, a choice of the proper method can be based on the costs of each procedure.

As a rough approximation, in large-scale works, 95% of optimum density can be obtained at a cost of 2 to 4 cents per cubic yard.   This is reported as the experience of the U.S. Bureau of Reclamation on Embankments and Foundations by Walker and Holtz.

Proper gradation of the soil compacted is desirable.   Under present techniques, the maximum possible density is more easily obtained with fine-grained soils; large percentages of grain sizes above ¼ in. reduce the density obtained with constant compactive effort.

Modern sheepsfoot rollers weigh 15 tons and will compact a 10-ft strip with 640 psi on each "foot" to a depth of 6 in. below the surface. The tendency in recent years has been to use heavy rubber-tired rolling equipment for compaction, with some extremely heavy "supercompactors" for the larger operations. These units with 80 to 100 psi tire pressures and 25,000-lb wheel loads have proved effective in compacting 18-in. layers of gravelly soil with fewer passes than were required by the use of sheepsfoot rollers. None of these machines can provide compaction to the top surface, which must be prepared either with smooth-surface rollers or by blading off the top layer.

Field density determinations are used for control and acceptance of compaction operations. In minor work, a simple test is to run a light automobile over the surface being compacted and swing the car around in a fairly sharp curve. Tire marks show if the soil is too moist, and dust will fly off the tires if the soil needs more sprinkling.

Overcompaction is dangerous where later changes in temperature and moisture may cause serious heaving. The density increase of soils improves their strength, but too high a compression will produce an incipient unstable internal structure.

Some experimental work has recently been reported by W. Kjellman of Sweden, where soil layers are compacted by covering with a membrane and surcharged by exhausting the air below the membrane. One form of membrane used in actual work consisted of a sand cover on a clay soil. Similar densification and stability have been noted where wellpoint suction creates a partial vacuum in the soil.

More difficulty must be expected in obtaining uniform density in glacial-drift deposits or blends of granular soils than in the finer soils. Using the modified Proctor test, of a 10-lb weight falling 18 in. and with 25 blows per layer, the following results were obtained with two natural glacial deposits and a blend of the same:

Deposit	Optimum moisture, %	Max dry density, lb per cu ft
Brown sand with trace of silt..........	6.9	120.6
Brown silt with trace of sand..........	8.1	122.1
50% of each........................	9.5	127.6

Note that the blended soil required a higher moisture content but gave a considerably higher density than either of the natural deposits.

SPREAD FOOTINGS

The most economical foundation support for a load is that which transmits the load most directly to the soil. That makes the spread footing for an isolated column load the most frequent type of foundation.

4-14. Bearing Capacity with Spread Footings. Sometimes, the complete solution of this subject is given in one simple equation:

$$A = \frac{P}{S} \qquad (4-4)$$

where area of footing needed A equals the load to be carried P divided by the unit bearing value of the soil S. Unfortunately, this equation has no real meaning; nor is it even approximately correct without some limitations on each factor.

Actually, the equation should read: The area of a footing required to comply with the limitation of a desired amount of settlement of the column carried—for a known distribution of loading on the base of the footing and for known elastic characteristics of the footing—approximately equals the actual average load divided by the average bearing of the soil.   But this relationship holds only for footings of the same shape and size, under the same unit loading, for a definite subsidence in the desired time period.

The purpose of a footing is to support a definite assigned portion of a building. Since all footings will settle, i.e., the load imposed will cause a displacement, all footings in a perfect design will be displaced equally, both horizontally and vertically.

4-15. Cause of Settlement of Footings.   Since there are on record many cases of foundation failures but very few footing failures, it must be concluded that the ground on which the footings rest is the usual cause of the trouble.

The displacement of the load carried can be one or several of the following movements:

1. Compression of the footing material elastically.
2. Deflection of the footing unit elastically.
3. Compression of the soil directly below the footing elastically.
4. Vertical yield of the soil directly below the footing because of horizontal transfer of stress, with consequent horizontal strain—elastic and plastic—possibly not equally in all directions.
5. Vertical yield of the soil due to change in character of the soil, such as squeeze of water content under pressure, change in volume at contact planes of different materials, change in chemical constituents of soil or rock.

It should be kept in mind that items 3, 4, and 5 may be caused not only by the direct loading but also by loadings on adjacent footings.   Also, the loading at the bottom of a footing is not uniform over its entire area.

The action of loads on soil is pictured by Hogentogler as a series of interrelated phases, chiefly:

1. The load compresses the soil directly below it.
2. The compressed soil bulges laterally.
3. The bulge compresses the side soil areas.
4. The side soil areas resist and distort, sometimes showing definite surface bulges. Fehr and Thomas found ripples in sand surfaces beyond loaded test areas.

4-16. Amounts of Settlement.   From data on settlement of structures that have been accumulated it can be safely concluded that:

1. In soft rock, hardpan, and dense glacial deposits, settlements of from $\frac{1}{4}$ to $\frac{3}{8}$ in. must be expected and will occur almost immediately under loads up to 10 tons per sq ft.
2. In dry sands, settlements of $\frac{1}{2}$ to $\frac{3}{4}$ in. must be expected under loads from 3 to 4 tons per sq ft and will occur almost immediately.
3. In wet sands, settlement of $\frac{1}{4}$ to $\frac{1}{2}$ in. will occur immediately under loads from 2 to 3 tons per sq ft and will increase to $\frac{3}{4}$ in. in a period of months, especially if the sand is drained.
4. In dense clays, usually mixed with gravel or sand, settlements under loads of 3 to 4 tons per sq ft will be $\frac{1}{2}$ in. immediately and will increase to about 2 in. in a period of 2 years.
5. In soft clays, settlements under 1 to 2 tons per sq ft will be 1 in. immediately and will increase to 3 in. in 3 years.   The increase will continue with time.   Values of 6 to 9 in. are not unusual.

These values are for small areas.   The settlement of large areas in granular soils will not be uniform, chiefly because the base pressures are not uniform.   The settlement of large areas in plastic soils will not be uniform, because the base pressures are not uniform and the effect of plastic flow is much less in the interior regions.

4-17. Consolidation of Subsoil.   The settlements in Art. 4-16 are for isolated footings.   The total settlement of a structure will be increased by two factors:

1. Consolidation of the subsoil by the added load.
2. Effect of adjacent loads on the footing in question.

The relative importance of subsoil consolidation can be evaluated from Terzaghi's statement that 80% of settlement comes from the compression of soil within a depth one and a half times the width of the footing.   (Cummings computed the unit stresses at various depths under different base-pressure distributions and concluded that the stress at a depth of twice the footing width is independent of the base-pressure distribution.)

The effect of adjacent loads is a more serious factor. For example, F. Kögler (*Harvard Soil Mechanics Conference*, Vol. 3, p. 66, 1936) describes, as the reason for the tipping of large tanks toward each other, the greater consolidation of the soil between tanks due to the addition of compression from several loadings, as against the lesser compression on the outside of the cluster of tanks. In tall buildings founded on clays, the interior footings will settle more than those along the street lines. The seriousness of building adjacent footings at different levels, with resultant unequal restraint of the subsoil under the footings, is proved by cracked walls and tipped structures. This effect becomes most serious when continuous footings under walls are built with stepped subgrades.

A related cause of trouble is the upheaval of the bottom of excavations due to lateral pressure of the banks, causing a decrease of soil density during construction. In clays, such as those in Texas, excavated pits are immediately covered with a mat of concrete, at least 3 in. thick. In water-bearing areas, the excavation is kept flooded to prevent unbalanced pressures on the subgrade.

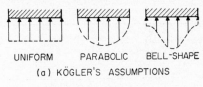

UNIFORM   PARABOLIC   BELL-SHAPE

(a) KÖGLER'S ASSUMPTIONS

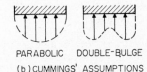

PARABOLIC   DOUBLE-BULGE

(b) CUMMINGS' ASSUMPTIONS

Fig. 4-1. 8-ft 2-in. square footing on 3-ton-capacity soil as designed at various times.

Fig. 4-2. Some assumed distributions of loadings at the base of a spread footing.

The effect of uplift due to changing water levels, as occurs along many streams as well as along tidal waters, must be considered when the design has footings at different depths. Along shores, very light bungalows on spread footings will move with the tides.

4-18. Pressure Distribution under Spread Footings. Even though the settlement characteristics of a soil are determined, the actual expected settlement cannot be even approximated unless the distribution of pressure at the base of the footing is known. Without such information, the design of a footing is impossible.

In the past, concrete footings were made very rigid. Prior to 1910, for example, footings 8 ft square were usually made about 4½ ft deep (Fig. 4-1); combined footings for two columns were layers of steel-grillage beams, embedded in concrete. The rigidity so obtained forces a uniform indenture into the soil; a uniform deformation meant a uniform soil resistance. The pressure distribution, therefore, was different from that under a reinforced-concrete footing.

For flexible (i.e., appreciably elastic deformable) footings, the base pressure is a simple function of the elastic curve for any soil loaded below the permanent set or flow value. This is another way of saying that additional settlement is directly proportional to the additional load.

Kögler, in 1936, stated that the base-distribution pressure must be assumed as either uniform, parabolic with zero at the edges, or bell-shaped with a constant minimum along the edges and a maximum under the center of the footing area (see Fig. 4-2a).

A. E. Cummings (*Transactions of the ASCE*, 1935) stated that the pressure-distribution curve is a direct function of the elastic curve formed by the footing. There are two general cases: (1) a parabolic distribution for a rigid footing on a dense sand, and (2) a double-bulge shape, with maxima near the quarter points for a less rigid footing on a rigid or elastic material. There is a great difference in the footing design under the two cases (see Fig. 4-2b).

Unit bearing capacity for equal settlement varies with the size and shape of footing; it is greater for smaller areas and smaller for round areas. W. S. Housel (*University of Michigan Research Bulletin* 13, 1929) reported on tests of four round plates and four square plates, each shape with areas of 1, 2, 4, and 9 sq ft. He concluded that for equal settlement, the bearing value P equals the area A times the strength of the pressure bulb m plus the perimeter S times the edge shear resistance of the soil n. Thus, $P = Am + Sn$. If m and n are assumed constant for any one soil, two load tests on different areas are sufficient for a complete solution.

According to A. W. Skempton (1951 London Building Congress), clays with zero internal friction, but with cohesive strength, have the ultimate bearing value given by $(cN + p)$, where c is the tested cohesion or shear strength of the soil, p is the total overburden pressure at foundation level, and N is a factor dependent upon the shape of the footing. If R is the ratio of depth of the bottom to width of footing, values of N are:

When R is	0	0.25	0.5	0.75	1.0	1.5	2.0	2.5	3.0	4.0+
For circular footings	6.2	6.7	7.1	7.4	7.7	8.1	8.4	8.6	8.8	9.0
For strip footings	5.1	5.6	5.9	6.2	6.4	6.8	7.0	7.2	7.4	7.5

The ultimate bearing value should be divided by the chosen factor of safety to obtain a safe unit value of the clay.

For the purpose of footing design, knowledge of the pressure distribution in the soil below the contact area is necessary when soft layers are encountered that may fail

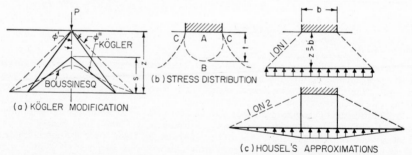

FIG. 4-3. Assumed distribution of pressure from a spread footing to subsoil.

under the combination of stresses from various loads. Or it may be needed for estimating the total expected settlement of the structure. In weak soils, the initial settlement either compresses the material to a denser and less yielding one, or continuous settlements occur, with only one result—ultimate failure.

In 1885, Boussinesq published a solution for the distribution of stress in an elastic material caused by a point load on a horizontal surface. This solution is applicable approximately to pressure distribution in the deeper soil layers under footings. The vertical stress at any point in the mass equals $3Pz^3/2\pi R^5$, where z is vertical depth, P is the load, and R is the radius vector. In 1935, A. E. Cummings recommended that, in place of a constant exponent 3 for z in the numerator, an amount varying from 3 for hard dry clays to 6 for sands be used.

Kögler modified the Boussinesq distribution by substituting for the curve average straight lines, somewhat steeper than the curve, with a somewhat larger maximum stress vertically below the load (Fig. 4-3a). If S is maximum unit pressure at a depth z according to Kögler, and t maximum depth of permanent set in the soil, ϕ' the slope from the vertical to the point of zero stress according to Boussinesq, ϕ'' the slope according to Kögler, then (the area above a horizontal at any depth being equal to the load P):

For loose sand: $\phi' = 35$ to $40°$ $t = 6.0$ to 3.5 ft
For medium sand: $\phi' = 40$ to $55°$ $t = 3.5$ to 2.7 ft
For dense sand: $\phi' = 35$ to $65°$ $t = 2.7$ to 1.5 ft

ϕ' =	40°	50°	60°	75°	90°
ϕ'' =	35°	40°	45°	50°	55°
S^2/P =	2.04	1.34	0.96	0.65	0.478

If z is greater than t, ϕ' is $90°$, and $S = 0.478P/z^2$.

The distribution of load from a footing into the subsoil can be pictured by a division of the soil into three types of affected areas (Fig. 4-3b):

A. Circular shape or volume of permanent deformation, passing through the edges of the load and of maximum depth t.

B. The remainder of the area, in which there is elastic deformation.

C. Areas between the top of the ground and somewhat curved lines making angles of ϕ' with the verticals passing through the edges of the load, in which there is no effect.

Housel modifies this picture for the soil below the depth equal to the width of the loaded area by the assumption that the pressure is uniformly distributed over the width within 1:1 slope lines from the edges of the footing—or as an alternate, is uniformly distributed over the width of the footing and then reduces to zero at the intersection with a 1:2 slope line from the edge of the footing (Fig. 4-3c).

4-19. Footing Loadings. The load to be used for footing design must be at least the dead load, including the weight of all fixed partitions, furniture, finishes, etc. However, it is doubtful whether the live load has any effect on settlements, except in such structures as grandstands, where the live-load increment may be over 150 psf during the minutes before and after a touchdown.

Where city building codes are enforced, the loads used in foundation design usually are fixed by a code. Two requirements are common:

1. Footings to be designed to sustain full dead load and a reduced summation of live loads on all floors, the percentage of reduction increasing with the number of stories, but seldom exceeding 50%. Pressures under the footings are limited by listed maximum unit pressures for various classes of soils.

2. Footings to be designed as in 1, but the areas of the footings are to be proportioned for equal soil pressure under dead load only.

In method 2, unit base pressures under dead plus live load are greater for interior footings than for wall footings. Since wall footings are usually rectangular—and if at street lines, on soil less affected by adjacent loads—the opposite condition would be more conducive to equal settlements. In method 1, since the computed live loads seldom, if ever, exist, the actual base pressures on the interior footings are less than those on the exterior footings.

4-20. Effect of Pressure Distribution on Footing Design. The rigid solution of the stresses in a footing for a pressure distribution on the base that is a function of the settlement is many times indeterminate. As compared with a uniform distribution, the effect of the variable distribution on the computed bending moments in a single loaded footing (whether square, round, or strip shape) may be large, but the effects on computed shear, as well as unit shear and bond stresses in the concrete, may be disregarded from both the point of safety as well as economy. Where bending moment controls the design, as well as in combination footings of either the mat, cantilever, or combined types, the departure from uniform distribution may affect both safety and economy.

Why, then, have there not been many structural failures of footings constructed from designs based on the assumption of uniform distribution? The usual explanations point to the surplus strength in the materials (factors of safety) as well as the nonexisting live loads included in the design. However, since unequal settlements probably occur, even though the total base pressures may be less than computed, another explanation is necessary. It is found in the theory of "limit design": In a closed system of forces and restraints, local failure cannot occur, because the continuity of the mass causes a transfer of load to the spots which can best take the load.

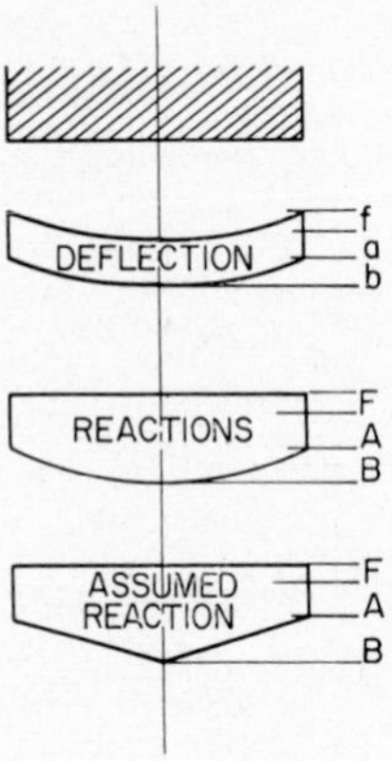

4-21. Footing Design. Despite the uncertainties of pressure distribution under footings, an approximate solution for some simple footings may be developed, the method being necessary only where large moments control the design. Where allowable soil pressures are above 3 tons per sq ft, uniform pressure distribution may be safely assumed in footing design [see Eq. (4-4), Art. 4-14].

The simplest case is a strip footing carrying a uniform continuous line load. The total load per foot on the footing w is equal to the summation of unit pressure below the footing. The shape of the loading curve is assumed similar to the deflection curve of the footing. The maximum unit pressure is $(F + A + B)$; the minimum is $(F + A)$, where F is the unit weight of the footing, A the minimum pressure, exclusive of footing weight, and B the maximum change in pressure from a uniform distribution due to deflection of the footing (Fig. 4-4).

FIG. 4-4. Soil reaction on a strip footing.

First, compute the maximum deflection of the footing as a cantilever, assuming the load w uniformly distributed: $b = wL^4/8EI$, where L is the cantilever length, E the modulus of elasticity, and I the moment of inertia based on an assumed section, footing weight being disregarded temporarily. Next, assume that the ratio of this deflection to the maximum settlement is the same as the ratio of the pressure for b to maximum soil pressure. Draw the resulting base-pressure curve, taking into account the fact that the area between the pressure curve and the zero axis must equal the total load. Assume that the deflection curve is a straight line to simplify the computation (assumed-reaction diagram, Fig. 4-4). Then, repeat the process using the new pressure curve in place of the assumed uniform distribution. Generally, the first approximation is close enough for economy.

Taking a specific example to illustrate the method, we shall compute the pressures for a strip footing 10 ft wide and 20 in. deep, which carries a wall load of 60,000 lb per lin ft, the soil being such that the average pressure, 6,000 psf, will cause a settlement of $\frac{1}{4}$ in.

Under uniform distribution, w is 6,000 psf; E for concrete will be taken as 2,000,000 psi; I is $12 \times 20^3/12$, or 8,000 in.[4].

$$b = \frac{wL^4}{8EI} = \frac{6,000 \times 5^4 \times 12^3}{8 \times 2,000,000 \times 8,000} = 0.05 \text{ in.}$$

$$B = \frac{0.05}{0.25} \times 6,000 = 1,200 \text{ psf}$$

Since the area of the pressure curve must equal 60,000 lb; i.e.,

$$\frac{L}{2}(2A + B) = P$$

$$A = 6,000 - \frac{1,200}{2} = 5,400 \text{ psf}$$

Footing weight of 250 psf must be added to these pressures. Base pressures then vary from 5,650 psf at the edge to 6,850 psf at the center.

For use in the next step, note that deflection of a cantilever under triangular load, with zero at the free end, is $WL^3/15EI$ where W is the total load. Assume the pressures just computed as the load. The new approximate deflection then is $12^3[5,400 \times 5^4/8EI + 1,200 \times 5^4/(15 \times 2EI)]$, or practically 0.05 in., differing less than 5% from the first approximation. Moments and shears can be computed from the pressures already obtained, with sufficient accuracy (see also Art. 5-69).

For a square footing with a point load, similar assumptions can be made. In addition, assume that the deflection of a corner is $wL^4/8EI$ and that of the middle of a side, two-thirds as much, so that the deflected footing is dish-shaped.

For a footing 10 × 10 ft by 30 in. thick carrying a load of 600,000 lb on a soil that settles ¼ in. under the average load, 6,000 psf, the deflections under a uniform 6,000 psf load are computed to be 0.050 and 0.033 in. at the corners and middle of the sides, respectively. The corresponding vertical ordinates of the dish-shaped loading curve are $0.05 \times 6,000/0.25 = 1,200$ and 800 lb (departure from uniform distribution). Consider half a quarter section, carrying an eighth of the load, or 75,000 lb on an area of 12.5 sq ft, and assume straight-line pressure variation from center to corners and to center of edges. The "loss" in bearing value, represented by a pyramidal volume with 5-ft altitude, is $(800 + 1,200)/2 \times \frac{5}{3} \times 5 = 8,300$ lb. Unit pressure at the center of footing, therefore, is $(75,000 + 8,300)/12.5 = 6,700$ psf. At the middle of the edge, the pressure is $6,700 - 800 = 5,900$ psf. And at the corner, the pressure is $6,700 - 1,200 = 5,500$ psf. To these units are to be added the weight of the footing, or 375 psf. Moments can then be computed from this distribution, and will show some saving over the assumption of uniform distribution (see also Art. 5-70).

4-22. Helpful Hints for Footing Design. Several practical considerations may be used as a guide in design and construction:

1. The more rigid the footing, the more uniform the pressure on the base.

2. Nonuniform distribution may be disregarded in footings resting on soils having a bearing value over 3 tons per sq ft.

3. On similar soils, with the same loads per unit area, square footings settle more than rectangular footings.

4. On the same soils, for the same shaped footings under the same average load intensity, the larger the footing, the greater the settlement.

5. Footings on the exterior of a building, not adjacent to other loads, will settle less than those affected by adjacent loads.

6. Footings will probably settle again when adjacent soil areas are loaded.

7. Bearing-value tests are reliable only when site conditions are duplicated exactly.

8. Flexible footings may be designed for smaller bending moments than are given by the assumption of uniform distribution.

9. Footing failures are seldom structural failures.

10. Uniform settlements of buildings can be obtained by taking into consideration: actual loadings to be expected; greater soil bearing value of exterior locations; provision for slip joints for settlement due to adjacent future loadings; effect of difference in levels of footings in close proximity; changes in portions of the soil area due to water, weathering, and vibration; and differences in bearing value of differently shaped footings.

11. Maximum soil pressure under centers of footings is no criterion of expected settlements, because of the distribution of load due to rigidity.

12. Bearing pressures of soil and expected settlements deduced from load tests in the field or laboratory tests on undisturbed samples have no value if the conditions in the construction work are not considered.

13. Exposure of soils during excavation may modify the soil structure and change all the characteristics.

14. All structures will settle, and provision must be made for the expected settlement by keeping them free of adjacent structures that have moved into a stable position.

15. Lateral resistance in soils must not be disturbed or reduced below that necessary to balance the lateral stresses resulting from the added loadings.

COMBINED FOUNDATIONS, MATS, AND RAFTS

In many cases, it is not possible or economical to provide a footing centrally located under each column and wall load.   There are two corrective procedures normally used for such cases: combination of loads for one footing or imposition of balancing loads to neutralize the eccentric relative positions of load and footing.   Two or more loads may be supported on a single footing, and in some locations an entire building may be constructed on a mat or raft.   Balancing of loads can be accomplished by means of structural beams acting as levers (often called "pan handles" or "pump handles") between column loads, or by imposition of counterbalancing moment resistance in the form of rigid frames.

Entire building areas may be covered by a single raft, or mat, where soils have extremely low bearing values at desired settlements and where the weight of the structure must sometimes be partly or wholly balanced by removal of soil weight to avoid soil failure.

4-23. Design of Combined Footings.   In isolated footings the form of soil-resistance distribution may not be a determining factor in the economy of structural design, since the bending moment of the pressures about the centrally located column usually does not control the design of either the concrete or the reinforcing.   The opposite condition holds, however, when the superimposed loads are not single and centrally located. And since very little is known concerning the true distribution of soil resistance at the contact face between soil and concrete, the usual design procedure is to assume uniform distribution, with sufficient soil resistance to counterbalance eccentricity of loading.

Once a design of this type is prepared, analysis of the deflections resulting from a uniform distribution (not to be carried to extreme precision because the accuracy of deflection computations for concrete structures is questionable) can be used to revise the shape of the soil-reaction curve.   The resulting moments will usually be found less than when computed for the uniform-reaction assumption.

For this computation, the soil-reaction modulus, or relationship between gross deformation of the soil and bearing value, must be known.   This can be taken from the results of a load-bearing test, but the effect of edge shears should be considered.

When more than one load is supported on a footing, the center of gravity of the loads should coincide with the geometric center of the footing.   In addition, axes of symmetry through the column loadings should coincide with axes dividing the footing into equal areas.   Since column loads are seldom of constant value, and since the variation in uncertain loadings (live load, impact, wind, etc.) is different even for adjacent columns, these requirements can only be approximately met.

When the soil is highly sensitive to load changes, combined footings should be avoided, if possible, since irreversible tipping may cause structural damage.   A simple example is to stand on a plank on soft soil and shift the weight from one leg to another.

For combined footings, a study must be made of different possible load combinations, and the shape of the footing should be adjusted so that there will be pressure over the entire base area at all times.   Any curling of the footing, especially in water-bearing soils, will permit softening of part of the base area.   Unequal settlements must result (see also Art. 5-72).

4-24. Mat Footings.   The application of the **Moseley principle** of least resistance— if a system of reactions statically stable can be shown to exist to counteract all external forces, then the structure will be safe if designed for such reactions—permits some economical modifications of the assumption of uniform base pressures.   This is especially true where the footings are extended to provide support for interior walls in addition to adjacent columns.   One assumption is to allot to an area symmetrically located about each column the load of that column, the area being determined by the full soil bearing value.   In that way the soil resistances are in the form of rectangular loads with blank spaces between, and the computed bending moments are considerably reduced.   In large mats, the same assumption will result in strips of loading under the lines joining the columns.   Some mats are constructed as such strips, with thinner slabs closing the "no-load" gaps.

One danger in the construction of mats or rafts, often overlooked, should be noted.

Since they are usually built on soft, saturated soils, where moisture removal means shrinkage and settlement, the absorption of moisture by the concrete mat and dissipation by evaporation within cellar spaces must be prevented.   Even with "good" concrete, such moisture travel can be appreciable, since the temperature gradient will always be upward.   A waterproof layer preventing moisture loss is a wise precaution.

4-25. Strapped Footings.   Used to support two columns, strapped footings consist of a pad under each column with a strap between them.   Where soil resistance is assumed only under the footings the strap connections (levers), often built on disturbed soil, or even a flexible form liner, are more economical than combined footings.   The usual assumptions are that base pressure is uniform under each pad, or bearing area, and that a rigid beam connects the two column loads, so that the center of gravity of the bearing areas coincides with the center of gravity of the column loads (see also Art. 5-73).

Any attempt to modify the assumption of uniform distribution results in complex detail founded on little fact; however, any distribution that reduces the eccentricity between load and resistance shows considerable return in economy.   Before starting an analysis based on nonuniform distribution, one should carefully consider the reliability of deflection and rigidity computations for reinforced concrete, because the only justification for nonuniform soil distribution is a relationship of soil resistance and deformation.

PILES AND PILE DRIVING

A pile is defined as a structural unit introduced into the ground to transmit loads to lower soil strata or to alter the physical properties of the ground.   It is of such shape, size, and length that the supporting material immediately underlying the base of the unit cannot be manually inspected.   This definition does not limit the type of materials making up the pile, the manner of insertion into the ground, or the loads to be transferred to lower strata.   However, where manual inspection of the bottom is possible, as in shallow pits or sufficiently wide, deep caissons, these types of construction are not classified as piles.

Piles transfer load to lower strata by frictional resistance along the surface in contact with the soil and by direct bearing into a compressed volume at or near the bottom of the pile.   The portion of the load carried by friction and by end bearing is known between limits.

The maximum frictional resistance between soil and pile surface is a definite limit to the amount of load that can be transferred by friction.

The bearing values of soils as normally determined, either by empirical classification or by load test, cannot be used to evaluate the end bearing resistance of a pile.   The confined character of the soil considerably increases its bearing value and a compressed volume of soil at the pile tip acts as an integral part of the base, of unknown total area.   Apparently, the total bearing area at the pile tip has a definite relationship to the area required to transfer that part of the pile load not taken up by skin friction.

4-26. Pile Deterioration.   Any analysis of load transfer and determination of pile load-carrying value is based on the premise that the pile structure will not change. That danger comes from many directions; the pile may rust away or rot, and exterior conditions, such as soil acidity, fluctuation in water levels, and loss of lateral support in the soil encasing the piles must be carefully considered and precautionary measures taken.

The rusting of steel surfaces in the ground (the average corrosion loss is 0.003 in. per year) cannot harm the load value of a pile, unless the mill scale becomes loose and surface friction is seriously affected.   The life of steel H and sheet piling is far beyond the normal life of a building.

4-27. Timber Piles.   Continuously kept wet, timber piles are quite permanent. But a narrow band of alternately wet and dry condition, sometimes caused by seasonal water-level fluctuations, will soon be apparent in pile failures.   Where many timber-pile foundations exist, a large-scale control of the water-table level by always maintaining full level, as is done at Amsterdam, Holland, is a necessary expense.

Almost every kind of timber can be used for a pile. Some species take the shock of driving better than others, and the species have different static compression values. Prime-grade sticks cannot be expected to be sold for piles; yet it is reasonable to insist on timber cut above the ground swell, free from decay, from unsound or grouped knots, from wind shakes and short reversed bends. The maximum diameter of any sound knot should be one-third the diameter of the pile section where the knot occurs, but not more than 4 in. in the lower half of pile length or more than 5 in. elsewhere. All knots should be trimmed flush with the body of the pile, and ends should be squared with the axis.

Piles should have reasonably uniform taper throughout the length and should be so straight that a line joining the centers of point and butt should not depart from the body of the pile. All dimensions should be measured inside the bark, which may be left on the pile if untreated but must be removed before treatment with any preservative. The diameter at any section is the average of the maximum and minimum dimensions; piles not exactly circular in section should not be rejected.

No timber pile should have a point less than 6 in. in diameter, except for temporary use. Where the point is reinforced with a steel shoe, the minimum dimension is at the upper end of such shoe. No untreated timber piles should be used where the cutoff or top level of the pile is below permanent water-table level. This level must not be assumed higher than the invert level of any sewer, drain, or subsurface structure, existing or planned, in the immediate vicinity, or higher than the water level at the site resulting from the lowest drawdown of wells or sumps.

Where timber piles may be partly above water level, the pile should be pressure-treated to a final retention of not less than 12 lb of creosote per cu ft of wood. Preservative should be a grade 1 coal-tar creosote oil, with penetration by the empty-cell process, both in accordance with Federal specifications No. TT-W-571-b or similar standard.

The tops of all creosoted piles as cut off should be below ground level and the cutoff section should be treated with three coats of hot creosote oil. Creosoted piles above ground level require some replenishment of preservative with age, as well as protection against fire damage.

Of the various timber species, cedar, western hemlock, Norway pine, spruce, or similar kinds are restricted to an average unit compression at any section of 600 psi; cypress, Douglas fir, hickory, oak, southern pine, or similar kinds are allowed a value of 800 psi. A maximum load of 20 tons is commonly allowed on timber piles with 6-in. points, and 25 tons where the point is 8 in. or more, subject, of course, to compliance with indicated or tested driving resistance and maximum stresses.

Timber piles are seldom used as end bearing piles, but there is no real objection to such use, if properly installed.

4-28. Steel H Piles. Where heavy resistances exist in layers that overlie the bearing depths, steel H piles will often take the punishment of the heavy driving much better than any other type. After insertion in the ground, the soil gripped between the web and inside faces of the flanges becomes an integral part of the pile, so that frictional resistance is measured along the surface of the enclosing rectangle and not along the metal surface of the section.

To prevent local crippling during driving, the section should have flange projections not exceeding 14 times the minimum thickness of metal in either web or flange and with total flange width not less than 85% of the depth of the section. All metal thicknesses should be at least $\frac{3}{8}$ in.

Other structural-steel sections, or combinations of sections, having flange widths and depths of at least 10 in. and metal thickness of at least $\frac{1}{2}$ in. may also be used—usually in combination with steel sheeting. Most rolling mills issue special sections for use as piles.

The load-carrying value of a steel pile is usually restricted to a maximum unit stress of 9,000 psi at any cross section.

4-29. Concrete Piles. Precast piles are most suitable for large projects. The necessity for accurate length determination and the added cost of cutoffs, plus the high cost of equipment to make and handle the piles, tend to make precast piles more expensive than the various cast-in-place types.

Precast piles must be reinforced for local stresses during lifting and driving and must be cured to full strength before use. Development of prestressed-concrete piles, some with the prestressed rods removable after the pile has been driven, improves economical possibilities for precast piles, since the cost of reinforcing is at least half the total cost of a precast pile before driving.

Cast-in-place concrete piles come in many variations, in which concrete fills premolded cavities in the soil. The cavity for a pile can be formed by removal of the soil or by forcing the volume displaced into the adjacent walls, as is done by timber or precast-concrete piles. The soil cavity can be made by auger or casing carried to a desired depth and filled with concrete. Volume displacement is accomplished by driving a thin, metal, closed-end shell stiffened with a retractable mandrel or a heavier cylindrical metal shell, which is retracted as the concrete filling is installed.

Retracted shells are usually heavy steel pipe, sometimes with reinforced cutting edges and with driving rings welded at the top to provide a grip for retraction.

In some types, the concrete is compressed by a vibrating or drop hammer and tends to squeeze out laterally below the casing to form annular expansions. These greatly increase the bearing value of the pile.

Whether the shell is left in place or not, one advantage of cast-in-place piles is the possibility of examining the cavity before placing the concrete, to check depth of penetration and variation from plumb or desired batter position.

Usually, the empirical resistance taken as a measure of pile value is indicated by the downward movement during casing driving, before any concrete is placed. It is therefore often claimed that the completed piles have much higher values than expected. The reasoning is that the concrete filling causes an expansion of the shell—or even with the shell removed, of the soil-contact cylinder—which must increase the frictional support value of the pile.

Shoes are sometimes integral with the shells; there are also several types of special shoes such as the flat boot, pointed castings of 60 and 45° cones, ball-pointed ribbed caps, inverted paraboloid, precast-concrete "button," and flat plates welded to the piles.

For all cast-in-place piles, care must be exercised to clean the cavity of all foreign matter and to fill the entire volume with concrete. If water enters the shell, tremie tubes may be necessary for pouring the concrete.

The structural concrete pile is designed as a short concrete column, with a maximum unit stress of 25% of the 28-day cylinder strength in compression and no allowance for any embedded reinforcement (except in precast piles) or for the steel shell if it is less than $\frac{1}{8}$ in. thick. For thicker shells left in place, an allowance of 9,000 psi for the steel cross-sectional area may be added to the capacity of the concrete.

4-30. Pile Splices. Piles are often made up of special sections of similar or different structural elements. Such composite piles are usually evaluated as equal to the weaker section. The splice must be designed to hold the sections together during driving, as well as to resist later effects from the driving of adjacent piles or from lateral loads. (Timber-to-concrete splice details and tests are given by H. D. Dewell, in *Civil Engineering*, September, 1938, p. 574.) Timber pile sleeves consist of a tight-fitting steel pipe section into which the pile ends are driven; sometimes drift pins or through bolts are used to hold the assembly together. Steel rolled sections and pipe piles are often extended by a full-strength weld. Concrete piles can be extended, but the detail is extremely expensive and should be employed in emergency cases only.

4-31. Soil Limitations on Piles. The structural pile can be relied upon within the limitations normally set on the materials. Maximum pile loading is more dependent on the nature of the soils into which the pile is driven than on the materials comprising the pile.

Structures on piles installed in unstable soil strata, which may be subject to lateral movements, should be braced by batter piles or completely tied with structural members having both tensile and compressive resistance in the plane of the pile caps.

Piles installed in soils that exhibit considerable subsidence and consolidation during driving, or where great depths of unconsolidated silts and mucks are penetrated, must be investigated for possible future loads when the consolidation occurs and the weight of these upper layers hangs on the piles. Several suggestions offered to avoid such overloading have been tried but found wanting. Among them are artificial lubrication of the pile, or surrounding the upper section with a loose paper or metal sleeve, to eliminate friction. It is true that the maximum weight that can hang on the pile is equal to the surface frictional resistance. However, the lateral strength of long piles driven through unconsolidated layers is so low that insertion of adjacent piles, weight of construction equipment, and unequal consolidations often cause lateral displacement of the piles. In these cases, immediate lateral staying of the piles is advisable, even before construction of the pile caps and bracing system between caps.

4-32. Reused Piles. Reuse of piles where structures are demolished, or even for new loading conditions, should be restricted to places where complete data are available on length and driving conditions of each pile. Where a group of piles is to be reused for new loadings, their supporting value should be restricted to 75% of rated capacity. Additional piles driven for the same structure should be of similar length and type as those being reused and should also be restricted to 75% of rated capacity.

4-33. Minimum Sizes of Piles. The usual liberal restrictions on pile sections are a minimum 6-in.-diameter point, with a minimum 8-in.-diameter butt at cutoff for a tapered pile. Piles of uniform section are limited to a minimum 8-in. diameter, or $7\frac{1}{2}$-in. side if not circular.

Actually, if the piles can satisfy stress restrictions as short columns, there is no justification for any dimensional limitations. Generally, such small sizes as given here are suitable only for end-bearing piles and have too little surface to develop sufficient skin friction.

4-34. Pile Spacing. Since, basically, the purpose of piles is to transfer loads into soil layers, pile spacing should be a function of the load carried and the capacity of the soil to take over that load.

Piles bearing on rock or penetrating into rock should have a minimum spacing center to center of twice the average diameter, or 1.75 times the diagonal of the pile, but not less than 24 in. This spacing will not overload the rock, even if the bearing piles are fully loaded and no load relief occurs from skin friction.

All other piles, transferring a major part of the load to the soil by skin friction, should have a minimum spacing center to center of twice the average diameter, or 1.75 times the diagonal of the pile, but not less than 30 in. For a pile group consisting of more than four piles, such minimum spacing must be increased by 10% for each interior pile, to a maximum of 40%; i.e., to 42-in. spacing, if the principal support of the piles is in soil with less than 6 tons per sq ft bearing value. Figure 4-5 gives the pile spacing for various groups where spacing is governed by soil value.

Studies of the load value of groups, as related to an individual-pile value, show definite reduction in average pile value as the cluster increases in size. From results of a large-scale test program of wood piles, the approximate formula was deduced that the value of a pile is reduced by one-sixteenth for each other pile within normal spacing (Fig. 4-5). Increased spacing tends to eliminate the difference and give the piles nearly their full values.

Where lot-line conditions, space restrictions, or obstructions prevent proper spacing of piles, the carrying capacity should be reduced for those piles that are too close to each other or less than half the required spacing from a lot line. The percentage reduction in load-carrying capacity of each pile should be taken as one-half of the percentage reduction in required spacing. If, for example, a pile is 24 in. from a lot line instead of 30 in., the percentage reduction of spacing is 20%; so pile capacity is reduced 2%, or 10%. Such reduction in values is sometimes economical where closer spacing permits the placing of a pile group below the columns and eliminates eccentricity straps or combined footings.

4-35. Pile Embedment. Piles require a definite grip in resistant soil. It is a wise precaution to insist on at least 10 ft of embedment in natural soil of sufficient stiffness to warrant a presumptive bearing value of at least 2 tons per sq ft. The embedment should be below grade or such elevation as will not be affected by future excavations.

Each pile must be braced against lateral displacement by rigid connection to at least two other piles in radial directions not less than 60° apart. Where fewer than three piles are in a group, or where extra lateral stability is made necessary by the nature of loads or softness of soil layers, concrete ties or braces must be provided between caps. Such bracing should be considered as struts, with minimum dimensions of one-twentieth the clear distance between pile caps, but not less than 8 in. All bars should be anchored in the caps to develop full tension value. A continuous reinforced-concrete mat 6 in. or more in thickness, supported by and anchored to the pile

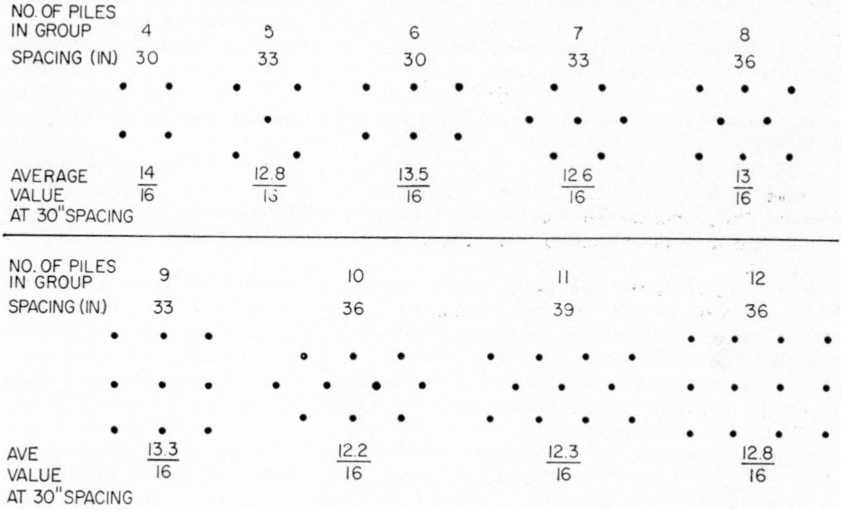

NO. OF PILES IN GROUP	4	5	6	7	8
SPACING (IN)	30	33	30	33	36
AVERAGE VALUE AT 30"SPACING	$\frac{14}{16}$	$\frac{12.8}{13}$	$\frac{13.5}{16}$	$\frac{126}{16}$	$\frac{13}{16}$

NO. OF PILES IN GROUP	9	10	11	12
SPACING (IN)	33	36	39	36
AVE VALUE AT 30"SPACING	$\frac{13.3}{16}$	$\frac{12.2}{16}$	$\frac{12.3}{16}$	$\frac{12.8}{16}$

FIG. 4-5. Recommended pile spacing and reduction in pile value for groups containing four or more piles from the valve permitted for single piles.

caps, or in which piles are embedded at least 3 in., may be used as the bracing tie, if the slab does not depend on the soil for the direct support of its own weight and loads.

Pile caps are designed as structural members distributing the load into the piles, with no allowance for any load support on the soil directly below the pile cap.

4-36. Tolerances for Piles. In designing a cap, each pile is considered a point load concentrated at the center of the cutoff cross section. However, only in ideal soil conditions and with perfect equipment will the piles all be inserted vertically and exactly in the planned position so that this assumption is true. Some practical rules of acceptance of piles not perfectly positioned must control every pile job:

A tolerance of 3 in. in any direction from the designated location should be permitted without reduction in load capacity—provided that no pile in the group will then carry more than 110% of its normal permitted value, even though the average loadings of the piles are much less. The distribution of column loads into the individual piles should be determined either analytically or graphically from a plotted graph of the surveyed locations of the cutoff centers. Where any later resurvey is expected, such centers should be marked by nails or chisel cuts.

Where any pile is overloaded, either additional balancing piles should be added to the group, or structural levers should be added for load redistribution or connection with adjacent groups.

Computation of actual pile loads can be simplified by plotting the pile and column locations to scale, then locating the center of gravity of the piles graphically and using the line between this point and the center of the column loads as an axis of symmetry.

Multiplying pile values by the offsets of all piles from the normal axis drawn through the center of gravity of the piles gives a total moment equal to the eccentricity moment. Assume a linear variation for reduction or increase of pile value with distance from the axis. If the maximum pile value is just beyond the 110% limit, a second approximation should be tried, relocating the center of gravity of the piles on a weighted basis, using the values from the first solution. This will slightly reduce the eccentricity and may be sufficient to permit approval of the pile group.

Where piles are installed out of plumb, a tolerance of 2% of the pile length, measured by plumb bob inside a casing pile or by extending the exposed section of solid piles, is permissible. A greater variation requires special provision to balance the resultant horizontal and vertical forces, using ties to adjacent column caps where necessary. For hollow-pipe piles, which are driven out of plumb or where obstructions have caused deviations from the intended line, the exact shape of the pile can be determined by the use of a magnetic shape-measuring instrument, or an electronic plumb bob. After the deflection curve of a pile is plotted, consecutive differentiation gives the slope, moment, and shears acting on the pile, from which the reduction in allowable load, if any, can be determined.

4-37. Pile-driving Hammers. Equipment and methods for installing piles should be such as to produce satisfactory piles in proper position and alignment. This involves the proper choice of equipment for the size and weight of pile, expected load value, and type of soil to be penetrated. Generally, heavier piles require heavier hammers.

Experience with wood piles indicates that a lighter hammer than required by some building codes should be used to reduce breakage of piles, certainly in areas where soil layers change suddenly in resistance to penetration. (T. C. Bruns, "Don't Hit Timber Piles Too Hard," *Civil Engineering*, December, 1941.) Although the usual argument that a big spike should not be driven with a tack hammer is true, so is the opposite statement that a long slender finishing nail should not be driven with a sledge.

The usual pile-driving hammers used on building foundations are listed in Table 4-3.

4-38. Jetting Piles into Place. Other methods of pile insertion include the Franki drop weight for pulling a pipe casing into the ground by acting on a compressed gravel or concrete plug in the bottom of the casing, or water-jet loosening of the soil allowing the pile to drop by gravity or under the weight of a hammer resting on the butt.

Jetting is not necessary or advisable in soils other than fairly coarse dense sands. Even there, it must be remembered that jetting is excavation of soil; it has been so decided by the New York State Supreme Court, and all legal restrictions concerning excavations along a property line are available protections for the adjacent owner.

Jetting should be stopped at least 3 ft above the final pile-tip elevation and the piles driven at least 3 ft to the required resistance. The condition of adjacent completed piles should be checked, and if loss of resistance is found, all piles should be redriven.

Use of jacks against static loads (in the form of existing structural mass or temporary setup of weights) is usually limited to adding piles for additional support during underpinning operations or within completed buildings.

4-39. Load Value of Piles. There are three general methods of evaluating the safe carrying capacity of a pile:

1. From the indicated resistance to the impact of a moving hammer.
2. From the net settlement under a static load.
3. From the computed shear resistance over the pile surface area.

Recent tendency is to give greater reliability to the load-test method and restrict the use of pile-driving formulas to the lower pile-load values and in areas of uniform soil conditions.

In the use of impact formulas, minimum necessary data are (1) the energy per blow —usually given by the manufacturer for a definite number of blows per minute, and for steam or air hammers, at definite pressures on the piston—and (2) the net penetration of the pile into the ground under a blow.

The net penetration is the gross penetration under impact less the rebound. It is measured along a scale on the fixed portion of the pile-driver frame.

Table 4-3. Pile-driving Hammers and Rated Values
1. Drop Hammers
Vulcan sizes from 500- to 3,000-lb weight of hammer, dropping 12 to 48 in.

Hammer type	Rated energy, ft-lb	Ram, lb	Stroke, in.
2. Single-acting Steam Hammers			
McKiernan-Terry No.:			
S3	9,000	3,000	36
S5	16,250	5,000	39
S8	26,000	8,000	39
S10	32,500	10,000	39
S14	37,500	14,000	32
Warrington-Vulcan No.:			
OR	30,200	9,300	39
0	24,300	7,500	39
1	15,000	5,000	36
2	7,260	3,000	29
3	3,600	1,800	24
4	965	550	21
3. Double-acting Steam or Air Hammers*			
Super-Vulcan No.:			
18C	3,600 at 150 s/m	1,800	$10\frac{1}{2}$
30C	7,260 at 133 s/m	3,000	$12\frac{1}{2}$
50C	15,100 at 120 s/m	5,000	$15\frac{1}{2}$
80C	24,450 at 111 s/m	8,000	$16\frac{1}{2}$
140C	36,000 at 103 s/m	14,000	$15\frac{1}{2}$
200C	50,200 at 98 s/m	20,000	$15\frac{1}{2}$
McKiernan-Terry No.:			
5	1,000 at 300 s/m	200	7
6	2,500 at 275 s/m	400	$8\frac{3}{4}$
7	4,150 at 225 s/m	800	$9\frac{1}{2}$
9-B-3	8,750 at 145 s/m	1,600	17
10-B-3	16,800 at 130 s/m	3,000	19
11-B-3	19,150 at 95 s/m	5,000	19
Special	55,000 at 90 s/m	10,000	24
Industrial Brownhoist No.:			
Short	6,000 at 150 s/m	1,600	16
Long	9,650 at 110 s/m	1,900	24
Union Ironworks No.:			
00	54,900 at 85 s/m	6,000	36
0A	22,050 at 90 s/m	5,000	21
0	19,850 at 110 s/m	3,000	24
1	13,100 at 130 s/m	1,850	21
1A	10,020 at 120 s/m	1,600	18
2	5,755 at 145 s/m	1,025	16
3	3,660 at 160 s/m	700	14
3A	4,390 at 150 s/m	820	$13\frac{1}{2}$
4	2,100 at 200 s/m	370	12
4. Diesel Hammers*			
Syntron No.:			
3000	3,000 at 110 s/m	1,200	33
5000	5,200 at 110 s/m	2,100	34
9000	9,000 at 105 s/m	3,800	34
16000	16,000 at 84 s/m	5,400	48

* s/m = strokes per minute.

For many of the pile formulas, additional weights of pile and other parts of the hammer, conditions at the surfaces of impact and other empirical constants also must be evaluated. In any case, the formulas can apply only to ideal conditions; penetration measurements are not reliable if made when a pile head is broomed or shows plastic flow, if new cushion blocks are used, and if frictional resistance hinders the free fall of the hammer. Note, too, that for piles driven to large batters, the true impact is the vertical component of the rated value.

Table 4-4. Common Pile-driving Formulas

General energy-resistance formula (Redtenbacher, 1859):

$$R = \frac{AE}{L}\left[-S \pm \sqrt{S^2 + WH\frac{(W + Pn^2)2L}{(W + P)AE}} \right]$$

where W = weight of hammer, lb
$\quad\quad H$ = height of drop of W, in.
$\quad\quad R$ = ultimate pile value, lb (no factor of safety)
$\quad\quad S$ = pile penetration per blow, in.
$\quad\quad E$ = modulus of elasticity of pile
$\quad\quad A$ = cross-sectional area of pile, sq in.
$\quad\quad P$ = weight of pile, lb
$\quad\quad L$ = length of pile, in.
$\quad\quad n$ = coefficient of restitution due to impact—zero for nonelastic soil; unity for elastic soil

The Redtenbacher formula, as used in Europe, takes $n = 0$.

If $n = 1$, this formula becomes $R = WH/(S + C)$, where C is a constant. This is the Wellington, or *Engineering News*, formula.

Boston Pile Code formulas:

For drop hammer:
$$R' = \frac{3WH'}{S + K}\frac{W}{W + P}$$

For single-acting hammer:
$$R' = \frac{3.6WH'}{S + K}\frac{W}{W + P}$$

For double-acting hammer:
$$R' = \frac{4F}{S + K}\frac{W}{W + P}$$

where H' = height of fall, ft
$\quad\quad S$ = average pile penetration for last 5 blows, in.
$\quad\quad R'$ = allowable pile value, lb
$\quad\quad F$ = actual hammer-blow energy, ft-lb
$$K = \frac{3R'L}{SAE} + C, \text{in.}$$
$\quad\quad C$ = 0.05 for wood pile or cap
$\quad\quad K$ = constant for various types and sizes of piles

Hiley formula often used in Britain (1930):

$$R = \frac{YWH}{S + \frac{1}{2}C}$$

where Y = efficiency of blow transmission, always less than unity
$\quad\quad C$ = sum of energy losses due to compression of driving head, of pile, and of ground

Many pile-driving formulas have been proposed; all have some disadvantages, and none can be used blindly. To correlate a static bearing value with the resistance to an impact—as some formulas attempt to do—is basically impossible; that the results have little correlation with load-test values is therefore not surprising. Some of the more common formulas are shown in Table 4-4.

Where no soft layers underlie firm soil layers (as would be shown by erratic reports on casing resistance), and where the expected maximum pile value does not exceed 30 tons, any of the common formulas can be used, with the proper constants for the corresponding hammer type.

The minimum impact blow should be related to the load value: a minimum of

15,000 ft-lb for 25- to 30-ton pile values, 12,000 ft-lb for 21 to 25 tons, 8,000 ft-lb for 15 to 20 tons. Restrictions on hammer weights based on pile diameter do not have any logical basis, as they require too heavy a hammer for a wood pile, with consequent breakage during driving, and permit too small a hammer for an 8-in. steel pile, which may carry 30 or more tons.

When the allowable pile load is to be determined by load tests, subsurface investigations must first prove that the conditions in the area are fairly uniform. For each 15,000 sq ft of building area or part thereof, three piles should be driven—distributed over the area—close to points where borings were made. A complete pile-driving log record should be kept. Driving should be carried to resistances indicated by dynamic formula for the desired load value. If the lengths of the piles or their driving records (blows per foot) vary more than 20%, additional piles should be driven until agreement is found.

Two piles in each area should be load-tested to 200% of the desired load. The load should be applied in eight equal increments, each to remain until the settlement is constant within 0.001 ft for 2 hr. The total load should remain until the settlement is constant within 0.001 ft for 48 hr. After that, the load should be removed in four equal decrements, with intervals of not less than 1 hr. The rebound should be measured after each removal and also 24 hr after the load is entirely removed.

Based on the plotted record of the test, the maximum allowable pile load is the smaller of the following: one-half the load causing a net settlement of 0.01 in. per ton of load, or one-half the load causing a gross settlement of 1 in.

In the subsequent driving of piles in that area, using the same equipment on the same type of pile, under similar operating conditions, all piles showing the same or greater resistance to penetration as was shown by the piles tested should be allowed the average values obtained from the load tests. Any piles that stop at higher levels and are one-third or more shorter than the average length of the tested piles should be rejected or load-tested.

Where piles are installed by jacking against static loads, the safe carrying capacity may be taken as 50% of the maximum jacking load required at final penetration. If the jacking load is held constant for a period of 10 hr, the carrying capacity can be taken as two-thirds the jacking load. In temporary underpinning work, piles may be used to support the full jacking load, but if the piles are to remain as permanent supports, not more than two-thirds the jacking load should be allowed.

Only piles receiving their support entirely from frictional resistances along their surface can be evaluated by summing the resistances in each layer penetrated. Such frictional unit resistances must be determined either from undisturbed samples taken within each soil layer or by means of a plunger cone or vane-type investigation.

Any attempt to combine theoretical end bearing with such surface friction should be discouraged. Not enough is known about the possibility of combined action; even with friction alone, the unproved assumption is made that the shearing strains in all soil layers are equal, or remain constant during failure; otherwise a summation of the resistances is not permissible.

The maximum unit shear coefficient at any depth cannot exceed the internal coefficient of shear of the soil, because failure will occur at the pile surface or within the soil adjacent to it.

The surface of shear resistance is cylindrical for all piles, the diameter of the cylinder for a battered or stepped pile being substantially the diameter at the butt of the pile. Noncylindrical shapes are more efficient friction piles.

As an approximation, subject to check by field determination, the maximum friction resistance may be taken as 10% of the normally safe bearing value for each soil encountered. In no case should a pile value be permitted above 50% of the accumulated computed surface-skin frictional resistance.

4-40. Pile Loads. For all types of piles, the design must safely support the maximum combination of the following loads:

1. All dead loads and the weight of the pile cap and superimposed loads.

2. All live loads, reduced as permitted because of floor area or number of stories in the building.

3. Lateral force and moment reactions, including the effect of eccentricity, if any, between the column load and the center of gravity of the pile group.

4. That amount of the vertical, lateral, and moment reactions resulting from wind and seismic loads in excess of one-third of the respective reactions totaled from 1, 2, and 3.

The maximum load permitted on a vertical pile is the allowable pile load, as determined by formula, test, or computation, applied concentrically in the direction of its axis. No lateral loads in excess of 1,000 lb per pile shall be permitted on a vertical pile, unless actual test shows that the pile will resist double the lateral load with less than $\frac{1}{2}$-in. lateral movement at the ground surface. If batter piles are used to take lateral forces, the resultant loads along the axis of the pile should not exceed the allowable pile value.

Piles are considered as columns fixed at a point from 5 to 10 ft below the surface; the lower value can be used whenever the soils at the top are compact. Unit stresses in any pile section must not be exceeded. The total pile load is considered as existing in all end bearing piles without relief to a depth of 40 ft and with a maximum reduction of 25% if the pile is longer.

For a friction pile, the entire load is assumed to exist at the section located at two-thirds the embedded length of the pile, measured to the top.

4-41. Bearing Piles. Piles driven to a resistance providing end bearing in rock or extremely tough and dense layers directly overlying bedrock are called bearing piles. For one type, an open casing is used, which can be cleaned out for visual inspection of the material at the bottom of the pile. Where exposure of bedrock is possible and the steel pipe is driven into the rock to ultimate resistance—denoted by less than $\frac{1}{4}$-in. net penetration under five blows of a hammer having a rated energy in foot-pounds of at least 25% of the desired pile value in pounds—the maximum pile value can be taken as 80% of the structural value of the combined steel and concrete section. The limit usually is 200 tons.

Piles of solid section similarly driven are similarly evaluated but usually are further restricted to a maximum value of 120 tons if driven into rock or 80 tons if the point stops above the rock surface. Such values cannot be used, unless checked by load tests; a maximum value of 40 tons should be set on end bearing piles evaluated by formula only.

There are a number of special pile forms used for very high load values, such as the drilled-in-caisson pile, where a core is cut into the rock bed, and the H pile driven into rock and encased in concrete within a shell that is first driven to good resistance.

4-42. Friction Piles. Piles not driven to a bearing on hard ground or rock are known as friction piles and are assumed to have no end bearing. When the piles stop in soils underlain by compressible layers, a careful analysis of the imposed loading on such layers is necessary, to determine what settlements are to be expected from consolidation. Usually, piles evaluated by impact formula only are restricted to a 30-ton value, with further restriction to 25 tons or less for wood piles.

Steel tubes 18 in. in diameter have been used as friction piles for 100 and 200 tons, but in some cases, it was evident that the soils could not take such load concentration in groups of four to six piles and that resistances dissipated with time, even when the piles were not loaded.

Bearing value of friction piles is affected by vibrations transferred to the piles. Tests under 500 to 850 vibrations per minute showed additional settlements in the range of 0.2 to 0.5 in. in silt and sand.

CAISSONS AND SHAFTS

Before the invention of heavy construction equipment, the only way that a foundation could be carried to considerable depths through soft soils was by slow, manual excavation within a protective construction. To a large degree, this development was a carry-over from experience gathered in well-sinking operations. (A parallel development in more recent times is the drilled-caisson procedure modeled on oil-well-exploration methods.) The sheeted and braced deep-water well logically became a construction shaft for a deep footing. The ancient masonry ring enclosure in a well, which was successively underpinned as the excavation progressed, as developed in many parts of North Africa, the Babylonian area of influence, and in India, is still copied, with only slight modifications, in very deep shafts.

4-43. Open Shafts for Foundations. Shafts are constructed to great depths, usually through saturated soft soil by the following methods:

1. Excavation, followed by sheeting the desired outline using braced horizontal or vertical members of wood, steel, or precast concrete.

2. Excavation, following the insertion of vertical sheeting, introducing bracing at the desired depths, when reached. This type of construction usually is called a **cofferdam.**

3. Method 2 sometimes is modified by setting up a completely braced shell, or **caisson,** which sinks from its weight (aided, if necessary, by temporary surcharge loadings) as the excavation undercuts the shell.

4. **Pneumatic caissons** are used for excavations carried to depths at which it would be impossible with ordinary caissons to control the flow of water or soil through the bottom. They are capped to provide a top seal and work is done under artificially applied air pressure, sufficient to counterbalance hydrostatic pressure. Entrance to the working chamber is through double-gated locks.

5. Resistance to sinking of a caisson limits the depth to about 100 ft; so the **nested caisson** was introduced. Lower sections of this type of caisson fit within the completed ring and can be jacked down against the resistance of the upper section. With this procedure, a three-section caisson has reached 400-ft depths.

6. Similar depths can be reached by freezing the ground around the volume to be excavated.

4-44. Soil Resistance When Sinking Caissons. In all the sinking methods, frictional soil resistance governs depth of penetration. The design of the sheeting and bracing depends on the pressure of the soil during sinking or during excavation within the enclosure.

In all types of sinking methods, where additional bearing area is required when the shaft reaches the desired depth, the base area can be extended by undercutting if the soil at that depth can be retained sufficiently to install the concrete base. In heavy clays, the cutting can be done without any special protection. In clays that squeeze or displace laterally on excavation of a free surface, the cost of sheeting and bracing to withstand such movement is prohibitive; the shaft must be carried down full size. In granular materials, sloping sheeting can be driven through the bottom of a caisson to cover and protect the conical section of enlargement.

Resistance to vertical penetration of a rigid body in any soil indicates that, during the period when there is actual relative motion, the soil is in a viscous state, and the nature of the material forming the rigid body has little effect on the resistance. The depth of cover also has little effect on the amount of resistance per unit area of buried surface. Apparently, the tackiness and adhesion of the soil to the caisson, plus the shear resistance of any projections on the surface, are always greater than the internal resistance of the soil, and therefore the lesser value governs the total resistance to be expected. Large additions of water or slurry along the interface will considerably reduce the resistance, especially in soils where cohesion to the caisson is a major factor in total internal resistance. Continuity of movement is desirable, to eliminate "freezing" of the interface that is caused by dissipation of enough free liquid to change the soil state from viscous to solid. (Jacob Feld, International Soil Mechanics Congress, Paper No. Vc5, vol. 7, Rotterdam, 1948.)

In addition to surface resistance, there is also the bearing resistance of any surfaces at the base of the moving caisson, which must be overcome by load to the point of failure; i.e., the amount of unit pressure must be enough to make the soil act as a nonsolid. From a summary of many caisson operations, the load required to overcome surface resistance has been found to range approximately as follows, in pounds per square foot of buried surface:

Dense clay, sometimes mixed with fine sand	700–800
Tight sand, clay, and silt mixtures	500–600
Saturated sands	400–500
Soft clay and wet sand mixtures	200–300

4-45. Pressure on Sheeting. Soil pressure on sheeting that is inserted into the ground without permitting soil expansion or movement depends on the ratio of width or diameter of excavation to depth.

In any type of soil, there is no lateral pressure at a certain depth, which depends on the width of the excavation. For derivation of theoretical earth-pressure formulas, see *Journal of the American Concrete Institute*, Vol. 16, pp. 441–451, 1945, from which Table 4-5 is reproduced.

Table 4-5. Soil Pressures in Pits

Angle of internal resistance	Ratio of width to depth			For a pit 5 ft wide unit pressure is zero at a depth of (ft)
	Zero unit pressure	Max unit pressure	Zero total pressure	
0	0	0	0	∞
5	0.054	0.108	0.036	93
10	0.098	0.196	0.065	51
15	0.126	0.252	0.084	40
20	0.147	0.294	0.098	34
25	0.159	0.318	0.106	31
30	0.167	0.334	0.111	30
35	0.168	0.336	0.112	30
40	0.165	0.330	0.110	30
45	0.159	0.318	0.106	31
50	0.149	0.298	0.099	34
55	0.135	0.270	0.090	37
60	0.120	0.240	0.080	52
65	0.104	0.208	0.069	48
70	0.084	0.168	0.056	60
75	0.065	0.130	0.043	77
80	0.042	0.084	0.028	119
85	0.024	0.048	0.016	209

It is noteworthy that zero unit pressure occurs in normal granular soils at a depth about six times the width of the pit or shaft. If surface resistance was a friction as normally encountered in solids, it could not restrict the depth of penetration, since the frictional value is a direct function of the pressure acting against the sheeting.

4-46. Types of Sheeting. Simplest pit sheeting consists of square-edge wood boards, successively placed one at a time below previously braced boards, following careful hand cutting of the soil to closely simulate the shape of the boards. When soil conditions do not permit such shaping and where the soil will not maintain a vertical face long enough to permit insertion of the next sheet, any one of several louver-type sheets may be used.

The basic requirement of **louver sheeting** is provision of packing in back of the sheets, to correct irregularities of excavation and to eliminate open voids in back of the sheeting. The simplest device is to interpose small blocks between adjacent sheets and thereby leave packing gaps. One patented unit provides a recessed gap in each sheet, which eliminates the handling of small blocks. An efficient method is to cut a diagonal from one edge of a board and tack it to the opposite edge, forming a parallelogram, so that an 8-in. board will cover 10 in. (if of 2-in. stock). The sharp lower edge permits digging into the bottom of the pit and rotating the board into position against the earth. The upper level protects the gap opening and simplifies the packing operation. Bracing of the pit sides can be accomplished in several ways, all copied from the methods used in making wooden boxes, and based on the support of each side by the two adjacent sides.

The **Chicago caisson** is an open circular pit lined with vertical plank staves, which are braced internally by steel rings wedged against the staves. The excavation is carried down for the depth equal to the length of staves—4 to 6 ft—and usually two bracing rings are inserted for each section. This type is suitable chiefly for easily cut clays that will stand unbraced for several hours and where free-flowing water or running silt is not encountered. This method has been used for many of the large structures in Chicago, to depths as great as 200 ft. Sometimes, enlargements are made at the bottom into the bearing stratum.

Where softer soils do not permit the use of box sheeting or lagging, a steel cylinder is sunk as a cutoff of soil and water until it reaches required soil bearing layers and can be excavated. If the bottom cannot be sealed off, excavation is under water and the concrete is poured by tremie method.

4-47. Gow Caisson. Developed in the Boston area, this caisson consists of a nest of steel cylinders from 8 to 16 ft high. Each cylinder is 2 in. smaller in diameter than the preceding. The caisson is driven down by impact or jacking as excavation proceeds. Since no internal bracing is required, the excavation is easily performed, and the cylinders can be withdrawn as concreting progresses.

4-48. Drilled-in Caisson. For very large loads and where bad filled ground must be penetrated, the **drilled-in caisson** (sometimes below 24 in. diameter and classed as a bearing pile) is employed. A heavy casing pipe is driven to rock or heavy bearing material. Soil and obstructions encountered are removed. A well drill bit is used to provide a socket in the rock into which a steel H or pipe section can be driven to increase the normal column strength of the concrete core, which is placed within a thin, steel-shell lining of the casing pipe. The casing pipe is then removed. These caissons have been constructed with lengths above 200 ft and for loads of 2,000 tons.

DRILLED-SHAFT FOOTINGS

As a development of power drilling for water and oil wells, there is a group of drilled-shaft procedures for obtaining economical exposures of suitable bearing layers.

4-49. Cored Shafts. In normal plastic soil, sometimes interspaced with limestone or sand seams, a spinning auger-bottom bucket is rotated by a square- or oblong-section Kelly bar to excavate a circular shaft 24 to 72 in. in diameter. The operation is rapid and simple. When the bottom is exposed, a sawtooth-bottom steel shell is rapidly spun and a cut made, until the desired hardness of material is reached, or else an underreamer is used to cut an enlargement to the desired area. The concrete pier is cast without forms. Skin friction is depended on to carry some of the load, although normally the base pressures are satisfactory. The concrete core may be reinforced to increase carrying capacity.

This development is chiefly used in Texas and Southern California, where sandy loams or clays can be cut and left standing for inspection of the bottom and concreting done without bracing. In the limestone areas near Dallas, cores or the bottom exposures are taken for testing and base-pressure values are correlated with the compressive strength of core samples.

Cored shafts have been carried to depths over 80 ft, but the economical range is about 40 ft.

The time and power used to lift each bucket of soil, and the special rigs required for the deep holes, make other methods quite competitive. For depths of about 20 ft where soft rock or equivalent can be reached, however, the cored caisson foundation will be found competitive in cost with a spread footing on the upper soil.

When running water is encountered, the shafts must be kept full of water during excavation to prevent caving of the side walls. If in addition, seams of fine sand or silt are cut, the shaft must be enclosed with a steel shell, usually with a serrated bottom edge for cutting into the layer that permits sealing off the running material. To prevent binding, the top of the shell has two or more outriggers, or recessed gripping cuts, for turning the shell part of a revolution every hour or so. Within the shell, the coring operation continues normally. As concrete is placed, the shell is retracted.

4-50. Montee Caisson. Used for deep foundations, this consists of a reinforced steel shell, with cutting edge of serrated hardened plate, which is connected to a large motor for continuous rotation. The action is similar to the circular saw used in some large granite quarries to remove cores of 8 and 10 ft diameter, to serve as weakening planes for freeing the rock sheets. To maintain completely fluid conditions, a slurry is fed into the cylinder to float the interior soil outward under the cutting edge and up along the outer surface of the shell.

The difficulty encountered in the use of the Montee caisson comes chiefly from rock surfaces encountered on a tilt. Well-bedded boulders or riprap are easily cut through, but a loose boulder may damage the cutting edge. When uneven rock is engaged, it is difficult to get a complete seating and seal to the rock. The apparatus requires a large investment; so the method cannot be considered except for large projects.

4-51. Driven Shafts. In a similar group of methods, soil in shafts is extruded by displacement, and piers are concreted in the voids so formed. One method that has been used for light structures on partly consolidated sanitary fill is to insert a steel flat-pointed 12 × 12 in. mandrel into the ground with a light pile hammer to a depth of 4 ft and place concrete in the voids. The consolidation from squeezing the 4 cu ft of soil into the immediate adjacent area may be sufficient strengthening to provide acceptable support.

The Franki extrusion "pile" is a similar foundation. A steel shell is set into a pit; the bottom is filled with run of bank gravel or dry concrete to a depth of two to three diameters; and the fill then is pushed into the soil by dropping a heavy ram inside the shell. The gravel packs and grips the shell sufficiently to pull it along through almost any type of soil. On reaching a desired depth, rapid impact with the ram breaks up the plug and extrudes it into the soil in the shape of an inverted mushroom. Concrete is added before the plug material has entirely cleared the shell. As the additional concrete is extruded, the shell is withdrawn. The result is a very rough-surfaced cylinder with a number of annular fins projecting into the soil. At the bottom is a mushroom-shaped expansion. Under load test, these piles carry much more load than is indicated by the area of the mushroom times the normally presumptive bearing value of the soil.

EARTH PRESSURES ON WALLS

In all soil-mechanics and foundation problems, four types of earth pressures are involved:

1. Active earth pressure. This exerts horizontal and vertical components against any structure that impedes the tendency of the earth to fall, slide, or creep into its natural state of equilibrium.

2. Passive earth resistance. This pressure is mobilized by the tendency of a structure to compress the earth.

3. Vertical load reaction of soil above a structure that has been built into the earth or which is covered with earth.

4. Vertical pressure distribution through a soil from an imposed loading.

Each of these pressures is dependent on many of the physical properties of the soil, as well as the relative rigidity of soil and structure. The most important properties of the soil appear to be density and coefficient of internal resistance, the latter being a direct factor in the ratio of active pressure to the weight of soil above the level considered. Some typical values for various soil types are given in Table 4-6.

4-52. Active Earth Pressure. This can safely and economically be determined by the following rules:

1. Horizontal component of active earth pressure for any material for a normal-type wall is closely given by the general wedge theory for the case of a vertical wall and substantially horizontal fill. The wall is assumed to be backfilled by usual construction methods and not so rigid that a small rotational movement (of the magnitude of 0.001

Table 4-6. Typical Soil Weights and Internal Resistance

Soil type	Average weight, w, lb per cu ft	Coefficient of internal resistance, $\tan \phi$
Soft flowing mud..........	105–120	0.18
Wet fine sand.............	110–120	0.27–0.58
Dry sand.................	90–110	0.47–0.70
Gravel....................	120–135	0.58–0.84
Compact loam............	90–110	0.58–1.00
Loose loam...............	75–90	0.27–0.58
Clay.....................	95–120	0.18–1.00
Cinders..................	35–45	0.47–1.00
Coke.....................	40–50	0.58–1.00
Anthracite coal...........	52	0.58
Bituminous coal..........	50	0.70
Ashes....................	40	0.84
Wheat...................	50	0.53

its height) cannot occur. The necessary rotation to mobilize the internal friction of the backfill is equivalent to an outward movement of $\frac{1}{4}$ in. at the top of a 20-ft wall.

The horizontal component of lateral pressure E_a is closely given for vertical walls and horizontal fills by the formula

$$E_a = \frac{1}{2}wH^2 \tan^2 \left(45° - \frac{\phi}{2} \right) = \frac{1}{2}wH^2K_a \qquad (4\text{-}5)$$

where w = average unit weight of fill, lb per cu ft
H = height of fill, ft
ϕ = angle whose tangent is coefficient of internal friction of fill
The value of $\tan^2 (45° - \phi/2)$ is often designated by the symbol K_a. Table 4-6 gives average values for w and $\tan \phi$. Table 4-7 gives values of $\tan^2 (45° - \phi/2)$ for various values of ϕ.

Table 4-7. Active and Passive Pressure Coefficients

Values of $K_a = \tan^2 \left(45° - \frac{\phi}{2} \right) = \dfrac{1 - \sin \phi}{1 + \sin \phi}$

and of $K_p = \tan^2 \left(45° + \frac{\phi}{2} \right) = \dfrac{1 + \sin \phi}{1 - \sin \phi}$

ϕ	$\tan \phi$	K_a	K_p
0	0	1.00	1.00
10	0.176	0.70	1.42
20	0.364	0.49	2.04
25	0.466	0.41	2.47
30	0.577	0.33	3.00
35	0.700	0.27	3.69
40	0.839	0.22	4.40
45	1.000	0.17	5.83
50	1.192	0.13	7.55
60	1.732	0.07	13.90
70	2.748	0.03	32.40
80	5.671	0.01	132.20
90	∞	0	∞

2. The general wedge-theory formulas (taking into account friction along the surface of a wall) may be used for evaluation of the horizontal component for all other conditions of wall batters and sloping fills. However, comparison with experimental results indicates that the results are somewhat too small for negative surcharges and somewhat too large for positive surcharges, but the differences are no greater than 10%. It is quite accurate enough, taking into account the uncertainties of conditions as to actual slope, to use a table of ratios, referred to the simplified case of vertical wall and horizontal fill (see Table 4-8).

Table 4-8. Lateral-Pressure Ratios for General Conditions

For Horizontal Fill

Wall Slope*	%
+1:6	107
+1:12	103
Vertical	100
−1:12	95
−1:6	90

For Vertical Walls

ϕ =	40°	30°	20°
Fill Slope†	%		
+10°	123	110	109
0	100	100	100
−10°	74	83	88

Note: Percentages apply to values given by Eq. (4-5) for the case of vertical wall and horizontal fill and for a specific value of ϕ. In computing the above values, the angle of friction between the wall and fill is assumed equal to ϕ, but not greater than 30°.
  * + represents a slope away from the fill; − represents a slope toward the fill.
  † + represents a slope uphill away from the wall; − represents a downhill slope.

3. The vertical component of lateral pressure, in all cases, is such that the resultant pressure forms an angle with the normal to the back of the wall equal to the angle of wall friction. However, under no condition can this angle exceed the angle of internal friction of the fill.

4. The pressure of soils that, because of lack of drainage and because of their nature, may become fluid at any time—whether such fluid material is widespread or only a narrow layer against the wall—is the same as hydrostatic pressure of a liquid having the same density as that soil.

5. The pressure of submerged soils is given by Eq. (4-5) with the weight of material reduced by buoyancy (for the solid fraction of the soil only) and the coefficient of internal friction evaluated for the submerged condition; in addition, full hydrostatic pressure of water must be included. For granular materials, submergence affects the coefficients of internal and wall friction very little; submergence changes silt materials to liquids.

6. The pressure of fills during saturation and prior to complete submergence and the pressure during drainage periods are affected by the rapidity of water movement. Drainage produces a slight temporary decrease in pressure from normal. Submergence produces an expansion of the fill with consequent increase in pressure. Such variations will not occur if adequate provision is made for drainage; if such provision is not made, the soil may become submerged and the pressure should be computed as for a submerged soil.

7. The pressure of granular fills may be increased about 10% by earthquake and other vibrations. The increase remains for a time and slowly disappears. Silt materials and some kinds of clay (thixotropic clays) under the action of earthquakes or vibrations by heavy trucking may become liquid.

8. The pressure of fills varies directly with temperature and normally decreases with age. Both factors can be safely disregarded in the design of abutments and walls.

9. Surface loading of the fill increases the lateral pressure on the wall. A trapezoidal pressure distribution—obtained by adding to the ordinary fill pressure the pressure computed from Eq. (4-5) for a depth of earth equivalent in weight to the surface loading or surcharge—may be assumed. Although not in complete accord with recent experimental work, this assumption is considered safe for walls because of the unlikely occurrence of full surcharge over the entire area of influence. For liquid fills, even though drained but remaining fluid, the moisture in the pores transmits the full weight of the surcharge to the wall. Hence, in such cases, that part of the horizontal pressure on the wall due to the surcharge equals the full weight of the surcharge at all depths.

10. The resultant horizontal pressure acts a distance from the base equal to 0.33 to 0.45 of the height of the wall. Liquid and negative-sloped fill pressures act at 0.33 of the height. Theoretical points of application of surcharge fills are listed in Table 4-9. Except for liquid and negative-sloped fill pressures, the point of application should be assumed no lower than 0.375 of the height, and higher if the surcharge ratio so requires. This assumption is on the safe side sufficiently to compensate for any effect of vibration, age, and local fill compaction. The location of the resultant affects wall design much more than corresponding accuracy in amount of pressure.

Table 4-9. Pressures from Surcharges on Fills

Ratio of surcharge equivalent to fill height	Ratio of height of resultant to fill height	Total pressure ratio (theoretical)	Total pressure ratio (Spangler)*
0	0.33	100	100
0.1	0.36	120	105
0.2	0.38	140	120
0.3	0.40	160	150
0.4	0.41	180	210
0.5	0.42	200	290
0.6	0.42	220	
0.7	0.42	240	
0.8	0.43	260	
0.9	0.43	280	
1.0	0.43	300	

* The Spangler ratios are based on data shown in Fig. 10, p. 63, *Highway Research Board Proceedings*, 1938, assuming normal unsurcharged pressure equal to 16 h^2, the extrapolation being from a single surcharge load (100 psf).

11. The pressure in pits and bins is not given by the wedge theory unless a correction for side-wall friction is made, in which case actual field observations of pressures are closely checked. (See Table 4-5.)

12. Many attempts have been made to derive a consistent formula for the pressure of cohesive soils, including a reduction factor for the cohesive resistance. Empirical evaluation indicates a formula of the form:

$$K = 0.75 - \frac{q}{wH} \tag{4-6}$$

where K = hydrostatic pressure ratio to be used in Eq. (4-5) for K_a
w = unit weight of soil, lb per cu ft
H = depth of excavation of fill, ft
q = the average unconfined compressive strength of soil samples, psf
(See chart by R. S. Knapp and R. B. Peck, *Engineering News-Record*, Nov. 20, 1941.)

4-53. Passive Earth Pressure. The horizontal component of passive (or maximum) resistance to pressure before failure (termed also "passive pressure") is often computed from the formula

$$E_p = wH^2 \tan^2 \left(45° + \frac{\phi}{2} \right) = \frac{1}{2}wH^2K_p \tag{4-7}$$

where w = average unit weight of fill, lb per cu ft
$\quad H$ = fill height, ft
$\quad \phi$ = angle whose tangent is the coefficient of internal friction of fill
$\quad K_p = \tan^2 (45° + \phi/2)$

Experimental work, especially with sheetpiles in sand, shows that actual values of passive resistance are larger than those given by Eq. (4-7). For the design of sheet-piling embedded in sandy materials, a maximum value of passive resistance equal to twice E_p may be recommended as permissible.

The vertical component of the passive resistance is such that resultant pressure is inclined from the normal to the back of the wall by the angle of wall friction.

Little is known about the location of the resultant passive pressure. It is probably affected by the rigidity of the wall. The usual assumption is that the distribution of lateral resistance is linear.

4-54. Pressures on Underground Structures. The vertical load reaction due to soil above a buried structure has been determined chiefly on culverts, although there are considerable data available from tunnel-construction experience. The relative rigidity or flexibility of surrounding earth and the intruding culvert, tunnel, or foundation has considerable influence on whether the load to be carried is greater than, equal to, or less than the weight of the soil directly above. A summary of general relationship is given in several reports of the Iowa State College Engineering Experiment Station, where a succession of fine work has been done on this problem from 1910 to the present. Generally, flexibility of the embedded structure reduces the load to be carried. Rigidity in the backfill has the same effect.

SHEETING AND BRACING OF EXCAVATIONS

The design of proper sheeting and bracing to hold excavation banks in safe position during a construction operation is often given too little attention. Legal responsibility for maintaining adjacent property and public streets with their buried utility services undamaged during and after construction is usually placed on the builder. Since the work to be done is temporary and is not a measurable item of completed production, the tendency is to minimize it and "take a chance." The results are usually expensive reconstruction, loss of valuable time, and lengthy litigation. Some cities require filing of a carefully prepared design for temporary sheeting.

4-55. Sheeting Design. Sheeting without special anchorage or buttresses can be used in several forms or combinations of shapes.

Any formula used for stresses in sheeting must be based on assumptions of the shape that the sheeting takes under load. In designing embedded poles subjected to unbalanced wire loading, the usual assumptions are:

1. The lateral passive resistance increases linearly with depth.
2. The point of inflection is at two-thirds the embedded length below the surface.

These assumptions may be safely used to determine depth of sheeting embedment for small structures, especially where reliable soil data are not available. On the assumption that the passive resistance increases linearly with depth and the maximum value at the bottom is the same on either side of sheeting and equals wK_pD, M. A. Drucker developed a formula that may be simplified to approximately

$$D = \frac{H}{3} \cdot \frac{1 + 3K_a}{1 - K_a} \tag{4-8}$$

where D = depth of embedment

H = height of retained fill

K_a = active pressure coefficient

K_p = passive-resistance coefficient (see Table 4-7)

(*Civil Engineering*, December, 1934.)

Equation (4-8) should not be used where the coefficient of internal friction of the soil is greater than unity. When soil so hard is encountered, (for values of ϕ greater than 45°) the formula to be used is

$$D = \frac{2K_a}{1 - 2K_a} \qquad (4\text{-}9)$$

These equations are applicable for cantilevered sheeting with no external supports other than the embedment below the level of excavation. Deeper types of steel sheeting can be used to depths of 20 ft or more and, even in saturated sands, when drained by well points, have permitted safe construction of foundations without interference from bracing. Where pile driving or other vibrations may occur, elimination of bracing is not advisable.

4-56. Bracing of Sheetpiles. Sheetpiling can be provided with additional supports by either bracing inside the cut or anchoring the top to buried "dead men" located outside. Where space is available, the latter procedure is more economical, taking the form of piles or buried masses of concrete, to which are attached adjustable lengths of cables or rods holding back a continuous horizontal whaler.

The reactions to be provided at each level of support cannot be definitely determined. The distribution of pressure on the sheeting depends on the flexibility of the sheeting, which in turn is affected by the relative stiffness of the supports. A liberal allowance at each level is therefore necessary, and the total of all the resistances should be considerably above the total pressure. However, unit stresses in the whalers, struts, and ties can be taken at much higher values than for permanent construction; one-half the elastic limits of the respective materials is quite proper.

If the final shape of the sheeting is known, graphical determination of moments and pressures is possible. The Baumann solution given in *Transactions of the ASCE*, 1935, is such a method. Standard sheetpile handbooks usually give the Blum-Lohmeyer method for load evaluation at the various supports.

Normally, water pressure need not be considered, since the excavation must be kept dry, and any hydrostatic pressures on the back of the sheeting can be easily relieved. However, if water can accumulate in back of the sheeting, such pressure must be considered. Equally important, saturation will reduce considerably the soil-anchorage reaction at the bottom of the sheeting and increase the upper reactions. Saturation of the bottom will also require longer penetration of the sheeting to avoid blowouts or boils along the sheeting, either of which will prove disastrous. Drainage is a cheap investment for safety.

No bracing system is any stronger than the resistance provided at the bottom of the struts. Unless very good soil is found, the struts should be provided with screw jacks to develop the necessary resistances in the sills and to permit continuous adjustments.

Bracing against previously completed footings is permissible only if the footings are properly braced against undisturbed soil or have enough lateral strength. In evaluating lateral strength, the frictional resistance on the base of footings (disregarding any cohesive forces) may be added to the passive resistance of the soil against vertical faces.

Lateral resistance of piles, for movements of $\frac{1}{4}$ in., is taken by the U.S. Corps of Engineers in the design of river works as: 4 tons per wood pile, 5 tons per concrete pile, and 6 tons per steel pile, when driven to the usual bearing values of each. For substantial movements laterally, the values should be reduced by 30%.

4-57. Anchorage of Sheeting. Where exterior anchorages are used, the pull-out resistance varies with the type of soil and size of the buried anchor. Relative values of pull-out resistance for soils are 1.0 for compact and stiff clay and 0.5 for fairly soft clay and loose sand.

For equal vertical depth of embedment, resistance increases with the slope of the pull from the vertical. If we assign a value of 1.0 for vertical pull, then the resistance is 1.5 at 1:1 slope; 2.0 at 1:2 slope; 2.1 at 1:3 slope; and 2.3 at 1:4 slope.

Where embedment is larger than the maximum dimension of the anchor, the resistances to vertical pull in rammed average soil in pounds per square foot of anchor face at various depths are:

Resistance, Psf	Depth, Ft
800	1.0
1,000	1.5
1,900	2.0
3,000	3.0
5,400	4.0
8,000	5.0

Sheeting should not be removed until all backfill is properly consolidated. Some additional fill and compaction are necessary as sheeting is removed to avoid internal slip and possible damage to adjacent pavements.

SETTLEMENT AND FAILURES

4-58. Unwanted Foundation Movements. Structures that show unwanted vertical or lateral movements as a result of foundation settlements, heaves, or displacements are examples where the foundation design is a failure. Rarely does a structural failure occur in the footing; the usual trouble is in the soil and a consequence of the assumption that movements either will not occur or will be uniform.

Failures can be classified as unwanted upward, downward, and lateral movements.

That many structures are affected by the heave of fine-grained soils is now common knowledge. Certain bentonitic clay soils undergo large volume changes with seasonal variation in moisture content—especially when lightly loaded. The phenomenon is further complicated by the shading effect, both under and toward the northerly side of the buildings, causing an inequality in the drying out of the soil.

Tidal intrusion of water along shore lines has caused upward movements of light frame structures.

Evaporation of moisture taken out by trees adjacent to foundations has caused sufficient volume change to tip and crack walls.

Consolidation of soil layers from drainage induced by sewer and other subsurface trenches, as well as the normal slower consolidation from normal pressure of overburden, can cause tipping of foundations. Even pile foundations have been known to settle and move laterally where unconsolidated layers—usually not uniform in thickness—start to shrink after the trigger action of pile driving or change in loading conditions.

A very common failure is the dragging down of an existing wall by new construction built in intimate contact; an open gap or sliding plane must be provided between any previously settled-in-place structure and new work. A similar trouble is the sympathetic settlement of existing structures on a stable foundation underlain by soft strata, which are compressed and bent by new loading, even if the two structures do not touch.

Settlements can be easily observed, and the trouble can often be recognized from the shape of the masonry cracks. Every design should be examined to see where and how foundation movements can occur, and design modifications should be made to eliminate the effects on other structures and to equalize movements, in amount and direction, in the new structure.

For example, a large structure designed by the Los Angeles County Flood Control District was to be founded partly on natural shale and partly on a blended compacted fill. The formula for the blending of fills was fixed by getting a mixture of decomposed granite and broken shale with the same triaxial shear-test value as the natural shale. The computed expected settlement was 0.014 ft. Under 90 % of the design load, the completed structure showed an actual settlement of 0.012 ft. Procedures of this type are available and should be used to avoid failures of the foundation design.

Settlements are possible for pile foundations or even footings on rock, and any assumption made that no settlement will occur can only lead to trouble. Pile foundations will settle as much as the supporting soils under the distributed loads. Certain rocks, of the shale and schist groups, will disintegrate under continuous loading. Unless bottoms of footings are sealed, any percolation of ground water, especially if it contains sewage or other wastes, will soften the contact layer sufficiently to permit lateral flow.

Compact hard dry clays do not remain in that condition if water is present. Backfill for basement walls with soils that shrink on dehydration—often caused by suction of the soil water into the concrete—show voids in the fill immediately adjacent to the wall. Such conditions have been known to be the cause of complete collapse immediately after a heavy rainfall, when enough water enters the voids to provide full hydrostatic pressure for which the wall was not designed.

Localized footing failures within buildings are often caused by the pipe trenches dug after the footings are completed, without regard to relative depths of excavations. Similar troubles often occur when new trunk sewers or even transit tunnels are built in public streets without proper underpinning of all footings above the surface of influence from the new excavation. Such work will also affect the normal ground-water table, and together with pumping for industrial and air-conditioning requirements, has lowered the water level sufficiently to cause rotting of untreated wood piles. This difficulty is so prevalent that many cities restrict the use of untreated piles for any area where ground water may not remain stable. Proximity of natural water areas is no proof of such stability; the ground-water level has been shown to be at 35 ft below sea level at only short distances from the bulkhead lines where industrial pumping was carried to excess.

A serious foundation failure of a heavy factory bearing on compact fine sand was caused by the decision to sink some wells within the building and get the process water from the subsoil. The underlying layers were reduced in thickness and a dish-shaped floor resulted.

Local overload on ground-floor slabs, transmitted to some footings, explains the odd-shaped roofs on many single-story warehouses.

All these troubles can be controlled, but only by a frank admission in the design that foundations will settle if the soil support is altered and that every new foundation will settle as the load is applied.

ADOBE AND SOIL HOUSES

Use of local soil for building material must be as old as the first human who imitated an earth-boring animal and provided shelter. From that earth cave, it is only a short step to shelters made of sod, used extensively after World War II in the reclamation areas in Europe, and of mud bricks, called adobe when they are sun-cured. The oldest known adobe house is at Sialk, an oasis in Iran, dated before 4000 B.C. Many of the houses in Damascus with walls and roof of local mud applied to woven willow mats are reputed to date to early Biblical times.

4-59. Types of Soil Walls. The use of soil for wall construction is in five different processes:

1. Cajob, where soil wall panels are supported in wood or concrete frames.

2. Mud concrete, or poured adobe, is a fluid mix poured into full-height forms or into movable forms, which are lifted as the work progresses.

3. English Cob, which is a stiff mud piled up by hand to form a wall without any forms or structural skeleton.

4. Rammed earth, or "pise de terre," a damp mix placed between sturdy wood forms, in layers of about 4 in. which are rammed to about 2½ in.

5. Sun-baked soil bricks, adobe, where shrinkage occurs before using in the wall, requiring 2 to 3 months' storage. A good brick will have compressive strength of 300 to 500 psi and tensile value of 50 psi.

4-60. Adobe Blocks. Machine-made adobe blocks are available with admixtures such as cement (really a cement-soil concrete), emulsified asphalt, resins, silicates, soaps, and similar water-repellent ingredients.   Rammed earth in mass or in blocks is fire-resistant, verminproof, and decay-proof and has excellent thermal insulation.

However, to reduce its susceptibility to moisture penetration, and to increase resistance to shrinkage, cracking, and surface deterioration, some soil-blending admixtures or ingredients become essential.   These not only immediately increase the cost of materials, but require some skilled help in the preparation of the mixtures.

The mechanical resistance of the product is directly proportional to the care and skill in blending and preparing the blocks or walls.   The soil in either should be compressed or rammed to a density of no less than 2.10 or 132 lb per cu ft—greater density than is normally accomplished by any compaction on a road or airport operation.

4-61. Materials for Soil Blocks or Walls.   The soil mix should not have any gravel of 1 in. or larger size, and the total gravel must be less than 40% by weight.   More gravel will cause the mix to coagulate, set badly on drying, and give fragile bricks. The sand should be clean and may require electrostatic treatment to be so ionized that the surfaces wet easily.   Clay should make up 20 to 35% of the mix, with silt sizes eliminated as far as possible.   If marl is to be used, it must not be too calcareous and should be broken up into a size range between $\frac{1}{16}$ and $\frac{1}{8}$ in.

Since optimum moisture conditions must be maintained, topsoils with vegetation should be avoided since they require too much water and shrink too much.

In France, binder stabilizers are found necessary.   Those used are fat lime or hydraulic lime (at least 170 lb per cu yd), or portland cement (170 to 300 lb per cu yd). Very good results are obtained with a blend of 1 part hydraulic lime and 2 parts cement, by weight.   A good report of strengths and densities possible with different percentages of cement and varying mixes of sand and clay sizes, based on work in Bogotá, Colombia, was given by Ralph Stone (*Civil Engineering*, December, 1952, p. 29).   Considerable work has been done by and many reports are available from the United Nations, both in the Technical Assistance Administration and in the Housing, Town and Country Planning Section of the Department of Social Affairs.

Section 5

CONCRETE CONSTRUCTION

MAURICE BARRON

Consulting Engineer
Farkas & Barron
New York, N.Y.

Concrete is "a compound of gravel, broken rock or other aggregate bound together by means of hydraulic cement, coal tar, asphaltum or other cementing materials. Generally, when a qualifying term is not used, portland cement concrete is understood." (Definition adopted in 1923 by the American Concrete Institute.)

Concrete differs from other structural materials in that generally it does not arrive at the job as a finished material. It usually is manufactured where it is used. Greater care must therefore be taken to assure that the concrete is of uniform and specified quality. For properties of portland cement and aggregates, see Sec. 2.

5-1. Proportioning Concrete Mixes. The exact proportions of fine and coarse aggregate, water, and cement that will give a desired strength and workability must be determined by experience or trial.

The following principles influence proportioning:

1. The strength of concrete depends on the water-cement ratio. When this ratio is high, the strength is low; when the ratio is low, the strength is high.

2. When the mix is diluted, the cost of the mix is lower. Water increases the workability of the mix and enables more aggregate to be introduced to maintain a required consistency. This means fewer bags of cement per cubic yard.

3. The ideal minimum amount of cement paste is that which will coat each aggregate particle and will fill all voids.

4. Economy of the mix decreases as the ratio of fine to coarse aggregate increases, because the large surface area of the fine aggregate requires more cement to coat it.

5. Shrinkage during setting is proportional to the amount of cement paste in a mix. Mixes with too much sand, therefore, will be subject to greater shrinkage since the cement content will be higher.

5-2. Water-Cement Ratio. The strength of concrete in terms of the water-cement ratio is expressed in Duff A. Abrams' formula: $S = 14,000/7^x$, where S is the 28-day compressive strength and x is the ratio of water to cement by volume. If rigid control is lacking, the formula is $S = 14,000/9^x$. These formulas hold only for a workable mix.

In 1932, Inge Lyse simplified these expressions by expressing the strength in terms of a linear equation with the variable C/W as the ratio of cement to water by weight: $S = 2,480C/W - 1,730$. However, modern portland cements are much improved in quality from those for which the above formulas were derived. The modern formulas are $S = 13,300/4.04^x$; $S = 2,700C/W - 760$.

Two and one-half gallons of water per sack of cement (assumed to be 1 cu ft) is sufficient for the hydration of cement. The strength quickly decreases as the quantity of mixing water is increased.

Professor Abrams, who introduced the concept of water-cement ratio, also introduced the **fineness modulus.** A measure of the grading of an aggregate, it is 0.01 the sum of the percentages of material coarser than each of the following U.S. Standard sieves: No. 100, 50, 30, 16, 8, 4, $\frac{3}{8}$-in., $\frac{3}{4}$-in., $1\frac{1}{2}$-in., and 3-in. The higher the modulus, the coarser the aggregate. Different aggregates may have the same fineness modulus, but it is found that different aggregates with the same fineness modulus will require equal amounts of mixing water to give the same plasticity and will produce concretes of different strengths. In practice, the problem of proportioning reduces to that of finding the best aggregate combination to use with the water-cement ratio for a required strength.

5-3. Consistency of Concrete Mixes. Consistency or plasticity is measured with a slump cone. This device is an open ended 12-in.-high truncated cone. Concrete is placed in the cone by a standardized procedure and then the cone is removed. The slump is the difference in the original height of the concrete and the height after the cone is removed. Some recommended slumps are:

Type	Max slump, in.	Min slump, in.
Mass concrete	3	1
Reinforced-concrete walls and footings	5	2
Plain footings, caissons, and substructure walls	4	1
Slabs, beams, and reinforced walls	6	3
Pavements	3	2

The above values for slump should be reduced by about one-third if high-frequency vibrators are used.

The maximum sizes of coarse aggregates that are recommended are given in Table 5-1 (ACI Standard, 613-54, "Selecting Proportions for Concrete").

Table 5-1. Maximum Size of Aggregate, Inches

Min dimension of section, in.	Reinforced walls, beams and columns	Unreinforced walls	Heavily reinforced slabs	Lightly reinforced or unreinforced slabs
$2\frac{1}{2}$-5	$\frac{1}{2}$-$\frac{3}{4}$	$\frac{3}{4}$	$\frac{3}{4}$-1	$\frac{3}{4}$-$1\frac{1}{2}$
6-11	$\frac{3}{4}$-$1\frac{1}{2}$	$1\frac{1}{2}$	$1\frac{1}{2}$	$1\frac{1}{2}$-3
12-29	$1\frac{1}{2}$-3	3	$1\frac{1}{2}$-3	3
30 or more	$1\frac{1}{2}$-3	6	$1\frac{1}{2}$-3	3-6

5-4. Methods of Proportioning Concrete. 1. *Void Determinations.* This method consists of determining the void content in the coarse aggregate and filling these voids with sufficient sand, then determining the void content of the sand and filling this with cement paste.

2. *Arbitrary Proportions.* This method is a variation of void determination. Experience shows that coarse aggregate contains approximately 50 % voids. When these voids are filled with sand, the ratio of fine to coarse aggregate will be 1:2. The mix is determined by experience. Some examples of mixes used are:

For columns or other structural members carrying unusually high compressive stress and structures exposed to severe weathering conditions (ratio of cement to fine aggregate to coarse aggregate): $1:1\frac{1}{2}:3$.

For floor slabs, beams, and other structural members carrying ordinary stresses and not exposed to severe weathering: $1:2:3\frac{1}{2}$.

For filling and massive work exposed to severe weathering: $1:3:5$.

This method does not result in uniform and reliable concretes.

3. *Mechanical Analysis.* In this method the aggregates are combined to give the densest mix by means of sieve analyses of the materials.

4. *Trial Mixes.* In this method the densest mix is found by mixing trial batches. Definite proportions of material are mixed and then tamped in a cylinder. The volume of the tamped mix is then recorded. A new mix is made in which the proportions vary slightly, and the procedure is repeated. After several trials, the mix that occupies the least volume for its weight is chosen.

5. *Surface-area Method.* This method assumes the strength of the concrete is dependent on the ratio of cement to the surface area of the aggregate.

5-5. Properties and Tests of Concrete. (See also Art. 2-18.) Concrete does not have a linear stress-strain relationship. Also, there is no well-defined yield point. Approximately, the modulus of elasticity $E_c = 1,000f'_c$, where f'_c is the 28-day cylinder strength, and E_c is the secant modulus of elasticity.

Concrete exhibits the property of plasticity; that is, the concrete permanently deforms slightly under load over a period of sustained loading. In elastic design, this is not taken into account, the concrete being assumed to act with a constant E_c.

Concrete cylinders usually are tested in compression at the end of 7 days and 28 days. According to W. A. Slater (*Proceedings of the American Concrete Institute,* 1926):

$$S_{28} = S_7 + 30 \sqrt{S_7} \tag{5-1}$$

where S_{28} = 28-day compressive strength
S_7 = 7-day strength

For S_{28}, Psi	S_7 Should Be at Least, Psi
4,000	2,500
3,500	2,115
3,000	1,745
2,500	1,385
2,000	1,035

The tensile strength of concrete is very small compared with the compressive strength and is usually neglected in design.

Weight of stone concrete varies from 140 to 160 lb per cu ft. It is customary to assume a weight of 150 lb per cu ft for reinforced concrete, and 145 for plain concrete.

Lightweight concretes, some weighing considerably less than 100 lb per cu ft, may have as coarse aggregate commercially manufactured aggregate, such as expanded clay or shale, vermiculite, perlite, or pumice. Usually, mixes made with these aggregates require an air-entraining agent or other admixture to obtain plasticity without introduction of excessive amounts of water.

Heavyweight concretes, some weighing about 200 lb per cu ft, are used in shields to absorb atomic radiation. Aggregates employed include barites, or barium sulfate, limonite, magnetite, and steel punchings and shot.

In some localities, coral may be the only available coarse aggregate, and sea water the only available water. It has been determined that sea water should be used with coral, but the surface of the concrete must be dense and impervious or the concrete will deteriorate quickly. Only the surface part of a coral bed should be quarried for aggregate, because the deeper layers (below 2 ft) will be very soft.

5-6. Concrete-mixing Plants. A concrete plant is an installation where the concrete for large projects is manufactured. The actual mixing may be done in truck mixers and not at the plant. The usual parts of a concrete plant are:

1. *Aggregate stockpiles.* Usually, different gradings are kept in separate piles.

2. *Cement silo.*

3. *Cement and aggregate elevators.* Usually, the cement and aggregate must be lifted up to be placed into the bins. This is usually done by elevators of the con-

tinuous bucket type. Cranes may also be used for this purpose. If the bin is located beside a vertical cliff, the aggregate may simply be dropped into the bin.

4. *Bin.* This is a metal container with an opening in the bottom through which the materials pass by gravity into the batcher. The bin is divided into several compartments for different cements and aggregates. The cement compartments are watertight.

5. *Batcher.* Here, the cement, aggregates, and water are weighed separately. The aggregates and cement are then discharged through an opening in the bottom of the batcher into the mixer.

6. *Mixer.*

5-7. Measuring of Materials for Concrete. The end product of scientific proportioning is the determination of the quantities of material that are to be mixed. The quality of concrete is largely dependent on the care used in measuring the materials that go into the mixer.

Cement is measured by volume or weight. A bag of cement weighs 94 lb and is assumed to be 1 cu ft. A barrel of cement contains 4 bags. Sometimes, however, cement is bought in bulk, and therefore, each batch must be weighed.

Aggregates also are measured by volume or weight. In order that the grading will be more uniform, coarse aggregates are sometimes weighed in two sizes. If sand is measured dry and loose, a "bulking factor" must be taken into account. When the sand contains moisture, the sand particles are separated by a film of water and the apparent volume is larger. More sand, therefore, must be added to compensate for the bulking and less water to offset the water in the aggregates. Absorbed water never is available for cement hydration.

An uncertainty arises in volume measurement because of the variations of compaction, and therefore, batching by weight is preferred. On small jobs, measurement is sometimes made by shovels or wheelbarrows. Concrete so made is quite variable.

Water must be very accurately measured. Allowance must be made for water in the aggregate. Sand usually has a moisture content of 3 to 8 %. If this is neglected, an excess of ¾ to 2 gal of water per sack of cement may result. Coarse aggregate usually has a moisture content of 1 or 2 %. Moisture contents are determined by weighing and heating a sample of the aggregate until the water has been driven off and then weighing the sample again. Sometimes alcohol is mixed with a sample of aggregate and ignited to drive off the water.

5-8. Concrete Mixing. Except for very small quantities, concrete is machine-mixed rather than hand-mixed. Machine mixing is much faster and gives a more reliable concrete.

The mixing is frequently done on the job, but mixers mounted on truck bodies also are used to deliver concrete ready-mixed to the job from a central batching plant.

Types of mixers include:

1. *Drum.* The materials are mixed in a rotating drum. Inside the drum are blades that agitate the concrete and promote uniform mixing. Discharge is through a trough inserted in the side of the drum; but in small types, the drum may be tilted.

2. *Trough.* These employ the rotation of blades in a trough. They are not as reliable as the drum mixer.

3. *Gravity.* The materials fall under the action of gravity through successive funnels and are incidentally mixed. It has a low first cost because of the saving in power. But concrete mixed in a gravity mixer is likely to be uncertain in quality.

4. *Pneumatic.* Compressed air is the mixing agent. Its use is restricted because of the large compresser that must be installed for each mixer.

5. *Truck-mounted.* This is essentially a mobile drum mixer. Capacity ranges from 2 to 6 cu yd.

6. *Countercurrent mixers.* In this device, mixing blades are not stationary but rotate in the direction opposite the drum rotation.

The mixer drum should operate at an approximate peripheral speed of 200 fpm. Speeds less than 100 fpm and greater than 225 fpm are inefficient. The peripheral speed for mixing efficiency is inversely proportional to the diameter of the drum.

Duration of mixing should never be less than 1 min. It is preferable to mix for

$1\frac{1}{2}$ min for mixers of 1 cu yd capacity and longer for mixers of greater capacity. A safe rule is $1\frac{1}{2}$ min for the first cubic yard and $\frac{1}{2}$ min for each subsequent cubic yard. Time of mixing should always be counted from the time that all the materials, including the water, are in the drum. Concrete should not be mixed longer than 20 min. It is important to remember that mixers should not be loaded beyond their rated capacity.

CONCRETE PLACEMENT

The principles governing concrete placement are:

1. Concrete should be placed in the forms continuously and evenly.
2. Concrete should not be placed in forms in any manner that promotes segregation.
3. Lateral flow of concrete should be avoided, since segregation of the aggregate may result.
4. As far as possible, the forms should be continuously filled without stoppage, to prevent laitance (a low-strength layer of fine particles that floats to the top) or stoppage planes.
5. Before new concrete is deposited on concrete that has set, precautions should be taken to secure a perfect bonding between the two.
6. Care should be taken to avoid entrapment of air.
7. Concrete should be manipulated in the forms to allow entrapped air to escape.
8. Puddling and tamping should be used to fill the forms completely and to insure intimate contact with the reinforcement.
9. Spading will insure the larger aggregate's being kept away from the forms so that a smooth finish is obtained.
10. Unconfined concrete should not be deposited in water.
11. Concrete that has been retempered after initial set should not be deposited in forms.
12. No concrete should be deposited in cold or very hot weather without special precautions.

5-9. Effect of Excess Water on Concrete. Because concrete is highly viscous, workmen often add water to it to make it flow freely and to make the work of placing it in the forms easier. Excess water is extremely detrimental for many reasons, some of which are:

1. Excess water reduces the strength of the concrete.
2. Water, when charged with gelatinous aluminates from cement, has ability to occlude great quantities of air. This air, in the form of minute bubbles, coats the aggregate and prevents cementation. Excess water aggravates this condition.
3. Excess water tends to leak out of the concrete before, or after, final set has taken place. This results in voids in the concrete. Voids and sand streaks are highly detrimental, since they adversely affect surface appearance and afford a passageway for water, which disintegrates the concrete.
4. Excess water results in "day's work planes." These are fault planes through which water may seep.
5. When concrete is continually dumped in one place, the excess water tends to carry away the finer materials, including the cement. These harden above the concrete to form a deposit of muck or laitance, which is chalky and of low strength. This laitance prevents bonding of any new concrete placed on it. For this reason, columns should always be poured in one section.

5-10. Bonding Set and New Concrete. The first essential in securing a good bond is removal of the laitance film from horizontal surfaces. At least $\frac{1}{2}$ in. of surface material should be removed, even if the concrete is several years old. It may be necessary to take out several inches before sound concrete is reached. The surface then should be washed, preferably with clean water, and all loose material removed. Vertical surfaces should be "hacked" or sandblasted. Rich grout should be brushed on the surface to provide a good bedment. Before the grout has dried, the new concrete should be placed, the first thin layer being tamped down solidly.

5-11. Removal of Undesirable Air. An excess of entrapped air is deleterious since it isolates the aggregate. Entrapped air is likely to result when concrete is dropped from a height. This air may be driven out by vibrating the concrete or by hitting the side of the forms. Some small amount of entrained air in the form of minute bubbles is actually beneficial.

5-12. Spudding, Puddling, Tamping, and Vibrating. These methods are used to fill the forms completely and to insure contact between the reinforcing bars and concrete. The concrete should be spaded back from the forms so that a smooth surface will exist at exposed surfaces.

5-13. Vibration of Concrete in the Forms. By vibrating, a harsh concrete is made plastic and may then be handled more easily. The advantages of vibrating concrete are: lowered costs of concrete through ease of placement and by reduced cement content, greater density and homogeneity of concrete, greater bond at construction joints, greater durability, and reduced shrinkage. Use of concretes with low slumps is feasible with vibration; concrete with 2-in. slumps may be placed easily.

The effectiveness of vibration is closely related to the frequency of the vibrator. The greater the frequency, the greater will be the effects of vibration. Speeds of vibrators may vary from 1,000 to more than 10,000 rpm.

Methods of vibration may be classified into two general categories—external and internal.

External vibration may be further divided into surface vibration, form vibration, and vibration of molds. In surface vibration, the vibrator rests or floats on the concrete surface. In form vibration, the vibrator is attached to the form, which transmits the impulses to the concrete. Vibrating tables are used to vibrate precast units placed on them.

Internal vibrators are inserted into the concrete. For general construction work, the internal vibrator is the most efficient. Vibratory motion is secured by means of a rotating eccentric element. In the ball or torpedo type, the vibrating element is the unbalanced rotor of the electric motor. In most cases, the motor is distinct and apart from the unit housing the eccentric element. The connection between motor and vibrator unit may be a short spline drive. Some vibrators are oil- or air-driven.

Excessive vibration should be avoided because it results in segregation. Continued vibration moves the ingredients of lower specific gravity upward toward the surface. Vibration also results in the removal of entrained air as well as entrapped air. When air-entrainment agents are used in concrete, care must be taken not to vibrate excessively.

5-14. Concreting in Cold Weather. Special concreting methods are required during cold weather, because the strength and durability of concrete are adversely affected when the concrete is exposed to low temperatures during the curing period.

Special methods should be planned well in advance of the anticipated cold weather. These methods should be used if the temperature drops below 40°F during the 24-hr period directly after placing and or below 30°F during the succeeding 6 days. The purposes of these methods are to:

1. Prevent damage to concrete from freezing and thawing at an early age.
2. Allow the concrete to develop early strength so that the forms may be quickly removed.
3. Maintain proper curing conditions.
4. Limit excessive or rapid temperature changes before the concrete has hardened sufficiently to resist temperature stresses.

The most reliable means of protecting concrete from frost damage at early ages is to build a temporary housing to enclose the whole volume to be occupied by the concrete structure, and to maintain the proper curing temperature in this enclosure by artificial heat. This has been done for structures of small size built in extremely cold weather. Generally, it is not economical.

Other methods include construction of canvas, plywood, sheetrock, plastic, Celotex, Sisalkraft, and other weatherproof enclosures around the forms only. These enclosures may be heated by means of steam unit heaters, steam jets, steam pipes, salamanders, etc.

Sometimes the concrete is placed at a temperature high enough that the loss of heat will be balanced by the heat of hydration of the cement. This method is limited to temperatures only a few degrees from freezing. Also, the concrete is likely to be damaged by a sudden drop in temperature, if no provisions are made for protecting it. Use of hot concrete leads to excessive cracking when the concrete cools. Hot concrete has low workability and a tendency toward flash set.

To heat the concrete during placing, it is convenient to heat the materials. For temperatures not lower than 30°F, the mixing water should be heated so that the concrete in the mixer will be between 50 and 70°F. On small jobs (less than 20 cu yd), the concrete may be heated by means of a torch inside the mixer. For air temperatures from 0 to 30°F, the water and fine aggregate should both be heated so the concrete in the mixer is between 50 and 70°F. To avoid flash set where either aggregate or water is heated in excess of 100°F, the loading of the mixer should be in such sequence that the cement does not come in contact with such hot materials. For air temperatures below 0°F, the coarse, as well as the fine, aggregate should be heated to bring the concrete mix to the 50 to 70°F range.

The above recommendations are somewhat different for mass concrete, since the interior of the concrete is protected from sudden temperature changes. If the temperature is likely to fall below 35°F in the 24-hr period after placing, precautions should be taken. For air temperatures not lower than 30°F, the water should be heated to bring the temperature of the concrete at the mixer to between 40 and 60°F. For air temperatures below 30°F, both water and fine aggregate are heated to bring the temperature of the mixer to between 40 and 70°F.

It is usually desirable to remove the forms as soon as possible so that further construction may proceed. Yet, low temperatures greatly retard the chemical reactions by which the concrete hardens. To speed up the hardening, high-early-strength cement may be used. However, this cement does not obviate the necessity of protecting the concrete from freezing and thawing, but it reduces the duration of such protection.

Calcium chloride or other accelerators may be used to hasten setting of the concrete. Calcium chloride should never be used in excess of 2% of the weight of cement. Use of calcium chloride or other soluble materials for the purpose of preventing freezing solely by lowering the freezing point of the mixing water should not be permitted.

A supply of moisture should be maintained on all exposed concrete surfaces during the curing period to promote development of strength and surface hardness.

A sudden cooling or a considerable temperature differential within the concrete structure will result in extensive and harmful cracking. This may occur when the forms are removed and the surface of the concrete becomes chilled. This is particularly serious in mass concrete where the heat of hydration of the cements may raise the internal temperature from 30 to 70°F above the temperature at which the concrete is placed.

5-15. Curing Concrete. "Curing, as applied to reinforced concrete, covers all the conditions both natural and artificially created that affect the extent and the rate of hydration of the cement." (Timms, "Curing of Concrete," *Journal of the American Concrete Institute*, May, 1952.) Many concrete structures are cured without protection of any kind; they are allowed to harden while exposed to sun, wind, and rain. This type of curing is unreliable because water may evaporate from the surface. As the term is usually applied, curing refers to the various means employed to control the moisture content or the temperature of the concrete. In practice, it consists of conserving the moisture within the concrete by furnishing additional moisture to replenish the water lost by evaporation. Usually, little attention is paid to temperature except in winter curing and steam curing.

Curing is beneficial in that it makes the concrete more watertight and increases the strength.

Methods for curing may be classified as:

1. Those that supply water throughout the early hydration process and tend to maintain a uniform temperature, such as ponding, sprinkling, application of wet burlap or cotton mats, wet earth, sawdust, hay, and straw.

2. Those designed to prevent loss of water, but having little influence on maintaining a uniform temperature, such as waterproof paper or impermeable membranes. These impermeable membranes usually consist of a clear or bituminous compound, which is sprayed on the concrete. It fills the pores and thus prevents evaporation. A fugitive dye in the colorless compound aids the spraying and inspection.

Calcium chloride may be used integrally or as a surface compound. If used integrally, it acts to accelerate the hardening and therefore reduces the time of curing.

A white pigment that gives infrared reflectance can be used in a curing compound to keep the concrete surface cooler.

5-16. Transporting and Placing Concrete Mixes. The following methods may be used for transportation and placing of concrete:

1. *Depositing Concrete through Water.* Concrete must never be deposited through water unless confined. A tremie is used for this purpose. This is a tube (commonly called an elephant trunk) about 1 ft or more in diameter at the top, slightly flaring at the bottom, and of sufficient length to reach the bottom of the water. The lower end is always kept immersed in the newly deposited concrete, and the tremie is always kept full of concrete. Discharge of the tremie is aided by moving its bottom slowly. As the concrete level rises, the tremie is also raised.

Concrete is sometimes lowered in water in loosely woven jute bags, but a closed bucket may be used instead. In general, concrete should be deposited through water only when it is impossible or prohibitive to dewater the forms.

2. *Barrows.* In the ordinary wheelbarrow, a man can carry $1\frac{1}{2}$ to 2 cu ft of concrete a distance of 25 ft every 3 min. The major disadvantage in using wheelbarrows is that a large proportion of the load is on the man's arms instead of on the wheel.

3. *Concrete Carts.* Two-wheel concrete carts overcome the disadvantage of wheelbarrows. Four and one-half cubic feet may be handled in each cart, since carts are heavier and wider than wheelbarrows, but more elaborate runways are required. Motorized carts with $\frac{1}{2}$ cu yd capacity also are available.

4. *Buckets.* Buckets are of various types. They may be transported to the forms by cableways or crane. They may be unloaded by overturning. Buckets with bottom dump also are common.

5. *Spouts or Chutes.* In this method, concrete is raised vertically in a tower and then distributed by gravity through chutes or channels. The radius covered may be as much as 300 ft. However, this method encourages the use of excess water to promote the flow of concrete through chutes when the angle with the horizontal is not large.

When spouts or chutes are used the following precautions must be taken:

    a. A uniform slope must be maintained throughout the chute line; otherwise the flow of concrete will not be uniform.

    b. The slope must be large enough so that the concrete will flow readily, but excessive concrete slump should be avoided.

    c. The slope should also be greater if the distance over which the concrete is transported is long. For instance, a wet concrete will flow 50 ft with a slope of 1:6. The slope must be increased to 1:4 for a distance of 100 ft, and to 1:3 for 300 or 400 ft.

6. *Pumping through Pipe.* Sometimes concrete is pumped through pipelines from the mixer to the chute.

7. *Pneumatically Placed Concrete* (shotcrete or gunite). Mortar or concrete is projected by an air jet directly onto the form. The force of the jet compacts the material in place.

Steps in the placement of shotcrete are as follows:

1. Aggregate and cement are mixed in a standard concrete mixer.

2. The dry mix is fed by gravity into a special mechanical feeder called the "gun."

3. Compressed air is introduced into the gun and the pressurized mix is fed through

a delivery hose to a special nozzle. The nozzle is provided with a perforated manifold through which water is admitted. The water mixes with the dry mix.

4. The moistened mix is jetted immediately onto the object to be shotcreted.

Advantages of shotcrete are as follows: It requires a relatively small, portable plant. The method of placement requires a lower water-cement ratio; the density obtained by the method of placement and the stiffness of the mix permit building up of many shapes without forms. Shotcrete has a high compressive strength. It is well adapted for thin walls; coatings over brick, concrete, steel, and masonry; encasement of steel for fireproofing; and repair of concrete surfaces.

Shotcrete must be placed by highly skilled workers, since the strength and surface texture are greatly affected by the skill of the workmen.

Experience shows that the best condition for shotcrete placement is through less than about 100 ft of hose. However, as much as 500 ft of hose may be used. The nozzle pressure should be from 25 to 60 psi. For rough or heavy work, 50 or 60 psi are required. The pressure may be increased to 75 psi on high lifts, or for long hose to prevent clogging.

REINFORCING STEEL

Plain concrete has practically no tensile strength, while it has significant compressive strength. Thus, plain concrete is extremely uneconomical in beams. Use of steel bars in the tension part of a beam's cross section gives to the concrete the tensile strength it does not have.

Steel is also used to take compression, in beams as well as in columns. This permits the cross section to be made smaller, since steel has a higher allowable stress. Steel is also used to control strains due to temperature and shrinkage and to distribute loads to the concrete, since some tension is likely to occur from these strains. Distribution steel is usually put into the structure perpendicular to the main steel. Its purpose is to insure that a local stress will be resisted by the main steel in a larger portion of the structure.

Steel is also used as placement steel; that is, it serves to tie reinforcing bars together so that they may be placed easily. In recent years, steel is used in prestressed concrete for a completely different function. Usually in the form of wires, it is used to put an initial compressive stress into the structure to counteract the tensile stresses due to design loads.

5-17. Types of Reinforcing. Most reinforcing is in the form of bars or rods. The bars may be either smooth or deformed. When stress is induced in a reinforced-concrete member, it is transmitted to the steel by the bond stress between concrete and steel. Deformed bars (steel with raised patterns), naturally, can develop a higher bond stress without slipping than smooth bars. In current practice, it is customary to use only deformed bars, except for the ¼-in. size, which cannot be conveniently deformed. Bar sizes range from ¼ to 1½ in.

Bars in this country were originally plain round or square; later twisted square bars were introduced. In recent years, these bars have been completely replaced by round deformed bars with closely spaced deformations. (Use of twisted squares was discontinued because of the small angle the bearing faces made with the axis of the bar.)

The new deformed reinforcing bars conform to American Society for Testing Materials Specification A305. This specification accurately describes the size, position, and spacing of the projections the bar must have to be considered deformed. The deformation must be spaced uniformly along the length of the bar at a distance not exceeding seven-tenths the nominal size of the bar, with the deformations on opposite sides similar in size and shape and placed so that the included angle with respect to the longitudinal axis is not less than 45°. Where the included angle is between 45 and 70°, the deformations must alternately reverse in direction on each side, or those on one side reverse from those on the opposite side. The length of the deformation must be such that the space between extreme ends of deformations on opposite sides of the bar does not exceed 12½% of the nominal perimeter. The average height of deformation varies slightly, being at least 4% for bars ½ in. and smaller, 4½% for ⅝ in., and 5% for ¾ in. and larger.

Deformed bars are numbered in eighths, from No. 3 to No. 11; e.g., a No. 5 bar designates a bar ⅝ in. diameter. Numbers 9, 10, 11 replace the bars formerly known as 1-in.-square, 1⅛-in.-square, and 1¼-in.-square, respectively. They have the same area and weight as the square bars. Plain round bars are made from numbers 2 to 11, inclusive.

Advantages of the deformed bars may be summarized as follows:

1. Greatly improved bond resistance, permitting safe working stresses of 10% of the ultimate concrete stress.

2. The equivalent of "special anchorage" within the meaning of the American Concrete Institute Building Code Requirements for Reinforced Concrete, permitting higher values of diagonal tension.

3. Accurate crack control. Evenly spaced hairline cracks are formed, instead of widely spaced large cracks.

4. Continuous bonding along the bar.

Reinforcement may also be used in the form of wire fabric. It is convenient and economical for slabs, pipes, and conduits.

Rust on reinforcing is not undesirable, because it makes the surface rougher. However, if the rust is of a loose or scaly nature, it should be cleaned off with hydrochloric acid solution consisting of 3 parts acid to 1 part water and then washed with running water. Bars should never be oiled or painted, since this impairs bond.

Reinforcing bars are usually specified as structural grade, intermediate grade, or hard grade, depending on the yield point of the steel. Intermediate-grade new-billet steel is the most common grade used; it is easy to cut and bend. Hard-grade steel bars or rerolled rail steel may be used to advantage in columns or where no bends are required.

5-18. Wire-fabric Reinforcement. This material is used for floors, roof, walls, vaults, etc. Wire fabric is made of cold-drawn steel wires crossing generally at right angles and secured at the intersections. The heavy wires run lengthwise and are called carrying wires. The transverse wires are called distributing or tie wires.

A distinct advantage of wire fabric is that the spacing between the steel is kept uniform.

There are several different types of wire reinforcement:

1. *Welded-wire Fabric.* This is made up of heavy longitudinal wires held together by transverse wires that cross the longitudinal wires at right angles and are welded to them at the intersections. The longitudinal wires are spaced from 2 to 16 in. in ½-in. increments. Transverse wires are spaced from 1 to 18 in. in 1-in. intervals.

2. *Triangle-mesh Wire Fabric.* In this fabric, the longitudinal wires, which are single or stranded, are connected by transverse wires woven to the longitudinal wires to form triangles.

3. *Unit Wire Fabric.* This is a rectangular mesh secured at the intersections by wires.

4. *Lock-woven Steel Fabric.* This fabric is a rectangular mesh woven together by the transverse wires. The longitudinal wires have an ultimate strength of 180,000 psi with an elastic limit of 125,000 psi.

5. *Expanded Metal.* This is made by slitting a sheet of soft metal and then expanding the metal in a direction normal to the axis of the sheet.

5-19. Bending and Placing Reinforcement. In general, bends are required for heavy beam and girder rods; vertical reinforcing rods of columns at or near floor level, where columns change size; stirrups or column hoops; slab reinforcement; and rods or wire that form spiral column reinforcement.

Care must be taken that the bars are bent accurately and that the steel is not injured during the operation.

In a lapped splice in slabs, beams, and girders, bars should overlap 24 bar diameters and at least 12 in.

All reinforcing bars should be wired or otherwise secured in place. Care must be exerted not to disturb or loosen the reinforcement before or during the placing of the concrete. Column, beam, and girder reinforcement are frequently assembled in a frame and then put into the form. Clear distance between parallel bars, except in columns, should not be less than the nominal diameter of the bars, 1⅓ times the maximum size of coarse aggregate, or 1 in.

5-20. Supports for Reinforcement. Many ingenious devices have been devised to support reinforcing bars in the forms. There are beam spacers that not only support the bar above the form, but also space the bars the proper distance. Small metal devices called chairs are used to provide the proper clearance. Some chairs are also designed to lock the bar in place as well.

JOINTS IN CONCRETE

Joints established between two successive concrete pours are termed construction joints. In long sections, expansion joints are provided to relieve compressive stresses that would otherwise result from a temperature rise. Contraction joints are provided to permit the concrete to contract under a drop in temperature, or to permit shrinkage without resulting tension stresses.

5-21. Construction Joints. The procedure for bonding new concrete to the old concrete is discussed in Art. 5-10. However, no matter how much the old concrete surface is roughened and cleaned, the bond between new concrete and old concrete cannot be so strong as the bond between concretes that have hardened at the same time. The construction joint, therefore, is a plane of weakness. It does not affect the compressive strength, but the shear and tensile strength across the joint are markedly reduced. Since the tensile strength of concrete is assumed nil, even where no construction joint exists, the only thing of concern is the shear.

Construction joints, therefore, should be located at sections of minimum shear. These sections will usually be at the center of beams and slabs where the bending moment is highest. They should also be located where it is most convenient to stop work. The construction joint is usually keyed to give the joint some shearing strength.

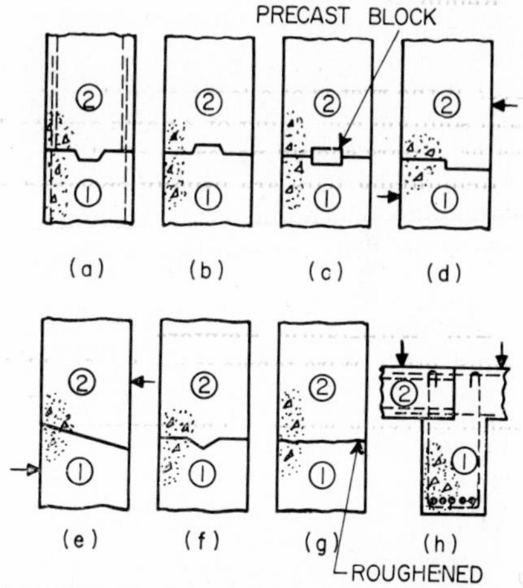

FIG. 5-1. Types of joints in concrete construction: (*a*) dropped key; (*b*) raised key; (*c*) key formed with block; (*d*) stepped joint; (*e*) sloping joint; (*f*) V key; (*g*) roughened-surface joint; (*h*) floor-to-beam connection.

If the floor area is small, it will be possible to concrete an entire floor with one pour. When more than one pour is necessary, the vertical joints are usually located in the center of the span. Horizontal joints usually are provided between columns and floor. The entire floor system, including slabs, beams, and girders, is concreted in one pour, the columns in another.

Various types of construction joints are shown in Fig. 5-1. The numbers on each section refer to the sequence of pours.

If the joint is horizontal, as in Fig. 5-1*a*, water may be trapped in the joint. If the joint is vertical, it is easily formed by nailing a wood strip to the inside of the forms. A raised key, as in Fig. 5-1*b*, makes formwork difficult.

In the joint in Fig. 5-1*c*, the key is made by setting precast concrete blocks into the concrete at intermittent intervals. The key in Fig. 5-1*d* is good if the shear acts as shown. The key in Fig. 5-1*e* theoretically is better but is more difficult to form.

The V-shaped key in Fig. 5-1*f* can be made by hand in the wet concrete.

In Fig. 5-1*g*, the key is eliminated, reliance being placed on the roughened surface.

This key may be used only if the shears are small and there are large compressive forces across the joint.

In Fig. 5-1*h* is a possible arrangement whereby the joint is located at the beam. Even though there is high shear across the joint, it cannot fail because it is supported by the beam. (C. W. Dunham, "Theory and Practice of Reinforced Concrete," 3d ed., McGraw-Hill Book Company, Inc., New York, 1953.)

5-22. Expansion and Contraction Joints. Expansion or contraction joints should be located at places where the concrete is likely to crack because of temperature changes or shrinkage. The joints should be located where there are changes in thickness and offsets. Ordinarily, joints should be spaced 30 ft c to c in exposed structures, such as retaining walls.

In expansion joints, there is usually a filler that separates the two pours of concrete. This filler should be a compressible substance like corkboard or premolded mastic. The filler must have such properties that it will not be squeezed out of the joint, will not slump when heated by the sun, and will not stain the surface of the concrete.

To make the joint waterproof, the joint must be sealed. Copper flashing may be used. It is folded into the joint so that the joint may open without rupturing the metal. The flashing must be strong enough to hold its position when the concrete is poured.

To avoid unsightly cracks due to shrinkage, a dummy-type contraction joint is frequently used. This is simply an indentation in the concrete. When contraction takes place, a crack occurs at this deliberately made plane of weakness. In this way, the crack is made to occur at an inconspicuous place. A joint may serve as a contraction joint or an expansion joint.

ADMIXTURES FOR CONCRETE

An admixture is defined in ASTM Specification C125 as "a material other than water, aggregates and portland cement (including air-entraining portland cement and portland blast-furnace slag cement), that is used as an ingredient of concrete and is added to the batch immediately before or during its mixing." Admixtures are added to concrete to modify the properties of the concrete so as to make it more suitable for a specific kind of work. Some of the objectives in using admixtures are as follows (*Journal of the American Concrete Institute*, October, 1954):

1. Improvement of workability.
2. Acceleration of the rate of strength development at early ages.
3. Retardation of initial stiffening or too rapid set.
4. Retardation or reduction of heat evolution.
5. Reduction in bleeding.
6. Increase in durability or in resistance to special conditions of exposure.
7. Control of alkali-aggregate expansion.
8. Decrease in capillary flow of water.
9. Decrease in permeability to liquids.
10. Production of cellular concrete.
11. In grout mixtures, improvement of penetration and pumpability and reduction of segregation.
12. Prevention of settlement or creation of slight expansion in concrete and mortar used for filling block-outs or other openings in concrete structures and in grout for seating machinery, columns, and girders.
13. Increase in bond to steel reinforcement.

The above objectives may sometimes also be accomplished by varying the cement or the proportions of the mix. Many admixtures will affect more than one property.

Admixtures may be classified as accelerators, retarders, air-entraining agents, gas-forming agents, cementitious materials, pozzolans, alkali-aggregate expansion inhibiters, dampproofing and permeability-reducing agents, workability agents, grouting agents, and miscellaneous. Commercial admixtures usually consist of a mixture of several types.

5-23. Accelerators. Accelerators are introduced in the concrete to increase the rate of early-strength development. They are used for concrete work where early removal of the forms is desirable, or it is desired to reduce the period of curing or of protection, as in winter concreting. High-early-strength cement may be used instead of an admixture.

Some accelerators are calcium chloride, soluble carbonates, silicates and fluosilicates, aluminous cements, and some organic compounds like triethanolamine.

Calcium chloride is the most widely used accelerator. It can be used safely in amounts up to 2 % of the weight of portland cement. The increase in strength obtained with 2 % calcium chloride reaches its maximum in 1 to 3 days and thereafter decreases.

Calcium chloride slightly increases the workability of the fresh concrete and reduces bleeding. It also increases heat development and expansion under moist curing and shrinkage but reduces moisture loss under drying conditions. It increases aggregate-alkali expansion, but the latter is effectively controlled by using a pozzolan or a low-alkali cement with the chloride. It does not cause corrosion of embedded steel, and it increases the resistance of the concrete to erosive and abrasive action.

Calcium chloride may be added dry or in solution. The usual solution contains 1 lb of calcium chloride per qt of water. The chloride is always added to the water and not vice versa. If added dry, care must be taken to see that the chloride is not caked.

5-24. Retarders. Retarders are used to slow the hardening of the concrete. They are often used in hot-weather concreting to counter the tendency to false set and also to enable the concrete to be placed in difficult positions.

These admixtures are sometimes placed on the inside of forms so that the setting of the outside surface of mortar is retarded. This permits the outside layer to be brushed away, to expose the aggregate, thus producing textural effects.

Retarders are especially used in grouting operations over a prolonged period of time, where the grout must be pumped a long distance and where hot-water flows are encountered.

The most commonly used retarders are starches or cellulose products, sugars and acids, or salts of acids containing one or more hydroxyl groups. They are added in very small amounts.

5-25. Air-entraining Agents. Incorporation of a small amount of air uniformly distributed in the form of minute bubbles in the concrete materially aids the ability of concrete to withstand frost action. Beside the increased durability, air-entrained concrete is considerably more plastic and workable than ordinary concrete. Tendencies toward segregation, bleeding, and water gain are reduced. The occurrence of planes of laitance (a low-strength layer of fine particles) at the top of vertical lifts is lessened.

Some air-entraining admixtures now in use are natural wood resins, fats, various sulfonated compounds, and oils. Air-entraining portland cement may also be used to entrain air in the concrete.

The strength of concrete is reduced in an amount proportional to the air entrained. Reduction in strength will rarely exceed 15 % for compressive strength and 10 % for flexural strength. The loss is more than balanced in many cases by the gain in durability. This pertains only to concretes where the air entrained is not more than 7 %.

Entrained air is used to good effect in the manufacture of concrete block; air entrainment permits greater compaction and a denser block. Appearance of the block is improved, and a closer reproduction of the contours of the mold is obtained. Also, breakage of green block is reduced.

Air entrainment is also used to make lightweight concrete. (Lightweight aggregates are also used for this purpose.) A cellular concrete is one in which all or part of the aggregate is replaced by air or gas.

Cellular concretes may be classified as gas concretes and foam concretes. They are made by using an admixture. Air may be entrained in amounts from 30 to 60 % by volume for structural concrete and 70 to 85 % for insulation. Entraining agents that are commonly used in foam concretes are sodium laurel sulfate, alkyl aryl sulfonate, certain soaps, resins, and other agents. In another process, the foam is produced by the addition of the same foaming agents used to combat gasoline fires, such as hydrolyzed waste protein.

There is a large variation of properties for foam concretes. They may weigh as little as 20 and as much as 110 lb per cu ft. The lightest ones usually possess only enough strength to retain their shape during handling and are used for acoustic or thermal insulation. The heavier types have sufficient strength to be used in structural elements.

"No-fines" concrete is one in which 20 to 30 % entrained air replaces the sand. Pea gravel is used as the coarse aggregate. The weight of this concrete is from 105 to 118 lb per cu ft, and its compressive strength is from 200 to 1,000 psi.

5-26. Gas-forming Agents. Gas-forming agents are used to counteract shrinkage and bleeding in the plastic concrete. Aluminum powder is a very common gas-forming agent. It reacts with the hydroxides present in the hydrating cement to produce minute bubbles of hydrogen.

The hydrogen bubbles cause a slight expansion in the plastic concrete, thus reducing shrinkage. This expansion increases bond with the reinforcing steel and improves the effectiveness of grout in filling joints. Very small quantities of aluminum powder are used (about 1 teaspoonful per sack of cement). The aluminum powder is generally premixed with a fine sand or pozzolan.

Lightweight concretes may be produced by using much larger quantities of aluminum powder (about $\frac{1}{4}$ lb per bag of cement). In some cases, additional alkali, such as sodium hydroxide or trisodium phosphate, is added to accelerate the reaction.

Zinc and magnesium powder will also entrain hydrogen in the concrete mass. Hydrogen peroxide and bleaching powder entrain oxygen. Other agents entrain chlorine and nitrogen.

5-27. Cementitious Materials as Admixtures. This group includes natural cements, hydraulic lime, and slag cement. They may be substituted for 10 to 25 % by weight of the portland cement. The effect is to increase workability, especially in harsh mixes, and to decrease bleeding, segregation, and heat of hydration. Strength is also reduced initially.

5-28. Pozzolanic Materials. A pozzolan is defined in ASTM Specification C129 as a "siliceous or siliceous and aluminous material, which in itself possesses little or no cementitious value but will, in finely divided form and in the presence of moisture, chemically react with calcium hydroxide at ordinary temperatures to form compounds possessing cementitious properties." The pozzolanic material is substituted for part of the portland cement. Use of pozzolanic material reduces permeability and increases resistance to sulfates and the corrosive action of sea water. These effects are greater for lean mixes than for rich mixes.

Pozzolans may also be added to instead of being substituted for the cement. The effects are similar but are most marked when the pozzolan is added to a mix originally deficient in fines.

Examples of pozzolans are fly ash, volcanic ash, heat-treated diatomaceous earths, and either heat-treated or raw shales or clays.

5-29. Alkali-aggregate Expansion Inhibitors. Alkali-aggregate expansion is a phenomenon believed to result from the interaction of the alkalies in portland cement and siliceous types of aggregates. This reaction produces expansion and cracking of the concrete. One remedy is to use portland cement with a low alkali content (0.60 % or less Na_2O). Many, but not all, pozzolans have the ability to reduce alkali-aggregate expansion.

Pozzolans that counteract alkali-aggregate expansion may be divided into three categories:

1. "Amorphous" siliceous or siliceous and aluminous substances. In this category are some opals and highly opaline rocks, certain volcanic glasses, diatomaceous earth, calcined clays of the kaolinite type, and some fly ashes.

2. Calcined clays of the montmorillonite type. These clays must not contain calcium as the exchangeable action, and they must be calcined in the 1000 to 1800°F range, but not at a temperature sufficiently high to destroy the crystalline structure.

3. Combinations of the above two. This category includes siliceous shales and pumicites.

The amount of pozzolan used usually ranges from 20 to 35 % by weight of the cement, but certain diatomaceous earths and opaline cherts are effective in amounts less than 15 % by weight of cement.

Air-entraining admixtures and aluminum powder may also reduce alkali-aggregate expansion. Other admixtures that are beneficial in this respect are lithium salts and certain protein air-entraining admixtures.

5-30. Dampproofing and Permeability-reducing Agents. (See also Sec. 14.) Many commercial admixtures employ calcium chloride as a waterproofing admixture, but it has very little value in this respect. Calcium chloride does accelerate the setting of the concrete and so reduces the period of time for which curing is necessary.

Admixtures that are also used are those classified as "soaps." These are inorganic salts of fatty acids, usually calcium or ammonium stearate or oleate. In commercial preparations, the soap content is 20 % or less, the remainder consisting of lime or calcium chloride. Soaps also increase the workability of the plastic concrete.

The action of butyl stearate is similar to that of soaps. Unlike the soaps, it does not have a frothing action and may therefore be used in greater quantity than soaps. It is usually added as an emulsion containing 1 % butyl stearate by weight of cement. Its effect on concrete strength is negligible if added in this amount.

Addition of a finely divided material will reduce the permeability of concrete deficient in fines. But it may have the opposite effect on a properly graded concrete. The fine material may be inert or reactive, such as a pozzolan.

Heavy mineral oil is also used to make concrete water-repellent. The oil should not contain vegetable or mineral components and should have a viscosity of about SAE 60. Asphalt cutback oils and asphalt emulsions have also been tried.

Air-entraining agents and workability agents may be classified as permeability-reducing agents since they facilitate manufacture of a denser and more uniform concrete.

Miscellaneous materials that are used as permeability reducing agents are:

1. Barium sulfate, calcium and magnesium silicates, and fatty acid.
2. Finely ground silica and naphthalene.
3. Colloidal silica and a fluosilicate.
4. Petroleum jelly and lime.
5. Cellulose materials and wax in an ammoniacal copper solution.
6. Silica, lime, and alum.
7. Coal tar cut with benzene.
8. Sodium silicate, together with an organic nitrogenous material.

5-31. Workability Agents. The workability of the mix (generally measured by the slump) will affect the cost of concrete construction. Increased workability is essential if the concrete is harsh (because of aggregate characteristics, or grading) when the concrete must be placed around closely spaced reinforcement, or when the concrete is placed by pumping or by tremie pipe.

Addition of fine material to a mix deficient in fines will generally increase workability of the mix. Also, certain organic compounds will increase the slump for a particular water content, as will air entrainment.

5-32. Grouting Agents. Accelerators are used to hasten the set when grout is used in a plugging operation. Calcium chloride or triethanolamine may be used.

Retarders are used to aid the pumpability of a grout. Mucic acid and several patented chemicals are commonly used as retarders.

Gas-forming agents are used to expand the grout so that it thoroughly fills a confined area, like a contraction joint.

Workability agents, such as fly ash, bentonite, pumicite, and diatomaceous earth, are sometimes added to increase pumpability.

5-33. Expanding Cements. These are not admixtures but are similar to them in their action. They are used to offset shrinkage, which is undesirable in concrete. A nonshrinking cement is one that does not shrink, and expanding cement is one that expands on drying.

Expanding cements may be made by the addition of a sulfoaluminous cement made by burning a mixture of gypsum, bauxite, and limestone. Powdered iron and an oxidizing agent may also be added to portland cement to make a nonshrinking concrete.

REINFORCED-CONCRETE BEAMS AND SLABS

5-34. Rectangular Beams (Elastic Design). The following assumptions are made in elastic analysis:

1. Plane sections remain plane after bending and perpendicular to the longitudinal fibers.

2. The material obeys Hooke's law: $f = E\epsilon$ (the stress-strain curve is a straight line).

3. $E_s/E_c = n$ is constant.

4. The concrete develops no tensile stresses.

The following formulas are derived from the above assumptions (see Table 5-2):

$$\frac{nf_c}{f_s} = \frac{k}{1 - k} \tag{5-2}$$

Design equation—balanced design:

$$k = \frac{1}{1 + f_s/nf_c} \tag{5-3}$$

Review equation:

$$k = \sqrt{2np + (np)^2} - np \tag{5-4}$$

$$j = 1 - \frac{k}{3} = \frac{3 - k}{3} \tag{5-5}$$

$$M_c = \tfrac{1}{2}f_c kjbd^2 = K_c bd^2 \tag{5-6}$$

where $K_c = \tfrac{1}{2}f_c kj$

$$M_s = f_s A_s jd = f_s pjbd^2 = K_s bd^2 \tag{5-7}$$

where $K_s = f_s pj$

5-35. Transformed Section. This is a useful concept in analysis of reinforced-concrete sections by elastic design. Since there is no slip between the steel and the concrete, the stress in the steel is related to the stress in the concrete at any point, as given

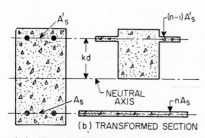

(a) ACTUAL SECTION

FIG. 5-2. Transformed section for a concrete beam substitutes an equivalent area of concrete for reinforcing bars.

by the equation $f_s = nf_c$. This suggests that the steel area may be replaced by an equivalent concrete area n times as large, as shown in Fig. 5-2.

With this equivalent area, the section may be analyzed like a homogeneous section; that is, the stress in the extreme fibers may be computed from $f = Mc/I$.

5-36. Balanced Design. This is a design in which concrete and steel are simultaneously stressed to the allowable maximum. It is not necessarily the most economical design.

When a beam is under-reinforced, the steel is critical; that is, the capacity of the steel determines the maximum moment that the beam will carry. If the beam were loaded to capacity, the steel would be stressed to the maximum allowable, but not the concrete.

When a beam is over-reinforced, the concrete is critical. Over-reinforced beams are rare in design, because they seldom are economical and because failures may occur without warning.

A beam with rectangular cross section is designed as follows:

1. From Eq. (5-3) or a table based on it, k is determined.   From k and allowable stresses, j and K are determined [Eqs. (5-5) and (5-6); they may also be taken from a design table].

2. From Eq. (5-6), bd^2 is determined.   When b and d are selected, the beam cross section is determined (see Art. 5-52).   This gives the d for balanced design, since Eq. (5-3) is for balanced design.

Table 5-2. Standard Symbols

(American Concrete Institute Building Code Requirements for Reinforced Concrete)

A_s = effective cross-sectional area of metal reinforcement in tension in beams or compression in columns

A_v = total area of web reinforcement in tension within a distance of s or the total area of all bars bent up in any one plane

b = width of rectangular beam or width of flange of T beam

b' = width of stem of T beam

C = total compressive force in concrete

C' = total compressive stress in reinforcement

d = depth from compressive surface of beam or slab to center of longitudinal tension reinforcement

d' = depth from compressive surface of beam or slab to center of compressive reinforcement

E_c = modulus of elasticity of concrete in compression

E_s = modulus of elasticity of steel in tension = 30,000,000 psi

f_c = compressive unit stress in extreme fiber of concrete

f'_c = ultimate compressive strength of concrete at age of 28 days, based on tests of 6 × 12-in. or 8 × 16-in. cylinders made and tested in accordance with the ASTM Standard Methods of Making and Storing Specimens of Concrete in the Field and the Tentative Methods of Making Compressive Tests of Concrete

f_s = tensile unit stress in longitudinal reinforcement

f'_s = compressive unit stress in longitudinal reinforcement

f_v = tensile unit stress in web reinforcement

I = moment of inertia of a section about the neutral axis for bending

j = ratio of lever arm of resisting couple to depth d

$jd = d - \bar{z}$ = arm of resisting couple

k = ratio of depth of neutral axis to depth d

L = span length of beam or slab

M = bending moment or moment of resistance in general

$n = E_s/E_c$ = ratio of modulus of elasticity of steel to that of concrete

Σ_o = sum of perimeters of bars in one set

p = ratio of effective area of tension reinforcement to effective area of concrete in beams
  = A_s/bd

p' = ratio of effective area of compressive reinforcement to effective area of concrete in beams = A'_s/bd

s = spacing of web members, measured at the plane of the lower reinforcement and in the direction of the longitudinal axis of the beam

t = thickness of flange of T beam

T = total tensile stress in longitudinal reinforcement

u = bond unit stress

v = shearing unit stress

w = uniformly distributed load per unit length of beam or unit area of slab

$\bar{z}$ = depth from compression surface of beam or slab to resultant of compressive forces

3. The steel area A_s is determined from Eq. (5-7).   From this formula, we see that A_s could have been reduced by increasing the depth d.   This results in under-reinforcing and is usually economical, since steel is saved.   The balanced-design value for j may still be used, since j changes only slightly with changes in d.   Min. $A_s = 0.005bd$.

However, the depth of the beam is usually fixed, especially for girders.   It will usually be found that the permissible depth is less than the balanced-design depth, and the beam is then over-reinforced.   Over-reinforced beams are uneconomical, because a relatively great amount of tension steel is required to increase the moment capacity of the over-reinforced beam.   This difficulty is surmounted by using compression steel.

5-37. One-way Slab. This type of slab has one span so much larger than the span in the transverse direction that it can be assumed to be supported only on its long sides. It may be designed or analyzed the same way as a beam spanning the short way. A 1-ft width is usually designed and the rest of the slab made similar (see also Art. 5-53). In addition to the main steel which runs in the short direction, tempera- ture or distribution steel is placed in the long direction. The purpose of this steel is to take temperature stresses and to distribute concentrated loads that act on the slab. The temperature steel is always placed so as to keep the main steel as close as possible to the tension face of the concrete. Minimum steel area $A_s = 0.0025bd$ for structural, intermediate, and hard-grade and rail reinforcing steel, and $0.002\ bd$ for steel with minimum yield point of 56,000 psi.

5-38. Shear and Bond. The maximum unit shear stress acting on a cross section with shear V is given by

$$v_{\max} = \frac{V}{bjd} \tag{5-8}$$

The bond stress is given by

$$u = \frac{V}{\Sigma_o jd} \tag{5-9}$$

where Σ_o is the sum of the bar perimeters. This formula applies only to tensile reinforcement. The critical section for bond is at the section of maximum shear, where the steel is still in the tension side of the section.

Anchorage is the distance that a bar must be embedded in order for it to develop a certain stress. It is given by

$$L = \frac{f_s a}{4u} \tag{5-10}$$

where a is the side of a square bar or the diameter of a round bar. It is customary to run bars 10 diameters past the section where they are no longer required for stress.

Shear is dangerous in a concrete beam because it is accompanied by diagonal ten- sion. Stirrups or bent-up bars are used to reinforce a beam for diagonal tension.

In designing for shear, part is assumed taken by the concrete (V_c) and part by the steel (V'), so that the total shear $V = V_c + V'$ (see American Concrete Institute Building Code Requirements for Reinforced Concrete). If A_v is the cross-sectional area of the legs of a stirrup, f_v the allowable tensile stress of the steel, and s the stirrup spacing, the stress in vertical stirrups is given by

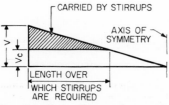

$$A_v f_v = \frac{V's}{jd} \tag{5-11}$$

For stirrups inclined at an angle α:

$$A_v f_v = \frac{V's}{jd(\sin \alpha + \cos \alpha)} \tag{5-12}$$

For stirrups inclined at 45°:

$$A_v f_v = \frac{0.707 V's}{jd} \tag{5-13}$$

FIG. 5-3. Shear diagram for a uni- formly loaded beam, with proportion of the shear carried by the concrete indicated by V_c. The shaded area must be carried by steel stirrups.

These formulas, however, are subject to limitations. The ACI Building Code (Art. 806) states that every potential 45° crack shall be crossed by at least one line of reinforcement.

From Eqs. (5-11) to (5-13), the spacing of stirrups may be determined. The first step is to draw a shear diagram as shown in Fig. 5-3. Then, shear carried by the con- crete V_c is found from $V_c = v_c bjd$, where v_c is the allowable unit shear stress in con- crete. The first stirrup is usually placed 2 in. from the face of the support.

There are many different devices and tables devised for determining stirrup size and spacing to carry the shear in excess of V_c.   The simplest is to compute the spacing at several points from Eqs. (5-11) to (5-13), and use a constant spacing between these points.   Thus, if the shear is changing rapidly, the stirrup spacing is changed several times.

Other methods are not practical except in very long beams, because they save only one or two stirrups and the spacing is constantly changed.   One of these other methods is to divide the shear diagram into $2N$ equal areas, where N is the number of stirrups needed, and to place a stirrup at each odd boundary.   The number of stirrups needed may be obtained by dividing the area of the shear diagram above V_c by the area of one stirrup A_v multiplied by the allowable stress f_v.   (See also Sutherland and Reese, "Reinforced Concrete Design," John Wiley & Sons, Inc., New York.)

This procedure works only for linearly varying shear.   Furthermore, the maximum spacing is fixed by the requirement that every potential crack be crossed by at least one line of reinforcement, as shown in Fig. 5-4.

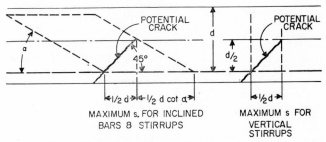

FIG. 5-4. Side view of a concrete beam showing reinforcing steel bent up to cross potential cracks (*left*) and vertical stirrups spaced to cross 45° cracks (*right*).

Stirrups are usually placed in the middle part of a beam even when they are not needed for diagonal tension.   They serve also as supports for the longitudinal steel. The spacing of such stirrups is usually 18 in.   Two bars are always placed in the top of the beam to support the stirrups.   At the beam supports, these bars serve as tension reinforcement; near the center, they are compression reinforcement but are usually not taken into account in stress computations.   If these two support bars are very heavy, it may be economical to cut them off and substitute lighter bars in the middle of the beam, as supports for the stirrups.

Stirrups may be used in conjunction with bent-up bars as web reinforcement.   In beams and girders, for instance, the positive reinforcement is often bent up so that it acts as tension reinforcement at the supports.   In this case, it is good practice to bend these bars up as close as possible to the supports where the shear is greatest.   This cuts down the number of stirrups that are necessary.

In some places, straight bars are used wherever possible because of the added expense incurred when bars are bent.   While material is usually saved when bent bars are used, the added cost of labor for bending and placing bent bars usually offsets this gain.

Stirrups must always be checked for anchorage.   If we assume the concrete below the neutral axis to be cracked, the stirrups, since they are in tension, are held in place by the bond developed with the concrete above the neutral axis and by the force developed in hooks.   The hooks are assumed to develop a force equal to 10,000 lb.

It is usual to use No. 3 bars as stirrups, but if the length of the stirrup is not sufficient for anchorage, larger bars or W stirrups may be used.

5-39. Bent-up Bars, Cutoff Points, and Other Placing Details. It is the usual practice to cut off bars or bend them when they are no longer needed.   Steel that is required in the center of the span is bent up so as to serve as tensile reinforcement at the support.   American Concrete Institute Building Code Requirements for Reinforced Concrete, however, specify that at least one-fourth of the bottom steel should not be bent up but should be carried into the support. Two bottom bars (see Fig. 5-4) would have to be carried into the support anyway to serve as supports for the stirrups. These two bars may be considered as compression reinforcement, if required.

The theoretical points where bars are cut off or bent up may be determined by drawing a curve of maximum moments. The curve is obtained by adding the moment due to dead load to the moment resulting from a loading of live load that will produce the maximum. If ACI moment coefficients are used, the curves of maximum moments are approximated by parabolas, one for positive moment and one for negative moment. The cutoff points may then be determined graphically, as shown in Fig. 5-5.

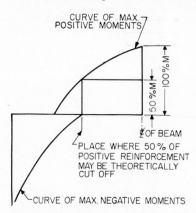

Fig. 5-5. Bending-moment diagram for half a beam, with resisting moments of the steel reinforcing indicated. At the intersection of resisting moments and moments due to load, the steel no longer is needed.

Bars that are cut off must be extended at least 10 diameters beyond the theoretical cutoff point, while bars may be bent up at the theoretical cutoff point. The top steel, at the supports, may be provided by bars bent up from the center of the span, bars bent up from the center of the adjacent span and straight bars, or by any combination of these bars.

5-40. Ultimate-strength Design of Beams. This article is concerned only with the ultimate strength of a reinforced-concrete beam based on its cross section. In statically indeterminate structures, the forces on a cross section may be found by a means of the theory of elastic displacements (see Sec. 3).

Arguments for ultimate design of reinforced concrete include:

1. The straight-line theory does not conform to experimental observations.

2. Ultimate design permits the use of different safety factors for live and dead loads —a more rational procedure.

3. Conventional column design is a modified ultimate design. Therefore, the design of members subject to both thrust and moment by elastic theory contains an inconsistency.

4. A better evaluation of the critical moment-thrust ratio for members subject to combined flexure and axial load may be found by ultimate-design procedure.

5. The design of prestressed concrete requires ultimate design.

Assumptions on which ultimate design is based are the same as in elastic design, except that the stress-strain relationship for concrete is not linear at ultimate strength (Fig. 5-6). The diagram of compressive-stress distribution of concrete may be assumed to be a rectangle, parabola, trapezoid, or any other shape that results in ultimate strength that agrees with tests (Fig. 5-7). The maximum fiber stress of concrete is assumed not to exceed $0.85f'_c$, and the steel stress not to exceed the yield point.

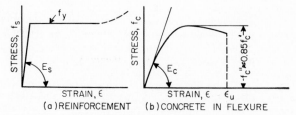

Fig. 5-6. Stress-strain diagrams for reinforcing steel and concrete in reinforced-concrete beams. Modulus of elasticity of steel E_s is constant up to the yield point, whereas E_c varies.

Let U = ultimate strength, B = effect of basic load consisting of dead load plus volume change (shrinkage, temperature), L = live load plus impact, W = wind load, E = earthquake forces, and $K = 2$ (for columns and members subject to combined

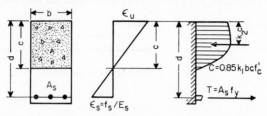

Fig. 5-7. Ultimate-load conditions for the cross section of a reinforced-concrete beam— strain variation is assumed linear, but the compressive stresses are nearly uniform across the top portion of the section, because of plastic flow.

bending and axial loads) and 1.8 (for beams and girders subject to flexure only). Members should be proportioned to carry the critical loads as follows:

Wind and earthquake not a factor.

$$U = 1.2B + 2.4L \tag{5-14}$$
$$U = K(B + L) \tag{5-15}$$

Wind a factor. If earthquake is considered, substitute E for W.

$$U = 1.2B + 2.4L + 0.6W \tag{5-16}$$
$$U = 1.2B + 0.6L + 2.4W \tag{5-17}$$

$$U = K\left(B + L + \frac{W}{2}\right) \tag{5-18}$$

$$U = K\left(B + \frac{L}{2} + W\right) \tag{5-19}$$

See ACI-ASCE Committee 327 Report, "Ultimate Strength Design," *Journal of the American Concrete Institute*, January, 1956, p. 505.

5-41. Ultimate-strength Design of Rectangular Beams with Tensile Reinforcement Only. For under-reinforced beams, where strength is limited by tension in the steel, the bending moment at ultimate strength is

$$M_u = A_s f_y d \left(1 - \frac{k_2}{k_1} \frac{p f_y}{0.85 f'_c}\right) \tag{5-20}$$

where A_s = area of tension reinforcement
f_y = yield point stress of steel, or 60,000 psi (whichever is lower)
k_2 = ratio of distance between extreme fiber and resultant of compressive stresses and distance between extreme fiber and neutral axis
k_1 = ratio of average compressive stress to $0.85f'_c$
p, f'_c, b, d = usual symbols (see Table 5-2, page 5-17)
k_2/k_1 depends on the assumed stress-strain relation. It is $\frac{1}{2}$ for rectangular stress distribution, and $\frac{2}{3}$ for a triangular one. The computed M_u should not be greater than

$$M_u \leq A_s f_y d \left(1 - \frac{0.59 p f_y}{f'_c}\right) \tag{5-21}$$

or
$$M_u \leq f'_c b d^2 q(1 - 0.59q) \tag{5-22}$$
where $q = p f_y / f'_c$. Also,

$$p_o = \frac{0.40 f'_c}{f_y} \quad \text{or} \quad q_o = 0.40 \tag{5-23}$$

where p_o is the maximum value of p, and q_o of q, that may be used in Eq. (5-22).   (See American Concrete Institute Building Code Requirements for Reinforced Concrete.)

5-42. Rectangular Beams with Compression Reinforcement (Elastic Theory). Design formulas (see Table 5-2, page 5–17):

$$k = \frac{1}{1 + f_s/nf_c} \tag{5-24}$$

$$f'_s = f_s \frac{kd - d'}{d - kd} \tag{5-25}$$

$$f'_s = nf_c \frac{kd - d'}{d - kd} \tag{5-26}$$

$$C = C_c + C'_s = T \tag{5-27}$$

$$\frac{f_s}{f_c} = \frac{k}{2[p - p'(kd - d')/(d - kd)]} \tag{5-28}$$

Review formulas (see Table 5-2, page 5–17):

$$k = \sqrt{2n\left(p + p'\frac{d'}{d}\right) + n^2(p + p')^2} - n(p + p') \tag{5-29}$$

$$\bar{z} = \frac{(k^3d/3) + 2np'd'[k - (d'/d)]}{k^2 + 2np'[k - (d'/d)]} \tag{5-30}$$

$$jd = d - \bar{z} \tag{5-31}$$

$$M_s = Tjd = A_s f_s jd \qquad f_s = \frac{M}{A_s jd} \tag{5-32}$$

$$M_c = \tfrac{1}{2}f_s jbd^2\left[k + 2np'\left(1 - \frac{d'}{kd}\right)\right] \tag{5-33}$$

$$f_c = \frac{2M}{jbd^2\{k + 2np'[1 - (d'/kd)]\}} \tag{5-34}$$

The above formulas are too involved and are used only for the computation of tables.   Some approximate formulas, which are very useful, are

$$M_1 = C_c\left(d - \frac{kd}{3}\right) = \frac{1}{2}f_c bkd\left(d - \frac{kd}{3}\right) \tag{5-35}$$

$$M'_s = M - M_1 = 2f'_s A'_s(d - d') \tag{5-36}$$

$$A'_s = \frac{M'_s}{2f'_s(d - d')} \tag{5-37}$$

In Eqs. (5-35) and (5-37), $2f'_s$ is substituted for f'_s.   According to the American Concrete Institute Building Code Requirements for Reinforced Concrete, compression steel is assumed to act as in plastic design, the steel taking twice the elastic stress, pro yided the allowable stress in tension of steel is not exceeded.

5-43. Ultimate-strength Design of Rectangular Beams with Compressive Reinforcement.   (See Table 5-2, pege 5–17, and Art. 5-41.)

$$M_u = (A_s - A'_s)f_y d\left[1 - \frac{0.59(p - p')f_y}{f'_c}\right] + A'_s f_y(d - d') \tag{5-38}$$

where $p - p'$ should not exceed $0.40f'_c/f_y$. A'_s = area of compressive reinforcement and $p' = A'_s/bd$.

5-44. T Beams (Elastic Theory).   When the floor or roof slab is concreted integrally with the beam, the slab is usually assumed to assist the beam.   The two act together as a T beam in regions of positive moment.   When the T beam is continuous, the sections subjected to negative moment are designed as a rectangular beam, since the flange of the beam will be in tension and therefore will not be any help.

If the neutral axis is within the flange, the analysis is the same as for a rectangular beam with width b, the same as that of the flange. However, b', the width of stem, must be used in shear computations.

If the neutral axis occurs within the stem, it is customary to neglect the compression in the stem. The effect of this compression is negligible.

The formulas for T beams with stem compression neglected are as follows (see Table 5-2, page 5–17):

$$k = \frac{1}{1 + f_s/nf_c} \tag{5-39}$$

$$C = \frac{1}{2} f_c \left(1 + \frac{kd - t}{kd}\right) bt = \frac{f_c bt}{2kd} (2kd - t) = T = A_s f_s \tag{5-40}$$

$$\frac{f_s}{f_c} = \frac{bt(2kd - t)}{2A_s kd} \tag{5-41}$$

$$kd = \frac{2ndA_s + bt^2}{2nA_s + 2bt} \tag{5-42}$$

$$\bar{z} = \frac{t(3kd - 2t)}{3(2kd - t)} \tag{5-43}$$

$$jd = d - \bar{z} \tag{5-44}$$

$$M_s = Tjd = A_s f_s jd \tag{5-45}$$

$$M_c = Cjd = \frac{f_c bt(jd)}{2(kd)} (2kd - t) \tag{5-46}$$

$$f_c = \frac{f_s}{n}\left(\frac{kd}{d - kd}\right) \tag{5-47}$$

Sometimes it is necessary to take the web compression into account. The formulas and design tables may be obtained from reinforced-concrete textbooks and handbooks, such as C. W. Dunham, "Theory and Practice of Reinforced Concrete," 3d ed., McGraw-Hill Book Company, Inc., New York, 1953; Sutherland and Reese, "Reinforced Concrete Design," John Wiley & Sons, Inc., New York; "Reinforced Concrete Design Handbook," American Concrete Institute; and "Concrete Reinforcing Steel Institute Handbook."

The shearing stress of T beams is governed by the equation

$$V = \frac{V}{b'jd} \tag{5-48}$$

Two approximate formulas that save much work in T-beam design are

$$M_s = A_s f_s \left(d - \frac{t}{2}\right) \tag{5-49}$$

$$M_c = \frac{1}{2} f_c bt \left(d - \frac{t}{2}\right) \tag{5-50}$$

In the last two equations, the moment arm jd is assumed equal to $d - t/2$. This results in slightly more steel than is necessary. In using Eq. (5-48), it is customary to assume $j = \frac{7}{8}$.

It is necessary to limit b, the width of flange. The ACI Code recommends the following limitations: b shall be less than one-fourth the span length; the overhanging width of flange shall not exceed eight times the slab thickness; and the overhanging width shall not exceed one-half the clear distance between beams.

A common procedure in designing T beams is as follows:

1. Determine economical depth and select desired values of stem width b' and total depth h.

2. Check the section for shear [Eq. (5-48)].

3. Check the fiber stress f_c at supports [Eq. (5-50)]. If the allowable stress is exceeded, compression steel may be added.

4. Determine tension steel areas A_s for bending-moment requirements [Eq. (5-49)].

5. Check tension steel for bond.

6. Determine anchorage requirements.

7. Design web reinforcement.

8. Recheck with Eqs. (5-42) to (5-46).

5-45. Ultimate-strength Design of T Beams. If the flange thickness exceeds $1.30qd$, where $q = pf_y/f'_c$, use Eq. (5-22) with p computed as for a beam of width equal to the flange width. For thinner flanges, use

$$M_u = (A_s - A_{sf})f_y d \left[1 - \frac{0.59(p_w - p_f)f_y}{f'_c} \right] + A_{sf}f_y(d - 0.5t) \qquad (5-51)$$

where $A_{sf} = 0.85f'_c(b - b')t/f_y$

f_y = yield stress of steel

t = flange thickness

b = over-all width of flange

b' = width of web

$p_w = A_s/bd$; $p_f = A_{sf}/b'd$

Note that $p_w - p_f$ should not exceed $0.40f'_c/f_y$.

5-46. Torsion in Reinforced-concrete Members. Spandrel beams and beams that frame openings are examples of beams subject to torsional stress. While torsion stresses are often neglected, they may at times be quite important. The shearing unit stresses due to torsion may be computed from Eqs. (3-93), (3-96), (3-98), (3-99), and (3-100). Equal tensile stresses exist on planes bisecting the angles between the planes of maximum shear.

Torsional reinforcement may consist of spiral reinforcement inclined at 45° so as to cross potential cracks perpendicularly. The required reinforcement for a square section is given by the expression

$$\frac{A_s}{p} = \frac{1}{17f_s r_s{}^2} \left(\frac{R}{v_m} \right)^3 [3v_m{}^4 - 4v_m{}^3 t_c + t_c{}^4] \qquad (5-52)$$

where A_s = cross-sectional area of one wire

p = longitudinal pitch of the spiral

v_m = maximum shear stress

R = radius of inscribed circle

t_c = allowable tensile stress

r_s = radius of spiral

5-47. Shrinkage Stresses. Concrete usually shrinks as it drys out. The extent of this shrinkage varies with exposure and with time. Maximum shrinkage will occur in regions of very low humidity. If the concrete could be unrestrained in all ways, no stresses would result from shrinkage.

Steel bars restrain the concrete from shrinking, because of the bond between the concrete and steel. This results in compression in the bars and tension in the adjacent concrete. These stresses are related by the formula

$$\frac{f'_s}{E_s} = s - \frac{f_t}{E_c} \qquad (5-53)$$

where f'_s = compressive stress in the steel

f_t = tensile stress in the concrete

s = shrinkage, in. per in.

The above formula generally is true only at the location of the bar; but it also holds for the entire cross section if the steel bars are symmetrically placed, as in an axially loaded column.

In a beam, where the steel is not placed symmetrically, shrinkage will result in bending. Since most of the steel in a beam is placed at the bottom of the cross section and since the shrinkage causes tension in the concrete around the bars, the shrinkage will result in an increased beam deflection (Dean Peabody, Jr., "Reinforced Concrete Structures," John Wiley & Sons, Inc., New York). The state of stress resulting from shrinkage is shown in Fig. 5-8.

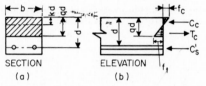

SECTION   ELEVATION
  (a)   (b)

FIG. 5-8. Shrinkage stresses are created across the section of a concrete beam because of the restraint offered by the reinforcing.

The concrete below depth qd is cracked and therefore can carry no stress. The following formulas give the state of stress in the structure:

$$f_c = \frac{2kp}{(q - 2k)q} f'_s \tag{5-54}$$

$$f_t = \frac{2(q - k)p}{(q - 2k)q} f'_s \tag{5-55}$$

$$f'_s = \frac{sE_s}{1 + [2np(1 - k)/q(q - 2k)]} \tag{5-56}$$

If the section is uncracked, $q = 1$ and $k = \frac{1}{3}$; the above formulas become

$$f_c = 2pf'_s \tag{5-57}$$
$$f_t = 4pf'_s \tag{5-58}$$

$$f'_s = \frac{sE_s}{1 + 4pn} \tag{5-59}$$

5-48. Formwork for Concrete Beams.   (See also Art. **5-52.**)   The requirements for forms are that they possess adequate strength to contain the concrete, be true to shape, and be well-braced and tight.

In designing a structure, an effort should be made to make it possible for the contractor to use the forms over again several times on the same project.   For economy of formwork, beam and slab dimensions should be chosen to enable standard lumber and plywood sizes to be used with no cutting or a minimum of cutting.

With structural-steel framing, slab forms are generally carried by the framing. For reinforced-concrete slabs and beams, forms are supported by a system of shores strong enough to carry the entire weight of the floor and adequately braced laterally and diagonally.   They should be so designed that beam sides and slab forms may be removed while the beam bottoms are still shored.   Posts can be replaced under the slab if necessary.

REINFORCED-CONCRETE COLUMNS

5-49. Axially Loaded Columns.   These are usually designed by ultimate-strength theory (ACI Building Code).   Compression members with length from three to ten times least lateral dimension are called short columns.

For spiral reinforced short columns, the ACI Code gives

$$P = 0.225f'_cA_g + f_sA_s \tag{5-60}$$

where f'_c = 28-day cylinder strength of the concrete
   A_g = gross area of section
   A_s = area of reinforcing steel

For lateral tied columns:

$$P = 0.18f'_c A_g + 0.8f_s A_s$$

The allowable load for a tied column is 80% of the allowable load for a spiral column. The explanation is as follows: As load is applied to a column, the longitudinal bars tend to buckle outward. Tests show that columns usually fail by a lateral bursting of the concrete. The concrete may be restrained by lateral ties, but spiral reinforcement is much more effective. Another reason is that tied columns fail suddenly, while spiral columns fail slowly, giving more warning. If spirals are used, the longitudinal bars must be arranged in a circle.

If the column is slender, its load capacity is less:

$$P' = P\left(1.3 - 0.03\frac{h}{d}\right) \qquad \text{when } \frac{h}{d} \geq 10 \tag{5-61}$$

where P = safe load on a column of same cross section but with $h/d < 10$
  h = unsupported length of column
  d = least dimension of column
Spiral reinforcement is determined from the following formula:

$$p' \geq 0.45(R - 1)\frac{f'_c}{f'_s} \tag{5-62}$$

where p' = ratio of volume of spiral reinforcement to volume of spiral core (out to out of spiral)
  R = ratio of gross area to core area
  f'_s = allowable yield-point stress of spiral reinforcement
Spiral reinforced columns should be designed for a minimum eccentricity of 5% of the depth of the section and tied columns for 10% of the depth.

5-50. Composite, Combination, and Pipe Columns. A composite column is a concrete compression member having a structural-steel or cast-iron core with a cross-sectional area not exceeding 20% of the gross area of the column. The concrete also contains spiral and longitudinal reinforcement. Its strength is given by

$$P = 0.225A_c f'_c + f_r A_r + f_s A_s \tag{5-63}$$

where A_c = net area of concrete section = $A_g - A_s - A_r$
  A_s = area of bar reinforcement
  A_r = cross-sectional area of steel or cast-iron core
  f_r = allowable stress of core—16,000 psi for a steel core; 10,000 psi for a cast-iron core
A combination column consists of a structural-steel column with concrete encasement that is at least 2½ in. thick over all metal (except rivetheads). In order that the concrete be considered as aiding the steel column, the concrete must be reinforced by a welded wire mesh wrapped completely around the column. This column may sustain a load

$$P = A_r f_r \left(1 + \frac{A_g}{100A_r}\right) \tag{5-64}$$

where f_r = the allowable unit stress for an unencased-steel column
A pipe column is a steel pipe filled with concrete. Its allowable load is given in Eq. (6-12), Art. 6-32.

5-51. Combined Bending and Axial Load. Since column design is based on ultimate strength and beam design may be based on elastic theory, the methods cannot be combined for members subjected to both axial load and bending. Satisfactory results, however, can be obtained by also applying ultimate-strength design with an appropriate safety factor to combined loading. Joint Committee 327 of the

American Concrete Institute and the American Society of Civil Engineers recommends:

$$P_u = 0.85f'_cbdk_uk_1 + A'_sf_y - A_sf_s \tag{5-65}$$

$$P_ue = 0.85f'_cbd^2k_uk_1 \left(1 - \frac{k_2}{k_1}k_uk_1 \right) + A'_sf_yd \left(1 - \frac{d'}{d} \right) \tag{5-66}$$

k_2/k_1 should not be less than 0.5, nor should k_1 be greater than 0.85 (see Art. 5-41). P_u = axial load; e = eccentricity; f_s = stress in tensile reinforcement (f_y, the yield point, if tensile reinforcement governs); k_ud = distance to neutral axis from extreme fiber; A_s = the area of tensile steel, and A'_s = area of compressive steel.

Tension governs when

$$P_u \leq \left[P_b = 0.72 \frac{90,000}{(90,000 + f_y)} f'_cbd + A'_sf_y - A_sf_y \right] \tag{5-67}$$

When $P_u < P_b$, then

$$P_u = 0.85f'_cbd \left\{ p'm' - pm + 1 - \frac{e}{d} \right.$$
$$\left. + \sqrt{\left(1 - \frac{e}{d}\right)^2 + 2\left[\frac{e}{d}(pm - p'm') + p'm'\left(1 - \frac{d'}{d}\right)\right]} \right\} \tag{5-68}$$

where $m = f_y/0.85f'_c$
$m' = m - 1$
$p = A_s/bd, p' = A'_s/bd$

For symmetrical reinforcement, Eq. (5-68) reduces to

$$P_u = 0.85f'_cbd \left\{ -p + 1 - \frac{e}{d} + \sqrt{\left(1 - \frac{e}{d}\right)^2 + 2p\left[m'\left(1 - \frac{d'}{d}\right) + \frac{e}{d}\right]} \right\} \tag{5-69}$$

With no compression reinforcement, Eq. (5-68) becomes

$$P_u = 0.85f'_cbd \left[-pm + 1 - \frac{e}{d} + \sqrt{\left(1 - \frac{e}{d}\right)^2 + \frac{2epm}{d}} \right] \tag{5-70}$$

When $P_u > P_b$, compression governs. Then

$$P_u = \frac{P}{1 + (P/P_b - 1)(e'/e'_b)} \tag{5-71}$$

where P = concentric load column can carry at ultimate strength
e' = eccentricity measured from centroid of section
e'_b = eccentricity of load P_b measured from centroid of section

For a circular section, two formulas that may be used are:
When compression controls,

$$P_u = \frac{A_sfy}{(3e'/d) + 1} + \frac{A_gf'_c}{[9.6De'/(0.8D + 0.67d)^2] + 1.18} \tag{5-72}$$

When tension controls,

$$P_u = 0.85D^2f'_c \left[\sqrt{\left(\frac{0.85e'}{D} - 0.377\right)^2 + \frac{p_tmd}{2.5D}} - \left(\frac{0.85e'}{D} - 0.377\right) \right] \tag{5-73}$$

where D = diameter of column

p_t = ratio of total area of longitudinal reinforcement A_s to A_g, the gross area of column

d = diameter of circle circumscribing reinforcement

e' = eccentricity of load from centroid

When the unsupported length L is greater than fifteen times the least lateral dimension, use a reduced load:

$$P'_u = P\left(1.6 - 0.4\frac{L}{d}\right) \tag{5-74}$$

The Building Code Requirements of the ACI recommend design by equations of the form (see Art. 6-30):

$$\frac{f_a}{F_a} + \frac{f_b}{F_b} = 1 \tag{5-75}$$

5-52. Formwork for Concrete Columns. (See also Art. **5-48.**) The following factors affect the design of forms:

1. *Method of Handling.* When forms are to be manually handled, the materials of which they are made should be very light and the panels small. Light spruce, dressed on two sides, is often used. Crane-handled members are constructed more heavily.

2. *Pouring Schedule.* This should be determined in advance and in such a way that forms may be reused.

3. *Method of Placing Concrete.* Forms must be designed to resist impact if concrete is placed rapidly in the forms.

4. *Class of Work.* Exposed work requires more careful forming than footings.

5. *Concrete Pressures.* Concrete wall and column forms must be designed to withstand lateral pressure exerted by liquid concrete.

When the concrete is placed the full height of the form within the period of time required for initial set, the pressure exerted by the concrete is assumed to have a triangular distribution (pressure increasing with depth) on the entire form. No relief of pressure due to the setting of the concrete can be assumed. The full-head analysis is used for fast pours of such deep members as columns, buttresses, and small walls. If the concrete is exceptionally slow-setting, a full-head analysis is also used.

The pressure used in full-head analysis varies from 85 to 125 psf per ft of height; 100 psf per ft is most commonly used. The maximum pressure of concrete in a form will never exceed 1,500 psf when the concrete is "placed" and 2,000 psf for heavy columns when the concrete is "dumped."

In limited-head analysis, account is taken of the fact that, as concrete hardens, the pressure it exerts on the forms is reduced because of internal friction. The maximum pressure P, in pounds per square foot, is a function of R in feet, the rise per hour of concrete in the forms and the temperature.

Temp, °F	P
70–80	$P = 150R$
60–70	$P = 187.5R$
50–60	$P = 225R$
40–50	$P = 262.5R$

Rectangular column forms are usually made of wood. The forms on two opposite sides of the column are made the exact width of the column; the other two forms overlap to give a tight fit. Many systems of cleats, bolts, clamps, wedges, etc., have been devised to keep the forms intact. The column form should be plumbed and braced after the reinforcing-steel assembly is installed.

A cleanout opening should always be left on two opposite faces of the column at the bottom.   This allows the removal of dirt, shavings, etc., before the concrete is poured. On top of the forms, openings are left to admit the beam and girder forms.

Steel forms are usually used for circular columns and capitals.

In all kinds of forms, bevel strips are usually placed to eliminate a sharp corner in the concrete, resulting in chamfered corners.   This will prevent the chipping of corners when the forms are removed.

REINFORCED-CONCRETE FLOOR AND ROOF SYSTEMS

There are a great many types of concrete floor systems.   A few of the more common ones are classified as follows:

1. One-way reinforcing systems (in which the main reinforcement in each element runs in one direction).

    a. Solid-slab beam and girder floors
    b. One-way ribbed floors; concrete joists with steel pan or concrete-tile fillers.
    c. Steel-joist floors (commonly used with steel frames).
    d. Precast systems:
        (1) Precast slab or deck.
        (2) Precast beams and girders.
    e. Concrete slab reinforced with steel deck.

2. Two-way reinforcing systems (in which the main reinforcement in the slab runs in two directions).

    a. Two-way solid slabs with beam supports.
    b. Two-way ribbed slabs with tile or steel-pan fillers and with beam supports.
    c. Flat-slab floors.
    d. Flat-plate floors.

5-53. Beam and Girder Floors and Roofs.   These are systems in which a one-way slab transmits its load to beams and the beams are supported by girders that rest on columns.   The beams are so spaced that they apply their load at the girder's midpoint, third points or quarter points.   The range of live loads for which this system is usually used is from 40 to 400 psf, and the column spacings range from 16 to 32 ft.

In normal beam and girder design (Art. 5-36), the height of the beam will be about twice its width.   This results in maximum economy for the beam, but the over-all economy may not be a maximum because the story height is greater.   The story height may be reduced by eliminating intermediate beams and using wide-shallow girders.   This is called slab-band construction.   It has been often used in multistory apartment and office buildings.

One-way slabs are frequently used with steel-frame construction.   In this case, the forms for the slab may be supported from the steel beams.   Main reinforcement is placed perpendicular to the steel beams.

In designing a beam and girder floor, it is customary to assume that the entire load of the slab goes to the beam, the clear span being used in design.   The load on the girder then consists of the concentrated loads transmitted by the beams, its own weight, and the live load that acts directly over it.

For figuring the maximum moments in the beam, design coefficients are given by the American Concrete Institute Building Code Requirements for Reinforced Concrete.   These coefficients, when multiplied by wL^2, give the moment in foot-pounds (w is the load in pounds per foot, and L is the clear span in feet).   They were derived for knife-edge supports, and the most unfavorable conditions of live load on a series of equal-span continuous beams with uniformly distributed load.   The coefficients are as follows:

Positive moment at center of span:

End spans.. $\frac{1}{14}wL^2$

Interior spans... $\frac{1}{16}wL^2$

Negative moment at exterior face of first interior support:

Two spans... $\frac{1}{9}wL^2$

More than two spans.. $\frac{1}{10}wL^2$

Negative moment at other faces of interior support...................... $\frac{1}{11}wL^2$

Negative moment at face of all supports for (1) slabs with spans not exceeding 10 ft and (2) beams and girders where ratio of sum of column stiffnesses to beam stiffnesses exceeds 8................ $\frac{1}{12}wL^2$

Shear in end members of first interior support........................... $1.15\dfrac{wL}{2}$

Shear at other supports.. $1.00\dfrac{wL}{2}$

If the end span rests freely on a wall, the negative moment there is negligible, but if it is cast integrally with a beam or a wall, the negative moment should be taken as $\frac{1}{24}wL^2$. If the end span is monolithic with a supporting column, $\frac{1}{16}wL^2$ should be used. However, if the ratio of column stiffness to beam stiffness exceeds 8, $\frac{1}{12}wL^2$, as shown in the table, should be used.

These coefficients are not applicable to unequal spans when the longest span exceeds the shortest by 20 %. Also, the live load should not exceed three times the dead load.

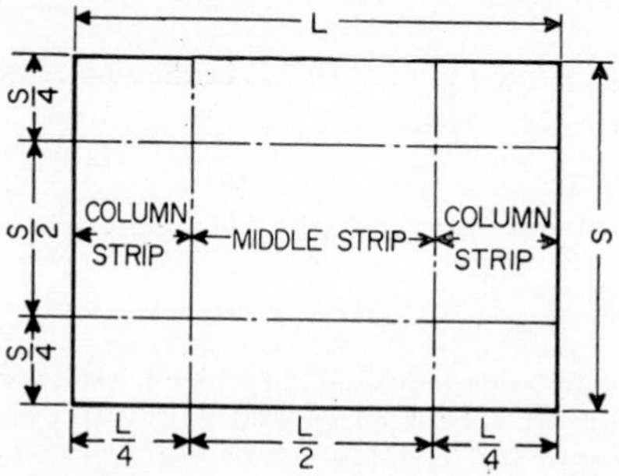

FIG. 5-9. Two-way slab is divided into column and middle strips for design purposes.

Where the spans and dead load–live load ratios exceed the specified limits, the use of the ACI moment coefficients will result in a design that is too conservative. In this case, an analysis for continuity, such as the moment-distribution method (Arts. 3-63, 3-64, and 3-68) may be used.

5-54. Two-way Slabs. A two-way slab is one in which the main reinforcement runs in two directions. Not only is it statically indeterminate, but its solution involves highly complicated formulas. Therefore, two-way slabs are usually designed by empirical methods. It is economical to design slabs that are square or nearly so as two-way slabs.

The following is an empirical method recommended by the American Concrete Institute Building Code Requirements for Reinforced Concrete. The slab is divided in both directions into a column strip and middle strip as shown in Fig. 5-9.

If m, the ratio of the short span to the long span (S/L), is greater than or equal to 0.5, the width of the middle strip in the short direction equals $L/2$, as shown.

If m is less than 0.5, the middle strip in the short direction has a width equal to $L - S$. The remaining width is divided equally between the two-column strips. However, when m is less than 0.5, most of the load would be carried in the short direction and it would be desirable to design the slab as a one-way slab.

A table in the ACI code presents coefficients C which, when multiplied by wS^2, give the moments in the middle strip per foot of width, w being the load in pounds per square foot. These coefficients are tabulated for different values of m, the ratio of short span to long span, and for different types of panels (see Table 5-3).

The moment in the column strip is assumed to be two-thirds that in the middle strip. The formula $A_s = M/f_s jd$ determines the steel area.

To design the carrying beams, the load is assumed to be distributed to the beams as shown in Fig. 5-10 (L. C. Urquhart, C. E. O'Rourke, and G. Winter, "Design of Concrete Structures," 5th ed., McGraw-Hill Book Company, Inc., New York, 1954).

Table 5-3. Moment Coefficients for Two-way Slabs, $C = M/wS^2$

	Short span S, values of $m = S/L$						Long span L, all values of m
	1.0	0.9	0.8	0.7	0.6	0.5 and less	
Case 1. interior panels:							
Negative moment at continuous edge..	0.033	0.040	0.048	0.055	0.063	0.083	0.033
Positive moment at mid-span.........	0.025	0.030	0.036	0.041	0.047	0.062	0.025
Case 2. one edge discontinuous:							
Negative moment at:							
Continuous edge.................	0.041	0.048	0.055	0.062	0.069	0.085	0.041
Discontinuous edge..............	0.021	0.024	0.027	0.031	0.035	0.042	0.021
Positive moment at mid-span........	0.031	0.036	0.041	0.047	0.052	0.064	0.031
Case 3. two edges discontinuous:							
Negative moment at:							
Continuous edge.................	0.049	0.057	0.064	0.071	0.078	0.090	0.049
Discontinuous edge..............	0.025	0.028	0.032	0.036	0.039	0.045	0.025
Positive moment at mid-span........	0.037	0.043	0.048	0.054	0.059	0.068	0.037
Case 4. three edges discontinuous:							
Negative moment at:							
Continuous edge.................	0.058	0.066	0.074	0.082	0.090	0.098	0.058
Discontinuous edge..............	0.029	0.033	0.037	0.041	0.045	0.049	0.029
Positive moment at mid-span........	0.044	0.050	0.056	0.062	0.068	0.074	0.044
Case 5. four edges discontinuous:							
Negative moment at discontinuous edge...........................	0.033	0.038	0.043	0.047	0.053	0.055	0.033
Positive moment at mid-span........	0.050	0.057	0.064	0.072	0.080	0.083	0.050

To find the moments in the supporting beams, the following equivalent uniform loads may be used: For the short span, $wS/3$; for the long span, $wS(3 - m^2)/6$.

Besides the main steel, reinforcing must be provided in the corners of the slab to resist the tendency of the corners to lift. Cracks tend to appear in the top of the slab perpendicular to the diagonal, and in the bottom of the slab parallel to the diagonal. If steel is placed so as to be perpendicular to the potential crack, four layers of reinforcement will result. If the slab is thin, it is customary to add additional steel parallel to the span directions in the vicinity of the corners (quarter span). If the steel is placed perpendicular to the crack, its area should equal the area of the short-span steel that resists the positive moment in the center half span. If placed

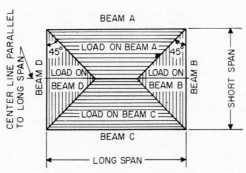

Fig. 5-10. Load distribution assumed for beams supporting a two-way slab.

parallel to the edges of the panel, the areas of steel should be equal to this area (A_s) multiplied by the secant of the angle that the bar makes with the expected crack, as shown in Fig. 5-11 (Dean Peabody, Jr., "Reinforced Concrete Structures," John Wiley & Sons, Inc., New York).

5-55. Flat-slab Construction. In this type of construction, peculiar to reinforced concrete, the slab is directly supported by the columns. There are no beams or girders. The columns flare out at the top to form **capitals,** giving the slab-column connection more rigidity. The capital flares out at a 45° angle.

The columns may be round, square, octagonal, or hexagonal, but are usually round. Exterior columns, however, are usually rectangular. The capital for an exterior column is sometimes only a bracket that projects toward the interior column.

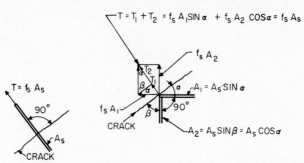

Fig. 5-11. Steel stresses when steel is placed normal to and at an angle with a crack.

The slab is often made thick around the columns. The thickened part of the slab is called a **drop panel.** This thickened area may be extended from column to column, in reality forming shallow beams, giving the effect of a paneled ceiling.

Flat slabs are much thicker and have more reinforcement than a slab in a beam-and-girder floor system. Advantages, however, are:

1. The ceiling, being flat, offers no obstruction to the passage of light.

2. Experience with fires shows that construction having many sharp corners fails more easily because spalling begins at the corners. Flat-slab construction has fewer sharp corners.

3. Fire protection is also better, because with a flat ceiling the water spray from the sprinkler system has better play.

4. A considerable saving in story height results for flat-slab construction.

5. The danger of sudden collapse due to overload is much less.

6. The slab formwork is much simpler. Forms for the columns are not expensive, because they have been standardized and are made of steel permitting unlimited reuse.

7. Cost of a flat-slab floor is favorable compared with beam-and-girder floors.

Structures to which flat slabs are adapted are warehouses, factories, cold-storage plants, garages and automobile service stations, wharves, coal-storage bins, and railroad terminals.

Marginal beams usually frame openings that occur in the slab.

Several different systems of reinforcement have been developed. They are as follows:

1. *Two-way System.* The reinforcement is placed in two directions. The column strip and the middle strip have the same limits as in the two-way slab (Art. 5-54). Principal steel in these strips runs in the same directions as in the two-way slab, but the amount of steel in the column strips is greater. Also the main bars in the column strip are in the bottom of the slab in the center and are bent up so as to be in the top of the slab as they pass over the columns. Main bars in the middle strip are also in the bottom of the slab in the center of the span and are bent up as they pass over the column-strip bars. In other words, the main bars are in the top of the slab to

resist negative moment and in the bottom to resist positive moment. Virtually all flat slabs built in this country today employ this system.

2. *Four-way System.* The column-strip steel is the same as that of the two-way slab. Instead of middle-strip steel, diagonal bands of steel are placed over the columns.

3 *Circumferential System.* Concentric circles of top bars are laid around each column, with radial top bars extending outward. The central area of the slab is reinforced in the bottom in like fashion.

4. *Three-way System.* Columns must be arranged so that the lines connecting them form equilateral triangles. Bands of steel run from column to column.

The method of designing flat slabs recommended in the American Concrete Institute Building Code Requirements for Reinforced Concrete was devised for a rectangular panel with a maximum ratio of length to width of 1.33. There must be at least three panels in each direction. This method is best suited for two-way slabs which have a simpler arrangement of reinforcement than other types of flat slabs. The total moment acting along the line connecting two adjacent columns and a parallel bisecting the panel is called M_o and is given by the expression

$$M_o = 0.09WL \left(1 - \frac{2c}{3L}\right)^2 \tag{5-76}$$

where W = total load on panel
L = distance between columns, center to center, perpendicular to strips under consideration
c = diameter of column capital

This moment is then divided into four parts—moments acting at mid-span in the column and middle strips and moments acting at the end in the column and middle strips. These moments will be the maximum positive and negative moments in the slab, respectively. A table in the ACI code furnishes these coefficients. They are listed for each interior panel, exterior panel, etc.

Aside from considerations of compressive strength and shear, the thickness of the slab is limited so as to prevent excessive deflection. Minimum thickness is not less than one-fortieth of the longer panel dimension for slabs with drops and one-thirty-sixth for slabs without drops.

Design mainly consists of assuming dimensions and then checking to see if the slab has sufficient strength. Then, steel is provided. It is usual to make the diameter of the column capital 0.20 to 0.35 of the average span.

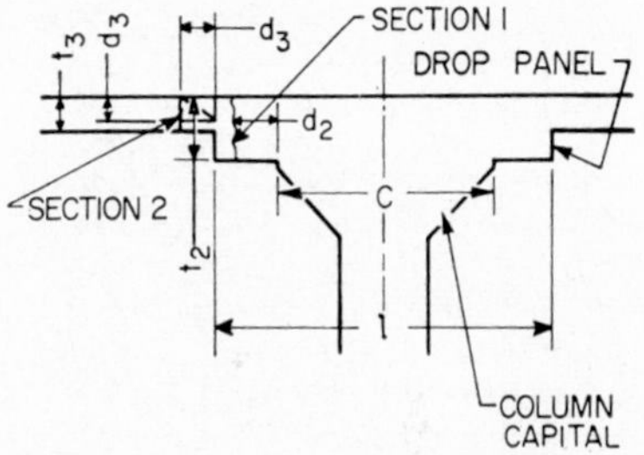

FIG. 5-12. Critical sections for shear in the slab and drop panel of a flat slab in the vicinity of an interior column.

The ACI code specifies that the difference in thickness of the slab and the dropped panel should not be more than one-fourth of the distance from the edge of capital to the edge of the drop.

To check for unit stress in the concrete, a balanced-design depth is found for the drop panel and the slab (Art. 5-36), and if equal to or less than the assumed thicknesses, the design is satisfactory for concrete unit flexural stress.

The slab is then checked for shear at two critical sections. Since the use of diagonal tension reinforcement is not desirable, the depth of the slab must be sufficient that the maximum allowable diagonal tension, or equivalent shear, is not exceeded. The critical sections are shown in Fig. 5-12 (Sutherland and Reese, "Reinforced Concrete Design," John Wiley & Sons, Inc., New York).

Effective depths of the slab and the drop panel are d_3 and d_2, respectively, and may be taken as $1\frac{1}{2}$ in. less than the corresponding thicknesses t_3 and t_2. As shown in Fig. 5-12, the critical sections are not taken at the sections of maximum shear, which are at the face of the drop panel and at the edge of the capital. The reason for this is that the diagonal tension is the quantity that must be investigated, not the shear. Large compressive forces, which enter from the column, result in a reduction of diagonal tension at the faces. Also, cracks are likely to occur as shown.

The shear is then found from the formula $v = V/bjd$, with j assumed to be $\frac{7}{8}$. For section 1 (Fig. 5-12), b will be the circumference of a circle with diameter equal to that of the column capital plus twice the effective depth of the drop panel $(c + 2d_2)$. For section 2, b will be the perimeter of a square if the drop is square, with sides equal to that of the drop panel plus twice the effective depth of the slab $(l + 2d_3)$.

The value of V is easily computed by noting that, by symmetry, there will be zero shear on the section formed by the center lines of the slabs. As shown in Fig. 5-13, this section forms a rectangle. The shear on section 1 or 2 (Fig. 5-12) will then be the total on this rectangular area minus the load carried on the area formed by a circle with diameter $c + 2d_2$ for section 1, and a square with side $l + 2d_3$ for section 2. Allowable shears are given in the ACI Code.

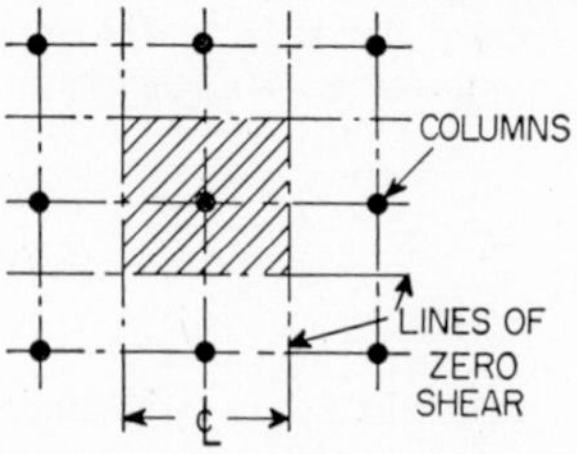

Bar lengths to satisfy bending moment and bond may be determined from Fig. 5-14 (ACI Code; also see Urquhart, O'Rourke, and Winter, "Design of Concrete Structures," 5th ed., McGraw-Hill Book Company, Inc., New York, 1954).

By a slight variation, the slab could be designed as a four-way slab. The same design moments are used as for the two-way slab. The steel for positive moment in the column strip is supplied entirely by the main bands, which may be bent or straight bars. The negative steel in the column strip is supplied by the main bands coming from both sides and by diagonal bands. For diagonal bars to supply the required steel, they must have a cross-sectional area equal to $A_s/\cos\theta$, where θ is the angle between the bar and the direction of the main bars.

FIG. 5-13. Flat slab uniformly loaded has zero shear on the boundaries of a rectangle around each column formed by the center lines of the panels, as indicated by the shaded area.

While concrete is placed, "high chairs," or precast-concrete blocks, are used to raise the top bars above the forms.

5-56. Ribbed Floors and Roofs. These consist of a series of small, closely spaced reinforced-concrete T beams framing into beams and girders, which in turn frame into columns. The T beams, which are called joists or ribs, are formed by placing rows of fillers in what would otherwise be a solid slab. The fillers may be special steel pans, hollow clay tile, lightweight concrete tile blocks, heavy-paper boxes or tubes, or ordinary wood forms. The girders that support the joists are usually built as regular T beams.

In effect, the one-way ribbed system is a one-way slab from which much of the tension concrete is removed, with considerable weight saving. Ribbed floors are economical for buildings such as apartment houses, hotels, and hospitals, where the live loads are small and the spans comparatively long.

5-57. Ribbed Floor with Steel-pan Fillers. Steel pans are available in lengths of 36 in. and depths of 6, 8, 10, 12, or 14 in. as forms for ribbed construction. Other sizes are made but are not so common. Most pans are tapered so they can be removed, but some types are designed to be left in place permanently. The most common width at the bottom of the pan is 20 in., but they may vary from 10 to 30 in.

With permanent types, metal lath is placed under the pans before they are put into position. The lath is anchored by metal clips which project into the joists. When the pans are removable, metal lath may be attached to the concrete, allowing the ceiling to be plastered. Sometimes the joists are left bare.

Reinforcement of the joists usually consists of two bars—one straight and one bent. The slab is reinforced primarily for temperature and shrinkage, with wire mesh or small bars placed at right angles to the joists. The area of the reinforcement is usually 0.25 % of the area of the slab.

Steel pans with the sides flared in the direction of the length are often used at the end of a row, where the joists frame into a beam. This results in a wider joist at the section of maximum shear. Also, sometimes the top of the pan is tapered.

Weight of this type of construction for design purposes may be obtained from manufacturer's catalogs. Also, the weight of the floor finish and the ceiling must be added.

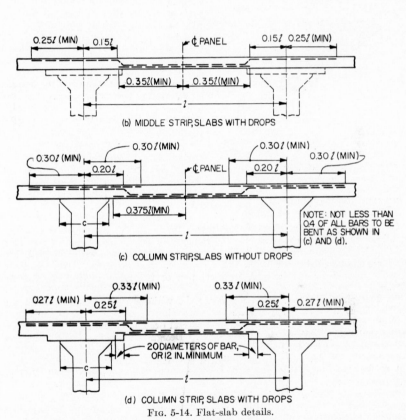

(a) MIDDLE STRIP, SLABS WITHOUT DROPS

(b) MIDDLE STRIP, SLABS WITH DROPS

(c) COLUMN STRIP, SLABS WITHOUT DROPS

(d) COLUMN STRIP, SLABS WITH DROPS

Fig. 5-14. Flat-slab details.

An allowance of 10 to 20 psf is usually included for partitions, if these partitions are not definitely located on the architect's plans or where there is a possibility that the location of the partitions may be changed. If the partitions are definitely located, and they run parallel to the joists, a thicker joist is placed under the partition. If a partition parallels the joists and lies between them, the adjacent joists and the slab between them may be thickened. When the partition runs perpendicular to the joists, the joist is designed with a concentrated load where the partition crosses.

Transverse bridging joists are often used at the center of spans of less than 24 ft and at the third points of larger spans. These act to stiffen the joists and to distribute concentrated loads.

The joists are designed for positive moment as T beams with a width of flange equal to the center-to-center spacing of joists. The shearing stress should be kept below the maximum allowable concrete stress possible, since the joists are too small to permit use of stirrups. In other respects, the design of the joist is the same as the design of a beam (Art. 5-36).

5-58. Ribbed Floors with Clay- or Concrete-Tile Fillers. These floors employ structural clay tile or concrete-tile blocks as fillers. The clay tile blocks are usually 12 in. square and can be obtained in thicknesses varying from 3 to 12 in. The blocks are laid flat, end to end, in rows between and at right angles to the girder forms. The usual clear distance between rows is 4 in., making the usual center-to-center spacing of the rows 16 in. Because the surface of the tiles is not smooth, the tiles become bonded to the concrete and remain in place. The entire ceiling may then be plastered.

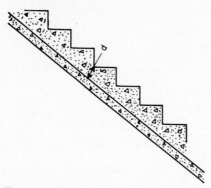

FIG. 5-15. Concrete stairs are reinforced and designed as one-way slabs.

Hollow concrete tiles come in various sizes. They are made of portland cement and a lightweight aggregate—cinders, slag, burned clay, or mineralized-organic substance.

The design of ribbed floors with clay-tile fillers is very much the same as that for floors with steel-pan fillers. One important difference is that, with tile fillers, advantage may be taken of the strength the tile adds to the floor, because of the bond between tile and concrete. In taking this into account, it is customary to add 1 or 1½ in. to the width of the joist in computing the resistance to bending moment and shear.

5-59. Two-way and Flat Slabs with Fillers. Just as in the case of one-way slabs, filler blocks or steel pans may be used to reduce the weight of a two-way slab or a flat slab. These fillers are placed on the forms in a grid pattern, with room between fillers for concrete joists running in two directions. In ribbed flat slabs, the drops are easily formed by eliminating the steel pan or tile fillers around the column capital.

5-60. Flat-plate Floors. These are flat slabs without drop panels and column capitals. They are used for light loads and fairly short spans (18 to 24 ft), such as in apartment houses, where they can be, with careful design, the most efficient system even for multistory projects up to 28 stories. Design is the same as for flat slabs, but shear resistance must be adequate.

5-61. Stairs. Stairways may be designed as a simple one-way slab with a span equal to the horizontal distance between supports. The effective depth d is as shown in Fig. 5-15.

5-62. Concrete Roofs. Design is similar to that for floors. In addition to structural requirements, the roofs must be impervious to water, must provide for adequate drainage and insulation, and must furnish protection against condensation.

A roof should be designed to carry its own weight plus the weight of any snow that may come on it. If the roof has considerable pitch, it must be designed for a wind load. Roof live load commonly assumed in temperate climates is 40 psf.

In concrete warehouses and like structures where no artificial heating is required, condensation can be eliminated by proper ventilation. Powerhouses, paper mills, roundhouses, etc., with concrete roofs will require the best insulation and ventilation to prevent condensation (see also Secs. 15 and 18).

PLAIN AND REINFORCED-CONCRETE RETAINING WALLS

Retaining walls are used to provide lateral support for a mass of earth or other material, the top of which is at a higher elevation than the earth or rock in front of the wall.

Free-standing retaining walls are primarily of three types: gravity, cantilever, and counterfort. Gravity walls can be built without steel reinforcement. The other types require reinforcement; they are shown in Fig. 5-16 (C. W. Dunham, "Theory and Practice of Reinforced Concrete," 3d ed., McGraw-Hill Book Company, Inc., New York, 1953).

For determination of pressures on retaining walls and under wall footings, see Art. 4-52.

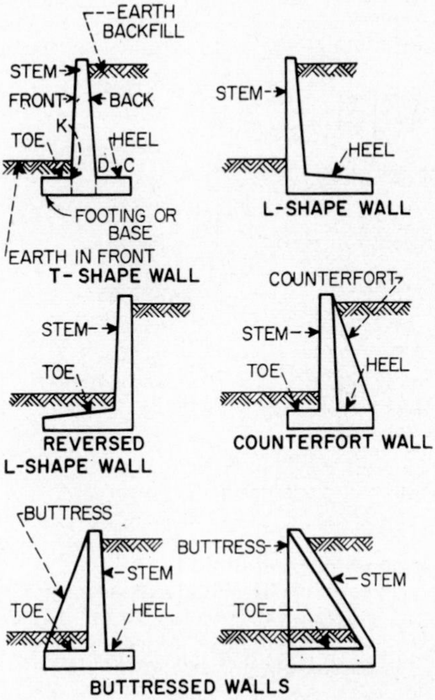

5-63. Concrete Gravity Walls. A gravity wall is designed to resist overturning moment through the action of its weight. The forces that act on the wall are its own weight, lateral earth pressure, and the resultant pressure on its base. Lateral earth pressure generally is assumed triangular in distribution. Gravity walls often are made of plain concrete.

There are two ways in which the wall may fail: It may be crushed or it may be pushed out of the way by the soil, by sliding or overturning.

A trial design must first be checked for stability. The sum of the righting moments and the sum of the overturning moments about the toe are found. It is assumed that, if the wall is overturned, it will overturn about the toe. A safety factor often used is 1.5, which means the righting moment is 1.5 times the overturning moment.

Next, the safety factor against sliding friction is determined. If μ is the coefficient of sliding friction, then the maximum horizontal resistance the soil can exert on the wall to resist sliding is μR_v, where R_v is the total downward force on the soil.

Next, the location of the vertical resultant R_v should be found. It must act in the middle third of the base in order that there be no tension in the bottom of the wall. The location of the resultant may be found by taking moments about the toe and dividing by R_v.

Finally, pressure distribution on the base should be computed. The maximum pressure should not exceed the allowable pressure for the soil.

To find the pressure distribution on the base of the wall, having determined the value of R_v and its location, use the formula:

$$P = \frac{R_v}{A} \pm \frac{Mc}{I} = \frac{R_v}{A}\left(1 \pm \frac{6e}{b}\right) \tag{5-77}$$

Pressure distributions for various locations of R_v are shown in Fig. 5-17 (Urquhart, O'Rourke, and Winter, "Design of Concrete Structures," 5th ed., McGraw-Hill Book Company, Inc., New York, 1954).

FIG. 5-16. Types of retaining walls.

When the resultant is outside the middle third of the base, it is assumed that the supporting medium can exert no tension on the base; pressure is exerted only on a portion of the footing, as shown in Fig. 5-17.

5-64. Cantilever Retaining Walls. This type of wall consists mainly of two parts—a cantilever slab, or vertical stem, and a base, or footing. The forces that act on the stem are earth thrust and resisting shear and moment. The forces acting on the base are its own weight and that of the earth above it, the upward pressure of the

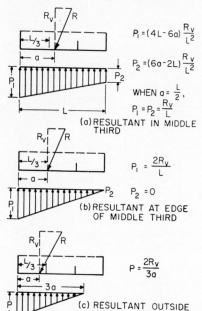

$$P_1 = (4L - 6a)\frac{R_v}{L^2}$$

$$P_2 = (6a - 2L)\frac{R_v}{L^2}$$

WHEN $a = \dfrac{L}{2}$,

$$P_1 = P_2 = \frac{R_v}{L}$$

(a) RESULTANT IN MIDDLE THIRD

$$P_1 = \frac{2R_v}{L}$$

$$P_2 = 0$$

(b) RESULTANT AT EDGE OF MIDDLE THIRD

$$P = \frac{2R_v}{3a}$$

(c) RESULTANT OUTSIDE MIDDLE THIRD

FIG. 5-17. Soil-pressure variation with location of resultant of superimposed loads.

soil and the internal resisting forces at the stem. The weight of the soil on the toe is seldom considered in design, since it acts to reduce the stresses in the toe and may not be in place when the wall is first loaded.

This type of wall is commonly used for walls of moderate height—18 to 20 ft. Higher walls are usually of the counterfort type.

Sometimes the toe is eliminated; that type of wall is called an L-shape wall (Fig. 5-16).

The procedure for design is as follows:

1. Design stem for moment, shear, and bond.

2. Select the base-slab size by checking whole slab for:

     a. Maximum soil pressure.

     b. Maximum friction on base.

3. Design of footing. If resistance to sliding is not fully furnished by friction, a key, or lengthwise projection, may be added on the bottom of the base slab to increase the resistance to sliding. It is important to keep in mind that only compacted undisturbed soil can develop adequate passive pressure and that fill, no matter how compacted, should not be considered as resisting the tendency of the wall to slide.

In investigating stability against overturning, the procedure is the same as for a gravity wall (Art. 5-63). To find the amount of steel in the stem, the procedure is the same as for design of a reinforced-concrete slab (Arts. 5-36 and 5-37). Web reinforcement is not usually provided; so unit shear in the concrete must be less than the allowable.

Since the moment is zero at the top and reaches a maximum at the foot of the stem, it is usual to make the wall taper from a maximum thickness at the bottom to a minimum thickness at the top. The total thickness at the top should preferably not be less than 12 in. to allow room for the concrete to be placed.

The main reinforcement will be vertical and lie in the back of the wall—the side against which the soil pressure will act. Some of the steel is usually cut off where it is no longer needed. The cutoff points may be determined graphically by drawing a bending-moment diagram and superimposing on it a diagram showing the moment resistance of the remaining steel, as indicated in Fig. 5-18.

The bars are not cut off at the theoretical cutoff points but are extended 12 bar diameters, as in beam design. The moment curve is a third-degree parabola; the steel-resistance curve is assumed a straight line. (The steel-resistance curve should actually be curved since j varies as well as d. However, this variation is slight.)

In addition to the main steel, transverse steel is put in both faces to act as temperature and shrinkage steel. The amount of this steel is usually made greater in the front face than in the back face since the temperature variation will be greater on the exposed face.

Design of the heel and toe portions of the footing is similar. For the heel, however, the main steel will be in the top; for the toe, it will be in the bottom. Temperature steel, running lengthwise, is also added. This steel also serves a useful purpose in tying the main steel together so it may be placed easily.

As usual, the steel is determined by $A_s = M/f_s jd$. The critical section is, of course, at the stem. Since the shear is great in comparision with the moment, it is possible that bond will determine the amount of steel. A fine balance may be obtained by using small-diameter bars, increasing the perimeter without increasing weight.

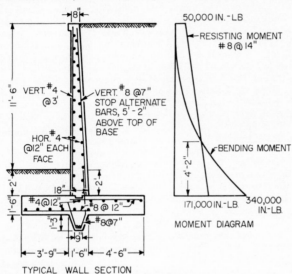

TYPICAL WALL SECTION

FIG. 5-18. Cantilever wall (*left*) has vertical main steel, placed near the earth face. Moment diagram (*right*) with resisting moments of main steel also plotted indicates No. 8 bars at 14 in. c to c are adequate 4 ft 2 in. above the base and higher. Below the spacing must be decreased to 7 in.

It is usually found when designing a short thick member like the base slab that shear, or rather diagonal tension, will determine thickness of slab. The width, as for the gravity footing, is determined entirely by external stability requirements; but depth of the footing usually is determined by shear $d = V/vbj$, where b is taken as 12 in., v is allowable unit shear, $j = \frac{7}{8}$, and V is shear per foot. Because of the heavy downward force coming from the wall, the maximum diagonal tension does not occur at the face of the wall. It is taken at a section at a distance from the face of the stem equal to the effective depth of footing. Since d is not yet known, it is assumed, and the required depth is found by cut and try. The required depth for bending is also found from the formula

$$d = \sqrt{\frac{M}{Kb}}$$

where M = maximum moment per ft in slab
   b = 12 in.
   K = $\frac{1}{2} f_c kj$
If this d is larger than the one required for shear, it controls.

If there is a key to resist sliding, the key is reinforced. It is, however, difficult to determine the forces acting on it. The steel in the key may be found by assuming the key is a cantilever subjected to passive earth pressure.

Since the wall and footing are never concreted at the same time, a construction joint is placed at the junction between stem and footing. Also, dowels tie the two together. To fulfill moment requirements, a dowel is provided for every stem bar and is of the same or greater diameter. The bars must fulfill anchorage requirements by extending into the stem and footing the full distance required to develop the bond stress. It will usually be found that the dowel must be bent over in the base slab to develop anchorage. Generally also, main steel in the toe is bent over into the stem so that it acts as a dowel. This may result in more steel than necessary in the toe, but placing is facilitated.

Improper drainage is the cause of most retaining-wall failures. The reason for this is that, after a rain, water may pile up behind the wall. Eventually, it will seep beneath the wall, but water seeps through soil very slowly. The water will fill the pores of the soil and will act on the wall with a lateral pressure for which the wall was not designed. The effect of water pressure is eliminated by placing holes in the wall, called weep holes, near the base of the stem. A porous pipe is placed at the back of the wall to conduct water to the weep holes. Sometimes crushed stone and gravel are also placed at the back of the wall so that the water will drain away quickly.

Sometimes, water will endanger a wall in quite another way, especially in northern climates, where frost action occurs. The moisture in the top of the soil freezes, expands, and then exerts a lateral pressure on the top of the wall. A lateral force of 700 lb per lin ft may be assumed and the wall designed to resist it.

To reduce shrinkage and temperature stresses in long walls, expansion joints are placed at intervals along the length. These will also act as construction joints.

Occasionally, masonry facing is placed on the front of the wall for appearance's sake. This masonry may be considered as adding strength to the wall if it is put in place before the concrete is placed or while the concrete is still wet and has not hardened, so that bond develops between masonry and concrete. In designing such a wall, Table 5-4 should be used.

Table 5-4. Properties of Stone Masonry for Wall Facings

Kind of masonry	Weight, lb per cu ft	Modulus of elasticity, psi	$n = E_s/E_m$	Allowable compressive strength, psi	
				Cement with lime mortar	Cement with mortar
Best granite ashlar.....	165	4,000,000	7.5	650	800
Medium granite ashlar..	160	4,000,000	7.5	500	700
Rubble..............	150	2,000,000	15	250	350

The wall may be designed as a reinforced-concrete wall. The following rules, however, must be followed:

1. Deduct 1 in. from front face to allow for weathering at joints.
2. Use allowable compressive stress and n from table if materials and workmanship are applicable.
3. Allow $f_s = 18,000$ psi for the reinforcement.
4. All stones must be well bonded to the concrete.
5. Use expansion joints as in reinforced-concrete walls.

5-65. Counterfort Walls. A counterfort wall, while resembling a cantilever wall in appearance, becomes an entirely different kind of structure by the addition of the counterforts, or braces, at the back (Fig. 5-16). The toe slab is a cantilever, as in the cantilever wall (Art. 5-64).

The counterforts are vertical ribs that tie the wall slab to the base at intervals. Thus wall slab and base slab are structurally similar—slabs supported on three sides.

On two opposite sides they are continuous over the counterfort, and on the third side, they are supported like a cantilever. The counterfort is almost completely in tension.

Instead of working with a 1-ft length of wall, the section of wall equal to the center-to-center spacing of counterforts is used in design. The external stability design is the same as for the other kinds of walls (Arts. 5-63 and 5-64). A key may also be provided in this wall, if necessary, to resist sliding. In computing lateral earth pressure two pressures are used—the earth pressure acting on the vertical wall, and that acting on the back of the counterfort.

The toe slab is designed as for the cantilever-wall footing (Art. 5-64).

The wall slab is designed as a continuous slab. Stresses thus computed will be larger than the actual stresses, since the resisting moments of the third edge are usually neglected. The latter usually are small and significant only in the direct vicinity of the junction of wall slab and base. For large walls, however, economy may be effected by taking into account the cantilever effect.

In the counterfort wall, the main steel is the horizontal steel. The vertical steel is the placement steel, the reverse of the situation for the cantilever wall. Negative-moment steel is placed near the earth face of the wall at the counterforts and positive-moment steel near the outer face between counterforts (Fig. 5-19). Vertical steel of about 0.3 to 1 % should be placed in the slab to act as placement steel and to resist the formation of cracks at the bottom of the wall.

As in continuous beams, one-fourth of the outward or top steel is extended over the supports. Bend points, the check for steel and bond, required depth, and steel are determined as for continuous slabs (Arts. 5-36 to 5-39).

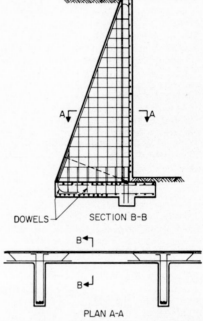

FIG. 5-19. Counterfort wall has main steel placed horizontally.

The loading w in pounds per foot will not be uniform over the entire height of the wall. The result of the lateral earth pressure, it will therefore have a triangular distribution. The required bar spacing for this loading should be computed for the bottom and several intermediate points. Thus, just as for stirrup spacing in beams, spacing of the horizontal bars is changed at several sections along the height of the slab.

Design of the heel of the base slab is almost identical with that of the wall slab. The forces acting on the footing are its own weight, upward pull of the counterforts, weight of the soil above, and the soil reaction below. Since the heel spans between counterforts as a continuous slab, longitudinal steel should be placed near the top face at counterforts and near the bottom between counterforts. The toe acts as a cantilever; so steel should be laid transversely in the bottom face. Dowels should be placed between wall and footing, and all steel anchorages checked, as recommended for cantilever walls (Art. 5-64). In neither base nor wall slab is there usually any web reinforcement.

Forces acting on the counterfort are the vertical and horizontal pressure of the soil and tensile forces acting on the planes where the counterfort is connected to the wall slab and base slab. Also there is shear along the plane where the counterfort joins the base slab because of the horizontal thrust of the soil. The counterfort acts essentially like a wedge-shaped cantilever, built in at the bottom of the base slab.

It acts as a T beam, with the wall slab as the flange. For this reason, concrete stresses are always low and need not be checked.

Maximum moment is at the section where the counterfort joins the footing. It is resisted by the main steel, which consists of bars in the sloping (earth) face of the counterfort. Dowel bars anchor the main steel to the base slab and are hooked in a large radius into the base slab for a distance sufficient to provide anchorage. Just as in the cantilever wall, the main steel is cut off where not required.

To compute the shear stress on a horizontal section of the counterfort, the formula $V_c = V_1/bjd$ is used, where $V_1 = V - M(\tan \theta + \tan \phi)/d$; M = moment at the section; V = shear; θ and ϕ = angles the longitudinal edges subtend with a normal to the section in question; and d = horizontal distance of the main steel to the front face of wall. In the case of most counterforts, the front face is vertical and the formula for V_1 reduces to $V_1 = V - M \tan \theta/d$, where θ is the angle the back face makes with the vertical.

Usually, the concrete will be found to be sufficient to take the shear. Nevertheless, horizontal bars, as shown in Fig. 5-19, anchor the counterfort to the wall slab. These horizontal bars are designed to counteract the pull of the wall slab and are thus designed for the full wall reaction. In like manner, vertical bars are placed in the counterfort to resist the pull of the base slab. These vertical bars are anchored to the base slab by dowels.

The base slab is concreted first; then the counterforts and wall slab are cast together. Thus all steel that must pass into the base slab from the wall slab or the counterfort must be doweled, while steel going from the wall slab to the counterfort need not be doweled.

When backfill is placed behind the wall, care should always be taken that the earth is laid in layers sloping downward away from the wall, to minimize earth pressure.

5-66. Formwork for Retaining Walls. The lumber used in formwork for walls should have a nominal thickness of at least $1\frac{1}{2}$ in. before surfacing, and should be of a good quality of Douglas fir, southern longleaf yellow pine, or plywood. The lumber for facework should be dressed on one side and on both edges to a uniform thickness and width. The lumber for backing and other rough work may be unsurfaced and of inferior grade.

Forms should be substantial and unyielding. They should be tight so that mortar does not leak out. Wales and other bracing should be adequate to carry the lateral pressures of liquid concrete (see Art. 5-52). Battered forms should be capable of resisting upward pressures.

The base slab is always cast directly on the earth, with only side forms.

REINFORCED-CONCRETE FOOTINGS

All the load and weight of a structure must ultimately be supported by the soil. Since the allowable pressure on the soil generally is much lower than the allowable stress in the building columns and walls, they must never be allowed to rest directly on the soil. Rather, load must be spread out on footings; or some other suitable foundation, such as piles, must be used.

Soil, as a structural material, is far more variable and uncertain than concrete. The bearing capacity of a soil is determined by tests made on samples of soil taken from the proposed site or by a soil-bearing-load test (Sec. 4). These bearing capacities are so determined that the total differential settlement of different parts of the structure will be a minimum.

5-67. Design Loads on Footings. In designing footings, the dead load is the weight of the structure itself. The live load, however, is not necessarily the sum of the full live load on all contributory floors and areas. In most structures, especially for commercial offices or residential occupancy, it is extremely unlikely that the full live load will ever exist on all floors simultaneously. Therefore, in computing the design loads for columns and footings, some reduction in load is allowed depending on the number of floors supported by each column or footing (Art. 4-19).

5-68. Types of Spread Footings. A wall footing is a strip of reinforced concrete sufficiently wider than the wall to distribute the pressure to the soil. A footing for a single column may be square or rectangular. If the column is built close to the property line, a strap footing or a combined footing may be used (Art. 4-23). A combined footing is simply a footing on which one or more columns rest. It may also be used when two columns are so close together that these footings, when designed, will be very close or overlapping. In a strap or connected footing, the exterior footing is placed eccentrically under its column in order not to project beyond the property line. Such a position would result in an uneven distribution of the bearing pressure and tipping of the footing. In order to counteract this, the footing is connected by a beam or strap to the nearest interior footing.

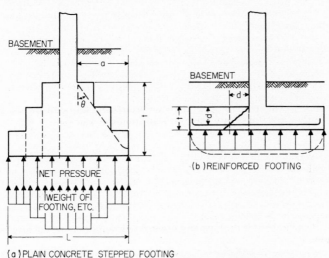

(a)PLAIN CONCRETE STEPPED FOOTING

Fig. 5-20. Wall footings may be made of plain concrete, in which case it must be very thick (a), or of reinforced concrete (b) designed to withstand bending stresses.

If the soil is weak or column loads too large, the required footing areas may become too large to be economical. In this case, a mat or raft foundation may be used (Art. 4-24). This is a thick concrete slab reinforced in both directions that provides great rigidity against differential settlement.

Sometimes, a beam-and-girder foundation is used. For design purposes, this may be considered as an inverted beam and girder floor. If the columns are in a square pattern, the slab is provided with two-way reinforcement. Inverted flat slabs, with capitals at the bottoms of the columns, are also used for mat foundations. In some buildings, the basement and the floor above, with the connecting columns and walls, are rigidly connected, thereby stiffening the foundation.

In designing footings it is customary to assume a linear distribution of pressure. Actually, the pressure distribution is quite complex, but there is not sufficient justification to use more refined methods (Arts. 4-20 to 4-22). The weight of the footing, soil, and basement load immediately above the footing causes pressure on the soil but does not cause shear forces or bending moments in the footing, since the supporting soil is in line with the loads. It is the wall or column loads, or net pressure, that cause bending and shear in the footing slab.

5-69. Wall Footings. These can be designed as a continuous cantilever slab 1 ft wide. They may either be plain concrete step footings of considerable thickness or a thinner reinforced slab of uniform thickness.

The shape of a stepped footing is shown in Fig. 5-20a.

The first step in its design is to estimate the weight of the 12-in. width of footing. This depends on the bearing capacity of the soil, strength of the concrete, and several other factors. It may be taken at about 6 to 12 % of the wall load. The estimated footing weight plus the wall load when divided by the allowable bearing pressure of the soil gives the required length L of the bottom of the footing. If θ, the angle of the step (see Fig. 5-20a), is made about 30° the footing will probably be safe for moment.

Shear, however, should be investigated. The critical section is at the face of the wall. For a 12-in.-wide strip of cantilever, the shear V is pa, where a is the distance in feet from the face of wall to end of footing and p is the net pressure in pounds per square foot (wall load divided by area of footing). The unit shear is given by $v_c = VQ/12I = V/8t$ from which the thickness of footing t, in inches, at the critical section is $V/8v_c$, with v_c limited to $0.02f'_c$.

Height of risers should be set to avoid the necessity of ripping planks to give correct form height. Sometimes the steps are omitted, but the footing is designed as a sloped footing. If the footing is sloped, a 6-in. platform between the wall and beginning of slope should be provided to support the wall forms.

After the dimensions of the footings have been found, the weight of the footing must be computed and checked against the assumed weight. If the true weight is much greater than the assumed weight, the allowable bearing pressure will be exceeded; so the footing dimensions must be redetermined.

In designing a reinforced-concrete wall footing, the footing weight is assumed first. It will, of course, weigh less than a plain concrete footing carrying the same load on the same soil. The required width and the net pressure are determined in the same way as for the plain concrete footing.

It is likely that shear will govern the design of the footing rather than moment. The required depth is given by $d = V/v_cbj$, where $j = 0.9$, since footings are usually under-reinforced. V is the shear on a section taken at a distance d from the face of the wall. V is then a linear function of d, which may be found by trial and error.

The allowable unit shear $v_c = 0.03f'_c$, since it is undesirable to use web reinforcement in footings. However, the American Concrete Institute Code limits the maximum v_c to 75 psi, which is the allowable shearing stress for 2,500 psi concrete. This factor limits the use of rich mixes in footings.

The footing should be checked for concrete compressive stress. The critical section for this is at the face of the wall. If required depth for bending [Eq. (5-6), Art. 5-34] is greater than the depth for shear, moment governs. The total thickness is found by adding the bar covers. A 3-in. cover under the reinforcing is normally required on average soil. If the soil is particularly poor, 5 in. may be necessary. The ACI Code further specifies that at least 6 in. of concrete must cover the top of the bars. This limits the minimum thickness of a footing to 10 in.

When the dimensions of the footing have been selected, the weight may be found and checked against the assumed weight. If they do not substantially check, the footing requires redesign.

In footings, it is usual to find the required number of bars to satisfy both area requirements for moment and perimeter requirements for bond. The required areas and perimeters may be computed from Eq. (5-7) (Art. 5-34) and Eqs. (5-8) and (5-9) (Art. 5-38). The bars should not be hooked unless the length for anchorage is inadequate.

In addition to the main steel, near the bottom of the footing, shrinkage or temperature reinforcement is always placed parallel to the wall. This reinforcement also facilitates placing of the main reinforcement. (Dean Peabody, Jr., "Reinforced Concrete Structures," John Wiley & Sons, Inc., New York.)

5-70. Single-column Footings. These are usually made square unless there are space restrictions or the columns are rectangular. Three types of footings are shown in Fig. 5-21. The footing in (a) is the usual type, a column resting on a concrete slab reinforced in two directions. The footing in (b) has, in addition, a pedestal. The pedestal provides a more favorable transfer of load and in many cases is required to provide the necessary length of dowels. The third type (c) is a sloped footing. This requires less concrete than type (b) but is more expensive to form.

The procedure for finding the required area and net pressure is the same as for wall footings (Art. 5-69), except the whole footing is considered, rather than a 12-in. strip. The critical sections for moment, bond, and shear, as specified by the American Concrete Institute Building Code Requirements for Reinforced Concrete, are shown in Fig. 5-22.

The critical section for bending and bond is ab in Fig. 5-22a. The shear V on ab is the upward load resulting from the net pressure acting on area $abcd$. The moment M is the moment about ab of the upward load on $abcd$. The area and the perimeter of the reinforcing steel should be designed for 85 % of the moment and shear so computed, according to the ACI code.

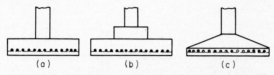

(a) (b) (c)

FIG. 5-21. Column footings: (a) column seated directly on a reinforced-concrete footing; (b) pedestal placed between column and reinforced-concrete footing; (c) sloped reinforced-concrete footing. In plan, they usually are square or rectangular, depending on column shape.

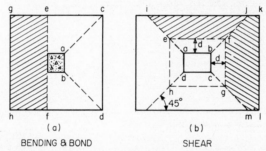

(a) (b)

BENDING & BOND SHEAR

FIG. 5-22. Critical design sections for reinforced-concrete column footings.

The critical section for shear is ef or fg in Fig. 5-22b, d distant from the face of the column. In the formula $v = V/bjd$, b is either ef or fg. The shear acting on ef is equal to the total upward pressure on $efij$, which is formed by drawing 45° lines from the corners of the column, while the shear on fg comes from $fgmlkj$. Since the effective footing depth d is not known initially, the critical section must be found by trial, as for wall footings (Art. 5-69).

In investigating the shear on ef and fg, it should be remembered that there is a different d in each direction, because the reinforcing is laid at different levels. For square footings, it is customary to determine A_s for the upper layer (smaller d) and to use the same value for the lower layer. Also to be noted is that the allowable bond stress in a two-way footing is less than the usual allowable bond stress. The reason is that the bond between a bar and the concrete is reduced by crossing bars.

In square or nearly square footings, the reinforcement is uniformly spaced. In rectangular footings, the reinforcement in the long direction is uniformly spaced over the shorter width of the footing. The bars running in the short direction, however, are closely spaced directly beneath the column and wider spaced toward the edges. The ACI Code recommends the following distribution for this steel: If S is the ratio of the long side to the short side of the footing, and B is a band centered on the column and having a width equal to the short side of the footing, the reinforcement in B, uniformly spaced, is given by twice the area of the reinforcing steel in the short direction divided by $(S + 1)$. The remainder of the reinforcement should be uniformly distributed in the outer portions of the footing.

Shear reinforcement is not provided in footings; therefore, the maximum permissible shear stress is $0.03f'_c$.

For round or octagonal columns, the rules for finding the critical section apply if the "face" of the column is taken as the side of a square having the same area as that of the column.

The compressive stress in the longitudinal bars of the column must be transferred to the footing. This is done by means of dowels. There should be at least one dowel for each column bar; the total area of the dowels should equal the total area of the column bars. The dowels lap the column bars 20 bar diameters for concretes with f'_c equal to or greater than 3,000 psi and 26.7 bar diameters for concretes of less strength. For plain bars use twice these values.

The dowels should extend into the footing 20 bar diameters. If the footing depth is insufficient, they may be bent.

In addition to the requirements of bond, shear, etc., the bearing pressure at the foot of the column on the footing must not exceed the allowable value for the concrete. This pressure is the load of the column divided by the bearing area, which may be the area of the column itself or of the pedestal if the column is seated on one. The ACI Code specifies the allowable bearing pressure on the full area (such as the base area of a pedestal) as $0.25f'_c$ and on a partly loaded area (such as the top area of a pedestal or footing) as $0.375f'_c$ if the loaded portion is one-third or less of the full area. The allowable stress on an area larger than one-third but less than the full area is obtained by a linear interpolation between the two values. If the stress on the bottom surface of the pedestal is greater than $0.25f'_c$, the pedestal must be designed as a column.

The reason the allowable bearing pressure for partly loaded areas is more than for fully loaded areas is that the concrete directly under the column or pedestal is restrained laterally by the unloaded concrete in much the same manner as the ties or spirals that laterally support the concrete in columns.

The check for bearing pressure should be made directly after the required area is found. The reason for this is that a pedestal may be required to spread the load. The critical sections are then determined using the dimensions of the pedestal rather than those of the column. (Urquhart, O'Rourke, and Winter, "Design of Concrete Structures," 5th ed., McGraw-Hill Book Company, Inc., New York, 1954.)

5-71. Footings Subjected to Overturning. Sometimes, footings must be designed to take moment as well as direct stress. This occurs when the column that rests on the footing carries a moment. In such cases, the pressure under the footing will be trapezoidal or triangular in distribution. When the overturning moments act parallel to one axis, it is often economical to make the footing rectangular with its long side in the direction of the overturning moment.

The pressure distribution and steel reinforcement under this type of footing are found in the same way as for a retaining wall.

5-72. Combined Footings. These should fulfill the following requirements:

1. They should have an area great enough to give the safe allowable soil pressures.
2. They should have a shape such that the resultant net soil pressure is uniform.

The last condition is satisfied when the resultant of the column loads acts at the center of gravity of the base area (Art. 4-23).

Combined footings may be rectangular or trapezoidal in plan. Consider two columns of a building—an exterior column carrying a light load and an interior column carrying a heavy load. If the footing cannot project beyond the exterior column, a combined rectangular footing may be used; but if the footing is also restricted from extending beyond the interior column, a trapezoidal footing must be used.

The design of a combined footing assumes that each column rests on a transverse beam and that these beams are supported by a longitudinal slab, which, in turn, rests on the soil.

The following procedure may be followed for designing a combined rectangular footing carrying an interior and exterior column (Fig. 5-23):

The weight of the footing is assumed. The total required area of the footing is computed from the loads and allowable soil pressure; then the center of gravity of the two column loads is calculated. This also is the center of gravity of the footing. Since the location of one end of the footing is known, the total length of the rectangular footing may be found by doubling the distance from the known face to the center of gravity of the column loads. The width of the footing is then the required area divided by the length.

With the net pressure and the column loads known, the shear and moment diagram for the footing in the longitudinal direction may be drawn. The maximum moment will be negative and will occur somewhere between the two columns. The maximum shears will occur at the faces of the column.

Authorities disagree as to where the critical design section for shear should be taken. Since the footing in the longitudinal direction has more of the proportions of a beam, it is safe to assume that the critical section is at the face of the column.

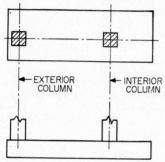

FIG. 5-23. Rectangular combined footing. Centroid of loads and footing coincide.

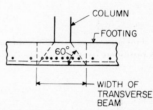

FIG. 5-24. Load distribution assumed for a column seated on a combined footing.

The depth of the footing is usually determined by the shear [Eq. (5-8), Art. 5-38]. As in other footings, web reinforcement should be avoided. However, if the loads are heavy and the required depth becomes too large, the footing may be designed for a higher allowable shear and with web reinforcement. After the required depth is determined for shear, the required depth for moment is found [Eq. (5-6), Art. 5-34], the larger value governing. As for slabs, b may be taken as 12 in., if M is the moment per foot.

Longitudinal steel will be required in the top of the footing between the columns and in the bottom under the columns, where the footing overhangs the columns and for a short distance on the exterior side of the interior column. Required steel areas and perimeters at the places of maximum moments are found as usual [Eqs. (5-7) and (5-9), with j usually as $\frac{7}{8}$]. Cutoff points are found from the moment diagram as in beams (Art. 5-39). Sometimes bent bars are used, as in beams. If web reinforcement is required, these bent bars may be considered as web reinforcement.

In order that the assumption of uniform pressure over the width of the column be valid, the loads that enter the footing through the columns are distributed transversely by bands of steel under each column. These transverse bars are placed in the bottom of the footing, since the transverse beam is a cantilever subjected to upward pressure. To determine the required amount of steel, a width of transverse distribution must be assumed. A conservative assumption is that the load spreads out at a 60° angle, as shown in Fig. 5-24.

The critical section for moment and bond in the transverse beams is taken at the face of the column. The only forces considered in producing shear and moment on these sections are the column load and the net pressure; shears and moments acting along the sides of the transverse beam are ignored.

The transverse beams should also be checked for shear. The section for shear is taken at a distance d away from the face of the column, where d is the effective depth. Also the transverse steel, under the interior column, is designed for an allowable bond for two-way steel since it will be crossed by the main longitudinal steel. However, the transverse steel under the exterior column is designed as one-way steel, since the longitudinal steel at this section usually is required only in the top. Some longitudinal steel should be put in the bottom even when not required, however, to serve as placement steel for the transverse reinforcing.

When the footing projection beyond both columns is limited, a trapezoidal area may be used (Fig. 5-25).

For this type of footing, the length of footing, location of centroidal axis (found from column loads), and the required area may be determined at the outset. With these data, two equations may be solved to find the maximum and minimum footing widths a and b. The net pressure per foot of length varies and is given by

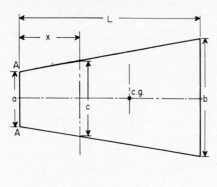

$$W = p_n c = p_n \left(a + \frac{b - a}{L} x \right)$$

where p_n = net pressure

The design procedure is the same as for rectangular footings except that the longitudinal steel is spread fanwise over the trapezoid. Alternate bars are cut off as the narrow end of the footing is approached. (Dean Peabody, Jr., "Reinforced Concrete Structures," John Wiley & Sons, Inc., New York.)

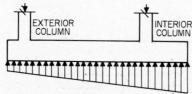

Fig. 5-25. Trapezoidal combined footing.

5-73. Strap or Connected Footings. These are used when the distance between exterior and interior columns is large and a common footing is necessary. The exterior footing is placed eccentrically beneath its column. To overcome the tendency of the exterior footing to overturn, it is connected by a beam or strap to the nearest interior footing.

The footing areas are so proportioned that the pressure under each is uniform, and the same. To accomplish this, the centroid of the combined area of the two footings must be made to coincide with the centroid of the loads (Art. 4-25). This can best be done by trial.

Strap footings may be designed in two ways. In one—the usual way—the strap is designed so that it does not bear on the soil (Fig. 5-26 from Urquhart, O'Rourke, and Winter, "Design of Concrete Structures," 5th ed., McGraw-Hill Book Company, Inc., New York, 1954). This is accomplished by casting the concrete strap on a bottom form instead of on the soil. In the second way, the strap is designed so that it bears on the soil. In this case, the soil pressure on the strap is considered.

It is important to note that the resultant of net soil pressure under the exterior or the interior footing does not necessarily equal the column load on that footing.

These pressures may be computed by the laws of statics. If the strap does not bear against the soil, its weight per foot is assumed and taken into account in finding moments and shears. This is not done in the case where the strap bears against the soil because the weight of the strap will pass directly into the soil. However, there will be an upward soil reaction that must be found, which will be the same as that acting on the footings, since the net pressure is uniform.

The moment and shear diagrams for the strap may be drawn, since all the loads on the strap are known. The loads acting on the strap are:

1. Exterior-column load.
2. Net soil pressure acting upward on the exterior footing.
3. Weight of the strap and net pressure of the soil on the strap.
4. Net pressure acting upward on the interior footing.
5. Interior-column load.

The strap is made wider than the interior or exterior columns; so the column forms may rest on the strap. The depth is determined by moment requirements.

Stirrups will usually be required at the ends, where the shear is high. Main tensile steel will be in the top, because the strap is subject to negative moment only. Steel is sometimes also placed in the bottom of the strap to guard against the possibility of differential settlement. The reinforcement of the strap is usually heavy; two rows of bars may be necessary. Part of the steel may be cut off where it is no longer needed.

The actual weight of the strap should be checked against the assumed weight, and the design modified, if necessary.

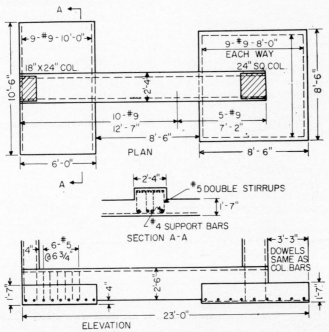

FIG. 5-26. Strap footing.

The exterior footing is designed like a wall footing (Art. 5-69), since the strap is assumed to distribute the load of the column over the length of the footing. The interior footing is designed as a single-column two-way footing (Art. 5-70). The net pressure is the same as that acting under the exterior footing.

5-74. Footings on Piles. If conditions warrant, piles are driven to support columns. There usually will be a cluster of piles for each column. The size of the footing for distributing the column load to the piles is determined by the number of piles and the spacing between them (Art. 4-34).

The piles usually project 6 in. into the footing. The distance from the center of outside piles to the edge of the footing must not be less than 18 in. Reinforcement usually has a clearance of 3 in. above the piles.

It is important that piles be cut off at the proper elevation, because if reinforcement is bent around a pile that is too high, the concrete above that pile is unreinforced.

Pile caps for footings are designed like a two-way single-column footing (Art. 5-70); the same critical sections are used. The piles are arranged symmetrically about the column so that all piles carry equal loads. In determining moments, the piles are considered as concentrated loads acting on the footing. In determining shear, the American Concrete Institute Building Code Requirements for Reinforced Concrete recommends the following:

"In computing the external shear, the entire reaction from any pile whose center is located 6 in. or more outside the section shall be assumed as producing shear on the section; the reaction of any pile whose center is located 6 in. or more inside the section shall be assumed as producing no shear on the section. For intermediate positions of the pile center, the portion of the pile reaction to be assumed as producing shear on the section shall be based on straight line interpolation between full value at 6 in. outside the section and zero value at 6 in. inside the section."

5-75. Formwork for Footings. Concrete need only be formed on four sides, since the earth provides the form for the bottom. In forming sloped footings, forms may be required for steep slopes. Holes are provided in the sloping forms into which concrete is poured. The holes are sealed as the level of the concrete rises.

REINFORCED-CONCRETE ARCHES

Arches are curved structures used in roofs for such buildings as hangars, auditoriums, rinks, etc., where long spans are desired. The great advantage of the arch in reinforced-concrete construction is that the whole cross section may be utilized. In reinforced-concrete beams, the part below the neutral axis is considered cracked and therefore does not contribute to bending strength. But by arching the beam, it is possible to make the axis conform to the line of thrust, thereby virtually eliminating bending moment. In other words, the entire cross section may be utilized in compression.

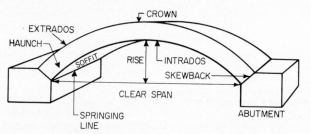

Fig. 5-27. Components of an arch.

The components of a fixed arch are shown in Fig. 5-27. For a discussion of different types of arches and stress analysis, see Arts. 3-82 to 3-84.

Since the depth of an arch generally varies along the length, several cross sections must be chosen for design, such as the crown, springing, haunches, and quarter points. Concrete compressive stresses and shear should be checked at each section and steel-reinforcing requirements determined. The sections are designed as rectangular beams or T beams subjected to bending and axial stresses, as indicated in Arts. 5-42 to 5-45 and 5-51.

5-76. Concrete-arch Details. When an arch is loaded, large horizontal reactions are developed at the supports. For roof arches, tie rods may be placed overhead or in or under a building floor to take the horizontal reaction.

Hinges for concrete arches must transmit the axial thrust and the shear but offer no resistance to bending. It is impossible to build a perfect concrete hinge, but a hinge is satisfactory if its resistance to bending is negligible compared with the resistance of other portions of the arch. Use of hinges results in a marked reduction in stresses due to shrinkage, temperature change, and settlement of supports.

Of the various types of hinges, steel hinges are best, but they are expensive. Hinges may be made of reinforced concrete, as shown in Fig. 5-28.

The Mesnager hinge (Fig. 5-28a) offers less resistance to rotation than the Considere (Fig. 5-28b), but the latter can carry very large thrusts. In the Mesnager hinge, the reinforcing bars are crossed over at the hinge; in the Considere, they are wrapped with a steel spiral.

It is recommended that, in a Mesnager hinge, the hinge opening should, at least, be equal to the concrete thickness t (preferably $h = 1.3t$). The crossed bars should not be too short or too thick. If the diameter of bars is too small, they will buckle. Their L/r should be between 20 and 40, where L is the length of the inclined bar between concrete faces, or $L = h/\cos \theta$; r is the radius of gyration and is equal to $D/4$ for round bars of diameter D.

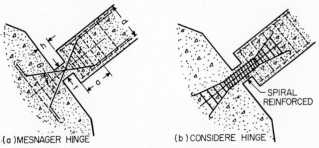

(a) MESNAGER HINGE   (b) CONSIDERE HINGE

Fig. 5-28. Concrete hinges.

Length of embedment of the bars should be 20 diameters, as for column dowels (Art. 5-70). To find the required area A_s of the hinge bars, it is assumed that they form a triangular truss. The compressive stress is given by

$$f'_s = \frac{N}{A'_s \cos \theta} + \frac{S}{A'_s \sin \theta} \tag{5-78}$$

where N = axial thrust through hinge
S = shear across the hinge
θ = angle bars make with arch axis
The stress f'_s should not exceed 30 % of the yield point.

The inclined bars exert a bursting force that must be resisted by lateral reinforcement (stirrups and ties). Only the lateral reinforcement that extends a distance $a = 8D$ from the face of the concrete at the hinge is considered effective in resisting the bursting force.

The stress in the lateral reinforcement is given by

$$f''_s = \frac{(N/2)\tan \theta + Sa/jd)}{0.005ab + A''_s} \tag{5-79}$$

where A''_s = combined area of lateral stirrups or ties located within distance $a = 8D$
b = horizontal width of hinge (usually equal to width of arch rib)
d = effective depth of arch rib
(Urquhart, O'Rourke, and Winter, "Design of Concrete Structures," 5th ed., McGraw-Hill Book Company, Inc., New York, 1954.)

Arch Formwork. Arches with spans less than 90 ft are usually constructed with ribs 3 or 4 ft wide. These are concreted in one day. The concrete may be placed continuously from both abutments toward the crown, so as to obtain symmetrical loading on the falsework.

For spans of 90 ft or over, however, arches are usually constructed by the alternate block or voussoir method—the arch is constructed in transverse blocks of such size that each can be completed in one pouring. This method reduces shrinkage stresses to a minimum. The blocks are cast in such order that the centering will settle uniformly. If blocks close to the crown section are not placed before blocks at the haunch and springing sections, the centering will rise at the crown, and placing of the crown blocks will then be likely to cause cracks in the haunch. The usual procedure is to cast two blocks at the crown, then the two springing blocks, and alternate until the complete arch is poured.

In construction by the alternate-block method, the block sections are kept separate by timber bulkheads. The bulkheads are kept in place by temporary struts between the voussoirs.

Keyways left between the voussoirs are concreted later. Near piers and abutments, a top form may be necessary. It is put on as pouring progresses.

If arch reinforcement is laid in long lengths, settlement and deformation of the arch centering will cause the steel to buckle. Therefore, lengths of steel greater than 30 ft should not be used, and splicing should occur in the keyways. An effort should be made to stagger the splices of adjacent rods and to locate the splices where there is minimum tension in the rods.

Upper reinforcement in arch rings may be held in place by means of spacing boards nailed to props, or by wiring the steel directly to transverse timbers supported above the surface of the finished concrete.

Forms for the arch may be supported on a timber falsework bent. This consists of joists and beams supported by timber posts that are braced together. Wedges are placed at the bottom of the posts so that the formwork may be conveniently lowered after the concrete has hardened sufficiently to take its own load. The false-work may also be made of metal.

THIN-SHELL CONCRETE STRUCTURES

Shells derive their strength from the fact that the loads are transmitted through the shell primarily by direct stresses, with some relatively small bending stresses that originate near the supports. Since reinforced concrete can carry direct compression on its entire cross section, it is possible to make the shell very thin. Since shells are always reinforced, the thickness of the shell is usually determined by the minimum thickness required to cover the reinforcement—usually 1 to $3\frac{1}{2}$ or 4 in. The shell is thickened near supports and stiffeners to about $5\frac{1}{2}$ to 7 in. because of the bending stresses in such areas.

Shells are most often used as roofs for such buildings as hangars, garages, theaters, and arenas where large spans are required and loads are light. The advantages of reinforced-concrete shells may be summarized as follows:

1. The most economical use of materials in a structural system.
2. Great freedom in architectural shapes.
3. Easy to provide natural lighting throughout the entire structure.
4. Ability to carry a very large unbalance of forces.
5. High fireproofing characteristics. This results from the absence of jutting corners and the fire resistance of concrete.
6. Reserve strength. Even if the shell is locally damaged at a critical point, it will not fail.

In spite of the above advantages, difficulties arise that make the design of large shell roofs a major problem. Formwork is usually very expensive; construction is presently difficult and unfamiliar to most contractors; and the design procedure involves higher mathematics and lengthy numerical computations.

5-77. Cylindrical Shells. These are the most commonly used thin-shelled structures. They are especially adapted for roofing rectangular-plan structures. For determination of stresses, see Art. 3-87.

The inclination of stress trajectories can be computed and principal stress trajectories drawn for the shell. It will be found that high tensile stress occurs near the longitudinal edge at mid-span.

It is difficult to put reinforcing in the shell to follow the tensile-stress trajectories. It is sufficient to put the steel in a rectangular pattern, but at a 45° angle at the edges. Steel also is provided where no tension from loads exists to act as shrinkage and temperature reinforcement. Wire fabric may be used.

Multiple-barrel shells are a series of cylindrical shells connected in parallel; that is, the shells are continuous across their longitudinal edges. The following conditions must be satisfied:

1. The vertical line load at the edge must equal the vertical component of the membrane transverse force.

2. Shearing-line load at edge must equal the membrane shearing force.

3. Horizontal displacement of edge must be zero.

4. Rotation of edge must be zero.

Each interior barrel acts the same; so only one need be analyzed and designed. The exterior barrel may be considered to have the same stresses as an interior barrel from the interior edge to the crown and the same stresses as a simply supported barrel from the crown to the exterior edge. Design procedure is the same as for a single shell.

To stiffen cylindrical shells, a beam is sometimes cast integrally along each longitudinal edge. This beam is subjected to more complex loading than beams normally met in practice. In addition to its own weight, a uniform vertical load, it is loaded with a sinusoidal vertical load and a sinusoidal shear load.

Also, shells may be stiffened by integral transverse ribs. A stiffener is designed as a T-section arch rib carrying its own weight plus the weight of the shell between planes of zero shear (see also Art. 3-87).

The possibility of failure of the shell by buckling is rare, because the shell is not often made thin enough for this to happen. For design purposes, the normal compressive stress should be kept below $0.2Et/r$ for long barrels, where E is the modulus of elasticity of the concrete, t the thickness of the shell, and r its radius of curvature. Since the modulus of elasticity is assumed to be 1,000 times the cylinder strength f'_c, this stress should not exceed $200f'_c t/r$.

If the allowable compressive stress for flexure is taken as $0.45f'_c$, the above formula indicates that buckling becomes critical in long barrels only when the r/t ratio is greater than $200/0.45$, or about 450.

5-78. Folded-plate Concrete Construction. This also is known as prismatic-shell and hipped-plate. This type of structure consists simply of several thin plates intersecting along their edges and supported by diaphragms normal to the edges (Art. 3-88). The formwork is simpler, but the bending moments are larger than in cylindrical shells, making this type of shell less suitable for long spans. Design is similar to that for cylindrical shells.

5-79. Formwork for Cylindrical Shells. This is essentially the same as for arches. However, it should be noted that, because of the great cost of forms, it is essential that the forms be designed for maximum reuse. Therefore, the entire shell is not cast at one time. The form for only a portion—say, one-sixth of the shell—is constructed. This portion of the shell is then cured, while the forms are moved on tracks to the next position and that section is concreted.

This method may be used for spherical domes and cones also, the forms being rotated about the vertical axis. This method of construction may be used for many types of shell structures.

PRECAST CONCRETE

As differentiated from cast-in-place concrete, which is cast in exactly the location it will permanently occupy, precast members are made of concrete that is first cast and then placed in the structure. Precast-concrete construction is similar to erection of structural steel.

With precast concrete, form costs are greatly reduced, since the forms do not have to be supported or suspended in their final position but may be located on the ground in any convenient position. For instance, a very thin wall would be extremely difficult to construct if the wall were cast vertically. The concrete would have to be placed in the narrow opening in the top of the form. However, this wall is very easily precast flat on the ground. Also, one side form is eliminated, as well as many bracing members needed to keep the vertical wall form in place. No time need be lost in construction waiting for the concrete on one floor to harden before the concrete for the next floor can be placed.

Many of the more complex thin-shell structures would be almost impossible to construct of cast-in-place concrete. Furthermore, prestressed members are rarely cast in place.

5-80. Precast Floor and Roof Systems. In addition to the cast-in-place floor and roof systems described in Arts. 5-53 to 5-62, precast systems may be used. Precast units are made of the following types as defined in American Concrete Institute Standard 711:

1. I-beam type with cast-in-place or precast slab.
2. Hollow-core-type joists.
3. Assembled-concrete-block type:

   a. With contact faces between units ground to provide a slight camber to the assembly (also known as "Dox floor and roof system").
   b. With contact faces parallel, but with a tension in the lower moment bars sufficient to align and hold the assembly together and to provide a slight camber (also known as "Strestcrete").

4. Precast inverted T-beam joist with precast filler block between. Two systems that are used are "Joistile" and the "F and A" system.
5. Integrally precast slab and T-beam joist. This system is known as the "Farhan" slab.

5-81. Protective Cover for Reinforcement. High-early-strength cement is often used for precast units. The 28-day cylinder strength of the concrete usually is at least 3,750 psi, but lower strengths are permitted if lightweight aggregate is used.

In precast joists, the coarse aggregate should be no bigger than one-third the least dimension of the member and is rarely larger than $\frac{3}{8}$ in. Because of the more careful methods of manufacture, the concrete in precast joists will be denser, less porous, and consequently more fireproof than cast-in-place concrete. A smaller protective cover may then be allowed.

The American Concrete Institute Building Code Requirements for Reinforced Concrete ordinarily requires that, for both precast and cast-in-place concrete, protective cover for reinforcement not exposed directly to the ground or weather should be at least $\frac{3}{4}$ in. for slabs and walls, and not less than $1\frac{1}{2}$ in. for beams, girders, and columns. In concrete joist floors in which the clear distance between joists is not more than 30 in., protective cover should be at least $\frac{3}{4}$ in.

Reinforcement of footings and other principal structural members in which the concrete is deposited against the ground should have at least 3 in. of concrete between it and the ground. If concrete surfaces after removal of forms are to be exposed to the weather or be in contact with the ground, the reinforcement should be protected with at least 2 in. of concrete for bars larger than No. 5 and $1\frac{1}{2}$ in. for No. 5 bars or smaller.

Concrete protection in all cases should at least be equal to the diameter of the bars. Fire-protective cover may be reduced to $\frac{5}{8}$ in. if the precast member is not exposed to weather, moisture, or fire hazard.

5-82. I-beam-type Precast Joists. These joists come in several standard sizes. Most common are the 8-, 10-, and 12-in. depths. Many different floor systems are possible with this type. The floor slab may be poured on, or mortised into the joist, or a precast slab may be bonded to the joist. If the slab is bonded to it, the joist may be designed as a T beam.

5-83. Hollow-core-type Precast Joists. Floors made of precast-concrete units, in which some portion of the cross section is left out at the time of casting for the purposes of reducing dead load, are called hollow-core-precast floors.

5-84. Assembled-concrete-block-type Joists. In the Dox system, the lightweight blocks, which have openings in them to reduce weight and to provide space for utilities, are tongued and grooved to provide an interlocking action that aligns each plank or slab with the one next to it. Each slab or plank is made up of blocks tied together by rods run through openings in the blocks. The rods are tensioned to tie the blocks firmly together and provide a camber. The entire beam is cured and the tie rods secured and protected by mortar.

Strestcrete is similar to the Dox system except grout joints bond the beams together instead of tongues and grooves. As in the Dox system, tensioned rods hold the blocks together to form a beam and to provide initial camber. Strestcrete can be used for walls as well as floors and roofs. It is manufactured in 3-, 4-, 6-, 8-, 10-, and 12-in. depths, and 16-in. widths. Top negative steel may be used in both systems if the beams are continuous.

5-85. T-beam-type Precast Joists. The F and A system is an outgrowth of the hollow-tile and concrete-joist floor system described in Art. 5-58. It employs a precast inverted T-beam joist. The flanges of the T beam form a shelf on which precast filler blocks may be set. A concrete topping is then placed over the whole assembly, bonding with the joists to form a T beam.

Joistile is similar to the F and A system.

5-86. Ribbed-slab-type Precast Units. In this type, the joist and slab are integrally cast.

5-87. Thin-shell Precast Concrete. This may be defined as a type of reinforced-concrete framing composed of relatively thin prefabricated members. The term "thin shell" denotes a slab or shell that may be as little as $\frac{1}{2}$ in. thick. (Design and formwork for thin-shell structures are described in Arts. 5-77 to 5-79.)

Most of the thin-shell elements that are precast are made in the form of panels consisting of a thin slab cast integrally with longitudinal side beams or joists. Small transverse rib beams are also provided to give rigidity to the panel. They are designed as two-way slabs supported on all four sides by side joists and transverse ribs. The slab portion is reinforced with wire mesh, the joists and ribs with bar reinforcement.

Methods of manufacture vary. One common method employs metal or plastic pans as molds, which form the bottom of the slab and the sides of the joists and ribs. The exterior side forms are made of metal. The panels are stripped from the forms pneumatically or hydraulically by admitting air or water under pressure through the bottom pan.

5-88. Tilt-up Construction. Essentially this method consists of casting a wall in a horizontal position and then tilting it to its final vertical position.

To cast the wall, a casting platform is required—simply a smooth, approximately horizontal surface. It may consist of any of the following types:

1. Earth, fairly smooth, compacted, and hard.
2. Concrete slab—usually the floor or an auxiliary concrete area.
3. Wood planks—not recommended because form marks show.
4. Plywood built on a platform—an emergency measure.
5. Casting table—used in commercial precast factories or yards.
6. Wood molds—required for ribbed sections of minimum quantity.
7. Concrete molds—expensive; require maximum reuse.

Tilt-up walls require forms only for the sides. These forms may be made of steel or wood.

The most important item in tilt-up construction is the bond-breaking agent, which must be applied to the surface of the casting platform. Modern bond-breaking agents in order of economy and practicality are:

1. Hunt's Process solution Bx 112-TU; Techkote tilt-up compound.
2. Hunt's Process curing solution 130; Techkote antibond No. 200.
3. Paraffin dissolved in gasoline.
4. Wax dissolved in petroleum ether or gasoline.
5. Green liquid soap.
6. Refined commercial pure soap in powder form dissolved in water.
7. Blend of castor oil and fuel oil.
8. Talcum powder.
9. Ground chalk dissolved in water and applied as paint.
10. Water glass.
11. Paper (sisalkraft or equivalent).
12. Canvas.
13. Rubber or plastic sheeting.

A crane or A frame is used to lift up the wall. If lifting cables are attached to an edge, great bending stresses develop at the center of the wall. It is therefore economical and convenient to attach the cables to intermediate points. Two-point or three-point pickup may be used. The points are located approximately as shown in Fig. 5-29.

Specially designed inserts are cast into the wall at points where the cables are to be attached and reinforcing bars are placed around them. These inserts contain devices for fastening the cable to the slab.

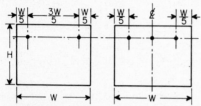

FIG. 5-29. Location of pickup points for tilt-up wall construction.

In addition to regular panel steel, reinforcing is added where necessary to resist bending stresses due to lifting. The wall may also be provided with braces when it is lifted.

Another method of lifting a wall slab is to use a vacuum mat. This consists of a steel mat with a rubber gasket along each edge, which is placed in contact with the slab. The air between the mat and the slab is pumped out. The mat then adheres to the slab because of the suction resulting from the vacuum.

It is often convenient to have the crane operate on the floor slab of the building. In this case, the floor must be designed for the concentrated load of the crane, and the inside of the wall slab must be shored up. If the crane is outside the building, the outside of the wall slab is shored up.

5-89. Lift-slab or Youtz-Slick Method. In this method, floor and roof slabs for a multistory building are cast on a base slab, one on top of the other, with a separating membrane between to prevent bond. Powerful jacks seated on the columns lift the slabs to their final position where they are structurally connected into place. This method eliminates practically all formwork.

PRESTRESSED CONCRETE

One of the disadvantages of reinforced concrete in bending is the waste of the concrete below the neutral axis, resulting from the assumption of a cracked section; i.e., concrete can take no tension. Also, concrete members that must be watertight have the additional disadvantage that their effective thickness in resisting the passage of water is reduced by cracks. Concrete may be prestressed to eliminate cracks.

5-90. Basic Principles of Prestressing (Wires, Bars, or Strands). Suppose a concrete beam is constructed in the following way: High-strength steel or tendons (with an ultimate tensile strength above 200,000 psi) are placed in the form, passing through holes in anchor plates at the end of the forms and tensioned to an initial force P_i. This may be done with jacks that bear against abutments at the ends of the casting bed. The concrete is then placed so that the anchor plates bear against it. After the concrete has attained sufficient strength, the steel is secured to the anchor plates and the jacks are removed. The tendons will tend to shorten and therefore will put compression in the concrete.

The steel bearing plates will exert a force P on the concrete after some time has elapsed. P will be somewhat smaller than P_i for the following reasons:

1. The compression in the concrete causes it to shorten, and the tendons also shorten, reducing the steel tensile stress, which is proportional to its elongation.

2. Further shortening results because of the creep of concrete under constant load.

3. If the steel is tensioned beyond its creep limit, it will stretch under constant stress, with consequent stress reduction.

Eccentrically applied, force P causes a stress distribution, as shown in Fig. 5-30a. The stress f_2 on the bottom is not allowed to exceed the permissible concrete compressive strength f_c, and f_1 on the top is not allowed to exceed the permissible concrete tensile stress. Usually, a slight compression is maintained on the top. When loads are applied, the net stresses remain compressive (Fig. 5-30b). The whole concrete cross section, therefore, is effective in resisting bending and there are no cracks. Sometimes, a small tension is permitted on the bottom.

High-strength concretes, with a cylinder strength of 5,000 psi or higher, are used in conjunction with high-strength steel. In the form of wires, the steel usually has an ultimate strength of the order of 220,000 psi. It is necessary to use such high steel stresses because of the loss of prestress due to plastic flow in the concrete.

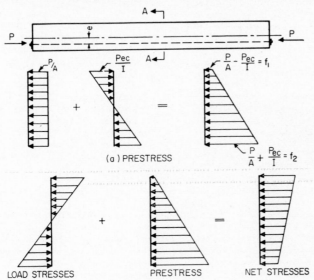

(a) PRESTRESS

LOAD STRESSES   PRESTRESS   NET STRESSES

(b) NET STRESSES AT SECTION A-A

Fig. 5-30. Stresses on the cross section of a posttensioned beam.

There are two methods of fabricating prestressed concrete: pretensioning and posttensioning. In pretensioning, the steel is stretched between external abutments before the concrete has hardened and released when it attains sufficient strength. The prestress is maintained without special anchorage by the bond between concrete and steel. Aiding this bond is the fact that the ends of the wires, being unstressed, expand laterally and wedge into the concrete, thus preventing slip. This system is highly suited for mass production. Often casting beds several hundred feet long between abutments are used in this operation, the entire length being cast simultaneously. The units later are cut into several lengths.

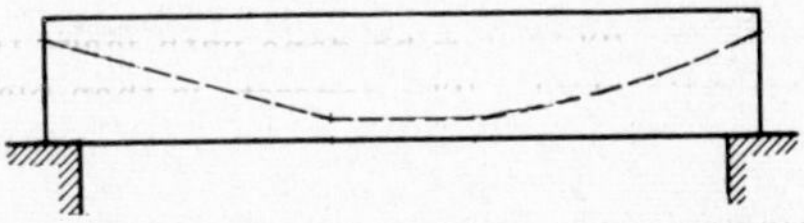

In posttensioning, the wires are placed in groups called "cables," which consist of wires uniformly spaced and kept separate from each other. The wires are stressed after the concrete has hardened, with bond prevented. (Generally, the cables are placed in sheathes to prevent bond during construction.)

Fig. 5-31. Posttensioned beam with tendons draped in a vertical curve.

Posttensioning has several advantages: No special abutments are required; the reinforcement need not be straight but may be bent up as shown in Fig. 5-31 to obtain a more advantageous stress distribution along the length of the beam.

Dead-weight stresses counteract some of the prestress; but at the ends of the beam there are no stresses due to dead load. If the beam is a pretensioned member with all the tendons straight, it will carry the same prestress throughout; consequently, the ends will be subject to negative moment and the top fibers may be in tension. The prestress at the ends is nullified by bending up wires as shown.

5-91. Allowable Stresses in Prestressed Concrete. There are actually two loading conditions for prestressed concrete: an initial prestress load, which is temporary, and the dead and live loads. Because of the different natures of these loads, different stresses are allowed. The allowable stresses for concrete under the temporary stresses are higher than those for the permanent stresses. The reason for this is that the prestress is actually in the nature of a test of the concrete; if the member fails during the prestress operation, no great harm is done.

Permissible temporary stresses are usually specified as a percentage of the concrete cylinder strength at the time of prestressing f'_{ci} rather than the 28-day cylinder strength f'_c because it is not usual to wait 28 days to prestress the concrete. Stresses are considered temporary if they are applied before creep and shrinkage take place. The permissible stresses are approximately as follows:

Temporary concrete:
  Compression in extreme fiber:
    Pretensioned................................ $0.60f'_{ci}$
    Posttensioned............................... $0.55f'_{ci}$
  Tension....................................... $0.05f'_{ci}$
  Prestressing steel............................. $0.80f'_s$
Stress under live and dead loads (after creep and
  shrinkage):
  Concrete:
    Compression in extreme fiber................... $0.45f'_c$
    Tension in extreme fiber....................... 0
  Prestressing steel............................. $0.6f'_s$ or $0.8f'_{sy}$, whichever is less

The allowable temporary compressive stress for concrete is higher for pretensioned than for posttensioned members. Also, allowance is made in steel stress for a drop in prestress. No tension is allowed in the concrete, however; if tension is shown by computations to be possible, ordinary reinforcement is added. But the computed tension in the concrete, before the unprestressed reinforcement is added, should not exceed $0.08f'_c$.

5-92. Loss of Prestress. It is necessary to compute the losses due to creep, shrinkage, elastic deformation, and friction. The ACI Code defines creep as the "inelastic deformation of concrete or steel, dependent on time and resulting solely from the presence of stress and a function thereof." Shrinkage is defined as the "contraction of concrete due to drying and chemical changes, dependent on time, but not on stresses due to external loading." The loss of prestress results from four causes:

1. *Shrinkage of Concrete.* The shrinkage in pretensioned members is assumed to be 0.0002 in. per in., causing the loss in tension in the steel to be

$$0.0002E_s = 0.0002 \times 30 \times 10^6 = 6,000 \text{ psi}$$

where E_s is the modulus of elasticity of the steel. For posttensioned members, shrinkage is assumed to have taken place when the steel is prestressed; in that case, the loss is only 3,000 psi.

2. *Elastic Compression of Concrete.* This equals P/AE_c, where E_c is the modulus of elasticity of the concrete.

3. *Creep of Concrete.* This is taken as 2.25 times the elastic compression.

4. *Creep of Steel.* If f_{si} is the stress in the tendons immediately after prestressing and creep is assumed to be 4%, the loss is $0.04f_{si}$.

When the tendons are curved, some allowance must be made for the loss in prestress due to the rubbing of the wires against the concrete. Even if the wires are straight, there may be friction because of the misalignment of the passageways. The stress in the wire may be found from the formula

$$T_o = T_x e^{(Kx + f\alpha)} \tag{5-80}$$

where T_o = stress at prestressing jack, psi
$\quad T_x$ = stress at a point x ft from the jack, psi
$\quad K$ = enclosure coefficient, which may vary from $1/200$ to $1/1,500$
$\quad f$ = coefficient of friction between prestressing steel and enclosure walls
$\quad \alpha$ = angle between element at jack and slope at given point, radians
$\quad e$ = 2.718
The following values of K may be used:

Preformed holes where concrete comes in direct contact with prestressing
steel.. $K = 1/1,000$
Galvanized-metal enclosure... $K = 1/1,000$
Ungalvanized-metal enclosure... $K = 1/500$

The following values of f may be used:

$\qquad$ Preformed holes................. $f = 0.50$
$\qquad$ Galvanized enclosure............. $f = 0.20$
$\qquad$ Ungalvanized enclosure.......... $f = 0.30$

5-93. Diagonal Tension in Prestressed Concrete. As in ordinary reinforced concrete, stirrups must be provided if the diagonal tension exceeds $0.03f'_c$. However, the effect of compressive stresses due to the prestress in reducing diagonal tension can be taken into account.

5-94. Bearing Stress under Anchor Plates. The stresses under the anchor plates should not exceed f'_c or

$$f_{cp} = 0.4f'_c \sqrt[3]{\frac{a_c}{a_p}}$$

where a_c = maximum area of that portion of beam end that is geometrically similar and concentric to anchor plate
$\quad a_p$ = the plate area.

5-95. Design of Prestressed Beams. The analysis may be accomplished by elastic or plastic assumptions. A prestressed beam acts in exactly the same way as a concrete member under combined compression and bending. If a straight-line stress-strain diagram is assumed, the prestress is given by

$$f = \frac{P}{A} \pm \frac{Pec}{I}$$

(See Fig. 5-30a.)
Also, the diagonal tension may be computed from

$$f = \frac{P}{2A} - \sqrt{\left(\frac{P}{2A}\right)^2 + V^2}$$

Part of the concrete in the middle portion of the beam may be dispensed with, as in steel beams, since it is not required for bending or diagonal tension. The most economical shape for a prestressed beam is an I, with a web strong enough to withstand the diagonal tension and shear. An I section is also efficient because the kern section is larger, and prestress applied in the lower flange will not produce as high tension stresses in the upper flange as it would for a rectangular section.

Design is essentially a trial-and-error procedure. However, tables have been devised for properties of common cross sections, as in the case of steel. The area of tendons required is determined by the amount of prestressing force that is required to put zero stress on the bottom fiber when full load occurs. When prestress is applied, the beam deflects upward so that the dead load of the beam will counteract the moment due to prestressing. This should prevent tension on the upper fiber even if the center of gravity of the steel is well outside the kern section.

In posttensioned members, it is usual to inject grout to develop bond between the steel and the concrete. This bond is not relied upon, however; the end anchor plates are designed to carry the entire prestress.

5-96. Construction of Posttensioned Beams. In Freyssinet's method, the tendons are usually sheathed in paper, metal, or bitumen to prevent bonding to the concrete. Each cable consists of 12 wires. The 12 wires are pulled simultaneously by a double-acting hydraulic jack. While one part of the jack induces and maintains the tension in the wires, another part of the jack forces a cone into the anchorage device, thus locking the wires in place.

In Magnel's system, rubber inlays are placed in the forms in the same positions that the steel reinforcing is to occupy. After the concrete has been cast, they are removed. The cables are then inserted. A cable consists of four wires per layer for as many layers as necessary. The wires are pulled in pairs. Each pair is anchored separately by a steel wedge in steel plates called sandwich plates.

Prestressed members are usually not cast in place as ordinary reinforced-concrete members are. They are precast elsewhere and lifted into place in much the same way as steel members. Usually, they are precast in a factory. Entire buildings may be constructed of precast, prestressed columns, beams, girders, and slabs.

STRENGTHENING AND DAMAGE REPAIR OF CONCRETE STRUCTURES

Corrective construction may be required to strengthen reinforced-concrete structures, thereby increasing safety or load-carrying capacity. Also, structures may have structural defects because of deterioration due to age or faulty construction methods, poor ingredients, improper design, or a combination of these causes. Another not uncommon cause for corrective construction is damage due to fire and spalling and "popping," caused by sudden change in temperature when cold water from a fire hose strikes heated concrete.

5-97. Corrective Construction. One of the most important objectives is the bonding of new concrete to the old so that both act, as nearly as possible, as though cast monolithically. To effect this, the folllwing steps are recommended;

1. The old concrete structure should be stress-relieved—usually accomplished by a controlled jacking operation. The jacking load may be a concentrated load, or a distributing device may be used to spread it. A concentrated jacking load, at the center of a bay, equal to about 60% of the distributed dead load in the bay, will cause an elastic deflection equal to uniform dead-load deflection, but in the opposite direction. The ideal jacking load is one that will restore the structure to the position it had when originally formed; i.e., when supported by the formwork and with no induced stresses. In addition to use of calibrated gages on the jacks, the jacking operation is carefully controlled by surveyor's level, extension dials (Ames or Mercer), and plaster of paris telltales (patches located at sections of maximum tension that show cracks well in advance of the jacking load that will cause distress in the structure). The structure should be shored and wedged to hold the position caused by the jacking operation; then the jacks may be removed.

2. The defective area should be scarified by hand chipping or by compressed-air chippers with a sharp chisel point to a depth of at least ¾ in. A greater depth, however, may be required to reach hard sound concrete. All laitance, old topping, and loose material should be removed, leaving coarse aggregate exposed in as rough a surface as possible.

3. The area should be cleaned of all loose material with stiff brooms, compressed air (or high-pressure water), and a commercial vacuum cleaner to remove loose dust and fine sand particles.

4. The area should be wetted down and kept moist for at least 14 hr. Free water should be avoided and removed if it collects in the low spots.

5. Slab areas requiring major strengthening should be provided with a mat of reinforcing bars. Studs $3/16$ or $1/4$ in. thick should be shot into the scarified slab but left projecting a distance that permits the mat to be held in exact position. The supporting bars should be welded to the top of the studs, and the top layer of the mat

should be fastened to the supporting bars, preferably by welding, but wire ties may be adequate. For this type of mat, the topping must be at least 2 in. thick.

For toppings less than 2 in. thick, wire-mesh fabric may be used to advantage. Varying degrees of strength may be obtained, dependent on the spacing of the wires, the gage, and the method of tying. For maximum strength, the heavier and more closely spaced fabric should be welded to the studs. The lightest fabric (2 × 2 by No. 14) may be tied to the studs ($3/16$-in. diameter, 18 in. c to c). For minor strengthening, or merely resurfacing, studs are not needed. In addition to strengthening, the mat and fabric act as temperature reinforcement and crack-control steel.

6. The rough surface should be soaked with water and kept damp for at least 14 hr prior to the next operation. However, all free water must be removed before application of the slush coat.

7. A rich mortar (1:1) is slushed onto the rough surface and worked into every recess with stiff brooms. The mortar coat should be thin and under no circumstances should it be permitted to set up before the topping is applied. A retarder should be used to insure proper bonding of the topping to the old concrete.

8. A low-slump rich topping should be carefully placed, using vibrators to insure intimate contact with the slush coat and the old concrete. Topping mixes may range from $1:1:1\frac{1}{2}$ for extremely high strengths (over 6,000 psi) to $1:1\frac{1}{2}:2\frac{1}{2}$. The coarse aggregate should be screenings or chips less than $3/8$ in. in size, or grit. A minimum amount of water should be used with a slump not to exceed 2 in. It is important to keep shrinkage to a minimum, and therefore the water content is very important. Retarders are beneficial because the heat of hydration is developed at a slower rate and is easily dissipated. Accelerators should obviously not be used. Surface hardeners and other admixtures that do not develop heat rapidly may be used for their advantages.

9. Camber should be provided by placing the topping with a high point at the center of the slab. The surface finishing should be executed in the usual manner.

10. Curing of the topping is second in importance only to the intimate bonding of the old and new concrete. To secure the maximum hydration of cement, the concrete should be kept continuously moist during the curing stage (at least 7 days). An effective and economical way to cure a slab is to build a low sand dam around the area and keep the area flooded with an inch or two of water.

11. After the topping has cured and attained desired strength, jacks are used to remove the load from the shores, which then are taken away. After that, the jacking load should be gradually reduced to zero, deflection readings being taken meanwhile. From these measurements, it is possible to determine the elastic behavior of the structure, the degree to which the topping has been bonded, the stresses the structure will develop under dead load, and superimposed live load.

12. Surfaces other than horizontal must be strengthened or refinished in a different manner. If possible, the structure should be stress-relieved. The surfaces may be roughened by sandblasting or hand chipping. The fabric may be tied or welded to existing exposed bars or welded to studs shot into the concrete. After soaking with water, pneumatically jetted mortar may be applied to the roughened surface. (Pneumatically applied mortar should not be used on floors because the "fly" settles back and forms weak planes in the topping.) For ceilings and vertical surfaces, the "fly" presents no problems other than the need for coating finished work.

Ceilings and surfaces not horizontal may be cured with a curing compound sprayed on the surface to seal in the water.

13. Most building codes require a load test to prove the safety and adequacy of a strengthened or repaired structure. Since the test load must be a uniform load, jacking loads are not used. The load may consist of sand, water, concrete blocks. or bags of cement uniformly distributed over a typical test area as specified in the code.

Section 6

STRUCTURAL-STEEL CONSTRUCTION

Henry J. Stetina

Regional Engineer
American Institute of Steel Construction

Structural-steel construction embraces only the range of hot-rolled steel sections (or shapes) and plates, of thicknesses not less than ⅛ in., together with such fittings as rivets, bolts, bracing rods, and turnbuckles.

The shop operation of cutting steel plates and shapes to final size, punching, drilling, and assembling the components into finished members ready for shipment is called **fabricating.** Some 400 companies comprise the structural-steel fabricating industry. The majority not only take contracts to furnish the fabricating services but also install or erect the steel—a branch of the industry called **erecting.**

The skilled laborers employed in the field to actually place and connect the steel in position are called **ironworkers.**

To promote uniformity in bidding practices, the American Institute of Steel Construction has adopted a more specific, although lengthy, definition for structural steel (see also "Code of Standard Practice"). It is well for the owner and his engineer to understand fully just what the fabricator will supply when the latter submits a price for furnishing "structural steel." When it is desired that bids should include any other material, such as ornamental iron and miscellaneous metalwork, a statement to that effect should appear in the bidding invitation.

6-1. Structural-steel Shapes. Steel mills have a standard classification for the many products they make, one of which is *structural shapes (heavy)*. By definition this classification takes in all shapes having at least one cross-sectional dimension of 3 in. or more. Shapes of lesser size are classified as *structural shapes (light)* or, more specifically, bars.

Shapes are identified by their cross-sectional characteristics—angles, channels, I beams, wide-flange beams and columns, light columns, tees, zees, bulb angles, and H piles. Each shape has its particular functional use, but the work horse of building construction is the wide-flange section.

Wide flanges, symbolically known as WF's, account for nearly one-half of the structural-shape (heavy) tonnage. Two mills, Bethlehem Steel and U.S. Steel, produce an entire range of sizes, there being about 160 different sections listed in the current AISC "Manual of Steel Construction." A small percentage of wide flanges is produced by two other mills; Kaiser Steel, with a range of 12 sizes, and Inland Steel, with a range of 30 sizes. A couple of other mills possess equipment for rolling a few of the lighter wide-flange sections, but their production is sporadic.

The wide-flange shapes rolled by the two major mills may not be precisely identical because of differences in rolling methods. Many of Bethlehem's WF shapes have a 5% slope on the inside face of flanges, whereas all of U.S. Steel's WF's have parallel-

6–1

face flanges. The table of properties in the AISC "Manual" gives the smaller values, but the difference is negligible.

6-2. Tolerances for Structural Shapes. Mills are granted a tolerance because of variations peculiar to working of hot steel and wear of equipment. Limitations for such variations are established by Specification A6 of the American Society for Testing Materials.

A wide-flange beam or column, for example, may vary in depth by as much as $\frac{1}{2}$ in.; i.e., $\frac{1}{4}$ in. over and under the nominal depth. The designer should always keep this in mind. Particularly, he should appreciate the fabricator's and erector's efforts to control these variations. Fillers, shims, and extra weld metal may not be desirable, but often they are the only practical solution.

Cocked flanges on column members are particularly troublesome to the erector, for it is not until the steel is erected in the field that the full extent of mill variations becomes evident. This is particularly true for a long series of spans or bays, where the accumulating effect of dimensional variation of many columns may require major adjustment. Fortunately, the average variation usually is negligible and nominal erection clearance allowed for by the fabricator will suffice.

Mill tolerances also apply to beams ordered from the mills cut to length. Where close tolerance may be desired, as sometimes required for welded connections, it may be necessary to order the beams long and then mill the ends in the fabricating shop to the precise dimensions.

6-3. Cambered Beams. Frequently, designers want long-span beams slightly arched (cambered) to offset deflection under load and to prevent a flat or saggy appearance. Such beams may be procured from the mills, the required camber being applied to cold steel. The AISC "Manual of Steel Construction" gives the maximum cambers that mills can obtain and their prediction of the minimum cambers likely to remain permanent. Smaller cambers than these minimums may be specified, but their permanency cannot be guaranteed. It should be observed that nearly all beams will have some camber as permitted by the tolerance for straightness, and advantage may be taken of such camber in shop fabrication.

A method of cambering, not dependent on mill facilities, is to employ heat. In welded construction, it is commonplace to flame-straighten members that have become distorted. By the same procedure, it is possible to distort or camber a beam to desired dimensions.

6-4. Obsolete Steel Sections. Over the years, there have been numerous changes in the size of beam and column sections. The reasons are many: efficiency, popularity, stocking, standardization, simplification, and conservation. Occasionally, an engineer is called on to investigate an existing building, possibly because of increased floor loadings or because an additional story or two is to be added. Whatever the reason, he may be faced with the task of identifying sections that are no longer rolled and for which physical properties are not readily obtainable. To aid the designer in this problem, the American Institute of Steel Construction published in 1953 a complete compilation of steel and wrought-iron beams and columns that were rolled in this country during the period 1873–1952.

6-5. Codes and Specifications. Uniform quality is an outstanding characteristic of structural steel. There is no significant metallurgical or physical difference between the products rolled by the several structural mills. This high degree of uniformity is achieved through acceptance of the nationally recognized American Society for Testing Materials Specification A7, "Steel for Bridges and Buildings."

Companion ASTM specifications are used for the several types of fasteners and appurtenant materials:

Rivets: A141.
Bolts and nuts: A307.
High-tensile-strength bolts, washers, and nuts: A325.
Welding electrodes: A233.

Appropriate material specifications are also available for cast iron, cast steel, malleable iron, and forgings.

The American Institute of Steel Construction "Specification for the Design,

Fabrication and Erection of Structural Steel for Building," a recommendation adopted originally in 1923, has been prominent in standardizing structural practice. It is revised from time to time to keep abreast of professional thoughts and the results of research. Incorporated in the specification are all the pertinent requirements for welding as promulgated by the American Welding Society's "Standard Code for Arc and Gas Welding in Building Construction."

The AISC recommended basic allowable unit stress for tension and bending of structural steel is 20,000 psi. Nevertheless, local code requirements should be checked.

This basic unit stress of 20,000 psi is in the ratio of 1 to 1.65 to the minimum yield point of 33,000 psi, the A7 requirement. This ratio, sometimes called the factor of safety, has been a constant for more than four decades.

ASTM Specification A373, "Tentative Specification for Structural Steel for Welding," was conceived as the result of repeated demands from many bridge engineers and welding theorists who sought to limit the carbon and manganese contents in structural steel of A7 specification. Although this "controlled" steel has already found favor for welded bridges, its usage in building construction at present is obscure. Probably it will be confined to special applications, Federal construction (Type II steel, QQ-S-741a), and for plates and shapes in the thicker range. Its lower yield point, 32,000 psi as against 33,000 psi for A7 steel, is not believed to be a deterrent for popular usage. Principal handicap is the satisfactory record of A7 in welded building construction.

It should never be taken for granted that all steel in existing buildings conforms to A7 or to preceding specifications for structural-grade mild-carbon steel. In some instances, various low-alloy steels, structural silicon steel, and others have been rolled into structural shapes and used in building construction.

It is very seldom that the building engineer can justify a high-strength low-alloy steel (ASTM A242 or similar) on the basis of economy alone. Extra mill costs must be offset by weight saving and value attached to superior resistance to atmospheric corrosion. Also, the quantity involved must be sufficient to justify rolling each of the several sizes that would normally be required.

STEEL-FRAMING SYSTEMS

Steel construction may be classified into three broad categories: wall bearing, skeleton framing, and long-span construction. Depending on the functional requirements of the building itself and the materials used in constructing its roof, floors, and walls, one or more of these methods of framing may be employed in a single structure.

6-6. Wall-bearing Framing. Probably the oldest and commonest type of framing, wall-bearing framing (not to be confused with bearing-wall construction), occurs wherever a wall of a building, interior or exterior, is used to support ends of main structural elements carrying roof or floor loads. The walls must be strong enough to carry the reaction from the supported members and thick enough to insure stability against any horizontal forces that may be imposed. Such construction is limited to relatively low structures, because load-bearing walls become massive and uneconomical in taller structures. Generally, a three-story wall-bearing structure is close to the economical limit. Nevertheless, on occasion, a wall-bearing system may be advantageous for certain parts of taller buildings.

A common application of wall-bearing construction may be found in many one-family homes. A steel beam, usually 8 or 10 in. deep, is used to carry the interior walls and floor loads across the basement with no intermediate supports, the ends of the beam being supported on the foundation walls. The relatively shallow beam depth affords maximum headroom for the span. In some cases, the spans may be so large that an intermediate support becomes necessary to minimize deflection—usually a steel pipe column serves this purpose.

Another example of wall-bearing framing is the member used to support masonry over windows, doors, and other openings in a wall. Such members, called **lintels,** may be a steel angle section (commonly used for brick walls in residences) or, on

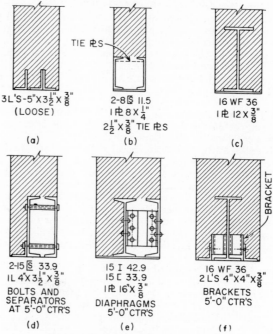

TIE ₽S

3 L'S-5"X3½"X⅜"
(LOOSE)

2-8 Ⓢ 11.5
1 ₽ 8 X ¼"
2½"X⅜" TIE ₽S

16 WF 36
1 ₽ 12 X ⅜"

(a)   (b)   (c)

BRACKET

2-15 Ⓢ 33.9
1 L 4"X3½"X⅜"
BOLTS AND
SEPARATORS
AT 5'-0" CTR'S

15 I 42.9
15 C 33.9
1 ₽ 16"X ⅜"
DIAPHRAGMS
5'-0" CTR'S

16 WF 36
2 L'S 4"X4"X⅜"
BRACKETS
5'-0" CTR'S

(d)   (e)   (f)

FIG. 6-1. Lintels supporting masonry.

longer spans and for heavier walls, a fabricated assembly.   A variety of frequently used types is shown in Fig. 6-1.   In types (b), (c), and (e), a continuous plate is used to close the bottom, or soffit, of the lintel, and to join the load-carrying beams and channels into a single shipping unit.   The gap between the toes of the channel flanges in type (d) may be covered by a door frame or window trim, to be installed later. Pipe and bolt separators are used to hold the two channels together to form a single member for handling (see also Art. 6-75).

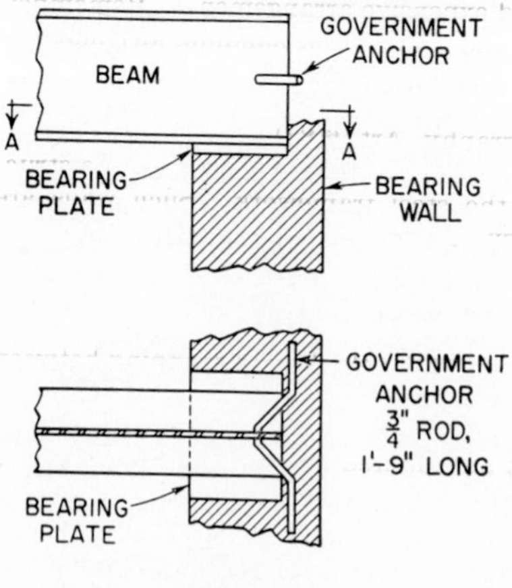

BEAM

GOVERNMENT ANCHOR

BEARING PLATE

BEARING WALL

A ← A

GOVERNMENT ANCHOR
¾" ROD,
1'-9" LONG

BEARING PLATE

SECTION A-A
FIG. 6-2. Wall-bearing beam.

Because of the low allowable unit pressures on masonry, bearing plates (sometimes called masonry plates or grillages) are usually required under the ends of all beams that rest on masonry walls, as illustrated in Fig. 6-2. Even when the pressure on the wall under a member is such that an area no greater than the contact portion of the member itself is required, wall plates are sometimes prescribed, if the member is of such weight that it must be set by the steel erector.   The plates, shipped loose and in advance of steel erection, are then set by the mason to provide a satisfactory seat at the proper elevation.

Wall-bearing beams are usually anchored to the masonry. Of the two common methods shown in the American Institute of Steel Construction "Manual of Steel Construction," **government anchors** as illustrated in Fig. 6-2 have been preferred.

Aside from residential use, another common application for the wall-bearing system is in one-story commercial and light industrial-type construction. The masonry side walls support the roof system, which may be rolled beams, open-web joists, or light trusses. Clear spans of moderate size are usually economical, but for longer spans (probably over 40 ft), wall thickness and size of buttresses (pilasters) must be built to certain specified minimum proportions commensurate with the span distance—a requirement of building codes to assure stability. Therefore, the economical aspect should be carefully investigated. It may cost less to introduce steel columns and keep wall size to the minimum permissible. On the other hand, it may be feasible to cut the span length in two by introducing intermediate columns and still retain the wall-bearing system for the outer end reactions.

There is one disadvantage of wall-bearing construction that needs to be emphasized: Before the steel can be set by the ironworkers, the masonry must be built up to the

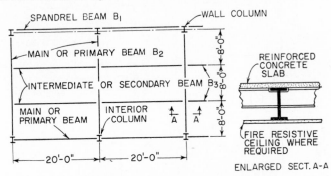

Fig. 6-3. Typical steel beam-and-column framing.

proper elevation to receive it. When these elevations vary, as is the case at the end of a pitched or arched roof, then it may be necessary to proceed in alternate stages, progress of erection being interrupted by the work that must be performed by the masons, and vice versa. The necessary timing to avoid delays is seldom obtained. A few columns or an additional rigid frame at the end of a building may cost less than calling trades to a job on some intermittent and expensive arrangement. Remember, too, that labor-union regulations may prevent the trades from handling any material other than that belonging to their own craft. An economical rule may well be: Lay out the work so that the erector and his ironworkers can place and connect all the steelwork in one continuous operation (Bibliography, Art. 6-87).

6-7. Skeleton Framing. In skeleton framing all the gravity loadings of the structure, including the walls, are supported by the steel framework. Such walls are termed **nonbearing** or **curtain walls.** This system made the skyscraper possible. Steel, being so much stronger than all forms of masonry, is capable of sustaining far greater load in a given space, thus obstructing less of the floor area in performing its function.

With columns properly spaced to provide support for the beams spanning between them, there is no limit to the floor and roof area that can be constructed with this type of framing, merely by duplicating the details for a single bay. Erected tier upon tier, this type of framing can be built to any desired height. Fabricators refer to this type of construction as "beam and column"; a typical arrangement is illustrated in Fig. 6-3.

The spandrel beams, marked B1 in Fig. 6-3, are located in or under the wall so as to reduce eccentricity caused by wall loads. Figure 6-4 shows two methods for connecting to the spandrel beam the shelf angle that supports the outer course of masonry over window openings 6 ft or more in width. In order that the masonry contractor may proceed expeditiously with his work, these shelf angles must be in alignment with the face of the building and at the proper elevation to match a masonry joint. The connection of the angles to the spandrel beams is made by bolting; shims are provided to make the adjustments for line and elevation (Art. 6-75).

Figure 6-4a illustrates a typical connection arrangement when the outstanding leg of the shelf angle is about 3 in. or less below the bottom flange of the spandrel beam; Fig. 6-4b illustrates the corresponding arrangement when the outstanding leg of the shelf angle is more than about 3 in. below the bottom flange of the spandrel

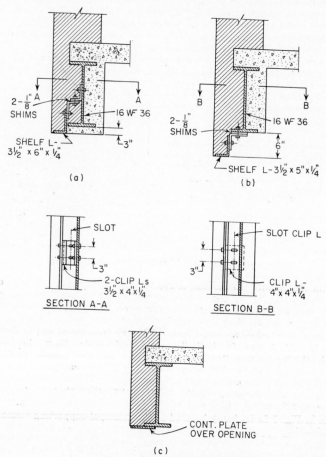

FIG. 6-4. Typical steel spandrel beams.

beam. In the cases represented by Fig. 6-4b, the shelf angles are usually shipped attached to the spandrel beam; however, if the distance from the bottom flange to the horizontal leg of the shelf angle is greater than 10 in., a hanger may be required.

In some cases, as over door openings, the accurate adjustment features provided by Fig. 6-4a and b may not be needed. It may then be more economical to simplify the detail, as shown in Fig. 6-4c. The elevation and alignment will then conform to the permissible tolerances associated with the steel framework (Bibliography, Art. 6-87).

6-8. Long-span Steel Framing. Large industrial buildings, auditoriums, gymnasiums, theaters, hangars, and exposition buildings require much greater clear distance between supports than can be supplied by beam and column framing. When the clear distance is greater than can be spanned with rolled beams, several alternatives are available. These may be classified as *girders, simple trusses, arches, rigid frames,* and *cantilever-suspension spans.*

Girders are the usual choice where depths are limited, as over large unobstructed areas in the lower floors of tall buildings, where column loads from floors above must be carried across the clear area. Sometimes, when only slightly more strength is required than is available in rolled beams, cover plates are added to the flanges (Fig. 6-5a) to provide the additional strength.

When depths are over 36 in.—the limit for rolled beams—the girder must be built up from plates and shapes, as shown in Fig. 6-5b to i. Type g employs a channel section for the top flange, thus providing greater horizontal bending strength. Crane girders are of this type. Type a may be assembled by either riveting or welding; types b to g are adapted for riveted fabrication; types h and i are designed for welding. Type h illustrates the simplest composition—three elements, all plates. See also Fig. 6-20, Art. 6-26, and Fig. 6-22, Art. 6-27.

Welded construction affords maximum flexibility; e.g., the flange plates need not be parallel but may be arched or uniformly tapered to suit design and architectural requirements. Also, a welded girder offers the most opportunity for weight reduction.

Each cover plate is limited in thickness by either of two rules: (1) plate thickness should not exceed the thickness of the flange angles or beam flange; or (2) the punchable thickness as determined by the capacity of shop equipment, usually a ⅞-in.

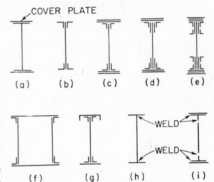

FIG. 6-5. Typical built-up girders.

plate, is the maximum. In the case of type g, there is no restriction on the thickness of the flange plate, single plates being preferred to two or more plates superimposed. A series of single plates of short lengths may be butt-welded together to form a continuous flange from end to end.

When the depth limitation is not binding, a more economical way of spanning long distances is with *trusses,* for both floor and roof construction. Because of their greater depth, trusses usually provide a greater stiffness against deflection when compared pound for pound with the corresponding rolled beam or plate girder that otherwise would be required. Five general types of trusses frequently used in building frames are shown in Fig. 6-6, together with modifications that can be made to suit particular conditions.

Trusses in Fig. 6-6a to d may be used as the principal supporting members in floor and roof framing; types e to j serve a similar function in the framing of symmetrical roofs having a pronounced pitch. As shown, types a to d have a top chord which is not quite parallel to the bottom chord. Such an arrangement is used to provide for drainage of flat roofs. Most of the connections of the roof beams (**purlins**), which these trusses support, can be identical, which would not be the case if the top chord were dead level and the elevation of the purlins varied. When used in floors, truss types a to d have parallel chords.

Properly proportioned, bow-string trusses (Fig. 6-6j) have the unique characteristic that the stress in their web members is relatively small. The top chord, which usually is formed in the arc of a circle, is stressed in compression, and the bottom chord in tension. In spite of the relatively expensive operation of forming the top chord, this type of truss has proved very popular in roof framing on spans of moderate lengths up to about 100 ft.

Transverse cross sections through a number of typical buildings having roof trusses of the general type just discussed are shown diagrammatically in Fig. 6-7. Cross section (a) might be that of a storage building or a light industrial building. A Fink truss has been used to provide a substantial roof slope. Roofs of this type are often designed to carry little loading, if any, except that produced by wind and snow, since the contents of the building are supported on the ground floor. For light construction, the roof and exterior wall covering may consist of thin, cold-formed metal or asbestos-cement sheets, lapped at their seams so as to shed rain. Lighting and

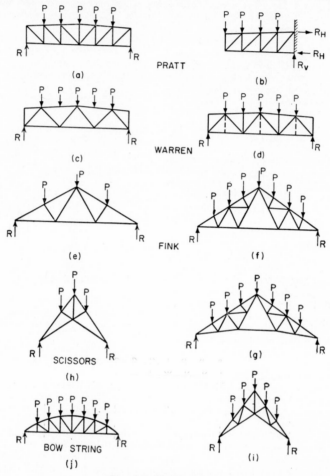

Fig. 6-6. Steel trusses.

ventilation, in addition to that provided by windows in the vertical side walls, frequently are furnished by means of sash installed in the vertical side of a continuous monitor, framing for which is indicated by the dotted lines in the sketch.

Cross section (b) shows a scissors truss supporting the high roof over the nave of a church. This type of truss is used only when the roof pitch is steep, as in ecclesiastical architecture.

A modified Warren truss, shown in cross section (c), might be one of the main supporting roof members over an auditorium, gymnasium, theater, or other assembly-type building where large, unobstructed floor space is required. Similar trusses are used in the roofs of large garages, terminal buildings, and airplane hangars, for spans ranging from about 80 up to 200 ft.

The Pratt truss (Fig. 6-7d) is frequently used in industrial buildings, while (e) depicts a type of framing often used where overhead traveling cranes handle heavy loads from one point on the ground to another.

When very large clear spans are needed, the transverse bent framing required to support walls and roof may take the form of solid or open-web *arches*, of the kind shown in Fig. 6-8. A notable feature of bents (a) and (b) are the heavy steel pins

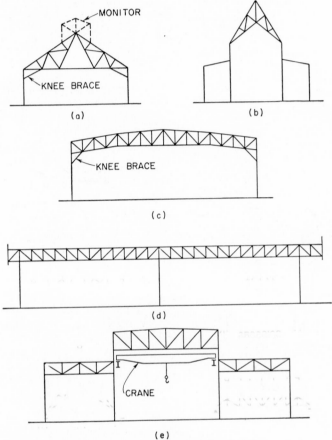

Fig. 6-7. Structures with trussed roofs.

at points *A*, *B*, and *C*, connecting the two halves of the arch together at the crown and supporting them at the foundation. These pins are designed to carry all the reaction from each half arch, and to function in shear and bearing much as a single rivet is assumed to perform when loaded in double shear.

Use of hinge pins offers two advantages in long-span frames of the type shown in Fig. 6-8. In the first place, they simplify design calculations. Secondly, they simplify erection. All the careful fitting and the heavy riveting required to develop the needed strength at the ends of the arch can be performed in the shop and at ground level. When these heavy members have been raised in the field about in their final position, the upper end of each arch is adjusted, upward or downward, by means of jacks near the free end of the arch. When the holes in the pin plates line up exactly, the crown pin is slipped in place and secured against falling out by the attachment of keeper plates. The arch is then ready to carry its loading. Bents of the type shown in Fig. 6-8a and b are referred to as **three-hinged arches.**

When ground conditions are favorable and foundations are properly designed, and if the loads to be carried are relatively light, as, for example, for a large dirigible hangar, a **hingeless arch** similar to the one shown diagrammatically in Fig. 6-8c may offer advantage in over-all economy.

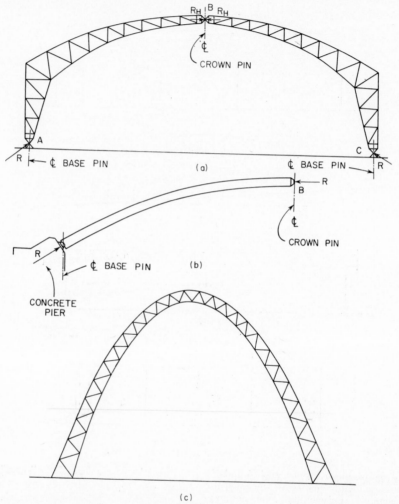

Fig. 6-8. Steel arches.

In many cases, the arches shown in Fig. 6-8a and b are designed without the pins at B (**two-hinged arch**). Then, the section at B must be capable of carrying the moment and shear present. Therefore, the section at B may be heavier than for the three-hinged arch, and erection will be more exacting for correct closure.

Another type of long-span bent is the **rigid frame.** In its design, the stiffness afforded by beam-to-column connections is carefully evaluated and counted on in the design to relieve some of the bending moment that otherwise would be assumed as occurring with maximum intensity at mid-span. Typical examples of rigid frame bents are shown in Fig. 6-9. When completely assembled in place in the field, the frames are fully continuous throughout their entire length and height. A distinguishing characteristic of rigid frames is the absence of pins or hinges at the crown, or mid-span.

In principle, single-span rigid-frame bents are either two-hinged or hingeless arches—the latter, when the column bases are fully restrained by large rigid foundations, to which they are attached by a connection capable of transmitting moment

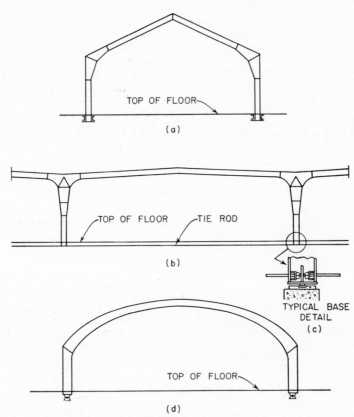

FIG. 6-9. Steel rigid frames.

as well as shear. Since such foundations may not be economical, if at all possible, because of soil conditions, the usual practice is to consider the bents hinged at each reaction. However, this does not imply the necessity of expensive pin details; in most cases, sufficient rotation of the column base can be obtained with the ordinary flat-ended base detail and a single line of anchor bolts placed perpendicular to the span on the column center line. Many designers prefer to obtain a hinge effect by concentrating the column load on a narrow bar, as shown in Fig. 6-9c; this refinement is worthwhile in larger spans.

Regardless of how the frame is hinged, there is a problem in resisting the horizontal shear that the rigid frame imparts to the foundation. For small spans and light thrusts, it may be feasible to depend on the foundation to resist lateral displacement. However, more positive performance and also reduction in costs is usually obtained by connecting opposite columns of a frame with tie rods, as illustrated in Fig. 6-9b, thus eliminating these horizontal forces from the foundation.

For ties on small spans, it may be possible to utilize the reinforcing bars in the floor slabs or floor beams, by simply connecting them to the column bases. On larger spans, it is advisable to use tie rods and turnbuckles, the latter affording the opportunity to prestress the ties and thus compensate for elastic elongation of the rods when stressed. Prestressing the rod during erection to 50% of its value has been recommended for some major installations; but, of course, the foundations should be checked for resisting some portion of the thrust.

Rigid frames have been fabricated and erected economically in both riveted and welded construction. However, the make-up of the usual frame has provided impetus for the widespread use of the latter fabrication method. The architecturally pleasing haunches (more often called "knees"), tapered columns when specified, variable-depth or parabolic-shaped girders, and clean lines, afforded by simple-plate stiffeners and absence of rivetheads, are a few features that enhance welded construction.

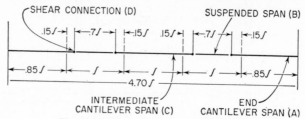

Fig. 6-10. Hung-span steel construction.

One of the principal problems associated with long-span construction is that of locating field splices compatible with the maximum sizes of members that can be shipped and erected. Field splices in frames are generally located at or near the point of counterflexure, thus reducing the splicing material to a minimum. In general, the maximum height for shipping by truck is 8 ft, by rail 10 ft. Greater over-all depths are possible, but these should always be checked with the carrier; they vary with clearances under bridges and through tunnels.

Individual shipping pieces must be stiff enough to be handled without buckling or other injury, light enough to be lifted by the raising equipment, and capable of erection without interference from other parts of the framework. This suggests a study of the entire frame to insure orderly erection, and to make provisions for temporary bracing of the members, to prevent jackknifing, and for temporary guying of the frame, to obtain proper alignment.

In certain applications, for example, large one-story buildings, an arrangement of **cantilever-suspension** (**hung**) spans (Fig. 6-10) has proved economical and highly efficient. This layout was made so as to obtain equal maximum moments, both negative and positive, for the condition of uniform load on all spans. A minimum of three spans is required; that is, a combination of two end spans (A) and one interior span (B). The connection at the end of the cantilever (point D) must be designed as a shear connection only. If the connection is capable of transmitting moment as well as shear, it will change the design to one of continuity and the dimensions in Fig. 6-10 will not apply. This scheme of cantilever and suspended spans is not necessarily limited to one-story buildings.

As a rule, interior columns are separate elements in each story. Therefore, horizontal forces on the building must be taken solely by the exterior columns (Bibliography, Art. 6-87).

6-9. Steel and Concrete Framing. A fourth category or framing system could be added, wherein a partial use of structural steel has an important role, namely, the *reinforced-concrete–structural-steel combination framing.*

Reinforced-concrete columns when employed in tall buildings and for large spans become excessively large. The loss in floor area and the bulky appearance are objectionable. The practice is to reduce the column size to that required for structural steel by using a steel column for the core. In principle, the column load is carried by both the steel column and the concrete that surrounds the steel shape; building codes usually contain an appropriate formula for this condition.

A number of systems employ a combination of concrete and steel in various ways. One method features steel columns supporting a concrete floor system by means of a steel grillage connected to the columns at each floor level. The shallow grillage is embedded in the floor slab, thus obtaining a smooth ceiling without drops or capitals.

Another combination system is the **lift-slab** method. In this system, the floor slabs are cast one on top of another at ground level. Jacks, placed on the permanent steel columns, raise the slabs, one by one, to their final elevation, where they are made secure to the columns. The columns may be boxed in with any one of many noncombustible materials available for that purpose. The merit of this system is the elimination of formwork and shoring that is essential in conventional reinforced-concrete construction (Bibliography, Art. 6-87).

FLOOR AND ROOF SYSTEMS

In most types of buildings, floor and roof systems are so intimately related to the structural frame that the two must be considered together in the development of a steel design. Both are important, but floors usually predominate in tier-type structures.

6-10. Factors Affecting Floor Design. Selection of a suitable and economical floor system for a steel-frame building involves many considerations: load-carrying capacity, durability, fire resistance, dead weight, over-all depth, facility for installing power, light, and telephones, facility for installing air conditioning, sound transmission, appearance, maintenance, and construction time.

Building codes set minimum design live loads for those structures within jurisdictional areas. In the absence of a code regulation, one may use "Minimum Design Loads in Buildings and Other Structures" (American Standard A58.1, American Standards Association), a summary of which is given in Tables 3-1 and 3-2 (Art. 3-2). Naturally, a floor must be designed to support the actual loading or these minimum loads, whichever is larger. Most floors can be designed to carry any given load. However, in some instances, a building code may place a maximum load limit on particular floor systems without regard to calculated capacity. Resistance to lateral forces is usually disregarded, except in areas of seismic disturbances where floors may be employed as horizontal diaphragms to distribute seismic shears to walls designed to transmit them to the ground.

Obviously, it is a question of durability when a floor is subject to loads other than static or moderately kinetic types of forces. For example, a light joist system may be just the floor for an apartment or an office building but may be questionable for a manufacturing establishment where a floor must resist heavy impact and severe vibrations. Shallow floor systems deflect more than deep floors; the system selected should not permit excessive or objectionable deflections.

Fire resistance and fire rating are very important factors, because building codes, in the interest of public safety, specify the degree of resistance that must be provided. Many floor systems are rated by the codes or by fire underwriters for purposes of satisfying code requirements or basing insurance rates (see Arts. 6-81 to 6-86).

The dead weight of the floor system, including the framing, is an important factor affecting economy of construction. For one thing, substantial saving in the weight and cost of a steel frame may result with lightweight floor systems. In addition, low dead weight may also reduce foundation costs.

Sometimes, the depth of a floor system is important. For example, the height of a building may be limited for a particular type of fire-resistant construction or by zoning laws. The thickness of the floor may well be the determining factor limiting the number of stories that can be built. Also, the economy of a deep floor is partly offset by the increase in height of walls, columns, pipes, etc.

Another important consideration, particularly for office buildings and similar-type occupancies, is the need for furnishing an economical and flexible electrical wiring system. With the accent on movable partitions and ever-changing office arrangements, the readiness and ease with which telephones, desk lights, and electric-powered business machines can be relocated is of major importance. Therefore, the floor system that by its make-up provides large void spaces or cells for concealing wiring possesses a distinct advantage over competitive types of solid construction. Likewise, the problem of recess lighting in the ceiling may disclose an advantage in one system over another. Furthermore, air conditioning and ventilation are a must in new office buildings; a competitive necessity in older structures, if at all possible. So location of ducts and method of attachment warrant study of several floor systems for optimum results.

Sound transmission and acoustical treatments are other factors that need to be evaluated. A wealth of data is available in BMS 17 and Supplements 1 and 2, BMS 42 and TRBM 44 (National Bureau of Standards). In general, floor systems of sandwich type with air spaces between layers will afford better resistance to sound transmission than solid systems, which do not interrupt sound waves. Although the ideal soundproof floor is impractical, cost-wise, there are several reasonably satisfactory systems. Much depends on type of occupancy, floor coverings, and ceiling finish—acoustical plaster or tile.

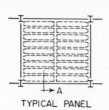

TYPICAL PANEL

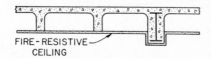

FIRE-RESISTIVE
CEILING

ENLARGED SECTION A

Fig. 6-11. Concrete joist floor.

Appearance and maintenance are also weighed by the designer and the owner. A smooth, neat ceiling is usually a prerequisite for residential occupancy; a less expensive finish may be deemed satisfactory for an institutional building.

Speed of construction speaks for itself. Contractors are alert to the systems that enable the follow-up trades to work immediately behind the erector and with unimpeded efficiency.

In general, the following constructions are commonly used in conjunction with steel framing: concrete arch, concrete joists (removable pan), steel joists, and cellular steel.

6-11. Concrete-arch Floors. The old-type floor used in office and industrial buildings consists of a reinforced-concrete slab, about 4 in. thick, supported on steel beams spaced about 8 ft apart. These beams are designated secondary or intermediate, whereas the beams or girders framing into columns and supporting secondary beams are the primary members (Fig. 6-3). It is called an "arch" floor because it evolved from earlier construction with thick brick and tile floors that were truly flat-top arches; some of the early reinforced-concrete floors also were cast on arch-shaped forms.

The arch system is so much heavier than the contemporary lightweight systems that it has lost most of its earlier appeal for light-occupancy construction. It ranks high, however, where heavy loads, durability, and rigidity are key factors. It is without competition wherever building codes restrict the use of other types. The system works well with the steel frame because all formwork can be supported directly, or by wire suspension, on the floor beams, thus obviating vertical shoring.

6-12. Concrete-pan System. Concrete floors cast on removable metal forms or pans, which form the joists, are frequently used with steel girders in certain areas. Since the joists span the distance between columns, intermediate steel beams are not needed (Fig. 6-11). This floor generally weighs less than the arch system but still considerably more than the lightest types.

There are a number of variations of the concrete-joist system, such as the "grid" or "waffle" system, where the floor is cast on small, square, removable pans, or domes, so that the finished product becomes a two-way joist system. Others such as the "Republic," "Schuster," and "Nassau" systems employ permanent filler blocks—usually a lightweight tile. Some of these variations fall in the heaviest floor classification; also the majority require substantial forms and shoring.

6-13. Open-web Joist Floors. The lightest floor system in common use is the open-web joist construction shown in Fig. 6-12. It is popular for all types of light occupancies, principally because of initial low cost.

Many types of open-web joists are on the market. Some employ bars in their make-up, while others are entirely of rolled shapes; they all conform to standards and good-practice specifications promulgated by the Steel Joist Institute. All joists conform to the standard loading tables and carry the same size designation so that the designer need only indicate on his drawings the standard marking without reference to manufacturer, just as he would for a steel beam or column section.

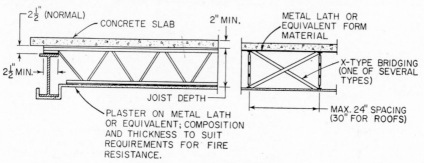

FIG. 6-12. Open-web steel joist.

Satisfactory joist construction is assured by adhering to SJI recommendations. Joists should not be spaced more than 2 ft c to c; they should be adequately braced (with bridging) during construction to prevent rotation or buckling; and to avoid "springy" floors, they should be carefully selected to provide sufficient depth.

One of the main appeals of this system is the elimination of falsework. Joists are easily handled, erected, and connected to supporting beams—usually by tack welding. Temporary coverage and working platforms are quickly placed. The open space between joists, and through the webs, may be utilized for ducts, cables, light fixtures, and piping. A thin floor slab is cast on steel lath, corrugated-steel sheets, or wire-reinforced paper lath laid on top of the joists. A plaster ceiling is suspended or attached direct to the bottom flange of the joist.

Lightweight beams, or so-called "junior" beams, are also used in the same manner as the open-web joists, and with the same advantages and economy, except that the solid webs do not allow so much freedom in installation of utilities. In using solid-web beams, the designer is not restricted to the 2-ft maximum spacing required by specifications for open-web joists. Beams may be spaced according to their safe load capacity; 3- and 4-ft spacings are common. As a type, therefore, the light-weight-steel-beam floor is intermediate between concrete arches and open-web joists.

6-14. Cellular-steel Floors. Light-gage steel decking has rapidly advanced to the forefront of floor systems, particularly for modern office buildings. One type is illustrated in Fig. 6-13. Other manufacturers make similar cellular metal decks, the primary difference being in the shape of the cells.

Two outstanding advantages held for this system are the ease by which present and future connections can be made to telephone, light, and power wiring, each cell serving as a conduit; and rapidity of erection. Each deck unit becomes a working platform immediately on erection, thus enabling the several finishing trades to follow right behind the steel erector.

While generally thought to be high in initial costs as compared with other floor systems, the cost differential can be narrowed to competitive position when equal consideration for electrical facility is imposed on the other systems; e.g., the addition of 4 in. of concrete fill to cover embedded electrical conduit on top of a concrete flat-slab floor.

The fill on top of the cellular decking usually serves only to level off the surface and provide fire protection; consequently, low-strength lightweight concrete is often employed. Cellular steel floors have low dead weight, comparable with the open-web joist-steel-frame system.

6-15. Effect of Intermediate Beams on Costs. The joist systems, either steel or concrete, require no intermediate support, since they are obtainable in lengths to meet the normal bay dimensions in tier building construction. On the other hand, the concrete arch and cellular steel floors are usually designed with one or two intermediate beams within the panel. The elimination of secondary beams does not necessarily mean over-all economy just because the structural-steel contract is less. These beams are simple to fabricate and erect and allow much duplication. An

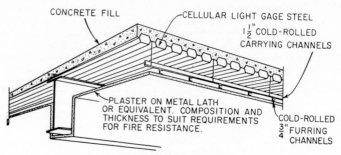

FIG. 6-13. Cellular steel floor.

analysis of contract prices shows that the cost per ton of secondary beams will average 20% under the cost per ton for the whole steel structure; or viewed another way, the omission of secondary beams increases the price per ton on the balance of the steel-work by 3½% on the average. This fact should be taken into account when making a cost analysis of several systems.

6-16. Other Floor Systems. Aside from the basic floor systems of Arts. 6-11 to 6-14, there are numerous adaptations and proprietary systems, such as these:

Cofar (corrugated form and reinforcing), where concrete reinforcement is shop-welded to corrugated sheets, which serves as the form for the concrete slab. Clear spans up to 14 ft are possible.

Smooth ceilings, where the floor slab is supported with the aid of short cantilever steel beams, or grids, rigidly connected to the columns and embedded in the slab—a system that eliminates beams between columns.

Dox, a system of precast-concrete blocks tied together in the shop with steel rods to form beams or slabs.

Lith-I-Bar, a prefabricated, light, reinforced-concrete joist; in effect, a light metal joist encased in concrete.

Flexicore, a prefabricated, light, concrete floor plank, achieving weight saving through the use of circular, longitudinal, hollow spaces.

Battledeck or steel-plate floor, the concrete slab of the arch system being replaced with a steel plate. It requires close spacing of secondary beams.

And in addition, there are available a number of precast floor planks (or tiles) of concrete or gypsum, some featuring lightweight aggregates.

6-17. Roof Systems. These are similar in many respects to the floor types; in fact, for flat-top tier buildings, the roof may be just another floor. However, when roof loads are smaller than floor loads, as is usually the case, it may be economical to lighten the roof construction. For example, steel joists may be spaced farther apart; the Steel Joist Institute recommends 30-in. maximum spacing, as against 24-in. for floors. Where roof decking is used, the spacing of the joist is determined by the load-carrying ability of the applied decking and of the joists.

Most of the considerations listed for floors are also applicable to roof systems (Arts. 6-10 to 6-16). In addition, however, due thought should be given to weather resistance, heat conductance and insulation, moisture absorption and vapor barriers, and especially to maintenance.

Many roof systems are distinctive as compared with the floor types; for example, the corrugated sheet-metal roofing commonly employed on many types of industrial or mill buildings. The sheets rest on small beams, channels, or joists, called **purlins,** which in turn are supported by the trusses. A table in the American Institute of Steel Construction "Manual of Steel Construction" gives the carrying capacities for corrugated-steel sheets from which the purlin spacing can be fixed (see also Sec. 15).

BASIC DESIGN PROBLEMS

Structural-steel members are designed for any one, or any combination, of five possible stress conditions: bending, shearing, web crippling, direct or axial tension, and direct or axial compression. There are other conditions that must be investigated under special conditions: local buckling, excessive deflection, and torsion.

6-18. Design of Laterally Supported Steel Beam. *Condition:* Laterally supported; i.e., stayed from deflecting sideways (Art. 6-36). Maximum allowable working stress for bending on the extreme fibers is 20,000 psi, in either tension or compression. Loads produce a bending moment of 150,000 ft-lb.

Solution: Required section modulus $S = M/f$, where M is the bending moment in inch-pounds and f is the allowable unit stress in pounds per square inch.

$$S = \frac{150,000 \times 12}{20,000}$$
$$S = 90$$

From the Section Modulus Table of Rolled Beams in the American Institute of Steel Construction "Manual of Steel Construction," the closest S (on the safe side) is 92.2 for a 14 WF 61; however, the most economical (lightest weight) is an 18 WF 55 with S of 98.2. If depth is restricted, a 16 WF 58 with S of 94.1, or a 12 WF 72 with S of 97.5 may be used. A 10 WF 89 is also available to meet extreme depth limitations but is definitely uneconomical.

Extremely helpful in selecting beams are the safe-load beam tables in the AISC "Manual"; however, the tables are based on uniform loadings only. Capacities of beams supporting concentrated loads must be computed (Bibliography, Art. 6-87).

6-19. Design of Steel Beam for Buckling. *Condition.* Bending moment of 150,000 ft-lb and a laterally unsupported span of 25 ft; i.e., not stayed from deflecting sideways (Art. 6-36). Maximum allowable stress for the compression flange is determined by the physical properties of the beam and the length between lateral supports. (Examples of laterally unsupported beams—crane-runway beams, trolley beams, etc.) This working stress is computed from the formula*

$$f = \frac{12,000,000}{ld/bt} \qquad (6\text{-}1)$$

where l = unsupported length in inches
d = beam depth in inches
b = flange or beam width in inches
t = thickness of the compression flange in inches

Equation (6-1) applies only when ld/bt exceeds 600. Examination of Eq. (6-1) reveals that its application requires a solution by trial, since allowable stress is dependent on the physical characteristics of the beam selected.

* For derivation and application, see "Strength of Beams as Determined by Lateral Buckling," *Transactions of the American Society of Civil Engineers,* 1947; also Art. 6-37).

Solution: The equivalent or trial section modulus S' is determined from the formula

$$S' = \frac{SL}{50} \frac{d}{bt}$$

where S = section modulus for same beam laterally supported (20,000 psi allowable)
L = length of span, ft

$$S = \frac{M}{f} = \frac{150,000 \times 12}{20,000} = 90$$

$$S' = \frac{90 \times 25}{50} \frac{d}{bt} = 45 \frac{d}{bt} \tag{6-2}$$

At this point an assumption of beam size must be made. The tedious work of trying several sizes has been eased by publishing the d/bt values for all beams in the AISC "Manual of Steel Construction." The equivalent section modulus S' must be larger for the laterally unsupported beam than it is for the supported condition. Consequently, by inspection, d/bt must exceed 2 in this case. Let us take as a trial beam an 18 WF 60, with $S = 107.8$ and $d/bt = 3.48$. From Eq. (6-2),

$$S' = 45 \times 3.48 = 157$$

Since this is greater than the section modulus of the 18 WF 60, the trial selection, we reenter the section-modulus table and select a larger 18-in. beam, 18 WF 70, with $S = 128.2$ and $d/bt = 2.74$; from this, $S' = 123$.
Checking the allowable compression unit stress with Eq. (6-1),

$$f = \frac{12,000,000}{ld/bt} = \frac{12,000,000}{25 \times 12 \times 2.74} = 14,600 \text{ psi}$$

The resisting moment then is

$$M = fS = \frac{14,600 \times 128.2}{12} = 156,500 \text{ ft-lb}$$

This indicates the 18 WF 70 has a reserve capacity of 6,500 ft-lb over the moment required. Further investigation will reveal that this section is neither the shallowest nor the lightest that could be used to satisfy this problem. A 14 WF 68 is the most efficient; in fact, the allowable stress on this section is not reduced from the maximum of 20,000 psi until the clear span exceeds 25.5 ft.

To further simplify this "cut-and-try" procedure, the AISC includes in the "Manual" a set of charts for laterally unsupported beams. Having nothing more than the span and the bending moment, one can immediately select the beams of various depths that satisfy the problem. The most economical section is likewise immediately apparent.

Every beam section has a span L_u based on its cross-sectional dimensions, associated with it. For greater spans, the allowable maximum 20,000 psi stress must be reduced, unless lateral supports are provided. For convenience, the L_u values are tabulated in the AISC "Manual" (Bibliography, Art. 6-87).

6-20. Design of a Steel Beam for Shear. When vertical loads are applied to beams, they produce, in addition to longitudinal bending stresses, transverse shears. The total shear at the end of a beam is equal to the beam reaction at that end. In Fig. 6-14a, an imaginary failure is pictured between the right-hand reaction and the nearest applied load. (With a uniform load, it would occur just clear of the reaction.) The point of greatest shear always occurs at the ends of simple beams, and therefore, the investigation is limited to the beam ends. Actually, failure of the type pictured, due to high transverse shear stresses, never occurs. Long before this happens, a complex stress pattern would cause buckling of the web. The only time that transverse shear is a problem occurs when a beam has to be coped top or bottom as shown in Fig. 6-14b. Investigations must be made on the plane XX.

Given: Coped beam shown in Fig. 6-14b and an end reaction of 25.8 kips. Allowable shearing unit stress is 13,000 psi.

Solution: Disregarding the flange as affording resistance to shear, the net area of the web is $7 \times \frac{5}{16}$, or 2.18 sq in. Resisting shear = $2.18 \times 13{,}000 = 28.3$ kips, which satisfies the problem.

It is customary to consider the web depth as including the flange thicknesses. If the shear had exceeded the capacity of the beam web, it would have been necessary to add reinforcement to the web—usually in the form of shear plates on one or both sides of the web, depending on the amount of shear area required. Shear plates must be fully developed, i.e., attached to the beam web so as to function with the beam in the transmission of shear (Bibliography, Art. 6-87).

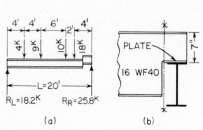

FIG. 6-14. Critical section for shear in a simple beam.

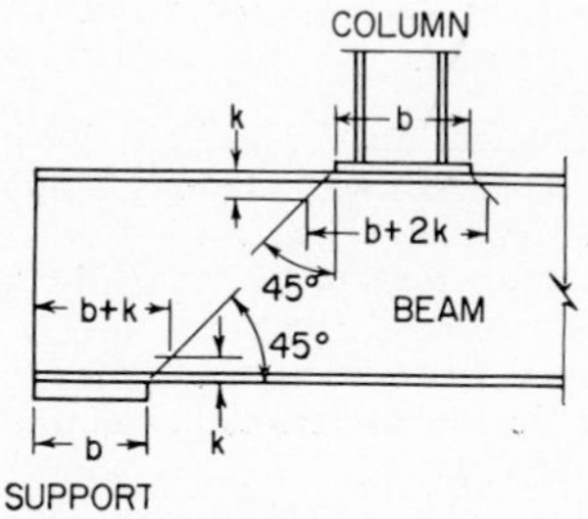

FIG. 6-15. Web crippling in a simple beam. Critical web section is assumed at fillet.

6-21. Design of Beam for Web Crippling. As indicated in Art. 6-20, the probability of failure by vertical shear of the web is remote; usually some form of web buckling will occur first. When a load or end reaction is concentrated on the web, a check should be made on the capacity of the web to transmit the forces safely. Specifications recognize the fact that loads are resisted not only by the part of the web directly in line with them, but also by the web immediately adjacent. A 45° distribution is usually assumed, as illustrated in Fig. 6-15 for two common conditions. The k distance is determined by the point where the fillet of the flange joins the web; it is given in the AISC "Manual of Steel Construction" beam tables.

Given: A 25.8-kip load on a 16 WF 40. Assume an 8-in.-wide bearing (distance b in Fig. 6-15). Allowable unit bearing stress is 24,000 psi.

Solution: Web thickness is $\frac{5}{16}$ in. and k distance is 1 in. for a 16 WF 40. The unit stress for a 25.8-kip end reaction is.

$$f_b = \frac{25{,}800}{(8+1)\frac{5}{16}} = \frac{25{,}800}{2.82} = 9{,}150 \text{ psi}$$

Given: Column reaction of 90 kips on the same beam. Column base to be supported is 8 in. wide (distance b in Fig. 6-15). Allowable unit bearing stress is 24,000 psi.

Solution: $f_b = \dfrac{90{,}000}{(8+2)\frac{5}{16}} = 28{,}800 \text{ psi}$

The web is overstressed since the allowable stress of 24,000 psi is exceeded. The most efficient method of strengthening the web is to provide web stiffeners—plates for welded construction, angles for riveted work (Bibliography, Art. 6-87).

6-22. Design of Beam for Unsymmetrical Bending. This case is frequently found in roof construction where the position of the beams (purlins) and the loads is as shown in Fig. 6-16.   In this case, the beam must be checked about both axes and the resulting stresses combined to give the maximum unit stresses.   Because of the low section modulus about the weaker YY axis (in plane of beam web), sag rods are used to reduce the span for bending about this axis.   Maximum unit stress is given by

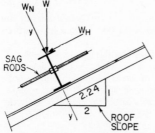

$$f = \frac{M_X}{S_X} + \frac{M_Y}{S_Y} \qquad (6\text{-}3)$$

Fig. 6-16. Unsymmetrical bending in a purlin.

where M_X and M_Y = bending moments
S_X and S_Y = section moduli of the beam about XX and YY axes
   The effect of the sag rods is to make the purlin a continuous beam.   If the moment M_Y is computed with the entire span assumed simply supported, the effect of the sag rods is to reduce the simple-span moment for the horizontal load by the following factors:
   For a single row of sag rods, divide M_Y by 4.
   For two rows of sag rods, divide M_Y by 11.25.
   For three rows of sag rods, divide M_Y by 20.
   Given: Assume the purlin in Fig. 6-16 has to carry 400 lb per lin ft on a span of 20 ft and that the roof decking provides lateral support, thus permitting maximum allowable bending stress in compression.

Solution: $W_X = \dfrac{2}{2.24} \times 400 = 358$ lb per lin ft

$\qquad\quad W_Y = \dfrac{1}{2.24} \times 400 = 179$ lb per lin ft

$\qquad\quad M_X = \dfrac{20^2}{8} \times 358 = 17{,}900$ ft-lb

Without sag rods:

$$M_Y = \frac{20^2}{8} \times 179 = 8{,}950 \text{ ft-lb}$$

Since the objective is to obtain the most economical purlin we shall start with a lightweight beam—10B17, with

$$S_X = 16.2 \qquad \text{and} \qquad S_Y = 1.72$$
$$f_X = \frac{17{,}900 \times 12}{16.2} = 13{,}300$$
$$f_Y = \frac{8{,}950 \times 12}{1.72} = 62{,}500$$
$$f = 75{,}800 \text{ psi}$$

   It is obvious that the full span must be reduced by introducing lateral rods; by inspection, two lines of rods (moment-reduction ratio of 11.25) appear necessary to bring the stress below the 20,000 psi allowable.

$$f_X = \frac{17{,}900 \times 12}{16.2} = 13{,}300$$
$$f_Y = \frac{8{,}950 \times 12}{1.72 \times 11.25} = \frac{5{,}600}{18{,}900 \text{ psi}}$$

The size of the sag rods must also be computed. Assume there are five purlins on each side of the peak, the eave purlin carrying one-half the load of the other purlins.

$$W_Y \text{ for full 20-ft span} = 20 \times 179 = 3{,}580 \text{ lb}$$
$$W_Y \text{ for } \tfrac{1}{3} \text{ the span} = 1{,}193 \text{ lb}$$
$$P = 4.5 \times 1{,}193 = 4{,}770 \text{ lb}$$

$$A = \frac{4{,}770}{20{,}000} = 0.238 \text{ sq in.}$$

Net area of a ¾-in.-diameter threaded rod is 0.302 sq in., which would be satisfactory. Since the rods are used in short lengths, extending from purlin to purlin, they could diminish in size as the load drops off, but for practical reasons all rods are specified with the same diameter.

In this problem, the decking was assumed to give lateral support, and therefore, the allowable bending stress of 20,000 psi governed. If the purlins actually are laterally unsupported (see Art. 6-36) the analysis should follow the line of reasoning in Art. 6-19. With two lines of sag rods (lateral supports), the allowable bending stress for moments about the major axis is given by Eq. (6-1) as

$$f = \frac{12{,}000{,}000}{6.67 \times 12 \times 7.7} = 19{,}500 \text{ psi}$$

For simplicity, the total stress about the major and minor axis will be compared with this allowable stress. Since 18,900 is less than 19,500, the 10B17 is satisfactory. In this particular problem, the question of lateral support contributed by the decking did not affect the solution, but this is not always the case.

As used in this problem, the sag rods serve a dual purpose: first, to relieve the purlins by supporting the full lateral (in plane of roof surface) component of the vertical load, for which they act in pure tension; and second, to provide lateral support for the purlins at third points. In the latter case, the rods function in tension, except at the eave purlin, where the rod is on one side only and can offer but negligible resistance when the buckling thrust is against the rod. A pipe section may be used to stiffen this rod or else some strutlike element (sometimes light trusswork) should be employed.

(a)   (b)

Fig. 6-17. Typical crane girders.

In some roof designs, sag rods are used for only one purpose—to hold alignment of purlins until the decking is installed and secured to purlins (Bibliography, Art. 6-87).

6-23. Design of Crane Beam. This is another example of bending in two planes as discussed in Art. 6-22, but with a variation in treatment. Specifications require that 10 % of the weight of the lifted load and crane trolley be applied as a lateral force normal to the runway rail. A rolled beam is sometimes used to support the rails for light cranes, but generally, a better design practice is to use a combination of a channel and a beam, two common types of which are illustrated in Fig. 6-17.

Given: Span and crane loadings as shown in Fig. 6-18a. Find the size of a crane beam of the type in Fig. 6-17a.

Solution: The loads will be placed for maximum moment, which occurs when one of the loads and the center of gravity of the loads are the same distance on either side of the center line of the span. The vertical reactions and maximum moment are:

$$R_L = (7 + 11) \times {}^{20}\!/_{20} = 18 \text{ kips}$$
$$R_R = (9 + 13) \times {}^{20}\!/_{20} = 22 \text{ kips}$$
$$M_V = 9 \times 18 = 162 \text{ ft-kips}$$

The horizontal reactions and maximum moment are:

$$R_L = (7 + 11) \times {}^{1}\!/_{20} = 0.9 \text{ kips}$$
$$R_R = (9 + 13) \times {}^{1}\!/_{20} = 1.1 \text{ kips}$$
$$M_H = 9 \times 0.9 = 8.1 \text{ ft-kips}$$

Try a section made up of an 18 WF 50 and a 12-in. 20.7-lb channel. First step is to locate the center of gravity of the section and compute the moment of inertia.

Section	A	y measured from mid-depth of 18 WF 50	Ay	Ay^2	I
18 WF 50.....	14.71	0	0	0	800.6
12 channel 20.7	6.03	8.58	51.74	443.93	3.9
Sum..........	20.74	....	51.74	443.93	804.5

$$\bar{y} = \frac{51.74}{20.74} = 2.49 \text{ in. (see Fig. 6-18}b).$$

$$I_x = 443.93 + 804.5 - (20.74 \times 2.49^2) = 1{,}119.8 \text{ in.}^4.$$

In crane-beam design, only the top-flange material is considered to resist the lateral force.

$$I_y = (\text{channel} + \text{top flange}) = 128.1 + \left(\frac{7.5^3 \times 0.57}{12}\right) = 148.1 \text{ in.}^4.$$

The crane beam is laterally unsupported between vertical supports; so the allowable unit stress should be determined from the ld/bt formula [Eq. (6-1), Art. 6-19].

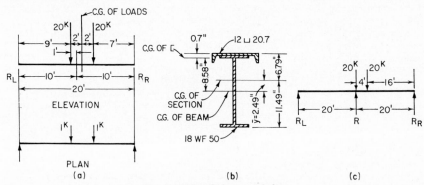

Fig. 6-18. Loaded crane girder.

It should be observed that bt represents flange area; therefore, the recommended practice is to take the full area of the channel and the beam flange. In this case,

$$bt = 6.03 + (7.5 \times 0.57) = 10.33 \text{ sq in.}$$

$$\frac{ld}{bt} = \frac{20 \times 12 \times 18.28}{10.33} = 425 < 600$$

Therefore, allowable stress of 20,000 psi does not have to be reduced. Total bending stress is, from Eq. (6-3),

$$f = \frac{162 \times 12 \times 6.79}{1{,}119.8} + \frac{8.1 \times 12 \times 6}{148.1}$$
$$= 11.80 + 3.94 = 15.74 \text{ kips per sq in.}$$

and, as a check on the tension flange for vertical load only,

$$f = \frac{162 \times 12 \times 11.49}{1{,}119.8} = 19.95 \text{ kips per sq in.}$$

For the maximum end reaction, the loads are placed as shown in Fig. 6-18c.

$$R = (1\tfrac{6}{20} + 1)20 = 36 \text{ kips}$$

The beam should be checked for web shear and crippling as indicated in Arts. 6-20 and 6-21.

Comparison between computed combined bending stress and the allowable stress based on the ld/bt expression [Eq. (6-1)] is admittedly conservative. The channel-beam combination obviously possesses an inherently better resistance to lateral buckling than a plain beam section, for which the formula was developed. Consequently, it may be safe to permit a combined unit bending stress up to the maximum allowable of 20,000 psi, but in any event, allowable working stress for vertical

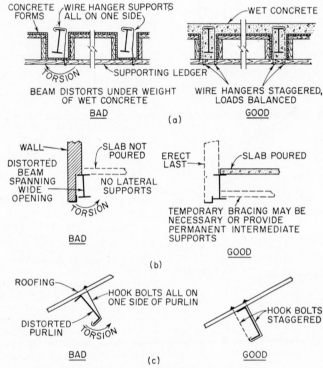

FIG. 6-19. Steel beams subjected to torsion.

loading alone should be limited to that computed from Eq. (6-1) (Bibliography, Art. 6-87).

6-24. Design of Laterally Unsupported Channels. Occasionally steel channels are used as beams. Application of the laterally unsupported beam formula to channel beams is questionable, since, theoretically, the basic formula [Eq. (6-1)] was derived for a symmetrical section. Within the limits of normal design practice, if a channel is not supported laterally by the construction that it supports vertically, the ld/bt formula may be expected to yield reasonably conservative results if bt is taken as the area of one flange. The inevitable eccentricity of loading, however, makes it advisable that a single channel never be used as a beam under conditions where lateral support is totally lacking for relatively large clear spans.

Other than this assumption for bt, design of laterally unsupported channel beams is carried out for bending as in Art. 6-19, for web shear and web crippling as in Arts. 6-20 and 6-21.

6-25. Design of Beam Sections for Torsion. This is a special type of load application, since in normal practice eccentric loads on beams are counterbalanced to the point where slight eccentricities may be neglected. For example, spandrel beams supporting a heavy masonry wall may not be concentric with the load, thus inducing torsional stresses, but these will largely be canceled out by the equally eccentric loads of the floor, partitions, attached beams, and similar restraints. For this reason, one seldom finds any ill effects from torsional stresses.

It is during the construction phase that torsion may be in evidence, usually the result of faulty construction procedure. In Fig. 6-19 are illustrated some of the bad practices that have caused trouble in the field. When forms for concrete slabs are hung on one edge of a beam (usually the light secondary beam), the weight of the wet concrete may be sufficient to twist the beam. Figure 6-19a shows the correct method, which reduces torsional effect to the minimum. Likewise for spandrels, the floor ties, if any, forms, or the slab itself should be placed prior to the construction of the eccentric wall (Fig. 6-19b). Connectors for heavy roofing sheets when located on one side of the purlin may distort the section; the condition should be corrected by staggering, as indicated in Fig. 6-19c.

Equations for computing torsional stresses are given in Arts. 3-77 and 3-78.

6-26. Design of Riveted Plate Girders. For a number of reasons, such as capacity, depth requirements, weight, availability of rolled beams in the heaviest and deepest range, and economy, it may be necessary to "build up" a girder with plates and angles. Although it is feasible to add cover plates to rolled beams, it generally

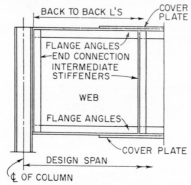

(a) GIRDER SUPPORTED ON END BEARINGS

(b) GIRDER FRAMING INTO COLUMNS

Fig. 6-20. Plate girder components.

may be more economical to employ a plate girder; common types are illustrated in Fig. 6-5, Art. 6-8. The principal elements of a plate girder are shown in Fig. 6-20.

There are two methods of design for a plate girder—the flange-area method and the moment-of-inertia method. In the latter method, the moment of inertia may be based on the net section or on the gross section. The American Institute of Steel Construction suggests proportioning plate girders by using the moment of inertia of the gross section and that no deduction be made for the standard shop or field rivet holes in flanges. In special cases, however, where the reduction of area of either flange by holes exceeds 15% of the gross flange area, the excess should be deducted. The following procedure is generally used in the design of a plate girder:

1. Compute the loads to be carried by the girder.
2. Compute the maximum bending moments and maximum shear.
3. Set the depth of the web and the distance back to back of flange angles.
4. Determine the web thickness to carry the shear.
5. Determine the trial flange section by the flange-area method.

6. Check to see if the reduction in area of either flange by rivet holes is in excess of 15 % of the gross flange area.

7. Compute the moment of inertia of the cross section and check the unit stress at point of maximum moment.

8. Determine length of cover plates, if any are needed.

9. Design and locate intermediate and end stiffeners.

10. Determine the spacing of rivets in cover plates and flange angles.

11. Design splices and end details.

To illustrate the basic design principles of a plate girder, the following example will be confined to a simple girder without cover plates, to carry a maximum bending moment of 1,250 ft-kips and maximum vertical shear of 200 kips. Span is 38 ft and maximum depth is limited to 39 in. Rivets are to be $\frac{3}{4}$ in. diameter. Compression flange is laterally supported at ends and center.

Solution: Design by flange-area method.

Assume a 38-in. web; distance back to back of flange angles, therefore, is $38\frac{1}{2}$ in. Also assume 4-in. legs of flange angles will be placed against the web. Depth of unsupported web then is $38.5 - 2 \times 4 = 30.5$ in. Since maximum unsupported depth of web usually is 170 times the web thickness, minimum web thickness $= 30.5/170 = 0.179$, or $\frac{1}{4}$ in. For an allowable unit stress of 13 kips per sq in., web area required for shear $= {}^{200}\!/_{13} = 15.4$ sq in.

$$\text{Web thickness for shear} = \frac{15.4}{38} = 0.405$$

Therefore, furnish a $\frac{7}{16}$-in.-thick web. Note, too, that a $\frac{7}{16}$-in. web is advantageous in that the $\frac{3}{4}$-in. rivets are developed for double-shear values.

Assume $8 \times 4 \times \frac{7}{8}$ in. flange angles. Allowable maximum bending stress for half the span length (distance between lateral supports) is, from Eq. (6-1),

$$f = \frac{12,000,000}{ld/bt} = \frac{12,000,000}{19 \times 12 \times 38.5/(16.44 \times \frac{7}{8})} = 19,670 \text{ psi}$$

Assume the center of gravity of the flange to coincide with the gravity axis of the flange angles, 1.0 in. from the back of the angles. Unit stress at this center of gravity is

$$f_{av} = 19,670 \times 36.5/38.5 = 18,650 \text{ psi}$$

$$\text{Required flange area} = \frac{1,250 \times 12}{36.5 \times 18.65} = 22.04 \text{ sq in.}$$

$$\text{Deduct effective web area} \frac{A}{6} = 2.77$$

$$\text{Required gross flange area} = \overline{19.27} \text{ sq in.}$$

Area supplied by two $8 \times 4 \times \frac{7}{8}$ in. angles is 19.46 sq in.

It is advisable to check at this point for the loss in gross area because of rivet holes in either flange. Assume two $\frac{7}{8}$-in.-diameter holes. The percentage reduction in area then is

$$\frac{2 \times \frac{7}{8} \times \frac{7}{8}}{19.46} \times 100 = 7.9 \% < 15 \%$$

For the check by the moment-of-inertia method A = gross area, d = distance center of gravity of section to center of gravity of flange angles, I_o = moment of inertia about own axis, I_{gr} = moment of inertia of gross section.

Section	A	d	Ad^2	I_o	I_{gr}
Web—38 × $\frac{7}{16}$	16.63	.....	......	2,000	2,000
4 angles—8 × 4 × $\frac{7}{8}$	38.92	18.25	12,960	42	13,002
Total	55.55	.....	......	.....	15,002

Required section modulus $= \dfrac{M}{f} = \dfrac{1{,}250 \times 12}{19.67} = 762$ in.^{3}.

Furnished section modulus $= \dfrac{I}{c} = \dfrac{15{,}002}{19.25} = 779$ in.^{3}.

No cover plates are required. If the trial section was inadequate, then additional flange area could be obtained by using thicker angles, flange angles with longer vertical legs, or by addition of cover plates. The last is the most efficient expedient, since the area added at the greatest distance from the neutral axis will provide the greatest increase in moment of inertia.

When cover plates are indicated, the components should be proportioned for the most effective results. In this example, 6 × 4 angles with 13-in. cover plates would have been a better selection than 17-in. cover plates on 8-in. legs. Main considerations are that the thickness of components is punchable with respect to rivet size, and that the total cross-sectional area of cover plates does not exceed 70% of the total flange area.

When cover plates are specified, the designer should determine their length. The following formula applies to girders with uniform loading:

$$l = L \sqrt{\frac{A_p}{A_f}} \tag{6-4}$$

where l = length of cover plate

L = length of span

A_p = area of cover plate whose length is being determined plus all covers over it

A_f = flange area (including one-sixth of gross web area)

The cover plates for a uniformly loaded girder are located symmetrically about the mid-span of the girder. Determining lengths of cover plates for unsymmetrically loaded girders is more complicated. Suggested procedure is to plot a moment diagram from which the cover lengths are easily obtained by superimposing on this diagram the resisting moments of the section with successive covers removed.

Stiffeners are located in accordance with specifications (local building code or AISC recommendation) at ends, concentrated loads, and intermediate points.

Unit horizontal shear between flange angles and web is given by the formula $v = VQ/I$, where Q is the statical moment of the area of the two flange angles about the horizontal axis of the girder:

$$v = \frac{200{,}000 \times 19.46 \times 18.25}{15{,}002} = 4{,}730 \text{ lb per lin in.}$$

Rivet capacity for $\frac{3}{4}$-in. diameter and a $\frac{7}{16}$-in. web plate is 13,130 lb.

Maximum pitch = 13,130/4,730 = 2.78 in.

Minimum allowable pitch = 3 rivet diameters = 2.25 in.

Therefore, a rivet spacing of 2.75 in. will be used at the ends of the girder. Since the loading is uniform, the pitch may be progressively increased from this maximum end pitch to the maximum permitted at the center. Specifications limit the maximum in built-up compression members to sixteen times the thinnest outside plate or shape, or twenty times the thinnest enclosed plate or shape, or to 12 in., whichever is the least.

For flange angles, $16t = 16 \times \frac{7}{8} = 14$ in. For web plate, $20t = 20 \times \frac{7}{16} = 8.75$ in. This spacing governs.

Web splices are avoided when possible because of added shop costs and additional weight. However, they must be employed when (1) length of web is beyond mill limits, (2) length is beyond shop capacity to handle, or (3) cambering can be facilitated by web joints. Figure 6-21 shows some of the commonest types of girder web splices. Type (*a*) is primarily a shear splice but can also be developed for moment; most specifications require web splices to transmit both moment and shear. Types (*b*) and (*c*) are more direct as to moment design, because the splice material is more efficiently located; also shear and moment can be treated independently.

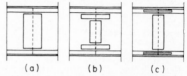

(a)   (b)   (c)

Fig. 6-21. Plate girder web splices.

It should be noted that for the particular example in this article a rolled section, 36 WF 230, with S of 835.5, would also satisfy the conditions, but with substantial increase in weight (Bibliography, Art. 6-87).

6-27. Design of Welded Plate Girders. In the simplest form, shown in Fig. 6-5*h* (Art. 6-8), a welded girder requires three main elements—all plates—whereas the equivalent in a riveted girder is made of five pieces, four angles, and a web plate. Considerable weight may be saved by welding, because all splices are butt-welded, flange plates may be reduced in thickness to suit design needs, and web stiffeners consist of plates. In contrast, the riveted girder requires splicing material at all joints, flange angles are of the same size throughout, web stiffeners are angles, and, in addition, filler plates are necessary to adjust for variations in thickness. Despite this obvious saving in weight, the question of which is most economical—riveted or welded construction—cannot be firmly established.

Sometimes welded beams, composed of plates, are successfully used in lieu of rolled sections. Frequently, however, the decision is not based strictly on economy but rather on availability; during national emergencies, the problem of supply and delivery of mill products has been very tight and uncertain, areas remote from sources of supply being most acutely affected.

Given: Span of 38 ft, maximum moment of 1,250 ft-kips, maximum shear of 200 kips, as in Art. 6-26. Use the same depth, $38\frac{1}{2}$ in.

Solution: The $8 \times 4 \times \frac{7}{8}$-in. flange angles of the riveted girder (area of 19.46 sq in.) used for the girder in Art. 6-26 suggest a $1\frac{1}{8}$-in. or $1\frac{1}{4}$-in. flange plate of about

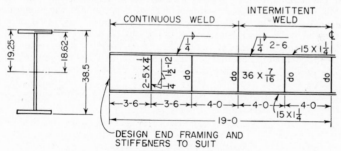

Fig. 6-22. Typical welded plate girder.

16-in. width; try $1\frac{1}{4}$-in. thickness. (See Fig. 6-22 for details.) Therefore, web depth $= 38.5 - 2.5 = 36.0$ in. Minimum thickness, based on unsupported depth $= \frac{36}{170} = 0.212$ in. With an allowable unit shear stress of 13 kips per sq in., required shear area $= \frac{200}{13} = 15.4$ sq in. Minimum thickness for shear $= 15.4/36 = 0.427$ in.

Therefore, furnish a $36 \times \frac{7}{16}$-in. web. (Plate widths are preferable in even inches, although $\frac{1}{2}$-in. increments are obtainable.) For the web, moment of inertia is $I_w = \frac{7}{16} \times 36^3/12 = 1{,}700$ in.[4]. For the flange plates, with b = plate width:

$$I_f = Ad^2 = 2 \times b \times 1.25 \times 18.62^2 = 867b$$
$$I = I_w + I_f = 867b + 1{,}700$$

Assume 20 kips per sq in. as the allowable bending stress. Then,

$$f = \frac{Mc}{I} = \frac{1{,}250 \times 12 \times 19.25}{867b + 1{,}700} = 20$$
$$b = 14.6, \text{ or } 15 \text{ in. wide}$$

(With $1\frac{1}{8}$-in. thick plates, the width would have to be at least $16\frac{1}{2}$ in.)
For a final check, the moment of inertia is computed:

Section	A	d	Ad^2	I_o	I_{gr}
$36 \times \frac{7}{16}$	15.75	0	......	1,700	1,700
$2{-}15 \times 1\frac{1}{4}$	37.50	18.62	13,000	50	13,050
Total......	53.25	.....	......	.....	14,750 in.[4]

Allowable bending stress is 20,000 psi, since

$$\frac{ld}{bt} = \frac{19 \times 12 \times 38.5}{15 \times 1.25} = 470 < 600$$

Required $S = \dfrac{1{,}250 \times 12}{20} = 750$ in.[3].

Furnished $S = \dfrac{14{,}750}{19.25} = 766$ in.[3].

The thickness of flange plates may be reduced to suit the lesser moment area required near the ends of the girder. Specifications permit these plates to be laid end to end and the junctions butt-welded. This usually results in substantial weight reduction, particularly if there is no change in the basic unit stress. In this illustration the unit stress of 20,000 prevails until ld/bt exceeds 600; to find the plate thickness at which this occurs,

$$t = \frac{ld}{600b} = \frac{19 \times 12 \times 38.5}{600 \times 15} = 0.98 \text{ or } 1 \text{ in.}$$

It is doubtful whether a reduction of $\frac{1}{4}$ in. in flange thickness would be economical in this example. For the sake of illustration, however, assume 20,000 psi governs throughout, as would be the case if additional lateral support is provided; then, a reduction in flange thickness to $\frac{5}{8}$ in. may be economically justified. The length of the $1\frac{1}{4}$ plate then is determined from the formula for uniform loading [Eq. (6-4)], with

$$A_f = 15 \times 1\frac{1}{4} = 18.75 \quad \text{and} \quad A_p = 15 \times (1\frac{1}{4} - \frac{5}{8}) = 9.33 \text{ sq in.}$$
$$l = L \sqrt{\frac{A_p}{A_f}} = 38 \sqrt{\frac{9.33}{18.75}} = 26.8 \text{ ft}$$

Therefore, the $15 \times 1\frac{1}{4}$-in. plates will be 27 ft long, with $15 \times \frac{5}{8}$-in. plates butted at each end for the rest of the girder.

It should be noted that specifications permit a minimum plate thickness of $\frac{1}{16}$ the nominal half width of the flange; in this example, $\frac{1}{2}$-in.-thick plates could be considered. In actual practice, many engineers treat the increased flange thickness in the same way as cover plates on riveted work; they extend the length of the plate beyond the theoretical termination, as computed by Eq. (6-4), to develop with continuous welding the proportionate share of flange stress that is taken by the increase in material. This stress is obtained from the following equation:

$$\text{Total stress in added area} = Af\frac{S_2 - S_1}{S_1} \tag{6-5}$$

where A = area of smaller flange
f = maximum allowable unit stress
S_2 = section modulus of larger section
S_1 = section modulus of smaller section

Flange plates are connected to the web with sufficient welds to transmit the shear in much the same manner as flange elements are connected with rivets to the web (Art. 6-26). Since vertical shear is greatest at the support v, the unit horizontal shear per linear inch is computed from $v = VQ/I$, with $Q = 15 \times 1\frac{1}{4} \times 18.62 = 349$, for the case where the $15 \times 1\frac{1}{4}$-in. plate extends the full length of girder. As computed previously, $I = 14,750$ in.[4] Therefore,

$$v = 200,000 \times 349/14,750 = 4,730 \text{ lb per lin in.}$$

The maximum size fillet weld is limited by the safe shearing capacity of the web; therefore, for a web with thickness t and allowable unit shear stress in base metal of 13,000 psi and in weld metal of 13,600 psi, the weld size for a fillet weld on both sides of the web is computed from

$$13,000t = 2a \times 0.707 \times 13,600$$
$$a = 0.675t \text{ or roughly } \tfrac{2}{3}t$$

For $\frac{7}{16}$-in. web, the maximum weld size is $\frac{2}{3} \times \frac{7}{16} = \frac{14}{48}$, or $\frac{5}{16}$ in.

Try $\frac{1}{4}$-in. welds. These have a capacity of $2 \times 0.707 \times 0.25 \times 13,600 = 4,800$ lb per in. Continuous $\frac{1}{4}$-in. welds will therefore be employed for the end portions, say up to the third point. Intermittent welds could be used for the middle third, calculated on the basis of the reduced vertical shear at the third point, although some designers prefer continuous welds throughout, particularly if the girder is exposed and maintenance is a problem. Specifications require that the clear spacing between intermittent welds joining the parts of compression members, in the direction of stress, be not greater than sixteen times the thickness of the inner part. In this case, the maximum interval is $16 \times \frac{7}{16}$, or 7 in.; in no case can the clear spacing between welds exceed 12 in.

In this example, the shear at the third point is 67 kips.

$$v = 67,000 \times \frac{349}{14,750} = 1,590 \text{ lb per lin in.}$$

Two $\frac{1}{4} \times 2$-in. fillet welds are good for $2 \times 4,800 = 9,600$ lb. So the spacing of welds, center to center, required in the middle third of the girder is $9,600/1,590$, or 6 in. A longer girder would warrant further reduction of the amount of flange welding.

Specifications require that stiffeners be placed on the web plate at points of concentrated loads and end reactions, the purpose being to transmit the forces directly into or out of the web area. Intermediate stiffeners may be required when the clear depth between flange plates is equal to or greater than seventy times the web thickness; in this example, the clear depth is 36 in. and

$$70t = 70 \times \frac{7}{16} = 30.6$$

Stiffeners must be provided where the unit shear exceeds

$$v = \frac{64,000,000}{(h/t)^2} \tag{6-6}$$

where h = clear distance between flange plates

$$v = \frac{64,000,000}{(36/0.43)^2} = 9,150 \text{ psi}$$

Since the unit shear in the end panel is $200,000/(36 \times \frac{7}{16}) = 12,700$ psi, stiffeners must be supplied near the girder ends. The AISC recommends that maximum spacing of stiffeners be limited to 84 in. or that given by the following formula, whichever is less:

$$d = \frac{11,000t}{\sqrt{v}} \tag{6-7}$$

where d = clear distance between stiffeners, in.
  t = web thickness, in.
  v = unit shear stress

$$d = \frac{11,000 \times \frac{7}{16}}{\sqrt{12,700}} = 42.5 \text{ in.}$$

The cross-sectional area of a pair of stiffener plates must satisfy this formula:

$$I_s = 0.00000016h^4 \tag{6-8}$$

where h = clear distance between flange plates

$$I_s = 0.00000016 \times 36^4 = 0.27 \text{ in.}^4$$

Assuming two $5 \times \frac{1}{4}$ in. plates:

$$I_s = \frac{1}{12} \times \frac{1}{4} \times 10.43^3 = 23.6 \text{ in.}^4 > 0.27 \text{ in.}^4$$

These stiffeners must be attached to the web by welds with clear spacing of not more than 12 in. Use of $1\frac{1}{2} \times \frac{1}{4}$-in. welds, 12 in. c to c, is suggested.

Stiffeners at points of concentrated loads are designed as columns, made up of a pair of stiffener plates and a centrally located strip of the web. This portion of the web may not exceed $25t$ in width at interior locations and $12t$ at end bearings, where t is the web thickness. The design of this column section is based on the column formula for compression members; l in the l/r ratio is taken to be not less than three-quarters the depth of girder (Bibliography, Art. 6-87).

6-28. Design of Member for Axial Tension. Axial tension is produced in a member when the forces are applied parallel to and at its center line, the forces tending to stretch or elongate the member. A fundamental assumption of design is that the unit stress f is uniform over the cross-sectional area A; i.e., $f = P/A$, where P = total axial force or load.

The design of a tension member with no holes in it consists only of choosing a section with sufficient area that the intensity of stress is within permissible limits. No loss of section because of holes occurs with welded construction, or with the tension rods used to brace buildings.

Typical tension members are illustrated in Fig. 6-23. Types (a), (b), and (c) are used for bracing and light trusses; (d), (e), and (f) for heavier trusses, the latter two being adaptable for combined bending and axial tension; and types (g) to (j) for the heaviest-type trusses found in buildings.

If the area of a member has been reduced at any point, for example, by a rivet hole, the value of f increases at that point. The increase is due to the reduction of the area over which the load may be distributed, regardless of whether the hole is filled by a rivet or tight-fitting bolt.

There are two cases to consider in obtaining the net area over which the tensile force is distributed. The first is a cross section with only one hole, and the second is one with a group of holes. In the latter case, a zigzag section between staggered holes may have less tensile strength than along a section normal to the applied load.

In Fig. 6-24a, it is logical to expect that the failure will be on a line through the rivet hole, normal to the direction of stress; but in Fig. 6-24b, the failure line could follow a variety of paths—*ABCDEF, ABCDG, ABDG, ABDEF,* or *ABEF.*

According to the American Institute of Steel Construction specifications, the net width is obtained by deducting from the gross width the sum of the diameters of all holes in the line of possible failure and adding, for each transverse (gage) space in the chain, the quantity $S^2/4g$, where S is the longitudinal spacing of the holes (pitch) and g is the transverse spacing (gage).

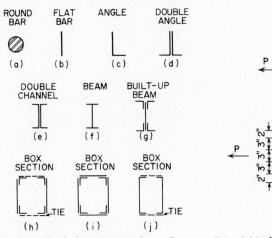

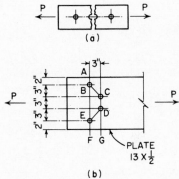

FIG. 6-23. Typical tension members. Lower ones are used for heavy loads.

FIG. 6-24. Net section of riveted tension members.

Given: Plate shown in Fig. 6-24b, ⅞-in.-diameter rivets. Find its tensile capacity for a 20,000 psi allowable unit stress.

Solution: Specifications require that the diameter of the hole be taken ⅛ in. greater than nominal diameter of rivet; in this case 1 in. Net widths of different chains are:

$$ABCDEF: 13 - (4 \times 1) + \frac{3^2}{4 \times 3} + \frac{3^2}{4 \times 3} = 10.5 \text{ in.}$$

$$ABCDG: 13 - (3 \times 1) + \frac{3^2}{4 \times 3} \qquad\qquad = 10.75 \text{ in.}$$

$$ABDG: 13 - (2 \times 1) + \frac{3^2}{4 \times 6} \qquad\qquad = 11.38 \text{ in.}$$

$$ABDEF: 13 - (3 \times 1) + \frac{3^2}{4 \times 6} + \frac{3^2}{4 \times 3} = 11.13 \text{ in.}$$

$$ABEF: 13 - (2 \times 1) \qquad\qquad\qquad = 11.0 \text{ in.}$$

The minimum width is on paths *ABCDEF* and is equal to 10.5 in.; therefore, the tensile capacity is

$$P = 10.5 \times \tfrac{1}{2} \times 20,000 = 105,000 \text{ lb}$$

All tension members, unless vertical, must support their own dead load in bending, but bending stresses usually are neglected in the design of the member. The choice of sections for long members may be influenced by their slenderness, or l/r ratio. Specifications, like that of the AISC, may limit the l/r ratio for main members to 240 and for secondary (bracing) members to 300, the reason being that some stiffness is desirable as a matter of good practice.   Tension rods, however, are excluded from this provision (Bibliography, Art. 6-87).

6-29. Design of Member for Axial Compression.   When the axial force tends to squeeze or shorten the member, the resulting stress is compression.   In contrast with the tension member in Art. 6-28, loss of area due to rivet or bolt holes is not a factor, because it is assumed the rivet or tight-fitting bolt fills the hole (or else after a tiny slippage it will bear against the adjoining material); therefore, only the gross area is considered.

Also, in contrast with axial tension, which tends to hold a member in a straight line, members subject to compressive loads have a tendency to bend out of the plane of applied forces.   The amount of working stress that a compression member can sustain is dependent upon two factors: length l and a cross-sectional property called radius of gyration r (Arts. 3-70 to 3-76).   Unlike the uniform 20,000 psi allowable unit stress applicable for all tension problems, there are variable values for working stresses in compression.

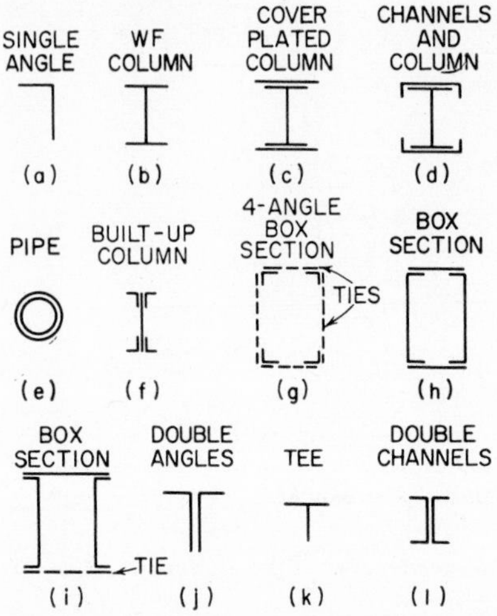

The less rigid a member is between braced points (r is a measure of rigidity), the lower will be its load-carrying capacity, and consequently, the lower the allowable unit stress.   Similarly, an increase in length for a given r will also lower the allowable stress.   Hence, the *slenderness ratio* l/r must be determined before an allowable working stress in compression can be prescribed for any compression member.

Figure 6-25 illustrates some of the common types of compression members.   Single angles (*a*) are frequently used for bracing but rarely for main compression members because of difficulty in loading concentrically.   The WF (wide-flange) sections with or without cover plates, (*b*), (*c*), and (*d*), are the columns commonly used in tier buildings.   Pipe columns (*e*) are frequently used for light loads (low-height commercial

SINGLE ANGLE (a) | WF COLUMN (b) | COVER PLATED COLUMN (c) | CHANNELS AND COLUMN (d)

PIPE (e) | BUILT-UP COLUMN (f) | 4-ANGLE BOX SECTION TIES (g) | BOX SECTION (h)

BOX SECTION TIE (i) | DOUBLE ANGLES (j) | TEE (k) | DOUBLE CHANNELS (l)

FIG. 6-25. Typical compression members.

structures, for example).   Usually, the void space is filled with concrete (see Art. 6-32).   Built-up columns (*f*) or the open-web type (*g*) are occasionally used in special situations.   Types (*j*), (*k*), and (*l*) are commonly used in light trusswork; whereas types (*b*), (*h*), and (*i*) are usually selected for heavy building trusses.

Given: Load of 60 kips, unsupported length 16 ft.   Find a suitable column section.

Solution: The solution requires "cut and try."   One helpful approach is the rule of thumb: take r as one-tenth the unbraced length in feet as a start.   Thus, trial r is assumed as 1.6.   A table of steel section properties gives for an 8 WF 24 a minimum r of 1.61 and an area of 7.06 sq in.   The allowable unit stress is given by the American Institute of Steel Construction specification as

$$f = 17,000 - 0.485 \left(\frac{l}{r}\right)^2 \tag{6-9}$$

when l/r is not greater than 120.   For an 8 WF 24

$$\frac{l}{r} = \frac{16 \times 12}{1.61} = 119$$

$$f = 17,000 - 0.485 \left(\frac{16 \times 12}{1.61}\right)^2 = 10,102 \text{ psi}$$

$$P = fA = 10,102 \times 7.06 = 71,320 \text{ lb}$$

Therefore, the trial section 8 WF 24 is satisfactory to carry 60,000 lb. To simplify this work, the AISC publishes tables in the "Manual of Steel Construction," which enable the designer to select proper-size columns without any computation. Other design tables also are available.

In this solution, the member was assumed to be a main compression element— one whose failure might be expected to cause an immediate collapse of the whole structure or a substantial portion, and consequently was within the limits set forth by the specification; i.e., the slenderness ratio must not exceed 120. If the member were of secondary importance, such as bracing, then l/r may range between 120 and 200, and f, the allowable unit stress, is obtained from

$$f = \frac{18,000}{1 + l^2/18,000r^2} \qquad (6\text{-}10)$$

Some specifications permit main compression members in the 120 to 200 slenderness range, but only at reduced unit stresses. The allowable unit stress in Eq. (6-10) for secondary compression members is reduced by multiplying by the fraction

$$1.6 - \frac{l}{200r}$$

The reduction varies from zero for $l/r = 120$ to 40% for $l/r = 200$.

The advantage of long slender main columns is apparent in certain buildings. For example, an open shed supporting only a small roof load, with a 120 limitation on l/r, would be permitted absurdly low unit stresses by Eq. (6-9), and consequently, there would be an unnecessary waste of material (Bibliography, Art. 6-87).

6-30. Design of Member for Combined Axial and Bending Stresses. Common examples of a member with combined stresses are a horizontal chord member in a truss supporting a vertical load as a beam, and an eccentrically loaded column, such as pictured in Fig. 6-26. As a matter of fact, most columns are subjected to wind moments; consequently, the problem of combined axial loads and bending moments is commonplace in building design.

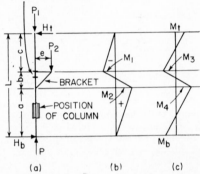

FIG. 6-26. Eccentrically loaded column.

The American Institute of Steel Construction specification requires that such members be proportioned so that the quantity $f_a/F_a + f_b/F_b$ does not exceed unity. F_a is the allowable axial unit stress if axial stress existed alone, F_b the allowable bending unit stress if bending stress existed alone, f_a the actual axial unit stress obtained by dividing the area of member into the total direct load and f_b the actual unit bending stress obtained by dividing the section modulus of the member into the bending moment.

Given: Eccentrically loaded column in Fig. 6-26a, with $P_1 = 10$ kips; $P_2 = 30$ kips; $e = 16$ in.; $L = 20.0$ ft; $a = 12.5$ ft; $b = 1.5$ ft, $c = 6.0$ ft. Find the column size to suit the design condition of hinged ends illustrated in b.

Solution: $H_b = H_t = \dfrac{P_2e}{L} = \dfrac{30 \times 16}{20 \times 12} = 2.0$ kips

$M_1 = H_t c = 2.0 \times 6.0 = 12.0$ ft-kips
$M_2 = H_b a = 2.0 \times 12.5 = 25.0$ ft-kips

The column is laterally supported near the top of the bracket, say 13 ft 6 in. above the column base.

At this point a trial section must be assumed—the "cut-and-try" method. The AISC "Manual of Steel Construction" offers a convenient method for obtaining the approximate size column. Bending factors—area divided by section modulus A/S—are tabulated for all sections. These permit conversion of bending moments into equivalent direct loads; then, columns may be selected from the column tables for the total direct load. Without such a table, the designer will have to approximate the size according to his judgment, or "rule-of-thumb" methods he has at his command.

Try an 8 WF 28; $r = 1.62$, $A = 8.23$, $S = 24.3$.

$$\frac{l}{r} = \frac{13.5 \times 12}{1.62} = 100$$

$$F_a = 17,000 - 0.485 \left(\frac{l}{r}\right)^2 = 17,000 - 0.485(100)^2 = 12,150 \text{ psi}$$

(Here again, the AISC "Manual" aids the designer with a convenient table of stresses for l/r values.)

$$P = P_1 + P_2 = 10 + 30 = 40$$

$$f_a = \frac{40,000}{8.23} = 4,850 \text{ psi}$$

$$F_b = 20,000 \text{ psi (since } L_u = 18.5 > 13.5. \text{ See Art. 6-19)}$$

$$f_b = \frac{25,000 \times 12}{24.3} = 12,300 \text{ psi}$$

$$\frac{f_a}{F_a} + \frac{f_b}{F_b} = \frac{4,850}{12,150} + \frac{12,300}{20,000} = 0.40 + 0.61 = 1.01$$

Unity is exceeded, but the margin of 0.01 is deemed to be within the tolerance of accepted good practice. Thus the 8 WF 28 is satisfactory.

Figure 6-26 typifies the crane column in a mill building. The assumption of hinged ends, used here to simplify the problem, is not always the case; more often, the columns are considered to be fixed or partly fixed at the base, and details are provided to fulfill this assumption. Likewise, the top of the column may be braced by a truss, so that a fixed-end moment will exist. In that case, the moment diagram will resemble Fig. 6-26c. Naturally, computation of such moments is more involved.

In the preceding example, the moment, and consequently, the bending stresses were taken about the strong axis. It was not necessary to reduce F_b because the L_u distance of the selected column shape exceeded the unsupported length of 13.5 ft. In another case, it may be necessary to reduce F_b to that allowed by the ld/bt formula [Eq. (6-1), Art. 6-19)]. Frequently, however, there is additional bending about the minor axis. This introduces a third stress that needs to be added to the total; that is, stress limitation becomes

$$\frac{f_a}{F_b} + \left(\frac{f_b}{F_b}\right)_X + \left(\frac{f_b}{20}\right)_Y \lessgtr 1 \tag{6-11}$$

A stress of 20,000 psi is permissible about the minor or weak axis for the following reason: When a member is subjected to bending about the strong axis, it tends to buckle or rotate into the plane of the weak axis. However, when the bending originates about the weak axis, there is no reverse tendency, there being no weaker planes into which the member can seek relief. Consequently, the full allowable stress of 20,000 psi will govern for bending stresses about the YY axis, whereas the allowable stress for bending about the XX axis will be as given by the lateral buckling formula, Eq. (6-1) (Bibliography, Art. 6-87).

6-31. Design of Member for Combined Wind and Axial Stresses. This is a variation of the design problem in Art. 6-30; it differs primarily in the magnitude of allowable stresses and application of governing specifications. For example, the AISC specification contains this rule:

"Member subject to stresses produced by a combination of wind and other loads may be proportioned for unit stresses 33⅓ % greater than those specified for dead and live load stresses, provided the section thus required is not less than that required for the combination of dead load, live load, and impact (if any). A corresponding increase may be applied to the allowable unit stresses in their connecting rivets, bolts or welds."

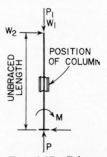

FIG. 6-27. Column with wind and axial loads.

This provision can be expressed another way: Structural members designed for dead and live loads can absorb, without increasing the size of members, additional stress caused by wind loads up to one-third of their designed capacity.

Given: Column loaded as in Fig. 6-27, with P_1 = axial load (dead plus live) = 50 kips; W_1 = axial wind load = 10 kips; W_2 = wind load producing moment M = 2 kips. Unbraced column length l is 10 ft.

Solution: The problem requires at least two steps, possibly three:

STEP 1. For the section required for axial load P_1 without wind, try the lightest 6-in. column, a 6 WF 15.5, with area A = 4.62, section modulus S = 10.1, and minimum radius of gyration r = 1.45.

$$\frac{l}{r} = \frac{10 \times 12}{1.45} = 82.7$$

From Eq. (6-9), the allowable compressive unit stress is

$$F_a = 17,000 - 0.485 \left(\frac{l}{r}\right)^2 = 17,000 - 0.485(82.7)^2 = 13,700 \text{ psi}$$

The actual unit stress is less:

$$f_a = \frac{P_1}{A} = \frac{50,000}{4.62} = 10,800 \text{ psi}$$

Therefore, the trial section, 6 WF 15.5, is ample.

STEP 2. Check this section for combined stresses:

$$P = P_1 + W_1 = 50 + 10 = 60 \text{ kips}$$
$$f_a = \frac{60,000}{4.62} = 13,000 \text{ psi}$$

The actual maximum bending stress is

$$f_b = \frac{M}{S} = \frac{2 \times 10 \times 12 \times 1,000}{10.1} = 23,800 \text{ psi}$$

$$F_a = \frac{4}{3} \times 13,700 = 18,200 \text{ psi}$$

$$F_b = \frac{4}{3} \times 20,000 = 26,700 \text{ psi}$$

$$\frac{f_a}{F_a} + \frac{f_b}{F_b} = \frac{13,000}{18,200} + \frac{23,800}{26,700} = 0.71 + 0.89 = 1.60$$

Since unity is exceeded a larger section must be selected.

STEP 3. Try an 8 WF 24, with $A = 7.06$, $S = 20.8$, minimum $r = 1.61$.

$$\frac{l}{r} = \frac{10 \times 12}{1.61} = 74.5$$

$$F_a = \frac{4}{3}\left[17,000 - 0.485\left(\frac{l}{r}\right)^2\right] = \frac{4}{3}[17,000 - 0.485(74.5)^2] = 19,100 \text{ psi}$$

$$F_b = \frac{4}{3} \times 20,000 = 26,700 \text{ psi}$$

$$f_a = \frac{60,000}{7.06} = 8,500 \text{ psi}$$

$$f_b = \frac{20 \times 12}{20.8} = 11,500 \text{ psi}$$

$$\frac{f_a}{F_a} + \frac{f_b}{F_b} = \frac{8,500}{19,100} + \frac{11,500}{26,700} = 0.45 + 0.43 = 0.88$$

Since this is less than and reasonably close to unity, the trial section 8 WF 24 is satisfactory.

In this problem a larger column was needed for the combined loads than for the dead- and live-load condition, but this is not always the case. Had we not introduced the moment and simply solved for direct axial loads, we would find that the 6 WF 15.5 could have taken a combined load of $4.62 \times 18,200$, or 84.0 kips, as against $4.62 \times 13,700$, or 63.3 kips, maximum for dead, live, and impact loads (Bibliography, Art. 6-87).

6-32. Design of Pipe Columns. As the name implies, the column shape is circular in cross section. Pipe columns are particularly useful in low-height buildings where simple axial loads prevail and where attractive architectural effects are derived from exposed steelwork. From a purely theoretical viewpoint, the circular column is ideal because the stiffness factor l/r is the same in every direction.

Pipe columns, however, are not well suited for multistory construction (say over four stories) or where bending moments are large. The cost and difficulty of connecting beams and girders to the round surface has been the outstanding deterrent to their use. However, growth of welding and development of special connections has alleviated many of the earlier objections. Still, it is doubtful that such construction can match the economy of ordinary rolled column sections in multistory buildings.

The American Institute of Steel Construction lists in the "Manual" three weight classifications for pipe—standard, extra strong, and double extra strong. The safe carrying capacity for concentric loading is given up to 26 ft of unbraced length; pipes range in diameters from 3 to 12 in. The safe loads are computed from the column formula, Eq. (6-9), Art. 6-29.

The AISC loads assume the pipe is made of steel at least as strong as the basic steel generally used for plates and structural shapes. In practice, pipes are frequently supplied to meet specifications for steel having higher yield points. No increase in allowable stresses is suggested, since higher yield points do not appreciably increase the load-carrying capacity of a column.

The void space in the pipe is usually filled with concrete, the idea being to seal the inaccessible area and to gain additional bearing capacity because of the ability of the concrete core to share this load. The generally accepted standard for computing the capacity of concrete-filled steel pipe columns is that given in "Building Code Requirements for Reinforced Concrete," of the American Concrete Institute:

$$P = 0.25f'_c\left(1 - 0.000025\,\frac{h^2}{K_c{}^2}\right)A_c + f'_r A_s \tag{6-12}$$

where f'_c = compressive strength of concrete (28 days)

$\quad A_c$ = cross-sectional area of concrete

$\quad A_s$ = cross-sectional area of steel pipe

$\quad h$ = unbraced column length

$\quad K_c$ = least radius of gyration of concrete section

f'_r is given by $17{,}000 - 0.485\, h^2/K_s{}^2$, with K_s as the least radius of gyration of the pipe section, when $h/K_s \lessgtr 120$ and the yield point of the pipe is at least 33,000 psi.

To aid the designer in quickly obtaining f'_r and f'_c values corresponding to various l/r ratios, HHFA published a chart, which is reproduced in Fig. 6-28. ("Structural

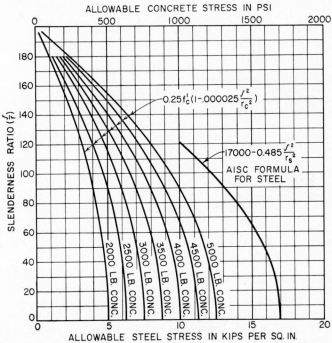

FIG. 6-28. Allowable stress in concrete-filled pipe columns.

Properties of Light-gage Tubular Columns," *Housing Research Paper* 21, Housing and Home Finance Agency, Washington, D.C.)

Design of a pipe column is no different in procedure from the solutions given in Arts. 6-29 and 6-30. With eccentric loading (combined axial and bending stresses) the steel must resist the combined stress, the resultant not exceeding unity according to the interaction formula, whereas the concrete core is computed for axial loads only.

6-33. Design of Trusses. A truss is a framework so arranged as to form a series of rigid triangles, the bending moments being translated into axial stresses applied concentrically to the members. The assumptions that such stresses are applied along the center of gravity of each member and that these stress lines meet at a point are not always precise truth. Steel angles, for example, in riveted construction are located so that gage lines, not gravity axes, are on the stress lines. Naturally, for wide angles with two gage lines, the line closest to the gravity axis is centered on the stress line to minimize eccentricity. Secondary stresses caused by such eccentricity should be avoided or minimized wherever possible.

As a general rule, members framing into trusses are located at panel points—the intersections of three or more members.   When loads are introduced between panel points, the truss members subjected to them must be designed for combined axial stress and bending.

The design problems encountered with trusses are the same as the basic problems previously discussed and illustrated for tension, compression, and combined stresses (Bibliography, Art. 6-87).

6-34. Design for Deflection.   The question of how much deflection is permissible before it becomes objectionable is one that the engineer must resolve for specific cases.   In many instances, a relatively small quantity of steel is ample to satisfy strength requirements but is insufficient to avoid excessive deflection.   Good-practice rules have been developed over the years.   For example, the American Institute of Steel Construction specification contains such rules expressed in terms of depth-to-span ratio, deflection-to-span ratio, and camber.   These may be summarized as follows:

Depth-span ratios (Minimums for single spans):

1 to 24 for floor beams and girders.

1 to 20 for floor beams and girders subject to impact.

When members of less depth are used, the unit stress in bending should be decreased in the same ratio the depth is decreased.

1 to 24 (maximum of 30) for roof purlins.

1 to 90 for secondary tension members where the "span" is the horizontal projection of the length.

Deflection-span ratio (maximum):

1 to 360 for live-load deflection for beams and girders supporting plastered ceilings.

Camber:

Trusses 80 ft or greater should be cambered for dead-load deflection.   Crane girders 75 ft or greater should be cambered for deflection under dead plus one-half live load.

Deflection formulas:

Formulas have been worked out for the common conditions of loading (concentrated, uniform, variable, partial, etc.) and for the various design systems (simple, rigid, continuous, cantilever, etc.).   These may be found in the specialized handbooks.   See also Figs. 3-30 to 3-41.

BRACING

Bracing as it applies to steel structures includes secondary members incorporated into the system of main members to serve these principal functions:

1. Slender compression members, such as columns, beams, and truss elements, are braced, or laterally supported, so as to restrain the tendency to buckle in a direction normal to the stress path.   The rigidity, or resistance to buckling, of an individual member, is determined from its length and certain physical properties of its cross section.   Economy and size usually determine whether bracing is to be employed.

2. Since most structures are assemblies of vertical and horizontal members forming rectangular (or square) panels, they possess little inherent rigidity.   Consequently, additional rigidity must be supplied by a secondary system of members or by rigid or semirigid joints between members.   This is particularly necessary when the framework is subject to lateral loads, such as wind, earthquakes, and moving loads.   Exempt from this second functional need for bracing are trusses, which are basically an arrangement of triangles possessing an inherent ideal rigidity both individually and collectively.

3. There is a need for bracing frequently to resist erection loads and to align or prevent overturning of trusses, bents, or frames during erection.   Such bracing may be temporary; however, usually bracing needed for erection is also useful in supplying rigidity to the structure and therefore is permanently incorporated into the building. For example, braces that tie together adjoining trusses and prevent their overturn-

ing during erection are useful to prevent sway—even though the swaying forces may not be calculable.

6-35. Column Bracing. Interior columns of a multistory building are seldom braced between floor connections. Bracing of any kind generally interferes with occupancy requirements and architectural considerations. Since the slenderness ratio l/r in the weak direction usually controls column size, greatest economy is achieved by using only wide-flange column sections.

It is frequently possible to reduce the size of wall columns by introducing knee braces or struts in the plane of the wall, or by taking advantage of deep spandrels or girts that may be otherwise required. Thus the slenderness ratio for the weak and strong axis can be brought into approximate balance. The saving in column weight may not always be justified; one must take into account the weight of additional bracing and cost of extra details.

Column bracing is prevalent in industrial buildings because greater vertical clearances necessitate longer columns. Tall slender columns may be braced about both axes to obtain an efficient design.

Undoubtedly, heavy masonry walls afford substantial lateral support to steel columns embedded wholly or partly in the wall. The general practice, however, is to disregard this assistance.

Concrete encasement (when used) of steel columns is usually credited with partial lateral support. This is reflected in an increase in allowable load-carrying capacity. For example, the American Concrete Institute Building Code contains a formula for a combination column, where the minimum thickness of concrete is $2\frac{1}{2}$ in. and where the concrete is of specified strength and reinforced with wire mesh; the allowable safe load is given by

$$P = A_s f_s \left(1 + \frac{A_c}{100 A_s} \right) \tag{6-13}$$

where A_s = cross-sectional area of steel column
$\quad\quad f_s$ = allowable stress for unencased steel column
$\quad\quad A_c$ = total area of concrete

An important factor in determining column bracing is the allowable stress for the column section [Eqs. (6-9) and (6-10), Art. 6-29]. Column formulas for obtaining this stress are based on the ratio of two variables, length l and the physical property called radius of gyration r.

The question of when to brace (to reduce the unsupported length and thus slenderness ratio) is largely a matter of economics and architectural arrangements; thus no general answer can be given.

Use of Eq. (6-10) with a reduction factor is limited to conditions where columns will not be subject to shock or vibratory loads. Where it can be used, reduced Eq. (6-10) makes possible an economical-size column of long length for light loads.

6-36. Beam Bracing. Economy in size of member dictates whether laterally unsupported beams should have additional lateral support between end supports. Lateral support at intermediate points should be considered whenever the allowable stress obtained from the reduction formula [Eq. (6-1), Art. 6-19] falls below some margin, say 25%, of the 20,000 psi allowed for the fully braced condition. There are cases, however, where unit stresses as low as 4,000 psi have been justified, because intermediate lateral support was impractical.

The question often arises: When is a steel beam laterally supported? There is no fixed rule in specifications (nor any intended in this discussion) because the answer requires application of sound judgment based on experience. Tests and studies that have been made indicate that it takes rather small forces to balance the lateral thrusts of initial buckling.

In Fig. 6-29 are illustrated some of the common situations encountered in present-day practice. In general, positive lateral support is provided by:

(a) and (b). All types of cast-in-place concrete slabs (questionable for vibrating loads and loads hung on bottom flange).

(*c*). Metal and steel plate decks, welded connections.

(*d*). Wood decks nailed securely to nailers bolted to beam.

(*e*) and (*f*). Beam flange tied or braced to strut system, either as shown in (*e*) or by means of cantilever tees, as shown in (*f*); however, struts should be adequate to resist rotation.

(*g*). Purlins used as struts, with tees acting as cantilevers (common in rigid frames and arches).

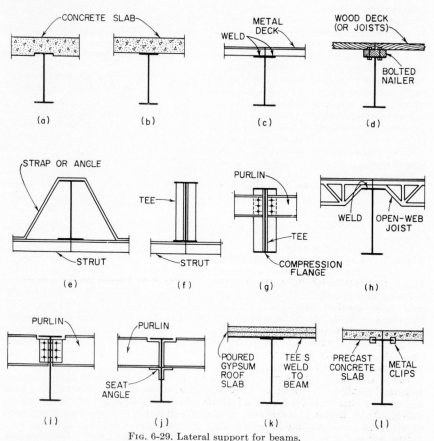

FIG. 6-29. Lateral support for beams.

(*h*). Open-web joists tack-welded (or the equivalent) to the beams; but the joists themselves must be braced together (bridging), and the flooring so engaged with the flanges that the joists, in turn, are adequately supported laterally.

(*i*). Purlins connected close to the compression flange.

(*k*). Tees (part of cast-in-place gypsum construction) welded to the beams.

Doubtful lateral support is provided by:

(*j*). Purlins seated on beam webs, where the seats are distant from the critical flange.

(*l*). Precast slabs not adequately fastened to the compression flange.

The reduction formula [Eq. (6-1)] for steel beams does not apply to those fully encased in concrete, even though no other lateral support is provided.

Introducing a secondary member to cut down the unsupported length does not necessarily result in adequate lateral support. The assumed thrust, or rather the resistive capacity of the member, must be traced through the system to ascertain its effectiveness. For example, the system in Fig. 6-30a may be free to deflect laterally as shown. This can be prevented by a rigid floor system that acts as a diaphragm, or in the absence of a floor, it may be necessary to X-brace the system as shown in Fig. 6-30b.

The corollary question then arises: What size brace should be used? A popular rule among structural designers is: Design braces for 2% of the axial load on a column or 2% of the total compressive flange stress in a beam. Studies show that this assumption is conservative.

Singleton's "Manual of Structural Design" (H. M. Ives & Sons) contains a method for determining an equivalent lateral force, uniformly applied, that is needed to compensate for the probable buckling thrust of a beam laterally unsupported between its ends. A unit stress is found by subtracting the allowable stress given by the reduction formula [Eq. (6-1)] from the basic unit stress, 20,000 psi. Assuming this computed stress occurs in the compression flange acting alone as a horizontal beam, the horizontal uniform load that would produce this stress is determined and compared with the passive resistance of the slab or other elements that are in contact with the flange. Naturally, such frictional resistance is dependent on the values assumed for the coefficient of friction. This is estimated to range from 10 to 25% of the vertical load on the beam.

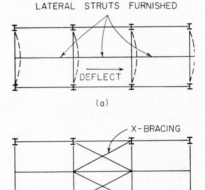

FIG. 6-30. Lateral bracing systems.

6-37. Reduction Formula for Buckling of Beams. The reduction formula for beams [Eq. (6-1), Art. 6-19] was adopted by the American Institute of Steel Construction following the publication of Karl deVries' paper, "Strength of Beams as Determined by Lateral Buckling," *Transactions of the American Society of Civil Engineers*, 1947. The allowable compression stress on the extreme fibers of rolled sections, plate girders, and built-up members is limited to 20,000 psi for ld/bt not exceeding 600 and $12,000,000/(ld/bt)$ psi for ld/bt exceeding 600, where l is the laterally unsupported length (see Art. 6-36), d the beam depth, b the flange or beam width, and t the thickness of the compression flange.

The parameter of 12,000,000 was suggested for the condition of uniform loading applied to the top flange of a simply supported, symmetrically shaped beam. This loading and point of application is the most critical of several cases investigated. Therefore, the general acceptance of this single parameter, in the interest of simplification, errs on the conservative side when it is used for other conditions of loading.

The deVries reduction formula is most satisfactory within the range of normal design practice and the field of rolled-beam sections. Application to plate girders, unsymmetrical sections such as channels, crane girders compounded from channels and beams, etc., frequently gives results that should be tempered with sound judgment. For a short, but exceptionally deep girder; e.g., the side of a bin, Eq. (6-1) may give too low values, whereas treating the flange as a column would be more realistic.

Application of Eq. (6-1) to sections other than hot-rolled beams; e.g., plate girders with flange angles, plate girder with cover plates or channels, etc., in which selection of the proper value for t is not apparent, may be aided by obtaining the product bt as given by the expression $6I_y/b^2$ for welded assemblies, or as given by $5I_y/b^2$ for riveted assemblies, where I_y is the moment of inertia of the whole girder about the vertical axis, and b is the maximum width of the top flange. When the top and bottom flanges are of unequal size, the value of I_y is twice the moment of inertia of the compression flange.

In the case of a channel functioning as a laterally unsupported beam and other unsymmetrical sections or assemblies, an alternate method for obtaining bt, erring on the conservative side for sections usually encountered, is to consider the product bt as representing flange area.

6-38. Lateral Forces on Building Frames. Design of bracing to resist forces induced by wind, seismic disturbances, and moving loads, such as those caused by cranes is not unlike, in principle, design of members that support vertical dead and live loads. These lateral forces are readily calculable. They are collected at points of application and then distributed through the structural system until delivered to the ground. Wind loads, for example, are collected at each floor level and distributed to the columns that are selected to participate in the system. Such loads are cumulative; that is, columns resisting wind shears must support at any floor level all the wind loads on the floors above the one in consideration.

6-39. Bracing Tall Buildings. If the steel frame of the multistory building in Fig. 6-31a is subjected to lateral wind load, it will distort as shown in Fig. 6-31b, assuming that the connections of columns and beams are of the standard type, for which rigidity (resistance to rotation) is nil. This can be visualized readily by assuming each joint is connected with a single pin. Naturally, the simplest method to prevent this distortion is to insert diagonal members—triangles being inherently rigid, even if all the members forming the triangles are pin-connected.

Bracing of the type shown in Fig. 6-31c, commonly called "X" bracing, is both efficient and economical. Unfortunately, X bracing is usually impracticable because of interference with doors, windows, and clearance between floor and ceiling. Architects of modern office buildings require clear floor areas; this offers flexibility of space use, with movable partitions. But about the only place for X bracing in this type of building is in the elevator shaft, fire tower, or wherever a windowless wall is required. As a result, additional bracing must be supplied by other methods. On the other hand, X bracing is used extensively for bracing industrial buildings of the shed or mill types.

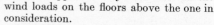

(a)   (b)   (c)

(d)   (e)   (f)

Fig. 6-31. Wind bracing for multistory buildings.

In lieu of X bracing in tall buildings, the designer has a choice of several methods. Knee braces, shown in Fig. 6-31d, or portal frames, shown in Fig. 6-31e, may be used in outer walls, where they are likely to interfere only with windows. However, the trend to window walls has decreased use of this type of bracing. The type that has emerged for almost uniform application is the bracket type (Fig. 6-31f). It consists simply of developing the end connection for the calculated wind moment. Connections vary in type, depending on size of members, magnitude of wind moment, and compactness needed to comply with floor-to-ceiling clearances.

Figure 6-32 illustrates a number of bracket-type wind-braced connections. The minimum type, represented in Fig. 6-32a, consists of angles top and bottom; they are ample for moderate-height buildings. Usually the outstanding leg (against the column) is of a size that permits only one gage line; a second line of rivets would not be effective owing to the eccentricity. When greater moment resistance is needed, the type shown in Fig. 6-32b should be considered. This is the type that has become rather conventional in multistory construction. Figure 6-32c illustrates the maximum size with beam stubs having flange widths that permit additional gage lines, as shown. It is thus possible on larger wide-flange columns to obtain 16 rivets in the stub-to-column connection.

The resisting moment of a given connection varies with the distance between centroids of the top and bottom connection piece.   To increase this distance, thus increasing the moment, an auxiliary beam may be introduced as shown in Fig. 6-32d, provided it does not create an interference.

All the foregoing types may be of welded construction, rather than riveted or bolted.   In fact, it is not unusual to find mixtures of both because of the fabricator's decision to shop-rivet and field-weld, or vice versa.   Welding, however, has much to offer in simplifying details and saving weight, as illustrated in Fig. 6-32e and f. The latter represents the ultimate efficiency with respect to weight saving, and furthermore, it eliminates interfering details.

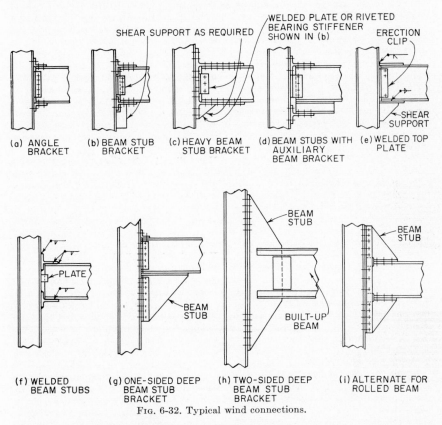

FIG. 6-32. Typical wind connections.

Deep wing brackets (Fig. 6-32g, h, and i) are sometimes used for wall beams and spandrels designed to take wind stresses.   Such deep brackets are, of course, acceptable for interior beam bracing whenever the brackets do not interfere with required clearances.

Not all beams need be wind-braced in tall buildings.   Usually the wind is concentrated on certain column lines, called bents, and the forces are carried through the bents to the ground.   For example, in a wing of a building, it is possible to concentrate the wind load on the outermost bent; to do so may require a stiff floor or diaphragm-like system capable of distributing the wind loads laterally, one-half to the outer bent and one-half to the main building to which the wing connects.

Braced bents are invariably necessary across the narrow dimension of a building. The question arises as to the amount of bracing required in the long dimension, since wind of equal unit intensity is assumed to act on all exposed faces of structures.

In buildings of square or near square proportions, it is likely that braced bents will be provided in both directions. In buildings having a relatively long dimension, as compared with width, the need for bracing diminishes. In fact, in many instances, wind loads are distributed over so many columns that the inherent rigidity of the whole system is sufficient to preclude the necessity of additional bracing.

Why all the emphasis on beam-to-column connections and not on column-to-column joints, since both joints are subjected to the same wind forces? Columns are compression members and as such transmit their loads, from section above to section below, by direct bearing between milled ends. It is not likely, in the average building, for the tensile stresses induced by wind loads ever to exceed the compressive pressure due to dead loads. Consequently, there is no theoretical need for bracing a column joint. Actually, however, column joints are connected together with nominal splice plates for practical considerations—to tie the columns during erection and to obtain vertical alignment.

This does not mean that one may always ignore the adequacy of column splices. In lightly loaded structures, or in exceptionally tall but narrow buildings, it is possible for the horizontal wind forces to cause a net uplift in the windward column due to the overturning action. The commonly used column splices should then be checked for their capacity to resist the net tensile fiber stresses produced in the column flanges. This computation and possible heavying up of the splice material may not be thought of as bracing; yet, in principle, the column joint is being "wind-braced" in a manner similar to the wind-braced floor-beam connections.

6-40. Shear Walls. It is well known that masonry walls enveloping the steel frame, interior masonry walls, and perhaps some of the stiffer partitions can resist a substantial amount of lateral load. Rigid floor systems participate by distributing the shears induced at each floor level to the columns and walls. In fact, in seismic design, where assumed lateral loads are relatively large, a major part of the load is frequently transmitted by the floor system into specially designed shear walls. Walls normally needed for fire towers, elevator shafts, divisional walls, etc., may be extended and reinforced for this purpose and may relieve the steel frame of cumbersome bracing of uneconomical proportions.

It is common design practice to carry wind loads on the steel frame, little or no credit being given to the substantial resistance rendered by the floor and the walls. In the past, some engineers deviated from this conservatism by assigning a portion of this load to the floor and walls; but even then the steel frame carried the major share. The present trend in multistory building design, particularly for offices, is to walls of glass; thin metallic curtain walls; lightweight floors; and removable partitions, and this imposes on the steel frame almost complete responsibility for transmittal of wind loads. Consequently, the importance of wind-bracing tall steel structures should not diminish.

In fact, in tall, slender, partitioned buildings, such as hotels and apartments, the problem of preventing or reducing to tolerable limits the cracking of rigid-type partitions has been related to the wracking action of the frame caused by excessive deflection. One solution that may be used in exceptionally slender frames (those most likely to deflect excessively) is to supplement the normal bracing of the steel frame with shear walls, in much the same fashion as for seismic design. The walls, usually of reinforced concrete, are located on transverse bents and spaced at such intervals as to be effective and compatible with the architectural arrangements.

6-41. Bracing Industrial-type Buildings. Bracing of low industrial buildings for horizontal forces presents fewer difficulties than bracing of multistory buildings, because the designer is virtually free to select the most efficient bracing without regard to architectural considerations or interferences. For this reason, conventional X bracing is widely used—but not exclusively. Knee braces, struts, and sway frames are used where needed.

Wind forces acting upon the frame shown in Fig. 6-33a, assuming hinged joints at the top and bottom of supporting columns, would cause collapse as indicated in Fig. 6-33b. In practice, the joints would not be hinged. However, a minimum-type connection at the truss connection and a conventional column base with anchor bolts located on the axis transverse to the frame would approximate this theoretical consideration of hinged joints. Therefore, the structure requires bracing capable of preventing collapse and undue deflection.

In the usual case, the connection between truss and column will be stiffened by means of knee braces (Fig. 6-33c). The rigidity so obtained may be supplemented by providing partial rigidity at the column base by simply locating the anchor bolts in the plane of the bent.

In buildings containing overhead cranes, the knee brace may interfere with crane operation. Then, the problem may be resolved by fully anchoring the column base so that the column may function as a vertical cantilever (Fig. 6-33d).

The method often used for very heavy industrial buildings is to obtain substantial rigidity at both ends of the column so that the behavior under lateral load will resemble the condition illustrated in Fig. 6-33e. In both (d) and (e), the footings must be designed for such moments.

A common assumption in wind distribution for the type of light mill building shown in Fig. 6-34 is that the windward column takes a large share of the load acting on the side of the building and delivers it directly to the ground. The remaining wind load on the side is

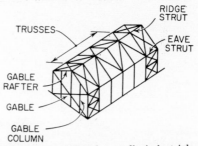

FIG. 6-33. Relative stiffness of mill-building frames.

FIG. 6-34. Braced, small industrial building.

delivered by the same columns to the roof system, where it joins with the wind forces imposed directly on the roof surface. Then, by means of diagonal X bracing, working in conjunction with the struts and top chords of the trusses, the load is carried to the eave struts, thence to the gables and, through diagonal bracing, to the foundations.

Since wind may blow in all directions, the building also must be braced for the wind load on the gables. This bracing becomes less important as the building increases in length and conceivably could be omitted in exceptionally long structures. The stress path is not unlike that assumed for the transverse wind forces. The load generated on the ends is picked up by the roof system and side framing, delivered to the eaves, and then transmitted by the diagonals in the end side-wall bays to the foundation.

No distribution rule for bracing is intended in this discussion; bracing can be designed many different ways. Whereas the foregoing method would be sufficient for a small building, a more elaborate treatment is suggested for larger structures.

Braced bays, or towers, are usually favored in the better-braced structures, such as in Fig. 6-35. There, a pair of transverse bents are connected together with X bracing in the plane of the columns, plane of truss bottom chords, plane of truss top chords, and by means of struts and sway frames. It is assumed that each such tower can carry the wind load from adjacent bents, the number depending on assumed rigidities, size, span, and also on sound judgment. Usually every third or fourth bent should become a braced bay. Participation of bents adjoining the braced bay can be assured by insertion of bracing designated "intermediate" in Fig. 6-35b. This bracing is of greater importance when knee braces between trusses and columns cannot be used. When maximum lateral stiffness of intermediate bents is desired, it can be obtained by extending the X bracing across the span; this is shown with broken lines in Fig. 6-35b.

Buildings with flat or low-pitched roofs, shown in Fig. 6-7d and e (Art. 6-8), require little bracing because the trusses are framed into the columns. These columns are designed for the heavy moments induced by wind pressure against the building side. The bracing that would be provided, at most, would consist of X bracing in the plane of the bottom chords for purpose of alignment during erection and a line or two of sway frames for longitudinal rigidity. Alignment bracing is left in the structure since it affords a secondary system for distributing wind loads.

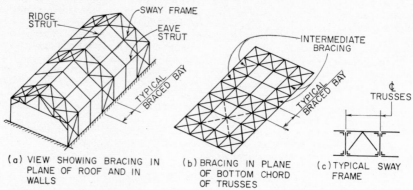

(a) VIEW SHOWING BRACING IN PLANE OF ROOF AND IN WALLS

(b) BRACING IN PLANE OF BOTTOM CHORD OF TRUSSES

(c) TYPICAL SWAY FRAME

Fig. 6-35. Braced, large industrial building.

6-42. Bracing Crane Structures. All buildings that house overhead cranes should be braced for the thrusts induced by sideway and longitudinal motions of the cranes. Bracing used for wind or erection may, of course, be assumed to sustain the lateral crane loadings. These forces are usually concentrated on one bent. Therefore, normal good practice dictates that adjoining bents share in the distribution. Most effective is a system of X bracing located in the plane of the bottom chords of the roof trusses.

In addition, the bottom chords should be investigated for possible compression, although the chords normally are tension members. A heavily loaded crane is apt to draw the columns together, conceivably exerting a greater compression stress than the actual tension stress obtainable under condition of zero snow load. This may indicate the need for intermediate bracing of the bottom chord.

6-43. Design of X Bracing. X bracing may consist of rods (probably the least expensive) or stiffer shapes, such as angles. Rods are unsuitable for compression, whereas an angle may be able to take some compression and thereby aid another diagonal member in tension. Generally, the rod or the angle is designed to take all the stress in tension.

One objection to rods is that they may rattle, particularly in buildings subjected to vibrations. Angle bracing is often larger than need be for the calculated stress. The American Institute of Steel Construction, to assure satisfactory service under normal operation, requires that tension members (except rods) have a minimum slenderness ratio l/r of 300 and, further, that the length (or horizontal projection) should not exceed ninety times the depth.

6-44. Bracing Rigid Frames. Rigid frames of the type shown in Fig. 6-9a (Art. 6-8) have enjoyed popular usage for gymnasiums, auditoriums, mess halls, and with increasing frequency, industrial buildings. The stiff knees at the junction of the column with the rafter imparts excellent transverse rigidity. Each bent is capable

of delivering its share of wind load directly to the footings. Nevertheless, some bracing is advisable, particularly for resisting wind loads against the end of the building.
Most designers emphasize the importance of an adequate eave strut; it usually is so
arranged as to brace the inside flange (compression) of the frame knee, the connection
being located at the mid-point of the transition between column and rafter segments
of the frame. Intermediate X bracing in the plane of the rafters is usually omitted.

FASTENERS

There are three basically different methods for connecting steel members together—
rivets, welds, and *unfinished bolts*—and three types of rivet substitutes—*turned bolts,
ribbed bolts,* and *high-tensile-strength bolts.*

Many variables affect the selection of a fastener. To name a few: code requirements, available equipment, labor supply (e.g., scarcity of riveters or abundance of
welders), designer's experience, fabricator's preference, and relative economy. Riveting and welding are the common shop methods, shops generally being geared for
one or the other, but sometimes for both methods. All methods are used in the field.
It is not uncommon to find such combinations as shop rivets and field bolts, shop
rivets and field welds, shop welds and field rivets, or shop welds and field bolts. The
variables leading to these decisions are too numerous and often too controversial to
permit establishment of fixed rules.

6-45. Hot-driven Rivets. These are the time-honored fasteners for connecting
structural-steel elements. The method is extremely efficient for shop assembly
because most shop rivets are driven with heavy machines capable of rapid production.
In the field, rivets are driven with compressed-air riveting guns, the equipment being
limited in size to permit manual operation.

Rivets are calculated on the basis of their ability to resist shear and bearing stresses;
occasionally they may function in pure tension or combination of tension and shear
(Art. 6-56). Within the range of working stresses and with the usual factor of safety
for loads, it is unlikely that rivets will function as designed to resist shear and bearing
under static loads. The initial tension in the rivet, as obtained upon cooling, due to
shrinkage, usually develops friction between components of the joint of sufficient
magnitude to support the working loads. However, this may not be true for moving
loads or for framing subject to vibrations. Therefore, no consideration is given in
design to the clamping force developed by hot rivets. But clamping force, although
ignored in rivet design, is fundamental for design with high-strength bolts.

Shear and bearing do occur after frictional resistance is exceeded and slippage
takes place.

Rivet material conforming to American Society for Testing Materials Specification
A141 has a minimum yield point of 85 % and a minimum ultimate strength of 87 %,
respectively, of that required for steel for plates and shapes (Specification A7). Tests
show that hot-working this material will increase the yield and ultimate strengths to
approximately the values specified for A7 steel.

6-46. Cold-driven Shop Rivets. These have been tried by some fabricators, but
the heavier driving equipment that is needed has cast doubt on the relative economy
over hot-driven rivets. Advantages claimed for cold driving are the superior filling
of rivet holes (when well driven), increased strength of rivet due to cold working, and
elimination of rivet heating.

6-47. Unfinished Bolts. Known in construction circles by several names—
ordinary, common, machine, or rough—unfinished bolts are characterized chiefly
by rough appearance of the shank. They fit into holes $\frac{1}{16}$ in. larger in diameter
than the nominal bolt diameter. Building codes and specifications, such as those
of the American Institute of Steel Construction, give allowable working stresses for
unfinished bolts of about two-thirds the shear and bearing stresses allowed for rivets,
thus making allowance for less accurate dimensions (Art. 6-57).

The allowable values also take into account the possibility (which is high) that
the threaded part of the shank will extend into the grip, this being necessary when
no washer is employed under the nut. With washers, it is customary to terminate

the threads outside the grip; in that case, some specifications (AISC) permit $12\frac{1}{2}\%$ increase in allowable unit stresses for shear and bearing.

One advantage of unfinished bolts is the ease of making the joint; nothing more than a wrench is required. On larger operations, however, erectors find they can do the task more economically and efficiently with a pneumatic impact wrench. Power tightening probably yields greater uniformity, all bolts having about the same initial tension. The disadvantage of larger numbers of bolts and possibly larger connections because of smaller allowable stresses, as compared with rivets, is usually offset by less labor in making the joint.

At one time, most building codes restricted unfinished bolts to minor applications, such as small secondary (or intermediate) beams in floor panels and in certain parts of one-story structures. Satisfactory experience and growing realization that their efficiency had been underrated have led to a much greater field of application. It is not difficult to find today multistory buildings, say up to 12 stories, in which all joints are connected with unfinished bolts.

6-48. Welding. The method of joining together steel by fusion at high temperatures is generally recognized as being on par with riveting for nonrestricted application. Most building codes accept the recommendations of the American Welding Society—"Standard Code for Arc and Gas Welding in Building Construction," the recognized authority in the field. The American Institute of Steel Construction specification embodies all of this code's salient features.

Weld metal is as good as or better than the base or parent metal. As a result, all major building codes assign the same allowable unit tensile and bending stresses to both the weld and base metals (Art. 6-58). Allowable shear stresses for fillet welds may vary slightly with that accorded to base metal to permit convenient computations.

In some types of structures, welding has proved to be economical; in others it may not be so apparent, if at all. In general, a welded connection can be made with fewer connecting details; consequently, the method conserves steel. Its biggest opportunity lies where continuity is desired, because of the relatively simple connections.

Aside from economic aspects, welding has the asset of being quiet. Therefore, it is frequently used for hospital additions, hotels, and structures in congested areas. The most satisfactory results occur when structures are designed for welding and are not a modification of a riveted design.

6-49. Turned Bolts. As the name implies, a turned bolt is one whose body, or shank, is machined to close tolerance to provide a snug fit with the hole, usually within $\frac{1}{50}$ in. Naturally, the holes must be truly cylindrical; reaming or drilling is deemed necessary. Washers are used to give full grip under the head.

Turned bolts are expensive. Their main function is to replace rivets where the latter cannot be driven to satisfaction. (For allowable stresses, see Art. 6-57.) On occasion, they are used where portability is desired.

6-50. Ribbed Bolts. Many building codes permit ribbed bolts (sometimes referred to as rivet-bolts), which are characterized chiefly by raised fins or ribs uniformly spaced around the shank and extending the length of the grip. The outside diameter (rib to rib) is slightly larger than the hole diameter. Therefore, when driven, the ribs cut into the sides of the holes, necessitating a driving force produced by either a maul or a riveting gun.

Test data supplied by the several manufactures indicate ribbed bolts are at least as strong as rivets (see also Art. 6-57). The material itself is usually of high-tensile-grade steel, with approximately 70,000 psi minimum yield strength. Washers or recessed nuts are needed to assure full grip on the ribbed shanks. Specifications that permit use of these bolts do so on the basis that they are equivalent size for size to rivets.

With ribbed bolts, length of grip, number of plies being connected, accuracy of holes, and type of driving equipment on hand may affect the results obtained. These bolts may require more extensive use of field reaming than for rivets. They are also critized by some engineers because of the notches cut in the base steel by the ribs, these being most objectionable in structures subject to fatigue and heavy impact loads. Nevertheless, the bolts are quite popular and from all indications are performing satisfactorily.

6-51. Locking Devices for Bolts. Unfinished, turned, and ribbed bolts are usually supplied with conventional American Standard threads and nuts. Properly tightened, this construction gives satisfactory service in most statically loaded connections. However, when the connection is subject to vibratory loads or heavy dynamic service, it is usually advisable to provide some locking device to prevent the nut from loosening.

Locking devices may be classified according to method employed—special threads, special nuts, special washers, and what may be described as "field" methods.

Instead of conventional threads, bolts may be supplied with a patented self-locking thread known as "Dardalet."

Locking features are sometimes built into the nuts. Patented devices, the "Automatic-Nut," "Union-Nut," and "Pal-Nut" are among the common ones.

Washers may be the familiar split ring or specially toothed.

The field methods generally used include "checking" the threads by jamming with a chisel or locking by tack welding the nuts. The latter method affords a very positive lock but, of course, makes it more difficult to unlock should portability be desired.

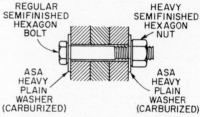

FIG. 6-36. High-tensile-strength bolt.

6-52. High-strength Bolts. Newest in the field of structural fasteners, high-strength bolts (Fig. 6-36) were developed to overcome deficiencies of rivets. The initial tension of cooled rivets is often insufficient to resist dynamic and fatigue-type loads; subsequently, rivets loosen and vibrate, eventually require replacement. But if that initial tensile force were substantially increased, it could afford sufficient resistance to those loads; this is the principle of high-tensile bolts.

To obtain the benefits inherent in high-strength bolts, while waiting for specific design data to be developed through research, the Research Council on Riveted and

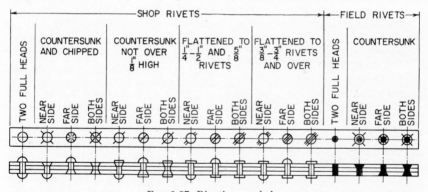

FIG. 6-37. Riveting symbols.

Bolted Structural Joints of the Engineering Foundation recommends that these bolts be substituted, size for size, for rivets in connections designed according to usual specifications governing riveted work (see also Art. 6-57). This procedure is deemed ultraconservative in view of the accumulated test data obtained from both laboratories and field applications conclusively demonstrating the superiority of high-strength bolts. It is expected that the results of current research may culminate in a more efficient design method, one that will reduce the number of bolts required

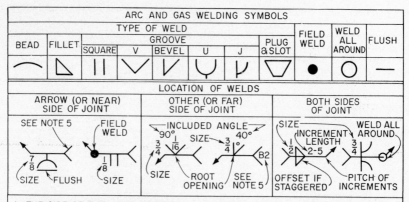

(a)

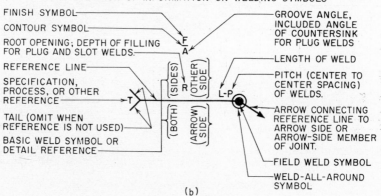

(b)

FIG. 6-38. Welding symbols.

under the present specification ("Assembly of Structural Joints Using High-strength Steel Bolts").

The material used for high-strength bolts is given by ASTM Specification A325. The stock used for $\frac{7}{8}$- and 1-in. bolts must possess a minimum tensile strength of 120,000 psi and a minimum yield strength of 81,000 psi.

In practice, the bolts are drawn up or "torqued" to a minimum tension equal to

90 % of the minimum elastic proof load.   This is readily obtained by means of manual torque wrenches or by pneumatic-powered impact wrenches.   Special calibrated wrenches have been developed to facilitate control of the tensioning process.   An alternate procedure starts with the joint material drawn up tight and the nut finger-tight, after which the nut is given a 360° turn.

Employing the clamping force obtained by initial tension eliminates the need for body-bound bolts.   Accordingly, the usual $\frac{1}{16}$-in. clearance between rivet and hole diameters also prevails for high-tensile bolts.

Specifications require hardened steel washers, under both head and nut, thus permitting easier tightening and better distribution of axial stresses.   No locking device is necessary.

One distinction in the employment of high-strength bolts in statically loaded buildings, in contrast to dynamically loaded structures, is that it is permissible to

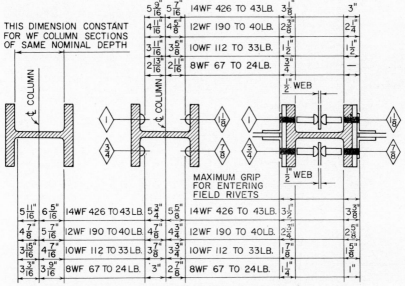

FIG. 6-39. Field-rivet and erection clearances for wide-flange columns.

shop-paint contact surfaces, whereas for bridges and other dynamic connections, all contact surfaces should be free from paint.   Permitting a shop coat for buildings obviates the additional costs entailed in marking up drawings and noting the unpainted areas in the shop.   The practice is justified on grounds that a tiny slip, if it should occur, would be tolerable in building construction.

6-53. Combinations of Fasteners.   On occasion, the question arises whether rivets or bolts can be combined with welds in a connection.   The AISC specification sets forth two conditions, depending on whether the structure is new or old:

For new work, the combination is not permitted; i.e., the stress in a specific connection cannot be distributed in part to rivets or bolts and in part to weld metal. Of course, one leg of a connection angle may employ one method, whereas a different method may be used on the other leg.   The stress is transferred into the angle by one method, then transferred out of the angle by another method.   This condition is commonplace, since one method may be selected for shopwork while a different method is preferred for the field connection.

For old buildings, the problem of making connections with a combination of fasteners is less restrictive.   Usually, the problem arises when new additions are connected to existing buildings, the latter being either riveted or bolted.   Welding is frequently employed to connect the new steel, because of its more efficient characteristics. The rule is to utilize existing rivets for carrying stresses from dead loads up to the allowable maximum and to provide welds to carry all excess dead loads and the design live loads.

6-54. Fastener Symbols. Fasteners are indicated on designs, shop drawings, and field erection plans by notes and symbols. A simple note may suffice for rivets or

No.	Max. Rivet	Diam. D, In.	Str. In.	Wt, Lb.	A		B		All hammers except No. 130 and No. 11 can be fitted with inverted handles. These are for crowded work and are only provided by special arrangement. No. 130 is a jam riveter for close-quarter work.
					Length L, In.	Clear. C, In.	Length Li, In.	Clear. C, In.	
130	$\frac{7}{8}$	$3\frac{1}{16}$	4	15	....	..	9	12	⎫ Used only to drive in
50	$\frac{3}{4}$	$2\frac{5}{16}$	5	20	....	..	14	17	⎰ close quarters
60	$\frac{3}{4}$	$2\frac{7}{16}$	6	23	$19\frac{1}{2}$	24	$15\frac{1}{2}$	19	Rarely used
80	1	$2\frac{7}{16}$	8	25	$21\frac{1}{2}$	26	$17\frac{1}{2}$	21	Used for all except heaviest riveting
90	$1\frac{1}{4}$	$2\frac{7}{16}$	9	26	$23\frac{3}{4}$	28	$19\frac{3}{4}$	23	⎫ Used for heaviest rivet-
11	$1\frac{1}{2}$	$2\frac{7}{16}$	11	32	$26\frac{1}{2}$	31	....	..	⎰ ing

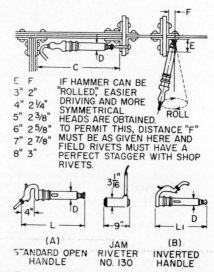

E F   IF HAMMER CAN BE
3" 2"   "ROLLED," EASIER
4" 2¼"   DRIVING AND MORE
5" 2⅜"   SYMMETRICAL
6" 2⅝"   HEADS ARE OBTAINED.
7" 2⅞"   TO PERMIT THIS, DISTANCE "F"
8" 3"   MUST BE AS GIVEN HERE AND
    FIELD RIVETS MUST HAVE A
    PERFECT STAGGER WITH SHOP
    RIVETS.

(A) STANDARD OPEN HANDLE   JAM RIVETER NO. 130   (B) INVERTED HANDLE

FIG. 6-40. Erection clearances for inserting and driving rivets.

bolts; for example: "$\frac{7}{8}$-in. rivets, except as noted." Welds require more explicit information, since their location is not so obvious as that of holes for bolts or rivets.

Symbols are standard throughout the industry. Figure 6-37 shows the symbols for rivets, Fig. 6-38 the symbols for welds. The welding symbols (Fig. 6-38a) together with the information key (Fig. 6-38b) are from American Welding Society standards.

6-55. Erection Clearances for Fasteners. All types of fasteners require clearance for proper installation in both shop and field. Shop connections seldom are a problem, since each member is easily manipulated and wholly under control of the shop and drafting-room personnel. Field connections, however, require careful planning, because connections can be made only after all members are erected and aligned in final position. It becomes the responsibility of the shop draftsmen to arrange connection details in such manner that adequate clearance is provided in the field.

Clearances are necessary for two reasons: (1) to permit entry, as in the case of rivets and bolts entering into holes, and (2) to permit driving of rivetheads with riveting hammers, tightening of bolts with pneumatic bolting machines, and movement of electrodes in welding.

Principal dimensions and maximum grips for entering of field rivets in column flanges are illustrated in Fig. 6-39. Minimum clearances needed for driving of rivets are shown in Fig. 6-40. As a rule, rivets that can be entered can be bucked up; that is, held in place with a "dolly bar" during the driving operation. Although no standard is published, it is customary to provide a few inches of additional clearance

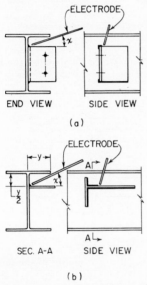

Fig. 6-41. Welding clearance near projecting flanges.

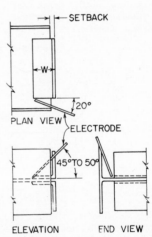

Fig. 6-42. Welding clearance for end-connection angles.

over the minimum needed for entering, so as to afford freedom of movement for the bucking-up operation.

In general, these rivet clearances are applicable to pneumatically tightened bolts. However, bolts may be secured with manual wrenches requiring less clearance. This is the case, of course, for turned bolts, since they are used because tight conditions prevent driving of rivets. Current practice with high-strength bolts, which are tightened with automatically controlled air machines, is to allow the same clearance as given for rivets. The newness of this fastening method and progressive development of new equipment have not warranted standardizing clearances peculiar to the method.

Somewhat less standardized, but equally important, are the clearances for welded joints. Ample room should be provided for the operator to observe the weld as it is deposited and to manipulate the welding electrode. In many respects, more latitude is afforded to the welder since he can shorten the electrode (12 to 18 in. initially) and even prebend it to accommodate a tight situation.

In general, the preferred position of the electrode for fillet welding in the horizontal position is in a plane forming an angle of 30° with the vertical side of the weld. Frequently, this angle must be varied to clear a projecting part, as illustrated in Fig. 6-41a and b. Satisfactory results can be obtained when the weld root is visible to the operator and when the clear distance to a projection that may interfere with the electrode is not less than one-half the projection height ($y/2$ in Fig. 6-41b).

Still another example of welding clearance is illustrated in Fig. 6-42, where the problem is to weld an end-connection angle to a beam web, which is in a horizontal plane, as it would lie on shop skids. The 20° angle in the plan view is the minimum for satisfactory welding with a straight electrode. Assuming a ½-in. setback for the end of the beam and a ⅜-in. outside diameter of the electrode, this distance could not be less than 1¼ in. for an angle whose width W is 3 in., or less than 1⅝ in. where W equals 4 in.

Although both the foregoing examples illustrate shop welding, the beams being laid in positions most favorable to the work, the limiting positions of the electrode are equally applicable to comparable situations that may arise with field connections.

CONNECTIONS

Design of connections and splices is a specialized art of the structural-steel industry known as *detailing*. As a rule, the designer of a structure simply indicates the type of connection desired, e.g., "standard connections Type A." For wind-resisting connections in multistory buildings, the wind moments would be given on the plans, and perhaps a sketch of a typical connection showing the type of wind bracing desired.

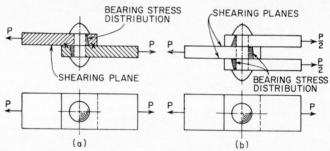

FIG. 6-43. Rivet connection—shear and bearing.

Complete development of each connection becomes the responsibility of the fabricator's engineering organization.

6-56. Stresses in Rivets. *Single shear* occurs when opposing forces act on a rivet as shown in Fig. 6-43a, the plates tending to slide on their contact surfaces. The body of the rivet resists this tendency; a state of shear occurs on the cross-sectional area of the rivet on plane XX. Specifications permit an allowable working stress of 15,000 psi on this area; therefore, a ¾-in.-diameter rivet has a shear value of 6,630 lb, a ⅞-in.-diameter rivet 9,020 lb, etc.

The distribution of shearing stresses may not always be so simple as for the joint in Fig. 6-43a. Frequently, the load is applied eccentrically as illustrated in Fig. 6-44a. Then, the resultant shear R is made up of two components F_v, the proportional share of load P, and F_e, the shear caused by the eccentricity of P, which produces a moment Pl. R is the controlling single-shear stress on the furthermost rivet from the center of gravity of the group; it may not exceed the capacity of this rivet based on a permissible working stress of 15,000 psi.

It should be observed that in Fig. 6-43a the load is transferred from plate to rivet and from rivet to plate by bearing of the plate against the body of the rivet. This is called *single bearing*, for which current specifications allow a stress intensity of 32,000 psi. The effective bearing area is thickness of plate times rivet diameter. It should be noted, however, that the bearing is nonuniform, the greatest concentration being at the inner edges of the plates, shown in Fig. 6-43a, the result of elastic deformation of the rivet.

Since the allowable bearing unit stress is more than double the shear value, it follows that bearing seldom controls the minimum strength of a connection; but, of course, it should be investigated when exceptionally thin material is used.

One other detail may affect the strength of this connection and that is the depth of the plate material behind the rivet. It should be sufficient to prevent tearing out; the minimum edge distance required by specifications is usually an ample safeguard.

Double shear takes place whenever three or more plates act on a rivet as shown in Fig. 6-43*b*. There are two parallel shearing surfaces, one on each side of the middle plate. Accordingly, the shear strength of the rivet is measured by its ability to resist two single shears. A state of single bearing, identical to the condition shown in Fig. 6-43*a*, exists on the outer plates. The bearing on the center plate is uniformly distributed. This condition represents double shear and *enclosed* bearing. Current specifications allow 40,000 psi for double bearing, the higher value a consequence of the uniform distribution of bearing.

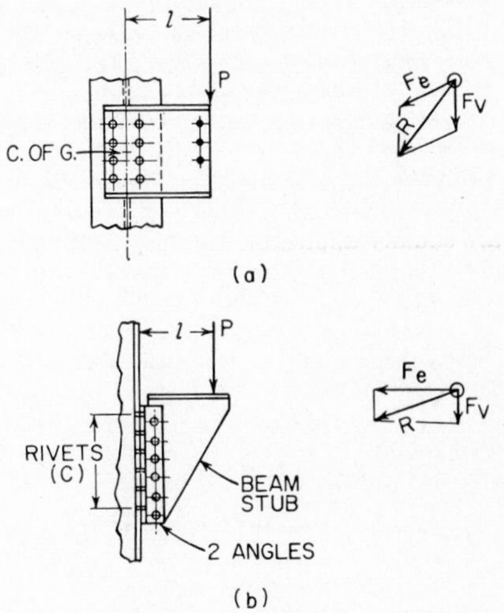

In the final analysis, the strength value of a rivet, such as the one in Fig. 6-43*b*, is measured by the lesser of the two stresses, double shear or double bearing. Tests indicate, however, that overstress in bearing is of little or no import except possibly for very thin material.

(a)

(b)

FIG. 6-44. Eccentrically loaded rivet groups.

Rivets in *tension* at one time were designed on the theory that the tension imposed by the load is additive to the initial tension generated by cooling. Research has conclusively disproved that theory; i.e., tests show the stresses are nonadditive.

Rivets may be used safely in tension, as shown in Fig. 6-45. The load P is transferred from plate (*a*) to angles (*b*) by means of rivets (*c*), which act in double shear and double and single bearing. From the angles, the load goes to the supporting beam (*d*) through rivets (*e*), which are stressed primarily in tension. The full basic 20,000 psi tensile stress for structural steel is also accorded to the rivets, the effective area being computed using the nominal diameter.

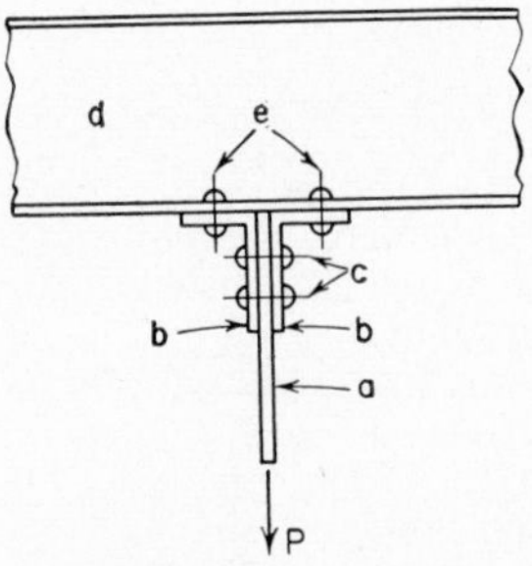

Combined shear and tension in rivets occurs in many connections similar to that in Fig. 6-44*b*, where the rivets (*c*) connecting the bracket to the column are subjected to both types of stresses. The total shear on any rivet in the group is the proportionate share of the load. The tension stress, however, is not uniformly distributed but varies with the resisting moment of each rivet. Obviously, the rivet furthermost from an assumed axis of rotation will be stressed the most.

FIG. 6-45. Rivets in tension.

While several methods of computing the moment are acceptable, the simplest, erring on the safe side, is to assume that the center of rotation coincides with the center of gravity of the rivet group and that the total compressive stress on the rivets below the neutral axis of the group is equal to the total tension stress on the rivets above the axis; the intensity on each rivet is assumed to vary directly with the distance to the neutral axis. The maximum stress on the furthermost rivet is the resultant of this tensile stress and the vertical shear stress, the two stresses functioning in planes at 90° to each other (see also Art. 6-63). The intensity of this resultant for combined shear and tension is limited to that permitted for shear alone—15,000 psi—

according to current AISC specification. Recent studies and research indicate that a higher limit could be safely considered (Bibliography, Art. 6-87).

6-57. Stresses in Bolts. In practice, all bolts are assumed to behave in the same manner as rivets; therefore, the principles of design for shear, bearing (not a factor with high-strength bolts), and tension are identical. Turned bolts, ribbed bolts, and high-strength bolts are currently given the same allowable values as rivets, except for minor variations for tension. Allowable rivet tension is based on nominal diameter, whereas for bolts (other than high-strength) tension is computed on the net area at the root of the thread. Gross area is used for high-strength bolts, because the bolt material has a much greater tensile strength than ordinary rivet steel (Art. 6-52). Lower allowable stresses for shear and bearing are applied to unfinished bolts: 10,000 psi for shear, 20,000 psi for single bearing, and 25,000 psi for double bearing. In tension, however, the unfinished bolt is accorded 20,000 psi, as are rivets (Bibliography, Art. 6-87).

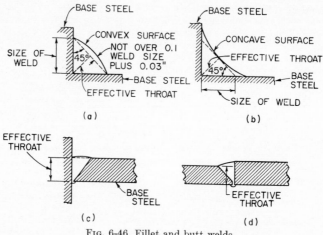

Fig. 6-46. Fillet and butt welds.

6-58. Stresses in Welds. Most welds used in building construction are of the *fillet* type (Fig. 6-46a and b). All stresses, regardless of direction or eccentricity, are resolved in only one manner—as shear on the throat of the weld. The effective throat dimension is indicated in Fig. 6-46a and b, which also show the permissible variation in profiles of fillet welds. Specifications allow a maximum working stress of 13,600 psi on the throat. For a 1-in. side, or leg, the throat dimension is 0.707 in.; therefore, the allowable stress on the throat is 9,615 lb—in round figures, 9,600 lb. Dividing this by 16 gives the familiar and convenient value of 600—the allowable stress for each $\frac{1}{16}$ in. of leg size and each inch of length. Thus, a $\frac{1}{4}$-in. weld ($\frac{4}{16}$ in.) is good for 4 × 600, or 2,400 lb per lin in.

Butt welds of the type shown in Fig. 6-46c and d, assuming steps are taken to assure complete penetration, are allowed the same basic stresses for tension, compression, shear, and bending as the base or parent metal. Complete penetration is assured by either removing the slag inclusions of the initial weld deposited in the exposed root or by using "backing strips" on which the initial pass may be deposited (Figs. 6-55 and 6-56). Failure to take such measures invokes a penalty: the basic stresses are reduced 25% (Bibliography, Art. 6-87).

6-59. Types of Beam Connections. In general, all beam connections are classified as either *framed* or *seated*. In the framed type, the beam is connected to the supporting member with fittings (short angles are common) attached to the beam web. With seated connections, the ends of the beam rest on a ledge or a seat, in much the same manner as if the beam rested on a wall.

6-60. Standard Riveted Framed Connections. The American Institute of Steel Construction "Manual of Steel Construction" lists a complete range of standard fittings suitable for beams from 6 to 36 in. in depth. Figure 6-47 illustrates several standard fittings that could be used for a 16-in.-deep beam. Respective strengths, as indicated in the diagram, depend on the shear value of the rivets in the outstanding legs of the connection angles. In most cases, however, lower capacities will prevail, depending on the bearing strength (double bearing) of the rivets connecting the angles to the beam web. Information tabulated in the "Manual" makes possible expeditious selection of the most economical connections.

Two points with regard to standard connection angles are worthy of mention: First, these industry-developed standards are not mandatory, nor is it a violation of good practice to depart from the standards. A standard connection for a specific size of beam is capable of supporting the maximum end reaction that the beam is normally required to carry safely. Consequently, in most cases where the load is less than maximum, it follows that the standard connection may be stronger than necessary. There may be some excess, but usually the economy and efficiency of the standard will offset the expense of extra material. Designers, however, may elect to detail the connections precisely for the calculated loads; sometimes such efforts may result in a substantial reduction of rivets, particularly expensive field rivets.

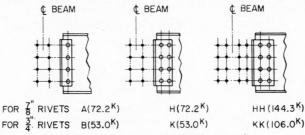

FOR $\frac{7}{8}''$ RIVETS   A(72.2^K)   H(72.2^K)   HH(144.3^K)
FOR $\frac{3}{4}''$ RIVETS   B(53.0^K)   K(53.0^K)   KK(106.0^K)

Fig. 6-47. Standard riveted framed connections.

The second point to bear in mind is that the capacity of standard frame-type connections is computed without considering the effect of eccentricity. Numerous tests have proved the complete adequacy of this practice. Evidently, the basic assumptions for computing rivet stresses are sufficiently conservative to absorb, without any further compensation, the small eccentricities that are induced in this type of connection.

6-61. Standard Bolted Framed Connections. The standard fittings for framed riveted connections are applicable also to bolted construction. The safe capacity loads assigned to the standards for riveted work will also apply when ribbed bolts or high-strength bolts are used in lieu of rivets. When unfinished bolts are used, however, strength values must be reduced, because of the lower shear and bearing unit stresses allowed (Art. 6-57). So a connection with unfinished bolts must contain 50% more bolts than rivets of the same size. To avoid cumbersome details, the designer should compare the capacity of the standard bolted connection with the actual or computed loads; in some instances, minimum-size standard connections will be sufficient without an increased number of bolts.

6-62. Standard Riveted-seat Connections. Seated connections, as illustrated in Fig. 6-48, are standardized and pertinent data for them are tabulated in the American Institute of Steel Construction "Manual." Two types are available—stiffened seats (Fig. 6-48a) and seats without stiffeners (Fig. 6-48b). Obviously, the capacity of the unstiffened seat is limited because of the flexibility of the horizontal leg of the seat angle. A 4-in. outstanding leg is the practical limit. As a result, unstiffened seats are satisfactory only for loads up to 35 kips; above 35 kips, the recommended practice is to use a stiffened seat.

Seated connections afford some outstanding advantages. From the viewpoint of economical fabrication, the beams are merely punched and are free from shop-riveted details.   They pass from the punching machine to the paint shed, after which they are ready for delivery.   In erection, seated connections are advantageous because the seat provides an immediate rest for the beam while the erector aligns connecting holes. The top angle is used to prevent accidental rotation of the beam during construction. Another advantage is that seated connections allow more erection clearance for entering the trough formed by column flanges than do framed connections.   The framed beam is usually detailed to within $\frac{1}{16}$ in. of the column web.   This provides about $\frac{1}{8}$ in. total clearance, whereas the seated beam is cut about $\frac{1}{2}$ in. short of the column web; thereby, a total clearance of 1 in. is obtained.   Then, too, each seated connection is wholly independent, whereas, for framed beams on opposite sides of the web, there is the problem of aligning the holes common to each connection.

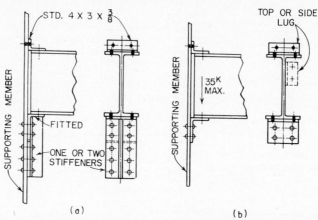

FIG. 6-48. Standard riveted seat connections.

Frequently, framed connections are shop-attached to columns—one angle for a connection may be riveted while the other is loose to permit erection.   This detail cannot be used on column webs because the column flanges obstruct the driving of rivets through the beam web; in this case, a seated connection has a distinct advantage.

Stiffened beam seats (Fig. 6-48a) may be supplied with either one or two stiffener angles, depending on the load to be carried.   As a rule, stiffeners with leg widths less than 5 in. are not connected together.   Therefore, torsion on the vertical line of rivets, whether for one stiffener or two, is taken into account in determining the strength of the connection. However, eccentricity of the load on the outstanding leg of stiffeners under 5 in. is customarily ignored, though included for stiffeners over 5 in. In the latter case, the eccentricity is taken to be one-half the leg width minus $\frac{1}{2}$ in., and the stresses are computed as for the bracket in Fig. 6-44b.

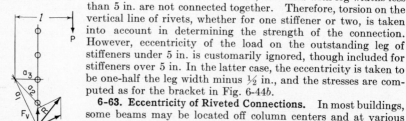

FIG. 6-49. Stresses on rivets due to eccentricity.

6-63. Eccentricity of Riveted Connections.   In most buildings, some beams may be located off column centers and at various angles with the column axes, thus necessitating special connections in which eccentricity must be taken into account.   Therefore, the fundamentals of computing rivet stresses should be well understood.

In Fig. 6-49, the n rivets are unequally stressed because of the eccentricity of load P. The vertical stress on each rivet, assuming equal distribution, is given by

$$F_v = \frac{P}{n} \qquad\qquad (6\text{-}14)$$

F_e, the rivet stress due to eccentricity of P, is proportional to the distance from the geometric center of the group and acts at right angles to the line connecting the rivet to the center. Let x equal the unknown force due to the moment Pl on an imaginary rivet at unit distance from the center of the rivet group. Then, for any rivet located at distance a from the geometric center, the force F_e is equal to ax and the resisting moment is a^2x. The sum of all the rivet moments is, of course, equal to Pl. For example, for the ten rivets in Fig. 6-49, equating the resisting and applied moments yields

$$4a_1{}^2x + 4a_2{}^2x + 2a_3{}^2x = Pl$$

For the farthermost rivet,

$$F_e = a_1x = \frac{Pla_1}{4a_1{}^2 + 4a_2{}^2 + 2a_3{}^2}$$

The resultant R of the two components may be found by any convenient method; a graphical solution is usually sufficiently accurate. The stress so obtained must not exceed the allowable value of the rivet in shear (Arts. 6-56 and 6-57) (Bibliography, Art. 6-87).

6-64. Standard Welded Framed Connections. An outstanding effort to encourage standardization of welded connections was made in 1946 (LaMotte Grover, "Manual of Design for Arc Welded Steel Structures," Air Reduction, New York). Not long after, the American Institute of Steel Construction adopted standards, the essentials of which are shown in Fig. 6-50. Eccentricity of load induces stresses in the welds that must be taken into account, but computation of such stresses is extremely complicated (see, for example, Art. 6-66); therefore, standard connections with predetermined capacities are most welcome.

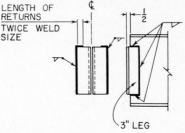

FIG. 6-50. Standard welded framed connections.

Erection bolt holes should be provided in the connection angles to permit securing the beam in place; erection bolts also serve to draw the material into tight contact before field welds are deposited. It should be noted that the length of connection angles now available in the AISC standards varies in increments of 1 in. from 4 to 32 in.; thus, an appropriate size with stated capacity may be selected for any depth of beam rolled in this country.

6-65. Standard Welded-seat Connections. Analogous to riveted seats are welded counterparts that have been standardized. Figure 6-51 shows the types adopted by the AISC. In general, the allowable loads for unstiffened seats (Fig. 6-51a) are identical to those listed in the riveted standards, except for the thicker seat angles, where it becomes advantageous with welded connections to develop the material fully. Consequently, the maximum end reaction reaches 50 kips, in contrast to 35 kips for riveted seats.

Welded stiffened seats (Fig. 6-51b) are simpler than those for riveted work. The seat is a beam stub, tee section, or two perpendicular plates. A far greater range of capacities is offered for the welded standards than for riveted—up to 266 kips maximum allowable load, more than double the maximum for riveted seats. These limits are not binding; similar connections of greater capacity may be specified, but the capacities must be computed.

6-66. Eccentricity in Welded Connections. Frequently, fillet-welded connections are subjected to eccentric stresses. A few of the more commonly used nonstandard types are illustrated in Fig. 6-52.

The underlying design principles for eccentric welded connections are very much like those employed for eccentric riveted connections (Art. 6-63). Referring to Fig. 6-53, the first step is to compute the center of gravity of the weld group. This is done by

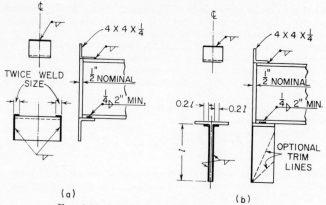

FIG. 6-51. Standard welded seat connections.

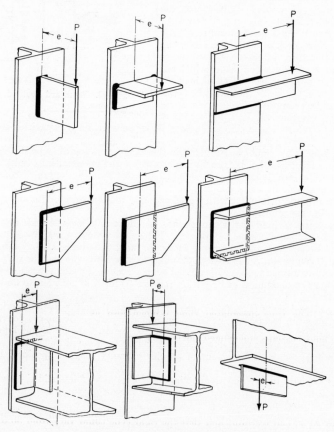

FIG. 6-52. Typical eccentric welded connections.

the conventional area-moment method, assuming the lines of welds to be "areas" of unit width. The eccentricity l is the distance from the load P to the center of gravity.

The moment Pl is resisted by the moment of the weld group, the maximum stress being exerted on the farthermost weld element from the center of gravity. Distances may be measured or computed. The maximum stress may be expressed as $F_e = Pl/S$, where S is the polar section modulus of the weld group. To find S, first compute the moments of inertia of the welds I_x about the XX axis and I_y about the YY axis (or the polar moment of inertia J about the center), assuming again weld "areas" of unit width: $S = J/a = (I_x + I_y)/a$, where a is the distance from the center to the farthermost weld element. The vertical shear component is given by $F_v = P/n$, where n is the total linear inches of weld. The resultant R of F_e and F_v should not exceed the capacity of the weld computed from the maximum permissible stress (Bibliography, Art. 6-87).

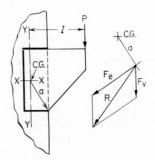

FIG. 6-53. Stresses on welds due to eccentricity.

6-67. Fixity of End Connections. Specifications recognize three types of connections: simple, rigid, and semirigid. The type designated *simple* (unrestrained) is intended to support beams and girders for shear only and leave the ends free to rotate

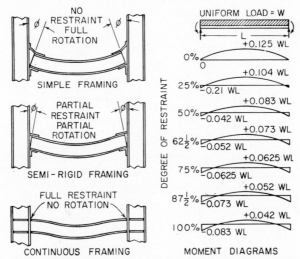

FIG. 6-54. Effect of rigidity of end connections on end moments.

under load. The type designated *rigid* (known also as rigid-frame, continuous, restrained frame) aims at not only carrying the shear but also providing sufficient rigidity to hold virtually unchanged the original angles between members connected. *Semirigid*, as the name implies, assumes that the connections of beams and girders possess a dependable and known moment capacity intermediate in degree between the simple and rigid types. Figure 6-54 illustrates these three types together with the uniform-load moments obtained with each type.

Although no definite relative rigidities have been established, it is generally conceded that the simple or flexible type could vary from zero to 15% (some researchers recommend 20%) end restraint and that the rigid type could vary from 90 to 100%. The semirigid types lie between 15 and 90%, the precise value assumed in the design being largely dependent on experimental analysis. These percentages of rigidity represent the ratio of the moment developed by the connection, with no column rotation, to the moment developed by a fully rigid connection under the same conditions, multiplied by 100. (See also "Structural Steel Connections," Engineering Research Institute, University of Michigan.)

Standard connections offer little or no restraint. In addition, several other arrangements are in common use within the scope of simple-type connections, although they appear to offer greater resistance to end rotations. For example, in Fig. 6-55a, a top plate may be used instead of an angle for lateral support, the plate being so designed that plastic deformation may occur in the narrow unwelded portion. Naturally, the plate offers greater resistance to beam rotation than a light angle, but it can provide sufficient flexibility that the connection can be classified as a simple type. Plate and welds at both ends are proportioned for about 25% of the beam moment capacity.

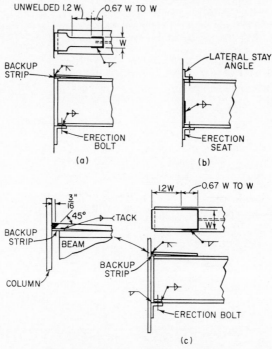

FIG. 6-55. Flexible welded connections.

The plate is shaped so that the metal across the least width is at yield-point stress when the stresses in the wide portion, in the butt welds, and in the fillet welds are at allowable working values. The unwelded length is then made about 20% greater than the least width to assure ductile yielding. This detail can also be developed as an effective moment-type connection.

Another flexible type is the direct web connection in Fig. 6-55b. Figured for shear loads only, the welds are located on the lower part of the web, where the rotational effect of the beam under load is the least, a likely condition when the beam rests on erection seats and the axis of rotation centers about the seat rather than about the neutral axis.

Tests indicate that considerable flexibility also can be obtained with a properly proportioned welded top-plate detail as shown in Fig. 6-55c without narrowing it as in Fig. 6-55a. This detail is usually confined to wind-braced simple-beam designs. The top plate is designed for the wind moment on the joint, at the increased stresses permitted for wind loads.

The problem of superimposing wind bracing on what is otherwise a clear-cut simple beam with flexible connections is a complex one. Some compromise is usually effected between theory and actual design practice. Two alternates usually are permitted by building codes:

1. Connections designed to resist assumed wind moments should be adequate to resist the moments induced by the gravity loading and the wind loading, at specified increased unit stresses.

2. Connections designed to resist assumed wind moments should be so designed that larger moments, induced by gravity loading under the actual condition of restraint, will be relieved by deformation of the connection material.

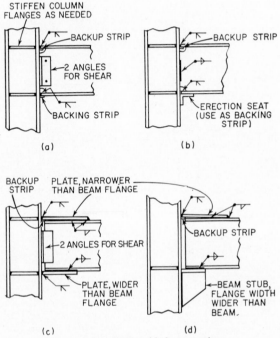

FIG. 6-56. Rigid welded connections.

Obviously, these options envisage some nonelastic, but self-limiting, deformation of the structural-steel parts. Innumerable wind-braced buildings of riveted, bolted, or welded construction have been designed on this assumption of plastic behavior and have proved satisfactory in service.

Fully rigid riveted connections have never enjoyed much popularity because of the awkward, bulky details, which, if not interfering with architectural clearances, are often so costly to design and fabricate as to negate the economy gained by using smaller beam sections. In appearance, they resemble the types shown in Fig. 6-32 for wind bracing; they are developed for the full moment-resisting capacity of the beam.

Much easier to accomplish and more efficient are welded rigid connections (Fig. 6-56). They may be connected simply by butt-welding the beam flanges to the columns—the "direct" connection shown in Fig. 6-56a and b. Others may prefer the "indirect" method, with top plates, because this detail permits ordinary mill tolerance for beam length. Welding of plates to stiffen the column flanges, when necessary, is also relatively simple.

A comparison of fixities intermediate between full rigidity and zero restraint in Fig. 6-54 reveals an optimum condition attainable with 75 % rigidity; end and center-span moments are equal, each being $WL/16$, or one-half the simple-beam moment. The saving in weight of beam is quite apparent.

Perhaps the deterrent to a broader usage of semirigid connections has been the proviso contained in specifications: "permitted only upon evidence that the connections to be used are capable of resisting definite moments without overstress of the fasteners." As a safeguard, the proportioning of the beam joined by such connections is predicated upon no greater degree of end restraint than the minimum known to be effected by the connection. Suggested practice, based on research with welded connections, is to design the end connections for 75 % rigidity but to provide a beam sized for the moment that would result from 50 % restraint; i.e., $WL/12$. ("Report of tests of Welded Top Plate and Seat Building Connections," *The Welding Journal*, Research Supplement 146S–165S, 1944.) The type of welded connection in Fig. 6-55c, when designed for the intended rigidity, is generally acceptable.

Test data for semirigid riveted and bolted connections are also available. ("Riveted Semi-rigid Beam-to-Column Building Connections," *Progress Report* 1, American

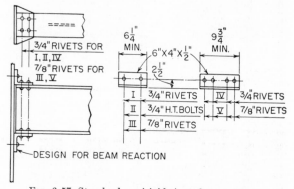

FIG. 6-57. Standard semirigid riveted connections.

Institute of Steel Construction.) Five types of connections (Fig. 6-57) are listed for beams 10 to 21 in. in depth, with lengths ranging up to 34 ft. Included in the data is the dependable percentage of rigidity that is obtainable for each size of beam and span, together with a recommended design procedure that greatly simplifies computations. For an average condition, beams are about one size less than would be required by the simple-beam assumption, thus indicating a weight saving of 10 to 20 %.

6-68. Column Splices. Column-to-column connections are usually determined by the change in section. In general, a change is made at every second-floor level, where a shop or field splice is located. From an erection viewpoint, as well as for fabrication and shipment, splices at every third floor may be more economical because of the reduced number of pieces to handle. Naturally, this advantage is partly offset by extra weight of column material, because the column size is determined by loads on the lowest story of each tier, there being an excess of section for the story or two above.

Splices are located just above floor-beam connections, usually about 2 to 3 ft above the floor. Since column stresses are transferred from column to column by bearing, the splice plates are of nominal size, commensurate with the need for safe erection and bending moments the joint may be subjected to during erection. From the viewpoint of moment resistance, a conventional column splice develops perhaps 20 % of the moment capacity of the column.

Although column splices are not standardized, as are beam connections, they are generally uniform throughout the industry. Figure 6-58 illustrates the common types of column splices for riveted and bolted work. In Fig. 6-58a and b, the upper column bears directly on the lower column; filler plates are supplied in (*b*) when the differences in depth of the two columns are greater than can be absorbed by erection clearance.

As a rule, some erection clearance should be provided. When columns of the same nominal depth are spliced, it is customary to supply a $\frac{1}{16}$-in. fill under each splice plate on the lower column or, as an alternate, to leave the rivet holes open on the top gage line below the milled joint until the upper shaft is erected; the latter procedure permits the erector to spring the plates apart to facilitate entry of the upper column.

When the upper column is of such dimension that its milled end does not wholly bear on the lower column, one of two methods must be followed: In Fig. 6-58*c*, a portion of the bearing area that overhangs the lower column is transferred by means of flange plates that are milled to bear on the lower column. These bearing plates must be attached with sufficient single-shear rivets to develop the load transmitted through bearing on the milled surface.

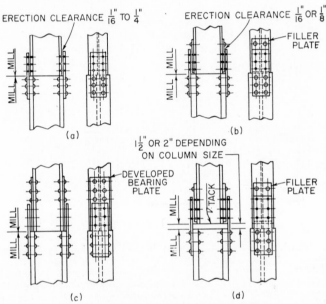

FIG. 6-58. Riveted and bolted column splices.

When the difference in column size is pronounced, the practice is to use a horizontal bearing plate as shown in Fig. 6-58*d*. These plates, known as *butt plates*, may be attached to either shaft with tack welds or clip angles. Usually it is attached to the upper shaft, because a plate on the lower shaft may interfere with erection of the beams.

Somewhat similar are welded column splices. In Fig. 6-59*a*, a common case, holes for erection purposes are generally supplied in the splice plates and column flanges as shown. Some, however, prefer to avoid drilling and punching of thick pieces and use instead clip angles welded on the inside flanges of the columns, one pair at diagonally opposite corners, or some similar arrangement. Figure 6-59*b* and *c* corresponds to the riveted splices in Fig. 6-58*c* and *d*. The shop and field welds for the welded butt plate in Fig. 6-59*c* may be reversed, to provide erection clearance for beams seated just below the splice. The erection clip angles would then be shop-welded to the underside of the butt plate, and the field holes would pierce the column web. Attachment of the lower column to the butt plate requires an overhead weld, a type that is usually avoided.

The butt-weld splice in Fig. 6-59*d* is the most efficient from the standpoint of mate-

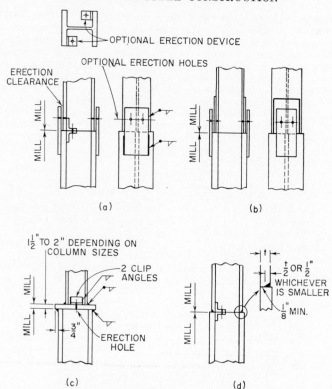

FIG. 6-59. Welded column splices.

rial saving.　The depth of the bevel as given in the illustration is for the usual column splice, in which moment is unimportant. However, should the joint be subjected to considerable moment, the bevel may be deepened; but a $\frac{1}{8}$-in. minimum shoulder should remain for the purpose of landing and plumbing the column (Bibliography, Art. 6-87).

6-69. Beam Splices. These are required in rigid frames, suspended-span construction, etc. Such splices are usually located at points of counterflexure, where the moments are zero, or at points where moments are relatively small. Therefore, splices are of moderate size. Flanges and web may be spliced with plates or butt-welded.

For one reason or another it is sometimes expedient to make a long beam from two short lengths. A welded joint usually is selected, because the beams can be joined together without splice plates

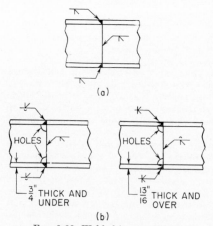

FIG. 6-60. Welded beam splices.

and without loss of section due to rivet holes. Also, from the viewpoint of appearance, the welded joint is hardly discernible.

Two possibilities are shown in Fig. 6-60: When the splice is located away from the point of maximum moment—at a section where 75 % efficiency is tolerable—then Fig. 6-60a may be used. All welding is done from one side, without cleaning out the root of the initial pass. Specifications term this "incomplete penetration"; strengths of the welds are figured at 75 % of nominal values.

More often, the beam joint must be 100 % efficient, to develop the full section. Figure 6-60b illustrates such a detail. The back side of the initial weld is gouged or chipped out; access holes in the beam webs facilitate proper edge preparation and depositing of the weld metal in the flange area in line with the web. Such holes are usually left open, because plugs would add undesirable residual stresses to the joint (Bibliography, Art. 6-87).

STEEL ERECTION

A clear understanding of what the fabricator furnishes or does not furnish to the erector, particularly on fabrication contracts that may call for delivery only, is all-important—and most fabricated steel is purchased on delivery basis only.

Purchasing structural steel has been greatly simplified by the industry's Code of Standard Practice for Buildings and Bridges—an American Institute of Steel Construction publication. A contract provision making the code part of the contract is often used, since it establishes a commonly accepted and well-defined line of demarcation between what is, and what is not, to be furnished under the contract. Lacking such a provision, the contract, to avoid later misunderstandings, must enumerate in considerable detail what is expected of both parties to the contract.

Under the code—and unless otherwise specifically called for in the contract documents—such items as steel sash, corrugated-iron roofing or siding, and open-web steel joists, and similar items, even if made of steel and shown on the contract design drawings, are not included in the category "structural steel." Also, such items as door frames are excluded, even when made of structural shapes, if they are not fastened to the structure in such way as to comply with "constituting part of the steel framing." On the other hand, loose lintels shown on design plans or in separate schedules are included.

According to the code, a fabricator furnishes with "structural steel," to be erected by someone else, the field rivets and unfinished bolts required for fastening the steel. However, the fabricator does not furnish the following items unless specified in the invitation to bid: turned bolts, high-strength bolts, ribbed bolts, special bolts, washers, shims, fitting-up bolts, drift pins, temporary cables, or welding electrodes.

The code also defines the erection practices. For example, the erector does not paint field boltheads and nuts, field rivetheads, field welds, or touch up abrasions in the shop coat, or perform any other field painting unless required in specifications accompanying the invitation to bid.

6-70. Erection Equipment. If there is a universal piece of erection equipment, it is the crane. Mounted on wheels or tractor treads, it is extremely mobile, both on the job and in moving from job to job. Practically all buildings are erected with this efficient raising device. The exception, of course, is the skyscraper whose height exceeds the reach of the crane. Operating on ground level, cranes have been used to erect buildings of about 12 stories, the maximum height being dependent on the length of the boom and width of building.

Cranes are also mounted on locomotive cars. Their use in building construction is limited to heavy plant construction serviced by railroads. By laying the rails early in the construction schedule, the erector can bring in the heavy steelwork on railway cars and use a heavy-duty locomotive crane for erection.

The guy derrick has emerged as the best raising device for tall buildings. Its principal asset is the ease by which it may be "jumped" from tier to tier as erection proceeds upward. The boom and mast reverse position; each in turn serves to lift up the other. It requires about 2 hr to make a two-story jump.

Two other rigs are sometimes used, usually in the role of auxiliaries to cranes or guy derricks, namely, the gin pole and the stiff-leg derrick. Gin poles are the most elementary—simply a guyed boom. The base must be secure because of the danger of kicking out. The device is useful for the raising of incidental materials, for dismantling and lowering of larger rigs, and for erection of steel on light construction where the services of a crane are unwarranted.

Stiff-leg derricks are most efficient where they may be set up to remain for long periods of time. They have been used to erect multistory buildings but are not in popular favor because of the long time required to jump from tier to tier. Among the principal uses for stiff legs are (1) unloading steel from railroad cars for transfer to trucks, (2) storage and sorting, and (3) when placed on a flat roof, raising steel to roof level, where it may be sorted and placed within reach of a guy derrick.

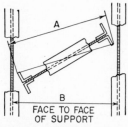

FIG. 6-61. Erection clearance for beams.

6-71. Clearance for Erecting Beams. Clearances for driving rivets, tightening bolts, and welding are discussed in Arts. 6-55 and 6-68. In addition, there is also the problem of providing sufficient field clearance so as to permit erection without interference with members previously erected. The shop draftsman should always arrange the details so that the members can be swung into their final position without shifting the members to which they connect from their final positions. The following examples illustrate the type of problem most frequently encountered in building work:

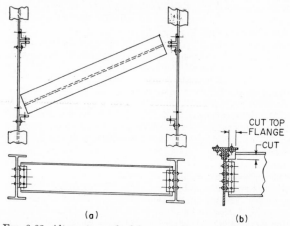

FIG. 6-62. Alternate method for providing erection clearance.

In framed beam connections (Fig. 6-61) the slightly shorter distance out-to-out of connection angles ($B - \frac{1}{8}$ in.), as compared with the face-to-face distance between supporting members, is usually sufficient to allow forcing the beam into position. Occasionally, however, because the beam is relatively short, or because heavy connection angles with wide outstanding legs are required, the diagonal distance A may exceed the clearance distance B. If so, the connection for one end must be shipped bolted to the framed beam to permit its removal during erection.

An alternate solution is to rivet one connection angle of each pair to the web of the supporting beam, bolting the other angle to the same web for shipment, as shown in Fig. 6-62a. The beam should be investigated for the clearance in swinging past riveted connection angles. Attention must also be paid to possible interference of rivetheads in swinging the beam into place when the supporting member is a plate girder (Fig. 6-62b).

Another example is that of a beam seated on column-web connections (Fig. 6-63). The first step is to remove the top angles and shims temporarily. Then, while hanging from the derrick sling, the beam is tilted until its ends clear the edges of the column flanges, after which it is rotated back into a horizontal position and landed on the seats.   The greatest diagonal length G of the beam should be about ⅛ in. less than the face-to-face distance F between column webs.   It must also be such as to clear any

obstruction above; e.g., G must be equal to or less than C, or the obstructing detail must be shipped bolted for temporary removal.   To allow for possible overrun, the ordered length L of the beam should be less than the detailing length E by at least the amount of the permitted cutting tolerance.

Frequently, the obstruction above the beam connection may be the details of a column splice.   As stated in Art. 6-68, it may be necessary to attach the splice material on the lower end of the upper shaft, if erection of the beam precedes erection of the column in the tier above.

6-72. Erection Sequence.   The order in which steel is to be fabricated and delivered to the site should be planned in advance so as not to conflict with the erector's methods or his construction schedule.   For example, if steel is to be erected with derricks, the approximate locations at which the derricks will be placed will determine the shipping installments, or sections, into which the frame as a whole must be segregated for orderly shipment.   When installments are delivered to the site at predetermined locations, proper planning will eliminate unnecessary rehandling.   Information should be conveyed to the drafting room so that the

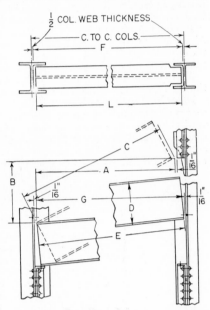

Fig. 6-63. Clearance for beams seated on column webs.

shipping installments can be indicated on the erection plans and installments identified on the shipping lists.

In erecting multistory buildings with guy derricks, the practice is to hoist and place all columns first, spandrel beams and wall bracing next, and interior beams with filler beams last.   More specifically, erection commences with bays most distant from the derrick and progresses toward the derrick, until it is closed in.   Then, the derrick is jumped to the top and the process is repeated for the next tier.   Usually, the top of the tier is planked over to obtain a working platform for the erectors and also to afford protection for the trades working below.   However, before the derrick is jumped, the corner panels are plumbed; similarly when panels are erected across the building, cables are stretched to plumb the structure.

There is an established sequence for completing the connections.   The raising gang connects members together with temporary fitting-up bolts.   The number of bolts is kept to a minimum, just enough to draw the joint up tight and take care of the stresses caused by dead weight, wind, and erection forces.   Permanent connections are made as soon as alignment is within tolerance limits.   Usually, riveting, bolting, or welding follow on the heels of the raising gang.   Sometimes, the latter moves faster than the gang making the permanent connections, in which case it may be prudent to skip every other floor, thus obtaining permanent connections as close as possible to the derrick—a matter of safe practice.

6-73. Field Welding Procedures.   The main function of a welding sequence is to control distortion due primarily to the effects of welding heat.   In general, a large input of heat in a short time tends to produce the greatest distortion.   Therefore, it is always advisable, for large joints, to weld in stages, with sufficient time between each stage to assure complete dispersal of heat.   Equally important, and perhaps more efficient from the erector's viewpoint, are those methods that balance the heat input in such manner that the distortional effects tend to cancel out.

Welding on one flange of a column tends to leave the column curled toward the welded side cooling, because of shrinkage stresses. A better practice, for beams connecting to both sides of a column, is to weld the opposite connections simultaneously. Thus the shrinkage on each flange is kept in balance and the column remains plumb.

If simultaneous welding is not feasible, then the procedure is to weld in stages. About 60 % of the required weld might be applied on the first beam, then the joint on the opposite flange might be completely welded, and finally, welding on the first beam would be completed. Procedures such as this will go far to reduce distortion.

Another rule is to weld the opposite exterior columns of a narrow bent at the same time. This, too, helps balance distorting forces.

Experience has shown that it is good practice to commence welding at or near the center of a building and work outward. Columns should be frequently checked for vertical alignment, because shrinkage in the welds tends to shorten the beams between columns. Even though the dimensional change at each point is very small, it can accumulate to an objectionable amount in a long row of columns. The condition can become acute in a column row in which beams connect to column flanges, because the shrinkage shortening could possibly combine with the mill under-run in column depths. Occasionally, it may be necessary to correct the condition by adding filler plates or building out with weld metal.

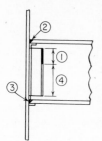

FIG. 6-64. Indication of sequence in welding connections.

Some designers of large welded structures prefer to detail the welding sequence for each joint. For example, on one project, the procedure for the joint shown in Fig. 6-64 called for four distinct operations, or stages: First, the top 6 in. of the shear weld on the vertical connection was made; second, the weld on the top flange; third, the bottom-flange weld; and fourth, the remaining weld on the vertical connection. The metal was allowed to return to normal temperature before starting each stage. One advantage of this procedure is the prestressing benefits obtained in the connecting welds. Tensile stresses are developed in the bottom-flange weld on cooling; compressive stresses of equal magnitude are consequently produced in the top flange. Since these stresses are opposite to those caused by floor loads, welding stresses are useful in supporting the floor loads. Although this by-product assistance may be worthwhile, there are no accepted methods for resolving the alleged benefits into design economy.

6-74. Field Tolerances. The only tolerances that have been covered as a standard are those for vertical and level alignment—"plumbing up" in trade circles. In general, a vertical member is plumb and a horizontal member is level when the error does not exceed 1 in 500. However, for a multistory building, exterior columns and those adjacent to elevator shafts are considered plumb when the error does not exceed 1 in 1,000.

No tolerance has been established for milled joints in column splices; yet because of a number of variables, column joints are not always in tight bearing over the entire cross-sectional area. While no rule is suggested, it would seem that insistence on bearing on the column web is ultraconservative.

6-75. Adjusting Lintels. Lintels supported on the steel frame (sometimes called shelf angles) may be permanently fastened in the shop to the supporting spandrel beam, or they may be attached so as to allow adjustment in the field (see Fig. 6-4, Art. 6-7). In the former case, the final position is solely dependent on the alignment obtained for the spandrel itself; whereas for the latter, lintels may be adjusted to line and grade independently of the spandrel. Field adjustment is the general rule for all multistory structures. Horizontal alignment is obtained by using slotted holes in the connection clip angles; vertical elevation (grade) is obtained with shims.

When walls are of masonry construction, a reasonable amount of variation in the position of the lintels may be absorbed without much effort on the part of the masons. So the erector can adjust the lintels immediately following the permanent fastening of the spandrels to the columns. This procedure is ideal for the steel erector, since it allows him to complete his contract without costly delays and without interference with other trades. Subsequent minor variations in the position of the lintels, due to deflection or torsional rotation of the spandrel when subjected to dead weight of the floor slab, are usually absorbed without necessitating further lintel adjustment.

However, with lightweight curtain walls, the position of the lintels is important, because large paneled areas afford less latitude for variation. As a rule, the steel erector is unable to adjust the lintels to the desired accuracy at the time the main framework is erected. If he has contracted to do the adjusting, he must wait until the the construction engineer establishes the correct lines and grades. In the usual case, floor slabs are concreted immediately after the steelwork is inspected and accepted. The floor grades then determined become the base to which the lintels can be adjusted. At about the same time, the wall contractor has his scaffolds in place, and by keeping pace with wall construction, the steel erector, working from the wall scaffolds, adjusts the lintels.

In some cases, the plans call for concrete encasement of the spandrel beams, in which case concreting is accomplished with the floor slab. Naturally, the construction engineer should see that the adjustment features provided for the lintels are not frozen in the concrete. One suggestion is to box around the details, thus avoid chopping out concrete. In some cases, it may be possible to avoid the condition entirely by locating the connection below the concrete encasement where the adjustment is always accessible.

The whole operation of lintel adjustment is one of coordination between the several trades; that this be carried out in an orderly fashion is the duty of the construction engineer. Furthermore, the desired procedure should be carefully spelled out in the job specifications so that erection costs can be estimated fairly.

Particularly irksome to the construction engineer is the lintel located some distance below the spandrel and supported on flexible, light steel hangers. This detail can be troublesome because it has no capacity to resist torsion. Avoid by developing the lintel and spandrel to act together as a single member.

PAINTING

Protection of steel surfaces has been, since the day steel was first used, a vexing problem for the engineers, paint manufacturers, and maintenance personnel. Over the years, there have been many developments, the result of numerous studies and research activities. However, it was not until 1950 that a concerted attempt was made to correlate all available data. Then, the Steel Structures Painting Council was organized, and an effort was made to determine and outline the best methods developed up to the present time, issue specifications covering practical and economical methods of surface preparation and painting steel structures, and engage in further research aimed at reducing or preventing steel corrosion.

Results are published in the "Steel Structures Painting Manual." This work is in two volumes—Volume I, "Good Painting Practice," and Volume II, "Systems and Specifications" (Steel Structures Painting Council, 4400 Fifth Avenue, Pittsburgh 13, Pa.). Each of the Council's paint systems covers the method of cleaning surfaces, types of paint to be used, number of coats to be applied, and techniques to be used in their applications. Each surface treatment and paint system is identified by uniform nomenclature; e.g., Paint System Specification SSPC-PS27-54T, which happens to be the identity of the minimum-type protection as furnished for most buildings. Undoubtedly, these paint systems will eventually become a national standard.

The Council, because of its broad representation, did not confine its work to bridges and buildings but has embraced the entire field of protection for all types of steel structures; viz., tanks, ships, pipelines, petroleum refineries, chemical plants, sewage works, coke ovens, etc., and under all kinds of service conditions. All kinds of paints, oils, lacquers, and metalizing methods are reviewed.

6-76. Corrosion of Steel. Ordinarily, steel corrodes in the presence of both oxygen and water, but corrosion rarely takes place in the absence of either. For instance, steel does not corrode in dry air, and corrosion is negligible when the relative humidity is below 70%, the critical humidity at normal temperature. Likewise, steel does not corrode in water that has been effectively deaerated. Therefore, the corrosion of structural steel is not a serious problem, except where water and oxygen are in abundance and where these primary prerequisites are supplemented with corrosive chemicals such as soluble salts, acids, cleaning compounds, and welding fluxes.

In ideal dry atmospheres, a thin transparent film of iron oxide forms. This layer of ferric oxide is actually beneficial, since it protects the steel from further oxidation.

When exposed to water and oxygen in generous amounts, steel corrodes at an average rate of roughly 5 mils loss of surface metal per year. If the surface is comparatively dry, the rate drops to about $\frac{1}{2}$ mil per year after the first year, the usual case in typical industrial atmospheres. Excessively high corrosion rates occur only in the presence of electrolytes or corrosive chemicals; usually, this condition is found in localized areas of a building.

Mill scale, the thick layer of iron oxides that forms on steel during the rolling operations, is beneficial as a protective coating, provided it is intact and firmly adheres to the steel. In the mild environments generally encountered in most buildings, mill scale that adheres tightly after weathering and handling offers no difficulty. In buildings exposed to high humidity and corrosive gases, broken mill scale may be detrimental to both the steel and the paint. Through electrochemical action, corrosion sets in along the edges of the cracks in the mill scale and in time loosens the scale, carrying away the paint.

Galvanic corrosion takes place when dissimilar metals are connected together. Noble metals such as copper and nickel should not be connected to structural steel with steel rivets or bolts, since the galvanic action destroys the fasteners. On the other hand, these metals may be used for the fasteners, because the galvanic action is distributed over a large area and consequently little or no harm is done. When dissimilar metals are to be in contact, the contacting surfaces should be insulated; paint is usually satisfactory.

6-77. Preparation of Steel for Paint. Authorities agree that the most important factor in obtaining long paint life, with attendant protection of steel, is in the proper treatment of the surface on which paint is to be applied. The Steel Structures Painting Council recognizes the following methods of surface preparation: (1) nominal cleaning, (2) solvent cleaning, (3) hand cleaning, (4) power-tool cleaning, (5) flame cleaning, (6) blast cleaning, and (7) pickling. All these methods, except the first, are covered by Surface Preparation Specifications (Steel Structures Painting Council, Pittsburgh, Pa.).

The first three, and to some extent the fourth, of the listed methods are common practices for building construction. The last three are rarely, if ever, used in building work. In fact, structural-steel fabricators, except for those majoring in bridgework or specialized plate fabrication, do not have the facilities to perform them.

Experts also agree that surface preparation is directly related to the type of priming paint, anticipated exposure, and expected service. In general, a slow-drying paint containing oil and rust-inhibitive pigments and one possessing good wetting ability may be applied on nominally cleaned steel. On the other hand, a fast-drying paint with poor wetting characteristics requires exceptionally good surface cleaning, which could well include complete removal of mill scale. Therefore, in specifying a paint, the engineer should also include the type of surface preparation. Frequently, the specified paint is to be used on a surface that is not adequately prepared. Either the paint should be changed or the surface cleaning improved.

Paint selection and degree of surface cleaning are a matter of economics. A precise cleaning job can be very expensive and the extra years of protection are not always justified. Most helpful to the engineer will be the Council's paint systems, in which the surface treatment is correlated with the paint specification and service conditions.

Nominal cleaning does not entail any more effort than that needed to remove weld flux and slag, easily removed weld spatter, heavy deposits of soil, oil, and grease, and some very loose mill scale and rust.

A far more thorough job is indicated by the hand-cleaning method—this being covered in detail by the Council's specification SSPC-SP2-52T. It requires complete removal of weld residues, rust scale, and grease and oil with solvents, after which the entire surface is vigorously brushed with approved wire brushes. It also requires painting of welds and adjacent areas within 1 in. of the weld with a special primer. All loose scale is removed, and the final surface must be dust-free. This method will cost more than the usual "nominal" cleaning method and therefore should be specified only when it is essential to the paint system as a whole. On the other hand, it is low-cost relative to more precise descaling methods, and when properly carried out in conformance with the specification, it provides a satisfactory base for heavy-duty service.

6-78. Shop-painting Steel. At least three general situations confront those concerned with shop-painting steel for building construction. These are (1) a fully enclosed building in which the steelwork is completely covered, (2) a fully or partly enclosed building in which steel is exposed but not subject to corrosive contaminants, and (3) an industrial plant subject to corrosive atmosphere in some degree.

The general practice of the fabrication industry—and a stipulation contained in most building codes—is to furnish a shop coat of paint on all new work—except that it is generally omitted on steel that will be embedded in concrete and on edges and surfaces that later will be welded. The practice does not entail any more rigorous surface preparation than that obtained by nominal cleaning methods, the purpose being to remove loose mill scale, weld slag, spatter, rust, oil, and foreign matter in general. The average shop paint used in the industry is of the best quality commensurate with fast drying and over-all economy. At best, one-coat shop paint is intended only for short-term protection.

Most buildings, apartments, hotels, offices, hospitals, schools, etc., are of the type identified as situation (1). The steelwork is completely enveloped with other construction materials or is surrounded with dead air space, so that at no time in its service lifetime is the steel exposed to the elements or factors that induce corrosion. When old buildings are razed, it is ever surprising to see the original paint, including the piece-identification marks, almost intact. However, should there be a break, say in the outer wall, through which moisture may seep, then the retarding effect of the one-coat shop paint is nil.

The point to remember is that one-coat shop paint is not intended to offer protection beyond the normal exposure period measured from the time the steel leaves the shop until it is covered in the field. Paint failure may occur where, for one reason or another, construction has been unduly delayed. Steel to be stored in the field for lengthy periods should be given additional coats of paint if the owner objects to the shop paint failing with attendant corrosion.

Examples of buildings in situation (2) are auto-parking decks, garages, arenas, warehouses, gymnasiums, etc., where the steel is exposed to changing atmosphere and consequently is subject to humidity changes but not to corrosive gases, even though located in industrial areas. The standard shop coat of paint, properly applied on nominal cleaned steel, is considered ample for the base or prime coat, providing all exposed steel will receive at least one coat of field paint. Before applying the field coat, a careful touch-up of the shop coat is advisable. All failure spots, abraded areas, field rivetheads, etc., should be cleaned and coated with priming paint.

For parking decks, the floor beams should be fully protected from drippings containing de-icing salts brought into the structure by automobiles. Should steel plate decks be used, then the problem of protection from this condition requires special attention, unless the structure is located in an area where de-icing is not employed. Steel Structures Painting Council should be consulted for the best methods currently recommended.

Steel protection in industrial plants, situation (3), usually calls for a somewhat more durable shop primer than that suggested for groups (1) and (2). In addition, surface treatment is more exacting, in that hand-cleaning and solvent-cleaning methods are recommended by the Council (Specifications SSPC-SP1-52T Solvent Cleaning and SSPC-SP2-52T Hand Cleaning). The type of paint and surface pretreatment to be used are dependent on the anticipated severity of corrosive agents.

Two methods of paint application are acceptable: (1) hand brushing and (2) spraying. When properly performed, with emphasis on adequate paint thickness, either method will yield a good job.

6-79. Field-painting Steel. There is some question on the justification for shop-painting steelwork embedded in masonry or otherwise sealed within dead air spaces (Art. 6-78). This statement needs to be qualified, however, for the case of steel members embedded in or in contact with exterior masonry walls, which though built according to good workmanship standards, may not be impervious to moisture. For example, in many instances, the masonry backing for a 4-in. brick wall is omitted to make way for column flanges. Very definitely, a 4-in. wall will not prevent penetration of water. In many cases, also, clearance is provided between a wall and steelwork, but as is usual, mortar drippings fall into the space and form bridges over which water may pass, to attack the steel. The net effect is premature failure of both wall and steel. Walls have been shattered—sheared through the brick—by the powerful expansion of rust formations. The preventatives are: (1) coat the steel with suitable paint and (2) good wall construction (see Sec. 10).

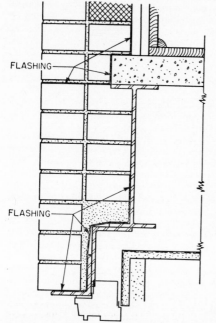

FLASHING

FLASHING

FIG. 6-65. Flashing at spandrels and lintels.

A typical building code reads: "Special precautions shall be taken to protect the outer surfaces of steel columns located in exterior walls against corrosion, by painting such surfaces with waterproof paints, by the use of mastic, or by other methods or waterproofing approved by the building inspector."

In most structures an asphalt-type paint is used for column-flange protection. The proviso is sometimes extended to include lintels and spandrels, since the problem of corrosion is similar, depending on the closeness and contact with the wall. However, with the latter members, it is often judicious to supplement the paint with flashing, either metallic or fabric. A typical illustration, taken from an actual apartment-building design, is shown in Fig. 6-65.

In general, all building codes require a coat of shop paint, but they differ on field paint; either a coat is stipulated or the code is silent. From a practical viewpoint, the question of field painting cannot be properly resolved with a single broad rule. For an enclosed building in which the structural members are enveloped, for example, a field coat is sheer wastage, except for exterior steel members in contact with walls. On the other hand, exposed steel subject to high-humidity atmospheres and to exceptionally corrosive gases and contaminants may need two or three field coats.

Manufacturing buildings should always be closely scrutinized, bearing in mind that original conditions are not always permanent. As manufacturing processes change, so do the corrosive environments stimulated by new methods. It is well to prepare for the most adverse eventuality.

Special attention should be given to steel surfaces that become inaccessible; e.g., tops of purlins in contact with roof surfaces. A three-coat job of particularly suitable paint may pay off in the long run, even though it delays placement of the roof covering.

6-80. Steel in Contact with Concrete or Masonry. According to the "Steel Structures Painting Manual," Vol. I, "Good Painting Practice" (Steel Structures Painting Council, Pittsburgh, Pa.):

1. Steel that is embedded in concrete for reinforcing should not be painted. Design considerations require strong bond between the reinforcing and the concrete so that the stress is distributed; painting of such steel does not supply sufficient bond. If the concrete is properly made and of sufficient thickness over the metal, the steel will not corrode.

2. Steel that is encased or fireproofed with lightweight concrete that is porous should be painted with at least one coat of good quality rust-inhibitive primer. When conditions are severe, or humidity is high, two or more coats of paint should be applied, since the concrete may accelerate corrosion.

3. When steel is enclosed in concrete of high density or low porosity, and when the concrete is at least 2 in. to 3 in. thick, painting is not necessary, since the concrete will protect the steel.

4. Steel enclosed in masonry should be painted with at least one coat of rust-inhibitive primer, because leaks in flashings, condensation permeating the masonry, etc., may cause localized corrosion.

5. Steel in partial contact with concrete is generally not painted. This creates an undesirable condition, for water may seep into the crack between the steel and the concrete, causing corrosion. A sufficient volume of rust may be built up, spalling the concrete. The only remedy is to chip or leave a groove in the concrete at the edge next to the steel and seal the crack with an alkali-resistant calking compound (such as bituminous cement).

6. Steel should not be encased in concrete that contains cinders, since the acidic condition will cause corrosion of the steel.

FIRE PROTECTION FOR STRUCTURAL STEEL

Structural steel is an incombustible material; i.e., it does not support combustion. It is therefore satisfactory for use without protective coverage in many types of buildings where incombustibility is sufficient, from the viewpoint of either building ordinances or owner's preference. When structural steel is used in this fashion, it is described as "exposed" or "unprotected." Naturally, unprotected steel may be selected wherever building codes permit combustible construction; the property of incombustibility makes it more attractive than competitive materials not possessing this property.

Exposed or unprotected structural steel is commonly used for industrial-type buildings, hangars, auditoriums, stadiums, warehouses, parking garages, billboards, towers and low stores, schools, and hospitals. In most cases, these structures contain or house little combustible materials; in others, where the contents are highly combustible, sprinkler or deluge systems may be incorporated to protect the steelwork.

6-81. Need for Fire Protection of Steel. The deleterious effect on steel of heat generated by a fire is well known (see also Art. 6-83). Steel building frames and floor systems must be covered with fire-resistant materials in certain buildings. These may be tall buildings, such as offices, apartments, and hotels, or low-height buildings, such as warehouses, where there is a large amount of combustible content. The buildings may be located in congested areas, where the spread of fire is a strong possibility. So for public safety, as well as to prevent property loss, building codes regulate the amount of fire resistance that must be provided.

The following are some of the factors that enter into the determination of minimum fire resistance for a specific structure: height, floor area, type of occupancy (a measure of combustible contents), fire-fighting apparatus, sprinkler systems, and location in a community (fire zone), which is a measure of hazard to adjoining properties.

6-82. Fire-protection Engineering. At one time, most building codes designated all buildings as fireproofed or nonfireproofed, sometimes with an intermediate grade of semifireproofed, but usually without consideration of the combustible contents. However, it is just as logical to design a building for a fire resistance compatible with intended occupancy as it is to design the structure to support the live load for that occupancy. Fire-protection engineers are motivated by the desire to eliminate or reduce the waste in protection that was engendered by the older building codes.

Too little significance has been given to the meaning of "fireproofed." Some so-called "fireproof" buildings have been totally destroyed by fire, while others suffered no physical damage to their frame—like a good stove—but loss of life was great.

Credit for progress in fire protection is due to efforts by many organizations and individuals. Perhaps the most outstanding work is that of the National Bureau of Standards. Its Report BMS 92, "Classifications of Building Constructions" (Government Printing Office, Washington, D.C., 1942) is a recognized milestone. Also noteworthy is the detailed compilation in "Fire Protection through Modern Building Codes" (American Iron and Steel Institute, New York).

The modern concept of fire-resistive construction has followed two courses: (1) Buildings are designed to resist the potential fire severity of their combustible contents; (2) the fire-resistance ratings obtainable with various materials of construction are established by performance tests that are nationally recognized.

The first course is based on the evidence that there is a fairly definite relationship between the amount of combustible contents and resulting fire severity. Combustible

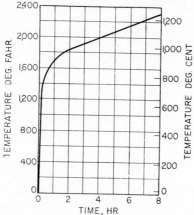

FIG. 6-66. Time-temperature curve for standard fire test.

contents may be readily expressed in terms of weight per square foot of floor area (see BMS 92 and 149).

Fire severity is a measure of the intensity and duration of a fire. It is expressed in terms of time of exposure equivalent to that in the standard furnace test—an internationally recognized standard (Fig. 6-66). For any stated period of duration of test, the rise in temperature must approximate the gradient shown by the curve; e.g., at 2 hr the structural assembly under test is exposed to a temperature of 1850°F, but in attaining this temperature, the furnace must record: 1000°F in 5 min, 1300°F in 10 min, 1550°F in 30 min; these being recorded on nine or more thermocouples distributed in the furnace near the test specimen. This performance test approximates the actual conditions encountered in real fires. Many fires, however, are of the smoldering type—of low intensity. Consequently, they could burn for hours in what may be not more than 1-hr resistive construction. Therefore, established ratings are a measure of time and intensity related together according to the standard curve in Fig. 6-66.

The relationship of weight of combustibles to fire severity is given in Table 6-1. Included also is the type of occupancy commensurate with the amount of combustibles usually found. This realistic appraisal of fire load is not necessarily a recommendation. In authoring building-code regulations, it becomes necessary to evaluate other factors; e.g., height, area, fire zones, etc.

Of equal importance are the ratings assigned to the fire resistance of various building components—trusses, girders, floor systems, columns, and walls—based on a common standard (ASTM E119, "Standard Methods of Fire Tests of Building Construction and Material"). It is applicable to assemblies of masonry units and to composite assemblies of structural materials for buildings, including walls, partitions, columns, girders, beams, slabs, and composite slab-and-beam assemblies for floors and roofs.

The test specimens must be a certain minimum size; e.g., a floor assembly must have an area exposed to fire of not less than 180 sq ft, with neither dimension less than 12 ft. Furnace temperatures must adhere to the standard time-temperature relationship (Fig. 6-66). Critical end points for terminating the test are fixed for each type of construction. For example, one of the critical end points of a floor assembly is reached when the heat penetrating the floor raises the temperature on the unexposed surface more than 250°F above its initial temperature. Similarly, the critical end point of a steel-column test is reached when the average temperature of the steel across any one of four test levels reaches 1000 or 1200°F on any single reading.

Table 6-1. Fire Severity of Various Occupancies

Average weight of combustibles, psf floor area	Fire severity, hr	Building type
5	$\frac{1}{2}$	Hospitals
$7\frac{1}{2}$	$\frac{3}{4}$ $\Big\}$	
10	1	Hotels, apartments, schools, department stores
15	$1\frac{1}{2}$	Furniture storage, offices
20	2	Laundries
30	3	
40	$4\frac{1}{2}$	
50	6	Heavy storage and warehouses
60	$7\frac{1}{2}$	

6-83. Effect of Heat on Steel. A moderate rise in temperature of structural steel, say up to 550°F, is beneficial in that the strength is about 25 % greater than the normal value. Above 550°F, strength falls off, until at 800°F it is approximately equal to the normal temperature strength. At a temperature of 1000°F, the compressive strength of steel is about the same as the maximum allowable working stress in columns. Therefore, it is permissible for tension and compression members to carry their maximum working stresses if the average temperature in the member does not exceed 1000°F, or the maximum at any one point does not exceed 1200°F (for ASTM A7 steel; for other steels some adjustment may be necessary).

Unprotected steel members have a rating of about 15 min, based on tests of columns with cross-sectional areas of about 10 sq in. Heavier columns, possessing greater mass for dissipation of heat, afford greater resistance—20 min perhaps. Columns with reentrant space between flanges filled with concrete, but otherwise exposed, have likewise been tested; where the total area of the solid cross section approximates 36 sq in., the resistance is 30 min, and where the area is 64 sq in., the resistance is 1 hr.

The average coefficient of expansion for structural steel between the temperatures of 200 and 1100°F is given by the formula

$$C = 0.0000061 + 0.0000000022t \qquad (6\text{-}15)$$

in which C = coefficient of expansion per °F

t = temperature, °F

From 1100 to 1400°F, there is a slight variation in the coefficient, and below 200°F the variation is less than that at the higher temperatures.

Structural steel maintained at any of various constant temperatures has, for any of these constant temperatures, a constant modulus of elasticity up to the elastic-limit stress (between the elastic-limit stress and the yield-point stress, the rate of deformation with stress is a variable). The modulus of elasticity of steel decreases as the temperature increases. The initial, or tangent modulus of elasticity in psi, for temperatures between 200 and 1300°F, is given approximately by the formula

$$E = 32,400,000 - 17,000t \qquad (6\text{-}16)$$

in which t = temperature, °F

Between room temperature and 200°F, there is a smaller variation in E.

Equation (6-16) does not apply for stresses above the elastic or proportional limit, which varies with the temperature approximately as follows:

200°F elastic limit = 33,000 psi
300°F elastic limit = 28,000 psi
500°F elastic limit = 16,000 psi
700°F elastic limit = 12,000 psi
900°F elastic limit = 8,000 psi
1100°F elastic limit = 5,000 psi
1300°F elastic limit = 2,000 psi

6-84. Materials for Improving Fire Resistance. Structural steel has been protected with many materials—brick, stone, concrete, tile, gypsum, and various fire-resistant plasters. Some measure of their relative insulating efficiency may be obtained from various test reports (see Table 6-2).

Table 6-2. Fire-Insulation Properties

	Steel side, °F	Insulation, in.	Furnace side, °F
Concrete, 41 tests	1292 min	$1\frac{1}{2}$	1962
	1256 min	$2\frac{1}{2}$	1962
	1112 min	$3\frac{1}{2}$	1962
Clay tile, 8 tests	1445 min	$1\frac{1}{2}$	1962
	1373 min	$2\frac{1}{2}$	1962
	1265 min	$3\frac{1}{2}$	1962
Gypsum 28 tests	698 min	$1\frac{1}{2}$	1962
	293 min	$2\frac{1}{2}$	1962
	221 min	$3\frac{1}{2}$	1962
Vermiculite gypsum	1142	1	2000
	878	$\frac{7}{8}$	1925

Concrete insulation serves well for column protection, in that it gives additional stability to the steel section. Also, it is useful where abrasion resistance is needed. Concrete, however, is not an efficient insulating medium compared with fire-resistant plasters. Normally, it is placed completely around the columns, beams, or girders, with all reentrant spaces filled solid. Although this procedure contributes to the stability of columns and effects composite action in beams and slabs, it has the disadvantage of imposing great weight on the steel frame and foundations. For instance, full protection of a 12 WF column with stone concrete weighs about 355 psf, whereas plaster protection weighs about 40 psf. However, lightweight concretes may be used, made with such aggregates as perlite, vermiculite, expanded shale, expanded slag, pumice, pumicite, and sintered flyash.

Considerable progress has been made in the use of lightweight plasters with aggregates possessing good insulating properties. Two aggregates used extensively are perlite and vermiculite; they replace sand in the sanded-gypsum plaster mix. A 1-in. thickness weighs about 4 psf, whereas the same thickness of sanded-gypsum plaster weighs about 10 psf.

Typical details of lightweight plaster protection for columns are shown in Fig. 6-67.

Generally, vermiculite and perlite plaster thicknesses of 1 to 1¾ in. afford protection of 3 and 4 hr, depending on construction details.

For buildings where rough usage is expected, a hard dense insulating material such as concrete, brick, or tile would be the logical selection for fire protection.   Concrete made with lightweight aggregates may be suitable.

For many buildings, finished ceilings are mandatory.   It is therefore logical to employ the ceiling for protecting roof and floor framing.   All types of gypsum plasters

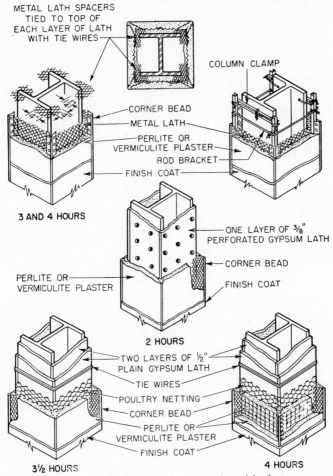

METAL LATH SPACERS
TIED TO TOP OF
EACH LAYER OF LATH
WITH TIE WIRES

COLUMN CLAMP

CORNER BEAD
METAL LATH
PERLITE OR
VERMICULITE PLASTER
ROD BRACKET
FINISH COAT

3 AND 4 HOURS

ONE LAYER OF ⅜"
PERFORATED GYPSUM LATH

CORNER BEAD

PERLITE OR
VERMICULITE PLASTER

FINISH COAT

2 HOURS

TWO LAYERS OF ½"
PLAIN GYPSUM LATH
TIE WIRES
POULTRY NETTING
CORNER BEAD
PERLITE OR
VERMICULITE PLASTER
FINISH COAT

3½ HOURS   **4 HOURS**

FIG. 6-67. Typical column fire protection with plaster.

are used extensively for this dual purpose.   Figure 6-68 illustrates typical installations.   For 2-hr floors, ordinary sand-gypsum plaster ¾ in. thick is sufficient.   Three and four-hour floors may be obtained with perlite gypsum and vermiculite gypsum in thickness range of ¾ to 1 in.   This is in sharp contrast with the 2½ or 3 in. of plaster and other materials previously required for 3-hr or better floor systems.

Aside from dual functioning of ceiling materials, partitions, walls, etc., being of incombustible material, often with no additional assistance, also protect the structural steel.   Fireproofing costs, therefore, may be made a relatively minor expense in the over-all costs of a building through dual use of materials.

6-85. Pierced Ceilings. Some buildings require recessed ceiling fixtures and duct openings for air-conditioning systems, thus interrupting the continuity of ceilings. Standard fire tests have provided data on the effect of these openings on the fire resistance. Accordingly, the rule that has evolved is that ceilings should be continuous, except that openings for noncombustible pipes, ducts, and electrical outlets are permissible if they do not exceed 100 sq in. in each 100 sq ft of ceiling area. Furthermore, duct openings must be protected with approved dampers. Reports of these tests are available through Underwriters' Laboratories ("Fire Resistance Ratings," National Board of Fire Underwriters).

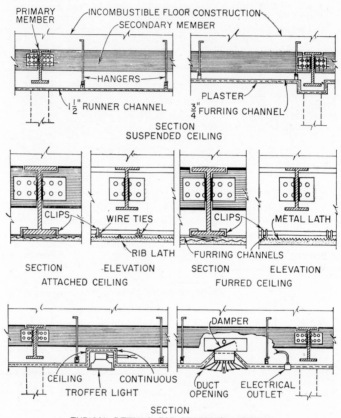

Fig. 6-68. Plaster-ceiling fire protection for floor framing.

6-86. Fire-resistance Ratings. Most standard fire tests on structural-steel members and assemblies have been conducted at one of two places—the National Bureau of Standards, Washington, D.C., or the Underwriters' Laboratories, Chicago. Their test reports form the basis for establishing ratings. Summaries of these tests, together with tabulation of recognized ratings, are published by a number of organizations listed below. The trade associations, for the most part, limit their ratings to those constructions employing the material they represent.

The National Board of Fire Underwriters, 85 John St., New York 38, N.Y.

The National Bureau of Standards, Washington 25, D.C.

Gypsum Association, 20 N. Wacker Drive, Chicago 6, Ill.

Metal Lath Manufacturers Association, Engineers Building, Cleveland 14, Ohio.
Perlite Institute, 10 East 40th St., New York 16, N.Y.
Vermiculite Institute, 1720 Madison St., N.E., Minneapolis 13, Minn.
American Iron and Steel Institute, 150 E. 42nd St., New York 17, N.Y.

6-87. Bibliography

Title	Author	Publisher
Steel Design (General Application of Structural Theory)		
"Design of Steel Structures"	Gaylord and Gaylord	McGraw-Hill
"Structural Members and Connections"	Hool and Kinne	McGraw-Hill
"Steel and Timber Structures"	Hool and Kinne	McGraw-Hill
"Elementary Structural Engineering"	Urquhart, O'Rourke, and Winter	McGraw-Hill
"Structural Design in Metals"	Williams and Harris	Ronald
"Simplified Design of Structural Steel"	H. Parker	Wiley
"Design of Steel Buildings"	Hauf and Pfisterer	Wiley
"Architectural Construction"	T. Crane	Wiley
"Stress Analysis and Design of Elementary Structures"	J. H. Cissel	Wiley
"Structural Frameworks"	Morris-Carpenter	Wiley
"Structural Design in Steel"	T. C. Shedd	Wiley
"Structural Design"	Sutherland and Bowman	Wiley
"Elementary Theory and Design of Flexural Members"	Vawter-Clark	Wiley
"Elementary Structural Problems in Steel and Timber	Young-Morrison	Wiley
"Design of Modern Steel Structures"	L. E. Grinter	Macmillan
"Applied Structural Design"	T. H. McKaig	F. W. Dodge Corp.
"Design in Structural Steel"	J. E. Lothers	Prentice-Hall
"Steel Designers Manual"	C. S. Gray	Fred Ungar
Handbooks, Data Books, Specialized Works		
"Civil Engineering Handbook"	L. C. Urquhart	McGraw-Hill
"Manual of Structural Design"	J. Singleton	H. M. Ives & Sons
"Design-data Book for Civil Engineers"	E. E. Seelye	Wiley
"Structural Engineers' Handbook Library"	Hool and Kinne	McGraw-Hill
"Procedure Handbook of Arc Welding—Design and Practice"	Lincoln Electric Co.	Lincoln Electric Co.
"Manual of Design for Arc Welded Steel Structures"	LaMotte Grover	Air Reduction
"Manual of Steel Construction"		AISC
"Structural Shop Drafting Textbook" (3 vols.)		AISC
"Structural Drafting"	C. T. Bishop	Wiley
"Structures, Their Elements and Details" Part I, "Steel Structures"	J. B. Gribbin	Edwards
"Steel Rigid Frames Manual"	M. P. Korn	Edwards
"Simplified Design of Roof Trusses for Architects and Builders"	H. Parker	Wiley
"Single Span Rigid Frames in Steel"	J. Griffiths	AISC
"Grandstand and Stadium Design"	W. N. Woodbury	AISC

Section 7

LIGHTWEIGHT STEEL CONSTRUCTION

F. E. Fahy

Bethlehem Steel Co.

The lighter types of steel construction have been found especially suitable for use in the floor framing of light-occupancy structures and in roof framing. Such construction takes many forms, and a great number of proprietary designs of structural members and framing systems have been developed. These make use of many different shapes and grades of steel—small angles, bars, rods, special rolled shapes, wire, and hot-rolled and cold-rolled sheet and strip steel shaped cold to form structural framing members and panels of various kinds.

OPEN-WEB STEEL-JOIST CONSTRUCTION

As defined by the Steel Joist Institute, open-web steel joists are lightweight steel trusses designed for use in light-occupancy buildings to support floor and roof panels between main supporting beams, girders, trusses, and walls.

Open-web steel-joist construction, as defined by that institute, refers to a particular kind of assembly of steel joists and top slab or deck in which the maximum permissible spacing of the joists is 24 in. on centers in floors and 30 in. on centers in roofs.

As usually employed in floor construction, open-web steel joists are covered by a slab of concrete, 2 to $2\frac{1}{2}$ in. thick, placed on permanent forms. An open-web steel-joist floor assembly, with ceiling, is illustrated in Fig. 7-1.

Open-web steel joists are usually supported on either structural-steel framing or masonry bearing walls. When used with structural steel, they are preferably welded to the supporting framework but may be bolted or clipped. For wall-bearing applications, wall anchors are usually specified.

In addition to light weight, one of the advantages claimed for open-web steel-joist construction is that the open-web system provides space for electrical work, ducts, and piping.

Standardization of open-web steel joists under Simplified Practice Recommendation R94-53 of the U.S. Department of Commerce consists essentially of standardization of depths, number designations, and load-carrying capacities. Further standardization under the specifications of the Steel Joist Institute consists of definition of product, specification of bridging lines, and specification of design basis. Most manufacturers have adopted uniformity of certain details, such as end depths, which are desirably standardized for interchangeability. Exact forms of the members, configuration of web systems, and method of manufacture are matters for the individual manufacturers of these joists, and a number of proprietary designs have been developed.

Open-web joists are manufactured in standard depths of 8, 10, 12, 14, 16, 18, and 20 in., to span up to 40 ft for roofs, and in different weights. These joists are desig-

7-1

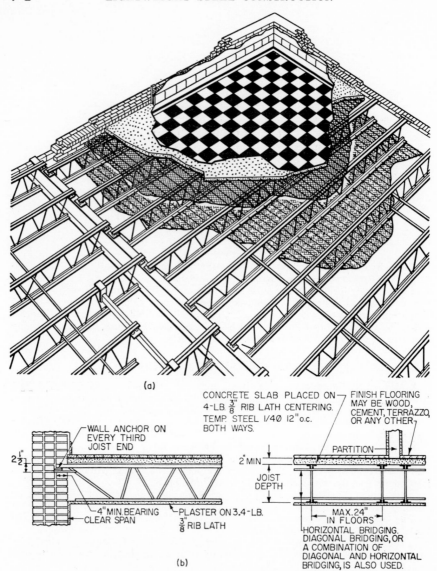

(a)

CONCRETE SLAB PLACED ON
4-LB. $\frac{3}{8}''$ RIB LATH CENTERING.
TEMP. STEEL I/4∅ 12"o.c.
BOTH WAYS.

FINISH FLOORING
MAY BE WOOD,
CEMENT, TERRAZZO,
OR ANY OTHER

WALL ANCHOR ON
EVERY THIRD
JOIST END

$2\frac{1}{2}''$

2" MIN

JOIST
DEPTH

PARTITION

4" MIN. BEARING
CLEAR SPAN

PLASTER ON 3.4-LB.
$\frac{3}{8}''$ RIB LATH

MAX. 24"
IN FLOORS

HORIZONTAL BRIDGING.
DIAGONAL BRIDGING, OR
A COMBINATION OF
DIAGONAL AND HORIZONTAL
BRIDGING, IS ALSO USED.

(b)

FIG. 7-1. Open-web steel-joist construction.

nated by a prefix SJ.   The safe load-carrying capacities of each are shown in the Steel
Joist Institute loading table reproduced in Table 7-1.

7-1. Joist Fabrication.   Open-web steel joists are different in one important respect
from the fabricated structural-steel framing members commonly used in building construction; that is, they are usually manufactured by production-line methods with
special equipment and assembly jigs designed to yield a uniform product.   On the
basis of method of manufacture, there are two types—expanded joists and welded
joists.

Expanded joists are manufactured by slitting and expanding special I-shaped

Table 7-1. Standard Loading Table*

(Allowable total safe loads, lb per lin ft of open-web standard and nailer steel joists)

The prefix letters SJ should precede joist designations given below, i.e., SJ81, SJ81W, SJ82, SJ82W, etc.

Joist Designation SJ	81 / 81W	82 / 82W	102 / 102W	103 / 103W	104 / 104W	123 / 123W	124 / 124W	125 / 125W	126 / 126W	145 / 145W	146 / 146W	147 / 147W	166 / 166W	167 / 167W	186 / 186W	187 / 187W	207 / 207W
Depth, in.†	8	8	10	10	10	12	12	12	12	14	14	14	16	16	18	18	20
Approx weights, lb per lin ft‡	3.5	4.0	4.0	4.75	5.75	5.0	5.75	7.0	8.0	7.0	8.0	10.0	8.5	10.0	9.0	10.5	10.5
Resisting moment, in.-kips	29.5	52.5	63	82	100	92	115	142	175	156	205	246	232	281	255	310	340
Max end reaction, kips	1.60	1.90	1.90	1.95	2.20	2.20	2.30	2.50	2.70	2.90	3.10	3.40	3.20	3.60	3.60	3.80	3.90
Span, ft																	
7	401																
8	307																
9	243																
10	197	350															
11	163	289															
12	137	243	292														
13	116	207	249														
14	100	179	214			313											
15	87	156	187	243		273											
16	77	137	164	214	260	240											
17			145	189	231	212	265										
18			130	169	206	189	237			321							
19			116	151	185	170	212	262		288							
20			105	137	167	153	192	237		260							
21						139	174	215		236							
22						127	158	196	241	215							
23						116	145	179	221	197	258						
24						106	133	164	203	181	237				295		
25										166	219	262	247		272		
26										154	202	243	229		251		
27										143	187	225	212	257	233		
28										133	174	209	197	239	217	264	
29													184	223	202	246	
30													172	208	189	230	252
31													161	195	177	215	236
32													151	183	166	202	221
33															156	190	208
34															147	179	196
35															139	169	185
36															131	159	175
37																	166
38																	157
39																	149
40																	142

* Adopted by the Steel Joist Institute Aug. 20, 1929, and revised to Sept. 16, 1952.
† Indicates nominal depth of standard steel joists only. See manufacturers' catalogs for depths of nailer steel joists.
‡ Approximate weights per linear foot of joists include accessories but do not include wood nailer strip.

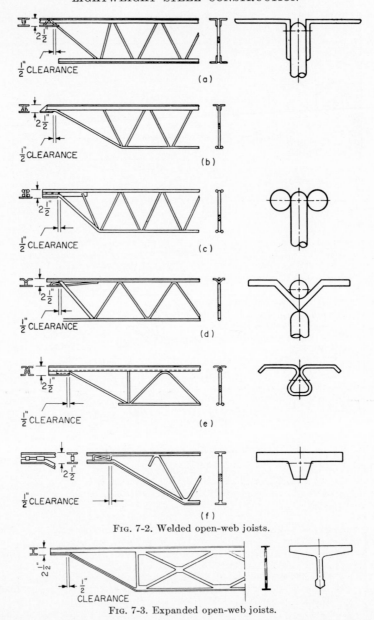

Fig. 7-2. Welded open-web joists.

Fig. 7-3. Expanded open-web joists.

blanks. The result is a double-lattice web system in which the ends are finished subsequent to expanding. This is done in special jigs that bend up the lower-chord ends and weld them to the upper chord. Welded joists are made by joining the component parts together by either resistance or manual arc welding. Various designs of joists are illustrated in Figs. 7-2 and 7-3.

7-2. Nailer Joists. Open-web steel nailer joists have one or both chords adapted to receive common nails for attachment of collateral materials. Most manufacturers use wood strips attached to the chords of regular open-web joists. Some manufacturers, however, have special chord sections to receive the wood strips; others bolt the strips to the chord sections of regular joists. There are also available joists with cold-formed chord sections adapted to receive nails directly. Details of nailer joists are shown in Figs. 7-4 and 7-5.

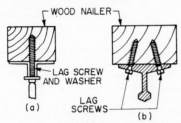

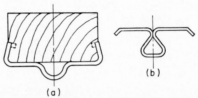

FIG. 7-4. Attachment of nailer strips to joists. The wood nailer can be attached to top or bottom chord.

FIG. 7-5. Nailer-joist chord sections. (a) Truscon Steel Division, Republic Steel Corp.; (b) Macomber, Inc.

Nailer joists are designated by the suffix W on the standard joist designation number. For instance, SJ166W refers to a nailer joist having the same depth (exclusive of nailer strip) and load-carrying capacity as standard joist SJ166.

Wood sleepers may be anchored as shown in Fig. 7-6.

7-3. Design of Open-web Joist Floors. Open-web joists are primarily designed to be used under uniformly distributed loading, and at substantially uniform spacing, in much the same way as wood joists are used. The chords of open-web joists are ordinarily not designed to resist bending caused by loads applied between panel points; published safe-load tables do not include any allowance for such bending.

In general, however, concentrated loads can be safely carried by open-web joists. But such loads should be applied over a concrete top slab that will adequately support and distribute them, or they should be applied at the panel points of the joists.

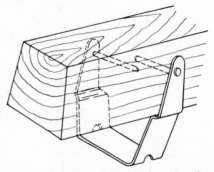

FIG. 7-6. Wood sleeper and anchor for concrete subfloor.

The standard specifications of the Steel Joist Institute state that bending stresses in the top chords of open-web joists need not be considered under the following conditions:

1. When steel joists support cast-in-place concrete slabs having a thickness of more than one-fourteenth the distance between supports under the top chords; however, when the concrete slabs are thinner, the theoretical bending stress in the top chord for a uniform load should be considered.

2. When a wood sleeper (nailing screed) is embedded in a top slab of cast-in-place concrete at least 2 in. thick—if the wood sleeper (nailing screed) is elevated a minimum of 1 in. above the top chord of the steel joist.

3. When a wood nailer strip adequate to carry the supported load to the panel points is attached to the top chord in accordance with the provisions of Sec. 103 (e) of these specifications. In the design of open-web nailer steel joists, the nailer strip should not be assumed to carry any part of the stresses in the steel joists, but, if adequate, may be assumed to carry the supported load to the panel points.

4. When precast interlocking top slabs are used over open-web steel joists and are of sufficient width and rigidity to transmit a uniform load to the panel points without the assistance of the top chords between panel points.

Open-web joists are not designed to be used as individual framing members, although special joists have been used under special conditions. Openings between joists requiring a span not larger than 4 ft may usually be framed with angle headers supported on adjacent joists (Fig. 7-7). Larger openings should be framed in structural steel.

Headers should preferably be located so that they are supported at panel points of the trimmer joists. In any case in which that is not practicable, consideration must be given to the bending stresses induced in the top chords of the trimmer joists by the concentrated loads from the header.

As with wood joists, open-web steel joists can be doubled and even tripled where necessary. Although a partition running crosswise of the joists constitutes a concentrated load, its weight usually is considered satisfactorily distributed by the concrete floor slab and is assumed not to cause any local bending in the top chord of the joists.

The method of selecting joist sizes for any floor will depend on whether or not the effect of any cross partitions or other concentrated loads must be considered. Under uniform loading only, joist sizes and spacings are most conveniently selected from a table of safe loads. Where concentrated or nonuniform loads exist, calculation must be made of the bending moments, end reactions, and shears, and the joists selected accordingly.

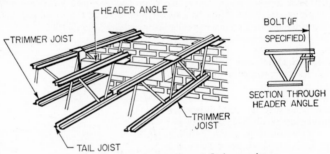

FIG. 7-7. Header construction at floor openings.

The deflection of open-web steel joists can be computed in the same way as for other types of beams. In computing moment of inertia of the cross section, however, the chords only should be considered, neglecting the web system. In general, deflections so computed will be slightly less than those computed by more accurate methods— possibly by 10 or 15%. When closer determination is desirable, deflections should be calculated as for a truss.

The chord sections and web details are different for different joist designs made by different manufacturers; information relating to the size and properties of the members has to be obtained from manufacturers' catalogs.

Some manufacturers recommend that, to avoid a feeling of springiness in a steel-joist floor, the clear span should not exceed twenty-one times the depth of the joist. For roofs, it is customary to allow spans twenty-four times the depth of the joist, as with structural-steel beams.

Figure 7-8 shows a portion of a framing plan for a typical open-web joist floor.

7-4. Bridging and Bracing for Open-web Joists. It is essential that bridging be installed between joists as soon as possible after the joists have been placed and before application of construction loads. When properly made and installed, open-web steel joists are capable of withstanding all usual service requirements. They are, however, very flexible in a lateral direction; they are not intended to be used without proper lateral support. The principal function of bridging is to provide such support during the construction period.

Bridging details vary with different manufacturers. The most commonly used types are (1) a double system of diagonal struts, and (2) continuous horizontal bridging composed of rods fastened to the top and bottom chords of the joists. Combinations of the two have also been used. It is also important that masonry anchors be used on wall-bearing joists and that where the joists rest on steel beams they should be welded, bolted, or clipped to the beams. The standard specifications of the Steel Joist Institute should be followed in all such details.

Care must be exercised even after the bridging has been installed to avoid undue concentrations of construction loads.

7-5. Slab Forms for Joist Construction. Centering usually consists of corrugated-steel sheets or expanded metal rib lath or paper-backed welded-wire mesh.

The wire-reinforced paper must be stretched rather tightly across the joists to avoid undue sag under the weight of the concrete, and in stretching it, care must be exercised not to bow the joists laterally. This type of form and metal lath is usually fastened to the joists with wire clips. When corrugated sheets are used, they can be welded to the joists, with a bent washer to reinforce the weld and provide anchorage to the slab, or fastened with drive screws. Bent washers also are advisable when drive screws are used. Clips have also been used for this purpose.

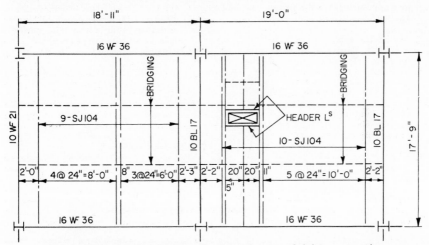

Fig. 7-8. Framing plan for part of a floor of open-web joist construction.

Although various kinds of removable forms have been tried in steel-joist construction, none of them has yet proved as economical as permanent centering of the types described above.

7-6. Slab Reinforcement in Steel-joist Construction. When the usual cast-in-place floor slab is used, it is customary to install ¼-in. reinforcing bars at about 12 in. c to c in two perpendicular directions, or welded wire fabric 6 × 6/No. 10 × No. 10. No other reinforcement is usually considered necessary. Precast units, which are sometimes used as decking on open-web joists, are, of course, provided with suitable reinforcement.

7-7. Open-web Joists in Roof Construction. Although standard open-web joist construction contemplates a maximum spacing of 30 in. for open-web joists in roof construction, such joists are frequently used as purlins at spacings considerably wider than 30 in.—determined by the load-carrying capacity of the decking. The joists should be properly braced, and on steep sloping roofs, sag rods should be provided, as for structural-steel purlins. Spacing of sag rods, in general, will have to be considerably closer than for structural-steel purlins. In considering the effect of load components parallel to the slope of the roof, the top-chord section only should be considered effective.

7-8. Fire Resistance of Open-web Joist Construction. Almost any desired degree of fire resistance can be obtained in steel-joist construction with proper protection,

Table 7-2. Fire-resistance Ratings for Steel-Joist Construction

1. ¾-hr fire resistance*
   Top slab: 1-in. nominal tongue-and-groove single wood floor on 2 × 2 in. wood strips attached to steel joist
   Ceiling: ¾-in. sanded gypsum plaster on expanded metal or wire lath, 1:2 for scratch coat and 1:3 for brown coat

2. 1-hr fire resistance†
   Top slab: 2-in. reinforced concrete, or 2-in. precast reinforced gypsum tile
   Ceiling: ¾-in. portland-cement sand plaster, 1:2 for scratch coat and 1:3 for brown coat, with 15 lb of hydrated lime and 3 lb of short asbestos fiber per bag of portland cement; or ¾-in. sanded gypsum plaster, 1:2 for scratch coat and 1:3 for brown coat

3. 1½-hr fire resistance†
   Top slab: 2-in. reinforced concrete, or 2-in. precast reinforced gypsum tile
   Ceiling: ¾-in. portland-cement sand plaster, 1:2 for scratch coat and 1:3 for brown coat, with 15 lb of hydrated lime and 3 lb of short asbestos fiber per bag of portland cement; or ¾-in. sanded gypsum plaster, 1:2 for scratch coat and 1:3 for brown coat

4. 2-hr fire resistance†
   Top slab: 2¼-in. reinforced concrete, or 2-in. reinforced gypsum tile, the latter with ¼-in. mortar finish
   Ceiling: ¾-in. sanded gypsum plaster, 1:2 for scratch coat and 1:3 for brown coat

5. 2½-hr fire resistance
   a. Top slab:† 2-in. reinforced concrete, or 2-in. reinforced gypsum tile, the latter with ¼-in. mortar finish
   Ceiling: 1-in. neat gypsum plaster or ¾-in. gypsum-vermiculite plaster; ratio of weight of gypsum to fine heat-expanded vermiculite in the range 2:1 to 3:1.
   b. Top slab:‡ 2½-in. reinforced concrete
   Ceiling: ⅞-in. sanded gypsum plaster, 1:2 for scratch and brown coats

6. 3-hr fire resistance
   a. Top slab:† 2½-in. reinforced concrete, or 2-in. reinforced gypsum tile, the latter with ½-in. mortar finish
   Ceiling: 1-in. neat gypsum plaster, or ¾-in. gypsum vermiculite plaster; ratio of weight of gypsum to fine heat-expanded vermiculite in the range 2:1 to 3:1
   b. Top slab:¶ 2-in. concrete floor slab on metal lath or 2¾-in. reinforced portland cement concrete plank
   Ceiling: 1-in. gypsum-vermiculite plaster on metal lath, ratio of gypsum to vermiculite 4:1 by weight

7. 4-hr fire resistance†
   Top slab: 2½-in. reinforced concrete, or 2-in. reinforced gypsum slabs, the latter with ½-in. mortar finish
   Ceiling: 1-in. gypsum vermiculite plaster applied on metal lath and proportioned in the range 2:1 to 3:1 gypsum to heat-expanded vermiculite by weight

NOTE: Fire resistance ratings established in National Bureau of Standards Report BMS-92 require that:
   "The plaster for the ceiling shall be applied on metal lath (expanded metal, woven wire, or paper-backed wire lath) of appropriate weight for the spacing of the supports. The lath shall be tied (or clipped) to the supports to give the equivalent of single No. 18-gauge steel wire ties on 5-inch centers. The thickness of plaster shall be the depth from the back side of flat lath and to the back of the flat portion of ribbed lath.
   "The plaster proportions are by dry weight of materials.
   "The slab thicknesses are measured from the top flange of the joists and unless otherwise indicated are for monolithic poured construction. To obtain the fire resistance ratings herein given, the average thickness of the slabs cast in place should be one-quarter (¼") inch greater than at the joists. This greater average thickness usually results from the sag of metal lath forming or the placing of the more rigid forms under the top flange of the joists."
   Precast slabs shall have joints grouted.
   Wood nailers may be placed in top slabs provided they are separated from the top of the steel joist by the following minimum thickness of concrete or gypsum:
   1½-hr fire-resistive construction: 1 in.
   2-hr fire-resistive construction: 1⅛ in.
   2½-hr fire-resistive construction: 1⅜ in.
   3-hr fire-resistive construction: 1⅝ in.
   4-hr fire-resistive construction: 1⅝ in.
   * In accordance with National Bureau of Standards Report TRBM-44.
   † In accordance with National Bureau of Standards Report BMS-92.
   ‡ Interpolated by S. H. Ingberg, National Bureau of Standards, from other test results.
   ¶ In accordance with the National Board of Fire Underwriters Building Code, 1949 Edition.

The ratings shown in Table 7-2 are given in Sec. 113 of the Steel Joist Institute Standard Specifications for Open-web Steel Joist Construction, Oct. 9, 1951.

COLD-FORMED SHAPES

The term "cold-formed shapes" refers to relatively small, thin sections made by bending sheet or strip steel in roll-forming machines, press brakes, or bending brakes. Because of the relative ease and simplicity of the bending operation and the comparatively low cost of forming rolls and dies, the cold-forming process lends itself well to the manufacture of special shapes for special purposes and makes it possible to use thin material shaped for maximum stiffness.

The use of cold-formed shapes for ornamental and other non-load-carrying purposes is commonplace. Door and window frames, metal-partition work, non-load-bearing studs, facing, and all kinds of ornamental sheet-metal work employ such shapes. The following deals with cold-formed shapes used for structural purposes in the framing of buildings:

There is no standard series of cold-formed structural sections, such as those for hot-rolled shapes, although groups of such sections have been designed ("Light Gage Steel Design Manual," American Iron and Steel Institute). For the most part, however, cold-formed structural shapes are designed to serve a particular purpose. The general approach of the designer is therefore similar to that involved in the design of built-up structural sections; namely, to fit a particular application.

As a general rule, cold-formed shapes will cost considerably more per pound than hot-rolled sections. They will accordingly be found to be economical under the following circumstances:

1. Where their use permits a substantial reduction in weight relative to comparable hot-rolled sections. This will occur usually where relatively light loads are to be supported over short spans, or where stiffness rather than strength is the controlling factor in the design.

2. In a special case where a suitable combination of standard rolled shapes would be heavy and uneconomical.

3. Where the quantities required are too small to justify the investment in equipment necessary to produce a suitable hot-rolled section.

7-9. Material for Cold-formed Shapes. Cold-formed shapes are usually made from sheet or strip steel. In the thicknesses in which it is available, hot-rolled material is usually used. Cold-rolled material, that is, material that has been cold reduced to the desired thickness, is used in the thinner gages or where for any reason the surface finish, mechanical properties, or more uniform thickness that results from cold reducing are desired. Manufacture of cold-formed shapes from plates for use in building construction is infrequent.

The commercial distinction between steel plates, sheets, and strip is principally a matter of thickness and width of material and is unaffected by whether or not the material is furnished in flat form or in coils. Although the manufacturers' classification of flat-rolled steel products by size is subject to change from time to time, that given in Table 7-3 is fairly representative.

Cold-formed shapes may be either "black"—that is, uncoated—or galvanized. Because of its increased cost, galvanized material is used only where exposure conditions warrant paying for the increased protection afforded against corrosion. Carbon steel is generally used. Material to be used for structural purposes generally conforms to one of the standard specifications of the American Society for Testing Materials for structural-quality carbon-steel sheet and strip (A245 and A303).

The choice of grade of material usually depends on the severity of the forming operation required to make the desired shape. Most shapes used for structural purposes in buildings are made from Grade C material, which has a yield point of 33,000 psi, corresponding to the minimum yield point permitted under ASTM Specification A7, "Steel for Bridges and Buildings."

Some manufacturers of cold-formed shapes use special high-strength carbon steel having a specified minimum yield point of about 40,000 psi. Such steel should be

Table 7-3. Classification by Size of Flat-rolled Carbon Steel

Hot-rolled

(The sheet classification includes hot-rolled and hot-rolled pickled)

Widths, in.	Thicknesses, in.			
	0.2300 and thicker	0.2299–0.2031	0.2030–0.1800	0.1799–0.047
To 3½ incl...........	Bar	Bar	Strip	Strip
Over 3½ to 6 incl...	Bar	Bar	Strip	Strip
Over 6 to 8 incl........	Bar	Strip	Strip	Strip
Over 8 to 12 incl.......	Plate	Strip	Strip	Strip
Over 12 to 48 incl......	Plate	Sheet	Sheet	Sheet
Over 48..............	Plate	Plate	Plate	Sheet

Cold-rolled

Width, in.	Thickness, in.		
	0.2500 and thicker	0.2499–0.0142	0.0141 and thinner
To 12, incl....................	Bar	Strip* †	Strip*
2 to 12, incl.................	Bar	Sheet‡	Strip
Over 12 to 23¹⁵⁄₁₆, incl........	Strip†	Strip†	Strip
Over 12 to 23¹⁵⁄₁₆, incl........	Sheet¶	Sheet¶	Black plate¶
Over 23¹⁵⁄₁₆..................	Sheet	Sheet	Black plate

* When the width is greater than the thickness with a maximum width of ½ in. and a cross-sectional area not exceeding 0.05 sq in., and the material has rolled or prepared edges, it is classified as flat wire.

† When a particular temper as defined in ASTM Specification A109, or a special edge, or special finish is specified, or when single-strand rolling is specified in widths under 24 in.

‡ Cold-rolled sheet coils and cut lengths, slit from wider coils with No. 3 edge (only) and in thicknesses 0.0142 to 0.0821 in., inclusive, carbon 0.20% maximum.

¶ When no special temper, edge, or finish (other than dull or luster) is specified, or when single-strand rolling widths under 24 in. are not specified or required.

Table 7-4. Application of ASTM Specifications to Structural-quality Carbon-stee Sheets and Strip

Width, in.	(Theoretical) thickness, in., incl.						
	0.2299–0.2031	0.2030–0.1800	0.1799–0.0568	0.0567–0.0449	0.0448–0.0344	0.0343–0.0255	0.0254–0.0225
Up to 3½, incl......	....	A303	A303	A303	A303	A303	A245
Over 3½ to 6, incl...	....	A303	A303	A303	A303	A245	A245
Over 6 to 12, incl....	A303	A303	A303	A245	A245	A245	A245
Over 12 to 48, incl...	A245	A245	A245	A245	A245	A245	A245
Over 48.............	....	....	A245	A245	A245	A245	A245

Table 7-5. Principal Mechanical Properties of Structural-Quality
Carbon Sheet and Strip Sheet (A245 and 303)

	Grade A		Grade B		Grade C	
Tensile strength, min. psi......	48,000	45,000	52,000	50,000	55,000	52,000
Yield point, min, psi..........	25,000		30,000		33,000	
Elongation..................	Varies—see individual specifications					

BENDING PROPERTIES. Bend-test specimens shall stand being bent as follows at room temperature in any direction without cracking on the outside of the bent portion:
Grade A: Flat on itself.
Grade B: 180° around one thickness of the material.
Grade C: 180° around one and one-half thicknesses of the material.

Table 7-6. Manufacturers' Standard Gage for Steel Sheets
[Thickness equivalents are based on 0.023912 in. per lb per sq ft (reciprocal of 41.820 psf per in. thick)]*

Manufac- turers' standard gage No.	Psf	In. equivalent for steel sheet thickness	Manufac- turers' standard gage No.	Psf	In. equivalent for steel sheet thickness
3	10.0000	0.2391	21	1.3750	0.0329
4	9.3750	0.2242	22	1.2500	0.0299
5	8.7500	0.2092	23	1.1250	0.0269
6	8.1250	0.1943	24	1.0000	0.0239
7	7.5000	0.1793	25	0.87500	0.0209
8	6.8750	0.1644	26	0.75000	0.0179
9	6.2500	0.1495	27	0.68750	0.0164
10	5.6250	0.1345	28	0.62500	0.0149
11	5.0000	0.1196	29	0.56250	0.0135
12	4.3750	0.1046	30	0.50000	0.0120
13	3.7500	0.0897	31	0.43750	0.0105
14	3.1250	0.0747	32	0.40625	0.0097
15	2.8125	0.0673	33	0.37500	0.0090
16	2.5000	0.0598	34	0.34375	0.0082
17	2.2500	0.0538	35	0.31250	0.0075
18	2.0000	0.0478	36	0.28125	0.0067
19	1.7500	0.0418	37	0.26562	0.0064
20	1.5000	0.0359	38	0.25000	0.0060

* The density of steel is ordinarily taken as 489.6 lb per cu ft, 0.2833 lb per cu in., or 40.80 psf per in. thick. However, since sheet weights are calculated on the basis of the specified width and length, with all shearing tolerances on the over side, and also since sheets are somewhat thicker at the center than they are at the edges, a further adjustment must be made to obtain a closer approximation for inter-changeability between weight and thickness. This value for sheets has been found to be 41.820 psf per in. thick. ("Steel Products Manual," Carbon Steel Sheets, American Iron and Steel Institute, June, 1954.)

used only where the quantities required are sufficient to justify the expense and controls involved in setting up a satisfactory special grade, and where the resulting saving in weight is sufficient to compensate for any added cost per pound.

In addition to the carbon steel covered by Specifications A245 and A303 and the special high-strength carbon steel used by a few manufacturers, low-alloy high-strength steel having a relatively high degree of corrosion resistance and conforming generally to ASTM Specification A242, "Low-alloy Structural Steel," is sometimes used. Stainless-steel and aluminum sheets are frequently used for facing purposes in building construction but are not often shaped to form load-carrying structural

Table 7-7. Galvanized-sheet Gage Numbers, Unit Weights, and Thicknesses

Galvanized sheet gage No.	Psf	Thickness equivalent for galvanized-sheet gage No.
8	7.03125	0.1681
9	6.40625	0.1532
10	5.78125	0.1382
11	5.15625	0.1233
12	4.53125	0.1084
13	3.90625	0.0934
14	3.28125	0.0785
15	2.96875	0.0710
16	2.65625	0.0635
17	2.40625	0.0575
18	2.15625	0.0516
19	1.90625	0.0456
20	1.65625	0.0396
21	1.53125	0.0366
22	1.40625	0.0336
23	1.28125	0.0306
24	1.15625	0.0276
25	1.03125	0.0247
26	0.90625	0.0217
27	0.84375	0.0202
28	0.78125	0.0187
29	0.71875	0.0172
30	0.65625	0.0157
31	0.59375	0.0142
32	0.56250	0.0134

members. Low-carbon sheets coated with vitreous enamel are also frequently used for facing purposes, but not as a rule to perform any load-carrying function.

Thicknesses of cold-formed shapes are frequently expressed in terms of the manufacturers' standard gage number of the material from which they are formed (although the use of decimal parts of an inch is to be preferred). These gage numbers are applicable only to sheets, strip thicknesses being referred to in decimal parts of an inch. The relationships between gage number, weight, and thickness for uncoated sheets are given in Table 7-6, and for galvanized sheets in Table 7-7.

Although the material specifications discussed cover the thickness range from 0.0225 to 0.2299 in., inclusive (24 to 4 gage approximately) most building codes limit the thickness of metal used for individual structural members; i.e., framing members, to a minimum of 18 gage. Thickness of steel used to form load-carrying panels, such as ribbed steel roof-deck construction and floor deck, is usually limited to a minimum of 22 gage. Use of material $\frac{3}{16}$ in. or more in thickness for cold-formed shapes in building construction is infrequent, because where material this thick is required hot-rolled structural sections will usually be found to be more economical. The descriptions and design procedures of this section are intended to apply only to material thinner than $\frac{3}{16}$ in.

7-10. Types of Cold-formed Sections. Many cold-formed shapes used for structural purposes are similar in their general configuration to hot-rolled structural sections. Channels, angles, and zees can be roll-formed in a single operation from one piece of material. I sections are usually made by welding two channels back to back or by welding two angles to a channel. All sections of this kind may be made with either plain flanges as in Fig. 7-9a to d, j and m, or with flanges stiffened by lips at outer edges, as in Fig. 7-9e to h, k and n.

In addition to these sections, which follow somewhat conventional lines and have their counterparts in hot-rolled structural sections, the flexibility of the forming process makes it relatively easy to obtain inverted U, or hat-shaped, sections and open box sections (Fig. 7-9o to q). These sections are very stiff in a lateral direction and can be used without lateral support where other more conventional types of sections would fail because of lateral instability.

Other special shapes are illustrated in Fig. 7-10. Some of these are nonstructural in nature; others are used for special structural purposes.

An important characteristic of cold-formed shapes is that the thickness of the section is uniform throughout. (A slight reduction in thickness may occur at bends but may be ignored for computing weights and section properties.) This means that, for a specified gage, the amount of flange material in a section, such as a channel, is almost entirely a function of the width of the section—except where additional flange has been obtained by doubling the material back on itself. Another distinguishing feature of cold-formed sections is that the corners are rounded on both the inside and outside of the bend, since the shapes are formed by bending flat material.

Sharp corners, such as can be obtained with hot-rolled structural channels, angles, and zees, cannot be obtained in cold-formed shapes, except with very soft material and in a coining or upsetting operation, as distinguished from a simple bending operation. This is not customary in the manufacture of structural cold-formed sections; and in proportioning such sections for Grade C material, the inside radius of bends should not be less than three-quarters of the thickness and should preferably be not less than the thickness. For softer grades of material, correspondingly smaller bend radii may be used.

Special joist and stud sections with curved webs designed to receive nails are shown in Fig. 7-11.

Deck and panel sections, such as are used for floors, roofs, and walls, are as a rule considerably wider, relative to their depth, than are the structural framing members shown in Figs. 7-9 to 7-11. Such shapes are illustrated and discussed in Arts. 7-29 to 7-35.

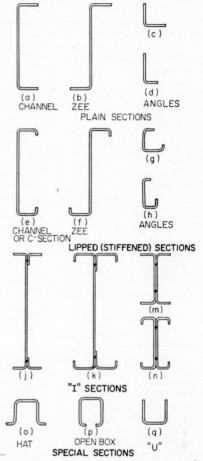

FIG. 7-9. Typical cold-formed structural sections.

7-11. Design Principles for Cold-formed Sections. The structural behavior of cold-formed shapes follows the same laws of structural mechanics as does that of conventional structural-steel shapes and plates. Thus, design procedures commonly used in the selection of hot-rolled shapes are generally applicable to light-gage cold-formed sections. Although only a portion of a section, in some instances, may be considered structurally effective, computation of the structural properties of the effective portion follows conventional procedure.

The uniform thickness of most cold-formed sections, and the fact that the widths of the various elements comprising such a section are usually large relative to the thickness, make it possible to consider, in computing structural properties (moment of inertia, section modulus, etc.), that such properties vary directly as the first power of the thickness. So in most cases, section properties can be approximated by first assuming that the section is made up of a series of line elements, omitting the thickness dimension, and then multiplying the result by the thickness to get the final value. With this method, the final multiplier is always the first power of the thickness, and first-power quantities such as radius of gyration and those locating the centroid of the section do not involve the thickness dimension. The assumption that the area, moment of inertia, and section modulus vary directly as the first power of the thickness is particularly useful in determining the required thickness of a section after the

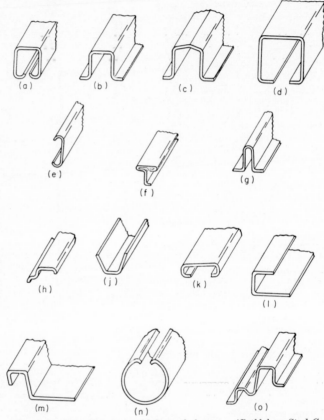

Fig. 7-10. Miscellaneous cold-formed shapes.   (*Bethlehem Steel Co.*)

lengths of the various elements that comprise it have been fixed. Although the method is sufficiently accurate for most practical purposes, it is well, particularly where the section is fairly thick relative to the widths of its elements, to check the final result through an exact method of computation.

Properties of thin elements are given in Table 7-8.

One of the distinguishing characteristics of light-gage cold-formed sections is that they are usually composed of elements that are relatively wide and thin, and as a result, attention must be given to certain modes of structural behavior customarily neglected in dealing with heavier material.

When wide thin elements are in axial compression—as in the case of a beam flange or a part of a column—they tend to buckle elastically at stresses below the yield point. This local elastic buckling is not to be confused with the general buckling that occurs in the failure of a long column or of a laterally unsupported beam. Rather local buckling represents failure of a single element of a section and conceivably may be relatively unrelated to buckling of the entire member. In addition, there are other factors—such as shear lag, which gives rise to nonuniform stress distribution; torsional instability, which may be considerably more pronounced in thin sections than in thicker ones, requiring more attention to bracing; and other related structural phenomena customarily ignored in conventional structural work that sometimes must be considered with thin material. Simplified means of taking care of these factors in ordinary structural design were made available when the American Iron and Steel Institute published, in 1946, the first edition of the Specification for the Design of Light Gage Steel Structural Members. The following discussion is based on that specification and the research work that resulted in some of its provisions.

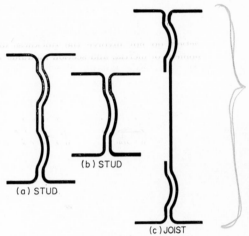

(b) STUD

(a) STUD

(c) JOIST

FIG. 7-11. Cold-formed sections with nailing grooves. (*Stran-Steel Division, Great Lakes Steel Corp.*)

7-12. Structural Behavior of Flat Compression Elements. It is convenient, in discussing buckling of plates, or flat compression elements in beams, columns, or other structural members, to use the term **flat-width ratio.** It is the ratio w/t of the width w of a single flat element, exclusive of edge fillets, to the thickness t of the element (Fig. 7-12).

For structural design computations, flat compression elements of cold-formed structural members can be divided into two kinds—stiffened elements and unstiffened elements. **Stiffened compression elements** are flat compression elements; i.e., plane compression flanges of flexural members and plane webs and flanges of compression members, of which *both* edges parallel to the direction of stress are stiffened by a web, flange, stiffening lip, or the like (AISI Specification for the Design of Light Gage Steel Structural Members). A flat element stiffened at only *one* edge parallel to the direction of stress is called an **unstiffened element.** If the sections shown in Fig. 7-12 are used as compression members, the webs are considered stiffened compression elements. The lips that stiffen the outer edges

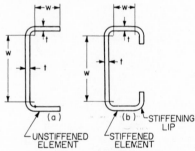

(a) UNSTIFFENED ELEMENT

(b) STIFFENED ELEMENT ⎿STIFFENING LIP

FIG. 7-12. Compression elements.

of the flanges are, in turn, unstiffened elements. Any section composed of a number of plane portions, or elements, can be broken down into a combination of stiffened and unstiffened elements.

In order that a compression element may qualify as a stiffened compression element, its edge stiffeners should comply with the following:

$$I_{\min} = 1.83t^4 \sqrt{\left(\frac{w}{t}\right)^2 - 144} \qquad (7\text{-}1)$$

where w/t = flat-width ratio of stiffened element
$I_{\min}$ = minimum allowable moment of inertia of stiffener (of any shape) about its own centroidal axis parallel to stiffened element

Table 7-8. Properties of Area and Line Elements

Area   Line

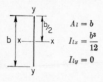

$$A = bt$$
$$I_x = \frac{b^3 t}{12}$$
$$I_y = \frac{bt^3}{12}$$

Rectangle

$$A_l = b$$
$$I_{lx} = \frac{b^3}{12}$$
$$I_{ly} = 0$$

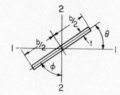

$$I_1 = \frac{bt}{12}(b^2 \sin^2 \theta + t^2 \cos^2 \theta)$$
$$I_2 = \frac{bt}{12}(b^2 \sin^2 \phi + t^2 \cos^2 \phi)$$

Inclined Rectangle

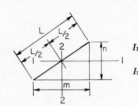

$$I_1 = \frac{Ln^2}{12}$$
$$I_2 = \frac{Lm^2}{12}$$

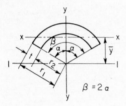

$$\beta = 2\alpha$$

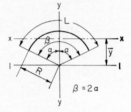

$$\beta = 2\alpha$$

$$A = \beta t \left(\frac{r_1 + r_2}{2}\right)$$
$$\tilde{y} = \frac{2}{3A}(r_1^3 - r_2^3) \sin \frac{\beta}{2}$$
$$I_x = \tfrac{1}{8}(r_1^4 - r_2^4)(\beta + \sin \beta) - A\tilde{y}^2$$
$$I_y = \tfrac{1}{8}(r_1^4 - r_2^4)(\beta - \sin \beta)$$

Circular Arc

$$L = R\beta$$
$$\tilde{y} = 2R \frac{\sin \frac{\beta}{2}}{\beta}$$
$$I_x = R^3 \left(\frac{\beta + \sin \beta}{2} - \frac{4 \sin^2 \frac{\beta}{2}}{\beta}\right)$$
$$I_y = \tfrac{1}{2}R^3(\beta - \sin \beta)$$

$$A = \frac{\pi}{4} t(r_1 + r_2)$$
$$= 0.7854t(r_1 + r_2)$$
$$\tilde{y} = \frac{4}{3\pi} \frac{(r_1^3 - r_2^3)}{t(r_1 + r_2)}$$
$$= 0.424 \frac{(r_1^3 - r_2^3)}{t(r_1 + r_2)}$$
$$I_x = \frac{\pi}{16}(r_1^4 - r_2^4) - A\tilde{y}^2$$
$$= 0.1964(r_1^4 - r_2^4) - A\tilde{y}^2$$

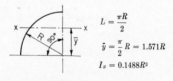

$$L = \frac{\pi R}{2}$$
$$\tilde{y} = \frac{\pi}{2} R = 1.571R$$
$$I_x = 0.1488R^3$$

90° Circular Corner

For small radii:

r_2	A	$\tilde{y}$	I_x
$2t$	$3.927t^2$	$1.613t$	$2.549t^4$
$1.5t$	$3.142t^2$	$1.300t$	$1.369t^4$
t	$2.356t^2$	$0.990t$	$0.635t^4$
$0.75t$	$1.963t^2$	$0.838t$	$0.400t^4$
$0.5t$	$1.571t^2$	$0.690t$	$0.235t^4$

Where the stiffener consists of a simple lip bent at right angles to the stiffened element, the required over-all depth d of such a lip may be determined with satisfactory accuracy from the following formula:

$$d = 2.8t \sqrt[6]{\left(\frac{w}{t}\right)^2 - 144} \qquad (7\text{-}2)$$

A simple lip should not be used as an edge stiffener for any element having a flat-width ratio greater than 60.

The values of I_{min} and d from Eqs. (7-1) and (7-2) are plotted in Fig. 7-13.

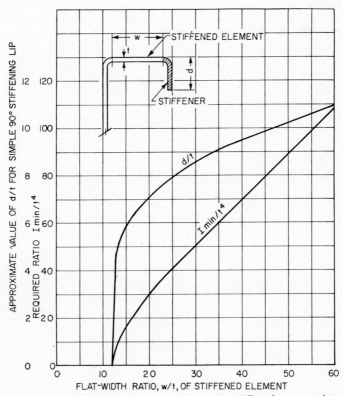

Fig. 7-13. Minimum dimensions of edge stiffeners for stiffened compression elements.

The discussion of stiffened compression elements in this section deals primarily with simple elements shown in Figs. 7-9 to 7-12. *Multiple-stiffened elements;* i.e., elements that have longitudinal stiffeners placed between webs or between a web and an edge, are sometimes encountered, particularly in deck and panel work. For methods of computing the effectiveness of such elements and for requirements for stiffeners for such elements, see the AISI Specification for the Design of Light Gage Steel Structural Members.

Whether or not local buckling of a flat compression element must be considered depends on its flat-width ratio. For unstiffened elements, (local) elastic buckling usually does not have to be considered unless the flat-width ratio exceeds 12 for sections formed of sheet and strip steel. For stiffened elements, which behave in buckling in a substantially different manner from unstiffened elements, the flat-width ratio beyond which allowance must be made for local buckling varies with the unit stress in the element. The effect of local buckling may be ignored for stiffened elements with flat-width ratios equal to or less than $(w/t)_{\text{lim}}$ in Eqs. (7-3) and (7-4).

For safe-load determination, i.e., in computing effective area and section modulus:

$$\left(\frac{w}{t}\right)_{\text{lim}} = \frac{3{,}790}{\sqrt{f}} \tag{7-3}$$

where f = computed unit stress in psi in the element based upon effective width.

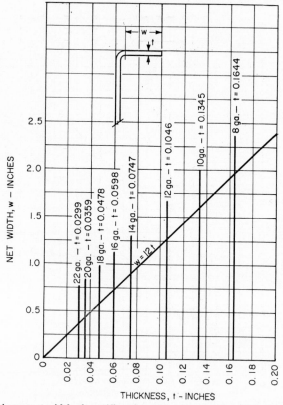

FIG. 7-14. Maximum net width of unstiffened compression elements without stress reduction.

Equation (7-3) is based on a safety factor of about 1.85 against yield stress at the outer fiber of the section. For any other safety factor m multiply the right-hand side of Eq. (7-3) by $\sqrt{1.85/m}$.

For deflection determinations, i.e., in computing moment of inertia to be used in deflection calculations or other calculations involving stiffness:

$$\left(\frac{w}{t}\right)_{\text{lim}} = \frac{5{,}160}{\sqrt{f}} \tag{7-4}$$

As long as the proportions of cold-formed sections are such that there are no unstiffened compression elements having net flat-width ratios greater than 12, and there are no stiffened compression elements having flat-width ratios greater than the limits established by Eq. (7-3), they can be treated, in their structural use as beams and columns, in the same general way as ordinary structural shapes, and without any modification to take into account local buckling. The maximum widths of flat compression elements that may be so used are shown in the charts of Figs. 7-14 and 7-15.

When the above limits are exceeded the treatment in Arts. 7-13 and 7-14 is recommended. (American Iron and Steel Institute "Light Gage Steel Design Manual." See also George Winter "Strength of Thin Steel Compression Flanges," *Cornell University Engineering Experiment Station Bulletin 35*, Part 3; George Winter, Warner

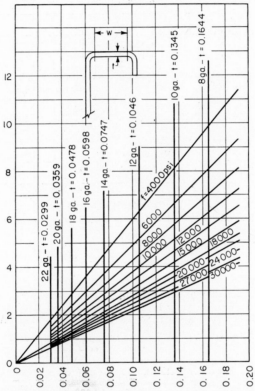

FIG. 7-15. Maximum net width for full effectiveness of stiffened compression elements.

Lansing, and R. B. McCalley, Jr., "Four Papers on the Performance of Thin Walled Steel Structures," Reprint No. 33.)

7-13. Unstiffened Light-gage Elements Subject to Local Buckling. Compute section properties of the full section in the conventional manner but allow a reduced compressive stress on the unstiffened element. Equations (7-5) to (7-8) are applicable.

For a flat-width ratio w/t greater than 12 but not over 30, the compressive stress should not exceed:

$$f_c = \frac{5}{3} f_b - 5{,}430 - \frac{1}{18} (f_b - 8{,}150) \frac{w}{t} \tag{7-5}$$

where f_b = basic design stress
w = width of element
t = thickness

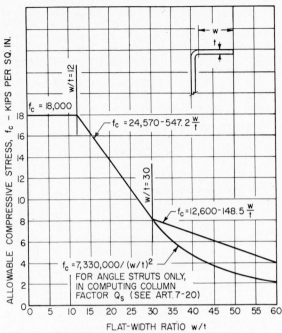

FIG. 7-16. Allowable compressive stress in unstiffened elements (grade C steel).

If $f_b = 18,000$ psi, this formula reduces to

$$f_c = 24,570 - 547.2 \frac{w}{t} \tag{7-6}$$

For w/t greater than 30 (but not over 60), the compressive stress should not exceed f_c as given by Eqs. (7-7) and (7-8).

For angle struts (see note on Fig. 7-16 and Art. 7-20),

$$f_c = \frac{7,330,000}{(w/t)^2} \tag{7-7}$$

For other sections,

$$f_c = 12,600 - 148.5 \frac{w}{t} \tag{7-8}$$

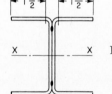

FIG. 7-17. Double-channel beam.

Equations (7-6) to (7-8) are plotted in Fig. 7-16.

As an example of the application of these formulas, consider the double channel section shown in Fig. 7-17, which is to be used as a simply supported beam about axis xx with the top flange in compression. The two legs of that flange are unstiffened compression elements.

If the thickness is $\frac{1}{8}$ in., then the flat-width ratio of these elements is 12, and if made of Grade C steel, the section can be used as a beam at the full basic working stress—usually 18,000 psi under gravity loads (see Arts. 7-17 to 7-21).

If the thickness is $\frac{1}{16}$ in., then the flat-width ratio of these unstiffened compression flange elements becomes 24, and according to Eq. (7-6), the allowable stress would be only 11,440 psi. If the thickness of the section is further reduced to, say, 18 gage (0.048 in.), then the flat-width ratio of these unstiffened compression elements is about 31, and the allowable stress according to Eq. (7-8) would be 8,000 psi.

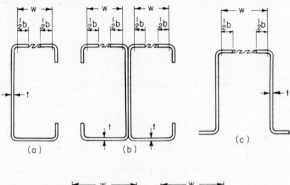

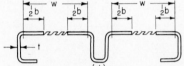
BEAMS – TOP FLANGE IN COMPRESSION

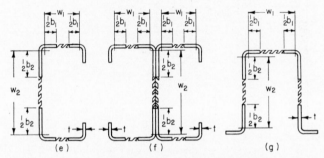
COLUMNS – EFFECTIVE AREA FOR COMPUTING COLUMN
FACTOR Q_a

FIG. 7-18. Effective width of stiffened compression elements.

7-14. Stiffened Light-gage Elements Subject to Local Buckling. Compute section properties based on an *effective width* of each stiffened compression element (Fig. 7-18). Determine the effective width b by means of Eqs. (7-9) and (7-10).

For safe-load determinations, i.e., in computing effective area and section modulus (including moment of inertia),

$$\frac{b}{t} = \frac{7,590}{\sqrt{f}} \left[1 - \frac{1,900}{(w/t)\ \sqrt{f}} \right] \tag{7-9}$$

where f = unit stress in psi in the element computed on basis of reduced section
  w = width of the element
  t = thickness

For deflection determinations, i.e., in computing moment of inertia to be used in deflection calculations or in other calculations involving stiffness,

$$\frac{b}{t} = \frac{10,320}{\sqrt{f}} \left[1 - \frac{2,580}{(w/t)\ \sqrt{f}} \right] \tag{7-10}$$

with f, w, and t the same as for Eq. (7-9).

As shown in Fig. 7-18, that portion of the element not considered to be effective should be located symmetrically about the center line of the element.

The curves of Figs. 7-19 and 7-20 were plotted from Eqs. (7-9) and (7-10) and may be used to determine the ratio b/t for different values of w/t and unit stress.

The effective width b in Eqs. (7-9) and (7-10) is dependent on the unit stress f, and since reduced-section properties are a function of effective width, the reverse is also true. In the general case of flexural members, therefore, determination of effective width by these formulas requires successive approximations: First, a unit stress is assumed for the compression flange; with that stress, b is computed; next, the section modulus and unit stress in the compression flange are calculated for the reduced section; and then the process is repeated if the effective width so computed should be significantly different from that for the stress first assumed.

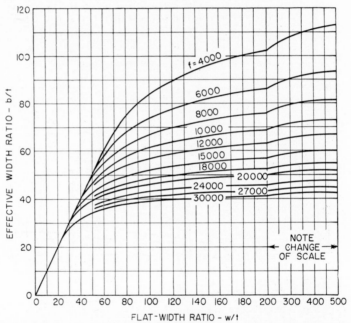

Fig. 7-19. Effective width for safe-load determination where local buckling may occur.

However, this somewhat cumbersome procedure can be avoided and the correct value of b/t obtained directly from the formulas when f is known or is held to a specified maximum allowable value (usually 18,000 psi for flexural members of Grade C steel) and the neutral axis of the section is closer to the tension flange than the compression flange so that the stress in the compression flange always controls. The latter condition holds for symmetrical channels, zees, and I sections used as flexural members about their major axes, such as (e), (f), (k), and (n) in Fig. 7-9. For hat and box sections, such as (o) and (p) in Fig. 7-9, or unsymmetrical channels, zees, and I sections, where w/t of the compression flanges does not exceed about 60 and Grade C steel is used with an allowable working stress of 18,000 psi in beams, the error introduced by basing the effective width of the compression flange on an f value of 18,000 will generally be negligible, even though the neutral axis is above the geometric center line. For wide, inverted, pan-shaped sections, such as deck and panel sections, a somewhat more accurate determination will frequently prove desirable; but extreme accuracy in the determination of the effective width of the compression flange is not essential, since relatively large variations in effective width will have relatively little effect on section modulus and moment of inertia.   Two approximations will almost always suffice.

In computing moment of inertia for deflection or stiffness calculations, properties of the full unreduced section can be used without significant error when w/t of the compression elements does not exceed 60.

As an example of effective-width determination, consider the hat section in Fig. 7-21a, which is to be made of Grade C steel and used as a simply supported beam with

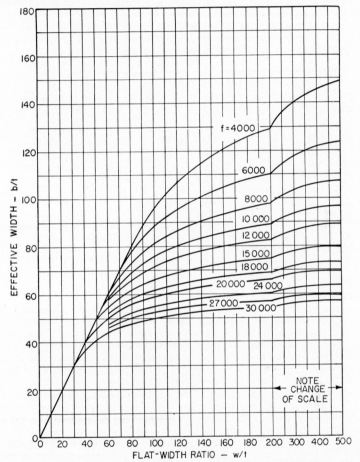

FIG. 7-20. Effective width for deflection determination where local buckling may occur.

the top flange in compression, at a basic working stress of 18,000 psi.   Safe load-carrying capacity is to be computed.

The top flange is a stiffened compression element.   If the thickness is $\frac{1}{8}$ in., then the flat-width ratio is 24.   For a unit stress of 18,000 psi, $(w/t)_{lim}$ according to Eq. (7-3) is 28.2, and the properties of the section may be computed in the usual manner, with the entire section considered structurally effective.   If, however, the thickness is $\frac{1}{16}$ in., then the flat-width ratio becomes 48, and Eq. (7-9) applies.   For this value of w/t and $f = 18,000$, Eq. (7-9) gives the ratio b/t as 40; thus, only 83 % of the top flange is considered effective.   The neutral axis of the section will lie below the horizontal center line; so the compression-flange stress will control.   Since that stress is limited to 18,000 psi, the effective width may be accurately determined from Eq. (7-9) for 18,000 psi.

For the section in Fig. 7-21b, in which the horizontal centroidal axis will be much nearer the compression than the tension flange, the stress in the tension flange controls. Determination of the unit stress in the compression flange and the effective width of that flange requires a trial-and-error procedure.

7-15. Light-gage Members with Unusually Wide Flanges on Short Spans. The phenomenon known as *shear lag*, resulting in nonuniform stress distribution in the flanges of a flexural member, requires recognition only in comparatively extreme cases of concentrated loads on spans very short relative to the width of the member. Its effect can be taken care of by an effective-width procedure applicable to both tension and compression flanges. The American Iron and Steel Institute Specification for the Design of Light Gage Steel Structural Members provides methods for handling this situation (see the AISI "Light Gage Steel Design Manual"). This specification should be consulted in any case of concentrated loading in which the span of a beam is less than thirty times the half width of flange for I-beam and similar sections or thirty times half the distance between webs for box or U-type sections.

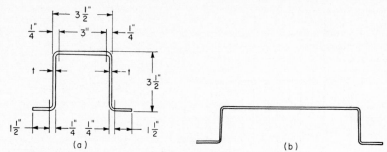

Fig. 7-21. Hat sections.

7-16. Maximum Flat-width Ratios for Light-gage Elements. When the flat-width ratio exceeds about 30 for an unstiffened element and 250 for a stiffened element, noticeable buckling of the element is likely to develop at relatively low stresses. Present-day practice is to permit buckles to develop in the sheet and to take advantage of what is known as the post-buckling strength of the section. The effective-width formulas [Eqs. (7-9) and (7-10)] are based on this practice. However, to avoid excessive deformations, over-all flat-width ratios, disregarding intermediate stiffeners and based on the actual thickness of the element, should not exceed the following:

Stiffened compression element having one longitudinal edge connected to a web or flange, the other to a simple right-angle lip.................................... 60
Stiffened compression element having both edges stiffened by other stiffening means than a simple right-angle lip... 90
Stiffened compression element with both longitudinal edges connected to a web or flange element such as in a hat, U, or box type of section...................... 500
Unstiffened compression elements.. 60

In special kinds of panel work, where the flat compression element may be stiffened by insulation board or other similar material fastened to it with an adhesive, elastic buckling does not occur with the same freedom as without such stiffening. The extent to which the stiffening effect of collateral materials may be utilized has to be determined by tests in each case. It will further depend on the extent to which the adhesive can be relied on to furnish continuous permanent bond between the two materials, and whether or not such bond is likely to be affected by fire or other external actions. In general, it is unwise to rely on collateral materials to prevent elastic buckling in the compression element.

7-17. Unit Stresses for Light-gage Steel. For sheet and strip of Grade C steel, with a specified minimum yield point of 33,000 psi, a basic working stress of 18,000 psi in tension and bending is commonly prescribed. For high-strength steel a basic stress of 54 % of the yield point (corresponding to a safety factor of 1.85 on yield point) may be used. As noted in Art. 7-13, this basic stress must be reduced for wide unstiffened compression elements. An increase of $33\frac{1}{3}$ % in allowable stress is customary for combined wind and gravity loads.

7-18. Laterally Unsupported Light-gage Beams. In the relatively infrequent cases in which light-gage cold-formed sections are used as laterally unsupported beams, the unit stress in the compression flange should not exceed f'_c in the formula

$$f'_c = \frac{250,000,000}{(L/r_y)^2} \qquad (7\text{-}11)$$

where L = unbraced length of member, in.

r_y = radius of gyration of full section about its centroidal axis parallel to web, in.

Because of the torsional flexibility of light-gage channel and zee sections, their use as beams without lateral support is not recommended. In the usual case in which one flange of such a section is connected to a deck or sheathing material, bracing of the other flange may or may not be needed to prevent twisting of the member, depending on: (1) whether or not the deck or sheathing material and its connection to the beam will effectively restrain the connected beam flange from lateral deflection and twist; (2) the dimensions of the member and the span; and (3) whether the unbraced flange is in compression or tension. In any doubtful case, a load test should be made to determine whether or not additional bracing is necessary. When bracing against twist is required, means of proportioning such bracing can be found in the American Iron and Steel Institute Specification for the Design of Light Gage Steel Structural Members. Bracing details will depend on the particular form of the sections involved. Bridging, such as is used with open-web steel-joist construction (Art. 7-4), can be effectively used.

In any case in which laterally unsupported beams must be used, or where lateral buckling of a flexural member is likely to be a problem, consideration should be given to use of relatively bulky sections having two webs, such as hat or box sections, as illustrated in Fig. 7-9o and p. Sections for which the moment of inertia about the vertical y axis is equal to or greater than that about the horizontal x axis do not fail because of lateral instability; but as the ratio I_y/I_x decreases, the section becomes more susceptible to failure by lateral buckling. (George Winter, "Strength of Slender Beams," *Transactions of the ASCE*, Vol. 109, 1944; and K. Bentley, "Lateral Stability of Beams," Preliminary Publication, 4th Congress International Association for Bridge and Structural Engineering, 1952.) Thus, double-web sections almost always are considerably more stable laterally than single-web sections of normal proportions. Hat sections (Fig. 7-9o) are especially suitable where lateral stiffness is necessary, and when the flat-width ratios of the individual elements are low enough to be fully effective structurally (Art. 7-12), design of the section is simple and straightforward. Sections of the kind shown in Fig. 7-10c having a top width of 2 in., depth of $2\frac{1}{2}$ in., and bottom flanges $\frac{5}{8}$ in. wide have been successfully used under floating loads without any lateral support on spans up to 7 ft, or 42 times the top width.

Even with hat sections, extreme proportions should be avoided. With very high narrow sections made of thin material, lateral instability may result from lack of stiffness in the webs, though the flat-width ratio of the compression flange may be low. It is desirable also to keep the flat-width ratio of the bottom flanges relatively low to avoid the necessity for using a low allowable stress (Art. 7-13) when the section is to be used as a continuous beam and the bottom flanges are in compression over the interior supports.

7-19. Web Stresses in Light-gage Members. As for ordinary structural-steel sections, the shear on the gross web section in light-gage cold-formed flexural members is usually limited to two-thirds of the basic working stress in tension and bending, or

$$v = \frac{64,000,000}{(h/t)^2} \qquad (7\text{-}12)$$

whichever is smaller.   In this expression h/t is the ratio of depth to web thickness, or of stiffener spacing to web thickness, as for plate-girder construction.   Where the web consists of two sheets, as in the case of two channels fastened back to back to form an I section, each sheet should be considered as a separate web carrying its share of the shear.   For Grade C steel, the maximum allowable shear on gross section of the web is usually specified as 12,000 psi (except for such increases as may be allowed for combined gravity and wind loading).

Use of webs in which h/t exceeds 150 is not recommended.

The buckling effect of combined shear and bending stresses in beam webs will rarely be critical.   However, it may be when high h/t values and high-strength steel are being used, with high working stresses, and then only where high shear and high bending stresses occur at the same section.   An interaction formula for investigating such a case can be found in the American Iron and Steel Institute Specification for the Design of Light Gage Steel Structural Members.

Empirical formulas for design against web crippling also can be found in this specification.   Those formulas are summarized in Tables 7-9 to 7-11 for Grade C steel and for sections where inside-corner radii are equal to the thickness of the material.   Care must be taken not to extend them beyond the tabular ranges of B/t.   Tables 7-9 and 7-10 apply to all cases of unreinforced webs, including hat sections as well as channels and zees.   Table 7-11 applies only where the web is backed up by an opposing web or portion of a web, such as in an I section made by welding two angles to a channel.

For other grades of steel or other corner radii, adjust the tabular values as indicated by Eqs. (7-17) and (7-18).

Multiply the values in Table 7-9 by the quantity

$$k \left(1.15 - 0.15 \frac{r}{t} \right) (1.33 - 0.33k) \qquad (7\text{-}17)$$

Multiply the values in Table 7-10 by the quantity

$$k \left(1.06 - 0.06 \frac{r}{t} \right) (1.22 - 0.22k) \qquad (7\text{-}18)$$

where k = specified minimum yield point of steel divided by 33,000
  r = corner radius

7-20. Light-gage Steel Columns.   When cold-formed sections are used as columns, there need be no modification of conventional procedure if the section does not contain any elements that exceed the limits $w/t = 12$ for unstiffened elements and $3,790/\sqrt{f}$ for stiffened elements, where f is the basic design stress—18,000 psi for Grade C steel (Art. 7-12).   Where either of these limits is exceeded, and provision must be made against failure by local buckling, the reduced strength of the section can be taken into account by the introduction of a form factor or buckling factor into the basic column formula.

The column-design formulas recommended by American Iron and Steel Institute specifications consist of a family of Johnson parabolas all tangent to a single Euler curve.   It can be shown that an infinite number of such parabolas can be drawn, all having the form

$$\frac{P}{A} = \frac{f_y}{C} - \frac{f_y^2}{D} \left(\frac{L}{r} \right)^2 \qquad (7\text{-}19)$$

and all tangent to a single Euler curve represented by

$$\frac{P}{A} = \frac{D/4C^2}{(L/r)^2} \qquad (7\text{-}20)$$

In Eqs. (7-19) and (7-20), C and D are constants that depend on the safety factor, eccentricity allowance, and end fixity, and f_y is the yield point of the material.   Observe

Table 7-9. Maximum End Reaction, or Concentrated Load on End of Cantilever, for Single Unreinforced Web of Light-gage Steel

(Grade C steel, corner radii = thickness of material)

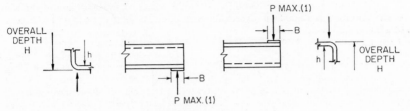

t = web thickness
h = clear distance between flanges
B = length of bearing
H = over-all depth

$$P \max (1) = 100t^2 \left(980 + 42\frac{B}{t} - 0.22\frac{B}{t}\frac{h}{t} - 0.11\frac{h}{t} \right)$$ (7-13)

NOTE: In solving this formula, B should not be assigned any value greater than h.

Gage and thickness	H, in.	P max (1), lb, for different values of B					
		1 in.	2 in.	3 in.	4 in.	6 in.	8 in.
No. 18, 0.0478 in.	1	390					
	2	380	530				
	3	360	500	620			
	4	340	450	570	670		
	6	290	360	430	500		
No. 16, 0.0598 in.	1	550					
	2	560	740				
	3	540	720	890			
	4	510	680	845	990		
	6	470	590	710	830		
	8	420	500	580	660		
No. 14, 0.0747 in.	2	820	1,050				
	3	800	1,050	1,260			
	4	770	1,000	1,230	1,430		
	6	730	910	1,100	1,280	1,620	
	8	680	820	960	1,100	1,390	
	10	640	730	830	930	1,120	
No. 12, 0.1046 in.	2	1,470	1,790				
	3	1,450	1,820	2,120			
	4	1,420	1,780	2,140	2,420		
	6	1,380	1,690	2,000	2,310	2,870	
	8	1,330	1,600	1,870	2,130	2,670	3,150
	10	1,280	1,510	1,730	1,960	2,400	2,850
	12	1,240	1,420	1,600	1,780	2,140	2,500
No. 10, 0.1345 in.	2	2,300	2,680				
	3	2,270	2,780	3,150			
	4	2,250	2,730	3,220	3,570		
	6	2,200	2,640	3,080	3,520	4,280	
	8	2,160	2,550	2,950	3,340	4,130	4,810
	10	2,110	2,460	2,810	3,160	3,860	4,560
	12	2,060	2,370	2,680	2,980	3,600	4,210
No. 8, 0.1644 in.	3	3,280	3,910	4,330			
	4	3,250	3,860	4,470	4,880		
	6	3,200	3,770	4,340	4,900	5,850	
	8	3,160	3,680	4,200	4,720	5,760	6,640
	10	3,110	3,590	4,060	4,540	5,500	6,450
	12	3,060	3,490	3,930	4,360	5,230	6,100

Table 7-10. Maximum Interior Reaction or Concentrated Load on Single Unreinforced Web of Light-gage Steel

(Grade C steel, corner radii = thickness of material)

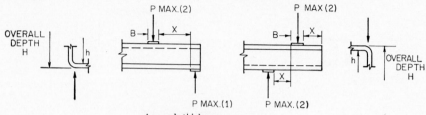

t = web thickness
h = clear distance between flanges
B = length of bearing
H = over-all depth

$$P \text{ max (2)} = 100t^2 \left(3{,}050 + 23\frac{B}{t} - 0.09\frac{B}{t}\frac{h}{t} - 5\frac{h}{t}\right) \tag{7-14}$$

NOTE: In solving this formula, B should not be assigned any value greater than h. This table and formula apply only where the distance x is greater than $1.5h$. Otherwise Eq. (7-13) and Table 7-9 govern.

Gage and thickness	H, in.	P max (2), lb, for different values of B					
		1 in.	2 in.	3 in.	4 in.	6 in.	8 in.
No. 18, 0.0478 in.	1	770					
	2	740	830				
	3	710	790	870			
	4	680	750	830	900		
	6	610	670	730	780		
No. 16, 0.0598 in.	1	1,180					
	2	1,150	1,260				
	3	1,120	1,230	1,330			
	4	1,080	1,180	1,280	1,370		
	6	1,000	1,080	1,170	1,250		
	8	920	990	1,050	1,120		
No. 14, 0.0747 in.	2	1,790	1,920				
	3	1,740	1,890	2,010			
	4	1,690	1,830	1,970	2,090		
	6	1,600	1,720	1,840	1,960	2,180	
	8	1,510	1,610	1,710	1,810	2,020	
	10	1,420	1,500	1,580	1,670	1,830	
No. 12, 0.1046 in.	2	3,470	3,650				
	3	3,410	3,620	3,790			
	4	3,340	3,550	3,760	3,920		
	6	3,220	3,410	3,600	3,790	4,130	
	8	3,100	3,270	3,440	3,610	3,950	4,260
	10	2,980	3,130	3,280	3,430	3,740	4,040
	12	2,850	2,990	3,120	3,260	3,530	3,800
No. 10, 0.1345 in.	3	5,620	5,900	6,110			
	4	5,540	5,820	6,090	6,300		
	6	5,390	5,650	5,900	6,160	6,610	
	8	5,240	5,480	5,720	5,960	6,440	6,850
	10	5,080	5,310	5,530	5,750	6,190	6,640
	12	4,930	5,140	5,340	5,540	5,950	6,360
No. 8, 0.1644 in.	3	8,380	8,730	8,970			
	4	8,290	8,630	8,980	9,210		
	6	8,100	8,430	8,760	9,080	9,630	
	8	7,920	8,230	8,540	8,850	9,470	9,980
	10	7,740	8,030	8,320	8,610	9,190	9,780
	12	7,560	7,830	8,100	8,380	8,920	9,470

Values above and to right of heavy lines should be checked to see that shear in web does not exceed allowable value recommended in Art. 7-19.

Table 7-11. Maximum Reactions and Concentrated Loads Bearing on Restrained Webs of Light-gage Steel

(Grade C steel, corner radii = thickness of material)

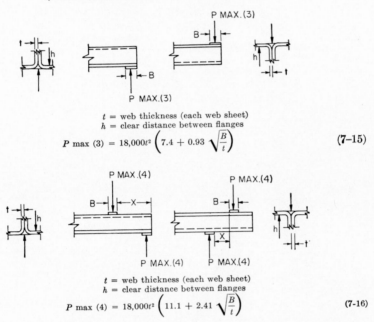

t = web thickness (each web sheet)
h = clear distance between flanges

$$P \text{ max (3)} = 18,000t^2 \left(7.4 + 0.93 \sqrt{\frac{B}{t}} \right) \qquad (7\text{–}15)$$

t = web thickness (each web sheet)
h = clear distance between flanges

$$P \text{ max (4)} = 18,000t^2 \left(11.1 + 2.41 \sqrt{\frac{B}{t}} \right) \qquad (7\text{–}16)$$

Values of P max (4) apply only where the distance x is greater than $1.5h$. Otherwise use P max (3). The effective length of bearing B for substitution in the above formulas should not be taken as greater than h, and tabular values of P for values of B greater than h should not be used.

Gage and thickness	End bearing. P max (3) lb, for different values of B						Interior bearing. P max (4), lb, for different values for B					
	1 in.	2 in.	3 in.	4 in.	6 in.	8 in.	1 in.	2 in.	3 in.	4 in.	6 in.	8 in.
No. 18, 0.0478 in....	480	550	610	650	.....	.....	910	1,100	1,240	1,360		
No. 16, 0.0598 in....	720	820	900	970	.....	.....	1,350	1,610	1,810	1,980		
No. 14, 0.0747 in....	1,080	1,230	1,340	1,430	1,580	.....	2,000	2,370	2,650	2,890	3,280	
No. 12, 0.1046 in....	2,020	2,260	2,440	2,590	2,840	3,060	3,650	4,260	4,730	5,120	5,780	6,340
No. 10, 0.1345 in....	3,240	3,580	3,840	4,060	4,430	4,750	5,740	6,640	7,320	7,890	8,860	9,670
No. 8, 0.1644 in.....	4,720	5,180	5,530	5,830	6,330	6,760	8,290	9,490	10,410	11,180	12,480	13,580

Tabular values are for one web thickness t. Multiply by 2 for double-thickness webs.

that f_y does not appear in Eq. (7-20). The point of tangency between the equations is always at a P/A value equal to half the initial value ($f_y/2C$).

If a form factor or buckling factor Q is introduced such that

$$Q = \frac{f_{cr}}{f_y} \qquad (7\text{–}21)$$

where f_{cr} represents the reduced strength of the section due to the presence of wide thin elements that buckle locally at stresses below the yield point of the material, then it is a simple matter to transform Eq. (7-19) into a consistent set of column curves applicable to any value of Q, all tangent to a single curve of Eq. (7-20):

$$\frac{P}{A} = \frac{f_y}{C} Q - \frac{f_y{}^2}{D} Q^2 \left(\frac{L}{r}\right)^2 \tag{7-22}$$

[When the effective-width treatment of stiffened elements is used (Art. 7-14), Q can be defined as the ratio between effective area and total area of the cross section, and A in the quantity P/A can mean total area of section.]

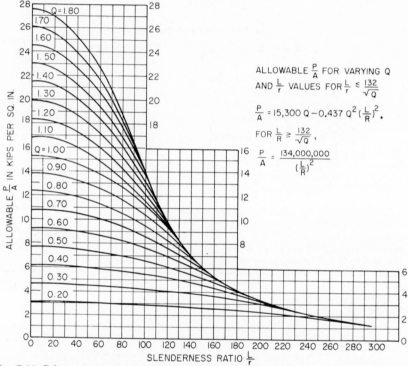

ALLOWABLE $\dfrac{P}{A}$ FOR VARYING Q
AND $\dfrac{L}{r}$ VALUES FOR $\dfrac{L}{r} \leq \dfrac{132}{\sqrt{Q}}$

$\dfrac{P}{A} = 15{,}300\, Q - 0.437\, Q^2 \left(\dfrac{L}{R}\right)^2 .$

FOR $\dfrac{L}{R} \geq \dfrac{132}{\sqrt{Q}}$,

$\dfrac{P}{A} = \dfrac{134{,}000{,}000}{\left(\dfrac{L}{R}\right)^2}$

FIG. 7-22. Column design curves for cold-formed shapes (Grade C steel). The chart may be used for other grades by multiplying the Q value of the section by the ratio of its yield-point stress to 33,000. Chart values of Q greater than 1.00 do not apply to Grade C steel. (*American Iron and Steel Institute.*)

Since f_{cr} can never be greater than f_y, the value of Q as a form factor or buckling factor can never exceed 1.0. For any section that does not contain any element with a flat-width ratio exceeding that for full effectiveness ($w/t = 12$ for unstiffened elements and $3{,}790/\sqrt{f}$ for stiffened elements), $Q = 1.0$ and disappears from the equation.

If a design formula of the form of Eq. (7-22) is written for a particular grade of steel by inserting the proper values for f_y, C, and D, it can be extended to any grade of steel by expanding the meaning of the factor Q to include the ratio between the yield point f_y of the grade of steel upon which the formula is based and the yield point f'_y of any other grade.

Provisions of the American Iron and Steel Institute specification for compression members made of Grade C steel are given in Art. 7-21 and plotted in Fig. 7-22.

7-21. Unit Stress for Axially Loaded Cold-formed Members. For cold-formed, axially loaded compression members of Grade C steel, the allowable unit stress P/A shall be

For L/r less than $132/\sqrt{Q}$:

$$\frac{P}{A} = 15,300Q - 0.437Q^2 \left(\frac{L}{r}\right)^2 \tag{7-23}$$

For L/r greater than $132/\sqrt{Q}$:

$$\frac{P}{A} = \frac{134,000,000}{(L/r)^2} \tag{7-24}$$

(AISI Specification for the Design of Light Gage Steel Structural Members)
where P = total allowable load, lb
    A = full, unreduced cross-sectional area of member, sq in.
    L = unsupported length of member, in.
    r = radius of gyration of full, unreduced cross section, in.
    Q = a factor determined as follows:

a. For members composed entirely of stiffened elements, Q is the ratio between the effective design area, as determined from the effective-design widths of such elements, and the full or gross area of the cross section. The effective design area used in determining Q is to be based on the basic design stress allowed in tension and bending—18,000 psi for Grade C steel.

b. For members composed entirely of unstiffened elements, Q is the ratio between the allowable compression stress for the weakest element of the cross section (the element having the largest flat-width ratio) and the basic design stress.

c. For members composed of both stiffened and unstiffened elements, the factor Q is to be the product of a stress factor Q_s computed as outlined in *b* above and an area factor Q_a computed as outlined in *a* above. However, the stress on which Q_a is to be based shall be that value of the unit stress f_c used in computing Q_s; and the effective area to be used in computing Q_a shall include the full area of all unstiffened elements.

The following L/r limits are recommended:

a. Columns, and other primary compression members, except as provided otherwise in this section, 120 max. The slenderness ratio L/r of a main compression member may exceed 120, but not 200, provided its unit stress under full design load does not exceed the following fraction of that stipulated by Eqs. (7-23) and (7-24):

$$1.6 - \left(\frac{L}{200r}\right)$$

b. Load-bearing studs, 160 max. However, the slenderness ratio of a load-bearing wall stud may exceed 160—but not 200—if its unit stress under full design load does not exceed the following fraction of that stipulated by Eqs. (7-23) and (7-24):

$$2.6 - \frac{L}{100r}$$

c. Secondary members, 200 max.
Exception: During construction only, L/r may exceed the foregoing limits but should not exceed 300.

If members temporarily unbraced during construction are to act as permanent load-carrying members in the completed structure, they must be so braced prior to completion of the structure as to reduce the L/r ratio to a value not exceeding that given in *a, b,* or *c* above, whichever may apply.

Combined axial and bending stresses in light-gage cold-formed sections can be handled in exactly the same way as for other sections.   The straight-line interaction criterion

$$\frac{f_a}{F_a} + \frac{f_b}{F_b} = 1.0 \qquad (7\text{-}25)$$

is usually used; f_a is the computed axial stress, F_a the allowable compressive stress, f_b the computed compressive stress due to bending and F_b the allowable flexural stress in the compression flange.

7-22. Braced Wall Studs.   A fairly common application of cold-formed shapes—and one that requires special treatment—is as load-bearing wall studs in small light-occupancy buildings.   Cold-formed steel studs are usually I, channel, or zee sections, to both flanges of which collateral materials are fastened.   The American Iron and Steel Institute Specification for the Design of Light Gage Steel Structural Members permits the strength of studs to be computed on the assumption that they are laterally supported in the plane of the wall.   However, the wall material and its attachments to the studs must comply with the following:

1. Wall sheathing is attached to both faces or flanges of the studs.
2. The spacing in inches of attachments of wall material to each face or flange of the stud does not exceed a in either Eq. (7-26) or (7-27):

$$a = 0.22 \frac{r_2^2}{A} k \qquad (7\text{-}26)$$

$$a_{\max} = \frac{L}{2} \frac{r_2}{r_1} \qquad (7\text{-}27)$$

where L = length of stud, in.
  A = full cross-sectional area of stud, sq in.
  r_1 = radius of gyration of full cross section of stud about its axis parallel to wall, in.
  r_2 = radius of gyration of full cross section of stud about its axis perpendicular to wall, in.
  k = combined modulus of elastic support, or spring constant, of one attachment of wall material to stud and of wall material tributary to that attachment, lb per in.

For any other steel than Grade C, having a yield point f_y, a computed from Eq. (7-26) should be multiplied by $(33,000/f_y)^2$.

For continuous attachment—by an adhesive, for example—a should be taken as unity in solving Eq. (7-26) for k.

One attachment and the wall material tributary to it should be able to exert on the stud a force in the plane of the wall at least equal to

$$F_{\min} = \frac{kLP}{2,600,000 \sqrt{I_2(k/a)} - P} \qquad (7\text{-}28)$$

where I_2 = moment of inertia of full cross section of stud about its axis perpendicular to wall
  P = load on stud

For continuous attachment, $a = 1$.

Values of k and F for any particular combination of stud, wall material, and attaching means can only be determined by test.   The following table shows the range of values obtained at Cornell University on five different wallboards fastened to channel studs with $\frac{3}{16}$-in.-diameter bolts and washers.   (Green, Winter, and Cuykendall, "Light Gage Steel Columns in Wall-braced Panels," *Cornell University Engineering Experiment Station Bulletin* 35, Part 2, October, 1947.)

Wallboard	Range of k values	Range of F values, lb
½-in. standard-density wood and cane-fiber insulating boards..	390–603	67.5–157.5
½-in. paper-base insulating board...................	915–1,460	162–227
⅜-in. gypsum board sheathing......................	775–1,535	125–292
³/₁₆-in. medium-density compressed-wood fiberboard...	2,010–4,560	140–256
⁵/₃₂-in. high-density compressed-wood fiberboard.......	3,960–7,560	435–600

The above values were obtained from relatively simple tension tests. Pieces of wall material are fastened to two short pieces of studs at about the contemplated spacing. Starting with a small initial load P_o (50 lb or so), increments of load are applied, and the distance between studs is measured at each increment. The test should be carried to failure. A satisfactory value of k can be determined from the expression

$$k = \frac{0.75P_{ult} - P_o}{0.5ny} \tag{7-29}$$

where P_{ult} = ultimate load
P_o = initial or zero load
n = number of attachments
y = average change in length between attachments of each of the stud pieces from initial load P_o to $0.75P_{ult}$

For continuous attachment, use n equal to four times the attached length along each faying surface. If it is desired to simulate conditions at a joint in the wallboard, the specimen can be altered accordingly.

For any particular assembly, it may be considered somewhat more direct to test a stud specimen to which collateral materials have been fastened in direct compression as a column. Thereby, it can be determined from the manner of failure whether or not the collateral materials and their attachments to the studs furnish sufficient lateral support in the plane of the wall. This procedure, however, should be used only under expert supervision. The instrumentation and technique necessary to perform and interpret such tests properly call for a high degree of skill. Among other precautions, care must be exercised to see that the collateral materials do not obscure the results by carrying part of the axial load on the stud.

It can be seen from the values of k and F from the Cornell tests, which are for one kind of stud with one kind of attachment, that a very wide variation can be expected in the ability of collateral materials to provide lateral support for studs. Tests have shown that even apparently minor changes in fasteners or technique can produce significant differences in the values of k and F (*Cornell University Bulletin* 35, Part 2). Fortunately, however, the degree of lateral support actually required to hold a column straight against buckling below its yield point is usually very small. With any reasonable spacing of attachments and strength of wall covering, sufficient lateral support will be provided.

7-23. Electric-arc Welding of Light-gage Steel. Electric-arc welding can be effectively used for making joints in light-gage steel construction. Care must be exercised not to use electrodes too large relative to the thickness of material being welded. Care also must be taken to avoid burning through the material because of the use of too much current. Proper current range and electrode type and size are a matter for determination by the fabricator.

Joints made by electric-arc welding in shapes formed of structural-quality carbon-steel sheet and strip can be designed in the same way and on the same strength basis as in structural-steel shapes and plates, with the working stresses specified for welds in structural-steel shapes and plates. The welding of special grades of steel is a matter for consideration in each individual case.

Butt welds and other edge-to-edge welds in thin material should be made only when proper alignment of the parts being joined and proper backup are provided. For details, the reader is referred to texts dealing with welding techniques and procedures, such as "Welding Handbook," American Welding Society.

7-24. Resistance Welding. Resistance welding is defined as "a group of welding processes wherein coalescence is produced by the heat obtained from resistance of the

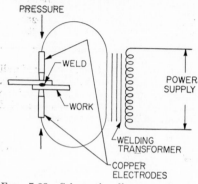

FIG. 7-23. Schematic diagram of spot-welding process.

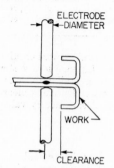

FIG. 7-24. Electrode clearance in spot welding.

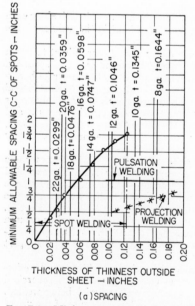

(a) SPACING

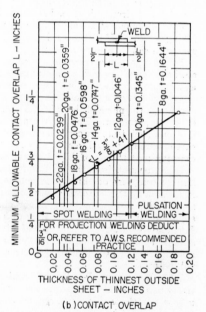

(b) CONTACT OVERLAP

FIG. 7-25. Minimum spacing and contact overlap for spot welds in clean, scale-free low-carbon steel used for cold-formed structural shapes.

work to the flow of electric current in a circuit of which the work is a part, and by the application of pressure." ("Welding Handbook," American Welding Society).

Although there are a number of different resistance-welding processes, **spot welding** is the simplest. It is commonly used in the manufacture of built-up or compound shapes of sheet and strip steel for structural purposes. In spot welding, the work is held under pressure between two electrodes through which an electric current passes, and the weld is made at contact interfaces between the pieces being joined (Fig. 7-23).

Resistance welding is essentially a shop process, because of the size of the equipment required for good work. Although portable resistance welders are available and will produce good results in very light work, electric-arc welding is generally more satisfactory for field use.

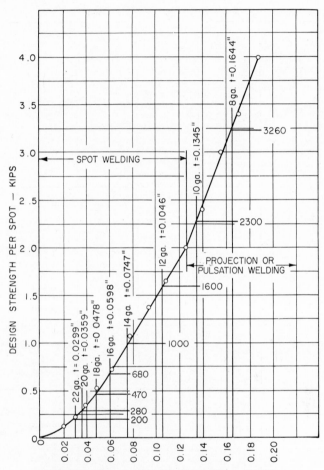

Fig. 7-26. Design strength of spot welds.

For structural design purposes, spot welds can be treated in the same way as rivets, except that no reduction in net section due to holes need be made. Table 7-12 and the curves of Figs. 7-25 and 7-26 show essential information for design purposes based upon "Recommended Practices for Resistance Welding," American Welding Society, 1950.

Based on the shear strengths in Table 7-12 and a safety factor of about 2½, the allowable shear on spot welds for design purposes may be read from the curve of Fig. 7-26.

The thickest material listed in Table 7-12 for plain spot welding is ⅛ in. For welding material thicker than $\frac{1}{8}$ in., variations of spot welding known as pulsation welding or projection welding are usually used unless large-capacity machines are available.

Projection welding is a form of spot welding wherein the weld is made through projections (usually consisting of buttons or protuberances in one or more of the pieces being joined) so as to localize the welding current and pressure. Thus, the welds can be made with somewhat lighter equipment than required for ordinary spot welding.

Table 7-12. Spot-welding Data

Thickness t of thinnest outside piece, in.	Min OD of electrode D, in.	Min contacting overlap, in.	Min weld spacing c to c, in.	Approx diam of fused zone, in.	Min shear strength per weld, lb	Diam of projection D, in.
			Plain Spot Welding			
0.021	3/8	7/16	3/8	0.13	320	
0.031	3/8	7/16	1/2	0.16	570	
0.040	1/2	1/2	3/4	0.19	920	
0.050	1/2	9/16	7/8	0.22	1,350	
0.062	1/2	5/8	1	0.25	1,850	
0.078	5/8	11/16	1 1/4	0.29	2,700	
0.094	5/8	3/4	1 1/2	0.31	3,450	
0 109	5/8	13/16	1 5/8	0.32	4,150	
0.125	7/8	7/8	1 3/4	0.33	5,000	
			Pulsation Welding			
1/8	1	7/8	.....	3/8	5,000	
3/16	1 1/4	1 1/8	.....	9/16	10,000	
			Projection Welding			
0.125	...	1 1/16	9/16	0.338	4,800	0.281
0.140	...	3/4	5/8	7/16	6,000	0.312
0.156	...	13/16	11/16	1/2	7,500	0.343
0.171	...	7/8	3/4	9/16	8,500	0.375
0.187	...	15/16	1 3/16	9/16	10,000	0.406

Pulsation welding, more accurately called multiple-impulse welding, can be defined as the making of spot welds by more than one impulse of current. Except where requirements for very small weld spacing or edge distance make it necessary to use projection welding, the choice between pulsation welding and projection welding is a matter for the fabricator to decide, based on the nature of the work, the number of pieces to be made, the capacity and limitations of the equipment, and other operating considerations.

Design values in Fig. 7-26 are based on the assumption that welding is to be performed in accordance with the American Welding Society's "Recommended Practices for Resistance Welding." When it is, these values may be applied to any of the grades of carbon steel covered by American Society for Testing Materials specifications, for structural-quality sheet and strip (Art. 7-9). In the absence of other information, they may also be applied to higher-strength steel; but spot welds in higher-strength steel yield somewhat higher shear strengths than those in Table 7-12 and may require special welding conditions. For further information, reference should be made to the American Welding Society's recommended practices.

Material for spot welding should be free from scale; therefore, either hot-rolled and pickled, or cold-rolled material is usually specified. Steel containing not more than 0.15% carbon is more readily weldable than is higher-carbon material. However, higher-carbon material can be successfully spot-welded with the proper equipment and technique.

It is important that the minimum contacting overlap shown in Table 7-12 be observed in detailing spot-welded joints. If smaller overlaps are used, the weld strengths will be difficult to maintain under shop conditions, or distortion of the lapping sheets may occur in welding. The minimum spacing specified should also be observed, so that no special precautions need be taken to compensate for the current-shunting effect of the adjacent welds. In detailing compound sections to be spot-welded, it is important to allow sufficient electrode clearance between the line of welds and the nearest interference (Fig. 7-24).

In addition to observing the minimum spacing of spot welds, it is also necessary to observe certain precautions with respect to the maximum spacing that may be permitted. These are as follows:

1. The spacing should not exceed that required to transmit the shear between the connected parts. This refers, of course, to the primary function of the welds to act in the same way as rivets in structural connections.

2. The American Iron and Steel Institute Specification for the Design of Light Gage Steel Structural Members recommends that, in order to avoid failure of a cover plate or sheet by column action or cylindrical buckling between welds, the weld spacing in line of stress should not exceed $6,000t/\sqrt{f}$, where f is the stress in the cover plate or sheet and t is its thickness. That specification also provides that the spacing, in line of stress, of welds, rivets, or other means connecting a compression cover plate or sheet to a stiffener or other element should not exceed three times the flat width of the narrowest unstiffened compression element (Art. 7-12) in that portion of the cover plate or sheet that is tributary to the welds, or thirty-six times the thickness of such element, whichever is the larger.

7-25. Riveting Light-gage Members. Although riveting of sheet metal is widely practiced in aircraft work, it finds relatively little application today with cold-formed shapes for structural purposes in buildings. When it is used for such purposes, ordinary structural practice can usually be followed in design and strength calculations. In special cases, the design may be based on test results. Rules relating to maximum allowable spacing of spot welds in cover plates or sheets (Art. 7-24) also apply to rivets.

7-26. Bolting Light-gage Members. Bolting is employed as a common means of making field connections in light-gage steel construction. The AISI Specification for the Design of Light-gage Steel Structural Members requires that the distance between bolt centers, in line of stress, and the distance from bolt center to edge of sheet, in line of stress, shall not exceed $1\frac{1}{2}$ times the bolt diameter nor

$$\frac{P}{f_b t}$$

where P = load on bolt, lb
t = thickness of thinnest connected sheet, in.
f_b = basic design stress, psi

That specification also recommends a limit of $3.5f_b$ for the bearing stress, and a maximum allowable tension stress on net section of

$$\left(0.1 + 3\frac{d}{s}\right)f_b$$

where d = bolt diameter, in.

s = spacing perpendicular to line of stress, in.

Rules relating to maximum allowable spacing of spot welds in cover plates or sheets (See Art. 7-24) also apply to bolts.

Care must be used in making use of test results of bolted joints in thin material because of the variation in strength that can result from variations in texture of the surfaces being joined, hole clearances, and tightening torques.

7-27. Self-tapping Screws for Joining Light-gage members.   Self-tapping screws, sometimes called sheet-metal screws, are frequently used for making field joints in light-gage steel construction, especially in connections that do not carry any calculated gravity load.   Such screws are of several types (Fig. 7-27).   They provide a rapid and efficient means of making light-duty connections and are especially useful for such

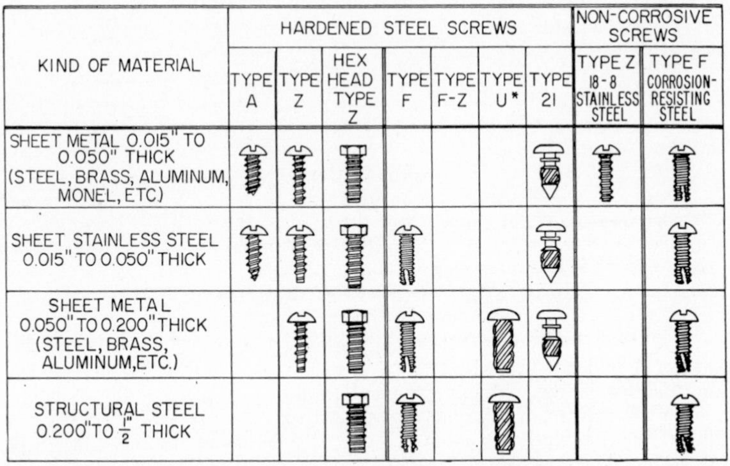

KIND OF MATERIAL	HARDENED STEEL SCREWS							NON-CORROSIVE SCREWS	
	TYPE A	TYPE Z	HEX HEAD TYPE Z	TYPE F	TYPE F-Z	TYPE U*	TYPE 21	TYPE Z 18-8 STAINLESS STEEL	TYPE F CORROSION-RESISTING STEEL
SHEET METAL 0.015" TO 0.050" THICK (STEEL, BRASS, ALUMINUM, MONEL, ETC)									
SHEET STAINLESS STEEL 0.015" TO 0.050" THICK									
SHEET METAL 0.050" TO 0.200" THICK (STEEL, BRASS, ALUMINUM, ETC.)									
STRUCTURAL STEEL 0.200" TO $\frac{1}{2}$" THICK									

NOTE: A blank space does not necessarily signify that the type of screw cannot be used for the purpose.   It denotes that the type of self-tapping screw will not generally give the best results in that material.

* Type U is not recommended for use in material the thickness of which is less than one diameter of the screw.

FIG. 7-27. Self-tapping screws.   (*Parker-Kalon Division General American Transportation Corporation.*)

purposes as fastening sheet-metal siding and roofing to framing members and for making joints in siding and roofing.   Such screws are sometimes used for fastening light studs, particularly non-load-bearing studs, to sill plates or channel tracks.   They may also be used for fastening bridging to sheet-metal joists and studs, and for similar purposes.   There are no standard design rules covering safe loads on such screws; they should be used for load-carrying purposes only under controlled conditions in which allowable loads have been determined by proper tests, or on the basis of the manufacturer's recommendations.

Essential dimensions for some types of self-tapping screws are shown in Table 7-13.

7-28. Special Fasteners for Light-gage Steel.   Special fasteners such as tubular rivets, blind rivets (capable of being driven from one side only), special bolts used for "blind insertion," special studs, lock nuts, and the like, and even metal stitching, which is an outgrowth of the common office stapling device, are all used for special applications.   In any particular case in which such a fastener is required, reference should be made to the manufacturer's catalogs, and any structural strength that may be attributed to it should be based on the results of carefully made tests or on the manufacturer's recommendation.

Table 7-13. Average Diameters of Self-tapping Screws

No. or size	Avg diam, in.*				
	Type A		Type B or Z†		Type U
	Outside diam	Root diam	Outside diam	Root diam	Outside diam
4	0.112	0.080	0.112	0.084	0.114
6	0.138	0.099	0.137	0.101	0.138
8	0.165	0.119	0.163	0.119	0.164
10	0.191	0.129	0.186	0.138	0.179
12	0.218	0.158	0.212	0.160	0.209
14	0.251	0.181	0.243	0.188	0.239
5⁄16 in.	.....	.....	0.312	0.240	
3⁄8 in.	.....	.....	0.375	0.304	

* Dimensions for Types A and B or Z are averages of standard maximum and minimum dimensions adopted under American Standard ASA B18.6-1947. Dimensions for Type U from Parker-Kalon Division, General American Transportation Corp.

† Type B is the designation used in ASA B18.6-1947 for the thread which is designated as Type Z in Fig. 7-27.

RIBBED STEEL ROOF DECK

Ribbed steel roof deck usually consists of ribbed-steel sheets with overlapping or interlocking edges designed to serve primarily for the support of roof loads. A typical roof-deck assembly is illustrated in Fig. 7-28.

7-29. Types of Ribbed Steel Deck. There has been very little standardization of roof-deck sections. In general, however, ribbed steel roof decking consists of long narrow sections having narrow longitudinal ribs from 1½ to 2 in. deep spaced about 6 in. c to c. Such sections are shown in Fig. 7-29.

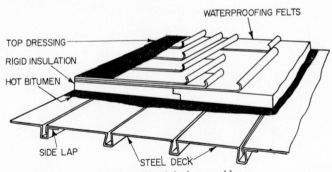

FIG. 7-28. Roof-deck assembly.

Usual spans for sections of the kind shown in Figs. 7-28 and 7-29 are from 6 to 10 ft, depending on depth of section, gage of material, and details of the design. In addition to the shallow ribbed sections in Fig. 7-29, some manufacturers make special long-span roof-deck sections, such as are shown in Fig. 7-30. The cellular floor constructions described in Arts. 7-34 and 7-35 may also be used in roofs.

Weight of the roof-deck sections in Fig. 7-29 varies, depending on the dimensions and details. With 20-gage metal, sections 1½ to 2 in. deep will weigh between 2 and

3 psf. For structural design purposes, 2.5 psf is an average figure for 20-gage deck, and 3.3 psf for 18-gage.

Steel roof deck is usually made of structural-quality sheet or strip, either black or galvanized.

Black material is given a shop coat of paint by the roof-deck manufacturer. Galvanized material may or may not be painted.

Common gages are No. 18 and 20. Most building codes permit the use of 22 gage, and a considerable number of manufacturers furnish it. One manufacturer produces 24 and 26 gages in a short-span section with ribs spaced 4 in. c to c and ¾-in. deep. The deep long-span sections of Fig. 7-30 are furnished in heavier gages, ranging from 18 to 12.

7-30. Load-carrying Capacity of Ribbed Steel Deck. Because the strength of a wide shallow section, such as is illustrated in Fig. 7-29, is a rather sensitive function of

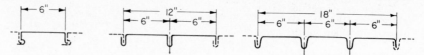

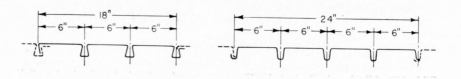

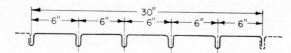

Fig. 7-29. Typical ribbed steel roof-deck sections.

the depth of ribs and the width at the bottoms of the ribs, and because each manufacturer's section is different from that of others, there has not yet been any standardization of section properties or safe-load tables. In order that the calculation of section properties and load-carrying capacity may be on a reasonably uniform basis for similar sections, the Metal Roof Deck Technical Institute has developed "Specifications, Code of Recommended Practice and Fire Ratings" (1954). In this is a recommendation that structural properties of steel roof-deck sections of the types illustrated in Fig. 7-29 with ribs spaced 6 in. c to c resting on structural supports not more than 10 ft apart be computed with an effective width of top flange between ribs as follows:

For 18-gage material, take three-fourths of the clear flat width as effective.

For 20-gage material, take five-eighths of the clear flat width as effective.

The American Iron and Steel Institute recommends, in addition, that one-half of the clear flat width may be considered effective for 22-gage material ["Building Code Modernization (A Series of Reference Bulletins)," V—Steel Regulations, American Iron and Steel Institute, June, 1949].

These approximate effective width percentages cannot be applied indiscriminately to sections of other shapes or dimensions. Other provisions of the AISI Specification for the Design of Light Gage Steel Structural Members, and the general procedures discussed in Arts. 7-11 to 7-19 are applicable to metal roof deck as to other cold-formed sections.

The following excerpts from the "Specification for Steel Roof Deck Construction" (Metal Roof Deck Technical Institute, 1949) apply to the type of roof decking in Fig. 7-29 and described in Art. 7-29:

"*Moment and Deflection Coefficients.* Where steel roof-deck units are welded to the supports, a moment coefficient of $\frac{1}{10}$ (applied to WL) shall be used for 3 or more spans, and deflection coefficient of $\frac{3}{384}$ (applied to WL^3/EI) shall be used for all except simple spans. All other steel roof-deck installations shall be designed as simple spans.

"*Maximum Deflections.* The deflection under live load shall not exceed $\frac{1}{240}$ of the clear span. (Suspended ceilings shall not be supported by the roof deck).

"*Anchorage.* Steel deck units shall be anchored to the supporting framework to resist the following gross uplifts:

45 psf for eave overhang
30 psf for all other roof areas

"The dead load of the roof-deck construction may be deducted from the above uplift forces."

For details of sections, section properties, and safe-load tables, refer to manufacturers' catalogs.

7-31. Details and Accessories for Ribbed Steel Deck. As illustrated in Fig. 7-29, all roof-deck sections have lapping or interlocking edges. Most sections are designed so that the ends lap (Fig. 7-31a). Special filler pieces or joint clips that fit between abutting sections are sometimes provided instead of end laps.

Special sections to fit various roofing details are furnished by most manufacturers of steel roof deck. The most common of these usually include side closure plates, ridge and valley plates, and cant strips. Although details and dimensions will vary with different manufacturers, the general shapes of these accessories are as shown in Fig. 7-31.

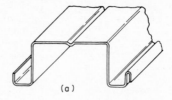

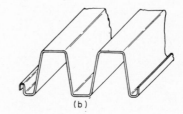

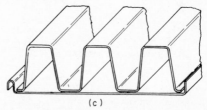

Fig. 7-30. Long-span roof-deck sections. (*a*) Detroit Steel Products Co.; (*b*) and (*c*) H. H. Robertson Co.

Most roof deck are fastened to structural-steel supports by electric-arc welding, but some manufacturers furnish clips for use where welding is not convenient. Self-tapping screws are also sometimes used for this purpose. In most decking installations, adjacent sections are fastened together at the supports and at one or more points between supports with short electric-arc welds or screws. In any particular instance, the details to be used depend on the circumstances surrounding the job and on the recommendations of the manufacturer.

7-32. Insulation of Roof Deck. Although insulation is not ordinarily supplied by the steel-roof-deck manufacturer, it is more or less standard practice to install insulation between the roof deck and the roofing. The Metal Roof Deck Technical Institute "Specifications, Code of Recommended Practice and Fire Ratings" contains the following recommendation with respect to insulation:

"All steel roof decks shall be covered by insulation of sufficient insulating value to prevent condensation under conditions to be experienced within the building. Insulation shall be completely hot mopped to the steel deck surface. When relatively high humidities and temperatures exist within a building, a vapor seal under the insulation

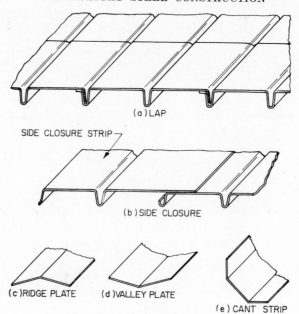

(a)LAP

SIDE CLOSURE STRIP

(b) SIDE CLOSURE

(c)RIDGE PLATE   (d)VALLEY PLATE

(e) CANT STRIP

FIG. 7-31. Roof-deck details.

shall be specified.   On jobs having a slope of more than 3 in. in 12 in., provision shall be made to prevent slipping of insulation."

Most manufacturers furnish clips or other fasteners for use where needed for this purpose.

7-33. Fire Resistance of Roof Deck.   The Metal Roof Deck Technical Institute "Specifications, Code of Recommended Practice and Fire Ratings" contains the fire-resistance ratings for steel-roof-deck construction given in Table 7-14.

Table 7-14. Fire-resistance Ratings, Steel Roof-deck Construction

Roof materials	Suspended ceilings of metal lath and plaster	Fire-resist-ance rating, hr
2-in. vermiculite concrete (or equivalent)	1-in. vermiculite—gypsum plaster on metal or wire lath	4
Minimum 1¾-in. insulation board of shredded wood, bonded with portland cement	1-in. vermiculite—gypsum plaster on metal or wire lath	3½
Minimum 1-in. insulation as described above	1-in. vermiculite—gypsum plaster on metal or wire lath	3
Minimum 1-in. insulation board of felted glass fiber	1-in. vermiculite—gypsum plaster on metal or wire lath	2
Minimum 1½-in. wood fiberboard insulation	1-in. sanded gypsum plaster, 1:2 mix	2
Minimum 1½-in. wood-fiber and cement-binder insulation	⅞-in. sanded gypsum plaster, 1:2 mix	2
Minimum 1-in. wood fiberboard insulation	¾-in. sanded gypsum plaster, 1:2, 1:3 mix	1½

CELLULAR STEEL FLOOR AND ROOF PANELS

A number of different designs of cellular steel panels for floor and roof construction are on the market. Sections of some of these panels are illustrated in Fig. 7-32. One form of cellular steel floor assembly showing concrete fill, utilities, and ceiling is illustrated in Fig. 7-33.

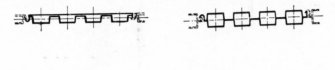

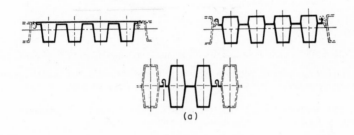

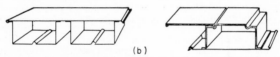

(a)

(b)

FIG. 7-32. Cellular steel floor sections. Cells can be used to carry wiring. (a) H. H. Robertson Co.; (b) Detroit Steel Products Co.

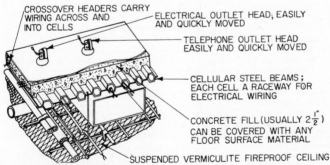

FIG. 7-33. Cellular steel floor assembly. (H. H. Robertson Co.)

One of the principal advantages claimed for cellular-type construction is that space is automatically provided to accommodate wiring. Particular emphasis is laid on the electrical-raceway capacity such floors provide, and on the ease with which changes in electrical services can be made. Such panels can also be provided with acoustic metal ceilings (Fig. 7-34).

7-34. Structural Design and Materials for Cellular Decking. Cellular floor and roof steel panels usually are made of 18-gage or heavier steel, complying with requirements of Grade C of American Society for Testing Materials specifications for structural-quality sheet or strip steel.   They may be either galvanized or painted.

Structural design of sheet-metal floor and roof panels is usually based on the design principles of Arts. 7-11 to 7-19.

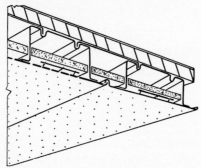

Fig. 7-34. Cellular steel floor panel with acoustic ceiling.   (*Detroit Steel Products Co.*)

Details of design and installation vary with types of panels and manufacturers.   In any particular instance, reference should be made to the manufacturer's recommendations.

7-35. Fire Resistance of Cellular Decking.   The following fire-resistance ratings have been published for cellular-steel floor and roof assemblies.

Rating, Hr

1. Steel formed into units of two or more cells; depth of unit not less than 3 in. and distance between cells not less than 2 in.*; portland-cement concrete (not less than $1\frac{1}{2}$ in. thick at top of cells, plus $\frac{1}{2}$ in. of $1:2\frac{1}{2}$ cement-sand finish—2 in. total thickness at top of cells) applied direct to top of steel units; ceiling $\frac{7}{8}$ in. gypsum vermiculite on metal or wire-lath plaster.   At least $2\frac{1}{4}$-in. air space between underside of cellular panel and back of lath†..................   4

2. Same as 1, except ceiling consists of 1 in. gypsum-vermiculite plaster on metal or wire lath and that air space shall not be less than 2 in.†...................   4

3. Same as 1, except ceiling consists of 1 in. unsanded gypsum plaster on metal or wire lath and that air space shall be not less than 2 in.†...................   4

4. 2-in. concrete slab; ceiling $\frac{7}{8}$ in. gypsum-perlite plaster—ratio of weight of gypsum to perlite in the range of $5:1$ to $5:1.5$; duct openings and electric outlets‡   4

5. Same as 1 except ceiling consists of 1 in. unsanded gypsum plaster on metal or wire lath and that air space shall be not less than 2 in.†...................   3

6. 2-in. concrete top slab; ceiling $1\frac{1}{8}$ in. asbestos fiber sprayed onto suspended metal lath‡..   3

7. $2\frac{1}{2}$-in. concrete top slab; ceiling 1 in. unsanded gypsum plaster or $\frac{3}{4}$ in. gypsum-vermiculite plaster—ratio of weight of gypsum to vermiculite in the range $2:1$ to $3:1$‡..   3

8. $2\frac{1}{4}$-in. concrete top slab; ceiling $\frac{3}{4}$ in. sanded gypsum plaster—mix $1:2$ for scratch, $1:3$ for brown coat‡...   2

9. 2-in. concrete top slab; ceiling $\frac{3}{4}$ in. sanded gypsum plaster—mix $1:2$ for scratch and $1:3$ for brown coat, or $\frac{3}{4}$-in. portland cement and sand plaster of like mix with 15 lb of hydrated lime and 31 lb of short asbestos fiber per bag of portland cement‡.. $1\frac{1}{2}$

* The detailed dimensions of the steel cells apply to the steel construction tested by Underwriters' Laboratories, Inc., but variation in these dimensions is not likely to affect the fire-resistance rating.

† B. L. Wood, "Fire Protection through Modern Building Codes," American Iron and Steel Institute, 1950.

‡ Detroit Steel Products Company.

Section 8

WOOD CONSTRUCTION

Verne Ketchum

Chief Engineer
Timber Structures, Inc.

Many years ago, when large trees grew on every hillside and in every valley, large timbers were plentiful. For the garage or store built on a 50-ft lot, the designer called for 50-ft-span sawn girders at 20-ft intervals, with wood joists spanning between them. Girders delivered by the lumber mill were swung into place with a crane or gin pole in a matter of minutes.

Here was roof framing in its easiest and cheapest form—little or no engineering, no fabrication, no assembly, no ironwork, and no lost time to get the building under roof. Today, such large timbers are difficult to obtain. Instead, designers resort to trusses, rigid frames, built-up girders, or glued-laminated timbers.

Up to and through the first decade of the twentieth century, engineers had one set of working stresses for all structural timbers. Soon thereafter, the industry set up grading rules that evaluated the strength of the clear wood and then reduced the stress values according to the growth characteristics permitted in each grade. Through the next 25 years, grades and their appropriate stress levels were refined, consolidated, and established as standards.

In 1943, because of wartime conservation of materials, the War Production Board raised all timber stresses 20%. After a long test program in 1948, the Forest Products Laboratory (FPL) at Madison, Wis., approved the higher stress levels for sawn timbers and the National Lumber Manufacturers Association, Washington, D.C., published the stress levels that are in effect today (National Design Specification for Stress-grade Lumber and Its Fastenings).

As soon as sawn-timber stress levels were established, FPL started a program to develop design and fabrication procedures for glued timbers. In 1951, this program was completed and the National Design Specification and West Coast Lumbermen's Association standards were revised and enlarged to include the new material.

Since then, glued-timber construction has been refined to accommodate modern machine production and available timber supplies. The timber truss now has a curved top chord, with increased efficiency; chords are glued-laminated to avoid shrinkage, and members are smaller.

8-1. Advantages of Timber Construction. Lumber and timbers can be planed, sawn, and joined with simple carpenter tools; so wood is the handiest and most easily worked construction material. Repairs, additions, and replacements are simple. New or repair construction requires little technical knowledge.

Lumber and timbers are everywhere available from the neighborhood yard and can be quickly transported by truck or car trailer.

While lumber grading on large projects is usually performed by experienced graders, all users are generally qualified to determine the general characteristics of lumber. The common shapes of shiplap, sheathing, 2 × 4 studding, and 2 × 10 joists are all known to builders, as are siding, shingles, moldings, and flooring.

Wood framing has an appearance of softness and warmth that makes it desirable for our immediate and intimate surroundings in homes, schools, churches, and other places where people worship, play, or relax.

Timber constructed to modern techniques can be strong and durable and often is much lower in cost than concrete or steel. Wood framing, and especially heavy timber construction, will often withstand fires better than unprotected steel construction. In addition, for certain electrical and nonmagnetic uses, wood can be used where steel cannot.

8-2. Disadvantages of Timber Construction. Timber construction is combustible and cannot be used in building types and in fire zones where code requirements limit all construction to incombustible materials. It is not suitable for extremely long-span trusses (300 ft or over). Nor is it suitable for building foundations. However, timber is suitable for piles, because the parts below ground water or under water do not decay.

Timber construction is not suitable for high-heat structures or for floor surfaces that have heavy wear. It has a higher ratio of deflection to load than does steel and so is not so adaptable to construction that requires great rigidity. For some uses, it is bulkier than steel, which has ten times the strength for the same area.

8-3. Plans for Timber Construction. These may be classified as design plans and shop details. Usually, an architect or engineer draws the design plans, and a fabricator produces shop details to conform to all design requirements. Sometimes, however, the design is also made by the fabricator.

The controlling dimensions of the structure are those established by the designer and shown on design plans. Dimensions should be clear and definite and provide the fabricator with spacings, spans, and anchorage locations so that accurate shop details can be made.

Design plans and specifications should give complete information on sizes, sections, and arrangements of members. Required camber should be shown. Species and grade of lumber, loads, design stresses, finish, paint, galvanizing, treatments, and appearance grades should be given in sufficient detail to convey the complete intent of the design.

Scale of design plans should be large enough to show information clearly. When required, large-scale illustrative details and sections may be provided.

Design plans should show information in such manner and to such completeness as will permit shop details to be made and the fabricator to determine fully the kind, quality, number, and extent of the items to be furnished and the operations to be performed under his contract.

Sizes shown on design plans should be nominal for stock sawn timbers and net for glued-laminated, mechanically laminated, plywood, and glued built-up timbers. Where special-size sawn timbers are used, net size should be given. Include appropriate descriptive words as "nominal" or "net," where necessary, to explain fully the intention of dimensions.

Shop details, giving complete information necessary for the fabrication and erection of the component parts of the structure, including the location, type, size, and extent of all connections, fastenings, and camber, should be prepared in advance of fabrication. Shop details may not, however, be required for timber items that have a minimum of fabrication or that can be shown or described in writing, such as lumber cut to length only. Nor should shop details be necessary to show fabrication or erection where sufficient information for one or both operations is adequately shown on design plans. Shop details should conform to the latest and best shop practices and have due regard for efficiency and economy in shop and field. Shop details should be submitted to the designer for approval before shopwork is begun.

8-4. Lumber Species for Building Construction. Southern pine and Douglas fir are the principal structural woods used in the United States and Canada. Western red cedar is used for roof and wall construction and oak for flooring. Some western hemlock is finding a place in both sawn and glued timber framing.

Douglas fir and southern pine are both excellent structural timber species, being light, strong, and about equal in strength for sawn and laminated timbers.

8-5. Grading Rules. Lumber is manufactured in a sawmill to grading rules of regional associations, such as the West Coast Lumber Inspection Bureau, Portland, Ore.; Southern Pine Inspection Bureau, New Orleans, La. As it leaves the saw, the wood is unseasoned. Much lumber is sold and used in this condition, though it is usually partly air-seasoned when it reaches the job.

In the United States there are not enough kilns to season all lumber produced, and air drying is a slow and expensive process. While seasoned lumber is always preferable, much construction can be well built with partly seasoned lumber. Construction lumber in houses, warehouses, and many minor structures is normally unseasoned, the material seasoning in place. For glued-laminated construction, however, lumber must be seasoned.

For stress grades, timbers are classified as: (1) joists and planks; (2) beams and stringers; (3) posts and timbers (see Table 2-31, Art. 2-41). Stress values for these sawn-lumber items are given in lumber inspection bureau grading and dressing rules. Lumber less than 2 in. thick is often graded as boards, sheathing, and form lumber. Boards and planks are used as laminations for glued-laminated construction. ("Guide to the Grading of Structural Timbers and the Determination of Working Stresses," U.S. *Department of Agriculture Miscellaneous Publication* 185, Forest Products Laboratory, Madison, Wis.)

Clear, straight-grained, unchecked wood of a given species, density, and moisture content has been found to be fairly uniform in strength. Tests, therefore, are made on small, clear specimens to secure strength data, and then separate investigations are made of the effect of the more important growth characteristics.

To secure basic stress values, the ultimate breaking strength of wood is reduced by a safety factor. This allows a safe margin below ultimate strength, compensates for the minor variabilities of clear wood, allows for effect of long-time loading, and provides adjustment for inaccuracies of design, fabrication, and grading (Art. 2-39).

8-6. Basic and Working Stresses for Timber. Basic stresses are the safe stress values of clear, straight-grained wood of structural-member size that have been determined by applying a safety factor to ultimate strength. Clear wood is not available commercially in structural sizes; so basic stress values cannot be used in design.

Strength ratio of wood represents the percentage of remaining strength left in commercial grades after making allowances for the effect on an unseasoned piece of the permitted growth characteristics, such as knots, cross grain, and shakes. Strength ratio for the particular grade is applied to basic stress to obtain working stress. Strength ratio is not, however, applied to modulus of elasticity.

Knots are formed when the part of a branch or limb embedded in a tree is cut through. They reduce bending strength of beams, having greater influence when near the top or bottom face in the center portion of the span or in any portion where bending moment is large. Knots near the center of the face parallel to the direction of load or near the ends have little or no effect.

Splits (separations of wood that extend through the piece), **shakes** (separations along the grain between annual growth rings), and **checks** (separations across the growth rings) reduce shear value approximately proportional to the reduction of shear-resisting area but do not greatly reduce bending or longitudinal compression strength. See Ketchum, May, and Hanrahan, "Are Timber Checks and Splits Serious," Timber Structures, Inc., Portland, Ore.

Cross grain—wood with fibers not parallel to sides or axis—affects bending and compression or tension-with-grain strength unfavorably.

Wane is bark or absence of wood or bark on an edge. It ordinarily has little effect on bending or compression-with-grain strength but may reduce bearing area under compression-across-grain and glue-line area in glued timbers.

The effect of these characteristics varies with size, shape, position, type of loading, type of stress, and size of member. In glued timbers, the effect of growth characteristics in lamination is determined by the position of the lamination.

The final values obtained by applying a safety factor and strength ratio to ultimate breaking strength of wood are termed working unit stresses. They apply equally to

Table 8-1. Allowable Unit Stresses for Stress-grade Lumber
(The allowable unit stresses below are for normal loading conditions)

Species and commercial grade*	Rules under which graded	Allowable unit stresses, psi				
		Extreme fiber in bending f and tension parallel to grain t	Horizontal shear H	Compression perpendicular to grain $c\perp$	Compression parallel to grain c	Modulus of elasticity E
(1)	(2)	(3)	(4)	(5)	(6)	(7)
Douglas fir, coast region:						
Dense select structural, J&P, B&S............		2,150	145	455	1,550	
Select structural, J&P, B&S............		1,900	120	415	1,450	
1,700f—Dense No. 1, J&P, B&S............		1,700	145	455	1,325	
1,450f—No. 1, J&P, B&S............	West Coast Bureau of Lumber Grades and Inspection	1,450	120	390	1,200	1,760,000
1,100f—No. 2, J&P............		1,100	110	390	1,075	
Dense select structural, P&T............		......	......	455	1,550	
Select structural, P&T............		......	......	415	1,450	
Dense No. 1, P&T............		......	......	455	1,400	
No. 1, P&T............		......	......	390	1,200	
Pine, southern:						
Dense select structural, J&P, B&S............		2,400	120	455	1,750	
Dense structural, J&P, B&S............		2,000	120	455	1,400	
Dense structural SE&S, J&P, B&S............		1,800	120	455	1,300	
Dense No. 1 structural, J&P, B&S............		1,600	120	455	1,150	
No. 1 dense 1,400f, J&P, B&S............		1,400	140	455	1,400	
No. 1 1,200f, J&P, B&S............	Southern Pine Inspection Bureau	1,200	120	390	1,200	1,760,000
No. 1 dense, J&P............		1,700	150	455	1,400	
No. 1, J&P............		1,450	125	390	1,200	
No. 2 dense, J&P............		1,250	100	455	1,025	
No. 2 dense 1,200f, J&P, B&S, P&T............		1,200	100	455	1,025	
No. 2, J&P............		1,100	85	390	875	
No. 2 1,050f, J&P, B&S, P&T............		1,050	85	390	875	
Dense select structural, P&T............		......	......	455	1,750	

Table 8-1. Allowable Unit Stresses for Stress-grade Lumber (*Continued*)

(The allowable unit stresses below are for normal loading conditions)

Species and commercial grade	Rules under which graded	Allowable unit stresses, psi				Modulus of elasticity E
		Extreme fiber in bending f and tension parallel to grain t	Horizontal shear H	Compression perpendicular to grain c⊥	Compression parallel to grain c	
(1)	(2)	(3)	(4)	(5)	(6)	(7)
Dense structural, P&T		....	....	455	1,400	
Dense structural SE&S, P&T		....	....	455	1,300	
Dense No. 1 structural, P&T		....	....	455	1,150	
No. 1 dense 1,400f, P&T		1,400	140	455	1,400	
No. 1 1,200f, P&T		1,200	120	390	1,200	
Pine, southern longleaf:						
Select structural longleaf, J&P, B&S		2,400	120		1,750	
Prime structural longleaf, J&P, B&S		2,000	120		1,400	
Merchantable structural longleaf, J&P, B&S		1,800	120		1,300	
Structural SE&S longleaf, J&P, B&S		1,800	120		1,300	1,760,000
No. 1 structural longleaf, J&P, B&S	Southern Pine Inspection Bureau	1,600	120	455	1,150	
No. 1 longleaf 1,400f, J&P, B&S		1,400	140		1,400	
No. 1 longleaf, J&P		1,700	150		1,400	
No. 2 longleaf, J&P		1,250	100		1,025	
No. 2 longleaf 1,200f, J&P, B&S, P&T		1,200	100		1,025	
Select structural longleaf, P&T		....	....		1,750	
Prime structural longleaf, P&T		....	....		1,400	
Merchantable structural longleaf, P&T		....	....		1,300	
Structural SE&S longleaf, P&T		....	....		1,150	
No. 1 structural longleaf, P&T		....	....		1,150	
No. 1 longleaf 1,400f, P&T		1,400	140		1,400	

* J&P = joists and planks; B&S = beams and stringers; P&T = post and timbers; SE&S = square edges and sound.

Table 8-2. Allowable Unit Stresses for Structural Glued-laminated Lumber
(The allowable unit stresses below are for normal loading conditions)

Species and combinations of lumber grades				Allowable unit stresses, psi							
Combination No.	Outer laminations		Inner laminations	Extreme fiber in bending f		Tension parallel to grain t		Compression parallel to grain c		Horizontal shear H	Compression perpendicular to grain $c\perp$
	Grade	No., each side	Grade	From 4 to 14 laminations	15 or more laminations	From 4 to 14 laminations	15 or more laminations	From 4 to 14 laminations	15 or more laminations		
Dry Conditions of Use											
Douglas fir, coast region:											
1	Clear (dense)	One	Dense select structural	3,000	3,000	3,000	3,000	2,400	2,500	165	455
2	Clear (dense)	One	Dense No. 1	3,000	3,000	2,600	3,000	2,200	2,300	165	455
3	Dense select structural	All	Dense select structural	2,800	3,000	3,000	3,000	2,400	2,500	165	455
4	Clear (close-grain)	One	Select structural	2,800	2,800	2,800	2,800	2,200	2,200	165	415
5	Select structural	All	Select structural	2,600	2,800	2,800	2,800	2,200	2,200	165	415
6	Select structural	⅕ of total	No. 1	2,600	2,800	2,400	2,600	2,000	2,000	165	415
7	Clear (medium grain)	One	No. 1	2,600	2,600	2,200	2,400	1,900	2,000	165	390
8	Dense No. 1	All	Dense No. 1	2,400	2,600	2,600	3,000	2,200	2,300	165	455
9	Dense No. 1	1/14 of total	No. 1	2,400	2,600	2,200	2,400	1,900	2,000	165	455
10	Select structural	One	No. 1	2,400	2,400	2,200	2,400	1,900	2,000	165	415
11	Select structural	⅕ of total	No. 2	2,200	2,600	2,400	2,600	1,900	2,000	165	415
12	Clear (medium grain)	One	No. 2	2,200	2,200	2,000	2,400	1,800	1,900	165	390
13	Select structural	One	No. 2	2,200	2,200	2,000	2,400	1,800	1,900	165	415
14	No. 1	All	No. 1	2,000	2,200	2,200	2,400	1,900	2,000	165	390
15	No. 1	One	No. 2	2,000	2,200	2,000	2,400	1,800	1,900	165	390
16	No. 2	All	No. 2	1,600	2,000	2,000	2,400	1,800	1,900	165	390
Pine, southern:											
1–1	No. 1 dense	All	No. 1 dense	3,000	3,000	3,000	3,000	2,400	2,500	200	450
1–2	B & B dense	One	No. 1	3,000	3,000	2,600	2,600	2,100	2,100	200	450
1–3	No. 1 dense	1/14 of total	No. 1	3,000	3,000	2,600	2,600	2,100	2,100	200	450
1–4	B & B dense	One	No. 2 dense	2,800	2,800	3,000	3,000	2,400	2,400	200	450
1–5	No. 1 dense	⅕ of total	No. 2 dense	2,800	3,000	2,800	3,000	2,300	2,400	200	450
1–6	No. 1	All	No. 1	2,600	2,600	2,600	2,600	2,100	2,100	200	385
1–7	B & B dense	1/14 of total	No. 2	2,400	2,800	2,600	2,600	2,000	2,000	200	450
1–8	B & B	One	No. 2	2,400	2,400	2,600	2,600	2,000	2,000	200	385

No.	Grade	Proportion	Limiting grade					Wet Conditions of Use			
1–9	No. 1	1/3 of total	No. 2	385	200	2,000	2,000	2,600	2,400	2,600	2,400
1–10	No. 2 dense	All	No. 2 dense	450	200	2,300	2,200	3,000	2,600	2,600	2,000
1–11	No. 2 dense	1/4 of total	No. 2	450	200	2,000	1,900	2,600	2,200	2,600	1,800
1–12	No. 2	All	No. 2	385	200	2,000	1,900	2,600	2,200	2,200	1,800
Douglas fir, coast region:											
1	Clear (dense)	One	Dense select structural	305	145	1,800	1,700	2,400	2,400	2,400	2,400
2	Clear (dense)	One	Dense No. 1	305	145	1,700	1,600	2,400	2,000	2,400	2,000
3	Dense select structural	All	Dense select structural	305	145	1,800	1,700	2,400	2,400	2,400	2,200
4	Clear (close-grain)	One	Select structural	275	145	1,600	1,600	2,200	2,200	2,200	2,000
5	Select structural	All	Select structural	275	145	1,600	1,600	2,200	2,200	2,200	2,000
6	Select structural	1/3 of total	No. 1	275	145	1,500	1,400	2,000	1,800	2,000	2,000
7	Clear (medium grain)	One	No. 1	260	145	1,400	1,400	2,000	2,000	2,200	2,000
8	Dense No. 1	All	Dense No. 1	305	145	1,700	1,600	2,400	1,800	2,200	2,000
9	Dense No. 1	1/4 of total	No. 1	305	145	1,400	1,400	2,000	1,800	2,000	2,000
10	Select structural	One	No. 1	275	145	1,400	1,400	2,000	1,800	2,000	1,800
11	Select structural	1/3 of total	No. 2	275	145	1,400	1,300	2,000	1,600	1,800	1,800
12	Clear (medium grain)	One	No. 2	260	145	1,400	1,300	1,800	1,800	1,800	1,800
13	Select structural	All	No. 2	275	145	1,400	1,400	2,000	1,600	1,800	1,600
14	No. 1	All	No. 1	260	145	1,400	1,300	1,800	1,600	1,800	1,600
15	No. 1	One	No. 2	260	145	1,400	1,300	1,800	1,600	1,800	1,600
16	No. 2	All	No. 2	260	145	1,400	1,300	1,800	1,600	1,600	1,200
Pine, southern:											
2–1	No. 1 dense	All	No. 1 dense	300	175	1,800	1,800	2,400	2,400	2,400	2,400
2–2	B & B dense	One	No. 1	300	175	1,500	1,500	2,000	2,000	2,400	2,400
2–3	No. 1 dense	1/4 of total	No. 1 dense	300	175	1,500	1,500	2,000	2,000	2,400	2,400
2–4	B & B dense	One	No. 2 dense	300	175	1,700	1,700	2,400	2,400	2,200	2,200
2–5	No. 1 dense	1/3 of total	No. 2 dense	300	175	1,700	1,700	2,400	2,000	2,000	2,000
2–6	B & B dense	All	No. 1	260	175	1,500	1,500	2,000	2,000	2,200	1,800
2–7	B & B	1/4 of total	No. 2	300	175	1,500	1,500	2,000	2,200	2,000	1,800
2–8	No. 1	One	No. 2	260	175	1,500	1,400	2,000	2,000	2,000	2,000
2–9	No. 2 dense	1/3 of total	No. 2	260	175	1,400	1,400	2,000	2,000	2,000	1,600
2–10	No. 2 dense	All	No. 2 dense	300	175	1,700	1,600	2,400	2,000	2,000	1,600
2–11	No. 2	1/4 of total	No. 2	300	175	1,400	1,400	2,000	1,800	2,000	1,600
2–12	No. 2	All	No. 2	260	175	1,400	1,400	2,000	1,800	1,800	1,400

unseasoned, unchecked, and to seasoned checked materials for sawn timbers; and when properly adjusted, they also apply to glued timbers. Values for commercial structural woods of the United States may be found in Tables 8-1 and 8-2, and in the National Design Specification of the National Lumber Manufacturers Association, Washington, D.C., and in grading and dressing rule books of lumber inspection bureaus.

Structural timbers, sawn and glued, are designed according to the type of stress, such as bending, compression-across-grain, tension-with-grain, compression-with-grain, horizontal shear, tension-across-grain, and modulus of elasticity. Minor properties, such as cleavage, hardness, and impact bending, are not usually considered for structural timber framing. ("Strength and Related Properties of Wood," Government Printing Office, Washington D.C.)

The allowable working stresses, for timber under normal loading conditions, in Tables 8-1 and 8-2 should be modified for duration of load in accordance with the provisions of the National Design Specification. Some of these modifications are listed below. (Modifications do not apply to modulus of elasticity, except when applied to columns.)

Full design load permanently applied—90%.

Two months' loading, such as snow—115%.

Several days' duration of load—125%.

Wind or earthquake—$133\frac{1}{3}$%.

Impact—200%.

8-7. Deflection of Timber Beams. Wood members supporting plastered ceilings should be so proportioned that deflection under full live and dead loads, exclusive of weight of plaster, should not exceed $\frac{1}{360}$ of the span.

For dry construction, deflection should not exceed $\frac{1}{240}$ of the span.

It is customary to design long-span trusses and girders with a minimum camber equal to twice the dead-load deflection. For light live loads, however, a ratio of 1.5 is used.

Deflection of beams and girders is proportional to the stiffness of the wood as defined by the modulus of elasticity of the species. Methods and formulas given in Sec. 3 may be used for wood construction.

Deflection of trusses and frames is dependent on the stiffness of the wood plus the take up in the connections. (See deflection formulas in Sec. 3 and "Douglas Fir Use Book," West Coast Lumbermen's Association, Portland, Ore.; and National Design Specification, National Lumber Manufacturers Association, Washington, D.C.)

8-8. Timber Beams and Girders. Timber flexural members, such as beams, girders, purlins, rafters, and joists, should be designed for bending moment, shear, and deflection.

Beam sizes are determined generally by allowable working stresses in bending or shear, or by deflection. In short, heavily loaded beams horizontal shear, however, is likely to control. In long beams, deflection may control (Art. 8-7). Formulas given in Sec. 3 can be used for stress and deflection computations.

For roof and wind loads, allowable stresses (Tables 8-1 and 8-2) may be increased as for short-duration loads (Art. 8-6).

In computing section properties, bear in mind that the actual sizes of dressed lumber are less than the nominal dimensions. For sawn lumber 2 to 4 in. thick, deduct $\frac{3}{8}$ in., and for thicker lumber, $\frac{1}{2}$ in., from nominal sizes. For sawn lumber 4 to 6 in. deep, deduct $\frac{3}{8}$ in., and for deeper members, $\frac{1}{2}$ in. Glued-laminated timbers, however, can be designed to exact size.

Example 1. Design a sawn wood roof beam spanning 20 ft to carry a total uniform load of 500 lb per lin ft and a mid-span concentrated load of 5,000 lb.

Maximum shear is $20 \times \frac{500}{2} + 5{,}000/2 = 7{,}500$ lb. From Table 8-1, for structural-grade pine, the allowable unit shear stress H is 120 psi. Therefore, the area required for shear is [Eq. (3-28), Art. 3-28]

$$bd = \frac{3V}{2v} = \frac{3 \times 7{,}500}{2 \times 120} = 93.7 \text{ sq in.}$$

Maximum bending moment is $500(20)^2/8 + 5,000 \times 2\%_4 = 50,000$ ft-lb, or $600,000$ in.-lb. From Table 8-1, for structural-grade pine, the allowable bending stress is $1,800$ psi. Therefore, the section modulus required is

$$\frac{bd^2}{6} = \frac{M}{f} = \frac{600,000}{1,800} = 333.3 \text{ cu in.}$$

$$bd^2 = 2,000 \text{ cu in.}$$

For deflection not to exceed $\frac{1}{240}$ of the span:

$$\frac{5}{384} \frac{wL^4}{EI} + \frac{PL^3}{48EI} = \frac{L}{240}$$

After multiplying both sides of the equation by $240/L$ and solving for the moment of inertia, we get

$$I = \frac{bd^3}{12} = \frac{25}{8} \frac{wL^3}{E} + \frac{5PL^2}{E} = \frac{(3.13 \times 500 \times 20 + 5 \times 5,000)20^2 \times 12^2}{1,300,000} = 2,500 \text{ in.}^4$$

$$bd^3 = 30,000 \text{ in.}^4$$

If we assume $b = 7.5$ in. for a nominal width of 8 in., then $d = 12.5$ in. for shear, 16.3 in. for moment, and 15.9 in. for deflection. Therefore, use an 8×18 in.

Tables 8-3 and 8-4 give properties of typical timber sections. A few typical beam, girder, and post connections are shown in Fig. 8-1.

Table 8-3. Properties of Sawn Timber Sections

Size, in.	Area, sq in.	Section modulus	Size, in.	Area, sq in.	Section modulus	Size, in.	Area, sq in.	Section modulus
2 × 3	4	1.9	8 × 8	56	70	14 × 14	182	410
4	6	3.6	10	71	113	16	209	540
6	9	8.6	12	86	165	18	236	689
8	12	15	14	101	227	20	263	855
10	15	24	16	116	300	22	290	1,040
2 × 12	19	36	18	131	382	24	317	1,243
			20	146	475	26	344	1,463
3 × 6	15	14	22	161	578	28	371	1,702
8	20	24	8 × 24	176	690	30	398	1,958
10	25	40				14 × 32	425	2,223
12	30	58	10 × 10	90	143			
3 × 14	35	80	12	109	209	16 × 16	240	620
			14	128	288	18	271	791
4 × 4	13	8	16	147	380	20	302	982
6	20	20	18	166	484	22	333	1,194
8	27	34	20	185	602	24	364	1,427
10	34	55	22	204	731	26	395	1,463
12	42	80	24	223	874	28	426	1,702
14	49	110	10 × 26	242	1,030	30	457	1,958
4 × 16	56	145				32	488	2,563
			12 × 12	132	253	34	519	2,899
6 × 6	30	28	14	155	349	16 × 36	550	3,256
8	41	52	16	178	460			
10	52	83	18	201	587			
12	63	121	20	224	728			
14	74	167	22	247	886			
16	85	220	24	270	1,058			
18	96	280	26	293	1,246			
6 × 20	107	475	28	316	1,449			
			12 × 30	339	1,668			

Table 8-4. Properties of Glued-laminated Beams with 1⅝-in. Laminations

Finished size, in.	Section modulus	Moment of inertia	Area of section	Wt. per ft, lb
3¼ × 6½	22.89	74.38	21.12	4.97
7 × 6½	49.29	160.2	45.50	10.74
5¼ × 9¾	83.18	405.5	51.19	12.09
9 × 8⅛	99.02	402.3	73.12	17.26
3¼ × 14⅝	115.9	847.2	47.53	11.22
7 × 11⅜	151.0	858.6	79.62	18.80
5¼ × 16¼	231.0	1,877	85.31	20.14
9 × 13	253.5	1,648	117.0	27.62
11 × 13	309.8	2,014	143.0	33.76
7 × 17⅞	372.8	3,332	125.1	29.54
9 × 16¼	396.1	3,218	146.2	34.52
9 × 17⅞	479.3	4,284	160.9	37.99
12½ × 16¼	550.1	4,470	203.1	47.95
5¼ × 26	591.5	7,690	136.5	32.40
7 × 24⅜	693.2	8,448	170.6	40.28
11 × 21⅛	818.2	8,642	232.4	54.87
9 × 24⅜	891.2	10,860	219.4	51.80
9 × 26	1,014	13,180	234.0	55.25
7 × 30⅞	1,112	17,170	216.1	51.02
11 × 26	1,239	16,110	286.0	67.52
11 × 27⅝	1,399	19,320	303.9	71.75
9 × 32½	1,584	25,750	292.5	69.06
11 × 30⅞	1,748	26,980	339.6	80.18
11 × 32½	1,936	31,470	357.5	84.40
12½ × 32½	2,201	35,760	406.2	95.90
12½ × 34⅛	2,426	41,390	426.6	100.72
9 × 42¼	2,678	56,560	380.2	89.77
11 × 40⅝	3,026	61,460	446.9	105.51
11 × 43⅞	3,529	77,420	482.6	113.94
12½ × 45½	4,313	98,120	568.8	134.30

Example 2. Design a tapered glued-laminated Douglas fir beam spanning 50 ft to carry a total uniform load of 45,000 lb. (NOTE: A tapered beam and a constant-section beam will deflect about the same amount if the tapered beam has the same cross section as the prismatic beam at a distance equal to 0.15 of the span from the center.) Use combination No. 15, Table 8-2, for the material.

Maximum shear is 45,000/2 = 22,500 lb. From Table 8-2, for combination No. 15, the allowable unit shear is 165 psi. Therefore, the area required for shear is

$$bd = \frac{3}{2}\frac{V}{v} = \frac{3 \times 22{,}500}{2 \times 165} = 205 \text{ sq in.}$$

With b assumed as 7 in., d = 29.2 in. at the ends of the beam.

Maximum moment is 45,000 × 50/8 = 281,000 ft-lb, or 3,370,000 in.-lb. From Table 8-2, for 15 or more laminations, the allowable bending stress is 2,200 psi. Therefore, the section modulus required at mid-span is

$$\frac{bd^2}{6} = \frac{M}{f} = \frac{3{,}370{,}000}{2{,}200} = 1{,}533 \text{ cu in.}$$

$$d = 36.3 \text{ in.}$$

Try twenty-three 1⅝-in. laminations, d = 37.4 in.

To check for deflection, we first compute d at a distance $0.15L$ from the center of the beam: $d = 37.4 - (37.4 - 29.2)0.15/0.5 = 35.0$ in. and $I = 7(35)^3/12 = 25{,}000$,

$$\delta = \frac{5}{384}\frac{WL^3}{EI} = \frac{5 \times 45,000 \times 50^3 \times 12^3}{384 \times 1,760,000 \times 25,000} = 2.88 \text{ in.} > \left(\frac{600}{240} = 2.50 \text{ in.}\right)$$

Since the deflection is greater than $\frac{1}{240}$ of the span, the depth must be increased. Use

$$d = 35.0 \sqrt[3]{\frac{2.88}{2.50}} = 36.7 \text{ in.}$$

and therefore increase the depth at mid-span to $29.2 + (36.7 - 29.2)0.5/(0.50 - 0.15)$ or 39.8 in.

Helpful design tables can be found in "Douglas Fir Use Book," West Coast Lumbermen's Association, Portland, Ore.; "Southern Pine Manual," Southern Pine Association, New Orleans, La.; National Design Specification, National Lumber Manufacturers Association, Washington, D.C.; and H. J. Hansen, "Timber Engineers' Handbook," John Wiley & Sons, Inc., New York.

8-9. Timber Joists. Joists are narrow deep beams spaced at intervals of 12 to 24 in. Lengths generally range from 8 to 30 ft, but spans over 22 ft are specials. They usually have sheathing or coverings securely fastened to top, or to top and bottom edges, which provide lateral support, so that no stress reduction need be applied for lateral buckling. Joists should be braced with solid or cross bridging when spans exceed 10 ft. Distance between bridging should not exceed 10 ft.

Good bearing should be provided under each end, and joists should be well nailed and securely anchored. Where joists rest on masonry walls, standard steel anchors should be provided at 8-ft intervals or less. Some codes require a sloping "fire-cut" on joist ends bearing above recesses in masonry walls, to assure that the joists will fall free if they collapse and not damage the wall. Where joists run parallel to masonry walls, anchors should extend back to the second joist. Anchors to masonry should be not less than $\frac{3}{16} \times 1\frac{1}{4}$-in. steel straps well nailed at ends.

Joists laid on a slope should be designed for loads on the horizontal projection of span. (Jack Singleton, "Design of Steel Purlins for Sloping Roofs," "Manual of Structural Design," H. M. Ives & Sons, Topeka, Kans.)

Thickness of joists should be not less than 2 in. nominal. Joists resting on masonry walls should have 3 in. or more bearing, and an air space should be left around the ends. Where floor live load does not exceed 100 psf, joist ends may rest on a 2×4 ledger nailed to beams. In placing joists, the crown should be turned up, and any large edge knots should be on top.

Actual sizes of dressed lumber are less than the nominal. For sawn lumber 1 in. thick, deduct $\frac{1}{32}$ in.; up to 2 in., $\frac{3}{16}$ in.; 2 to 4 in., $\frac{3}{8}$ in. For depths of 3 to 6 in., deduct $\frac{3}{8}$ in., and for deeper members, $\frac{1}{2}$ in. Grading rules give actual net sizes.

Joist spacing directly affects strength requirements of sheathing and coverings. In general 16- to 24-in. spacings will safely support 1-in. wood sheathing, while 2 in. or more is required for spacings over 24 in. Joist spacing, however, does not directly affect joist economy. Equal joist footages are required, regardless of spacing, for the same joist spans and for the same loads supported. Joists are most economical when spacing is such that each joist is loaded to full capacity.

Modulus of elasticity is not greatly affected by grade; so where stiffness is the controlling factor, low-grade joists may be used. For this reason, non-stress-grade lumber is extensively used for joists in dwellings and in other medium-span light-load applications.

For design, standard beam formulas, as given in Sec. 3, for bending, shear, and deflection can be used (see Art. 8-8). Often, deflection will govern size (Art. 8-7). One rule of thumb for joist size restricts the unsupported span to not more than twenty-four times joist depth for floors, and not more than thirty times joist depth for ceilings. Joist tables may be found in "Douglas Fir Use Book," West Coast Lumbermen's Association, Portland, Ore.; "Maximum Spans of Joists and Rafters," National Lumber Manufacturers Association, Washington, D.C., and H. J. Hansen, "Timber Engineers' Handbook," John Wiley & Sons, Inc., New York.

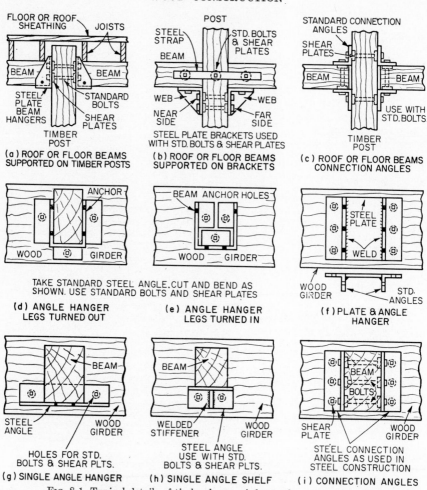

FIG. 8-1. Typical details of timber beam, girder, and post connections.

Tables 8-5 and 8-6 give load values of some sawn and glued-laminated joists.

8-10. Plank and Laminated Floors. A plank floor consists of tongue-and-grooved planks nailed directly to supporting members. Individual plank should be two bays in length, when possible, and should be laid to break joints every 4 ft. A laminated floor consists of plank set on edge, side by side, and firmly nailed together at 18-in. intervals with 20 or 30d nails, alternately at top and bottom.

Table 8-7 gives load values for some typical plank and laminated decks. More extensive tables, as well as instructions for laying and spacing of end joints with random-length stock are given in "Douglas Fir Use Book," West Coast Lumbermen's Association, Portland, Ore., and "Wood Structural Design Data," National Lumber Manufacturers Association, Washington, D.C.

One relatively new type is a double tongue-and-groove decking with a 3½-in. net depth, which is side-nailed. Nail holes are predrilled. Decking spans 8 to 20 ft, eliminating the need for joists, rafters, sheathing, and ceiling finish, and it has a high insulation value. Milled from western red cedar, Engelmann spruce, and Douglas fir, it provides a smooth, clear interior finish.

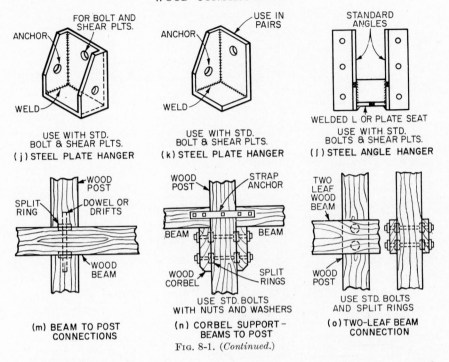

FIG. 8-1. (*Continued.*)

8-11. Wood Columns. Posts and columns are those vertical members stressed principally in compression-with-grain that support floors and roofs. Posts are less than story height and columns full story height. Column action is also found in struts, studs, truss chords, truss webs, and tower legs.

Columns may be of sawn, glued, nailed, or bolted timbers, which may be arranged to form solid or spaced members. When the slenderness ratio, or length divided by least dimension, exceeds 11, stiffness becomes important in determining allowable load. No arrangement of laminations in nailed or bolted timbers will produce a column as stiff as a solid column, but glued timbers are equally stiff.

Spaced columns of two or more leaves are often used for columns. They usually are economical in comparison with one-timber columns. They are well suited to connector-type construction. Made of thinner pieces, they are easily obtained and may season with less checking. Most compression truss chords are a series of spaced columns. Sawn, glued, nailed, or bolted timbers may be used in spaced columns, but maximum stiffness is obtained with sawn or glued timber.

Column load is considered as acting along the axis of the timber and of uniform intensity over the cross section. The load divided by working unit stress for compression-with-grain, adjusted for slenderness ratio of column, gives required cross-sectional area. When the ratio L/d of length to least dimension is greater than 11, the allowable working stress for short compression members must be modified.

For columns with square or rectangular cross section, the allowable stress when L/d is greater than 11 is limited to

$$\frac{P}{A} = \frac{0.3E}{(L/d)} \tag{8-1}$$

The modulus of elasticity E should be adjusted for duration of load (Art. 8-6).

Table 8-8 gives safe loads on some typical columns. More extensive design charts and tables are given in "Douglas Fir Use Book," West Coast Lumbermen's Associa-

Table 8-5. Safe Loads for Sawn Wood Joists

Size	Spacing	Span c to c of supports		
		Ceiling joists 10 psf	Roof joists 40 psf	Roof joists 60 psf
2 × 4	12	11′9″	9′0″	8′0″
	16	10′9″	8′0″	7′0″
	20	10′3″	7′6″	6′6″
	24	9′6″	7′0″	6′0″
	28	8′6″	6′6″	5′6″
	32	7′6″	6′0″	5′0″
2 × 6	12	16′0″	14′0″	13′0″
	16	15′0″	13′0″	12′0″
	20	14′0″	12′0″	11′0″
	24	13′0″	11′3″	10′3″
	28	12′0″	10′9″	9′9″
	32	11′0″	10′0″	9′0″
2 × 8	12	21′0″	18′0″	17′0″
	16	20′0″	17′0″	16′0″
	20	19′0″	16′0″	15′0″
	24	18′0″	15′0″	14′0″
	28	17′0″	14′0″	13′0″
	32	16′0″	13′0″	12′0″
2 × 10	12	24′0″	23′6″	22′0″
	16	23′0″	22′0″	20′0″
	20	22′0″	20′0″	18′0″
	24	21′0″	18′0″	16′0″
	28	20′0″	16′0″	15′0″
	32	19′0″	15′0″	14′0″
2 × 12	12	30′0″	26′0″	24′0″
	16	29′0″	25′0″	23′0″
	20	28′0″	23′0″	22′0″
	24	27′0″	22′0″	20′0″
	28	26′0″	21′0″	19′0″
	32	25′0″	19′0″	18′0″

tion, Portland, Ore.; "Wood Structural Design Data," National Lumber Manufacturers Association, Washington, D.C.; "Wood Columns," National Lumber Manufacturers Association, Washington, D.C.; and H. J. Hansen, "Timber Engineers' Handbook," John Wiley & Sons, Inc., New York.

Length of columns is limited by slenderness ratio L/d. Solid columns for heavy load are not economical where L/d exceeds 35 or 40 and should not be used for L/d greater than 50. Spaced columns should not be used for L/d of each timber greater than 80.

Structures with long compression members require additional bracing against lateral movement, to make the effective length of the column less. Such bracing should lie in at least two intersecting planes to resist buckling in all directions. For example, top-chord members in trusses must be braced not only in the plane of the truss, but also in the plane of the purlins.

Combined axial and bending stress must be considered in design where such action occurs. Codes require that P/A divided by the allowable unit compressive stress plus M/S divided by the allowable bending stress must not exceed unity.

Table 8-6. Safe Loads for Typical Glued-laminated Purlins

Span, ft	Spacing, ft	30 psf	35 psf	40 psf	45 psf	50 psf
10	4	$3\frac{1}{4} \times 4\frac{7}{8}$	$3\frac{1}{4} \times 4\frac{7}{8}$	$3\frac{1}{4} \times 4\frac{7}{8}$	$3\frac{1}{4} \times 4\frac{7}{8}$	$3\frac{1}{4} \times 6\frac{1}{2}$
	6	$3\frac{1}{4} \times 4\frac{7}{8}$	$3\frac{1}{4} \times 6\frac{1}{2}$	$3\frac{1}{4} \times 6\frac{1}{2}$	$3\frac{1}{4} \times 6\frac{1}{2}$	$3\frac{1}{4} \times 6\frac{1}{2}$
	8	$3\frac{1}{4} \times 6\frac{1}{2}$	$3\frac{1}{4} \times 6\frac{1}{2}$	$3\frac{1}{4} \times 6\frac{1}{2}$	$3\frac{1}{4} \times 6\frac{1}{2}$	$3\frac{1}{4} \times 8\frac{1}{8}$
12	4	$3\frac{1}{4} \times 4\frac{7}{8}$	$3\frac{1}{4} \times 6\frac{1}{2}$	$3\frac{1}{4} \times 6\frac{1}{2}$	$3\frac{1}{4} \times 6\frac{1}{2}$	$3\frac{1}{4} \times 6\frac{1}{2}$
	6	$3\frac{1}{4} \times 6\frac{1}{2}$	$3\frac{1}{4} \times 6\frac{1}{2}$	$3\frac{1}{4} \times 6\frac{1}{2}$	$3\frac{1}{4} \times 8\frac{1}{8}$	$3\frac{1}{4} \times 8\frac{1}{8}$
	8	$3\frac{1}{4} \times 6\frac{1}{2}$	$3\frac{1}{4} \times 8\frac{1}{8}$	$3\frac{1}{4} \times 8\frac{1}{8}$	$3\frac{1}{4} \times 8\frac{1}{8}$	$3\frac{1}{4} \times 8\frac{1}{8}$
14	4	$3\frac{1}{4} \times 6\frac{1}{2}$	$3\frac{1}{4} \times 6\frac{1}{2}$	$3\frac{1}{4} \times 6\frac{1}{2}$	$3\frac{1}{4} \times 6\frac{1}{2}$	$3\frac{1}{4} \times 8\frac{1}{8}$
	6	$3\frac{1}{4} \times 6\frac{1}{2}$	$3\frac{1}{4} \times 8\frac{1}{8}$	$3\frac{1}{4} \times 8\frac{1}{8}$	$3\frac{1}{4} \times 8\frac{1}{8}$	$3\frac{1}{4} \times 8\frac{1}{8}$
	8	$3\frac{1}{4} \times 8\frac{1}{8}$	$3\frac{1}{4} \times 8\frac{1}{8}$	$3\frac{1}{4} \times 9\frac{3}{4}$	$3\frac{1}{4} \times 9\frac{3}{4}$	$3\frac{1}{4} \times 9\frac{3}{4}$
16	4	$3\frac{1}{4} \times 6\frac{1}{2}$	$3\frac{1}{4} \times 8\frac{1}{8}$	$3\frac{1}{4} \times 8\frac{1}{8}$	$3\frac{1}{4} \times 8\frac{1}{8}$	$3\frac{1}{4} \times 8\frac{1}{8}$
	6	$3\frac{1}{4} \times 8\frac{1}{8}$	$3\frac{1}{4} \times 8\frac{1}{8}$	$3\frac{1}{4} \times 9\frac{3}{4}$	$3\frac{1}{4} \times 9\frac{3}{4}$	$3\frac{1}{4} \times 9\frac{3}{4}$
	8	$3\frac{1}{4} \times 9\frac{3}{4}$	$3\frac{1}{4} \times 9\frac{3}{4}$	$3\frac{1}{4} \times 9\frac{3}{4}$	$3\frac{1}{4} \times 11\frac{3}{8}$	$3\frac{1}{4} \times 11\frac{3}{8}$
18	4	$3\frac{1}{4} \times 8\frac{1}{8}$	$3\frac{1}{4} \times 8\frac{1}{8}$	$3\frac{1}{4} \times 8\frac{1}{8}$	$3\frac{1}{4} \times 9\frac{3}{4}$	$3\frac{1}{4} \times 9\frac{3}{4}$
	6	$3\frac{1}{4} \times 8\frac{1}{8}$	$3\frac{1}{4} \times 9\frac{3}{4}$	$3\frac{1}{4} \times 9\frac{3}{4}$	$3\frac{1}{4} \times 11\frac{3}{8}$	$3\frac{1}{4} \times 11\frac{3}{8}$
	8	$3\frac{1}{4} \times 9\frac{3}{4}$	$3\frac{1}{4} \times 11\frac{3}{8}$	$3\frac{1}{4} \times 11\frac{3}{8}$	$3\frac{1}{4} \times 11\frac{3}{8}$	$3\frac{1}{4} \times 13$
20	4	$3\frac{1}{4} \times 8\frac{1}{8}$	$3\frac{1}{4} \times 9\frac{3}{4}$	$3\frac{1}{4} \times 9\frac{3}{4}$	$3\frac{1}{4} \times 9\frac{3}{4}$	$3\frac{1}{4} \times 11\frac{3}{8}$
	6	$3\frac{1}{4} \times 9\frac{3}{4}$	$3\frac{1}{4} \times 9\frac{3}{4}$	$3\frac{1}{4} \times 11\frac{3}{8}$	$3\frac{1}{4} \times 11\frac{3}{8}$	$3\frac{1}{4} \times 13$
	8	$3\frac{1}{4} \times 11\frac{3}{8}$	$3\frac{1}{4} \times 11\frac{3}{8}$	$3\frac{1}{4} \times 13$	$3\frac{1}{4} \times 13$	$5\frac{1}{4} \times 11\frac{3}{8}$

Table 8-7. Safe Loads for Wood Plank and Laminated Floors, Psf

Span, ft	Depths, in.							
	2	3	4	5	6	8	10	12
5	190	500						
6	130	350	670	1,100				
7	100	260	500	800				
8	70	200	380	600	900			
9	. . .	160	300	500	730			
10	. . .	130	250	400	600	1,000		
11	. . .	100	200	330	490	850		
12	. . .	90	170	300	400	740	1,100	
13	. . .	75	140	230	350	620	1,000	
14	. . .	. . .	120	200	300	530	850	
15	. . .	. . .	100	170	260	460	750	1,000
16	. . .	. . .	90	150	230	400	650	960
17	. . .	. . .	80	140	200	360	600	850
18	. . .	. . .	70	120	180	320	520	750
19	. . .	. . .	. . .	110	160	300	480	680
20	. . .	. . .	. . .	100	150	260	420	600

Bending may be introduced into columns by uniform or concentrated transverse loads, wind loads, eccentric loading applied parallel to the column axis, or a combination of these. The location and magnitude of maximum moment determine the critical section for design of a column under combined stresses.

The critical section in columns supporting trusses most often occurs at the connection of knee brace to column. Where no knee brace is present, or where the column

Table 8-8. Safe Loads for Columns, Kips

Length, ft	6 × 6	8 × 8	10 × 10	12 × 12	14 × 14	16 × 16	18 × 18	20 × 20	22 × 22	24 × 24
5	36									
6	35	67								
7	34	66	108							
8	32	65	107							
9	30	64	106							
10	27	62	105	156						
11	23	60	103	155	218					
12	19	57	101	154	215	288				
13	16	53	99	152	214	284				
14	14	48	96	150	213	283	387			
15	12	42	92	147	211	287	363			
16	11	37	88	145	208	280	361	456		
17	9	33	82	141	205	278	369	450	554	
18	8	29	76	136	202	276	358	448	548	
19	...	26	68	131	198	273	355	446	546	719
20	...	24	61	125	194	269	353	444	544	654
21	...	...	56	118	188	265	349	442	543	652
22	...	...	51	109	182	261	346	439	540	650
23	...	...	...	100	176	256	342	435	538	648
24	...	...	...	92	168	249	337	431	534	646

supports a beam, the critical section for moment usually occurs at the bottom of the truss or beam. In such cases, a rigid connection must be provided to resist bending moment, or adequate diagonal bracing must be provided to carry wind loads into the support.

Wind pressures may be distributed among exterior and interior columns where connecting construction permits all the columns to form part of a resisting unit. Total panel wind load may be divided according to some rational weighing system and may be equally or unequally distributed between windward and leeward sides, as 50:50, 60:40, or some other ratio as construction warrants. Where column sizes vary, loads on individual columns should vary according to the moment of inertia of column cross section and according to position in structure and rigidity of connecting construction. Windward columns receive load more directly than others and so may take a greater part of the load.

Where wind pressure is involved, wind combined working stresses should be used, according to the governing code.

In heavy timber construction, girders and columns are often framed together with steel fittings (Fig. 8-1). Many types of post caps and beam hangers are on the market. Wood corbels with or without ring connectors are also used.

Concrete column caps, though seldom used, have been found by tests to permit the connection to outlast the column in fires, since heat is not built up in the joint as much as with steel post caps.

In timber buildings of several stories, bottom ends of upper story columns should not rest directly on beams or girders, since low bearing stress only is allowed for side grain, and beams and girders may shrink to cause settlement. Column ends should be supported on post caps or carried through to the upper ends of lower-story columns. Use of glued or seasoned girders eliminates the shrinkage hazard.

Exposed corners of wood columns should be chamfered. Keep the bottom of wood columns 3 in. or more above concrete floors to avoid decay due to water on the floor. Install a steel bearing plate and dowels or steel strap anchors at the base of columns. Always trim ends of columns neat and square for good bearing. Leave air pockets of ½ in. or more around all timber columns adjoining concrete or masonry walls.

Wood columns in basements built into partitions should be open on two or more sides.   Precautions should be taken to prevent columns from becoming damp from stagnant moist air or water from laundries or refrigerators.

The strength of posts in round form is greater than would be expected from ordinary engineering formulas.   The strength may be taken as identical with that of a square column of the same length and cross-sectional area.

Checks and splits of minor nature seen in wood columns that have been in service for some time do not usually lower load-carrying capacity.   Checks and splits are critical only when they are excessive in width beyond normal shrinkage, when they extend for a major proportion of the length of a column without being staggered, or when they tend to run out the sides.

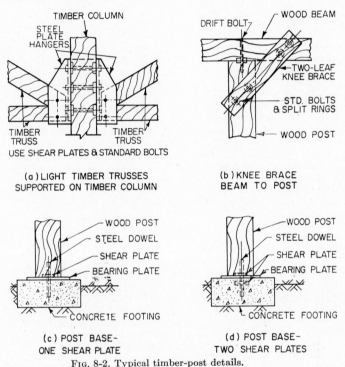

FIG. 8-2. Typical timber-post details.

A few typical column connections are shown in Figs. 8-1 and 8-2.

8-12. Plywood.   An important structural wood material, plywood, finds its best use where a combination of structural and enclosure qualities is needed.   It is used extensively for formwork, wall coverings, and diaphragms.   It consists of thin veneers glued together with the grain of alternate layers perpendicular to each other (Art. 2-44).

Strength qualities and construction details may be found in "Technical Design of Plywood," Douglas Fir Plywood Association, Tacoma, Wash.

There are two basic types—exterior and moisture-resistant.   The exterior type is made with an adhesive that is insoluble in water and is suitable for outdoor applications.   The other type is suitable for interior uses and short-time exterior exposure.

In computing tensile or compressive strength of plywood, it is customary to consider only those plies with grain parallel to the load.   And for bending, the moment of inertia usually is based on plies parallel to the span.   (H. J. Hansen, "Timber Engineers' Handbook," John Wiley & Sons, Inc., New York,; L. J. Markwardt and A. D.

Freas, "Approximate Tentative Methods of Calculating the Strength of Plywood," *Forest Products Laboratory Bulletin.*)

FASTENERS FOR TIMBER CONSTRUCTION

8-13. Bolts.   Standard machine bolts with square heads and nuts and standard threads are used extensively in timber construction.   Hexagonal heads and nuts are seldom used.

Construction bolts vary from $\frac{1}{2}$ in. to $1\frac{1}{4}$ in. or larger in diameter and from 3 to 30 in. in length.   Commercial stock lengths vary in $\frac{1}{2}$-in. increments up to 10 in. and in 1-in. increments from 10 to 30 in.   In large quantities, they may be ordered to any length direct from a manufacturer.

Length of bolts used in unseasoned or partly seasoned timber should be enough to extend just through the nut, so that later servicing may be performed with the available length of thread.   Specified bolt lengths should be the length of the bolt in the timbers, termed the *grip*, plus washer thicknesses, plus nut room.   Often, nut thickness is taken as equal to bolt diameter.   Leave room for lock nuts when used.

When five or more wood pieces are used with split-ring connectors at all contact faces, it may be necessary to furnish extra-length bolts, so that members may properly be strung on the bolts and pulled together.   Thread length must permit full take-up.

Since bearing values of bolts on steel plates are predicated on full contact, good practice requires, and many codes specify, that no bearing may be taken on the threaded portion.

Field men are great believers in long bolts, since they are more easily installed, but they should not be permitted to use excessive lengths.   Some jobs after completion or after servicing look too much like porcupines.

Bolt-order lists may be made up directly from design plans or shop details by an experienced estimator.   Overages that anticipate loss and breakage should be included; usually 2% is adequate.

Painting and galvanizing are not required under ordinary conditions for bolts on interior construction, but those on exterior construction do need protection and should be painted—or better still, galvanized.   Good practice requires that bolts and nuts be dipped in red lead and oil before use in either indoor or outdoor structures when galvanizing is not specified.   Also, for appearance grades of glued timbers and for ornamental exposed sawn timbers, used indoors or outdoors, it is good practice to shop-paint all hardware.

Appearance of timber construction is not enhanced by projecting rusty threads of bolts and the rusty streak that may extend from them.   Perhaps on glued timbers where servicing is not required, it may become the custom to use cap nuts, like those now used on machines, to cover the threaded end.

Remember that the bolthead has a better appearance than the threaded end, but the nut must be placed where it can later be reached by servicing wrenches.   Thus, end trusses should have nuts on the inside face, since the outside is nearly always covered by end-wall construction, so that the bolthead is concealed and therefore is inaccessible.

Concealed boltheads should be prevented from turning by some device, or servicing becomes difficult or impossible.   Washers with a raised lug to engage the bolthead and a projecting spur to engage the wood have been used but are no longer on the market.   Some builders drill holes in washers and drive nails alongside the bolthead.

Number of lengths and sizes of bolts should be kept to the absolute minimum.   Each new size requires another drill, wrench, overage, and extra clerical labor.   Most construction jobs are handled best with only two sizes of bolts.   Weights, sizes, and lengths may be taken from hardware catalogs.

Safety-head bolts provide the best solution to the problem of concealed locations.   Several companies make a safety-, or economy-head, bolt whose head is large, round, and flat and has lugs on the underside that engage the wood and resist turning.   The large head eliminates the need for a washer and so is economical of material and simple to install.   Such bolts save erection labor costs, since separate washers need not be handled; they are especially suitable where the head is covered by construction and inaccessible to servicing operations. Safety heads are not suitable for bearing on steel. They give timber construction a better appearance than ordinary bolts.

Safety plywood bolts have a flush head with lugs and spiral grooves on the underface to prevent turning. They are useful for timbers or plywood in railings or decks where the surface is exposed to wear or traffic. Safety plywood boltheads are not suitable for bearing on steel.

Carriage bolts are little used in construction except on equipment, railings, and on guards, or where traffic moves close to construction as in passages and galleries, and when large bearing area is not required. Carriage boltheads are not suitable for bearing on steel. They have an enlarged square neck, which must be considered when specifying washer or steel bearing under the head. They were designed for use in hardwoods.

Rods, in effect, are bolts with threads on both ends. They are normally used for tension members and sway bracing, or where the required length of bolt is greater than that of stock bolts. Often termed **double-end bolts,** rods are sometimes used in lieu of headed bolts to facilitate erection or demounting of adjoining steel assemblies. For plain rods, the critical section for computing allowable tension is at the root of threads. For upset rods, the strength of shank governs, since in standard upsets the strength at root of thread is greater than the strength of the shank itself. Lengths should be figured as for bolts, except length is out to out, and sufficient thread room should be provided for tightening in maintenance operations.

When specifying rods greater than $1\frac{1}{2}$-in. diameter, provide for an alternate size to the next larger $\frac{1}{4}$ in. if the specified size is a $\frac{1}{8}$-in. increment. This will expedite delivery and allow possible economy. Often, two smaller rods or bolts can be used to advantage in lieu of one large size.

Timber grips of steel with large round heads on each outer end and tapered, toothed interlocking inner ends are available. They have an enlarged tapered neck, which must be considered in specifying washers or holes in steel bearings under heads.

Drift bolts, sometimes termed drift pins, are bolts used primarily to prevent timbers from moving laterally in relation to each other, rather than to resist pulling apart. They are used more in dock and trestle work than in trusses and building frames. They may be headed or plain rods, either square or round, and may have square, wedge, or pointed ends. Cut from rod stock or purchased from hardware companies, they are usually driven in undersize holes. Size and number are usually decided by arbitrary standards, rather than by stress or load-carrying values.

Relative costs for various types of $\frac{3}{4} \times 12$ in. bolts with nuts are given in Table 8-9 with the cost of standard machine bolts taken as 100.

In comparing costs, note that safety-head, safety plywood, and carriage bolts require only one washer per bolt and other types require two washers per bolt when both head and nut bear on wood.

Table 8-9. Relative Cost of Bolts

Machine bolt, square head, black	100
Machine bolt, square head, galvanized	130
Safety-head bolt	225
Safety plywood bolt	111
Carriage bolt	112

8-14. Bolted Timber Joints. Design of bolted joints should be according to rules and load values of National Design Specification, National Lumber Manufacturers Association, Washington, D.C., or Uniform Building Code, International Conference of Building Officials, Los Angeles, Calif. UBC gives values somewhat more conservative than NDS. Increases in allowable loads for short-duration loading apply to bolts as well as timbers; construction conditions, however, often require reductions from tabulated values. See provisions of NDS or UBC.

Safe loads, in pounds, on bolts in seasoned lumber of the following species: eastern red cedar, southern cypress, Douglas fir (coast region), western larch, southern yellow pine, in joints consisting of three members (double shear) in which the side members are one-half the thickness of the main member, should not exceed values in Tables 8-10 and 8-11. For example, if a joint with three 2 × 8s were required to carry 2,000 lb, the number of ⅝-in. bolts needed is 2,000/670, or 3.

When a joint consists of two members (single shear) of equal thickness, one-half the tabulated load for a piece twice the thickness of one of the members should be used. When members of a two-member joint are of unequal thickness, one-half the tabulated load for a piece twice the thickness of the thinner member should be used.

Table 8-10. Holding Power of Bolts, Lb
(Loads perpendicular to grain, Douglas fir and southern pine)

Length of bolt in main members, in.	Diam of bolt, in.						
	½	⅝	¾	⅞	1	1⅛	1¼
2	590	670	750	820	890		
3	890	1,000	1,120	1,230	1,340		
4	1,040	1,330	1,490	1,640	1,790		
5	990	1,470	1,830	2,050	2,240	2,440	
6	.....	1,420	1,970	2,400	2,680	2,920	
7	.....	1,350	1,920	2,510	3,040	3,400	
8	.....	1,260	1,830	2,480	3,150	3,760	4,100
10	.....	.....	.....	2,300	3,000	3,790	4,600
12	.....	.....	.....	.....	2,790	3,590	4,460

Table 8-11. Holding Power of Bolts, Lb
(Loads parallel to grain, Douglas fir and southern pine)

Length of bolt in main members, in.	Diam of bolt, in.						
	½	⅝	¾	⅞	1	1⅛	1¼
2	1,180	1,560	1,910	2,230	2,550		
3	1,290	1,990	2,650	3,250	3,790		
4	1,290	2,010	2,890	2,830	4,720		
5	1,290	2,010	2,890	3,940	5,100	6,350	
6	.....	2,010	2,910	3,940	5,140	6,500	
7	.....	2,010	2,910	3,940	5,150	6,500	
8	.....	2,010	2,910	3,940	5,150	6,500	8,040
10	.....	.....	.....	3,940	5,150	6,500	8,040
12	.....	.....	.....	.....	5,150	6,500	8,040

For joints with more than three members, the load for each shear plane should be computed in the same manner as for a two-member joint.

When metal plates are used on each side of a wood member, tabulated bolt values may be increased one-quarter for values parallel to the grain.

A row of bolts is defined as a number of bolts placed in a line parallel to the direction of load. Minimum center-to-center spacing of bolts in any one row should be four times the bolt diameter. In no case should the bolt bearing capacity of any member be exceeded.

Spacing between rows of bolts for loads perpendicular to grain should be not less than 2½ times the bolt diameter for an L/d of bolt equal to 2, and not less than 5 times the bolt diameter for L/d of 6 or more. Intermediate values may be interpolated.

Spacing between rows of bolts for loads parallel to grain should be such that the net tension area remaining at a critical section should be not less than 80% for softwoods, and 100% for hardwoods, of the total area in bearing under all bolts in the timber.

End margin is defined as the distance from the end of a bolted member to the center of the nearest bolt hole. This distance, for a member in tension, shall be not less than seven times the bolt diameter for softwoods and five times for hardwoods. End margin for members in compression should be not less than four times the bolt diameter.

Bolt holes should be $\frac{1}{16}$ in. oversize.

8-15. Timber Connectors. Before the introduction of timber connectors, there were two obstructions to economical timber construction: (1) Under then existent design practices, joints were the weakest part of structures and denied to timber its latent economy; member sizes usually had to be much larger than required by stresses. (2) Normal construction methods of the time called for long timbers of large cross section, whereas the timber most readily available was in short lengths and of small cross section.

Timber connectors eliminated both objections. Joint efficiency is so enhanced that often the full working stress of timber may be developed. Large loads can be transmitted between members without seriously reducing the cross-sectional area of members joined, and small-sized structural-quality lumber works well as spaced members

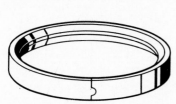

Fig. 8-3. Split-ring connector.   Fig. 8-4. Shear-plate connector.

joined by connectors. There are several types and sizes of connectors to fit various particular uses.

Timber connectors are steel rings that are placed in grooves in adjoining members to prevent relative movement or metal plates that are embedded in the faces of adjoining timbers. The purpose of bolts used with these connectors is to prevent the timbers from separating. Thus, the strength of a joint with timber connectors depends only on the connectors.

Split rings (Fig. 8-3) have a double bevel that permits easy assembly and increases load value. Split rings are used in wood-to-wood connections and shear plates (Fig. 8-4) in wood-to-steel connections or in wood-to-wood field joints or connections that need to be demountable. Other types of connectors are available but are not often used in building construction.

For very small jobs, routings for connectors can be made by hand tools, but power tools are far better, and for a quantity of routings a necessity.

Load values for connectors vary with style, size, and angle of load with the grain of the wood. Also, load values vary with duration of maximum load and moisture content of the wood. In addition, they are based on a minimum size of bolts and washers.

Connectors require considerable detailed information for proper use. (See "Teco Design Manual for Timber Connectors Construction" and "Typical Designs of Timber Connectors," Timber Engineering Co., Washington, D.C., for design and construction information.)

8-16. Lag Screws. These are often used in timber construction for steel-to-wood connections and sometimes for wood connections. A complete design method may be found in National Design Specification, National Lumber Manufacturers Association, Washington, D.C. See also "Strength of Lag Screws," West Coast Lumbermen's Association, Portland, Ore.

Lag screws usually need different size shank and screw holes. Lags should be screwed into prebored lead holes and not driven. The lead hole for the shank should have the same diameter as the shank and the same depth as the unthreaded portion of the shank. The lead hole for the threaded portion should have a diameter equal to 60 to 75% of the diameter of the shank and the same depth as the threaded portion.

In general, a penetration of the threaded portion equal to ten to twelve times the shank diameter in softwoods will develop the ultimate tensile strength of a lag screw.

8-17. Nails and Spikes. Connections of wood structural members with common nails and spikes should be designed in accordance with provisions of the National Design Specification, National Lumber Manufacturers Association, Washington, D.C., and Tables 8-12 and 8-13. (Grooved nails have greater holding power than wire nails.) Spikes are large nails.

Table 8-12. Safe Lateral Strength of Wire Nails
(Inserted perpendicular to the grain of the wood, lb per nail)

Kind of wood	Size of nail									
	6d	8d	10d	12d	16d	20d	30d	40d	50d	60d
	Length of nail, in.									
	2	2½	3	3¼	3½	4	4½	5	5½	6
Douglas fir and southern pine..	63	78	94	94	107	139	154	176	202	223

Table 8-13. Safe Resistance to Withdrawal of Wire Nails
(Inserted perpendicular to the grain of the wood, lb per lin in. of penetration into main member)

Kind of wood	Size of nail									
	6d	8d	10d	12d	16d	20d	30d	40d	50d	60d
Douglas fir....	29	34	38	38	42	49	53	58	63	68
Southern pine..	42	48	55	55	60	71	76	83	90	97

End distance, edge distance, and spacing of nails should be such as to avoid splitting of the wood. Nails should not be driven closer together than one-half their length, unless driven in bored holes, or closer to the edge of the timber than one-quarter their length. They should penetrate at least half their length into the timber farthest from the head. Holes for nails, when necessary to prevent splitting, should be smaller in diameter than the nails.

A wire nail inserted perpendicular to the grain of the wood should not be subjected to a greater load causing shear and bending than the safe lateral strength indicated in Table 8-12.

A wire nail driven parallel to the grain should not be subjected to more than three-fourths the lateral load allowable when inserted perpendicular.

A wire nail inserted perpendicular to the grain of the wood should not be subjected to a greater load tending to cause withdrawal than the safe resistance indicated in Table 8-13.

Nails driven nearly parallel to the grain or into the end grain should not be considered in computing withdrawal resistance. When nails or spikes are driven in unseasoned lumber, the allowable withdrawal load should be reduced 75%.

Design and detail of nail construction are given in the National Design Specification, National Lumber Manufacturers Association, Washington, D.C., and Uniform Building Code, International Conference of Building Officials, Los Angeles, Calif.

8-18. Wood Screws. Wood-screw connections should be designed for load values given in Tables 8-14 and 8-15. (See National Design Specification, National Lumber Manufacturers Association, Washington, D.C., and Uniform Building Code, International Conference of Building Officials, Los Angeles, Calif.)

A wood screw used to fasten wood to wood or a metal plate to a wood member should not be subjected to a greater load causing shear and bending than the safe lateral strength given in Table 8-14. Screws should have an embedment in the farthest member of at least six-tenths of the length of the screw, and the length should be not less than seven times the diameter.

A wood screw inserted perpendicular to the grain of the wood should not be subjected to a greater load tending to cause withdrawal than the safe resistance given in Table 8-15.

Table 8-14. Safe Lateral Resistance of Wood Screws, Lb per Screw

Kind of wood	Gage of screw					
	12	14	16	18	20	24
Douglas fir and southern pine........	185	232	284	342	406	548

Table 8-15. Safe Resistance of Wood Screws to Withdrawal
(Inserted perpendicular to grain of wood, lb per lin in. of screw embedment)

Kind of wood	Gage of screw					
	12	14	16	18	20	24
Douglas fir.............	160	179	199	218	237	276
Southern pine..........	214	240	266	292	317	369

A wood screw inserted in end grain or nearly parallel to the grain should not be considered in computing withdrawal resistance.

8-19. Washers. Boltheads and nuts that bear on wood require metal washers to distribute pressure and protect the wood against abrasion and crushing. Washers may be classified as cast, malleable, round-plate, square-plate, and cut. Washers should have sufficient area to avoid injury to wood fibers and be thick enough to resist breakage, corrosion, and cupping.

Washer types vary in material, size, thickness, cost, use, and appearance. They may control length of bolt. Best practice calls for large, cast, malleable, or square- or round-plate washers for all bolts engaging timber connectors, and smaller, more economical cut washers for other connections. Softwoods, such as pine and fir, need a larger washer than hardwoods, such as oak.

Square-plate washers cannot be used in countersinks. Where a countersink is needed and a standard round-plate washer is not large enough, use a combination of standard and oversize round-plate washers; i.e., for a $3\!/\!4$-in. bolt, we might use a 1- or

1¼-in. round-plate washer to bear against the wood, and then a ¾-in. standard round-plate washer under the head or nut. Usually, except in very large members, it is not possible to countersink for a malleable or cast washer, since the size of the hole becomes prohibitive. In many cases, it may be advantageous to place a larger washer under a standard-bolt washer.

It may be expedient to place a cast or malleable washer under the head or nut of a rod or bolt that bears on a steel plate. By this means, the required thickness of the steel plate may be reduced.

Cast-iron washers are heavy, thick, bulky, require a longer bolt, and are more expensive than malleable or square-plate washers. which give equal or greater bearing area. They do not, however, cup or easily corrode. They withstand excessive pressure but may sometimes break under shock or extreme temperatures. They should be used only on very heavy construction, where their size will not spoil appearance. They are well adapted to heavy construction along the seashore or in swampy regions, where corrosion is an extreme hazard. They are well adapted to use on docks, trestles, and bridge abutments but are too heavy and bulky in appearance for use on timber trusses or building framing of any kind. Cast washers are one of the oldest types of washer.

Malleable-iron washers are light, of medium thickness, and reasonable in cost. They do not cup under reasonable pressures nor corrode easily. They resist shock well but sometimes break under excessive pressure or other abuse. They are the most popular large washers.

Round-plate washers have a neat appearance and are the most economical type. Light in weight, they take little bolt room and are used extensively in timber construction. **Cut or wrought washers** are termed round-plate washers in some catalogs. These smaller standard washers do not have sufficient bearing area in softwood for important bolts that engage timber connectors but are quite satisfactory for all bolts in hardwood and for bolts in softwood without connectors.

Standard round-plate washers usually are called **cut washers**; those of large diameter and thickness for use with connectors are termed **round-plate washers.**

Square-plate washers are light in weight and of medium thickness. They have been used extensively when cast and malleable washers were unobtainable. They do not give a good appearance, because they are left turned at all angles. Plate washers should not be used in marine work, where corrosion is a hazard, unless they are galvanized.

Segmental cast washers have been developed to provide maximum packing under a bolthead or nut in servicing operations where shrinkage has occurred. These washers can be inserted without removal of the bolt or nut. Elimination of bolt removal is often an important saving, since considerable labor is involved, and sometimes bolt removal is impossible. ("Timber Maintenance Methods," Timber Structures, Inc., Portland, Ore.)

Horseshoe washers, similar to square-plate washers but with one open side, are used for servicing timber structures. They have the same advantage as segmental washers in that they do not require bolt or nut removal. They, however, are not so thick, and more of them must therefore be used to obtain the same packing results. They must be made to order, since they are not a standard commercial product. See "Timber Maintenance Methods" for description and use directions.

Spring or lock washers, used so extensively in mechanical work, are rarely found in construction. On crane runways, supports of rotating or vibrating machines, or in similar locations, lock nuts or other means should be used to avoid hazardous loosening of nuts.

Washers should be galvanized, parkerized, or given an equal protective coating where exposed to salt air or salt water. Washers used in outdoor structures and not exposed to salt-air hazards should be dipped in red lead and oil before being installed and given a good coat of lead and oil paint after installation. Washers used on interior construction need not be painted unless for appearance.

Washers are not needed under heads of plywood, safety, economy, or carriage head bolts; nor are they needed under boltheads or nuts that bear on ironwork, except to cover oversize holes in anchor plates or to distribute concentrated loads over greater steel areas.

Rods in tension such as tie rods, hangers, sway bracing, and tension members of structural frames may require large bearing washers. Engineers usually consider that commercial-size washers have sufficient area for ordinary bearing in structural woods, but when in doubt compression-across-grain stress (with allowed increase for small bearing lengths) and thickness to resist cupping should be checked.

In making up material lists, remember that small cut washers are not considered proper on bolts that engage timber connectors. Table 8-16 gives recommended sizes of washers for use in connector joints. Order lists should always contain overages that anticipate loss and breakage.

Table 8-17 shows weights and relative costs of various types of washers, with the cost of round-plate washers taken as 100.

Table 8-16. Recommended Sizes for Plate Washers for Connector Joints

Bolt, in.	Connectors	Hole, in.	Washer size, in.	
			Outside	Thickness
$\frac{1}{2}$	$2\frac{1}{2}$-in. split rings	$\frac{9}{16}$	$2\frac{1}{4}$ (round)	$\frac{3}{16}$
$\frac{3}{4}$	4-in. split rings, $2\frac{5}{8}$- and 4-in. shear plates	$1\frac{3}{16}$	3 (round)	$\frac{1}{4}$
$\frac{7}{8}$	4-in. shear plates	$1\frac{5}{16}$	3 × 3 (square)	$\frac{3}{16}$

Table 8-17. Cost and Weight of Washers for $\frac{3}{4}$-in. Bolts

Type	Relative cost	Weight per 100, lb
Cut.....................	40	11
Round-plate...........	100	50
Malleable..............	180	33
Cast..................	450	85

8-20. Ironwork in Timber Construction. Some ironwork is used in every timber structure for bearing plates, truss heel connections, splice plates, attachment angles, truss rods, and roof bracing. Do not embed the metal in timber members, except in special protected locations.

Ironwork used outdoors should be galvanized or well painted. Use oversize holes for all anchor bolts to ease installation.

Steel hangers and anchors are used extensively in timber construction. Many hangers are shop-detailed and made of structural-steel shapes. Some equipment companies manufacture hangers and anchors as stock items. Timber Engineering Co., Washington, D.C., for example, makes a line of Trip-L-Grip anchors of heavy sheet metal that serves well for many lightweight connections.

TIMBER FRAMING

8-21. Timber Trusses. Old-type trusses had single-piece timber chords, timber compression diagonals, and steel-rod tension verticals. Wood members were sawn timbers, usually unseasoned. Diagonals were dapped into chords and steel heel shoes transferred large end stress from top to bottom chord. Such trusses served well and still are often built, although connections become loose because of shrinkage, unless serviced until seasoned.

In modern trusses, extensive use is made of timber connectors. Usually chords are two- or three-leaf, thin members, interlaced with single-leaf or two-leaf web systems. Some trusses, such as for bridges, have large solid timber members with steel gussets and shear plate connections. Bowstring timber trusses (Fig. 8-5) give good service with little maintanance, while parallel-chord timber connector trusses (Fig. 8-6), though well designed, often require maintenance if built of unseasoned lumber.

Parallel-chord trusses or trusses with slightly sloping top chord and level bottom chord and separate leaf members are not too well adapted to timber construction. Chord stresses are maximum at the truss center and a minimum or even zero in end panels. Construction limitations, however, do not permit taking advantage of this tapering off of stress intensity. Chords usually are made uniform throughout their lengths, though they may be inefficient in many panels. Web stresses are many times those of an equivalent bowstring truss; so web members and web-to-chord connections must be very heavy.

Heavy web stresses must be transferred to chords through wide arcs; timber is at a disadvantage with parallel chords with multiple connector joints and eccentricity and tension across grain. The resulting stresses, plus seasoning shrinkage stresses, may form combinations too great for the timber to take, unless heavy and costly connections are provided. Conventional multiple-pattern bolt and connector joints may not be sufficient. Note that not only the heel connection but nearly every joint is important and critical.

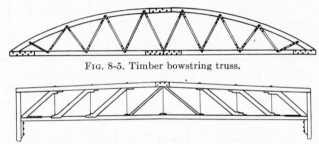

FIG. 8-5. Timber bowstring truss.

FIG. 8-6. Timber parallel-chord truss.

All species of timber are ill-adapted to resist tension-across-grain stresses, or those stresses produced by eccentric joints. Douglas fir is particularly vulnerable in this respect. Furthermore, unseasoned lumber is not well adapted to multiple-ring patterns. Though timbers may be surface-dry, they are seldom seasoned throughout until the second year of service. Shrinkage and some checking are a natural result of seasoning processes. Extensive field observation has led to the conclusion that such actions often cause distress in parallel-chord trusses: Secondary actions may become troublemakers in framing that has been well designed against all primary actions.

Good parallel-chord trusses are often built in timber, however, for moderate spans of sawn timbers, with two- or three-leaf chords and one- or two-leaf web system, in Howe, Pratt, or Warren web pattern.

Triangular wood trusses are adapted to short-span steep-pitched roofs, and only in such situations are they practical. All members are usually sawn timbers, and usually two-leaf chords with single-leaf web systems and timber connectors. Webs are sometimes extended through the top chords to engage and support purlins against sliding action. Such trusses often carry ceilings on the lower chords. Triangular trusses, because of high rise for a given span, are not often built for spans greater than 60 ft.

Ornamental steep-pitched trusses, such as scissors trusses, are frequently used for churches. Here appearance is highly important and worthy of extra cost. Dry material, chamfered corners, ornamental hardware, and other extras should be provided as desired, and as costs permit.

Bowstring trusses (Figs. 8-5 and 8-7) are by far the best type for timber construction. They are strong, stiff, and low in cost. They have been built in the United

States with spans of more than 200 ft. Web systems may be arranged in Warren, Pratt, or Howe patterns. Eccentricity of joints is no handicap since web stresses are very low. Warren web systems are used extensively.

Several reasons explain the utility and economy of bowstring trusses. Since they approximate a tied "ideal arch," chord stresses are nearly uniform throughout their lengths and web stresses are low, even for unbalanced loading. Chords can be of uniform section throughout and yet make efficient use of material for their full length. Webs and web-to-chord connections can be light.

Pleasing curved roof lines and low side walls are permitted by use of bowstring trusses. Roof end bays can be broached to permit low end walls without harming appearance. Webs can be extended up through the top chord to form build-ups, which permit flat or slightly sloping roof contours, and use of monitor or sawtooth roof construction.

Fig. 8-7. Industrial building with roof supported on bowstring trusses.

Strength of bowstring trusses depends mainly on three major units—the top chord, bottom chord, and heel connection that joins them. Careful design and construction of these items insure the safety of the entire truss.

Curved top chords are constructed in three general ways:

1. Overlapping segments with top edge sawn to a curve may be used to form a two-leaf chord with splices in alternate panels. This arrangement makes a strong stiff member, whose parts can be prefabricated from short-length lumber and conveniently shipped to the job site. For unusually heavy loads, three-leaf chords may be needed.

2. The chord may be laminated at the shop or job site from 2-in. stock-length lumber to form a curved two-leaf chord. Nails and stitch bolts hold the laminations together. Such chords cannot be routed for split rings or shear plates; so connections are limited to bolts or toothed rings. This type of chord is not particularly strong against axial or bending actions, except when laterally supported at frequent intervals; panel lengths should therefore be short. This type of chord is well adapted to field fabrication and assembly and has been widely used.

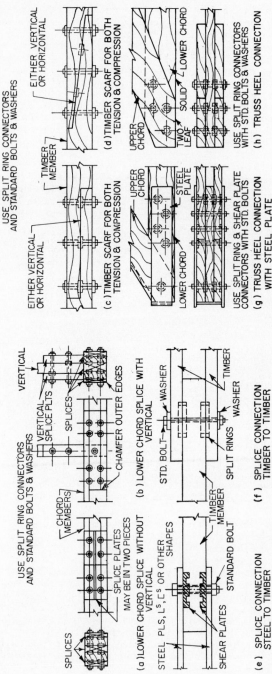

Fig. 8-8. Typical timber-truss details.

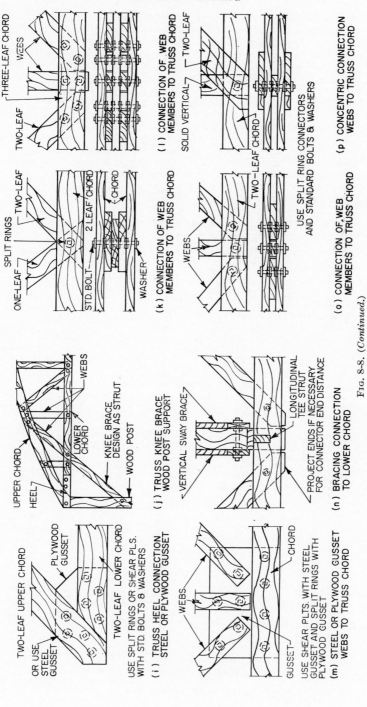

FIG. 8-8. (Continued.)

3. Glued-laminated curved chords, assembled as one- or two-leaf members, make the best top-chord members but are slightly higher in cost than other types. They should be shop-laminated, and field-spliced as necessary for handling and shipment. Such chords take high working stresses, so are small in size, and can be bored and routed for bolts and connectors. Bottom chords and webs of such bowstring trusses are usually sawn timbers. Heel plates and bottom-chord splice plates may be either wood or steel.

A monochord parallel-chord truss has been developed, which by use of new techniques, with dry glued timbers for chords and different types of connections, avoids nearly all the bad features of the separate-leaf, timber-connector type of parallel-chord truss. It is not so economical, however, as a bowstring truss of equal span and loading.

In truss design, span, spacing, and loads—dead and live, uniform and concentrated—are decided on first. (Wind rarely affects truss design, because of the larger stresses allowed.) Arrangement of truss members—depth, shape, and type of web system—is then selected. Purlins usually are placed at panel points. Closely spaced roof joists placed between panel points produce a uniform load along the top chord, which

Table 8-18. Dimensions, Sizes, and Weights of Typical Flat Roof Trusses

Span, ft	No. of panels	Truss height	Roof height	Camber, in.	Heel width, in.	Length of bearings, in.	Truss weight, lb
40	6	5'6''	6'6¼''	2	6	6	1,100
50	6	6'9''	7'9¼''	2½	6	6	1,500
60	6	8'0''	9'0¼''	3	6	8	2,100
70	6	9'6''	10'6¼''	3½	6	8	2,800
80	8	10'9''	11'9¼''	4	8	8	3,800
90	8	12'0''	13'0¼''	4½	8	10	4,400
100	8	13'3''	14'3¼''	5	8	10	5,000

NOTES: Tabular values are for average conditions. Individual designs may vary. Truss height is the vertical distance from bearing line to top of truss at mid-span. Roof height, as shown, is truss height plus depth of typical roof joists and thickness of 1-in. nominal sheathing. Dimensions were determined for typical case of 40 psf total loading and 20-ft spacing; i.e., 800 lb per lin ft of truss. Heel width is also minimum pilaster width.

Table 8-19. Dimensions, Sizes, and Weights of Typical Bowstring Roof Trusses

Span, ft	No. of panels	Truss height	Roof height	Arc length	Camber, in.	Heel width, in.	Length of bearings, in.	Truss weight, lb
40	6	5'9''	6'9½''	41'10¹¹⁄₁₆''	1½	6	5	950
50	6	7'2⅛''	8'2⅝''	52'4⁵⁄₁₆''	2	6	6½	1,120
60	6	8'7¾''	9'8¼''	62'10''	2½	6	8	1,530
70	6	10'0¾''	11'1¼''	73'3¹¹⁄₁₆''	2¾	6	9	2,180
80	8	11'6⅜''	12'6⅞''	83'9⁵⁄₁₆''	3	6	10	2,700
90	8	12'11½''	14'0''	94'3''	3½	6	11½	3,330
100	8	14'4½''	15'5''	104'8¹¹⁄₁₆''	4	6	12½	3,710
110	10	15'6⅛''	16'7¼''	115'2⅜''	4½	7¾	11½	5,100
120	10	16'11¾''	18'0¼''	125'8''	4¾	7¾	11½	6,230
130	10	18'4¾''	19'5¼''	136'1¹¹⁄₁₆''	5	7¾	12½	7,050
140	12	19'9⅞''	20'10¼''	146'7⅜''	5½	7¾	13½	8,170
150	12	21'3''	22'3½''	157'1''	5¾	7¾	14	9,460

NOTES: Tabular values are for average conditions. Individual designs may vary. Truss-height is the vertical distance from bearing line to top of truss at mid-span. Roof height, as shown, is truss height plus depth of typical roof joists and thickness of 1-in. nominal sheathing. Dimensions as determined for typical case of 40 psf total loading and 20 ft spacing; i.e., 800 lb per lin ft of truss. Heel width is also minimum pilaster width.

induces bending in that member. If trusses carry ceilings, compute the ceiling loads and concentrate them at lower-chord panel points. ("Typical Designs of Timber Structures," Timber Engineering Co., Washington, D.C.)

For simplicity, consider all loads concentrated at panel points and web and chord members as intersecting at these points. Determine stresses by one of the methods in Sec. 3.

Select chord-member sizes, taking into account column action in compression members, net sections in tension members, and types of connections. Where uniform or concentrated loads of roof or ceiling are placed on members between panel points, the members affected should be designed to resist both direct stress and bending. Determine the location of splices and type of heel joint. Web system should be arranged to meet or overlap chords. Tension members may be steel rods or structural shapes. Timber connectors and bolts may be used for connections.

As the design progresses, the designer should make a drawing showing loads, stress diagram, framing arrangement of trusses, purlins, joists, sheathing, bracing, and truss supports, as well as truss member and connection sizes and locations. Bracing should be provided to give lateral support to top and bottom chords of trusses. Knee braces or other supports capable of resisting lateral forces should be used between trusses and columns or walls unless the trusses rest on self-supporting walls.

End-panel connections often require multiple-ring patterns, since stresses are high. All timber trusses with spliced or glued-laminated bottom chord are cambered.

Many example of timber-truss designs can be found in "Typical Designs of Timber Structures" and "Trussed Rafters," Timber Engineering Co., Washington, D.C. See also "Timber Trusses and Bracing," American Institute of Timber Construction, Washington, D.C.

A few typical truss details are shown in Fig. 8-8. See also Tables 8-18 and 8-19.

8-22. Timber Arches. Used extensively in timber construction for both ornamental and utility units, arches may be two-hinged, with hinges at each base, or three-hinged, with hinges at crown and each base. They may be low-rise, like a bowstring truss, or high-rise, as used in steep-pitched church roofs.

Because of the horizontal thrust at the bases, buttresses, counterforts, tie rods, or other means must be provided. For low-rise arches, tie rods are often placed at ceiling level, and for high-rise arches, ties are usually placed under the floor.

Arches may be composed of overlapping segments, nailed-laminated or glued-laminated. Size of sections should permit shipment by road and rail. Glued-laminated arches should be built in a central shop, where equipment and personnel can produce a strong and durable glue line. They must have laminations thin enough to bend easily to the required curvature. In general, laminations are of 1- or 2-in. nominal stock.

Timber arches should have steel base shoes and a steel crown connection. For moderate spans, connections are not usually true hinges, but steel shoes that are adequate to transfer thrusts and reactions.

Many arches have been built with wood laminations and mechanical fastenings, such as nails and bolts, but no glue. In such members, relatively low shear stresses are developed, since the lamination joints are not so strong as glued joints; hence, mechanically laminated timbers are not so strong as sawn or glued timbers of equal size and grade. They should be used with caution and with a full realization of their limitations.

Constant-section arches (Fig. 8-9), sometimes called radial or barrel arches, may be of constant or variable radius. This type frequently is the most economical way to span wide areas; it has been used for spans of more than 200 ft.

The constant-section arch is of three types—tied arch, barrel arch, and buttressed arch.

Both tied and buttressed arches are low-rise. Steel tie rods, which resist the horizontal thrust of the tied arch, may be elevated slightly when they encroach unduly on headroom. The buttressed type has no tie rods, and overhead space is completely unrestricted. Soil conditions and height of buttresses are determining factors as to appropriateness and cost. Thrusts of constant-radius arches are given in Table 8-20.

With barrel arches, thrust is carried to the foundation itself, or to tie rods in or under the floor.

Tudor arches (Fig. 8-10) are one of the most practical as well as beautiful of the glued-laminated structural units.   Sides are vertical, making all space fully usable.

Common uses for Tudor arches include churches, gymnasiums, auditoriums, and store buildings.   In the shorter spans, they are excellent for contemporary residences where they permit any desired arrangement of rooms by eliminating the necessity of bearing partitions.

Spans of Tudor arches customarily range from 30 to 100 ft.   Wider spans also are possible, although long spans can be served more economically by the constant-section or barrel-type arch.   Typical haunch sections are given in Table 8-21.

8-23. Timber Rigid Frames.   These have been built as an alternate to Tudor arches.   Frames usually consist of separate wall and roof arms with rigid steel knees

Fig. 8-9. Constant-section timber-arch roof with 200-ft span in University of Montana field house.

at eaves and hinge joints at the ridge.   Wall and roof arms may be either sawn or glued-laminated timbers.

Rigid frames have the advantages of high interior clearances at walls and of easy shipment because component parts are straight shapes.

8-24. Lamellar Construction.   Lamellar timber roof frames, consisting of planks on edge arranged in a diamond pattern, have been built extensively in markets, auditoriums, and recreation buildings.   Lamellars are in short lengths, with the ends of two members carried at the center of a third piece, forming an attractive diamond net across the arched roof, and requiring no ceiling.   Such roof structures are erected on a scaffold because a large section must be in place before supporting action develops.

Nearly all lamellar roofs are designed and detailed by specialists in this field.

8-25. Wood-stud Walls.   Studs usually are set with wide faces perpendicular to the face of wall or partition but may be placed parallel to the face, provided the studs are considered as columns and are designed accordingly.   Stud walls should have top and bottom plates. Plates usually consist of two 2 × 4s, though sometimes one 4 × 4 is used. Joists may be supported by a let-in ribbon.

Exterior stud walls and bearing partitions for buildings of two stories or less should consist of not less than 2 × 4-in. studs; for buildings of three stories, the studs should be not less than 3 × 4 or 2 × 6 in. to the bottom of the second floor joists and 2 × 4 in. for the two upper stories.

Unless supported laterally by adequate framing, the maximum allowable height of 2 × 3-in. stud framing is 11 ft; of 2 × 4- and 3 × 4-in. stud framing, 15 ft; of 2 × 6-in. stud framing, 23 ft.

Except for one-story buildings, or the upper story of multistory wood-frame buildings, where 24-in. spacing may be used, no studs should be spaced more than 16 in.

Fig. 8-10. Tudor arch.

c to c unless vertical supporting members in the walls are designed as columns. However, walls may be constructed of 4 × 4-in. or larger posts spaced not more than 5 ft c to c, or may be of post-and-beam framing with plank sheathing not less than 1½ in. thick.

Angles at corners where stud walls or partitions meet should be framed solid so no lath may extend from one room to another. All exterior walls and main cross stud partitions should be effectively and thoroughly braced or sheathed, with panels adequately nailed along all edges.

Extensive tables of stud walls may be found in "Douglas Fir Use Book," West Coast Lumbermen's Association, Portland, Ore., and in "Wood Structural Design Data," National Lumber Manufacturers Association, Washington, D.C.

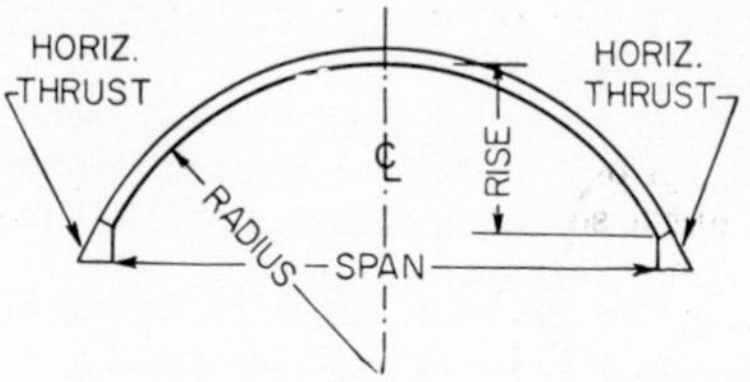

Table 8-20. Constant-radius–Constant-section Two-hinged Arches

High-rise (1/3 of Span)

Span, ft	Rise	Radius	Section sizes required, in. Design load on horizontal projection, lb per lin ft of arch: 400	600	800	1,000	1,200	Max horizontal thrust, lb per 100 lb of design load
			Depth Increments Based on 1 3/16-in. Laminations					
50	16′8″	27′1″	5 1/4 × 9 1/2	5 1/4 × 11 7/8	5 1/4 × 13 1/16	5 1/4 × 14 1/4	5 1/4 × 15 7/16	1,830
60	20′0″	32′6″	5 1/4 × 11 7/8	5 1/4 × 14 1/4	5 1/4 × 15 7/16	7 × 15 7/16	7 × 16 5/8	2,200
70	23′4″	37′11″	5 1/4 × 13 1/16	5 1/4 × 16 5/8	7 × 16 5/8	7 × 17 13/16	7 × 19	2,560
			Depth Increments Based on 1 5/8-in. Laminations					
80	26′8″	43′3″	5 1/4 × 16 1/4	7 × 16 1/4	7 × 17 7/8	7 × 21 1/8	7 × 22 3/4	2,930
90	30′0″	48′9″	7 × 16 1/4	7 × 17 7/8	7 × 21 1/8	9 × 21 1/8	9 × 22 3/4	3,290
100	33′4″	54′2″	7 × 17 7/8	7 × 19 1/2	9 × 21 1/8	9 × 22 3/4	9 × 24 3/8	3,660
110	36′8″	59′7″	7 × 19 1/2	9 × 19 1/2	9 × 22 3/4	9 × 24 3/8	9 × 26	4,030
120	40′0″	65′0″	7 × 21 1/8	9 × 21 1/8	9 × 24 3/8	9 × 26	9 × 29 1/4	4.390

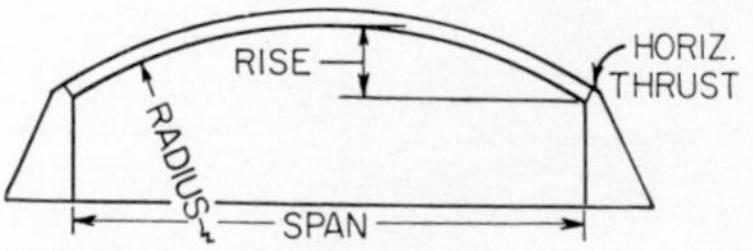

Low-rise (Radius Equals Span)

Depth Increments Based on 1 5/8-in. Laminations

Span, ft	Rise	Section sizes required, in. Design load on horizontal projection, lb per lin ft of arch: 400	600	800	1,000	1,200	Max horizontal thrust, lb per 100 lb of design load
50	6′8 3/8″	3 1/4 × 11 3/8	5 1/4 × 11 3/8	5 1/4 × 13	5 1/4 × 13	5 1/4 × 14 5/8	4,700
60	8′0 7/16″	5 1/4 × 11 3/8	5 1/4 × 13	5 1/4 × 14 5/8	5 1/4 × 16 1/4	7 × 16 1/4	5,640
70	9′4 9/16″	5 1/4 × 13	5 1/4 × 14 5/8	7 × 14 5/8	7 × 16 1/4	7 × 17 7/8	6,580
80	10′8 5/8″	5 1/4 × 14 5/8	7 × 16 1/4	7 × 17 7/8	7 × 19 1/2	7 × 21 1/8	7,520
90	12′1 7/16″	5 1/4 × 16 1/4	7 × 17 7/8	7 × 19 1/2	7 × 21 1/8	9 × 21 1/8	8,860
100	13′4 3/4″	7 × 16 1/4	7 × 19 1/2	7 × 21 1/8	9 × 21 1/8	9 × 22 3/4	9,400
110	14′8 7/8″	7 × 17 7/8	7 × 21 1/8	9 × 21 1/8	9 × 22 3/4	9 × 24 3/8	10,340
120	16′0 15/16″	7 × 19 1/2	9 × 21 1/8	9 × 22 3/4	9 × 24 3/8	9 × 27 5/8	11,280

NOTE: This table is based on conservation design criteria for construction with suitable structural-grade combinations but is subject to local considerations. Normal lateral support is assumed.

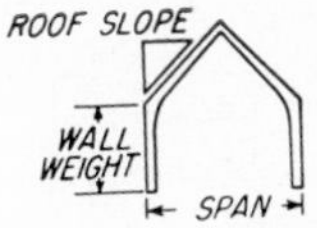

Table 8-21. Typical Haunch Sections, Tudor Arches, Three-hinged
(Depth increments based on ¾-in. laminations)

Roof slope	Wall height, ft	Vertical loading, lb per lin ft of span				
		400	600	800	1,000	1,200
Span 30 ft						
3/12	8	3¼ × 9¾	5¼ × 9	5¼ × 10½	5¼ × 12	5¼ × 15
	10	3¼ × 10½	3¼ × 12	5¼ × 12	5¼ × 14¼	5¼ × 15¾
	12	3¼ × 12	5¼ × 11¼	5¼ × 12¾	5¼ × 15	5¼ × 17¼
	14	5¼ × 10½	5¼ × 12¾	5¼ × 14¼	5¼ × 15¾	5¼ × 17¼
	16	5¼ × 11¼	5¼ × 13½	5¼ × 15	5¼ × 17¼	5¼ × 18¾
4/12	8	3¼ × 9	3¼ × 12	5¼ × 11¼	5¼ × 12¾	5¼ × 14¼
	10	3¼ × 10½	5¼ × 9	5¼ × 11¼	5¼ × 13½	5¼ × 15¾
	12	3¼ × 12	5¼ × 11¼	5¼ × 12¾	5¼ × 14¼	5¼ × 15¾
	14	5¼ × 10½	5¼ × 12¾	5¼ × 14¼	5¼ × 15¾	5¼ × 16½
	16	5¼ × 11¼	5¼ × 13½	5¼ × 15¾	5¼ × 17¼	5¼ × 17¼
6/12	8	3¼ × 9	3¼ × 10½	5¼ × 9	5¼ × 9¾	5¼ × 11¼
	10	3¼ × 10½	5¼ × 9¾	5¼ × 12	5¼ × 12¾	5¼ × 14¼
	12	5¼ × 9¾	5¼ × 12	5¼ × 13½	5¼ × 15	5¼ × 16½
	14	5¼ × 10½	5¼ × 12¾	5¼ × 14¼	5¼ × 16½	5¼ × 18
	16	5¼ × 11¼	5¼ × 13½	5¼ × 15¾	5¼ × 17¼	5¼ × 18¾
8/12	8	3¼ × 10½	3¼ × 12	5¼ × 11¼	5¼ × 12¾	5¼ × 13½
	10	3¼ × 12	5¼ × 11¼	5¼ × 12¾	5¼ × 14¼	5¼ × 15¾
	12	5¼ × 10½	5¼ × 12¾	5¼ × 14¼	5¼ × 15¾	5¼ × 17¼
	14	5¼ × 11¼	5¼ × 13½	5¼ × 15	5¼ × 17¼	5¼ × 18¾
	16	5¼ × 12	5¼ × 14¼	5¼ × 15¾	5¼ × 18	5¼ × 19½
12/12	8	3¼ × 10½	3¼ × 12	5¼ × 11¼	5¼ × 12	5¼ × 13½
	10	3¼ × 12	5¼ × 11¼	5¼ × 12¾	5¼ × 14¼	5¼ × 15¾
	12	5¼ × 10½	5¼ × 12¾	5¼ × 14¼	5¼ × 15¾	5¼ × 17¼
	14	5¼ × 11¼	5¼ × 13½	5¼ × 15	5¼ × 17¼	5¼ × 18¾
	16	5¼ × 12	5¼ × 14¼	5¼ × 16½	5¼ × 18	5¼ × 19½
16/12	8	3¼ × 10½	5¼ × 10½	5¼ × 12	5¼ × 13½	5¼ × 14¼
	10	3¼ × 12	5¼ × 11¼	5¼ × 13½	5¼ × 15	5¼ × 15¾
	12	5¼ × 10½	5¼ × 12	5¼ × 14¼	5¼ × 15¾	5¼ × 17¼
	14	5¼ × 11¼	5¼ × 12¾	5¼ × 15	5¼ × 16½	5¼ × 21
	16	5¼ × 11¼	5¼ × 13½	5¼ × 16½	5¼ × 18	7 × 17¼
Span 40 ft						
3/12	10	5¼ × 9¾	5¼ × 13½	5¼ × 16½	5¼ × 20¼	7 × 17¼
	12	5¼ × 12	5¼ × 14¼	5¼ × 16½	5¼ × 20¼	7 × 18
	14	5¼ × 13½	5¼ × 16½	5¼ × 18¾	5¼ × 21	7 × 20¼
	16	5¼ × 14¼	5¼ × 17¼	5¼ × 20¼	7 × 18¾	7 × 21¾
	18	5¼ × 15	5¼ × 18¾	7 × 18	7 × 21	7 × 22½
4/12	10	5¼ × 9¾	5¼ × 12	5¼ × 16½	5¼ × 19½	7 × 17¼
	12	5¼ × 12	5¼ × 15	5¼ × 16½	5¼ × 19½	7 × 17¼
	14	5¼ × 13½	5¼ × 16½	5¼ × 18¾	5¼ × 21	7 × 20¼
	16	5¼ × 14¼	5¼ × 17¼	5¼ × 20¼	7 × 19½	7 × 21¾
	18	5¼ × 15	5¼ × 18¾	7 × 18	7 × 21	7 × 22½

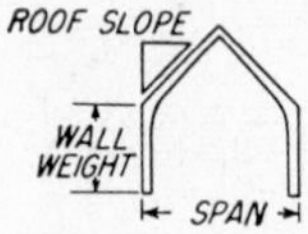

Table 8-21. Typical Haunch Sections, Tudor Arches, Three-hinged *(Continued)*

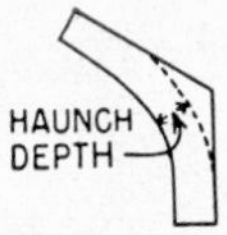

Roof slope	Wall height, ft	Vertical loading, lb per lin ft of span 400	600	800	1,000	1,200
Span 40 ft						
6:12	10	5¼ × 10½	5¼ × 12¾	5¼ × 15	5¼ × 16½	5¼ × 18
	12	5¼ × 12	5¼ × 15	5¼ × 17¼	5¼ × 18¾	5¼ × 20¼
	14	5¼ × 13½	5¼ × 16½	5¼ × 18¾	5¼ × 21	7 × 19½
	16	5¼ × 14¼	5¼ × 17¼	5¼ × 20¼	7 × 19½	7 × 21
	18	5¼ × 15	5¼ × 18¾	5¼ × 21	7 × 21	7 × 21¾
8:12	10	5¼ × 11¼	5¼ × 14¼	5¼ × 16½	5¼ × 18	5¼ × 19¼
	12	5¼ × 12¾	5¼ × 15¾	5¼ × 18	5¼ × 20¼	7 × 18¾
	14	5¼ × 14¼	5¼ × 16½	5¼ × 19½	5¼ × 21	7 × 20¼
	16	5¼ × 15	5¼ × 18	5¼ × 20¼	7 × 19½	7 × 21¾
	18	5¼ × 15¾	5¼ × 18¾	5¼ × 21	7 × 21	7 × 22½
12:12	10	5¼ × 11¼	5¼ × 14¼	5¼ × 15¾	5¼ × 18	5¼ × 19½
	12	5¼ × 12¾	5¼ × 15	5¼ × 17¼	5¼ × 19½	5¼ × 21
	14	5¼ × 13½	5¼ × 16½	5¼ × 18¾	5¼ × 21	7 × 20¼
	16	5¼ × 14¼	5¼ × 17¼	5¼ × 20¼	7 × 19½	7 × 21
	18	5¼ × 15	5¼ × 18	5¼ × 21	7 × 20¼	7 × 22½
Span 50 ft						
3:12	10	5¼ × 12	5¼ × 17¼	7 × 16½	7 × 19½	7 × 23¼
	12	5¼ × 14¼	5¼ × 18	7 × 18	7 × 21	7 × 23¼
	14	5¼ × 15¾	5¼ × 19½	7 × 18¾	7 × 22½	7 × 25½
	16	5¼ × 17¼	5¼ × 21	7 × 20¼	7 × 23¼	7 × 26¼
	18	5¼ × 18¾	7 × 19½	7 × 22½	7 × 25½	7 × 27¾
4:12	10	5¼ × 11¼	5¼ × 15¾	7 × 15¾	7 × 18¾	7 × 21¾
	12	5¼ × 13½	5¼ × 16½	7 × 16½	7 × 20¼	7 × 22½
	14	5¼ × 15¾	5¼ × 18¾	7 × 18¾	7 × 21	7 × 24
	16	5¼ × 17¼	5¼ × 20¼	7 × 20¼	7 × 22½	7 × 24¾
	18	5¼ × 18	7 × 18¾	7 × 21¾	7 × 24	7 × 26¼
6:12	10	5¼ × 12	5¼ × 15	5¼ × 17¼	7 × 16½	7 × 20¼
	12	5¼ × 14¼	5¼ × 17¼	5¼ × 19½	7 × 18¾	7 × 20¼
	14	5¼ × 15¾	5¼ × 18¾	7 × 18¾	7 × 21	7 × 22½
	16	5¼ × 16½	5¼ × 20¼	7 × 20¼	7 × 22½	7 × 24
	18	5¼ × 18	7 × 18¾	7 × 21	7 × 24	7 × 25½
8:12	10	5¼ × 12¾	5¼ × 15¾	5¼ × 18	7 × 18	7 × 18¾
	12	5¼ × 14¼	5¼ × 18	5¼ × 20¼	7 × 19½	7 × 21¾
	14	5¼ × 15¾	5¼ × 19½	7 × 18¾	7 × 21	7 × 23¼
	16	5¼ × 16½	5¼ × 20¼	7 × 20¼	7 × 22½	7 × 24¾
	18	5¼ × 17¼	5¼ × 21	7 × 21	7 × 24	7 × 26¼
12:12	10	5¼ × 12¾	5¼ × 15¾	5¼ × 18	7 × 17¼	7 × 18¾
	12	5¼ × 14¼	5¼ × 17¼	5¼ × 19½	7 × 18¾	7 × 21
	14	5¼ × 15	5¼ × 18¾	5¼ × 21	7 × 20¼	7 × 22½
	16	5¼ × 16½	5¼ × 19½	7 × 19½	7 × 21¾	7 × 24
	18	5¼ × 17¼	5¼ × 21	7 × 20¼	7 × 23¼	7 × 25½

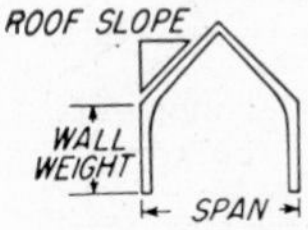

Table 8-21. Typical Haunch Sections, Tudor Arches, Three-hinged (*Continued*)

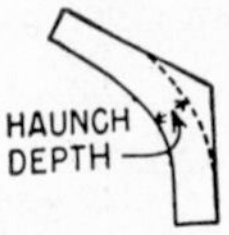

Roof slope	Wall height, ft	Vertical loading, lb per lin ft of span				
		400	600	800	1,000	1,200
Span 60 ft						
3/12	12	5¼ × 16½	7 × 17¼	7 × 21	7 × 24¾	9 × 24
	14	5¼ × 18¾	7 × 19½	7 × 21¾	7 × 26¼	9 × 24¾
	16	5¼ × 20¼	7 × 21	7 × 24	7 × 27	9 × 26¼
	18	7 × 18¾	7 × 22½	7 × 25½	9 × 25½	9 × 27¾
4/12	12	5¼ × 16½	5¼ × 20¼	7 × 19½	7 × 24	9 × 23¼
	14	5¼ × 18¾	7 × 19½	7 × 21¾	7 × 24¾	9 × 24
	16	5¼ × 20¼	7 × 21	7 × 24	7 × 26½	9 × 25½
	18	5¼ × 21	7 × 21¾	7 × 25½	9 × 24¾	9 × 27¾
6/12	12	5¼ × 16½	5¼ × 20¼	7 × 19½	7 × 21¾	7 × 24
	14	5¼ × 18	7 × 18¾	7 × 21	7 × 24	7 × 26¼
	16	5¼ × 19½	7 × 20¼	7 × 23¼	7 × 26¼	9 × 24¾
	18	5¼ × 21	7 × 21¾	7 × 24¾	7 × 27¾	9 × 26¼
8/12	12	5¼ × 17¼	5¼ × 20¼	7 × 20¼	7 × 21¾	7 × 24
	14	5¼ × 18¾	7 × 19½	7 × 21¾	7 × 24¾	7 × 27
	16	5¼ × 19½	7 × 20¼	7 × 23¼	7 × 26¼	9 × 25½
	18	5¼ × 20¼	7 × 21¾	7 × 24¾	7 × 27¾	9 × 27
11.2/12	12	5¼ × 16½	5¼ × 19½	7 × 19½	7 × 21¾	7 × 23¼
	14	5¼ × 17¼	5¼ × 21	7 × 21	7 × 23¼	7 × 25½
	16	5¼ × 18¾	7 × 19½	7 × 22½	7 × 24¾	7 × 27
	18	5¼ × 19½	7 × 20¼	7 × 26¼	7 × 26¼	9 × 25½
Span 70 ft						
3/12	14	5¼ × 21	7 × 22½	7 × 26¼	9 × 27	9 × 30
	16	7 × 20¼	7 × 24¾	7 × 27¾	9 × 28½	9 × 30
	18	7 × 21¾	7 × 26¼	9 × 26¼	9 × 30	9 × 32¼
	20	7 × 22½	7 × 27¾	9 × 27¾	9 × 30¾	9 × 33¾
4/12	14	5¼ × 21	7 × 22½	7 × 25½	7 × 27¾	9 × 27
	16	7 × 19½	7 × 24	7 × 27¾	9 × 27	9 × 30
	18	7 × 21	7 × 25½	9 × 25½	9 × 29¼	9 × 31½
	20	7 × 21¾	7 × 27	9 × 26¼	9 × 30¾	9 × 33
6/12	14	5¼ × 20¼	7 × 21¾	7 × 24¾	7 × 27¾	9 × 27
	16	7 × 19½	7 × 23¼	7 × 27	9 × 26¼	9 × 29¼
	18	7 × 20¼	7 × 24¾	9 × 25½	9 × 27¾	9 × 30¾
	20	7 × 21	7 × 25½	9 × 26¼	9 × 29¼	9 × 32¼
8/12	14	5¼ × 21	7 × 21¾	7 × 24¾	7 × 27¾	9 × 27
	16	7 × 19½	7 × 23¼	7 × 27	9 × 26¼	9 × 29¼
	18	7 × 20¼	7 × 24¾	9 × 24¾	9 × 27¾	9 × 30¾
	20	7 × 21	7 × 25½	9 × 26¼	9 × 29¼	9 × 31½
10.6/12	14	5¼ × 20¼	7 × 21	7 × 24	7 × 27	9 × 25½
	16	5¼ × 21	7 × 22½	7 × 25½	9 × 25½	9 × 27¾
	18	7 × 19½	7 × 23¼	7 × 27	9 × 27	9 × 29¼
	20	7 × 20¼	7 × 24¾	9 × 24¾	9 × 27¾	9 × 30¾

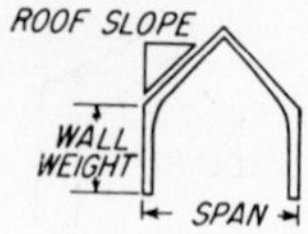

WOOD CONSTRUCTION

Table 8-21. Typical Haunch Sections,
Tudor Arches, Three-hinged (*Continued*)

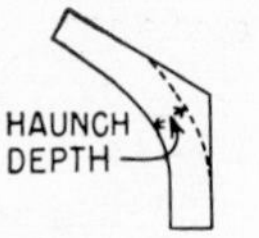

Roof slope	Wall height, ft	Vertical loading, lb per lin ft of span				
		400	600	800	1,000	1,200
		Span 80 ft				
3/12	14	7 × 20¼	7 × 24	9 × 25½	9 × 30	9 × 34½
	16	7 × 22½	7 × 27	9 × 27¾	9 × 30¾	9 × 35¼
	18	7 × 24	9 × 25½	9 × 29¼	9 × 32¼	9 × 36
	20	7 × 24¾	9 × 26¼	9 × 30¾	9 × 33¾	11 × 33¾
	22	7 × 25½	9 × 27	9 × 31½	9 × 35¼	11 × 35¼
4/12	14	7 × 19½	7 × 24¾	7 × 27¾	9 × 27¾	9 × 32¼
	16	7 × 21¾	7 × 27	9 × 27	9 × 29¼	9 × 33
	18	7 × 23¼	9 × 24¾	9 × 28½	9 × 31½	9 × 34½
	20	7 × 24¾	9 × 26¼	9 × 30	9 × 33¾	9 × 36
	22	7 × 26¼	9 × 27	9 × 30¾	9 × 35¼	11 × 33¾
6/12	14	7 × 18¾	7 × 23¼	7 × 27	9 × 26¼	9 × 28½
	16	7 × 20¼	7 × 24¾	9 × 25½	9 × 28½	9 × 30¾
	18	7 × 21¾	7 × 26¼	9 × 27	9 × 30	9 × 32¼
	20	7 × 23¼	9 × 24¾	9 × 27¾	9 × 31½	9 × 34½
	22	7 × 24¾	9 × 25½	9 × 29¼	9 × 33	9 × 36
8/12	14	7 × 19½	7 × 23¼	7 × 27	9 × 26¼	9 × 28½
	16	7 × 20¼	7 × 24¾	9 × 25½	9 × 28½	9 × 30¾
	18	7 × 21¾	7 × 26¼	9 × 27	9 × 30	9 × 32¼
	20	7 × 22½	7 × 27¾	9 × 28½	9 × 31½	9 × 33¾
	22	7 × 23¼	9 × 25½	9 × 29¼	9 × 32¼	9 × 35¼
10.2/12	14	5¼ × 21	7 × 22½	7 × 26¼	9 × 25½	9 × 27¾
	16	7 × 20¼	7 × 24	7 × 27¾	9 × 27	9 × 30
	18	7 × 21	7 × 25½	9 × 25½	9 × 29¼	9 × 31½
	20	7 × 21¾	7 × 27	9 × 27	9 × 30	9 × 33
	22	7 × 23¼	9 × 24¾	9 × 27¾	9 × 31½	9 × 34½

Three types of light wood-frame construction generally are used in the United States—eastern or braced frame, balloon frame, and platform frame.

Braced-timber framing is the oldest type. It originated in New England when the early settlers were required to cut framing members from logs. It is the strongest and most rigid type.

In modern adaptations, sometimes called the combination frame, a braced-timber exterior frame consists of a wood sill resting on the foundation wall; comparatively heavy posts at all corners and some intermediate points, seated on the sill; horizontal members, called girts, at second-floor level—"dropped girts" supporting ends of joists and "raised girts" paralleling the joists; a plate across the top of the frame, supporting roof rafters; and studs, 16 in. c to c between posts, extending from sill to girts and from girts to plate. Diagonal bracing is set between posts and sill, girts and plate. Posts are tenoned into sills, and girts are connected to posts with mortise-and-tenon joints.

Rough boards, ⅞ in. thick, generally are used to sheathe braced frames. Set horizontally, each board should be attached with at least two nails to each stud (three nails if boards are more than 6 in. wide).

Balloon framing, built almost entirely of 2-in. lumber, is distinguished by two-story-high studs, to the faces of which joists at all levels are nailed. Ends of the upper-story joists rest on a false girt, or "ribband." It differs from the braced frame also because of the omission of diagonal bracing; instead the frame is stiffened by diagonal sheathing. Fire stops—horizontal 2 × 4s—are placed between the studs at about mid-height and at floor level in each story.

Diagonal sheathing boards should be nailed to each stud with two or four nails. (Three nails are no better than two under racking action, because the center nail acts as a pivot and adds nothing to the strength.) Plywood sheathing, applied in large sheets, also imparts considerable rigidity to the frame. It should be nailed with 8d common nails, 6 in. c to c, for 5/8-in. material and with 6d nails, 2 1/2 in. c to c., for 1/4-in. material.

Platform framing, also known as western framing, is characterized by one-story-high walls supported by the floors at each level. At the bottom, joists rest on the sill and frame into headers of the same depth, which extend around the periphery of the building. Generally, before the superstructure is erected, the first-floor subflooring is laid on the joists to serve as a working platform. Then, a sole or shoe of the same size as the studs is set on top of the subfloor to form a base for the verticals. The studs extend to a plate at the next floor level. (Some builders assemble the wall framing in a horizontal position, then tilt it into place.) Joists are seated on the plate and frame into a header. After that, subflooring is placed over the joists, extending to the edge of the frame, another sole is laid, and the cycle is repeated. For this type of framing also, plywood or diagonal sheathing, well nailed, is highly desirable. (A. G. H. Dietz, "Dwelling House Construction," D. Van Nostrand Company, Inc., Princeton, N.J.)

8.26. Mechanically Laminated Members. Allowable unit stresses for individual pieces used in mechanically laminated members should comply with those established for sawn members.

Vertically laminated beams with laminations bolted together may be assumed to be as strong and stiff as solid beams of the same external net dimensions. Where end joints are used in laminations, the load capacity should be adjusted according to principles given in the National Design Specification, National Lumber Manufacturers Association, Washington, D.C.

Horizontally laminated beams should be designed as a summation of individual members, each equal to the individual lamination that forms the member, except where provisions have been made for shear and deformation.

Laminated columns, other than spaced columns, are those built up of several pieces spiked, bolted, or fastened together with timber connectors. Since no arrangement of laminations with mechanical fastenings will make a laminated column fully equal in strength to a solid sawn column of comparable material and like dimensions, the reduction of allowable stresses should be consistent with the recommendations in the "Wood Handbook," Government Printing Office, Washington, D.C.

8-27. Glued-laminated Construction. Wood plank or boards may be bonded together to form a glued-laminated structural member that is strong and durable (Fig. 8-11). The wide face of laminations in beams and girders may be either parallel or perpendicular to the applied load. Various lamination thicknesses, grades, and species may be combined in the same timber; if properties of individual laminations are taken into account, no loss of strength occurs. Lumber must be dry, and glue must be as strong and durable as the wood.

Laminating technique permits us to build curved members that have greater strength and added beauty (Fig. 8-12). Now we may discard costly pickling, steaming, and bandsawing operations that waste material and weaken the fiber.

Timbers can be fashioned into strong, compact top chords of trusses, graceful arches, and curved barn rafters. Laminating permits selection of material in a member to place high strength and good appearance where strength and looks are most needed, and permits location of less costly materials in positions where they are sufficient.

Since glued members are built of dry lumber, they do not warp, check, or split in

FIG. 8-11. Straight glued-laminated roof beams and sawn timber purlins.

FIG. 8-12. Curved glued-laminated girders and straight laminated purlins.

service, nor do they require servicing operations after installation. Laminated members have low field-assembly costs and require a minimum of hardware or ironwork.

Good members require good lumber, and because of net sizes of boards and scarfing losses, about one-third more lumber must be purchased for the same finished volume of glued as for sawn timbers. Also glue, plant, equipment, labor, and supervision must be added to production costs.

Glue lines of a glued member are assumed to be as strong and durable as the wood. Glued members are designed by the same engineering principles as sawn timbers. Load values of fastenings of glued members are the same as for sawn timbers of the same dryness, and they can be bored, routed, and trimmed as well.

When all end joints in laminations of a glued member are properly scarfed and effectively glued, and joints are sufficiently scattered the member may be considered as structurally effective for its full net cross section to resist bending action perpendicular to the wide faces of laminations.

The use in any lamination of improper scarfing, ineffective gluing, or insufficient stagger of end joints prohibits such lamination from being considered a fully effective structural part for bending action.

When laminations are 2 in. nominal or less, thickness has no bearing on the strength of glued timbers.

For curved timbers thin laminations may be a necessity, since they must be bent in the dry, and thin boards bend better than thick ones. Experience has shown that the thickness of laminations should not exceed $\frac{1}{120}$ of the radius of curvature. In general, $\frac{3}{4}$-in. boards can be bent to a radius of 9 ft 4 in., and $1\frac{5}{8}$-in. plank to 32 ft.

The following types of end joints are used in laminations of glued timbers:

1. *Butt joints* consisting of two abutting square ends. This type is the most economical of material, but it can transfer no stress of either tension or compression. Though ends are tight in layup, they may not be at the end of the pressure operation. Steel butt plates could add compressive capacity, but they are difficult to install.

Butt joints produce serious sources of stress concentration and are always undesirable in curved members. They should never be used in top or bottom laminations. They are not suitable for tension areas. For compression areas, design should disregard all laminations at a single cross section that have butt joints. In tension areas, design should disregard 1.2 times the area of all such laminations.

2. *Plain scarfs* have a straight slope from end to end. Usually, slopes vary from 1:8 to 1:12—the flatter the slope, the stronger the joint. Test programs have found little merit in slopes flatter than 1:12.

Many specification writers are concerned as to the exact spacing of scarf joints in a glued timber and require that certain distances be set up between joints in adjacent laminations. Such dimensional spacings did appear in early laboratory reports, but they are no longer considered necessary. Any such restriction requires a dry layup in the plant and so increases cost and delays the work.

Any appropriate working stress given in the standards and full cross section may be used without a more rigid requirement for arrangement of scarf joints in tension areas than the one of "well-scattered," and no requirement for compression areas.

3. *Pegged scarfs* are actually plain scarfs in which hardwood dowels have been inserted to hold them in proper position. Usually fabricators position holes by boring machines that form a part of the scarfer, so that holes are mechanically positioned. The peg adds no appreciable strength to the joint and so is not considered in the design.

4. *Stepped scarfs* are combinations of plain scarfs and steps. The step adds no appreciable strength but is helpful in positioning the scarf ends. In some types of gluing machines, they permit the leading piece to pull the trailing piece into the machine.

The customary pattern has a blunt end at each end of the scarf and a step at the center. Two plain scarf sections join these three cuts. Design requires that the step be deducted from the effective cross section. The two end cuts and center step can be made equal in depth and only one depth deducted from the cross section, since the three reductions all occur at different places along the length.

5. *Double- and triple-bevel scarfs* are patented modifications of the plain scarf. In

design, they are treated as a single plain scarf. The double and triple features act as positioners and seem to bind the joint together in a strong and durable manner. They resist twisting actions and have been successfully used in moderate-span arches to field-join wall arms, haunches, and roof arms.

6. *Special scarfs* or combinations of standard cuts may be used where design or test programs prove that they have a strength ratio equal to design assumptions.

8-28. Glued-laminated Appearance Grades. Appearance grades apply to the surfaces of glued-laminated members and include such items as growth characteristics, inserts, wood fillers, and surfacing operations, but not laminating procedures, stains, paints, varnishes, or other finishes, or wrappings, cratings, or other protective coverings. Appearance grades do not modify the design stresses, fabrication controls, grades of lumber used, and other provisions of the standards for structural glued-laminated lumber. Planed surfaces are satisfactory and sanding is not required.

Experience has shown that the following three appearance grades have a sufficient range to fulfill all normal requirements:

1. *Industrial-appearance Grade.* Ordinarily suitable for construction in industrial plants, warehouses, garages, and for other uses where appearance is not of primary concern.

2. *Architectural-appearance Grade.* Ordinarily suitable for construction where appearance is an important requirement. Any small voids should be filled by others than the fabricator if the final decorative finish so requires.

3. *Premium-appearance Grade.* For uses that require the finest appearance.

Application and specifications of appearance grades may be found in American Institute of Timber Construction Standards.

8-29. Protective Treatments for Timber. Timbers exposed to attack by wood-destroying organisms, decay, or damage by fire should be pressure-treated. Interior woodwork, except in termite-infested regions, is seldom given a preservative treatment. Specifying pressure treatment incurs an additional initial cost, which usually is offset by saving in replacement and maintenance costs. The economy of treating timber by pressure has been proved.

In general, preservatives are chemicals that are stable and have a high degree of permanence, possess good penetrating properties, and are harmless to wood as well as metal.

1. Creosote, creosote solutions, and oil-borne preservatives are relatively insoluble in water, so are usually recommended where a preservative is required to remain stable under varied conditions of use. Creosote, or creosote coal-tar solutions are the only preservatives recommended for use in structures subject to attack by marine borers. Creosote treatment is best for tidewater structures.

2. Salts preservatives are carried into the wood by a solution, with water or volatile solvents. Their use is generally recommended when a clean, odorless, paintable product is required.

3. Fire retardants are water-soluble salts which increase the fire resistance of wood so that it will not support its own combustion and will cease to burn if the source of the heat is removed. By specifying fire-retardant pressure treatment, it is possible to utilize the many inherent natural advantages of wood without the necessity of turning to a lumber substitute, and in certain instances, insurance-rate reductions may apply.

Each of the recognized preservatives and fire retardants (Art. 2-42) has certain distinct advantages, and the type of treatment specified should be determined by the end use of the material to be treated.

The same allowable stresses are used for designing with pressure-treated wood as when designing with untreated wood. Treated timber structures do not suffer any progressive loss in strength due to treatment or to decay or other wood-destroying agencies. The design weights used for pressure-treated wood are obtained by increasing the weights used for untreated wood by an amount equal to the retention specified. Pressure-treated wood reacts to changes in moisture content about the same as untreated wood; while the rate of moisture absorption or egress is slower, the ultimate amount of moisture is the same.

Glued-laminated material may be pressure-treated either before or after gluing, if exterior-type glues are used. Casein glue can be used with some types of salt treatments. Designers should keep in mind that, for members to be treated after gluing, the size and shape are limited by the size of the treating cylinders, which are usually 6 × 8 ft in diameter, with lengths ranging up to 150 ft. When material is pressure-treated before gluing, some dimensional changes may occur, and a final sanding or surfacing may be necessary to provide a uniform clean surface.

All fabrication that is practical should be accomplished prior to pressure treating, so that the material enters the treating cylinder in its final manufactured form. Fabrication should include boring holes, dapping, cutting to exact lengths, cutting odd angles, and grooving for splines or ring connectors. Cutting into the wood in any way after treatment may expose untreated timber; a brush treatment should be applied to any minor cuts made after treatment.

As an aid to uniform penetration, all sawn material, 3 in. or thicker, should be incised on all faces. Material less than 3 in. thick may be incised on the wide faces only. Incising consists of separating the outer fibers at regular intervals with knifelike teeth to facilitate penetration and distribution of preservatives. It has little effect on structural strength and is particularly desirable for fabricated material.

Incising also helps minimize checking and relieves internal stresses caused by rapid changes of moisture content. This operation may be omitted if it damages the fabrication or is objectionable from an appearance standpoint. At present, it is not considered desirable to incise glued-laminated timbers, since the material is dry and takes treatment well and incising knives tend to injure lamination edges. Preseasoning timber is not necessary.

Purchasers are cautioned against use of nonpressure processes that impart only a superficial coating of preservative. This coat may be easily ruptured, allowing untreated wood to be exposed to decay, insect, or marine-borer attack. The only satisfactory method of obtaining the desired penetration and retention of preservative is by the use of pressure processes conforming to the established standards of the American Wood Preservers' Association.

Section 9

WINDOWS

P. M. GRENNAN

Engineer-Associate

Office of Alfred Easton Poor, Architects
New York, N.Y.

Selection of a proper window for a building entails many considerations. Functional requirements are usually most important. However, size, type, arrangement, and materials very often establish the character of the building, and this external show of fenestration is an integral part of design and expression.

9-1. How Much Window Area? Distribution and control of daylight, desired vision of outdoors, privacy, ventilation control, heat loss, and weather resistance are all-important aspects of good design principles. Most building codes require that glass areas be equal to at least 10% of the floor area of each room. Nevertheless, it is good practice to provide glass areas in excess of 20% and to locate the windows as high in the wall as possible to lengthen the depth of light penetration. Continuous sash or one large opening in a room provides a more desirable distribution of light than separated narrow windows and eliminates the dark areas between openings.

Location, type, and size of window are most important for natural ventilation. The pattern of air movement within a building depends to a great extent on the angle at which the air enters and leaves. It is desirable, particularly in summer, to direct the flow of air downward and across a room at a low level. However, the type and location of windows best suited to ventilation may not provide adequately for admission of light and clear vision, or perhaps proper weather protection. To arrive at a satisfactory relationship, it may be necessary to compromise with these functional requirements.

While building codes may establish a minimum percentage of glass area, they likewise may limit the use of glass and also require a fire rating in particular locations. In hazardous industrial applications subject to explosions, scored glass is an added precaution for quick release of pressure.

Heat loss is of economic importance and can also seriously affect comfort. Weather stripping or the use of windows with integral frame and trim can minimize air infiltration. Double glazing or sealed double glazing make large glass areas feasible by materially reducing heat loss. Heat gain is accomplished mainly by the location of glass areas so that the rays of the sun can be admitted during the winter.

9-2. Window Materials. Window units are generally made of wood or metal. Plastics have been employed for special services.

Use of metal in window construction has been highly developed, with aluminum and steel most commonly used. Bronze, stainless steel, and galvanized steel are also extensively used for specific types of buildings and particular service. Use of metal windows is very often dictated by fire-resistance requirements of building codes.

9-3. Wood Windows. These can be used for most types of construction and are particularly adaptable to residential work. The most important factor affecting wood windows is weather exposure. However, with proper maintenance, long life and satisfactory service can be expected. Sash and frames have lower thermal conductivity than metal.

The kinds of wood commonly used to resist shrinking and warping for the exposed parts of windows are white pine, sugar pine, ponderosa pine, fir, redwood, cedar, and cypress. The stiles against which a double-hung window slide should be of hard pine or some relatively hard wood. The parts of a window exposed to the inside are usually treated as trim and are made of the same material as the trim.

9-4. Definitions for Wood Windows:

Sash. A single assembly of stiles and rails made into a frame for holding glass, with or without dividing bars. It may be supplied either open or glazed.

Window. One or more single sash made to fill a given opening. It may be supplied either open or glazed.

Window Unit. A combination of window frame, window, weather strip, balancing device, and at the option of the manufacturer, screen and storm sash, assembled as a complete and properly operating unit.

Measurements:

Between Glass. Distance across the face of any wood part that separates two sheets of glass.

Face Measure. Distance across the face of any wood part, exclusive of any solid mold or rabbet.

Finished Size. Dimension of any wood part over-all, including the solid mold or rabbet.

Wood Allowance. The difference between the outside opening and the total glass measurement of a given window or sash.

Stiles. Upright, or vertical, outside pieces of a sash or screen.

Rails. Cross, or horizontal, pieces of the framework of a sash or screen.

Check Rails. Meeting rails sufficiently thicker than the window to fill the opening between the top and bottom sash made by the check strip or parting strip in the frame. They are usually beveled and rabbeted.

Bar. Either vertical or horizontal member that extends the full width or length of the glass opening.

Muntin. Any short light bar, either vertical or horizontal.

Frame. A group of wood parts so machined and assembled as to form an enclosure and support for a window or sash.

Jamb. Part of frame that surrounds and contacts the window or sash the frame is intended to support.

Side Jamb. The upright member forming the vertical side of the frame.

Head Jamb. The horizontal member forming the top of the frame.

Rabbeted Jamb. A jamb with a rectangular groove along one or both edges to receive a window or sash.

Sill. The horizontal member forming the bottom of the frame.

Pulley Stile. A side jamb into which a pulley is fixed and along which the sash slides.

Casing. Molding of various widths and thicknesses used to trim window openings.

Parting Stop. A thin strip of wood let into the jamb of a window frame to separate the sash.

Drip Cap. A molding placed on the top of the head casing of a window frame.

Blind Stop. A thin strip of wood machined so as to fit the exterior vertical edge of the pulley stile or jamb and keep the sash in place.

Extension Blind Stop. A molded piece, usually, of the same thickness as the blind stop, and tongued on one edge to engage a plow in the back edge of the blind stop, thus increasing its width and improving the weathertightness of the frame.

Dado. A rectangular groove cut across the grain of a frame member.

Jamb Liner. A small strip of wood, either surfaced four sides or tongued on one edge, which, when applied to the inside edge of a jamb, increases its width for use in thicker walls.

9-5. Steel Windows. These are, in general, made from hot-rolled, structural-grade new billet steel. However, for double-hung windows, the principal members are cold-formed from new billet strip steel. The principal manufacturers conform to the specifications of The Steel Window Institute, which has standardized types, sizes, thickness of material, depth of sections, construction, and accessories.

The life of steel windows is greatly dependent on proper shop finish, field painting, and maintenance. The more important aspects of proper protection against corrosion are as follows:

Shop Paint Finish. All steel surfaces should be thoroughly cleaned and free from rust and mill scale. A protective treatment of hot phosphate, cold phosphate-chromate, or similar method such as bonderizing or parkerizing is necessary to protect the metal and provide a suitable base for paint. All windows should then be given one shop coat of rust-inhibitive primer, baked on.

Field Painting. Steel windows should receive one field coat of paint either before or immediately after installation. A second coat should then be applied after glazing is completed and putty set.

Hot-dipped Galvanized. Assembled frames and assembled ventilators should be galvanized separately. Ventilators should be installed into frames after galvanizing and bonderizing. Specifications must guard against distortion by the heat of hot dipping, abrasion in handling, and damage to the zinc galvanizing by muriatic acid used to wash brickwork. Painting is optional.

9-6. Aluminum Windows. Specifications set up by the Aluminum Window Manufacturers' Association are classified as residential, commercial, and monumental. These specifications provide for a minimum thickness of metal and regulate stiffness of the component parts, as well as limiting the amount of air infiltration.

The manufacturers offer about the same window types that are available in steel. However, in addition to these standard types, substantial progress has been made in the development of aluminum windows as an integral part of the walls of a building. With the exception of ventilator sections, which are shop-fabricated, some windows are completely assembled at the job. The wide range of extruded aluminum sections now manufactured has made it feasible to treat large expanses of glass as window walls. Picture windows with many combinations of ventilating sash are also furnished in aluminum. Many features are available,

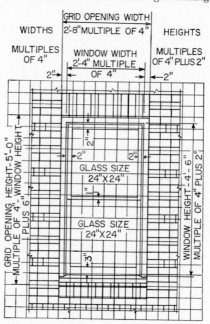

Fig. 9-1. Relation of modular standard double-hung wood window to grid opening in a brick wall.

such as aluminum trim and casing, weather stripping of stainless steel or Monel metal, combination storm sash and screens, sliding wicket-type screens, and metal bead glazing.

Aluminum windows should be protected for shipment and installation with a coating of clear methacrylate lacquer or similar material able to withstand the action of lime mortar.

9-7. Stainless-steel and Bronze Windows. These are high-quality materials used for durability, appearance, corrosion resistance, and minimum maintenance. Stainless steel is rustproof and extremely tough, with great strength in proportion to weight. Weather stripping of stainless steel is quite often used for wood and aluminum sash.

Bronze windows are durable and decorative and used for many fine commercial and monumental buildings.

9-8. Window Sizes. Manufacturers have contributed substantially toward standardization of window sizes and greater precision in fabrication. The American Standards Association has established an increment of sizing generally accepted by the building industry (A62 Guide for Modular Coordination, Modular Service Association, Boston, Mass.).

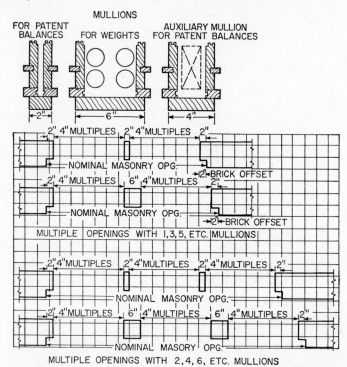

Fig. 9-2. Dimensions for multiple modular openings for double-hung wood windows.

The basis for this standardization is a nominal increment of 4 in. (Art. 1-31). However, it will be noted in Fig. 9-1 that for double-hung wood windows the 4-in. module applies to the grid dimensions, whereas the standard window opening is 4 in. less in width and 6 in. less in height than the the grid opening. Also, to accommodate 2- and 6-in. mullions for multiple openings in brick walls, it is necessary to provide a 2-in. masonry offset at one jamb. (Modular Standard, National Woodwork Manufacturers Association.)

Use of modular planning effects maximum economies from the producer and simplification for the building industry. At the same time, a given layout does not confine acceptable products to such a limited range.

9-9. Window Types. The window industry has kept well apace with modern advances in building design and has made available a wide range of window types to satisfy the ever-increasing scope of requirements. Windows are basically functional, but at the same time, they are usually employed as a means of architectural expression.

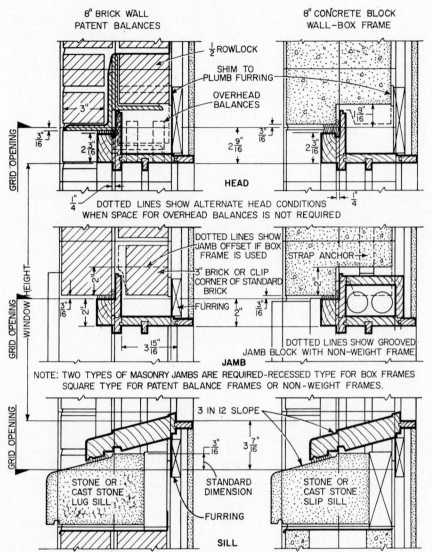

FIG. 9-3. Details of installation of double-hung wood windows. (*National Woodwork Manufacturers Association.*)

There are many materials, sizes, arrangements, details, and specific features from which to choose.

Types of windows (see symbols Fig. 9-4) include:

Pivoted windows, an economical, industrial window used where a good tight closure is not of major importance (Figs. 9-5 and 9-8). Principal members of metal units are usually $1\frac{3}{8}$ in. deep, with frame and vent corners and muntin joints riveted. However, when frame and vent corners are welded, principal members may be $1\frac{1}{4}$ in. deep. Vents are pivoted about 2 in. above the center. These windows are adaptable to multiunits, both vertical and horizontal, with mechanical operation. Bottom of vent swings out and top swings in.   No provision is made for screening.   Putty glazing is placed inside.

Commercial projected windows, similar to pivoted windows (Figs. 9-6 and 9-8). These are an industrial-type window but also are used for commercial buildings where economy is essential.   Vents are balanced on arms that afford a positive and easy control of ventilation and can be operated in groups by mechanical operators.   Maximum opening about 35°.   Factory provision is made for screens.

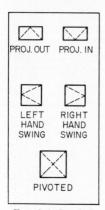

FIG. 9-4. Symbols for common window types (viewed from outside).

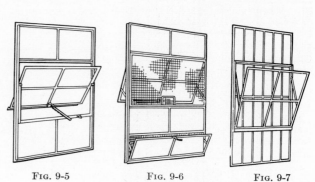

FIG. 9-5   FIG. 9-6   FIG. 9-7

FIG. 9-5. Pivoted window.
FIG. 9-6. Commercial projected window.
FIG. 9-7. Security window.

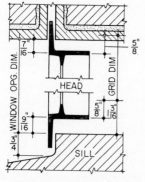

VERTICAL SECTION

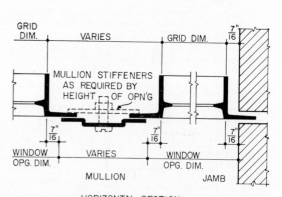

HORIZONTAL SECTION

FIG. 9-8. Details of installation of commercial projected, pivoted, and security windows.

Security windows, an industrial window for use where protection against burglary is important, such as for factories, garages, warehouses, rear and side elevations of stores (Figs. 9-7 and 9-8).   They eliminate the need for separate guard bars.   They consist of a grille and ventilated window in one unit.   Maximum grille openings are 7×16 in.   The ventilating section, either inside or outside the grille, is bottom-hinged or projected.   Muntins are continuous vertically and horizontally.   Factory provision is made for screening.   Glazing is placed from the inside.

Basement and utility windows, economy sash designed for use in basements, barracks, garages, service stations, areaways, etc. (Figs. 9-9 and 9-10).   Ventilator opens inward and is easily removed for glazing or cleaning, or to provide a clear opening for passage of materials. Center muntin is optional. Screens are attached on the outside.

Architectural projected windows, a medium-quality sash used widely for commercial, institutional, and industrial buildings (Figs. 9-11 and 9-12). Ventilator arrangement permits cleaning from inside and provides a good range of ventilation control with easy operation. Steel ventilator sections are usually 1¼ in. deep, with corners welded. Frames may be 1⅜ in. deep when riveted or 1¼ in. deep when welded. Screens are generally furnished at extra cost. Glazing may be either inside or outside.

Intermediate projected windows, high-quality ventilating sash used for schools, hospitals, commercial buildings, etc. (Figs. 9-13 and 9-14). When made of metal, corners of frames and ventilators are welded. Depth of frame and vent sections varies from "intermediate" to "heavy intermediate," depending on the manufacturer. Each vent is balanced on two arms pivoted to the frame and vent.

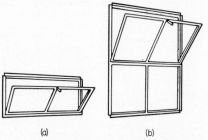

(a)   (b)

Fig. 9-9. Basement and utility windows.

The arms are equipped with friction shoes arranged to slide in the jamb sections. Screens are easily attached from inside. All

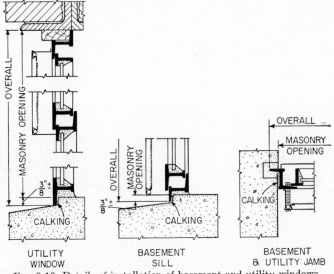

UTILITY
WINDOW

BASEMENT
SILL

BASEMENT
& UTILITY JAMB

Fig. 9-10. Details of installation of basement and utility windows.

cleaning is done from the inside. Glazing is set from the outside. Double insulating glass is optional.

Psychiatric projected windows, for use in housing for mental patients, to provide protection against exit but minimizing appearance of restraint (Fig. 9-15). Ventilators open in at the top, with a maximum clear opening of 5 to 6 in. Glazing is set outside. Screens also are placed on the outside but installed from inside. Metal casing can be had completely assembled and attached to window ready to install. Outside glass surfaces are easily washed from the inside.

Detention windows, designed for varying degrees of restraint and for different lighting and ventilating requirements. The guard type (Fig. 9-16) is particularly adaptable to jails, reform schools, etc. It provides security against escape through window openings. Ventilators are attached to the inner face of the grille and can be had with

a removable key-locking device for positive control by attendants. Screens are installed from inside between vent and grille. Glazing is done from outside, glass being omitted from the grille at the vent section.

Residential double-hung windows (Figs. 9-1 to 9-3 and 9-17), available in different designs and weights to meet various service requirements for all types of buildings. When made of metal, the frame and ventilator corners are welded and weathertight. These windows are also used in combination with fixed picture windows for multiple window openings. They are usually equipped with weather stripping, which maintains good weathertightness. Screens and storm sash are furnished in either full or half sections. Glazing is done from outside.

Residence casements, available in various types, sizes, and

FIG. 9-11. Architectural projected window.

weights to meet service requirements of homes, apartments, hotels, institutions, commercial buildings, etc. (Fig. 9-18). Rotary or lever operators hold the vent at the desired position, up to 100% opening. Screens and storm sash are attached to the inside of casement. Extended hinges on vents permit cleaning from inside. Glazing is done from outside.

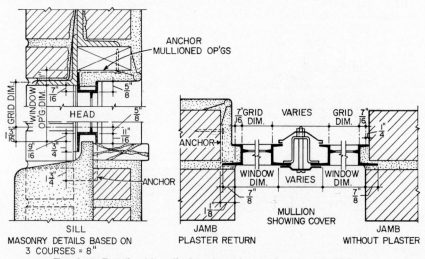

FIG. 9-12. Details of installation of architectural projected windows.

Intermediate combination windows, with side-hinged casements and projected-in ventilators incorporated to furnish flexibility of ventilation control, used extensively for apartments, offices, hospitals, schools, etc., where quality is desired (Fig. 9-19). They are available in several weights with rotary or handle operation. When made of metal, corners of vents and frames are welded. Factory provision is made for screens. All cleaning is done from inside. Glazing is set from outside. Special glazing clips permit use of double insulating glass.

Intermediate casements, a heavier and better quality than residence casements, used particularly for fine residences, apartments, offices, institutions, and similar buildings (Fig. 9-20). Frames and ventilators of metal units have welded corners. Easy control of ventilation by rotary or handle operation. Extended hinges permit safe cleaning of all outside surfaces from inside. Screens are attached or removed from inside. Single or double glazing is set from outside.

Awning windows, suitable for residential, institutional, commercial, and industrial buildings (Fig. 9-21), furnishing approximately 100% opening for ventilation. Mechanical operation can provide for the bottom vent opening prior to the other vents, which open in unison. This is desirable for night ventilation. Manual operation can be had for individual or group venting. All glass surfaces are easily cleaned from inside through the open vents. Glazing is set from outside, storm sash and screens from inside.

Jalousie windows (Fig. 9-22) combine unobstructed vision with controlled ventilation and are used primarily for sunrooms, porches, and the like where protection from the weather is desired with maximum fresh air. The louvers can be secured in any position. Various kinds of glass, including obscure and colored, often are used for privacy or decoration. They do not afford maximum weathertightness but can be fitted with storm sash on the inside. Screens are furnished interchangeable with storm sash.

Fig. 9-13. Intermediate projected window.

Ranch windows, particularly suited to modern home design and also used effectively in other types of buildings where more light or a better view is desired (Fig. 9-23). When made of metal, corners of frames and vents are welded. Depth of sections vary with manufacturers. These windows are designed to accommodate insulating glass or single panes. Screens are attached from inside.

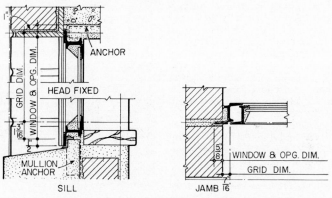

Fig. 9-14. Details of installation of intermediate projected window.

Continuous top-hung windows, used for top lighting and ventilation in monitor and sawtooth roof construction (Fig. 9-24). They are hinged at the top to the structural-steel framing members of the building and swing outward at the bottom. Two-foot lengths are connected end to end on the job. Mechanical operators may be either manual or motor-powered, with lengths of runs as specified in Table 9-1, p. 9-13. Sections may be installed as fixed windows. Glazing is set from outside.

Additional types of windows (not illustrated) include:

Vertical pivoted, which sometimes are sealed with a rubber or plastic gasket.

Horizontal sliding sash usually in aluminum or wood for residential work.

Vertical folding windows, which feature a flue action for ventilation.

Double-hung windows with removable sash, which slide up and down, or another type which tilts for ventilation but does not slide.

Austral type, with sash units similar to double-hung but which operate in unison as projected sash. The sash units are counterbalanced on arms pivoted to the frame, the top unit projecting out at bottom and the bottom unit projected in at top.

Picture windows, often a combination of fixed sash with or without auxiliary ventilating units.

Store-front construction, usually semi-custom-built of stock moldings of stainless steel, aluminum, bronze, or wood.

9-10. Windows in Wall-panel Construction. In the development of thin-wall buildings and wall-panel construction, windows have become more a part of the wall rather than units to fill an opening. Wall panels of metal and concrete incorporate windows as part of their general make-up; a well-integrated design will recognize this inherent composition.

Manufacturers of metal wall panels can furnish formed metal window frames specifically adapted to sash type and wall construction.

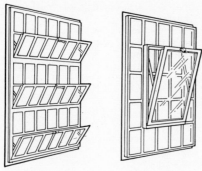

Fig. 9-15   Fig. 9-16

Fig. 9-15. Psychiatric projected window.
Fig. 9-16. Guard-type detention window.

In panel walls of precast concrete, window frames can be cast as an integral part of the unit (Fig. 9-25), or set in openings as provided. The cast-in-place method minimizes air infiltration around the frame and reduces installation costs on the job. Individual units or continuous bands of sash, both horizontal and vertical, can be readily adapted by the proper forming for head, jamb, and sill sections.

9-11. Mechanical Operators for Windows. Mechanical operation for pivoted and projected ventilators is achieved with a horizontal torsion shaft actuated by an endless hand chain or by motor power. Arms attached to the torsion shaft open and close the vents.

Two common types of operating arms are the lever and the rack and pinion (Fig. 9-26). The lever is used for manual operation of small groups of pivoted vents where rapid opening is desirable. The rack and pinion is used for longer runs of vents and can be motor-powered or manually operated. The opening and closing by rack and pinion is slower than by lever arm.

Usually one operating arm is furnished for each vent less than 4 ft wide and two arms for each vent 4 ft or more wide. Mechanical operators should be installed by the window manufacturer before glazing of the windows.

Continuous top-hung windows are mechanically controlled by rack-and-pinion or tension-type operators (Fig. 9-26).

Fig. 9-17. Double-hung windows.

Maximum length of run is given in Table 9-1.

9-12. Weather Stripping and Storm Sash. Weather stripping is a barrier against air leakage through cracks around sash. Made of metal or a compressible resilient material, it is very effective in reducing heat loss.

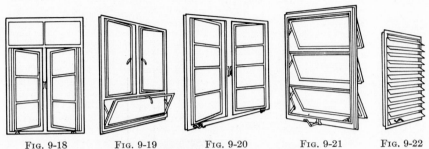

FIG. 9-18   FIG. 9-19   FIG. 9-20   FIG. 9-21   FIG. 9-22

FIG. 9-18. Residence casement window.
FIG. 9-19. Intermediate combination window.
FIG. 9-20. Intermediate casement window.
FIG. 9-21. Awning window.
FIG. 9-22. Jalousie window.

Storm sash might be considered an over-all outside transparent blanket that shields the window unit and reduces heat loss. Weather stripping and storm sash also reduce condensation and soot and dirt infiltration, as well as decreasing the amount of cold air near the floor.

Storm sash and screens are often incorporated in a single unit.

9-13. Window Glass. Various types of glass are used for glazing:

Clear Window Glass. This is the most extensively used type for windows in all classes of buildings. A range of grades, as established by Federal government standards, classifies quality according to defects. The more commonly used

FIXED LIGHTS 36"X 24" GLASS.
VENTS MAY BE PLACED AS DESIRED.

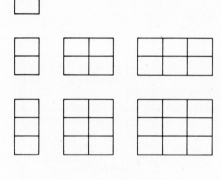

FIG. 9-23. Ranch windows.

CONTINUOUS TOP-HUNG WINDOWS

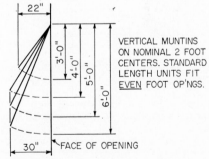

VERTICAL MUNTINS ON NOMINAL 2 FOOT CENTERS. STANDARD LENGTH UNITS FIT EVEN FOOT OP'NGS.

FACE OF OPENING

FIG. 9-24. Continuous top-hung windows.

grades are A and B. A is used for the better class of buildings where appearance is important, and B is used for industrial buildings, some low-cost residences, basements, etc.

With respect to thickness, clear window glass is classified as "single-strength," about $\frac{3}{32}$ in. thick; "double-strength," about $\frac{1}{8}$ in. thick; and "heavy-sheet," up to $\frac{7}{32}$ in. thick.   Maximum sizes are as follows: single-strength, 40 × 50 in.; double-strength, 60 × 80 in.; and heavy sheet, 76 × 120 in.

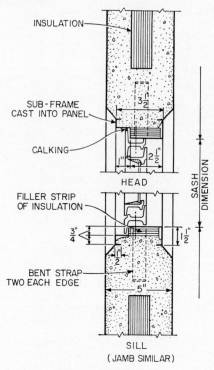

FIG. 9-25. Window installed in precast-concrete sandwich wall panel.   (*Marietta Concrete Corp.*)

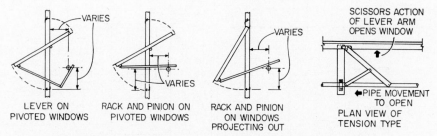

FIG. 9-26. Levers, rack-and-pinion, and tension-type window operators.

Polished plate glass is a superior-quality glass and more expensive.   It has better appearance and shows no distortion of vision at any angle.   Show windows, picture windows, and exposed windows in the better grades of buildings are usually glazed with polished plate glass.   Thickness of plate glass ranges from $\frac{1}{8}$ to about $1\frac{1}{4}$ in., with $\frac{1}{4}$ in. usually used for window glass.   There are two standard qualities, "silvering" and "glazing," the latter being employed for quality glazing.

Table 9-1. Maximum Run for Mechanical Operators, Ft

Operators for Pivoted Windows

Type of operator	Lever (1-in. pipe)				Rack and pinion (1-in. pipe)				
Control	Manual				Manual				Electric oil encl.
	Dust*		Oil†		Dust*		Oil†		
	Chain	Rod	Chain	Rod	Chain	Rod	Chain	Rod	
Sash open 16-in.	100	80	150	120	160	140	200	180	240

Operators for Projected Windows

Type of operator	Rack and pinion				
Control	Manual				Electric
	Dust*		Oil†		
	Chain	Rod	Chain	Rod	
	100	90	140	120	200

Operators for Continuous Top-hung Windows

Type of operator			Rack and pinion	Tension	
Control			Manual or electric	Manual	Electric
Limits	Sash	Height, ft	1-in. pipe	1-in. pipe	1-in. pipe
	Vertical	3, 4, 5, 6	150	200	300
	30° slope	3	120	160	240
		4	100	140	210
		5	80	120	180
		6	60	100	150

* Dust-protected—cast gearing.
† Oil-enclosed—cut gearing.

Processed glass and rolled figured sheet are general classifications of obscure glass. There are many patterns and varying characteristics. Some provide true obscurity with a uniform diffusion and pleasing appearance, while others may give a maximum transmission of light or a smoother surface for greater cleanliness. The more popular types include a clear polished surface on one side with a pattern for obscurity on the other side.

Wire glass is usually specified for its fire-retarding properties, although it is also used in doors or windows where breakage is a problem. It is considered as standard for continuous windows in monitor and sawtooth roof construction.

Prism glass has prism-shaped ribs on one side designed for deflecting light. The prisms can be had with different angles to suit various requirements. Prism wire glass is also available combining fire protection and deflection of light.

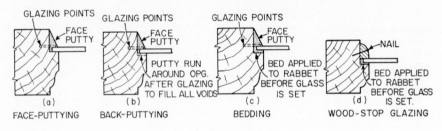

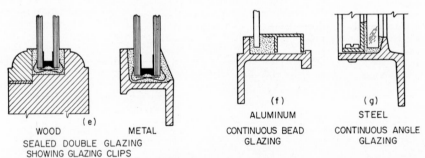

Fig. 9-27. Glazing details.

There also are many special glasses for specific purposes:

Actinic or heat-absorbing glass reduces heat, glare, and a large percentage of the ultraviolet rays, which bleach colored fabrics.

Quartz glass transmits ultraviolet rays. Hospital solariums employ this type to obtain maximum health benefits from the sun's rays.

Corrugated glass, corrugated wire glass, and corrugated plastic panels are used for decorative treatments, diffusing light, or as a translucent structural panel with color.

Safety and bulletproof glass are laminated transparent sheets that may crack under impact but will not shatter.

9-14. Glazing Compounds. Putty, glazing compound, rubber, or plastic strips and metal or wood molds are used for holding glass in place in sash. Metal clips for metal sash and glazing points for wood sash also are employed for this purpose.

Putty and glazing compounds are generally classified in relation to the sash material and should be used accordingly for best results.

"Bedding" of glass in glazing compound is desirable, because it furnishes a smooth bearing surface for the glass, prevents rattling, and eliminates voids where moisture can collect (Commercial Standards, U.S. Department of Commerce). Glazing terminology relative to putty follows:

Face Puttying (Fig. 9-27*a*). Glass is inserted in the glass rabbet and securely wedged where necessary to prevent shifting. Glazing points are also driven into the wood to keep the glass firmly seated. The rabbet is then filled with putty, the putty being beveled back against the sash and muntins with a putty knife.

Back Puttying (Fig. 9-27*b*). After the sash has been face-puttied, it is turned over and putty is run around the glass opening with a putty knife, thus forcing putty into any voids that may exist between the glass and the wood parts.

Bedding (Fig. 9-27*c*). A thin layer of putty or bedding compound is placed in the rabbet of the sash and the glass is pressed onto this bed. Glazing points are then driven into the wood and the sash is face-puttied. The sash is then turned over and the excess putty or glazing compound that emerged on the other side is removed.

Wood-stop Glazing (Fig. 9-27*d*). A thin layer of putty or bedding compound is placed in the rabbet of the sash and the glass is pressed onto this bed. Glazing points are not required. Wood stops are securely nailed in place. The sash is then turned over and the excess putty or glazing compound that emerged on the other side is removed.

Glazing beads (Fig. 9-27*f*) are designed to cover exterior glazing compound and improve appearance.

Continuous glazing angles (Fig. 9-27*g*) or similar positive supports for glass are usually required for "labeled windows" by the National Board of Fire Underwriters.

9-15. Sealed Double Glazing. This is a factory-fabricated sash composed of two panes of glass separated by a dehydrated air space. This type of sash is also manufactured with three panes of glass and two air spaces, providing additional insulation against heat flow or sound transmission.

Heat loss and heat gain can be substantially reduced by this insulated glass, permitting larger window areas and added indoor comfort. Heat-absorbing glass is often used for the outside pane and a clear plate glass for the inside. However, there are many combinations of glass available, including several patterned styles. Thickness of glass and air space between can be varied within prescribed limitations. In the selection of a window for double or triple glazing accommodation of the overall thickness of glass in the sash is an important consideration.

Section 10

WALLS AND PARTITIONS

FREDERICK S. MERRITT

Senior Editor
Engineering News-Record

MASONRY WALLS

Walls and partitions are classified as load-bearing and non-load-bearing. Different design criteria are applied to the two types.

Minimum requirements for both types of masonry walls are given in American Standard Building Code Requirements for Masonry, A41.1, prepared by the American Standards Association, under the sponsorship of the National Bureau of Standards. The following recommendations are based on this standard. See also John A. Mulligan, "Handbook of Brick Masonry Construction," McGraw-Hill Book Company, Inc., New York, 1942; H. C. Plummer and J. A. Blume, "Reinforced Brick Masonry and Lateral Force Design," Structural Clay Products Institute, Washington, D.C.

10-1. Masonry Definitions. Following are some of the terms most commonly encountered in masonry construction:

Architectural Terra Cotta. Plain or ornamental (molded or extruded) hard-burned building units, usually larger in size than brick, consisting of mixtures of plastic clays, fusible minerals, and grog, and having a glazed or unglazed ceramic finish.

Ashlar Facing. Wall facing composed of solid rectangular units usually larger in size than brick, having sawed, dressed, or squared beds, and mortar joints.

Ashlar Masonry. Masonry composed of rectangular units usually larger in size than brick and properly bonded, having sawed, dressed, or squared beds, and mortar joints.

Bonder. (See header.)

Brick. A solid masonry unit having a shape approximately a rectangular prism, usually not larger than 4 × 4 × 12 in. A brick may be made of burned clay, burned shale, fire clay, or mixtures thereof, lime and sand, cement and suitable aggregates, or other suitable materials.

Cross-sectional Area. Net cross-sectional area of a masonry unit is the gross area minus the area of cores or cellular space. Gross area of scored units is determined to the outside of the scoring but the cross-sectional area of the grooves is not deducted.

Grout. (See Mortar.)

Grouted Masonry. Masonry in which the interior joints are filled by pouring grout into them as the work progresses.

Header (Bonder). A masonry unit that ties two or more wythes (leaves) of the wall together by overlapping.

Height of Wall. The vertical distance from the foundation wall or other immediate support of such wall, to the top of the wall.

10–1

Hollow Masonry Unit. A masonry unit whose net cross-sectional area in any plane parallel to the bearing surface is less than 75% of its gross cross-sectional area measured in the same plane.

Masonry. A built-up construction or combination of building units of such materials as clay, shale, concrete, glass, gypsum, or stone, set in mortar; or plain concrete.

Mortar. A plastic mixture of cementitious materials, fine aggregates, and water used to bond masonry or other structural units. Mortar of pouring consistency is termed grout.

Partition. An interior wall one story or less in height.

Pier. An isolated column of masonry. A bearing wall not bonded at the sides into associated masonry is considered a pier when its horizontal dimension measured at right angles to the thickness does not exceed four times its thickness.

Rubble

Coursed Rubble. Masonry composed of roughly shaped stones fitting approximately on level beds, well bonded and brought at vertical intervals to continuous but approximately level beds or courses.

Random Rubble. Masonry composed of roughly shaped stones, well bonded and brought at irregular vertical intervals to discontinuous but approximately level beds or courses.

Rough or Ordinary Rubble. Masonry composed of nonshaped or field stones laid without regularity of coursing.

Solid Masonry Unit. A masonry unit whose net cross-sectional area in every plane parallel to the bearing surface is 75% or more of its gross cross-sectional area measured in the same plane.

Spandrel Wall. An exterior curtain wall at the level of the outside floor beams in multistory buildings. It may extend from the head of the window below the floor to the sill of the window above.

Walls

Bearing Wall. A wall that supports any vertical load in addition to its own weight.

Cavity Wall (Core Wall). (See Hollow Wall.)

Curtain Wall. A non-load-bearing exterior wall.

Faced Wall. A wall in which the masonry facing and the backing are of different materials and are so bonded as to exert a common reaction under load.

Hollow Wall. A wall of masonry so arranged as to provide an air space within the wall between the inner and outer parts (wythes) of the wall. A cavity or core wall is built of masonry units or of plain concrete, or of a combination of these materials, so arranged as to provide an air space within the wall (with or without insulating material) and in which the inner and outer wythes are tied together with metal ties.

Nonbearing Wall. A wall that supports no vertical load other than its own weight.

Parapet Wall. That part of any wall entirely above the roof.

Party Wall. A wall on an interior lot line used or adapted for joint service between two buildings.

Veneered Wall. A wall having a facing of masonry or other material securely attached to the backing, but not so bonded as to exert a common reaction under load.

Wythe (Leaf). Each continuous vertical section of a wall one masonry unit in thickness and tied to its adjacent vertical section or sections (front or back) by bonders (headers), metal ties, or grout.

10-2. Quality of Materials for Masonry. Materials used in masonry construction should be capable of meeting the requirements of the applicable standard of the American Society for Testing Materials.

Secondhand materials should be used only with extreme caution. Much salvaged brick, for example, comes from the demolition of old buildings constructed of solid brick masonry in which hard-burned bricks were used on the exterior and salmon brick as backup. Because the color differences that guided the original masons in sorting and selecting bricks become obscured with exposure and contact with mortar, there is a definite danger that the salmon bricks may be used for exterior exposure and may disintegrate rapidly. Masonry units salvaged from chimneys are not recommended because they may be impregnated with oils or tarry material.

Table 10-1. Types of Mortar

Mortar type	Parts by volume				Min avg compressive strength of three 2-in. cubes at 28 days, psi
	Portland cement	Masonry cement	Hydrated lime or lime putty	Aggregate measured in damp, loose condition	
M	1	1 (Type II)	....		2,500
	1	....	1/4		
S	1/2	1 (Type II)	....		1,800
	1	....	Over 1/4 to 1/2	Not less than 2 1/4	
N	...	1 (Type II)	....	and not more than	750
	1	....	Over 1/2 to 1 1/4	3 times the sum of	
O	...	1 (Types I or II)	....	the volumes of the	350
	1	....	Over 1 1/4 to 2 1/2	cements and limes	
K	1	....	Over 2 1/2 to 4	used	75

Table 10-2. Mortar Requirements of Masonry

Kind of Masonry — *Types of Mortar*

Foundations:
Footings... M or S
Walls of solid units............................... M, S, or N
Walls of hollow units.............................. M or S
Hollow walls....................................... M or S
Masonry other than foundation masonry:
Piers of solid masonry............................. M, S, or N
Piers of hollow units.............................. M or S
Walls of solid masonry............................. M, S, N, or O
Walls of solid masonry, other than parapet walls or rubble stone walls, not less than 12 in. thick or more than 35 ft in height, supported laterally at intervals not exceeding 12 times the wall thickness........................... M, S, N, O, or K
Walls of hollow units; load-bearing or exterior, and hollow walls 12 in. or more in thickness................. M, S, or N
Hollow walls less than 12 in. in thickness where assumed design wind pressure:
  a. Exceeds 20 psf.............................. M or S
  b. Does not exceed 20 psf.................... M, S, or N
Glass-block masonry................................ M, S, or N
Nonbearing partitions of fireproofing composed of structural clay tile or concrete masonry units............... M, S, N, O, or gypsum
Gypsum partition tile or block..................... Gypsum
Firebrick.. Refractory air-setting mortar
Linings of existing masonry........................ M or S
Masonry other than above........................... M, S, or N

10-3. Mortar. For unit masonry, mortar should meet the requirements of the American Society for Testing Materials Specification C270. This defines five types of mortar, as shown in Table 10-1. Each type is used for a specific purpose, as indicated in Table 10-2, based on compressive strength. However, it should not be assumed that higher-strength mortars are preferable to lower-strength mortars where lower strength is permitted for particular uses.

Mortars containing lime are generally preferred because of greater workability. Commonly used:

For concrete block, 1 part cement, 1 part lime putty, 5 to 6 parts sand.
For rubble, 1 part cement, 1 to 2 parts lime hydrate or putty, 5 to 7 parts sand.
For brick, 1 part cement, 1 part lime, 6 parts sand.
For setting tile, 1 part cement, 1/2 part lime, 3 parts sand.

10-4. Allowable Stresses on Masonry. In determining stresses in masonry, effects of loads should be computed on actual dimensions, not nominal.   The stresses should not exceed the allowable stresses given in American Standard Building Code Requirements for Masonry (A41.1), which are duplicated for convenience in Table 10-3.

Table **10-3.** Allowable Stresses in Unit Masonry

Construction	Allowable compressive stress on gross cross section, psi				
	Type M mortar	Type S mortar	Type N mortar	Type O mortar	Type K mort..r
Solid masonry of brick and other solid units of clay or shale; sand-lime or concrete brick:					
8,000 + psi	400	350	300	200	100
4,500–8,000 psi	2.0	225	200	150	100
2,500–4,500 psi	175	160	140	110	75
1,500–2,500 psi	125	115	100	75	50
Grouted solid masonry of brick and other solid units of clay or shale; sand-lime or concrete brick:					
4,500+ psi	350	275	200		
2,500–4,500 psi	275	215	155		
1,500–2,500 psi	225	175	125		
Solid masonry or solid concrete masonry units:					
Grade A	175	160	140	100	
Grade B	125	115	100	75	
Masonry of hollow units	85	75	70		
Piers of hollow units, cellular spaces filled	105	95	90		
Hollow walls (cavity or masonry bonded):*					
Solid units:					
Grade A or 2,500+ psi	140	130	110		
Grade B or 1,500–2,500 psi	100	90	80		
Hollow units	70	60	55		
Stone ashlar masonry:					
Granite	800	720	640	500	
Limestone or marble	500	450	400	325	
Sandstone or cast stone	400	360	320	250	
Rubble stone, coursed, rough, or random	140	120	100	80	

* On gross cross section of wall minus area of cavity between wythes.   The allowable compressive stresses for cavity walls are based on the assumption that floor loads bear on only one of the two wythes. Increase stresses 25 % for hollow walls loaded concentrically.

This standard recommends also that, in composite walls or other structural members composed of different kinds or grades of units or mortars, the maximum stress should not exceed the allowable stress for the weakest of the combination of units and mortars of which the member is composed.

Compressive strength of masonry depends to a great extent on workmanship and the completeness with which units are bedded.   Tensile strength is a function of the adhesion of mortar to a unit and of the area of bonding (degree of completeness with which joints are filled).   Hence, in specifying masonry work, it is important to call for a full bed of mortar, with each course well hammered down, and all joints completely filled with mortar.

10-5. Leakproof Walls. To minimize the entrance of water through a brick wall, follow the practices recommended in Art. 14-14.

In particular, in filling head joints, apply a heavy buttering of mortar on one end of the brick, press the brick down into the bed joint, and push the brick into place so that the mortar squeezes out from the top and sides of the head joint. Mortar should correspondingly cover the entire side of a brick before it is placed as a header. An attempt to fill head joints by slushing or dashing will not succeed in producing watertight joints. Partial filling of joints by "buttering" or "spotting" the vertical edge of the brick with mortar cut from the extruded bed joint is likewise ineffective and should be prohibited. Where closures are required, the opening should be filled with mortar so that insertion of the closure will extrude mortar both laterally and vertically.

Tooling of joints, if done properly, can help to resist penetration of water; but it is not a substitute for complete filling, or a remedy for incomplete filling of joints. A concave joint is recommended. Use of raked or other joints that provide horizontal water tables should be avoided. Mortar should not be too stiff at time of tooling, or compaction will not take place, nor should it be too fluid, or the bricks may move—and bricks should never be moved after initial contact with mortar. If a brick is out of line, it should be removed, mortar scraped off and fresh mortar applied before the brick is relaid.

Back-plaster, or parge, the back face of exterior wythes before backup units are laid. If the backup is laid first, the front of the backup should be parged. The mortar should be the same as that used for laying the brick and should be applied from ¼ to ⅜ in. thick.

(See also Type of Workmanship Recommended to Secure Dry Brick Walls; Specifications Recommended to Secure Dry Brick Walls; Type of Workmanship Recommended for Concrete Block Walls, Louisville Cement Co., Louisville, Ky. And *Proceedings of the Modern Masonry Conference*, Building Research Institute, Washington, D.C., 1956.)

10-6. Lateral Support for Masonry Walls. For solid masonry walls or bearing partitions, the ratio of unsupported height to nominal thickness, or the ratio of unsupported length to nominal thickness, should not exceed 20. However, if Type K mortar is used, the ratio should be limited to 12, or less. For hollow walls or walls of hollow masonry units, the ratio should be 18 or less.

In calculating the ratio of unsupported length to thickness for cavity walls, you can take the thickness as the sum of the nominal thicknesses of the inner and outer wythes. For walls composed of different kinds or classes of units or mortars, the ratio should not exceed that allowed for the weakest of the combinations. Veneers should not be considered part of the wall in computing thickness for strength or stability.

Cantilever walls and masonry walls in locations exposed to high winds should not be built higher than ten times their thickness unless adequately braced. Backfill should not be placed against foundation walls until they have been braced to withstand horizontal pressure.

In determining the unsupported length of walls, existing cross walls, piers, or buttresses may be considered as lateral supports, if these members are well bonded or anchored to the walls and capable of transmitting the lateral forces to connected structural members or to the ground.

In determining the unsupported height of walls, floors and roofs may be considered as lateral supports, if provision is made in the building to transmit the lateral forces to the ground. Ends of floor joists or beams bearing on masonry walls should be securely fastened to the walls. When lateral support is to be provided by joists parallel to walls, anchors should be spaced no more than 6 ft apart and engage at least three joists, which should be bridged solidly at the anchors.

Anchors for floor beams bearing on walls should be provided at intervals of 4 ft or less. The anchors should be solidly embedded in mortar and extend into the walls a distance of at least half the wall thickness. Interior ends of anchored joists should be lapped and spiked, or the equivalent, so as to form continuous ties across the building.

Unsupported height of piers should not exceed ten times the least dimension. However, when structural clay tile or hollow concrete units are used for isolated piers to support beams or girders, unsupported height should not exceed four times the least dimension unless the cellular spaces are filled solidly with concrete or either Type M or S mortar (see Table 10-1).

10-7. Masonry-thickness Requirements. Walls should not vary in thickness between lateral supports. When it is necessary to change thickness between floor levels to meet minimum-thickness requirements, the greater thickness should be carried up to the next floor level.

Where walls of masonry hollow units or bonded hollow walls are decreased in thickness, a course of solid masonry should be interposed between the wall below and the thinner wall above, or else special units or construction should be used to transmit the loads between the walls of different thickness.

Bearing walls should be at least 12 in. thick for the uppermost 35 ft of their height. Thickness should be increased 4 in. for each successive 35 ft or fraction of this distance measured downward from the top of the wall. Rough or random or coursed rubble stone walls should be 4 in. thicker than this, but in no case less than 16 in. thick. However, for other than rubble stone walls, the following exceptions apply to masonry bearing walls:

Stiffened Walls. Where solid masonry bearing walls are stiffened at distances not greater than 12 ft by masonry cross walls or by reinforced-concrete floors, they may be made 12 in. thick for the uppermost 70 ft but should be increased 4 in. in thickness for each successive 70 ft or fraction of that distance.

Top-story Walls. The top-story bearing wall of a building not over 35 ft high may be made 8 in. thick. But this wall should be no more than 12 ft high and should not be subjected to lateral thrust from the roof construction.

Residential Walls. In dwellings up to three stories high, walls may be 8 in. thick (if not more than 35 ft high), if not subjected to lateral thrust from the roof construction. Such walls in one-story houses and one-story private garages may be 6 in. thick, if the height is 9 ft or less or if the height to the peak of a gable does not exceed 15 ft.

Penthouses and Roof Structures. Masonry walls up to 12 ft high above roof level, enclosing stairways, machinery rooms, shafts, or penthouses, may be made 8 in. thick. They need not be included in determining the height for meeting thickness requirements for the wall below.

Plain Concrete Walls. Such walls may be 2 in. less in thickness than the minimum requirements for other types of masonry walls, but in general not less than 8 in.—and not less than 6 in. in one-story dwellings and garages.

Hollow Walls. Cavity or masonry bonded hollow walls should not be more than 35 ft high. In particular, 10-in. cavity walls should be limited to 25 ft in height above supports. The facing and backing of cavity walls should be at least 4 in. thick, and the cavity should not be less than 2 in. or more than 3 in. wide.

Faced Walls. Neither the height of faced (composite) walls nor the distance between lateral supports should exceed that prescribed for masonry of either of the types forming the facing and the backing. Actual (not nominal) thickness of materials used for facings should not be less than 2 in. and in no case less than one-eighth the height of the unit.

In general, parapet walls should be at least 8 in. thick and the height should not exceed three times the thickness. The thickness may be less than 8 in., however, if the parapet is reinforced to withstand safely earthquake and wind forces to which it may be subjected.

Nonbearing exterior masonry walls may be 4 in. less in thickness than the minimum for bearing walls. However, the thickness should not be less than 8 in. except that where 6-in. bearing walls are permitted, 6-in. nonbearing walls can be used also.

Nonbearing masonry partitions should be supported laterally at distances of not more than thirty-six times the actual thickness of the partition, including plaster. If lateral support depends on a ceiling, floor, or roof, the top of the partition should have adequate anchorage to transmit the forces. This anchorage may be accomplished with metal anchors or by keying the top of the partition to overhead work. Suspended ceilings may be considered as lateral support if ceilings and anchorages are capable of resisting a horizontal force of 150 lb per lin ft of wall.

10-8. Bond in Masonry Walls. When headers are used for bonding the facing and backing in solid masonry walls and faced walls, not less than 4 % of the wall surface of each face should be composed of headers, which should extend at least 4 in. into the backing. These headers should not be more than 24 in. apart vertically or horizontally (Fig. 10-1). In walls in which a single bonder does not extend through the wall, headers from opposite sides should overlap at 4 in. or should be covered with another bonder course overlapping headers below at least 4 in.

If metal ties are used for bonding, they should be corrosion-resistant. For bonding facing and backing of solid masonry walls and faced walls, there should be at least one metal tie for each $4\frac{1}{2}$ sq ft of wall area. Ties in alternate courses should be staggered, the maximum vertical distance between ties should not exceed 18 in., and the maximum horizontal distance should not be more than 36 in.

In walls composed of two or more thicknesses of hollow units, stretcher courses should be bonded by one of the following methods: At vertical intervals up to 34 in., there should be a course lapping units below at least 4 in. (Fig. 10-1). Or at vertical intervals up to 17 in., lapping should be accomplished with units at least 50 % thicker than the units below (Fig. 10-1). Or at least one metal tie should be incorporated for each $4\frac{1}{2}$ sq ft of wall area. Ties in alternate courses should be staggered; the maximum vertical distance between ties should be 18 in. and the maximum horizontal distance, 36 in. Full mortar coverage should be provided in both horizontal and vertical joints at ends and edges of face shells of the hollow units.

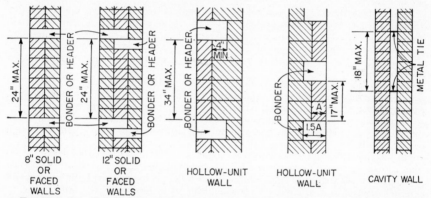

FIG. 10-1. Requirements for vertical spacing of bonding elements in masonry walls.

In ashlar masonry, bond stones should be uniformly distributed throughout the wall and form at least 10 % of the area of exposed faces.

In rubble stone masonry up to 24 in. thick, bond stones should have a maximum spacing of 3 ft vertically and horizontally. In thicker walls, there should be at least one bond stone for each 6 sq ft of wall surface on both sides.

For bonding ashlar facing, the percentage of bond stones should be computed from the exposed face area of the wall. At least 10 % of this area should be composed of uniformly distributed bond stones extending 4 in. or more into the backup. Every bond stone, and when alternate courses are not full bond courses every stone, should be securely anchored to the backup with corrosion-resistant metal anchors. These should have a minimum cross section of $\frac{3}{16} \times 1$ in. There should be at least one anchor to a stone and at least two anchors for stones more than 2 ft long or with a face area of more than 3 sq ft. Larger facing stones should have at least one anchor per 4 sq ft of face area of the stone, but not less than two anchors.

Cavity-wall wythes should be bonded with $\frac{3}{16}$-in.-diameter steel rods or metal ties of equivalent stiffness embedded in horizontal joints. There should be at least one metal tie for each $4\frac{1}{2}$ sq ft of wall area. Ties in alternate courses should be staggered, the maximum vertical distance between ties should not exceed 18 in. (Fig. 10-1), and the maximum horizontal distance, 36 in. Rods bent to rectangular shape should be used with hollow masonry units laid with cells vertical. In other walls, the ends of ties should be bent to 90° angles to provide hooks at least 2 in. long. Additional bonding ties should be provided at all openings. These ties should be spaced not more than 3 ft apart around the perimeter and within 12 in. of the opening.

When two bearing walls intersect and the courses are built up together, the intersections should be bonded by laying in true bond at least 50 % of the units at the intersection. When the courses are carried up separately, the intersecting walls should be regularly toothed or blocked with 8-in. maximum offsets. The joints should be provided with metal anchors having a minimum section of $\frac{1}{4} \times 1\frac{1}{2}$ in. with ends bent up at least 2 in. or with cross pins to form an anchorage. Such anchors should be at least 2 ft long and spaced not more than 4 ft apart.

10-9. Grouted Masonry. Masonry units in the outer wythes of grouted masonry walls should be laid with full head and bed joints of Type M or S mortar (see Table 10-1). All interior joints should be filled with grout.

Masonry units in the interior wythes should be placed or floated in grout poured between the two outer wythes.

One of the outer wythes may be carried up not more than three courses before grouting, but the other should be carried up not more than one course above the grout. Each grout pour should be stopped at least $1\frac{1}{2}$ in. below the top and stirred. Grouted longitudinal vertical joints should be at least $\frac{3}{4}$ in. wide. Bonders should not be used.

10-10. Glass Block. For control of light that enters a building and for better insulation than obtained with ordinary glass panes, masonry walls of glass block are frequently used. These units are hollow, $3\frac{7}{8}$ in. thick by 6 in. square, 8 in. square, or 12 in. square (actual length and height $\frac{1}{4}$ in. less, for modular coordination). Faces of the units may be cut into prisms to throw light upward or the block may be treated to diffuse light.

Glass block may be used as in nonbearing walls and to fill openings in walls. The glass block so used should have a minimum thickness of $3\frac{1}{2}$ in. at the mortar joint. Also, surfaces of the block should be satisfactorily treated for mortar bonding.

For exterior walls, glass-block panels should not have an unsupported area of more than 144 sq ft. They should be no more than 25 ft long, or more than 20 ft high between supports.

For interior walls, glass-block panels should not have an unsupported area of more than 250 sq ft. Neither length nor height should exceed 25 ft.

Exterior panels should be held in place in the wall opening to resist both internal and external wind pressures. The panels should be set in recesses at the jambs so as to provide a bearing surface at least 1 in. wide along the edges. Panels more than 10 ft long should also be recessed at the head. Some building codes, however, permit anchoring small panels in low buildings with noncorrodible perforated metal strips.

Steel reinforcement should be placed in the horizontal mortar joints of glass-block panels at vertical intervals of 2 ft or less. It should extend the full length of the joints but not across expansion joints. When splices are necessary, the reinforcement should be lapped at least 6 in. In addition, reinforcement should be placed in the joint immediately below and above any openings in a panel.

The reinforcement should consist of two parallel longitudinal galvanized-steel wires, No. 9 gage or larger, spaced 2 in. apart, and having welded to them No. 14 or heavier-gage cross wires at intervals of up to 8 in.

Mortar joints should be from $\frac{1}{4}$ to $\frac{3}{8}$ in. thick. They should be completely filled with mortar.

Exterior glass-block panels should be provided with expansion joints at sides and top. These joints should be kept free of mortar and should be filled with resilient material (Fig. 10-2).

10-11. Openings, Chases, and Recesses in Masonry Walls. Masonry above openings should be supported by arches or lintels of metal or reinforced masonry, which should bear on the wall at each end at least 4 in. Stone or other nonreinforced masonry lintels should not be used unless supplemented on the inside of the wall with iron or steel lintels, suitable masonry arches, or reinforced-masonry lintels carrying the masonry backing. Lintels should be stiff enough to carry the superimposed load with a deflection of less than $\frac{1}{360}$ of the clear span.

In plain concrete walls, reinforcement symmetrically disposed in the thickness of the wall should be placed not less than 1 in. above and 2 in. below openings. It should extend at least 24 in. on each side of the opening or be equivalently developed with hooks. Minimum reinforcement that should be used is one ⅝-in.-diameter bar for each 6 in. of wall thickness.

In structures other than low residences, masonry walls should not have chases and recesses deeper than one-third the wall thickness, or longer than 4 ft horizontally or in horizontal projection. There should be at least 8 in. of masonry in back of chases and recesses, and between adjacent chases or recesses and the jambs of openings.

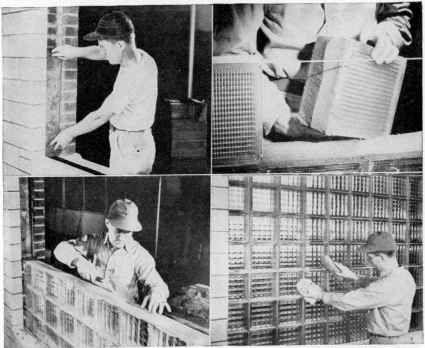

Fig. 10-2. (*Top left*) First step in installing a glass-block panel is to coat the sill with an asphalt emulsion to allow for movement due to temperature changes. Continuous-expansion strips are installed at jambs and head. (*Top right*) Block are set with full mortar joints. (*Bottom left*) Welded-wire ties are embedded in the mortar to reinforce the panel. (*Bottom right*) When all the block are placed, joints tooled to a smooth concave finish, and the perimeter of the panel calked, the block are cleaned.

Chases and recesses should not be cut in walls of hollow masonry units or in hollow walls but may be built in. They should not be allowed within the required area of a pier.

The aggregate area of recesses and chases in any wall should not exceed one-fourth of the whole area of the face of the wall in any story.

In dwellings not more than two stories high, vertical chases may be built in 8-in. walls if the chases are not more than 4 in. deep and occupy less than 4 sq ft of wall area. However, recesses below windows may extend from floor to sill and may be the width of the opening above. Masonry above chases or recesses wider than 12 in. should be supported on lintels.

Recesses may be left in walls for stairways and elevators, but the walls should not be reduced in thickness to less than 12 in. unless reinforced in some approved manner. Recesses for alcoves and similar purposes should have at least 8 in. of masonry at the back. They should be less than 8 ft wide and should be arched over or spanned with lintels.

10-12. Support Conditions for Walls. Provision should be made to distribute concentrated loads safely on masonry walls and piers. Heavily loaded members should have steel bearing plates under the ends to distribute the load to the masonry within allowable bearing stresses. Length of bearing should be at least 3 in. Lightly loaded members may be supported directly on the masonry if the bearing stresses in the masonry are within permissible limits and if length of bearing is 3 in. or more.

Masonry should not be supported on wood construction.

10-13. Corbeling. Except for chimneys, the maximum corbeled horizontal projection beyond the face of a wall should not exceed one-half the wall thickness. Maximum projection of one unit should not be more than one-half its depth or one-third the width (measured at right angles to the offset face).

Chimneys may not be corbeled more than 6 in. from the face of a wall more than 12 in. thick, and corbeling should not be permitted in thinner walls, unless there are equal projections on opposite sides of the wall. However, in the second story of two-story dwellings, corbeling of chimneys on the exterior of enclosing walls may equal the wall thickness. In every case, the corbeling should not be more than 1-in. projection for each course of brick projected.

10-14. Cold-weather Construction of Masonry Walls. Masonry should be protected against freezing for at least 48 hr after being laid. Unless adequate precautions are taken, no masonry should be placed when the temperature is below 32°F or below 40°F when the temperature at the work site is falling.

10-15. Chimneys and Fireplaces. Minimum requirements for chimneys may be obtained from local building codes or the National Building Code recommended by the National Board of Fire Underwriters. (See also H. C. Plummer, "Brick and Tile Engineering," Structural Clay Products Institute, Washington, D.C.)

In brief, chimneys should extend at least 3 ft above the highest point where they pass through the roof of a building and at least 2 ft higher than any ridge within 10 ft. They should be constructed of solid masonry units or reinforced concrete and lined with fire clay or other suitable refractory clay. In dwellings, thickness of chimney walls may be 4 in. In other buildings, the thickness of chimneys for heating appliances should be at least 8 in. for most masonry. Rubble stone thickness should be a minimum of 12 in.

Fireplaces should have backs and sides of solid masonry or reinforced concrete, not less than 8 in. thick. A lining of firebrick at least 2 in. thick or other approved material should be provided unless the thickness is 12 in.

Fireplaces should have hearths of brick, stone, tile, or other noncombustible material supported on a fireproof slab or on brick trimmer arches. Such hearths should extend at least 20 in. outside the chimney breast and not less than 12 in. beyond each side of the fireplace opening along the chimney breast. Combined thickness of hearth and supporting construction should not be less than 6 in. Spaces between chimney and joists, beams, or girders and any combustible materials should be fire-stopped by filling with noncombustible material.

The throat of the fireplace should be not less than 4 in. and preferably 8 in. above the top of the fireplace opening. A metal damper extending the full width of the fireplace opening should be placed in the throat. The flue should have an effective area equal to one-twelfth to one-tenth the area of the fireplace opening. For more details, see H. C. Plummer, "Brick and Tile Engineering," Structural Clay Products Institute, Washington, D.C.; C. G. Ramsey and H. R. Sleeper, "Architectural Graphic Standards," John Wiley & Sons, Inc., New York; and A. G. H. Dietz, "Dwelling House Construction," D. Van Nostrand Company, Inc., Princeton, N.J.

CURTAIN WALLS

With skeleton-frame construction, exterior walls need carry no load other than their own weight, and therefore, their principal function is to keep wind and weather out of the building—hence the name curtain wall. Nonbearing walls may be supported on the structural frame of a building, on supplementary framing (girts, for example) in turn supported on the structural frame of a building, or on the floors.

10-16. Functional Requirements of Curtain Walls. Curtain walls do not have to be any thicker than required to serve their principal function. Many industrial buildings are enclosed only with light-gage metal. However, for structures with certain types of occupancies and for buildings close to others, fire resistance is an important characteristic. Fire-resistance requirements in local building codes often govern in determining the thickness and type of material used for curtain walls.

In many types of buildings, it is desirable to have an exterior wall with good insulating properties. Sometimes a dead air space is used for this purpose. Sometimes insulating material is incorporated in the wall or erected as a backup.

The exterior surface of a curtain wall should be made of a durable material, capable of lasting as long as the building. Maintenance should be a minimum; initial cost of the wall is not so important as the annual cost (amortized initial cost plus annual maintenance and repair costs).

To meet requirements of the owner and the local building code, curtain walls may vary in construction from a simple siding to a multilayer-sandwich wall. They may be job-assembled or be delivered to the job completely prefabricated.

Walls with masonry components should meet the requirements of Arts. 10-2 to 10-14.

10-17. Wood Walls. Either in the form of boards or plywood, wood is often used as sheathing behind various types of facing materials. It is generally covered on the outside face with a waterproofing material before the facing is placed. Wood sheathing is most often used with wood framing, as in residential construction (Art. 8-25).

Wood is also applied as an exterior finish in the form of siding, shingles, half timbers, or plywood sheets. (A. G. H. Dietz, "Dwelling House Construction," D. Van Nostrand Company, Inc., Princeton, N.J.)

Siding may be drop, or novelty; lap, or clapboard; vertical boarding or horizontal flush boarding.

Drop siding can combine sheathing and siding in one piece. Tongued-and-grooved individual pieces are driven tightly up against each other when they are nailed in place to make the wall weathertight. It is not considered a good finish for permanent structures.

Lap siding or clapboard are beveled boards, thinner along one edge than the opposite edge, which are nailed over sheathing and building paper. Usually narrow boards lap each other about 1 in., wide boards more than 2 in. At the eaves, the top siding boards slip under the lower edge of a frieze board to make a weathertight joint.

When vertical or horizontal boards are used for the exterior finish, precautions should be taken to make the joints watertight. Joints should be coated with white lead in linseed oil just before the boards are nailed in place, and the boards should be driven tight against each other. Battens should be applied over the joints if the boards are square-edged.

Half timbers may be used to form a structural frame of heavy horizontal, vertical, and diagonal members, the spaces between being filled with brick. This type of construction is sometimes imitated by nailing boards in a similar pattern to an ordinary sheathed frame and filling the space between boards with stucco.

Plywood for exterior use should be an exterior grade, with plies bonded with permanent waterproof glue. The curtain wall may consist of a single sheet of plywood or of a sandwich of which plywood is a component. Also, plywood may be laminated to another material, such as a light-gage metal, to give it stiffness.

10-18. Wall Shingles. Wood, asphalt, or asbestos cement are most frequently used for shingles over a sheathed frame. Shingles are made in a variety of forms and shapes and are applied in different ways. The various manufacturers make available instructions for application of their products.

10-19. Stucco. Applied like plaster, stucco is a mixture of sand, portland cement, lime, and water. Two coats are applied to masonry, three coats on metal lath. The finish coat may be tinted by adding coloring matter to the mix or the outside surface may be painted with a suitable material.

The metal lath should be heavily galvanized.   It should weigh at least 2.5 lb per sq yd, even though furring strips are closely spaced.   When supports are 16 in. c to c, it should weigh 3.4 lb per sq yd.   The lath sheets should be applied with long dimensions horizontal and should be tied with No. 16 wire.   Edges should be lapped at least 1 in., ends 2 in.

The first, or scratch, coat should be forced through the interstices in the lath so as to embed the metal completely.   This coat may consist of 1 part quicklime putty or hydrated lime putty and 3 parts sand by volume, plus 1 bu of long hair or fiber per cu yd of sand.   To increase the rate of hardening, some of the lime may be replaced by portland cement.   A common mix is 1 part portland cement, 1 part lime putty, and 5 or 6 parts sand.

The second, or brown, coat may be based also on lime or portland cement.   With lime, the mix may be 1 part quicklime putty or hydrated lime putty and 3 parts of sand, by volume.   With cement, the mix may be 1 part portland cement to 3 parts sand, plus lime putty in amount equal to 15 to 25 % of the volume of cement.   The finish coat may have the same proportions as the brown coat.

For all mixes, the ingredients, except for the hair or fiber, are thoroughly mixed.   A small amount of water may be added for this purpose, though the hydrated lime may be mixed dry.   The mix should be left standing at least 24 hr.   So enough water should be added to the mix before this waiting period to prevent it from drying out. The hair or fiber and more water should be added and the ingredients thoroughly mixed just prior to use.

The brown coat may be applied as soon as the scratch coat has hardened sufficiently to withstand pressure without breaking the keys, usually in 1 week to 10 days.   For the finish coat it may be wise to wait several months to give the building a chance to settle and the base coats to shrink.

10-20. Metal and Asbestos-cement Siding.   Either in flat sheets or corrugated form, light-gage metal or asbestos cement may be used to form a lightweight enclosure. Corrugated sheets are stiffer than the flat.   If the sheets are very thin, they should be fastened to sheathing or closely spaced supports.

When corrugated siding is used, details should be planned so that the siding will shed water.   Horizontal splices should be placed at supporting members and the sheets should lap about 4 in.   Vertical splices should lap at least $1\frac{1}{2}$ corrugations. Sheets should be held firmly together at splices and intersections to prevent water from leaking through.   Consideration should be given to sealing strips at openings where corrugated sheets terminate against plane surfaces.   The bottommost girt supporting the siding should be placed at least 1 ft above the foundation because of the difficulty of attaching the corrugated materials to masonry.   The siding should not be sealed in a slot in the foundation because the metal may corrode or the asbestos-cement crack.   (C. W. Dunham, "Planning Industrial Structures," McGraw-Hill Book Company, Inc., New York, 1948.)

When flat sheets are used, precautions should be taken to prevent water from penetrating splices and intersections.   The sheets may be installed in sash like window glass, or the splices may be covered with battens.   Edges of metal sheets may be flanged to interlock and exclude wind and rain.

Pressed-metal panels, mostly with troughed or boxed cross sections, are also used to form lightweight walls.

Provision should be made in all cases for expansion and contraction with temperature changes.   Allowance for movement should be made at connections.   Methods of attachment vary with the type of sheet and generally should be carried out in accordance with the manufacturer's recommendations.   For typical details, see C. G. Ramsey and H. R. Sleeper, "Architectural Graphic Standards," John Wiley & Sons, Inc., New York.

10-21. Metal and Glass Facings.   In contrast to siding in which a single material forms the complete wall, metal and glass are sometimes used as the facing, which is backed up with insulation, fire-resistant material, and an interior finish.   The glass usually is tinted and is held in a light frame in the same manner as window glass. Metal panels may be fastened similarly in a light frame, attached to mullions or other secondary framing members, anchored to brackets at each floor level, or connected to the structural frame of the building. The panels may be small and light enough for one man to carry or one or two stories high, prefabricated with windows.

Provision for expansion and contraction should be made in the frames, when they are used, and at connections with building members. Metal panels should be shaped so that changes in surface appearance will not be noticeable as the metal expands and contracts. Frequently, light-gage metal panels are given decorative patterns, which also hide movements due to temperature variations ("canning") and stiffen the sheets. Flat sheets may be given a slight initial curvature and stiffened on the rear side with ribs, so that temperature variations will only change the curvature a little and not reverse it. Or flat sheets may be laminated to one or more flat stiffening sheets, like asbestos cement or asbestos cement and a second light-gage metal sheet, to prevent "canning."

It may be desirable in many cases to treat the metal to prevent passage of sound. Usual practice is to apply a sound-absorbing coating on the inside surface of the panel. Some of these coatings have the additional beneficial effect of preventing moisture from condensing on this face.

Metal panels generally are flanged and interlocked to prevent penetration of water. A good joint will be self-flashing and will not require calking. Care must be taken that water will not be blown through weep holes from the outside into the building. Flashing and other details should be arranged so that any water that may penetrate the facing will be drained to the outside.

10-22. Sandwich Panels. Walls may be built of prefabricated panels that are considerably larger in size than unit masonry and capable of meeting requirements of appearance, strength, durability, insulation, acoustics, and permeability. Such panels generally consist of an insulation core sandwiched between a thin lightweight facing and backing.

When the edges of the panels are sealed, small holes should be left in the seal. Otherwise, heat of the sun could set up sizable vapor pressure, which could cause trouble.

The panels could be fastened in place in a light frame, attached to secondary framing members, anchored to brackets at each floor level, or connected to the structural frame of the building. Because of the large size of the panels, special precautions should be taken to allow for expansion and contraction due to temperature changes. Usually such movements are provided for at points of support.

When light frames are not used to support the units, adjoining panels generally interlock, and the joints are calked and sealed with rubber or rubberlike material, to prevent rain from penetrating. Flashing and other details should be arranged so that any water that comes through will be drained to the outside. For typical details, see C. G. Ramsey and H. R. Sleeper, "Architectural Graphic Standards," John Wiley & Sons, Inc., New York; and "Precast Concrete Wall Panels," Portland Cement Association.

PARTITIONS

Partitions are dividing walls one story or less in height used to subdivide the interior space in buildings. They may be bearing or nonbearing walls.

10-23. Types of Partitions. Bearing partitions may be built of masonry or of wood or light-gage steel studs. The masonry or studs may be faced with plaster, wallboard, plywood, wood boards, plastic, or other materials that meet functional and architectural requirements. Masonry partitions should satisfy the requirements of Arts. 10-2 to 10-14.

Nonbearing partitions may be permanently fixed in placed, temporary (or movable) so that the walls may be easily shifted when desired, or folding. Since the principal function of these walls is to separate space, the type of construction and materials used may vary widely. They may be opaque or transparent; they may be louvered or hollow or solid; they may extend from floor to ceiling or only partway; and they may serve additionally as cabinets or closets or as a concealment for piping and electrical conduit.

Fire resistance sometimes dictates the type of construction. If a high fire rating is desired or required by local building codes, the local building official should be consulted for information on approved types of construction or the fire ratings of the National Board of Fire Underwriters should be used.

When movable partitions may be installed, the structural framing should be designed to support their weight wherever they may be placed.

Acoustics also sometimes affects the type of construction of partitions. Thin construction that can vibrate like a sounding board should be avoided. Depending on functional requirements, acoustic treatment may range from acoustic finishes on partition surfaces to use of double walls separated completely by an air space or an insulating material.

Light-transmission requirements may also govern the selection of materials and type of construction. Where transparency or translucence is desired, the partition may be constructed of glass, or of glass block or plastic, or it may contain glass windows.

Consideration should also be given to the necessity for concealing pipes, conduits, and ducts in partitions.

10-24. Structural Requirements of Partitions. Bearing partitions, of course, should be capable of supporting the superimposed loads in accordance with recommended engineering practice and should rest in turn on adequate supports that will not deflect excessively. Masonry partitions should meet the requirements of Arts. 10-2 to 10-14.

Nonbearing partitions should be stable laterally between lateral supports or additional lateral supports should be added. Since they are not designed for vertical loads other than their own weight, such partitions should not be allowed to take loads from overhead beams that may deflect and press down on them. Also, the beams under the partition should not deflect to the extent that there is a visible separation between bottom of partition and the floor or that the partition cracks.

Folding partitions, in a sense, are large doors. Depending on size and weight, they may be electrically or manually operated. They may be made of wood, light-gage metal, or synthetic fabric on a light collapsible frame. Provision should be made for framing and supporting them in a manner similar to that for large folding doors (Art. 11-3).

Section 11

DOORS

FREDERICK S. MERRITT

Senior Editor
Engineering News-Record

ORDINARY DOORS

Many types of doors are available to serve the primary purpose of barring or permitting access to a structure and between its interior spaces. They may be hinged on top or sides to swing open and shut; they may slide horizontally or vertically; or they may revolve about a vertical axis in the center of the opening.

A large variety of materials also is available for door construction. Wood, metal, glass, plastics, and combinations of these materials with each other and with other materials, in the form of sandwich panels, are in common use.

Selection of a type of door and door material depends as much on other factors as on the primary function of serving as a barrier. Cost, psychological effect, fire resistance, architectural harmony, and ornamental considerations are but a few of the factors that must be taken into account.

11-1. Door Types. **Swinging doors** are hung on butts or hinges. The part of a doorway to which a door is hinged and against which it closes is known as the door frame. It consists of two verticals, commonly called jambs, and a horizontal member, known as the head (Fig. 11-1).

To stop drafts and passage of light, the jamb about which the door swings has a rebate, or projection, extending the full height, against which the door closes. The projection may be integral with the frame, or formed by attaching a stop on the surface of the frame, or inset slightly. With single-acting doors, the opposite jamb also is provided with a stop, against which the door closes.

In thin walls, the frame width generally is the same as the wall thickness. In thick walls, frame width usually is less than the wall thickness; in that case, the location of the door should be chosen with care. For example, it is generally desirable to position an exterior door close to the inner face of the wall, because then if the door opens inward, it would be able to swing through a full semicircle. If it opens outward, while it may not be able to open more than 90°, at least it is protected from the weather. Usually also for interior doors in thick walls, the preferred position is the one that permits the largest swing of the door. The size of the hinge or butt also must be taken into consideration in deciding on the door location. With large butts having a sizable throw, the door can be set farther from the face of the wall and still open fully.

Door frames for swinging doors generally are fastened to rough construction members known as door bucks, and the joints between the frame and the wall are covered with casings, or trim. With metal construction, the trim is often integral with the frame and designed to grip the bucks. (Ramsey and Sleeper, "Architectural Graphic

11-1

Standards," John Wiley & Sons, Inc., New York.   For modular design, see A62 Guide for Modular Coordination, Modular Service Association, Boston, Mass.)

At the bottom of a door opening for an exterior door is a sill (Fig. 11-1), which forms a division between the finished floor on the inside and the outside construction.   The sill generally also serves as a step; for the door opening usually is raised above exterior grade to prevent rain from entering.   The top of the sill is sloped to drain water away from the interior.   Also, it may have a raised section in the plane of the door or slightly to the rear, so that water dripping from the door will fall on the slope.   The raised section may be integral with the sill or a separate threshold.   In either case, the rear portion covers the joint between sill and floor.   In addition, all joints should be sealed.

To weatherproof the joint between the bottom of the door and the threshold, a weather strip in the form of a hooked length of metal is attached to the underside of the door.   When the door is closed, the weather strip locks into the threshold to seal out water.

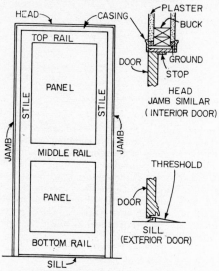

Fig. 11-1. Typical paneled door.

Horizontally sliding doors may roll on a track in the floor and have only guides at the top, or the track and rollers may be at the top and guides at the bottom.   Some doors fold or collapse like an accordion, to occupy less space when open.   A pocket must always be provided in the walls on either or both sides, to receive rigid-type doors; with the folding or accordion types, a pocket is optional.

Vertically sliding doors may rise straight up, may rise up and swing in, or may pivot outward to form a canopy.   Sometimes, the door may be in two sections, one rising up, the other dropping down.   Generally, all types are counterweighted for ease of operation.

In designing structures to receive sliding doors, the clearance between the top of the doors and the ceiling or structural members above should be checked—especially the clearance required for vertically sliding doors in the open position.   Also, the deflection of the construction above the door opening should be investigated to be certain that it will not cause the door to jam.

To keep out the weather, the upper part of a sliding door either is recessed into the wall above, or the top part of the door extends slightly above the bottom of the wall on the inside.   Similarly, door sides are recessed into the walls or lap them and are held firmly against the inside.   Also, the finished floor is raised a little above outside grade. Very large sliding doors require special study (Arts. 11-3 and 11-4).

Revolving doors are generally selected for entranceways carrying a continuous flow of traffic without very high peaks. They offer the advantage of keeping interchange of inside and outside air to a relatively small amount compared with other types of doors. They usually are used in combination with swinging doors because of the inability to handle large groups of people in a short period of time.

Revolving doors consist of four leaves that rotate about a vertical axis inside a cylindrical enclosure. The opening to the enclosure usually is between 4 and 5 ft. (See also Building Exits Code, National Fire Protection Association.)

11-2. Door Materials. Wood is used in several forms for doors. When appearance is unimportant and a low-cost door is required, it may be made of boards nailed together. When the boards are vertical and held together with a few horizontal boards, the door is called a batten door. Better-grade doors are made with panels set in a frame or with flush construction.

Paneled doors consist of solid wood or plywood panels held in place by verticals called stiles and horizontals known as rails (Fig. 11-1). The joints between panels and supporting members permit expansion and contraction of the wood with atmospheric changes. If the rails and stiles are made of a single piece of wood, the paneled door is called solid. When hardwood or better-quality woods are used, the doors generally are veneered; rails and stiles are made with cores of softwood sandwiched between the desired veneer.

Glass may be used instead of wood for one or more panels. In exterior doors, the light must be installed to prevent penetration of water, especially in veneered doors. One way is to insert under the glass a piece of molding that extends through the door and is turned down over the outside face of the door to form a drip. Another way is to place a sheet-metal flashing under the removable outer molding that holds the glass. The flashing is turned up behind the inside face of the glass and down over the exterior of the door, with only a very narrow strip of the metal exposed.

Flush doors also may be solid or veneered. The veneered type has a core of softwood, while the flat faces may be hardwood veneers. When two plies are used for a face, they are set with grain perpendicular to each other.

Flush doors, in addition, may be of the hollow-core type. In that case, the surfaces are made of plywood and the core is a supporting grid. Edges of the core are solid wood boards.

Metal doors generally are constructed in one of three ways: cast as a single unit or separate frame and panel pieces; metal frame covered with sheet metal; and sheet metal over a wood or other type of insulating core. The heavier metal doors of the swinging type usually are pivoted at top and bottom, rather than with the weight placed on hinges or butts.

Cast-metal doors are relatively high-priced. They are used principally for monumental structures.

Hollow metal doors, composed of a metal frame covered with sheet metal, are selected principally for rigidity, permanence, and fire resistance. The sheet metal is stiffened by a backup board of asbestos cement, and cork or other resilient material is incorporated at edges and sometimes behind the facings for acoustical reasons.

Metal-covered doors may be obtained with a wide variety of fire-resistance cores. A Kalamein door has a wood core (the wood will not burn as long as the sheet-metal cover prevents oxygen from reaching it).

Doors may be made wholly or partly transparent or translucent. Lights may be made of glass or plastic. Doors made completely of glass are pivoted at top and bottom because the weight makes it difficult to support them with hinges or butts.

Sliding doors of the collapsible accordion type generally consist of wood slats or a light steel frame covered with textile. Plastic coverings frequently are used.

SPECIAL-PURPOSE DOORS

Large-size doors, such as those for hangars, garages, and craneway openings in walls and for subdividing gymnasiums and auditoriums, often have to be designed individually. As distinguished from those made on a production basis, special-purpose doors require careful design of the main structure to support loads and to allow space for the open door and its controls.

Manufacturers classify special-purpose doors as horizontal-sliding, vertical-sliding, swing, and top or horizontal-hinge.

11-3. Horizontal-sliding Doors. Door leaves in the horizontal-sliding type are equipped with bearing-type bottom wheels and ride rails in the floor while top rollers operate in overhead guides. Two variations are in common use—telescoping and folding.

Telescoping doors (Fig. 11-2) are frequently used for airplane hangars. Normally composed of 6 to 20 leaves, they generally are center parting. They are built of

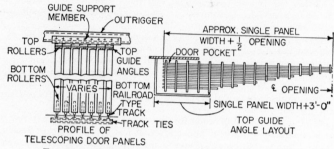

Fig. 11-2. Typical horizontal-sliding, telescoping door.

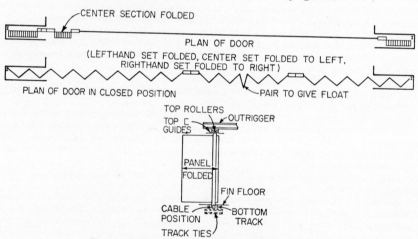

Fig. 11-3. Typical folding horizontal-sliding door.

wood, steel, or a combination of the two. Open doors are stacked in pockets at each end of the opening.

Telescoping doors are frequently operated by two motors located in the end pockets. The motors drive an endless chain attached to tops of center leaves. Remaining leaves are moved by a series of interconnecting cables attached to the powered leaf and arranged so that all leaves arrive at open or closed position simultaneously. Motor size ranges from 1 to 10 hp, travel speed of leaves from 45 to 160 fpm.

The weight of the leaves must be taken by footings below the rails. Provision also must be made to take care of wind loads transmitted to the top guide channels by the doors and to carry the weight of these channels.

Folding doors (Fig. 11-3) are commonly used for subdividing gymnasiums, auditoriums, and cafeterias and for hangars with very wide openings. This type of door is made up of a series of leaves hinged together in pairs. Leaves fold outward, and when the door is shut, they are held by automatic folding stays. Motors that operate the door usually are located in mullions adjacent to the center of the opening. The mullions are connected by cables to the ends of the opening, and when the door is to be opened, the mullions are drawn toward the ends, sweeping the leaves along. Travel speed may vary from 45 to 160 fpm.

Chief advantage of folding over telescoping types is that only two guide channels are required, regardless of width. Thus, less metal is required for guide channels and rails, and less material for the supporting member above. Also, since wind loading is applied to leaves that are always partly in folded position, the triangular configuration gives the door considerable lateral stiffness. Hence, panel thickness may be less for folding than for telescoping doors, and a lighter load may be used for designing footings.

11-4. Vertical-sliding Doors. When space is available above and below an opening into which door leaves can be moved, vertical-sliding doors are advantageous. They may be operated manually or electrically. Leaves may travel at 45 to 60 fpm. About $1\frac{1}{2}$ ft in excess of leaf height must be provided in the pockets into which the leaves slide. So the greater the number of leaves the less space needed for the pockets.

Vertical-sliding doors normally are counterweighted. About 15 in. of clear space back of the jamb line is needed for this purpose, but on the idler side only 4 in. is required.

Vertical loads are transmitted to the door guides and then by column action to the footings. Lateral support is provided by the jamb and building walls.

11-5. Swing Doors. When there is insufficient space around openings to accommodate sliding doors, swing types may be used. Common applications have been for firehouses, where width-of-building clearance is essential, and railway entrances, where doors are interlocked with the signal system.

Common variations include single-swing (solid leaf with vertical hinge on one jamb), double-swing (hinges on both jambs), two-fold (hinge on one jamb and another between folds and leaves), and four-fold (hinges on both jambs and between each pair of folds).

The more folds, the less time required for opening and the smaller the radius needed for swing. Tighter swings make doors safer to open and allow material to be placed closer to supports.

11-6. Horizontal-hinge Doors. Effective use of horizontal-hinge doors is made in such applications as craneway entrances to buildings. Widths exceeding 100 ft at or near the top of the building can be opened to depths of 4 to 18 ft. Frequently, horizontal-sliding doors are employed below crane doors to increase the opening. If so, the top guides are contained in the bottom of the crane door; so the sliding door must be opened before the swing door.

Top-hinged swing doors are made of light materials, such as structural steel and exterior-grade plywood. The panel can be motor-operated to open in 1 min or less.

Section 12

LATH AND PLASTER

Frederick S. Merritt

Senior Editor
Engineering News-Record

WET-TYPE CONSTRUCTION

Plaster finishes may consist of materials partly or completely prepared in the field or of prefabricated sheets (dry-type construction). Factors such as initial cost, cost of maintenance and repair, and speed of construction must be considered in choosing between them.

When field-prepared materials are used, the plaster finish generally consists of a base and two or more coats of plaster.

12-1. Gypsum Lath. One commonly used base is gypsum lath—a sheet generally 16 × 48 in. by $\frac{3}{8}$ or $\frac{1}{2}$ in. thick composed principally of calcined gypsum that has been mixed with water, hardened and dried, and sandwiched between two paper sheets. Perforated gypsum lath is produced, during the manufacturing process, by punching holes through the lath at regular intervals. Insulating gypsum lath is made by cementing a sheet of shiny aluminum to the back of plain lath. It is used for vapor control and insulation against heat loss.

When nailed to wood members, each lath should be attached with five nails to each framing member it covers. Nails should be blued gypsum lath nails, made of 13-gage wire, $1\frac{1}{8}$ in. long, with a $\frac{3}{8}$-in.-diameter head. They should be driven until the head is just below the paper surface without breaking the paper.

Ceiling framing members supporting the lath should never be spaced more than 16 in. c to c. Studs may be spaced up to 16 in. c to c with $\frac{3}{8}$-in. gypsum lath and up to 24 in. c to c with $\frac{1}{2}$-in. lath.

The lath should be applied to studs with long dimension horizontal, and vertical joints should be staggered. In ceilings, the long sides should span supports. Ends should rest on and be nailed to framing, headers, or nailing blocks. Each lath should be in contact with adjoining sheets, but if spaces are necessary the plaster should be reinforced with metal lath stapled or tied with wire to the gypsum lath.

Interior corners should be reinforced with cornerite stapled or tied with wire to the gypsum lath. Exterior corners should be finished with corner beads set to true grounds and nailed to the structural frame.

Plaster should be applied to the lath to a thickness of at least $\frac{1}{2}$ in. Grounds should be provided to mark off this thickness around all openings and wherever baseboards or moldings are to be used.

When clipped to steel furring, lath edges must be secured to the steel runners at each intersection. Cornerite should be used where the lath abuts a rigid plaster base at angles; otherwise, it is not necessary ("Manual of Gypsum Lathing and Plastering," Gypsum Association).

12-1

12-2. Metal Lath. Plaster holds to metal lath by a mechanical bond between the scratch coat and the metal. So it is important that the plaster completely surrounds and embeds the metal.

Three basic types are commonly used: woven wire, generally called wire fabric or wire lath; punched metal sheets, called metal lath; and punched and expanded metal sheets, called expanded metal lath.

Available in plain and stiffened sheets, expanded metal lath may be obtained in the form of diamond mesh, which is the plain unstiffened lath; flat- (⅛-in.) rib lath, and high- (⅜-in.) rib lath. Table 12-1 gives limiting spans for various types and weights of lath for ceilings and walls.

Table 12-1. Limiting Spans for Metal Lath in Inches

Type of lath	Min wt., lb per sq yd	Vertical supports			Horizontal supports	
			Metal		Wood or concrete	Metal
		Wood	Solid partitions	Others		
Diamond-mesh (flat expanded) metal lath	2.5	16	16	12	0	0
	3.4	16	16	16	16	13½
Flat-(⅛-in.) rib expanded metal lath...	2.75	16	16	16	16	12
	3.4	19	18	24	19	19
High-(⅜-in.) rib expanded metal lath*..	3.4	24	...	24	24	19
	4.0	24	...	24	24	24
Punched sheet........................	4.5	24	...	24	24	24
Wire lath.............................	2.48	16	16	16	13½	13½
V-stiffened wire lath.................	3.3	24	24	24	19	19
Wire fabric..........................	†	16	0	16	16	16

Standard A42.4-1950, American Standards Association.
* Rod-stiffened or V-stiffened diamond-mesh metal lath of equal rigidity and weight is permissible on the same spacings as ⅜-in. rib lath.
† Paper-backed wire fabric, 16-gage wire, 2 × 2-in. mesh, with stiffener.

Also available is self-furring metal lath, which is so designed that it is separated at least ¼ in. from the backing to which it is attached.

Wire mesh also is available in the form of a 2 × 2-in. mesh of 16-gage wire with stiffening ribs and attached to an absorbent fibrous paper-felt backing. The backing acts as a base to which plaster can adhere while hardening about the wire.

When metal furring is used, metal lath should be tied to it with 18-gage or heavier galvanized soft-annealed wire. With wood studs or joists, the lath should be secured with 6d nails or 1¼-in. 14-gage wire staples spaced 6 in. on centers and penetrating at least ⅞ in. Large collared nails penetrating at least 1 in. are recommended for absorbent fiber-backed wire mesh.

Metal lath should be applied with the long sides of sheets spanning supports. Similarly, rib lath should be fastened with ribs spanning supports. End laps should be placed only at supports. Sheets should lap at the sides at least ½ in. and at the ends 1 in. When rib lath is lapped, the outside ribs should be nested.

Normally, lath is applied first to the ceilings, the sheets being carried down 6 in. on walls and partitions. For plastering walls, the lath should be started one stud away from the corner and should be bent into the corner and continued along the intersecting wall to avoid a joint at the angle. However, high-rib lath may be butted into corners, if they are reinforced with **cornerite**—an L-shape strip of flat lath—which should be fastened to the lath along each edge but not in the angle. (See also Walls and Partitions; Specifications for Metal Lathing and Furring; and Technical Bulletins, Metal Lath Manufacturers Association, Cleveland 14, Ohio.)

Grounds must be provided around all openings and at baseboards to provide a minimum plaster thickness of ⅝ in. over the lath, ¾ in. from face of supports.

12-3. Fiber Insulation Lath. A semirigid plastering base may be secured simultaneously with good insulation with several types of board made from treated vegetable fibers. It is available in widths of from 16 to 24 in., lengths of from 32 to 64 in., and thicknesses of ½ and ¾ in. The ¾-in. thickness is recommended for 24-in. spacing of supports.

Fiber insulation lath is applied in the same manner as gypsum lath. Specifications for nailing, cornerite, and corner beads also are similar. However, this lath is not recommended for attachment to steel furring by clip methods.

12-4. Masonry Bases. Gypsum partition tile has scored faces to provide a mechanical bond as well as the natural bond of gypsum to gypsum. The 12 × 30-in. faces of the tile present an unwarped plastering surface because the tile is dried without burning; so a mechanic can lay a straighter wall than with other types of units. The Gypsum Association's "Manual of Gypsum Lathing and Plastering" recommends that only gypsum plaster should be applied to gypsum partition tile, since lime and portland cement do not bond adequately. Also, only gypsum mortar should be used for tile erection.

Brick and clay tile can be used as a plaster base if they are not smooth-surfaced or of a nonporous type. If the surface does not provide sufficient suction, it should offer a means for developing a mechanical bond, such as does scored tile.

Plaster should not be applied directly to exterior masonry walls because dampness may damage the plaster. It is advisable to fur the plaster at least 1 in. in from the masonry.

Properly aged concrete block may serve as a plaster base, but for block ceilings, bond plaster, as distinguished from wood-fiber plaster, should be applied. Bond plaster was developed specially for a first coat over concrete-block ceilings.

For precast or cast-in-place concrete with smooth dense surfaces, bond plaster should be used. However, if a plaster thickness of more than ⅜ in. is required for concrete ceilings or ⅝ in. for concrete walls, metal lath should be secured to the concrete before plastering, in which case sanded plaster or wood-fiber plaster can be used.

12-5. Plaster Base Coats. The base coat is the portion of the plaster finish that is applied to masonry or lath bases and supports the finish coat.

Plaster applications may be three-coat or two-coat. The former consists of (1) a scratch coat, which is applied directly to the plaster base, cross-raked after it has "taken up," and allowed to set and partly dry; (2) a brown coat, which is surfaced out to the proper grounds, darbied (float-finished), allowed to set and partly dry; and (3) the finish coat. Three-coat plaster is required over metal lath ("Manual of Gypsum Lathing and Plastering," Gypsum Association).

The two-coat application is similar except that cross raking of the scratch coat is omitted and the brown coat is applied within a few minutes to the unset scratch coat. Three coats are generally preferred because the base coat thus produced is stronger and harder.

12-6. Fibered Plasters. Wood fiber is added to some plasters for the purpose of adding bulk and coverage. Hair or sisal fibering are added to the scratch coat for applications to metal lath, to limit the amount of plaster that passes through the keys of the lath to what is needed for a good bond. For other uses, unfibered plaster should always be employed for both the scratch and the brown coats, since fibering adds no strength to the plaster.

12-7. Plaster Grounds. Thickness of plaster is controlled with grounds—wood or metal strips applied at the perimeter of all openings or continuous strips of plaster applied at intervals along a wall or ceiling, to serve as screeds. Plaster screeds should be used on all plaster surfaces of large area.

Grounds should be set to provide a minimum plaster thickness of ½ in. over gypsum lath, fiber insulation lath, and gypsum partition tile; ⅝ in. over brick, clay tile, or other masonry; and ⅝ in. from the face of metal to produce an over-all plaster thickness of at least ¾ in.

12-8. Plaster Ingredients. Plaster is generally composed of portland cement, or gypsum and lime; an aggregate (sand, vermiculite, perlite) and water. Lime mortar also may be used.

Sand should comply with American Society for Testing Materials Specification C35. It should be clean, free of organic material, more than about 5 % clay, silt, or other impurities, and should not contain salt or alkali. The proportion of sand in the plaster has an important bearing on the characteristics of the product. Oversanding results in considerable reduction in strength and hardness. A mix as lean as 4:1 by weight should never be used.

The Gypsum Association suggests that plasterers use a No. 2 shovel, which holds about 15 lb of moist sand, for maintaining proper proportions. Thus, with each 100-lb bag of plaster, a 1:2 mix requires 14 shovels of sand and a 1:3 mix 20 shovels ("Manual of Gypsum Lathing and Plastering").

Water should be clean and free of substances that might affect the rate of set of the plaster. It is not advisable to use water in which plasterers' tools have been washed because it might change the set. Excessive water is undesirable in the mix, because when the water evaporates, it leaves numerous large voids, which decrease the strength of the plaster. Hence, manufacturers' recommendations should be observed closely in determining water requirements.

Perlite and vermiculite are manufactured lightweight aggregates that are used to produce a lightweight plaster with relatively high fire resistance for a given thickness. Both aggregates should meet ASTM specifications for plaster aggregates, and the mix should be prepared strictly in accordance with manufacturers' recommendations.

12-9. Mixing Plaster. A mechanical mixer disperses the ingredients of a mix more evenly and therefore is to be preferred over box mixing. Recommended practice is as follows: (1) Place the anticipated water requirements in the mixer; (2) add about half the required sand; (3) add all the plaster; (4) add the rest of the sand; (5) mix at least 30 sec, but not more than 3 min, adding water, if necessary, to obtain proper workability; and (6) dump the entire batch at once.

The mixer should be thoroughly cleaned when it is not in use. If partly set material is left in it, the set of the plaster might be accelerated. For this reason also, tools should be kept clean.

For hand mixing, first sand and plaster should be mixed dry to a uniform color in a mixing box, water added, and the plaster hoed into the water immediately and thoroughly mixed. Undermixed plaster is difficult to apply and will produce soft and hard spots in the plastered surface.

Plaster should not be mixed more than 1 hr in advance. Nor should a new mix, or gaging, be mixed in with a previously prepared one. And once plaster has started to set, it should not be remixed or retempered.

12-10. Drying Plaster. A minimum temperature of 40°F should be maintained in the building during cold weather until the plaster is dry.

In hot dry weather, precautions should be taken to prevent water from evaporating before the plaster has set; plastered surfaces should not be exposed to drafts, and openings to the outside should be closed off temporarily.

After the plaster sets, the excess moisture it contains evaporates. Hence the room should be adequately ventilated to allow this moisture to escape.

12-11. Portland-cement Plaster. Portland cement, mixed with lime putty and sand, is used when a hard, sand finish, fire-retarding, non-water-absorbent plaster is desired and for all coats of stucco (Art. 10-19). It also is used for scratch and brown coats under Keene's cement finish and for scratch and brown coats that serve as a backing for tile wainscots. A typical mix for a coat consists of 1 part portland cement, ¼ part lime putty or hydrated lime, and 3 parts sand, by weight. For a scratch coat on metal lath, 1 lb of hair or fiber should be added per sack of cement.

12-12. Gypsum Base-coat Plasters. Four types of gypsum base-coat plasters are in general use: gypsum-cement plaster, sanded gypsum plaster, gypsum wood-fiber plaster, and bond plaster.

Gypsum-cement plaster, sometimes called hardwall or neat gypsum plaster, is sold in powder form and mixed with an aggregate and water at the construction site. Mixed with no more than 3 parts sand by weight, it makes a strong base coat at low cost. Scratch coats generally consist of 1 part plaster powder to 2 parts sand by weight, fibered or unfibered; the base coat in two-coat work usually is a 1:2½ mix; brown coats are 1:3 mixes.

Sanded gypsum plaster requires the addition only of water at the site, since it is sold in bags containing the proper proportions of aggregate and putty. It is specified when good plastering sand is high cost or not available, or to avoid the possibility of oversanding. It is equal in strength to gypsum-cement plaster but costs a little more because of the extra cost of transporting the sand.

Gypsum wood-fiber plaster, containing wood fiber to give the mix more bulk and coverage, also requires only the addition of water at the site. It is used where a high fire rating is required, also when good sand is high cost or not available and for alterations, repair, and patching. It is about three times stronger in compression and tension than sanded plaster and about 50% harder. The factory-prepared material costs more than gypsum cement plaster but application costs are about the same.

Bond plaster was developed primarily for applications to interior rough concrete surfaces. Factory-prepared, it requires the addition of only water at the site. Preparation of the concrete surface to receive bond plaster should be in accordance with American Standards Association Specification A42.1. Dust and loose particles should be removed with a wire brush; grease, oil, or efflorescence should be washed off with a solution of 1 part commercial muriatic acid to 4 parts water, and the surface then washed again with clean water. Smooth surfaces should be roughened to improve the bond with the plaster. If necessary, the masonry should be wetted, but not saturated. Cost of a base coat of bond plaster is about the same as for wood-fiber plaster.

The scratch coat of bond plaster must be thoroughly scratched into the concrete. Next, a doubling back coat should be applied to produce an even surface and left rough, ready to receive the finish coat. A gypsum-cement brown coat may be used instead of the doubling back coat of bond plaster, but the total plaster thickness should not be more than ⅜ in. on ceilings or ⅝ in. on walls. If these thicknesses cannot be maintained, the surfaces should be furred and plastered or the plaster should be applied to metal lath firmly attached to the masonry.

The scratch coat applied to lath should be laid on with enough pressure to form a strong clinch or key. The coat should cover the lath to a thickness of ¼ in. After the surface has been trued, it should be scratched horizontally and vertically with a toothed tool to form a good bonding surface, then left until dry. When the surface is so hard that the edges of the scoring do not yield easily under the pressure of a thumbnail, the brown coat may be applied. Hardening may take at least one day and sometimes as long as a week, depending on the weather and the amount of lime in the mix.

The brown coat not only forms the base for the finish coat but also is the straightening coat. Before it is applied, the scratch coat should be dampened, then time allowed for excess water to be evaporated. When plaster grounds are used, the plaster should be laid on with a steel float, trued, and finally roughened in preparation for the finish coat. With plaster screeds, the brown coat should be applied until flush with the screeds. It is put on with a darby, a two-handed long wood float.

12–13. Finish-coat Plasters. Several types of finish-coat plasters are available. In two of the most common—made with gaging plaster or Keene's cement—lime is an important ingredient, because it gives plasticity and bulk to the coat.

The lime is prepared first, being slaked to a smooth putty, then formed on the plasterer's board into a ring with water in the center. Next, gaging plaster or Keene's cement is gradually sifted into the water. Finally, all ingredients are thoroughly mixed and kneaded.

Gaging plasters are coarsely ground gypsum plasters, which are available in quick-setting and slow-setting mixtures; so it is not necessary to add an accelerator or a retarder at the site. Gaging plasters also are supplied as white gaging plaster and a slightly darker local gaging plaster.   Finish coats made with these plasters are amply hard for ordinary usages and are the lowest-cost plaster finishes.   However, they are not intended for ornamental cornice work or run moldings, which should be made of a finer-ground plaster.

Typical mixes consist of 3 parts lime putty to 1 part gaging plaster, by volume.   If a harder surface is desired, the gaging content may be increased up to 1 part gaging to 2 parts lime putty.

The lime-gaging plaster should be applied in at least two coats, when the brown coat is nearly dry.   The first coat should be laid on very thin, with sufficient pressure to be forced into the roughened surface of the base coat.   After the first coat has been allowed to draw a few minutes, a second or leveling coat, also thin, should be applied, and after this has been allowed to draw, the third coat, if desired, added.

The base coat draws the water from the finish coats; so the finished surface should be moistened with a wet bush as it is being troweled.   Pressure should be exerted on the trowel to densify the surface and produce a smooth hard finish.   Finally, the surface should be dampened with the brush and clean water.   It should be allowed to stand at least 30 days before oil paints are applied.

When a harder surface is required, or one with greater resistance to dampness than can be obtained with lime-gaging plaster, such as for gymnasiums, school corridors, trucking areas, and bathrooms, **Keene's cement** may be used with lime.   The regular cement sets initially in about $1\frac{1}{2}$ hr and has a final set of about 4 to 6 hr, but a quicker-setting variety is available with a 2-hr set.   Hardness of the surface depends on the lime content and the vigor with which the surface is troweled.

The base coat must be dry before a Keene's-cement finish is applied.   If suction is too great, however, the surface should be moistened with a wet brush.   The plaster should be applied in thin coats in the same manner as with lime-gaging plasters, except that Keene's-cement finishes may require additional troweling.

A prepared gypsum trowel finish also is available that requires only addition of water at the site.   The resulting surface may be harder than obtainable with Keene's cement and may be decorated as soon as dry.   It is applied in the same manner as lime-gaging plaster, but as with Keene's cement finishes, the base coat should be dry.   However, it has a moderately fast set and should be troweled before it sets.   For best results, three very thin coats should be applied and water should be used sparingly.

Sand float finishes are similar to gypsum trowel finishes, except that these float finishes contain a fine aggregate to yield a fine-textured surface and the final surface is finished with a float.   The base coat should be firm but only about 50 % dry when the finish coat is applied.

Prepared colored-gypsum float finishes also may be purchased, and only water need be added at the site.   These finishes require no additional decoration.   They also contain a high percentage of Keene's cement and therefore produce an exceptionally hard surface.   They are applied in the same manner as gypsum trowel finishes, except that the final surface is finished with a float.   To obtain surface uniformity, however, the suction of the base coat must be kept uniform, the finish must be applied to a uniform thickness, the floating motion must be uniform, and no water should be used in floating.

Molding plaster, intended for ornamental work, is made with a finer grind than other gaging plasters.   It produces a smooth surface, free from streaks or indentations as might be obtained with coarser-ground materials.   Equal parts of lime putty and molding plaster are recommended by the Gypsum Association for cornice moldings ("Manual of Lathing and Plastering").

DRY-TYPE CONSTRUCTION

To avoid construction delays due to the necessity of waiting for plaster to dry or to obtain different types of finishes, dry-wall construction may be used.   Rigid or semi-rigid boards, some of which require no additional decorative treatment, are nailed directly to studs or masonry or to furring.

Joints may be concealed or accentuated according to the architectural treatment desired. The boards may interlock with each other, or battens, moldings, or beads may be applied at joints.

When the boards are thinner than conventional lath and plaster, framing members should be furred out to conventional thicknesses so that stock doors and windows can be used.

12-14. Plywood Finishes. Available with a large variety of surface veneers, including plastics, plywood is nailed directly to framing members or furring. Small finish nails, such as 4d, should be used, with a spacing not exceeding 6 in. All edges should be nailed down, intermediate blocking being inserted if necessary. The plywood should also be nailed to intermediate members. When joints are not to be covered, the nailheads should be driven below the surface (set). With wood battens, ordinary flat-headed nails can be used. Water-resistant adhesive may be applied between plywood and framing members for additional rigidity.

12-15. Asbestos-cement Boards. Like other types of boards, asbestos-cement can be nailed directly to framing members or furring. Thin sheets usually are backed with plywood or insulation boards to increase resistance to impact. Joints generally are covered with moldings or beads.

12-16. Fiber and Pulp Boards. Fabricated with a wide variety of surface effects, fiber and pulp boards also are available with high acoustic and thermal insulation values. Application is similar to that for plywood. Generally, adjoining boards should be placed in moderate contact with each other, not forced.

12-17. Gypsum Board. Composed of a gypsum core enclosed in smooth tough paper, gypsum board generally comes in widths of 4 ft, lengths of 6 to 12 ft and thickness of $\frac{1}{4}$ to $\frac{5}{8}$ in. Boards $\frac{3}{8}$ in. thick are adequate for 16-in. spacing of supports, and $\frac{1}{2}$-in. for 24-in. spacing.

For $\frac{1}{4}$ and $\frac{3}{8}$-in. boards, 4d nails (flathead diamond point) $1\frac{3}{8}$ in. long should be used with wood framework; for $\frac{1}{2}$-in. board, 5d nails $1\frac{5}{8}$ in. long, with wood framework; for $\frac{5}{8}$-in. board and $\frac{1}{4}$- to $\frac{1}{2}$-in. board over old plaster, 6d nails $1\frac{7}{8}$ in. long. Nails should be driven at least 1 in. into wood framing.

Before gypsum board is applied, framing members should be checked for straightness and alignment, electrical outlets and heating ducts should be properly positioned, and nailing surfaces provided. Nailing should be started at the center studs and then continued on the outside edges. Nails should be spaced 5 to 7 in. apart on ceilings, 6 to 8 in. on walls. They should be placed no closer than $\frac{3}{8}$ in. to edges or ends of boards. They should be driven with a crown-headed carpenter's hammer until the head rests in a dimple in the board surface formed by the last hammer blow. The paper face should not be broken.

When joints are to be rendered unnoticeable, boards with depressed edges to receive a perforated tape are used. The channel is filled with a cement into which the tape is embedded, being forced into place with a 4-in. putty knife. A second, thin coat of cement is applied 24 hr later, feathered out 3 to 4 in. on each side of the channel. When this coat has dried thoroughly, another coat is applied, this time feathered out 8 to 10 in. About 24 hr later, the cement is sanded lightly until smooth and level with the wallboard surface. Inside corners are taped and cemented in a similar manner. Outside corners may either be taped and cemented or reinforced with a metal corner bead. Nailhead depressions and other dents should be filled in with at least two thin coats of cement and the hardened surface sanded smooth and level.

If ordinary gypsum board is to be finished with wallpaper, it should first be coated with sizing varnish; with some paints, a primer sealer should be applied first.

12-18. Lathing and Plastering Terms

Accelerator. Any material added to gypsum plaster that speeds the set.

Acoustical Plaster. A finishing plaster that corrects sound reverberations or reduces noise intensity.

Arris. A sharp edge, forming an external corner at the junction of two surfaces.

Band. A flat molding.

Base Coat. The plaster coat or combination of coats applied before the finish coat.

Bead. A small round member of a cornice.

Beaded Molding. A cast plaster string of beads set in a molding or cornice.

Bed Mold or Bed. A flat area in a cornice in which ornamentation is placed.

Blisters. Protuberances on the finish coat of plaster caused by application over too damp a base coat, or troweling too soon.

Boss. A Gothic ornament set at the intersection of moldings.

Brown Coat. Coat of plaster directly beneath the finish coat. In two-coat work, brown coat refers to the base-coat plaster applied over the lath. In three-coat work, the brown coat refers to the second coat applied over a scratch coat.

Buckles. Raised or ruptured spots that eventually crack, exposing the lath. Most common cause for buckling is application of plaster over dry, broken, or incorrectly applied wood lath.

Bull Nose. This term describes an external angle that is rounded to eliminate a sharp corner and is used largely at window returns and door frames.

Butterflies. Color imperfections on a lime-putty finish wall, caused by lime lumps not put through a screen, or insufficient mixing of the gaging.

Capital or Cap. The ornamental head of a column or pilaster.

Caisson. A panel sunk below the normal surface in flat or vaulted ceilings.

Case Mold. Plaster shell used to hold various parts of a plaster mold in correct position. Also used with gelatin and wax molds to prevent distortions during pouring operation.

Catface. Flaw in the finish coat comparable to a pock mark. Sometimes, base-coat knobs showing through the finish coat are referred to by this term.

Ceilings:

Contact. Lath is attached in direct contact with the construction above, without use of runner channels or furring.

Furred. Furring members are attached directly to the structural members of the building.

Suspended. Furring members are suspended below the structural members of the building.

Cross Furring. Furring members are attached at right angles to the underside of main runners or other structural supports.

Chamfer. A beveled corner or edge.

Chase. A groove in a masonry wall to provide for pipes, ducts, or conduits.

Check Cracks. Cracks in plaster caused by shrinkage, but the plaster remains bonded to its base.

Chip Cracks. Similar to check cracks, except the bond is partly destroyed. Also referred to as fire cracks, map cracks, crazing, fire checks, and hair cracks.

Coffered Ceilings. Ornamental ceilings made up of sunken or recessed panels.

Corner Bead. Fabricated metal with flanges and bead at junction of flanges; used to protect arrises.

Cornerite. Corner reinforcement for interior plastering.

Cornice. A molding, with or without reinforcement.

Cove. A curved concave, or vaulted, surface.

Dado. The lower part of a wall usually separated from the upper by a molding or other device.

Darby. A flat wood tool with handles about 4 in. wide and 42 in. long; used to smooth or float the brown coat; also used on finish coat to give a prelimina y true and even surface.

Dentils. Small rectangular blocks set in a row in the bed mold of a cornice.

Dope. Additives put in any type of mortar to accelerate or retard set.

Double-up. Applications of plaster in successive operations without a setting and drying interval between coats.

Dry Out. Soft chalky plaster caused by water evaporating before setting.

Efflorescence. White fleecy deposit on the face of plastered walls, caused by salts in the sand or backing; also referred to as "whiskering" or "saltpetering."

Egg and Dart. Ornamentation used in cornices consisting of an oval and a dart alternately.

Eggshelling. Plaster chip-cracked concave to the surface, the bond being partially destroyed.

Enrichments. Any cast ornament that cannot be executed by a running mold.

Expanded Metals. Sheets of metal that are slit and drawn out to form diamond-shaped openings.

Flat. Material accumulated on the trowel during the finishing operation and used to fill in small imperfections.

Feather Edge. A beveled-edge wood tool used to straighten angles in the finish coat.

Finish Coat. Last and final coat of plaster.

Fisheyes. Spots in finish coat about $\frac{1}{4}$ in. in diameter caused by lumpy lime due to age or insufficient blending of material.

Float. A tool shaped like a trowel with a handle braced at both ends and wood base or blade.

Furring. Strips that are nailed over studs, joists, rafters, or masonry to support lathing. This construction permits free circulation of air behind the plaster.

Gaging. Mixing of gaging plaster with lime putty to acquire the proper setting time and initial strength. Also denotes type of plaster used for mixing with lime.

Green Plaster. Wet or damp plaster.

Grounds. A piece of wood, metal, or plaster attached to the framing to indicate thickness of plaster to be applied.

Hardwall. Gypsum neat base-coat plaster.

Lath. A base to receive plaster.

Lime. Oxide of calcium produced by burning limestone. Heat drives out the carbon dioxide leaving calcium oxide, commonly termed "quicklime." Addition of water to quicklime yields hydrated or slaked lime.

Marezzo. An imitation marble formed with Keene's cement to which colors have been added.

Neat Plaster. A base-coat plaster to which sand is added at the job.

Niche. A curved or square recess in a wall.

Ogee. A curved section of a molding, partly convex and partly concave.

Pinhole. A small hole appearing in a cast because of excess water.

Putty. Product resulting from slaking, soaking, or mixing lime and water together.

Relief. Ornamented figures above a plane surface.

Return. The terminal of a cornice or molding that takes the form of an external miter and stops at the wall line.

Reveal. The vertical face of a door or window opening between the face of the interior wall and the window or door frame.

Scagliola. An imitation marble, usually precast, made of Keene's cement.

Scratch Coat. First coat of plaster in three-coat work.

Screeds. Long narrow strips that serve as guides for plastering.

Slaking. Adding water to hydrate quicklime into a putty.

Soffit. The underside of an arch, cornice, bead, or other construction.

Splay Angle. An angle of more than 90°.

Staff. Plaster casts made in molds and reinforced with fiber; usually wired or nailed into place.

Sweat Out. Soft damp wall area caused by poor drying conditions.

Temper. Mixing of plaster to a workable consistency.

Template. A gage, pattern, or mold used as a guide to produce arches, curves, and other various work.

Wadding. The act of hanging staff by fastening wads made of plaster of paris and excelsior or fiber to the casts and winding them around the framing.

Wainscot. The lower 3 or 4 ft of an interior wall when it is finished differently from the remainder of the wall.

Section 13

FLOOR COVERINGS

PERCY A. SIGLER

Technologist on Flooring Surfaces
National Bureau of Standards
Washington, D.C.

Flooring materials are quite diversified in both composition and construction. They range from relatively thin coverings contributing little or no structural strength to a building to much thicker materials capable of withstanding reasonable stresses, and in some designs, essential to the strength of the building.

Typical floor coverings in the thin class are plastic, rubber, linoleum, cork tile, asphalt tile, and felt-backed coverings having various compositions as a wearing surface. Concrete and wood are widely used to serve as both a structural floor and a floor surface. Floorings such as terrazzo, magnesite, and ceramic tile may be considered as in between the two previously mentioned classes. While they are compressed or indented very little by concentrated loads, they do require a rigid and structurally sound subfloor.

When selecting a floor covering for a particular location and type of occupancy, consideration should be given to the over-all economical performance of the floor. This includes design, subfloor preparation, method of installation, and subsequent repair and maintenance requirements. Proper installation and adequate maintenance will curtail the need for major repairs of practically all types of floors and will prolong and enhance their service life.

Federal specifications for such floor coverings as flexible and semiflexible vinyl plastic tiles, several types of linoleum, rubber floorings, asphalt tiles, cork tiles, ceramic tiles, and hardwood-block flooring, as well as departmental, trade association, and commercial specifications and standards, can be used as a basis for securing good-quality merchandise. However, they deal principally with the quality of a particular type of flooring material and not with the relative merits or outstanding properties of the various types. Comparable information on different types is of direct and economic interest to architects, builders, and consumers in selecting a flooring material to meet a particular need. In this section, space does not permit a detailed discussion of all the characteristics of different flooring materials. Generalized comments on their compositions, relative merits, and installation are presented.

A summary of the results of wear and indentation tests reported in National Bureau of Standards *Building Materials and Structures Reports* 34, 43, 68, 80, and 73 is given in Table 13-1.

13-1. Plastic Floor Coverings. These products are generally referred to as vinyl plastics, since polyvinyl chloride is the predominant synthetic resin used as a binder. In some floor coverings, the thermoplastic binder is made by copolymerizing vinyl

13-1

chloride with vinyl acetate, vinylidene chloride, or similar materials. The compositions range, with increasing plasticizer content, from semiflexible materials somewhat like asphalt tile to flexible materials comparable with rubber tile. Fine asbestos fibers, granular mineral fillers, and pigments are incorporated in various proportions.

The constructions range from homogeneous materials $\frac{1}{16}$ to $\frac{3}{16}$ in. thick, to vinyl compositions 0.20 to 0.50 in. thick, laminated onto an asphalt-saturated felt or a scrap or degraded vinyl backing. In a few floor coverings, the wearing surface consists of a clear transparent vinyl coating 0.006 to 0.020 in. thick, on a thin cork tile or over photogravure-printed patterns on felt.

Table 13-1. Relative Resistance of Flooring Materials to Wear and Indentation*

Flooring material	Nominal thickness, in.	Depth of wear, in.	Residual indentation, in.
Rubber	$\frac{1}{8}$	0.005	0.003
Linoleum, burlap-backed	$\frac{1}{8}$	0.004	0.005
Linoleum, felt-backed	$\frac{3}{32}$	0.005	0.010
Asphalt tile	$\frac{3}{16}$	0.017	0.004†
Asphalt tile	$\frac{1}{8}$	0.016	0.002†
Cork tile	$\frac{5}{16}$	0.016	0.061
Mastic felt-base	$\frac{5}{64}$	0.017‡	0.019
Enamel felt-base	$\frac{5}{64}$	0.009¶	0.015
Magnesium oxychloride	$\frac{1}{2}$	0.013	0.000
Cement-mortar, 1:2 mix	1	0.010	0.000
Concrete, 1:2:4 mix	4	0.025	
Maple, flat-grained	$2\frac{5}{32}$	0.004	0.000
White oak, flat-grained	$2\frac{5}{32}$	0.010	0.001
White oak, unit-block	$1\frac{5}{32}$	0.005	0.000
Red oak, unit-block	$1\frac{5}{32}$	0.007	0.001
Pecan, unit-block	$2\frac{5}{32}$	0.006	
Yellow pine, flat-grained	$2\frac{5}{32}$	0.010	0.003
Douglas fir, edge-grained	$2\frac{5}{32}$	0.033	0.006

* The wear measurements represent depth of wear caused by 24,000 passages of a large wheel, which was shod with wood blocks covered with abrasive cloth. The wheel produced a bearing load of 275 lb. The indentation measurements are the residual indentation 120 min after removal of a load of 100 lb, applied for 30 min on a $\frac{1}{4}$-in. flat-ended indenting tool. The measurements were made at a temperature of 72°F. The more recently developed vinyl plastic floor coverings were not included in the above tests, because they were not commercially available at that time. However, other tests indicate that they have as good resistance to wear and indentation as rubber tiles.

† Residual indentation much higher at temperature of 90°F (P. A. Sigler and Myrtle B. Woodward, "Indentation Characteristics of Floor Coverings," *Building Materials and Structures Report* 73, National Bureau of Standards, April, 1941).

‡ Mastic surface worn through in spots by 7,800 passages of abrasive-covered wheel (P. A. Sigler and E. A. Koerner, "Performance Test of Floor Coverings for Use in Low-cost Housing: Part 2," *Building Materials and Structures Report* 43, National Bureau of Standards, February, 1940).

¶ Enamel surface worn through in spots by 6,000 passages of abrasive-covered wheel (P. A. Sigler and E. A. Koerner, "Performance Test of Floor Coverings for Use in Low-cost Housing: Part 3," *Building Materials and Structures Report* 68, National Bureau of Standards, January, 1941).

Vinyl plastic floor coverings have been commercially available for a comparatively short time. Their price range is high in relation to that of other thin floor coverings. While their maintenance requirements are relatively low, they are scratched and smudged sufficiently by foot traffic to warrant an occasional scrubbing and waxing in order to keep their appearance satisfactory. In general, plastic floor coverings have very good resistance to wear and reasonably satisfactory indentation characteristics. Their dimensional stability has been greatly improved since their initial appearance on the market.

Vinyl plastic tiles are especially suited for use in kitchens, restaurants, and chemical laboratories, since they are impervious to water and are, in general, more resistant to grease, oils, alkalies, and many other reagents than most other types of thin floor coverings ("Resistance of Floor Coverings to Grease, Oils and Selected Reagents," *National Bureau of Standards Technical News Bulletin*, Vol. 36, No. 2, February, 1952). They are softened and damaged by some organic solvents such as acetone and xylene.

It has not been established that vinyl plastic floor coverings will give satisfactory service on concrete floors in direct contact with the ground where they are likely to be subjected to moisture on the underside, unless the concrete floor has been thoroughly waterproofed. Membrane waterproofing is discussed in detail in C. C. Fishburn, "Prevention of Dampness in Basements," *Journal of the American Concrete Institute*, February, 1948, p. 421, and "Concrete Floors on Ground," Portland Cement Association. Semiflexible vinyl tiles, referred to in the trade as vinyl-asbestos tile, in conjunction with an asphalt adhesive, are recommended by some manufacturers for concrete floors on ground, provided moisture conditions are not severe and there is good drainage away from the building.

Since many of the requirements for a satisfactory installation of thin floor coverings are similar, recommendations on methods and good practices for installing such floor coverings are treated in Art. 13-8.

13-2. Rubber Floor Coverings. Rubber floorings are vulcanized compounds of rubber, mainly synthetic rubber of the butadiene-styrene type (GR-S). In many of the floorings, reclaimed rubber is added. Mineral fillers, such as zinc oxide, magnesium oxide, and various clays, are added in considerable amounts along with mineral pigments. Rubber floorings can be obtained in tile or sheet form in thicknesses ranging from $\frac{3}{32}$ to $\frac{1}{4}$ in. In sheet form, the rubber compound is usually keyed to a cotton-cloth backing.

In general, rubber tiles have good resistance to wear and residual indentation, and are dimensionally stable under normal conditions (*Building Materials and Structures Reports* 43, 68, 73, 80, and 85, National Bureau of Standards). They are resilient and have a relatively high comfort value. Most rubber floorings swell and soften when in contact with petroleum distillates such as kerosene. Their resistance to vegetable oils and to dilute acids and alkalies varies considerably among different products ("Resistance of Floor Coverings to Grease, Oils and Selected Reagents," *National Bureau of Standards Technical News Bulletin*, Vol. 36, No. 2, February, 1952). Rubber tiles are not recommended for use on concrete floors in direct contact with the ground unless the concrete slab has been waterproofed (see also Art. 13-1).

13-3. Linoleum Floor Coverings. The binder in linoleum, or as it is called by manufacturers, "linoleum cement," consists of a mixture of oxidized linseed oil, Kauri gum, rosin, and other resins. This cement is intimately mixed with ground cork, wood flour, and pigments to form the linoleum composition. This composition is calendered onto a burlap backing or an asphalt-saturated felt backing. It is then cured in huge stoves or buildings, which are maintained at a constant temperature of about 140°F, for a period of from 2 to 4 weeks, depending on the thickness of the linoleum.

On a burlap backing, the usual thickness is $\frac{1}{8}$ or $\frac{3}{16}$ in. On a felt backing, the over-all thickness ranges from 0.065 to 0.125 in., and the thickness of the linoleum wearing surface from 0.022 to 0.085 in.

Linoleum floor coverings are available in either sheet or tile form. They cost less than rubber tile, but more than asphalt tile.

Linoleum has been on the market for more than 50 years and has a good performance record. It has good resistance to wear and, when properly protected from concentrated loads, satisfactory indentation characteristics (Table 13-1 and *Building Materials and Structures Reports* 34, 43, 68, 80, and 73). Linoleum is materially affected by alkaline cleaning solutions. It should not be installed on floors in direct contact with the ground (see also Art. 13-1 and P. A. Sigler and R. I. Martens, "Properties of Adhesives for Floor Coverings," *Building Materials and Structures Report* 59, September, 1950, National Bureau of Standards). Recommendations for installing linoleum on concrete and wood subfloors are given in Art. 13-8.

13-4. Cork Tiles. The quantity of cork tile used in the United States is small compared with most other types of floor coverings. The tiles are usually made from clean cork shavings with no added binder or inert fillers. A more recent process uses cork granules with some added binder. The cork particles are bonded together by subjecting them to a high compressive load and a baking process. The tiles are made in thicknesses of $\frac{1}{8}$, $\frac{3}{16}$, $\frac{5}{16}$, and $\frac{1}{2}$ in. and are priced relatively high.

Outstanding characteristics of cork tiles are their high sound absorption and resilience, which make them particularly suitable for libraries, churches, radio broadcasting studios, and other locations where quietness and comfort are of paramount importance. Their principal faults are poor resistance to wear and indentation, thus making them somewhat difficult to maintain (Table 13-1 and *Building Materials and Structures Reports* 73 and 80, National Bureau of Standards). The wear and maintenance problems can be improved by coating the tiles with a penetrating sealer and wax or some other recommended coating such as varnish or lacquer and wax. Cork tiles should not be used on below-grade or on-grade concrete floors which have not been adequately waterproofed (also Art. 13-1).

13-5. Asphalt Tiles. Gilsonite and petroleum asphalts are used as binders in dark-colored asphalt tiles. In the lighter shades, cumarone-indene resins, with very little or no asphalt, are used as binders. Various synthetic thermoplastic resins are used in grease-resistant asphalt tile. Fine asbestos fibers, ground limestone, and silica are used as fillers along with mineral pigments.

Asphalt tiles are made in thicknesses of $\frac{1}{8}$, $\frac{3}{16}$, and $\frac{1}{4}$ in. and are homogeneous in construction. Their price range is appreciably lower than plastic, rubber, linoleum, and cork tiles.

Asphalt tile is one of the few types of thin floor coverings that can be satisfactorily installed on a below-grade concrete floor subjected to appreciable moisture from the ground. For such installations, it is particularly important that the tiles show no tendency to curl when tested in accordance with Federal Specification SS-T-306b for Asphalt Tile.

The tiles are not so resistant to wear and indentation as plastic and rubber floor coverings. Indentations are materially increased at high temperatures and they are not so resilient as the softer types of floor coverings, such as rubber and linoleum (P. A. Sigler and M. B. Woodward, "Indentation Characteristics of Floor Coverings," *Building Materials and Structures Report* 73, April, 1941, National Bureau of Standards). Most regular asphalt tiles and some of the so-labeled "greaseproof" asphalt tiles are softened to a considerable degree by mineral and vegetable oils and show only fair resistance to animal fats ("Resistance of Floor Coverings to Grease, Oils and Selected Reagents," *National Bureau of Standards Technical News Bulletin*, Vol. 36, No. 2, February, 1952). Methods of installation are discussed in Art. 13-8.

13-6. Mastic Felt-base Floor Coverings. Mastic felt-base floor coverings consist of a fatty-acid pitch or a bituminous composition, intimately mixed with resins, mineral pigments, and fillers. The composition is calendered while hot onto an asphalt-saturated felt backing and cured in loose rolls at room temperature for at least several weeks. The thickness of the composition wearing surface is about 0.018 in.

Two types of surface are available, one smooth and the other rough or granular. The latter is made by incorporating abrasive granules, such as carborundum or emery, in the composition for the purpose of improving slip resistance, especially when wet (P. A. Sigler, M. N. Geib and T. H. Boone, "Measurement of the Slipperiness of Walkway Surfaces," *Journal of Research of the National Bureau of Standards*, May, 1948, p. 339). The floor coverings are priced very low and can be obtained in either sheet or tile form. Their patterns are limited to a few plain dark colors.

In general, mastic felt-base floor coverings have poor resistance to wear and indentation in relation to most other thin floor coverings. Their indentation characteristics are materially affected by temperature and they are softened appreciably by kerosene. Although they are bonded to a subfloor with an asphalt adhesive, they are not recommended for use on a below-grade concrete floor in direct contact with the ground.

13-7. Enamel Felt-base Floor Coverings. Probably the lowest-priced floor coverings on the market, these are available in rug form in various sizes, or in continuous pattern or roll form up to 9 ft wide.

The coverings are made of asphalt-saturated felt, painted on both sides to form smooth surfaces and prevent the asphalt from bleeding. The enamel design or pattern is applied to the coated felt by means of wood printing blocks, on each of which a portion of the design is in raised figures. A separate block is used for each color in the pattern; in some patterns as many as 24 blocks are used. The enameled felt is baked at a high temperature in large ovens similar to those used for curing linoleum. The thickness of the baked enamel ranges from 0.005 to 0.008 in., depending on the quality of merchandise involved.

Taking into consideration the thickness of the enamel wearing surface, the low initial cost, the ease of installation and maintenance, and the type of service for which enamel felt-base floor coverings are intended, they probably render more service per dollar than any other type of floor covering.

In many instances, especially in rug form, the floor coverings are not cemented to the subfloor. Since they tear readily, edges adjacent to doorways should be fastened to the subfloor with linoleum paste or with thin metal strips nailed to a wood subfloor.

In view of the thinness of the enamel surface, their service life is somewhat limited and their resistance to indentation relatively poor (*Building Materials and Structures Reports* 68, 73, and 80, National Bureau of Standards). The floor coverings are damaged by kerosene and strong alkaline cleaners.

13-8. Installation of Thin Floor Coverings. Most manufacturers and trade associations have definite instructions and printed specifications for the installation and maintenance of their particular type of floor covering. It is good practice to follow their recommendations.

One of the most important requirements for a satisfactory installation of a thin floor covering is a dry, even, rigid, and clean subfloor. Thin floor coverings will follow the contour of the underfloor and failures in bond are likely to result if the subfloor is unclean or wet at the time of the installation.

Loose coatings and paint should be thoroughly removed from concrete subfloors. This is of paramount importance for concrete floors in direct contact with the ground. A troweled-on underlayment of rubber latex composition or asphalt mastic composition is recommended for rough or uneven concrete subfloors. They can be troweled from a thickness of $\frac{1}{4}$ in. to a featheredge.

Wood subfloors should be suspended so as to insure ample ventilation to prevent the wood from becoming damp and subject to dry rot. They should be of double construction and of sufficient strength to carry intended loads without deflection. The surface flooring should be $\frac{25}{32}$-in. tongued-and-grooved flooring having not more than a $3\frac{1}{4}$-in. face.

All springy boards and loose ends in a strip-wood subfloor should be securely nailed. Warped and uneven floors should be sanded. While felt underlays are used extensively in installing thin floor coverings over strip-wood subfloors, the use of a $\frac{1}{4}$-in. hardboard or plywood underlayment is considered preferable. The hardboard or plywood should be nailed on 6-in. centers in each direction over the entire area with ringed or barbed nails at least $1\frac{1}{2}$ in. long. Two types of felt are commonly used, one a 15-lb asphalt-saturated felt, usually recommended for asphalt tile, and a semi-saturated felt used with burlap-backed linoleum.

Thin floor coverings may be cemented direct to even concrete subfloors and to hardboard or plywood underlayments. An asphalt-saturated felt underlayment in conjunction with asphalt tile, when installed on a concrete subfloor likely to be subjected to appreciable moisture from the ground, is beneficial in that it prevents accumulation around the edges of the tiles of partly soluble calcium and magnesium compounds in the ground moisture.

Lignin or so-called linoleum paste is used to cement felt underlays to wood subfloors. It is also most generally used to bond flexible vinyl tiles, rubber tiles, cork tiles, linoleums, and felt-backed floor coverings to suspended concrete and wood subfloors and to underlayments on such subfloors.   Since lignin paste is partly water-soluble, special resin cements or alumina cement-latex paste are recommended by some manufacturers where the surface of the floor tiles is apt to be exposed to appreciable water, such as in bathrooms, laboratories, and cafeterias.

Two types of asphalt adhesives—cutback and water-emulsion—are used to bond asphalt tile and semiflexible vinyl tile to concrete subfloors and to underlayments on suspended wood subfloors.   The cutback-type asphalt adhesive is considered preferable for use on concrete subfloors in direct contact with the ground.   However, particular care is required in the spreading and initial drying of this adhesive in order to prevent the adhesive from exuding between the joints of the tiles.   The recommended practice is to spread the adhesive uniformly with a serrated or notched edge of a trowel or spreader so that the thickness of the coating will not average more than $\frac{1}{32}$ in.   Before laying the tile, the adhesive should be allowed to dry until it will not adhere to the thumb when pressed onto the coating.   The V-shaped notches in the trowel should be $\frac{1}{16}$ in. deep and spaced $\frac{3}{16}$ in. on centers.   A similar serrated trowel is also used to spread other adhesives for floor coverings so that a thin uniform coating of adhesive is obtained.

It is good practice to keep heavy equipment and traffic off a new-laid floor covering until the adhesive has thoroughly set.   Also, exposure to water from washing and waxing should be avoided.   A period of at least 3 days is recommended.

All resilient-type floor coverings should be protected from concentrated indenting loads by equipping the legs of chairs and tables with adequate-size and flat-base glides ($\frac{3}{4}$ to $1\frac{1}{2}$ in. diameter) or large-diameter wide-wheel casters.—Rubber, plastic, or glass furniture cups should be placed under the legs of heavy equipment such as pianos, beds, desks, and bookcases.   The small metal domes usually attached to the legs of new furniture should be removed and replaced with large-surface protection devices.

13-9. Ceramic Tiles.   Ceramic floor tiles are produced from suitable combinations of clays, potter's flint, and feldspar or from natural clays; i.e., clays used without admixtures.   The tiles are matured in kilns at high temperatures and are available in various classes, sizes, and shapes.   The more common classes are unglazed porcelain tile, natural clay tile, and quarry tile (Tile, Ceramic; Floor, Wall and Trimmers, U.S. Federal Specification SS-T-308).

The tiles are made in thicknesses ranging from $\frac{1}{4}$ to $1\frac{1}{2}$ in.   They require a rigid subfloor and are usually set in a cement-mortar bed at least 1 in. thick.   Thin setting-bed methods are sometimes used ("Thin Setting-bed Methods and Materials," *Tile Council of America Booklet* K-400).

Special acid and alkali-resistant materials should be used to grout the joints of the tiles in locations where exposure to food acids are likely and sanitary requirements necessitate the use of severe cleansing methods, such as in breweries, dairies, and other establishments where foods and drinks are processed and packed.

Asphalt-saturated felt, and a metal-reinforced mortar setting bed should be installed on wood subfloors.

Ceramic tiles are high-priced in relation to thin floor coverings such as vinyl plastic and rubber tiles.

Ceramic tiles are very durable and have excellent resistance to wear and indentation. Although the tiles are not materially affected by alkalies, acids, oils, and many other reagents, the jointing material used may require careful selection to meet special conditions.

13-10. Terrazzo Floors.   Terrazzo floors usually consist of 1 part of portland cement to 2 parts of aggregate.   Crushed marble of various sizes, from $\frac{1}{8}$ to $\frac{1}{2}$ in., is the commonly used aggregate.   Colors are obtained by selecting aggregates of the desired hue; mineral pigments are sometimes added.

Terrazzo floors should be damp-cured for at least 6 days, after which the surface is ground so as to expose the colors of the marble chips.   The thickness of a terrazzo topping should be at least $\frac{5}{8}$ in.

Asphalt-saturated felt and a metal-reinforced mortar setting bed, at least $1\frac{3}{8}$ in. thick, should be placed over wood subfloors.

Any appreciable settlement or vibration in a building or expansion and contraction of the subfloor will cause terrazzo floors to crack. Placing the cement-mortar underbed on a ¼-in. bed of dry sand is recommended where such movements are anticipated.

Metal or plastic divider strips are often located at critical points to control and localize flexure cracks. Divider strips are also used to create decorative effects, such as panels. The panel size and shape may be varied to suit the particular room or occupancy. The divider strips are partly embedded in the underbed and extend to the surface of the terrazzo.

Terrazzo floors are relatively high in cost but are very durable. Their resistance to wear is influenced by the properties of the marble aggregates (D. W. Kessler, A. Hockman, and R. E. Anderson, "Physical Properties of Terrazzo Aggregates," *Building Materials and Structures Report* 98, May, 1943, National Bureau of Standards). They are damaged by acids and by some cleaning materials (D. W. Kessler, "Terrazzo as Affected by Cleaning Materials," *Journal of the American Concrete Institute*, September, 1948).

Terrazzo floors are available as conductive floors for hospital operating rooms or other locations where a spark from static electricity may ignite explosive mixtures of vapors or very fine particles of dust. (P. G. Guest, V. W. Sikora, and B. Lewis, "Static Electricity in Hospital Operating Suites: Direct and Related Hazards and Pertinent Remedies," *Bureau of Mines Report of Investigation* 4833, January, 1952; "Report of Committee on Explosions in Hospital Operating Suites," Public Building Service of General Services Administration, January, 1950; and Recommended Safe Practice for Hospital Operating Rooms, National Fire Protection Association Standard 56, June, 1952.)

Abrasive granules may be incorporated in a terrazzo mix or sprinkled on the surface before it sets, to improve the slip resistance of the floor. Slip resistance is particularly important for stairways, ramps, and floors likely to be wet. Most smooth-surface floors are slippery when wet. Good antislip properties under wet conditions are usually associated with rough particles that project through the film of water and thus prevent its action as a lubricant (P. A. Sigler, M. N. Geib, and T. H. Boone, "Measurement of the Slipperiness of Walkway Surfaces," *Journal of Research of the National Bureau of Standards*, Vol. 40, May, 1948).

13-11. Magnesium Oxychloride Floors. Magnesium oxychloride floors, more commonly known as "magnesite," are made by adding a 22° Baumé solution of magnesium chloride to powdered magnesium oxide. Various fibrous and mineral fillers are mixed into this paste, which sets to a hard mass comparable with concrete. Some of the more commonly used fillers are wood flour, hardwood fiber, cork, asbestos, talc, sand, marble flour, limestone fines, and mineral pigments. Marble chips are sometimes added to the mix and the surface ground to simulate terrazzo floors. Abrasive granules may be incorporated in the mix or embedded in the surface before it completely hardens to form a slip-resistant surface (P. A. Sigler, M. N. Geib, and T. H. Boone, "Measurement of the Slipperiness of Walkway Surfaces," *Journal of Research of the National Bureau of Standards*, Vol. 40, May, 1948).

Magnesite floors usually range in thickness from ½ to 1 in. on a concrete subfloor. It is essential that an existing concrete floor be thoroughly scarified and cleaned before the magnesite is installed to secure an adequate bond between the two monolithic floorings.

On a wood subfloor, a thickness of not less than ⅝ in. should be installed, along with a 15-lb asphalt-saturated felt and metallic reinforcing mesh nailed to the subfloor. A 2.5 lb per sq yd, diamond-mesh, expanded metal lath, conforming to Federal Specification QQ-B-1016, is a suitable anchoring and reinforcing medium. The lath should be nailed with 1½-in., large-head, galvanized roofing nails on 6-in. centers in two directions. The nails should be driven tight enough to secure the lath to the wood floor, but not hard enough to force the lath into and puncture the felt. Metal or plastic divider strips may be used if desired.

The physical properties of magnesium oxychloride floors are materially influenced by the care and workmanship used in properly proportioning the ingredients and in placing and troweling the mix. The fillers also play a predominant part (*Building*

Materials and Structures Reports 43, 68, and 80, National Bureau of Standards). The condition of set when the final troweling is made is quite important in order to obtain a smooth and dense surface.

Magnesite floors of specific composition are available as conductive and nonsparking floors for use in hospital operating rooms and munition plants (P. G. Guest, V. W. Sikora, and B. Lewis, "Static Electricity in Hospital Operating Suites: Direct and Related Hazards and Pertinent Remedies," *U.S. Bureau of Mines Reports of Investigations* 4833, January, 1952; "Report of Committee on Explosions in Hospital Operating Suites," Public Building Service of General Services Administration, January, 1950; and Recommended Safe Practice for Hospital Operating Rooms, National Fire Protection Association Standard 56, June, 1952).

Magnesium oxychloride compositions are not recommended for below-grade installations or where appreciable exposures to acid or alkaline solutions for prolonged periods are likely, such as in food-processing establishments, laundries, and breweries. They will withstand intermittent exposure to water, such as from occasional spillage and wet mopping.

13-12. Concrete Floors. A concrete topping may be applied before or after a concrete structural slab has hardened. The former is applied in a thickness of about $\frac{1}{2}$ in.; the latter in a thickness of about 1 in. In either case, the properties of the topping will be dependent to a considerable extent on a careful selection, grading, and proportioning of the cement, sand, and aggregates used; the water-cement ratio; the care and workmanship in placing, compacting, and troweling the mix; and adequate damp curing (M. B. Klock, "Monolithic and Bonded Floor Finishes," *Journal of the American Concrete Institute*, June, 1949).

The consistency of the concrete mix should be as dry as practicable for proper compacting and finishing. The surface of the topping should not be excessively troweled and should be damp-cured for at least 7 days. Where damp curing is not feasible, concrete toppings may be satisfactorily cured by spraying a curing compound of known merit on the surface as soon as it hardens sufficiently to be walked on. New concrete floors should not be exposed to heavy traffic for at least 10 days.

A topping with a maximum of coarse aggregates at the surface, where they are needed to withstand wear, can be produced from a relatively dry mix with a power float. Liquid surface treatments, such as solutions of magnesium fluosilicate, sodium silicate, aluminum sulfate, or zinc sulfate, are sometimes used to harden some concrete floors and decrease their tendency to dust. However, such treatments should not be considered as a cure-all for poor-quality concrete.

13-13. Wood Floors. Hardwoods most commonly used for flooring are maple, beech, birch, oak, and pecan. The softwoods consist of yellow pine, Douglas fir, and western hemlock ("Selection, Installation, Finish and Maintenance of Wood Floors for Dwellings," *U.S. Department of Agriculture Circular* 489, July, 1938). Hardwoods are more resistant to wear and indentation than softwoods; their densities reveal to some extent other desirable characteristics (*Building Materials and Structures Reports* 34, 68, 73, and 80, National Bureau of Standards).

Hardwood floorings are available in thicknesses of $1\frac{1}{32}$, $1\frac{5}{32}$, and $2\frac{5}{32}$ in., and in widths of $1\frac{1}{2}$, 2, $2\frac{1}{4}$, and $3\frac{1}{4}$ in.

Softwood floorings are usually $2\frac{5}{32}$ in. thick and can be obtained in widths of $2\frac{3}{8}$, $3\frac{1}{4}$, and $5\frac{3}{16}$ in.

The hardwoods are available as strips and as unit wood blocks. The softwoods are available as strips and as end-grain blocks for industrial establishments. Strip floorings over wood subfloors placed diagonally on wood joists are widely used to serve as both structural and surface floors.

For satisfactory performance, wood floorings require a protective coating such as penetrating sealer, varnish, or shellac in conjunction with wax.

13-14. Flooring Trade Associations. Detailed information on the installation and maintenance of flooring materials may be obtained from the following organizations:

Society of the Plastics Industry, Inc., 67 West 44th St., New York 18, N.Y.

The Rubber Manufacturers Association, Inc., 444 Madison Ave., New York 22, N.Y.

Asphalt Tile Institute, 101 Park Ave., New York 17, N.Y.

Cork Institute of America, 25 West 43rd St., New York, N.Y.

Tile Council of America, 10 East 40th St., New York 16, N.Y.

The National Terrazzo and Mosaic Association, 711 14th St., N.W., Washington 5, D.C.

Oxychloride Cement Association, 1028 Connecticut Ave., N.W., Washington 6, D.C.

Portland Cement Association, 33 West Grand Ave., Chicago, Ill.

Maple Flooring Manufacturers Association, 35 East Wacker Drive, Chicago 1, Ill.

National Oak Flooring Manufacturers Association, 814 Sterick Building, Memphis 3, Tenn.

Southern Pine Association, Canal Building, New Orleans 4, La.

Douglas Fir Plywood Association, Tacoma Building, Tacoma 2, Wash.

Section 14

WATER PERMEABILITY OF
MASONRY STRUCTURES

Cyrus C. Fishburn

Division of Building Technology
National Bureau of Standards

This section discusses the permeability of concrete and masonry structures subjected to water on exposed faces. It gives information on the construction of water-resistant above-grade and below-grade structures and the use of admixtures and coatings.

14-1. Definitions of Terms Related to Water Resistance

Permeability. Quality or state of permitting passage of water and water vapor into, through, and from pores and interstices, without causing rupture or displacement.

Terms used in this section to describe the permeability of materials, coatings, structural elements, and structures follow in decreasing order of permeability:

Pervious or Leaky. Cracks, crevices, leaks, or holes larger than capillary pores, which permit a flow or leakage of water, are present. The material may or may not contain capillary pores.

Water-resistant. Capillary pores exist that permit passage of water and water vapor, but there are few or no openings larger than capillaries that permit leakage of significant amounts of water.

Water-repellent. Not "wetted" by water; hence, not capable of transmitting water by capillary forces alone. However, the material may allow transmission of water under pressure and may be permeable to water vapor.

Waterproof. No openings are present that permit leakage or passage of water and water vapor; the material is impervious to water and water vapor, whether under pressure or not.

These terms also describe the permeability of a surface coating or a treatment against water penetration, and they refer to the permeability of materials, structural members, and structures whether or not they have been coated or treated.

14-2. Permeability of Concrete.
Concrete contains many interconnected voids and openings of various sizes and shapes, most of which are of capillary dimensions. If the larger voids and openings are few in number and not directly connected with each other, there will be little or no water penetration by leakage and the concrete may be said to be water-resistant.

Concrete in contact with water not under pressure ordinarily will absorb it. The water is drawn into the concrete by the surface tension of the liquid in the wetted capillaries.

The tendency for the water to rise above its level is known as the **capillary potential.** The potential capillary rise is termed the **equivalent negative hydraulic head.** The surface forces in the capillaries and the potential capillary rise increase inversely with the bore of the capillaries.

Rise of water into a system of interconnected capillaries in concrete tends to be limited by the potential of the largest capillaries in the system. The capillary potential of a large void or opening approaches zero but such openings may be bypassed by water contained in interconnected systems of smaller capillaries.

The relative humidity over the meniscus of water in a capillary is less than 100% and decreases with decrease in capillary bore. There will be a transfer of water vapor from the capillaries if the vapor pressure in the air adjacent to the concrete is lower than that of the air over the meniscus. The rate at which water enters the capillaries from below is dependent on the rate of evaporation in the capillaries.

Water under pressure and in contact with the exposed side and bottom of a concrete foundation floor or wall will tend to fill all capillaries in the concrete below the height of the hydrostatic pressure head. The water will tend to rise above this level to heights equivalent to the negative hydraulic head of the capillaries. The rise, however, may be greatly reduced if the rate of evaporation from the interior surfaces exceeds the rate of flow through the capillaries.

A slow percolation may occur from any capillary containing water at a hydrostatic pressure greater than the potential of the capillary. Some of the capillaries in concrete may be permeable to the flow of water under a low hydraulic head.

Tests of permeability, under pressure, of sand-and-gravel concrete indicate that, at a pressure of 20 psi, the rate of flow through a 5-in.-thick, lean, harsh specimen is 0.025 gal per sq ft per hr at a test period of 7 days (C. H. Jumper, "Tests of Integral and Surface Waterproofing for Concrete," *Journal of Research of the National Bureau of Standards,* Vol. 7, Research Paper No. 394, 1931). Richer and better-graded concretes were tested by Norton and Pletta (Paul T. Norton and Dan H. Pletta, "Permeability of Gravel Concrete," *Proceedings of the American Concrete Institute,* Vol. 27, p. 1093, 1931). The rate of flow reported for concrete having a water-cement ratio not exceeding 0.7 by weight and subjected to a pressure of 40 psi was less than 0.001 gal per sq ft per hr, at a test period of 50 hr. An increase of water-cement ratio tended to increase the rate of flow, but the rate was also affected by aggregate grading, richness of mix, and consistency of concrete. The rate of flow of water under pressure through the concretes decreased with time. It is evident that the rate at which water under pressure passes through capillaries in concrete is very small when compared with the possible rate of leakage through large interconnected voids, subjected to like pressure.

If a capillary in concrete is made repulsive to water with a water-repellent admixture, the capillary potential is of the same value but is reversed in sign. Such a capillary will not permit absorption of water that is not under pressure. If the water is under a pressure head greater than that of the capillary potential, the water will enter the concrete and will tend to rise to a height equal to the difference between the water pressure head and the equivalent positive hydraulic head of the capillary. This height will increase with increase in capillary bore and will equal the height of the pressure head in voids or openings having zero capillary potential.

Water-resistant concrete for buildings should be a properly cured, dense, rich concrete containing durable, well-graded aggregate. The water content of the concrete should be as low as is compatible with workability and ease of placing and handling. Information on the kind of concrete to be used in floors and walls is given in Arts. 14-7, 14-8, 14-9, and 14-11. More detailed information on the proportioning, mixing, placing, and curing of water-resistant concrete is given in Sec. 5. See also the 1953 Report of American Concrete Institute Committee 613 ("Recommended Practice for Selecting Proportions for Concrete," *Journal of the ACI,* October, 1953) and the report of the Joint Committee on Standard Specifications for Concrete and Reinforced Concrete ("Recommended Practice and Standard Specifications for Concrete and Reinforced Concrete," 1940).

14-3. Water-repellent Admixtures for Concrete. These are the most effective and widely used of the so-called integral "waterproofers" or "dampproofers" for concrete. They tend to keep the surfaces of voids and capillaries in concrete from being wetted by water.

For an ideal capillary, the contact angle between water and the walls of capillaries that are made repellent is changed from nearly 0 to almost 180°, the curvature of the meniscus is reversed, and the capillary potential is changed from an equivalent negative hydraulic head (rise) to an equivalent positive hydraulic head (depression).

A water-repellent admixture usually reduces the strength of concrete. For a given repellent, the strength reduction tends to increase with increase in repellency. The amount of water repellent commonly used is limited, rarely exceeding 0.2% of the weight of the cement.

Water-repellent concrete is permeable to water vapor. If a vapor-pressure gradient is present, moisture may penetrate from the exposed face to an inner face. The concrete is not made waterproof (in the full meaning of the term) by the use of an integral water repellent.

Whether or not a capillary is repellent, water under a sufficient pressure head will enter and pass through any capillary whose potential is less than that of the pressure head. Water will not enter a repellent capillary whose potential exceeds the applied water pressure head.

None of the water repellents tested by Jumper ("Tests of Integral and Surface Waterproofing for Concrete," *Journal of Research of the National Bureau of Standards,* Vol. 7, Research Paper No. 394, 1931) made the concrete impermeable to the penetration of water with a pressure head of 20 psi. However, they reduced the absorption of water by the concrete. The reduction in absorption resulting from the use of a water-repellent admixture may be a good measure of the probable effectiveness of the admixture against the capillary rise of water not under pressure.

The "soaps" or salts of fatty acids, such as calcium, aluminum, and ammonium stearates and oleates, are commonly used water-repellent admixtures for concretes. When used in amounts equal to about 0.2% by weight of cement, they may reduce the absorption of a concrete to roughly 70% of that of the plain untreated concrete. Tests by Jumper indicated that these repellents had little effect on the permeability of concrete subjected to water under pressure.

Butyl stearate used in amounts equal to 0.5 to 1.0% by weight of cement reduced absorption of concrete test specimens to about 35 and 55%, respectively, of that of plain concrete. Used in the form of an emulsion, the butyl stearate may become well distributed throughout the mass of the concrete without excessive foaming and possible reduction in strength of concrete. Permeability of concrete containing butyl stearate and tested under water pressure by Jumper was about equal to that of standard plain concrete. However, the butyl stearate was markedly superior to the "soaps" (salts of fatty acids) in reducing absorption.

Heavy mineral oil used in amounts equivalent to about 4% by weight of cement and containing 12% of stearic acid was found by Jumper to significantly reduce the permeability of concrete subjected to a water pressure of 20 psi. The absorption of the treated concrete was about 45% of that of the plain concrete and the compressive strength was 85% of that of the standard. Some engineers recommend that the viscosity of the oil should not be less than SAE 60 and that the oil should not saponify or emulsify with alkali and seriously impair the strength of the concrete.

Asphalt emulsions have been used as water-repellent admixtures and are claimed to be effective. Repellency of treated concrete may be increased if the concrete is dried sufficiently to permit the emulsion to "break."

Coal-tar pitch cut with benzene tested by Jumper indicated that addition of 1% of the pitch, by weight of cement, increased absorption, reduced compressive strength to about 85% of that of the standard, and decreased permeability, under pressure, of the concrete.

Powdered iron, with an oxidizing agent such as ammonium chloride, is not usually considered as an admixture for concrete. However, it is occasionally added to cementitious grouts and mortar that are applied as coatings for concrete and masonry. Oxidation of the iron begins when water is added and results in an expansion of the volume occupied by the iron particles. This expansion is claimed to control, reduce, or eliminate shrinkage of the grout or mortar.

Directions for the use of the iron may vary with different producers of the material. Equal parts by weight of portland cement and the chemically prepared iron are sometimes used in a grout. A trowel-applied mortar coat of portland cement, iron, and sand may contain as much as 25% of iron by weight of cement. Usually the grout coat is followed by one or more parge coats of a mortar. It is difficult to obtain a continuous coating with the iron alone and cement, or cement and sand, are usually added to obtain a workable mixture.

Permeability tests of surface coatings for concrete, made by Jumper, indicate that several coatings containing powdered iron and an oxidizing agent slightly reduced the absorption of cylindrical specimens of concrete immersed in water. Other data, some of which are unpublished, indicate the need for using portland cement, or portland cement and sand, with the iron to insure application of a continuous coating on highly permeable masonry walls. Although the data are meager, they indicate that trowel-applied mortar coatings are highly water-resistant whether or not they contain iron.

Many contractors specializing in preventive measures and remedial treatments against water penetration use chemically prepared iron powder in coatings applied to subgrade concrete and masonry surfaces. Use of iron may have some advantages, but it should be noted that coatings containing iron are permeable to the penetration of water by capillarity, whether or not the water is under hydrostatic head. Such a coating is not waterproof in the full sense of the term.

14-4. Permeability of Unit-masonry Walls. Most masonry units will absorb water. Some are highly pervious under pressure. The mortar commonly used in masonry will absorb water but usually contains few openings permitting leakage.

Masonry walls usually leak at the joints between the mortar and the units, however. Excepting single-leaf walls of highly pervious units, leakage at the joints results from failure to fill them with mortar and poor bond between the masonry unit and mortar. As with concrete, rate of capillary penetration through masonry walls is small compared with the possible rate of leakage.

14-5. Permeability of Concrete and Masonry Structures. Many above- and below-grade structures, built without surface coatings, membranes, and integral waterproofings, have given adequate protection against leakage under severe exposure conditions and have not become objectionably damp from the penetration of capillary moisture. Such structures contain few, if any, large openings permitting leakage of water in quantity.

Capillary penetration of moisture through above-grade walls that resist leakage of wind-driven rain is usually of minor importance. Such penetration of moisture into well-ventilated subgrade structures may also be of minor importance if the moisture is readily evaporated. However, long-continued capillary penetration into some deep, confined subgrade interiors frequently results in an increase in relative humidity, a decrease in evaporation rate, and objectionable dampness.

14-6. Drainage for Subgrade Structures. Subgrade structures located above ground-water level in drained soil may be in contact with water and wet soil for periods of indefinite duration after long-continued rains and spring thaws. Drainage of surface and subsurface water may greatly reduce the time during which the walls and floor of a structure are subjected to water, may prevent leakage through openings resulting from poor workmanship and reduce the capillary penetration of water into the structure. If subsurface water cannot be removed by drainage, the structure must be made waterproof or highly water-resistant.

Surface water may be diverted by grading the ground surface away from the walls and by carrying the runoff from roofs away from the building. The slope of the ground surface should be at least ¼ in. per ft for a minimum distance of 10 ft from the walls. Runoff from high ground adjacent to the structure should also be diverted.

Proper subsurface drainage of ground water away from basement walls and floors requires a drain of adequate size, sloped continuously, and where necessary, carried around corners of the building without breaking continuity.   The drain should lead to a storm sewer or to a lower elevation that will not be flooded and permit water to back up in the drain.

Drain tile should have a minimum diameter of 6 in. and should be laid in gravel or other kind of porous bed at least 6 in. below the basement floor.   The open joints between the tile should be covered with a wire screen or building paper to prevent clogging of the drain with fine material. Gravel should be laid above the tile, filling the excavation to an elevation well above the top of the footing.   Where considerable water may be expected in heavy soil, the gravel fill should be carried up nearly to the ground surface and should extend from the wall a distance of at least 12 in. (Fig. 14-1).

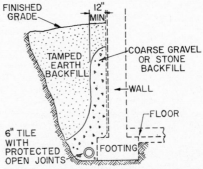

FIG. 14-1. Drainage of basement wall with drain tile along the footing and gravel fill.

14-7. Concrete Floors on Ground. These should preferably not be constructed in low-lying areas that are wet from ground water or periodically flooded with surface water.   The ground should slope away from the floor.   The level of the finished floor should be at least 6 in. above grade.   Further protection against ground moisture and possible flooding of the slab from heavy surface runoffs may be obtained with subsurface drains located at the elevation of the wall footings.

All organic material and topsoil of poor bearing value should be removed in preparation of the subgrade, which have a uniform bearing value to prevent unequal settlement of the floor slab.   Backfill should be tamped and compacted in layers not exceeding 6 in. in depth.

Except where the minimum winter air temperatures are above 35°F, slabs on ground of residences should be insulated at the edges.   A mineral insulating material, at least 1 in. thick, that will not absorb water should be used.   For best protection, the insulation should be placed along the outside edges and under the bottom of the slab for a distance of at least 18 in. from the edges.   In mild climates, the insulation may be placed along the outside edges downward to a distance of 12 in. below the bottom of the slab.

Where the subgrade is well-drained, as where subsurface drains are used or are unnecessary, floor slabs of residences should be insulated either by placing a granular fill over the subgrade or by use of a lightweight-aggregate concrete slab covered with a wearing surface of gravel or stone concrete.   The granular fill, if used, should have a minimum thickness of 5 in. and may consist of coarse slag, gravel, or crushed stone, preferably of 1-in. minimum size.   A layer of 3-, 4-, or 6-in.-thick hollow masonry building units is preferred to gravel fill for insulation and provides a smooth, level bearing surface.

Moisture from the ground may be absorbed by the floor slab thereby increasing the thermal conductivity of lightweight-aggregate concrete.   A waterproof membrane is effective in preventing such absorption only if it is continuous and not punctured or damaged during the concreting.   It is desirable, therefore, that the concrete be low absorptive.

Insulation also retards the capillary rise of ground moisture.

If the subgrade is not properly drained and the ground-water level should reach the bottom of the slab, the insulation value of granular fill, hollow masonry units, or lightweight-aggregate concrete will be greatly reduced.   In such cases, a waterproof layer of insulation may be needed beneath the slab.

Floor coverings, such as oil-base paints, linoleum, and asphalt tile, acting as a vapor barrier over the slab, may be damaged by a rise of capillary moisture and water vapor from the ground.   If such floor coverings are used and where a complete barrier against the rise of moisture from the ground is desired, a two-ply bituminous membrane waterproofing should be placed beneath the slab and over the insulating concrete or granular fill (Fig. 14-2). The top of the lightweight-aggregate concrete, if used, should be troweled or brushed to a smooth level surface for the membrane. The top of the granular fill should be covered with a grout coating, similarly finished. (The grout coat, $\frac{1}{2}$ to 1 in. thick, may consist of a 1:3 or a 1:4 mix by volume of portland cement and sand. Some $\frac{3}{8}$- or $\frac{1}{2}$-in. maximum-sized coarse aggregate may be added to the grout if desired.) After the top surface of the insulating concrete or grout coating has hardened and dried, it should be mopped with hot asphalt or coal-tar pitch and covered before cooling with a lapped layer of 15-lb bituminous saturated felt. The first ply of felt then should be mopped with hot bitumen and a second ply of felt laid and mopped on its top surface. Care should be exercised not to puncture the membrane, which should preferably be covered with a coating of mortar, immediately after its completion. If properly laid and protected from damage, the membrane may be considered to be a waterproof barrier.

Where there is no possible danger of water reaching the underside of the floor, a single layer of 55-lb smooth-surface asphalt roll roofing or a similar product of 55-lb

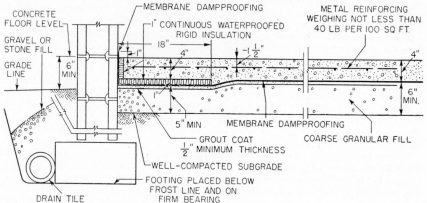

Fɪɢ. 14-2. Concrete slab on ground insulated and waterproofed with bituminous membrane.

minimum weight may be substituted for the membrane. Joints between the sheets should be lapped and sealed with bituminous mastic. Great care should be taken to prevent puncturing of the roofing layer during concreting operations. When so installed, asphalt roll roofing provides a low-cost and adequate barrier against the movement of excessive amounts of moisture by capillarity and in the form of vapor.

If a lightweight-aggregate insulating concrete slab is used, it is placed directly on the subgrade. The slab should have a minimum thickness of 4 in. and a minimum compressive strength of 1,500 psi. The coarse aggregate should not exceed 1 in. in size. If the insulating slab is to be covered with a membrane, it should be permitted to dry out after curing and before the membrane is placed. The concrete wearing surface applied over the membrane should be at least $2\frac{1}{2}$ in. and preferably 3 in. thick of 3,000 psi concrete and should be reinforced with welded wire fabric weighing at least 40 lb per square. A 6 × 6 mesh of No. 6 wire is suitable. If the concrete wearing slab is to be covered with an oil-base paint or a floor covering that is a vapor barrier, it should be in a thoroughly dry condition before it is covered.

A concrete slab placed over a granular fill, with or without a membrane, should have a minimum thickness of 4 in. The concrete should have a minimum compressive strength of 3,000 psi, should contain durable aggregate of not more than 1-in. maximum size and should be reinforced with welded wire fabric of 40-lb minimum weight.

14-8. Basement Floors in Drained Soil. Where a basement is to be used as living quarters or for the storage of things that may be damaged by moisture, the floor should be insulated and should preferably contain the membrane waterproofing described in Art. 14-7. In general, the design and construction of such basement floors is similar to that of floors on ground discussed in Art. 14-7.

If the ground adjacent to the structure is properly drained, the insulation obtained from a granular fill, hollow masonry units, or lightweight-aggregate concrete should suffice. No edge insulation of the slab is needed if the basement floor is more than 2 ft beneath the ground surface. Where insulation is needed and the exposure conditions are severe, for example, where the floor slab is in contact with water or wet ground for extended periods, a 1-in. thick layer of a nonabsorptive and waterproof mineral insulating material is preferred to granular fill and lightweight concrete.

If passage of moisture from the ground into the basement is unimportant or can be satisfactorily controlled by air conditioning or ventilation, the waterproof membrane need not be used. The concrete slab should have a minimum thickness of 4 in. and need not be reinforced, but should be laid on a granular fill or other insulation placed on a carefully prepared subgrade. The concrete in the slab should have a minimum compressive strength of 2,000 psi and may contain an integral water repellent.

A bituminous-filled joint between the basement walls and the floor will prevent leakage into the basement of any water that may occasionally accumulate under the slab. Space for the joint may be provided by use of beveled siding strips, which are removed after the concrete has hardened. After the slab is properly cured, it and the wall surface should be in as dry a condition as is practicable before the joint is filled to insure a good bond of the filler and to reduce the effects of slab shrinkage on the permeability of the joint. Hot asphalt or coal-tar pitch may be placed in the joint after its sides have been primed with a suitable bitumen.

14-9. Monolithic Concrete Basement Walls. These should have a minimum thickness of 6 in. Where insulation is desirable, as where the basement is used for living quarters, lightweight aggregate, such as those prepared by calcining or sintering blast-furnace slag, clay, or shale that meet the requirements of American Society for Testing Materials Standard C330, may be used in the concrete. The concrete should have a minimum compressive strength of 2,000 psi.

Wall form ties of an internal-disconnecting type are preferred to twisted-wire ties. Entrance holes for the form ties should be sealed with mortar after the forms are removed. If twisted-wire ties are used, they should be cut a minimum distance of $1\frac{1}{2}$ in. from the face of the wall and the holes filled with mortar.

The concrete should be placed in the forms in level layers, preferably not more than 18 in. thick. The concrete should be either vibrated or carefully tamped in the forms. Construction joints, where necessary, should be horizontal. Before concreting is resumed at a construction joint, the top surface of the wall should be cleaned of soft material to expose the aggregate. The cleaned top surface should be dampened and covered with a thin coating of a 1:2 mix of cement-sand grout, followed at once and before drying out with the next layer of concrete. The wall should be moist-cured for at least 7 days.

The resistance of the wall to capillary penetration of water in temporary contact with the wall face may be increased by the use of a water-repellent admixture. The water repellent may also be used in the concrete at and just above grade to reduce the capillary rise of moisture from the ground into the superstructure walls.

Where it is desirable to make the wall resistant to passage of water vapor from the outside and to increase its resistance to capillary penetration of water, the wall face may be treated with a bituminous coating. The continuity and the resultant effectiveness in resisting moisture penetration of such a coating is dependent on the smoothness and regularity of the concrete surface and on the skill and technique used in applying the coating to the dry concrete surface. Some bituminous coatings that may be used are listed below in increasing order of their resistance to moisture penetration:

Spray- or brush-applied asphalt emulsions.
Spray- or brush-applied bituminous cutbacks.
Trowel coatings of bitumen with organic solvent, applied cold.
Hot-applied asphalt or coal-tar pitch, preceded by application of a suitable primer.
Cementitious brush-applied paints and grouts and trowel coatings of a mortar

increase moisture resistance of monolithic concrete, especially if such coatings contain a water repellent.   However, in properly drained soil, such coatings may not be justified unless needed to prevent leakage of water through openings in the concrete resulting from segregation of the aggregate and bad workmanship in casting the walls.   The trowel coatings may also be used to level irregular wall surfaces in preparation for the application of a bituminous coating.

14-10. Basement Walls of Masonry Units.   Water-resistant basement walls of masonry units should be carefully constructed of durable materials to prevent leakage and damage due to frost and other weathering exposure.   Frost action is most severe at the grade line and may result in structural damage and leakage of water.   Where wetting followed by sudden severe freezing may occur, the masonry units should meet the requirements of the following specifications:

Building brick (solid masonry units made from clay or shale), American Society for Testing Materials Standard C62, Grade SW.

Facing brick (solid masonry units made from clay or shale), ASTM Standard C216, Grade SW.

Structural clay load-bearing wall tile, ASTM Standard C34, Grade LBX.

Hollow load-bearing concrete masonry units, ASTM Standard C90, Grade A.

For such exposure conditions, the mortar should be a Type S mortar (Table 10-1, Art. 10-3) having a minimum compressive strength of 1,800 psi when tested in accordance with the requirements of ASTM Standard C270.   For milder freezing exposures and where the walls may be subjected to some lateral pressure from the earth, the mortar should have a minimum compressive strength of 1,000 psi.

Rise of moisture, by capillarity, from the ground into the superstructure walls may be greatly retarded by use of an integral water-repellent admixture in the mortar. The water-repellent mortar may be used in several courses of masonry located at and just above grade.

Both the vertical and horizontal joints in brick masonry foundation walls should be completely filled with mortar.   Walls of hollow masonry units laid with the cells vertical should be bedded with mortar under all face shells of the units.   Mortar should also be spread on the cross webs, which serve as the bearing for the face shell of the units above, as where the wall contains two tiers, or wythes, of units.   Mortar for head joints should be buttered in the exposed faces of the wall a distance equal to the thickness of the face shells.   Side bearing units should be laid in full mortar beds. Both the bed and head joints of walls of solid concrete masonry units should be filled with mortar.

Thickness of basement walls should be as great as that of the wall they support and should not be less than one-twelfth of the vertical distance between lateral supports. Any requirement for the thermal conductance of the wall will also affects its thickness under usual conditions of service.   It is likely that, if the thermal conductance C of the wall does not exceed 0.4, or possibly 0.5 Btu per hr per sq ft per °F, there will be no surface condensation on the interior face.   This usually requires that masonry walls of hollow units be at least 12 in. thick.   If additional insulation is needed in the wall, insulation material of a nonabsorptive mineral type should be used.

All-brick basement walls containing two or three tiers of units can be built to be highly water-resistant (Arts. 14-14 and 14-16).   However, chief reliance against leakage of water through masonry basement walls, particularly those of hollow units, should be placed on use of trowel-applied mortar coats or pargings on the exposed faces of the walls.   The mortar coats should also be used on the outside faces of masonry foundation walls of basementless structures located where freezing temperature may occur, to prevent leakage and the subsequent freezing of water trapped in the masonry.

Two trowel coats of a mortar containing 1 part portland cement to 3 parts sand by volume should be applied to the outside faces of basement walls built of hollow masonry units.   One trowel coat may suffice on the outside of all-brick and of brick-faced walls.

The wall surface and the top of the wall footing should be cleaned of dirt and soil, and the masonry should be thoroughly wetted with water.   While still damp, the surface should be covered with a thin scrubbed-on coating of portland cement tempered to the consistency of thick cream. Before this prepared surface has dried, a ⅜-in.-thick trowel-applied coating or mortar should be placed on the wall and over the top of the footing; a fillet of mortar may be placed at the juncture of the wall and footing.

Where a second coat of mortar is to be applied, as on hollow masonry units, the first coat should be scratched to provide a rough bonding surface. The second coat should be applied at least 1 day after the first, and the coatings should be cured and kept damp by wetting for at least 3 days. A water-repellent admixture in the mortar used for the second or finish coat will reduce the rate of capillary penetration of water through the walls. If a bituminous coating is not to be used, the mortar coating should be kept damp until the backfill is placed.

The bituminous coatings described in Art. 14-9 may be applied to the plaster coating if resistance to penetration of water vapor is desired. The plaster coating should be dry and clean before the bituminous coating is applied over the surfaces of the wall and the top of the footing. Unless backed with a tier of masonry or a self-supporting layer of concrete, the bituminous coatings may fail, in time, to bond properly to the inner face of the masonry. They should not be used on the inner faces of the walls unless properly supported in position.

Expansion joints in both concrete and masonry foundation walls should be of bellows type made of 16-oz copper sheet, which should extend a minimum distance of 6 in. on each side of the joint. The sheet should be embedded between wyths of masonry units or faced with a 2-in.-thick cover of mortar reinforced with welded-wire fabric. The copper bellows may be backed with bituminous saturated fabric. The outside face of the expansion joint should be filled flush with the wall face with bituminous plastic cement conforming with the requirements of Federal Specification SS-C-153.

14-11. Basements Subjected to Hydrostatic Pressure, without Membranes. Basement walls and floors subjected to water under pressure should be designed and built to resist it. Where exposure conditions are severe, both walls and floors should be made of reinforced concrete. Expansion joints should be in the same vertical plane throughout walls and floors. These joints should be waterproof and of the bellows type, composed of noncorrosive metal sheet of sufficient strength and ductility to resist the anticipated maximum pressure and movement. The exposed face of the expansion joint should be sealed with plastic cement (Federal Specification SS-C-153).

Addition of an integral water repellent to concrete continuously subjected to water under pressure slightly increases permeability of the concrete. The increase has been partly attributed to difficulty in properly mixing the concrete, frothing of the mix, and entrapment of air in large-sized voids. Use of an integral water repellent in basement concrete subjected for long periods to hydrostatic pressure may not, therefore, be advisable.

If slow seepage of moisture by capillarity and passage of water vapor into a basement is not objectionable, or if the effects of such moisture penetration are controlled by ventilation or air conditioning, the walls and floor may not require the protection afforded by a bituminous membrane.

The concrete should be dense and should contain a well-graded, low-absorptive aggregate. The cement factor should be not less than 6 bags of portland cement per cubic yard and the water-cement ratio preferably should not exceed 0.45 by weight. The minimum 28-day compressive strength should be 3,000 psi. For maximum density, the concrete should be carefully handled and vibrated into place. If not vibrated, the concrete should have a maximum slump of 5 in. Construction joints in wall footings and walls should be keyed and should otherwise be made as described in Art. 14-9. The walls and floors should be carefully cured to avoid cracking due to shrinkage. Furthermore, the walls should be kept damp until after they have been backfilled.

The use of shotcrete or trowel-applied mortar coatings, ¾ in. or more in thickness, to the outside faces of both monolithic concrete and masonry unit walls greatly increases their resistance to penetration of moisture. Such coatings cover and seal construction joints and other vulnerable joints in the walls against leakage.   When applied in a thickness of 2 in. or more, they may be reinforced with welded-wire fabric. The reinforcement may reduce the incidence of large shrinkage cracks in the coating. However, the cementitious coatings do not protect the walls against leakage if the walls, and subsequently the coatings, are badly cracked as a result of unequal foundation settlement, excessive drying shrinkage, and thermal changes.

14-12. Bituminous Membrane.   This is a waterproof barrier providing protection against the penetration of water under hydrostatic pressure and water vapor.   To resist hydrostatic pressure, the membrane should be made continuous in the walls and floor of a basement.   It also should be protected from damage during building operations and should be laid by experienced workmen under competent supervision. It usually consists of three or more alternate layers of hot, mopped-on asphalt or coal-tar pitch and plies of bituminous saturated felt or woven cotton fabric.   The number of moppings exceeds the number of plies by one.

Bituminous saturated cotton fabric is stronger and is more extensible than bituminous saturated felt but is more expensive and more difficult to lay.   At least one or two of the plies in a membrane should be of saturated cotton fabric to provide strength, ductility, and extensibility to the membrane.   Where vibration, temperature changes, and other conditions conducive to displacement and volume changes in the basement are to be expected, the relative number of fabric plies may be increased.

The minimum weight of bituminous saturated felt used in a membrane should be 13 lb per 100 sq ft.   The minimum weight of bituminous saturated woven cotton fabric should be 10 oz per sq yd.

Although a membrane is held rigidly in place, it is advisable to apply a suitable primer over the surfaces receiving the membrane and to aid in the application of the first mopped-on coat of hot asphalt or coal-tar pitch.

Materials used in the membrane should meet the requirements of the following current American Society for Testing Materials standards:

Creosote primer for coal-tar pitch—D43.
Primer for asphalt—D41.
Coal-tar pitch—D450.
Asphalt—D449.
Woven cotton fabric, bituminous saturated—D173.
Coal-tar saturated felt—D227.
Asphalt saturated felt—D226.

The number of plies of saturated felt or fabric increases with the hydrostatic head to which the membrane is to be subjected.   Five plies is the maximum commonly used in building construction, but 10 or more plies have been recommended for pressure heads of 35 ft or greater.   The thickness of the membrane crossing the wall footings at the base of the wall should be no greater than necessary to reduce possible settlement of the wall due to plastic flow in the membrane materials.

The amount of primer to be used may be about 1 gal per 100 sq ft.   The amount of bitumen per mopping per 100 sq ft averages about 25 lb for asphalt and 30 to 35 lb for coal-tar pitch.   The thickness of the first and last moppings is usually slightly greater than the thickness of the moppings between the plies.

The surfaces to which the membrane is to be applied should be smooth, dry, and at a temperature above freezing.   Air temperature should be not less than 40°F.   The temperature of coal-tar pitch should not exceed 375°F and asphalt, 400°F.

If the concrete and masonry surfaces are not sufficiently dry, they will not readily absorb the priming coat, and the first mopping of bitumen will be accompanied by bubbling and escape of steam.   Should this occur, application of the membrane should be stopped and the bitumen already applied to damp surfaces should be removed.

The membrane should be built up ply by ply, the strips of fabric or felt being laid immediately after each bed has been hot-mopped.   One of several methods of laying the plies is the solid or continuous method, in which a portion of each strip of fabric or felt is in contact with the supporting base of the membrane.   The lap of succeeding plies or strips over each other is dependent on the width of the roll and the number of plies. In any membrane there should be some lap of the top or final ply over the first, initial ply. The American Railway Engineering Association requires a minimum distance of 2 in. for this lap (Fig. 14-3). End laps should be staggered at least 24 in., and the laps between succeeding rolls should be at least 10 in. ("AREA Manual," "Waterproofing," Chap. 29, 1953).

The floor membrane should be placed over a concrete base or subfloor whose top surface is troweled smooth and which is level with the tops of the wall footings. The membrane should be started at the outside face of one wall and extend over the wall footing, which may be keyed. It should cover the floor and tops of other footings to the outside faces of the other walls, forming a continuous horizontal waterproof barrier. The plies should project from the edges of the floor membrane and lap into the wall membrane.

The loose ends of felt and fabric must be protected; one method is to fasten them to a temporary vertical wood form about 2 ft high, placed just outside the wall face. Immediately after the floor membrane is laid, its surface should be protected and covered with a layer of portland-cement mortar, at least 1 in. thick.

After its completion, a wall membrane should be protected against damage and should be held in position by a facing of brick, tile, concrete block, mortar, asphalt plank, or asphalt block. Since this protective facing should be self-supporting, it preferably should have a minimum thickness of 4 in. and be of brick, structural clay tile, or concrete masonry units. Facings of asphalt plank, asphalt block, and mortar require considerable support from the membrane itself and give protection against abrasion of the membrane from lateral forces only. Protection against downward forces such as may be produced by settlement of the backfill is given only by the self-supporting masonry walls.

The kind of protective facing may have some bearing on the method of constructing the membrane. The membrane may be applied to the face of the wall after its construction, or it may be applied to the back of the protective facing before the main wall is built ("Architects and Engineers Reference Manual," Barrett Division, Allied Chemical and Dye Corp.). The first of these methods is known as the outside application; the second is known as the inside application (Fig. 14-4).

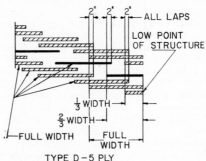

FIG. 14-3. Lapping of membranes recommended by American Railway Engineering Association.

For the inside application, a protective facing of considerable stiffness against lateral forces must be built, especially if the wall and its membrane are to be used as a form for the pouring of a main wall of monolithic concrete. Again, the inner face of the protecting wall must be smooth or else leveled with mortar to provide a suitable base for the membrane. The completed membrane should be covered with a ⅜-in.-thick layer of mortar to protect it from damage during construction of the main wall.

Application of wall membranes should be started at the bottom of one end of the wall and the strips of fabric or felt laid vertically. Preparation of the surfaces and laying of the membrane proceed much as they do with floor membranes. The surfaces to which the membrane is attached must be dry and smooth, which may require that the faces of masonry walls be leveled with a thin coat of grout or mortar. The plies of the wall membrane should be lapped into those of the floor membrane.

If the outside method of application is used and the membrane is faced with masonry, the narrow space between the units and the membrane should be filled with mortar as the units are laid. The membrane may be terminated at the grade line by a return into the superstructure wall facing.

Contraction joints in walls and floors containing a bituminous membrane should be the usual metal-bellows type. The membrane should be placed on the exposed face

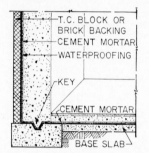 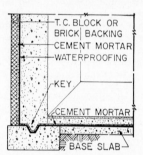

FIG. 14-4. Two methods of applying waterproofing membranes to walls.

of the joint and it may project into the joint, following the general outline of the bellows.

The protective facing for the membrane should be broken at the expansion joint and the space between the membrane and the line of the facing filled with a bituminous plastic cement.

Details at pipe sleeves running through the membrane must be carefully prepared. The membrane should be reinforced with additional plies and may be calked at the sleeve. Steam and hot-water lines should be insulated to prevent damage to the membrane.

14-13. Above-grade Water-resistant Concrete Walls.   The rate of moisture penetration through capillaries in above-grade walls is low and usually of minor importance. However, such walls should not permit leakage of wind-driven rain through openings larger than those of capillary dimension.

Monolithic, cast-in-place concrete walls are usually of sufficient thickness to permit readily the proper placing of a workable concrete. Construction joints should be carefully made, as described in Art. 14-9. Cracking of the concrete due to volume changes resulting from a fluctuation in temperature and moisture content of the concrete may be controlled by the use of steel reinforcement.

Walls of cellular concrete, made of aggregates containing no fines, are highly permeable and require surface coatings of grout or mortar to prevent leakage of wind-driven rain.

Tilt-up concrete panels, widely used in industrial construction, and architectural cast-stone panels, sometimes used in monumental buildings, are usually made of dense highly water-resistant reinforced concretes. However, the walls made of these panels are vulnerable to leakage at the joints. In tilt-up construction, edges of the panels may be recessed and the interior of vertical joints filled with grout after the panels are aligned.

Calking compound is commonly used as a facing for the joints. It has also been used to face the joints of rectangular architectural cast-stone panels 10 sq ft or more in area. Experience has shown that calking compounds often weather badly; their use as a joint facing creates a maintenance problem and does not prevent leakage of wind-driven rain after a few years' exposure.

The amount of movement to be expected in the vertical joints between tilt-up and cast-stone panels is a function of the panel dimension and the seasonal fluctuation in temperature and moisture content of the concrete. For such wall constructions, it may be more feasible to use an interlocking water-resistant joint, faced on the weather side with mortar and backed with either a compressible premolded strip or calking.

14-14. Above-grade Water-resistant Brick Walls. Brick walls 4 in. or more in thickness can be made highly water-resistant. The measures that need to be taken to insure there will be no leakage of wind-driven rain through brick facings are not extensive and do not require the use of materials other than those commonly used in masonry walls. The main factors that need to be controlled are the rate of "suction" of the brick at the time of laying and filling of all joints with mortar (Art. 10-5).

It may be noted, in general, that the greater the number of brick leaves, or wythes, in a wall, the more water-resistant the wall. Walls of hollow masonry units are usually highly permeable, and brick-faced walls backed with hollow masonry units are greatly dependent upon the water resistance of the brick facing to prevent leakage of wind-driven rain. Tests of water resistance of masonry walls subjected to a simulated wind-driven rain and the factors affecting the permeability of the walls are discussed by C. C. Fishburn, D. Watstein, and D. E. Parsons in "Water Permeability of Masonry Walls," *National Bureau of Standards BMS Report* 7, and C. C. Fishburn, "Water Permeability of Walls Built of Masonry Units," *BMS* 82.

Facing brick and building brick made of clay or shale should meet the current requirements of American Society for Testing Materials Standards C216 and C62, respectively. Methods of sampling and testing the brick are given in ASTM Standard C67. Brick meeting the requirements for Grades SW and MW of Standards C62 and C216 should be satisfactory for use in water-resistant brick walls.

The water absorption of the brick during complete immersion from a dry condition is of minor importance compared with the rate of absorption of the brick at the time of laying. This rate can be reduced by wetting the brick before laying. Medium absorptive brick may need to be thoroughly soaked with water. Highly absorptive brick may require total immersion in water for some time before brick "suction" is reduced to the low limits needed. The test for the rate of absorption of brick is described in Secs. 27 to 30, inclusive, ASTM Standard C67. The brick, in a flat position, is partly immersed in water to a depth of $\frac{1}{8}$ in. for 1 min, and the absorption is calculated for a net equivalent area of 30 sq in. For water-resistant masonry, the suction (rate of absorption) of the brick should not exceed 0.35, 0.5, and 0.7 oz, respectively, for properly constructed all-brick walls or facings of nominal 4-, 8-, and 12-in. thickness.

In general, method of manufacture and surface texture of brick do not greatly affect the permeability of walls. However, water-resistant joints may be difficult to obtain if the brick are deeply scored, particularly if the mortar is of a dry consistency. Loose sand should be brushed away or otherwise removed from brick that are heavily sanded.

Mortar to be used in above-grade, water-resistant brick-faced and all-brick walls should meet requirements of ASTM Standard C270, Type N, except that water retention of the mortar should not be less than 75%, and preferably 80% or more. For laying absorptive brick that contain a considerable amount of absorbed water, the mortars having a water retention of 80% or more may be used without excessive "bleeding" at the joints and "floating" of the brick.

The mortar may contain a masonry cement meeting the requirements of ASTM Standard C91, Type II, except that water retention should not be less than 75 or 80%. Excellent mortar may also be made with portland cement and hydrated lime, mixed in the proportion of 1:1:6 parts by volume of cement, lime, and loose damp sand. The hydrated lime should be highly plastic.   Type S lime conforming with the requirements of ASTM Standard C207 is highly plastic, and mortar containing it, in equal parts by volume with cement, will probably have a water retention of 80% or more.

Since capillary penetration of moisture through concrete and mortar is of minor importance, particularly in above-grade walls, the mortar need not contain an integral water repellent.   However, if desired, water-repellent mortar may be advantageously used in a few courses at the grade line to reduce capillary rise of moisture from the ground into the masonry.   To secure a strong water-resistant bond of the mortar to the brick, the mortar should be mixed to as wet a consistency as possible for the mason to handle.   The mortar should be of a type that does not stiffen rapidly on the board, except through loss of moisture by evaporation.

The amount of wetting the brick will require to control rate of absorption properly when laid should be known or determined by measurements made before the brick are used in the wall.   Some medium absorptive brick may only require frequent wetting in the pile; others may need to be totally immersed for an hour or more.   While the immersion method is more costly than hosing in the pile, it insures that all brick are more or less saturated when removed from immersion.   A short time interval may be needed before the brick are laid; but the brick are likely to remain on the scaffold, in a suitable condition to lay, for some time.   Brick on the scaffold should be inspected and moisture condition checked several times a day.

Mortar should be retempered frequently if necessary to maintain as wet a consistency as is practically possible for the mason to use.   At air temperatures below 80°F, mortar should be used or discarded within $3\frac{1}{2}$ hr after mixing; for air temperatures of 80°F or higher, unused mortar should be discarded after $2\frac{1}{2}$ hr.

The resistance of a brick facing to the penetration of rain may be increased if the mortar in the joints is compacted by tooling the joints concave with a rounded iron bar.   The tooling should be done after the mortar has begun to stiffen but care should be exercised not to displace the brick.

14-15. Above-grade Water-resistant Concrete Masonry Walls.   Exterior concrete masonry walls, without facings of brick, may be 8 or 12 in. thick and are usually highly permeable to leakage of wind-driven rain.   A water-resistant concrete masonry wall is the exception rather than the rule, and protection against leakage is obtained by facing the walls with a cementitious coating of paint, stucco, or shotcrete.

For walls of rough-textured units, a portland cement–sand grout provides a highly water-resistant coating.   The cement may be either white or gray.

Factory-made portland-cement paints containing a minimum of 65%, and preferably 80%, portland cement may also be used as a base coat on concrete masonry. Application of the paint should conform with the requirements of American Concrete Institute Standard 616.   The paints, stuccos, and shotcrete should be applied to dampened surfaces.   Shotcrete should conform with the requirements of ACI Standard 805.

Pneumatically applied coatings thinner than those discussed above and which contain durable-low absorptive aggregates are also highly water-resistant.

Shrinkage of concrete masonry due to drying and a drop in temperature may result in cracking of a wall and its cementitious facing.   Such cracks readily permit leakage of wind-driven rain.   The chief factor reducing incidence of shrinkage cracking is the use of dry block.   When laid in the wall, the block should have a low moisture content, preferably one that is in equilibrium with the driest condition to which the wall will be exposed.   A moisture content not exceeding 30% of the maximum absorption of the block is suitable for most parts of the United States.   This moisture content may be reduced in arid regions.

The block should also have a low potential shrinkage.   The linear shrinkage of saturated block during drying in a ventilated oven at 110°C should preferably not exceed 0.035% for block weighing 105 lb or more per cu ft and should preferably not exceed 0.045% for block weighing less than 105 lb.   A discussion of block shrinkage is given in the report of ACI Committee 716.   If block shrinkage exceeds these limits, greater precautions must be observed to control shrinkage.

Formation of large shrinkage cracks may be controlled by use of steel reinforcement in the horizontal joints of the masonry and above and below wall openings.   Where there may be a considerable seasonal fluctuation in temperature and moisture content of the wall, high-yield-strength, deformed-wire joint reinforcement should be placed in at least 50% of all bed joints in the wall.

Use of control joints faced with calking compound has also been recommended to control shrinkage cracking; however, this practice is marked by frequent failures to keep the joints sealed against leakage of rain.   Steel joint reinforcement strengthens a concrete masonry wall, whereas control joints weaken it, and the calking in the joints requires considerable maintenance.

14-16. Water-resistant Cavity Walls. Cavity walls, particularly brickfaced cavity walls, may be made highly resistant to leakage through the wall facing. However, as usually constructed, facings are highly permeable, and the leakage is trapped in the cavity and diverted to the outside of the wall through conveniently located weep holes.   This requires that the inner tier of the cavity be protected against the leakage by adequate flashings, and weep holes should be placed at the bottom of the cavities and over all wall openings.   Wall ties between the tiers should have drips to prevent a bridge for leakage water to cross the cavity.

Flashings should preferably be hot-rolled copper sheet of 10-oz minimum weight. They should be lapped at the ends and sealed either by solder or with bituminous plastic cement.   Mortar should not be permitted to drop into the flashings and prevent the weep holes from functioning.   The weep holes may be formed by the use of $\frac{3}{8}$-in.-diameter rubber tubing, withdrawn after the wall is completed.

14-17. Water-resistant Surface Treatments for Above-grade Walls. Experience has shown that leakage of wind-driven rain through masonry walls, particularly those of brick, ordinarily cannot be stopped by use of an inexpensive surface treatment or coating that will not alter the appearance of the wall.   Such protective devices either have a low service life or fail to stop all leakage.

Both organic and cementitious pigmented coating materials, properly applied as a continuous coating over the exposed face of the wall, do stop leakage.   Many of the organic pigmented coatings are vapor barriers and are therefore unsuitable for use on the outside, "cold" face of most buildings.   If vapor barriers are used on the cold face of the wall, it is advisable to use a better vapor barrier on the warm face to reduce condensation in the wall and behind the exterior coating.

The Housing and Home Finance Agency publication "Condensation Control" divides coatings into three groups, listed in increasing order of permeability to water vapor, as (1) water-vapor barriers; (2) intermediate coatings; and (3) breather-type coatings.

In Arts. 14-18 to 14-22, coatings for masonry are described and arbitrarily divided into five groups, as follows: (1) colorless coating materials; (2) cementitious coatings; (3) pigmented organic coatings; (4) joint treatment for brick masonry; and (5) bituminous coatings.

14-18. Colorless Coating Materials. The colorless "waterproofings" are often claimed to stop leakage of wind-driven rain through permeable masonry walls.   Solutions of oils, paraffin wax, sodium silicate, chlorinated rubber, silicone resins, and salts of fatty acids have been applied to highly permeable test walls and have been tested at the National Bureau of Standards under exposure conditions simulating a wind-driven rain.   Most of these solutions contained not more than 10% of solid matter.   These treatments reduced the rate of leakage but did not stop all leakage through the walls.

Solutions containing oils and waxes tended to seal the pores exposed in the faces of the mortar joints and masonry units, thereby acting more or less as vapor barriers, but did not seal the larger openings, particularly those in the joints.

Silicone water-repellent solutions greatly reduced leakage through the walls as long as the treated wall faces remained water-repellent.   After an exposure period of 2 or 3 hr, the rate of leakage gradually increased as the water repellency of the wall face diminished.   Some of these tests are described by publications such as C. C. Fishburn, D. Watstein, and D. E. Parsons, "Water Permeability of Masonry Walls," *National Bureau of Standards BMS Report* 7, and C. C. Fishburn and D. E. Parsons, "Tests of Cement-water Paints and Other Waterproofing for Unit-masonry Walls," *BMS* 95.

The test data show that colorless coating materials applied to permeable walls of brick or concrete masonry may not provide adequate protection against leakage of wind-driven rain.

Coatings of the water-repellent, breather type, such as silicone and "soap" solutions, may be of value in reducing absorption of moisture into the wall surface. They may be of special benefit in reducing the soiling and disfiguration of stucco facings and light-colored masonry surfaces. Again, they may be applied to tilt-up concrete panels and to facing panels of cast stone to reduce volume changes that may otherwise result from changes in moisture content of the concretes. However, it should be noted that a water-repellent treatment applied to the surface may cause water, trapped in the masonry, to evaporate beneath the surface instead of at the surface. If the masonry is not water-resistant and contains a considerable amount of soluble salts, as evidenced by efflorescence, application of a water repellent may cause salts to be deposited beneath the surface, thereby causing spalling of the masonry. The water repellents therefore should be applied only to walls having water-resistant joints.

Emulsions of waxes in water have also been used as water-resistant coatings for permeable masonry walls. Tests of two of these emulsions are described in *BMS Report* 95. One of these coatings, an emulsion, containing about 30% of waxes, did not greatly reduce the rate of leakage through the walls. Coatings of the other emulsion, which contained 45% of waxes, were effective and stopped leakage through brick masonry walls when tested soon after application. However, the treated walls were no longer water-resistant and leaked badly when again tested after exposure out of doors for a few months at Washington, D.C.

Claims for the effectiveness of colorless solutions and emulsions as waterproofings for masonry are often based on tests of small prisms of brick, stone, or concrete that have been treated and immersed in water. The treated specimens are found to absorb only a small percentage of the moisture taken up by similar but untreated specimens. Since highly permeable masonry walls, particularly brick masonry walls, leak at the joints and since the colorless solutions are known to fail in sealing such openings against leakage of wind-driven rain, the claims based on absorption tests are frequently fallacious. Furthermore, application of a colorless material makes the treated face of the masonry water-repellent and may prevent the proper bonding of a cementitious coating which could otherwise be used to stop leakage.

14-19. Cementitious Coatings. Coatings of portland-cement paints, grouts, and stuccos, and of pneumatically applied mortars are highly water-resistant. They are preferred above all other types of surface coatings for use as water-resistant base coatings on above-grade concrete masonry (see also Art. 14-15). They may also be applied to the exposed faces of brick masonry walls that have not been built to be water-resistant. Tests of the water permeability of some cementitious coatings are described in *National Bureau of Standards BMS Reports* 94 and 95.

The cementitious coatings absorb moisture and are of the breather type, permitting passage of water vapor. Addition of water repellents to these coatings does not greatly affect their water resistance but does reduce the soiling of the surface from the absorption of dirt-laden water. If more than one coating is applied, as in a two-coat paint or stucco facing job, the repellent is preferably added only to the finish coat, thus avoiding the difficulty of bonding a cementitious coating to a water-repellent surface.

The technique used in applying the cementitious coatings is highly important. The backing should be thoroughly dampened. Paints and grouts should be scrubbed into place with stiff fiber brushes and the coatings should be properly cured by wetting. Properly applied, the grouts are highly durable; some grout coatings applied to concrete masonry test walls were found to be as water-resistant after 10 years out-of-doors exposure as when first applied to the walls.

14-20. Pigmented Organic Coatings. These include textured coatings, mastic coatings, conventional paints, and aqueous dispersions. The thick-textured and mastic coatings are usually spray-applied but may be applied by trowel. Conventional paints and aqueous dispersions are usually applied by brush or spray. Most of these coatings are vapor barriers but some textured coatings, conventional paints, and aqueous dispersions are breathers. Excepting the aqueous dispersions, all the coatings are recommended for use with a primer.

Applied as a continuous coating, without pinholes, the pigmented organic coatings are highly water-resistant. They are most effective when applied over a smooth backing. When they are applied with paintbrush or spray by conventional methods to rough-textured walls, it is difficult to level the surface and to obtain a continuous water-resistant coating free from holes. A scrubbed-on cementitious grout used as a base coat on such walls will prevent leakage through the masonry without the use of a pigmented organic coating.

The pigmented organic coatings are highly decorative but may not be so water-resistant, economical, or durable as the cementitious coatings.

Fig. 14-5. Bituminous coating on inside face of permeable masonry wall blistered in rain test.

14-21. Joint Treatments for Masonry. Leakage of wind-driven rain through the joints in permeable brick masonry walls can be stopped by either repointing or grouting the joints. It is usually advisable to treat all the joints, both vertical and horizontal, in the wall face. Some "tuck-pointing" operations in which only a few, obviously defective joints are treated may be inadequate and do not necessarily insure that the untreated joints will not leak.

Repointing consists of cutting away and replacing the mortar from all joints to a depth of about ⅝ in. After the old mortar has been removed, the dust and dirt should be washed from the wall and the brick thoroughly wetted with water to near saturation. While the masonry is still very damp but with no water showing, the joints should be repointed with a suitable mortar. This mortar may have a somewhat stiff consistency to enable it to be tightly packed into place, and it may be "prehydrated" by standing for 1 or 2 hr before retempering and using. Prehydration is said to stabilize the plasticity and workability of the mortar and to reduce the shrinkage of the mortar after its application to the joints.

After repointing, the masonry should be kept in a damp condition for 2 or 3 days. If the brick are highly absorptive, they may contain a sufficient amount of water to aid materially in curing.

Weathering and permeability tests described in C. C. Fishburn, "Effect of Outdoor Exposure on the Water Permeability of Masonry Walls," *National Bureau of Standards BMS Report* 76 indicate that repointing of the face joints in permeable brick masonry walls was the most effective and durable of all the remedial treatments against leakage that did not change the appearance of the masonry.

Joints are *grouted* by scrubbing a thin coating of a grout over the joints in the masonry. The grout may consist of equal parts by volume of portland cement and fine sand, the sand passing a No. 30 sieve.

The masonry should be thoroughly wetted and in a damp condition when the grout is applied. The grout should be of the consistency of a heavy cream and should be scrubbed into the joints with a stiff bristle brush, particularly into the juncture between brick and mortar. The apparent width of the joint is slightly increased by some staining of the brick with grout at the joint line. Excess grout may be removed from smooth-textured brick with a damp sponge, before the grout hardens; care should be taken not to remove grout from between the edges of the brick and the mortar joints. If the brick are rough-textured, staining may be controlled by the use of a template or by masking the brick with paper masking tape.

Bond of the grout to the joints is better for "cut" or flush joints than for tooled joints. If the joints have been tooled, they should preferably not be grouted until after sufficient weathering has occurred to remove the film of cementing materials from the joint surface, exposing the sand aggregate.

Grouting of the joints has been tried in the field and found to be effective on leaky brick walls. The treatment is not so durable and water-resistant as a repointing job but is much less expensive than repointing. Some tests of the water resistance of grouted joints in brick masonry test walls are described in *National Bureau of Standards BMS Report* 76.

The cost of either repointing or grouting the joints in brick masonry walls probably greatly exceeds the cost of the additional labor and supervision needed to make the walls water-resistant when built.

14-22. Bituminous Coatings. Bituminous cutbacks, emulsions, and plastic cements are usually vapor barriers and are sometimes applied as "dampproofers" on the inside faces of masonry walls. Plaster is often applied directly over these coatings, the bond of the plaster to the masonry being only of a mechanical nature. Tests described in *National Bureau of Standards BMS Report* 95 show that bituminous coatings applied to the inside faces of highly permeable masonry walls, not plastered, will readily blister and permit leakage of water through the coating (Fig. 14-5). It is advisable not to depend on such coatings to prevent the leakage of wind-driven rain unless they are incorporated in the masonry or held in place with a rigid self-sustaining backing.

Even though the walls are resistant to wind-driven rain, but are treated on their inner faces with a bituminous coating, water may be condensed on the warm side of the coating and damage to the plastering may result, whether the walls are furred or not. However, the bituminous coating may be of benefit as a vapor barrier in furred walls, if no condensation occurs on the warm side.

Section 15

ROOF COVERINGS

JAMES MCCAWLEY

Editor
National Roofer

There exists today an amazing variety of roof coverings. Though they differ in structure of material employed, texture, color, and other characteristics, they can be classified into two main groups—single-unit roof coverings and multiple-unit, factory-processed roof coverings.

15-1. Types of Roofing. The single-unit type is designed for flat roof decks, where water can collect before proceeding slowly to drainage outlets. Included are built-up roofing of asphalt or coal-tar pitch, and flat-seam metal roofings.

While both these coverings are composed of a number of units, the finished roof is a single-unit, custom-built seamless product.

Multiple-unit coverings are designed for steep roof decks, where water pours swiftly over each exposed unit to gutters and leaders. They include asphalt shingles, asbestos-cement shingles, standing-seam metal panels, shingle metal roofing, wood shingles, clay tile, concrete tile, and slate.

Thus, multiple-unit roof coverings are designed for both water-shedding and water-proofing qualities, and single-unit coverings must of necessity be waterproof. The degree of effectiveness in water shedding by multiple-unit materials depends on the slope of roof and area of each unit exposed to the weather, the area exposed being greater as the slope increases. Slate, for instance, may have a 10-in. exposure on a 60° slope and a 5-in. exposure on a 45° slope.

Where, for decorative or other purposes, multiple-unit material is employed on slopes as low as 30°, the joints and laps may be sealed with mortar in the cases of clay tile or concrete tiles or have a waterproofed underlay of two or more plies of felt as is often done with asphalt shingles or concrete tile.

15-2. Roof Slopes. Roofs are constructed in a variety of shapes, of which the more common are gable or shed, hip, gambrel, mansard, sawtooth, and flat. The slope of a roof is generally referred to as the "pitch" and is expressed as the ratio between the rise of the roof and the horizontal span.

If the roof is dead flat, there is no rise. If a roof that spans a building 20 ft wide has the ridge, or peak, 10 ft above the eaves, the pitch is $^{10}\!\!/_{20}$ or half-pitch (also expressed as 6 in. on 12 in., or 6:12). Common roof pitches are $\frac{1}{4}$, $\frac{1}{3}$, $\frac{1}{2}$, and occasionally $\frac{5}{8}$ or $\frac{3}{4}$.

The greater the pitch, the more roofing material required to cover the roof. With added allowances for waste, pitches result in the following increase in area over a flat area: $\frac{1}{4}$—12%, $\frac{1}{3}$—20%, $\frac{1}{2}$—42%, $\frac{5}{8}$—60%, and $\frac{3}{4}$—80%. (See Table 15-1.)

15-3. Good Roofing Requires Good Roof Decks. Many roof failures can be traced to poorly designed roof decks, faulty preparation of the deck to receive the roofing, and abuse of the roof covering after it has been put in place.

Because heat-resisting materials impede heat flow through the roof in the winter, snow and ice build up to substantial live loads. This factor should be taken into consideration in rafter design to avoid trouble with the roof covering. Rafters, in addition, should be spaced adequately to prevent significant deflection of the roof deck and consequent damage to roofing.

Table 15-1. Variation of Roof Area with Slope

Classification	Incline		Inclined area per sq ft horizontal area	Percentage increase in area over flat roof
	In. per ft horizontal	Angle with horizontal		
Flat roofs	1/8	0°36′	1.000	0.0
	1/4	1°12′	1.000	0.0
	3/8	1°47′	1.000	0.0
	1/2	2°23′	1.001	0.1
	5/8	2°59′	1.001	0.1
	3/4	3°35′	1.002	0.2
	1	4°46′	1.003	0.3
	1 1/8	5°21′	1.004	0.4
	1 1/4	5°57′	1.005	0.5
	1 1/2	7°8′	1.008	0.8
	1 3/4	8°18′	1.011	1.1
	2	9°28′	1.014	1.4
Steep roofs	2 1/4	10°37′	1.017	1.7
	2 1/2	11°46′	1.021	2.1
	2 3/4	12°54′	1.026	2.6
	3	14°2′	1.031	3.1
	3 1/4	15°9′	1.036	3.6
	3 1/2	16°16′	1.042	4.2
	3 3/4	17°21′	1.048	4.8
	4	18°26′	1.054	5.4
	4 1/4	19°30′	1.061	6.1
	4 1/2	20°34′	1.068	6.8
	5	22°37′	1.083	8.3
	6	26°34′	1.118	11.8
	7	30°16′	1.158	15.8
	8	33°42′	1.202	20.2
	9	36°52′	1.250	25.0
	10	39°48′	1.302	30.2
	11	42°31′	1.356	35.6
	12	45°0′	1.414	41.4
Extra-steep roofs	14	49°24′	1.537	53.7
	16	53°8′	1.667	66.7
	18	56°19′	1.803	80.3
	20	59°2′	1.943	94.3
	22	61°23′	2.088	108.8
	24	63°26′	2.235	123.5

The roof-deck surface, whether of wood, metal, concrete, or other material, should be clean, smooth, and dry. Expensive roof failures have resulted from applying materials to wet or moisture-laden roof decks, for pressures developed by imprisoned moisture cause blisters and ruptures in the roof covering. Such failures are generally due to attempts to meet production schedules or to conform to construction-progress schedules—to meet building deadlines. Furthermore, a hasty installation is aggravated at times by periods of inclement weather, carelessness on the part of those responsible for adequate dry storage and application of the material, and the lack of knowledge of the destructive effects of moisture vapor.

15-4. Bituminous Roofing Materials. Expensive errors in roof application have resulted from failure of architects, builders, roofing contractors, and property owners to agree on trade terminology. As many as three or four different meanings have been conveyed by a term or phrase in a contract. With this in mind, in a discussion of bituminous materials, it is well to be clear on the meanings of terms involved:

Bitumen is a generic term that may be used to indicate either asphalt or coal-tar pitch.

Asphalt and coal-tar pitch are materials similar in appearance but with differing characteristics, which lend themselves to the solution of a variety of waterproofing and water-shedding problems.

Asphalt is a by-product of the refining processes of petroleum oils.

Coal-tar pitch is a by-product of crude tars derived from the coking of coal. The crude tars are distilled to produce coal-tar pitch.

In their solid state coal-tar pitch and asphalt resemble each other in appearance. However, there are major differences: Coal-tar pitch has a lower melting point and as a result melts faster. Because of this, a coal-tar-pitch roof must be protected by covering the final layer with gravel or slag.

Asphalt has a higher melting point and takes longer to melt. While it does not have the self-sealing feature of coal-tar pitch, its range of use is greater, because it can be used on higher slopes.

Both asphalt and coal-tar pitch are aided in water shedding and waterproofing by felted materials, manufactured largely of wood pulp, to which rag and asbestos fibers may be added—the former in the manufacture of asphalt and tarred felts and the latter in asbestos felts.

The terms asphalt felt and tarred felt refer merely to the saturating agents used in the manufacture of the felts.

15-5. Built-up Roofing. A built-up roof is a seamless piece of flexible, waterproofed material, custom-built to conform to the roof deck and to protect all angles formed by the roof deck and projecting surfaces. It consists of plies of felt mopped with asphalt or pitch.

Modern specifications for built-up roofing are easy to understand if it is remembered that the choice of a roofing depends on the answers to such questions as:

1. Can roofing material be nailed to the roof deck?
2. Is the roof deck a seamless, jointless single unit or composed of assembled units?
3. What type of surfacing is desired—mineral or smooth?
4. What is the slope of the deck?

A cast-in-place concrete deck, which is, in fact, one continuous unit over the entire roof area requires one ply of felt fewer than a wood-sheathed deck or a metal deck, which has a multiplicity of side and end joints.

While one ply of felt may be dispensed with for a cast-in-place concrete deck, one extra layer of bitumen is required to compensate for the lack of nailing the first two felts. Thus, a four-ply built-up roof over concrete is equal to a five-ply over wood (Fig. 15-1).

The five-ply built-up roof specification is the oldest of all the built-up roofing specifications (see Fig. 15-2). With the introduction of cast-in-place concrete roof decks, the four-ply specification made its appearance.

All subsequent specifications are modifications of the standard specifications for four- and five-ply roofing to take care of varying conditions. Minimum specifications have been achieved by reducing these standards by one or two plies of felt and one or two layers of bitumen or equal.

Roofing manufacturers who issue bond guarantees rate these maximum, medium, and minimum specifications in years of expected life of the roof—20, 15, and 10 years. However, experience has shown that the majority of roofs covered by these specifications have had years of life in excess of the bond termination.

For monolithic roof decks, such as cast-in-place concrete, poured gypsum, and similar type decks, felts can be cemented directly to the roof deck. For roof decks made up of units that permit nailing, the first two plies of felt are nailed to the deck, sealing the joints between the units from drippage and tying the roof covering to the deck. For multiple-unit-type roof decks that do not permit nailing, such as precast concrete slabs, the first ply of felt is cemented to the deck by a "strip mopping" operation—the slab or unit being mopped with bitumen to within 4 in. of its perimeter.

Where the slope of a roof deck is 2 in. on 12 in. or more, it is difficult to keep slag or gravel surfacing on a roof. The surfacing has a tendency to slide or be blown off the

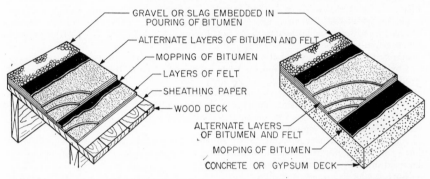

GRAVEL OR SLAG EMBEDDED IN POURING OF BITUMEN

ALTERNATE LAYERS OF BITUMEN AND FELT

MOPPING OF BITUMEN

LAYERS OF FELT

SHEATHING PAPER

WOOD DECK

ALTERNATE LAYERS OF BITUMEN AND FELT

MOPPING OF BITUMEN

CONCRETE OR GYPSUM DECK

(a) 5-PLY BUILTUP ROOF OVER WOOD   (b) 4-PLY BUILTUP ROOF OVER CONCRETE

FIG. 15-1. Built-up roofing is applied with bitumen mopping between each two layers.

FIG. 15-2. Five-ply built-up roofing.

roof. This has resulted in the specification of felts with a mineral surfacing embedded into the surface of the felt. Minimum weight of such mineral-surfaced "cap" sheets is 55 lb per square (100 sq ft). Maximum specifications require the cap sheets to be applied over two 15-lb felts—one mopped and the first one nailed.

Use of smooth-surfaced roofs on suitable slopes has resulted in specifications that eliminate the heavy surface coating in favor of a 30-lb felt nailed to the deck followed by three 15-lb felts and a final surfacing of asphalt roof coating at the rate of 10 lb to the square. The thin coating is preferable to a heavy coating because the thin film is not so subject to alligatoring, with the loss of volatile oils under solar radiation, as the thick films.

Slag, however, can be used on roofs up to 4 in. to the foot where special precautions are taken in its application. Mineral-surfaced cap sheets, too, may be used on such slopes.

These cap sheets are furnished in three forms. The simplest is a heavy sheet of saturated felt with its upper surface entirely covered with granules. The second type is similar except for an unsurfaced lap portion along one side. The third has about one-half its width surfaced with granules and may be assumed to be two-ply construction in the final assembly.

Known as "double-coverage" or "19-in. selvage edge" roofing, the third type should be applied so that each sheet laps the unsurfaced portion of the under sheet. It is particularly useful for sawtooth roof decks, where the unsurfaced portions can be nailed to the roof deck or to wood nailers embedded in the deck.

Because of the tendency of a flat deck to retain water, application of built-up roofing on a level roof requires greater mechanical skill and judgment than for steep roofs. Gravity helps even a badly constructed steep roof to shed water.

To prevent roof troubles, designers should not locate chimneys, skylights, vents, and other projections or openings in positions that make flashing and waterproofing difficult. Roofers should prepare roof-deck surfaces with care. Note that the four principal types of roof failures are:

1. *Blisters* caused by water and air in or between the roofing felts, in the roof insulation, or in or on the roof deck. Most of the moisture comes from exposure during construction or from poured decks that have not had enough time to dry adequately before the application of roofing. Blisters are also due to the roofer's failure to cement felts securely to each other, to the insulation, and to the deck.

2. *Wet insulation* due to exposure and to rain while in storage on the job during construction. But more often, it is caused by infiltration of vapor from within the building.

3. *Roof-deck failures* due to inability of roof decks to sustain the weight of design dead and live loads, to withstand traffic without deflection, and other design errors.

4. *"Condensation leaks"* due to lack of an effective vapor barrier over the roof deck, or failure to ventilate the building adequately during construction.

15-6. Cold-process Bituminous Roofing. This is used primarily for repair and maintenance, rather than for new construction. However, cold-process bituminous roofing is not limited to maintenance work.

To produce workable liquidity, the bituminous materials are thinned with solvents or emulsified with water. The solvent-thinned type is known as a cutback. Solvents include kerosene, in the manufacture of cutback asphalt, and toluene, in the manufacture of cutback tar. With cutbacks, the cementing process on the roof is achieved by evaporation of the solvents, leaving a film of bituminous material.

Bitumen emulsions are produced by melting the bitumen and dispersing it into tiny particles suspended in water by means of a soap or chemical emulsifying agent. On the roof, the water evaporates, leaving a solid film of bitumen on the surface. Clay-type emulsions, as contrasted with chemical emulsions, appear to have a greater life because of weather resistance of the bentonite-clay emulsion particles in the dry film, which support the asphalt and limit oxidation to the surface.

Felts and fabrics used with cold-process bitumen are different from those used with hot. Since cementing takes place on the evaporation of the solvents or emulsion water, it is necessary that the drying-out process be speeded. Porous mats made of glass fibers have the advantage that the open weave allows water vapor to travel through it—a breathing process that eliminates blisters. Glass fibers, however, require a heavy mastic-type emulsion, because light films are not strong enough to hold the fibers down.

Cold-process materials are applied by brush or spray, following a preparation of the roof surface to eliminate cracks, ruptures, holes, fish-mouths, and other characteristics of weathered roof decks.

Unfortunately, the field of roof-coating materials has more than its share of unprincipled producers who promote doubtful products of high unit cost by making extravagant advertising claims; so care must be exercised in selection of materials.

Cold-process roofing materials have a place in the roofing industry and can add years of life to roofs. But they are not cure-alls and will not add a second of life to roof coverings that have disintegrated. They will not bridge gaps in surfaces and will prolong life only in those materials in which life exists.

15-7. Asphalt Roofing Materials. Asphalt roofing materials, chosen wisely, serve every roofing need from slopes as low as 1 in. to the foot to the steeper slopes classified as follows:

1 in. per ft..........	19-in. selvage-edge roofing; built-up roofing
2 in. per ft..........	Mineral-surfaced roll roofing; blind-nailed, square-butt strip shingles with 2-ply felt underlay
3 in. per ft..........	Mineral-surfaced roll roofing, exposed nailed
4 in. per ft..........	Hexagonal, individual, 3-tab square butt, and lock-type shingles

15-8. Asphalt Shingles. These are manufactured of asphalt-saturated and coated felt in which is embedded a permanent mineral surfacing. They are cut into strips and units in a variety of designs ranging from individual shingles of 9 × 12 in. and 12 × 18 in. to strips 36 in. long and 10 to 13½ in. wide.

Square-butt strip shingles are strips slotted at the butts to present the illusion of individual units. Shingles are also manufactured in a variety of other shapes, for example, hexagonal.

With all asphalt-shingle materials, the first step in application is to fasten an underlay of No. 15 asphalt felt to the roof deck, lapping it 6 in. at the end and sides. A usual practice is to start off with a row of shingles turned upside down, over which is nailed a row of shingles right side up. However, while this insures a double thickness of material where it is needed most, a more desirable method is to apply a starting strip of mineral-surfaced roll roofing, 18 in. wide in normal-wind areas and 36 in. wide in high-wind areas.

Since a high proportion of backup leaks at eaves is caused by moisture traveling upward from the eaves—beneath the shingles—through capillary attraction, it is a wise precaution to cement the starter material to the roof deck, rather than nail it. In winter, should water dam up in the gutter, it may back up under the shingles and follow a nail puncture through the roof into the building interior.

Faulty shingle applications can be traced in part to too few nails, but a higher proportion can be attributed to nailing too high. If the shingle is nailed ½ in. above the slots, as in the case of square-butt asphalt shingles, the shingle will be held to the roof not just by the four nails called for in specifications, but by eight nails—four driven starting with this shingle and four others driven through the shingle on top. So each nail travels through two thicknesses of shingle material.

If the shingle is nailed 2 in. or more above the slots, it is held by only four nails at the top, and the shingle is a target for any vagrant wind.

Nails should be at least 1¼ in. long on new work and 1¾ in. long on reroofing. The usual recommendation is for hot-dipped, zinc-coated iron or steel nails, with bar-bed stems; but ordinary steel nails give very good service, and if the stems rust it appears to be all to the good, since the holding power of a rusty nail is excellent.

While shingle tabs are not required to be nailed, in high-wind areas it is a useful precaution to place a small dab of asphalt cement under each tab, which then should be pressed firmly onto the concealed portion of the underlying shingle.

Wind damage has been responsible for the popularity of lock-type asphalt shingles. The butt of this type locks into the sides of two adjoining lower-course shingles. This shingle has the advantage that it is economical in coverage in relation to the amount of material used.

15-9. Slating. This is one of the older mechanical arts—one in which skills are disappearing as the older craftsmen fade away.

Slate roofs may be divided into two classifications, standard commercial slate and textural slate, or random slating. The latter is the older and still popular form, in which slates are delivered to the job in a variety of sizes and thicknesses, to be sorted by slaters. The longer and heavier slates are placed at the eaves, medium-sized at the center, and the smallest at the ridge.

Standard commercial slating is a modern form of slating resulting from the grading of slates at the quarries. It is applied on the least expensive roofs. Slates are graded not only by lengths and widths, but by thickness—the latter approximating $\frac{1}{4}$ in.

The manufacture of slate calls for splitting the material, which results in a smooth and a rough side. The slates are applied on the roof with the smooth side down.

Slates should be laid with a lap not less than 3 in. over the second slate beneath it. Slate exposure, or margin, is found by deducting the lap from the total length of the slate and dividing the result by 2. For example, the exposure of a 20-in. slate with a 3-in. lap is $\frac{1}{2}(20 - 3) = 8\frac{1}{2}$ in.

Application starts with an undereaves course of slate fastened over a batten. Purpose of the batten is to cant the first course of slate to coincide with the angular projection of the remaining courses of the roof.

Slate is applied so that all joints are broken. It is nailed with noncorroding nails, which are not driven "home" but level with the slate. Slating nails, with a large thin head designed to fit within the countersunk hole in the slate, should be used.

15-10. Roofing Tile. Clay roofing tile offers a great deal of latitude in design and range of choice. It is manufactured from special clays, a favorite being shale—a claylike rock which when fired becomes as enduring as stone.

While there exists a variety of patterns, all tile falls into two classifications—roll and flat. Roll tiles are furnished in semicircular shape, reverse curve S shape, pan and cover, and flat-shingle design.

To lay tiles successfully, vertical and horizontal chalk lines should be struck as guide lines. In laying out these lines, it must not be assumed that the manufacturers' standard tile measurements coincide with the tile size delivered to the job. Although variations may be small, contractions occurring in the burning of the tile can cause enough difference to warrant checking of the delivered tile.

To insure a full-length tile at the ridge, and to avoid needless cutting at dormers, chimneys, and other projections, the horizontal guide lines should be adjusted—always in favor of increasing the lap. With interlocking tile, however, since the tile exposure and lap are governed by the locking device, it is impossible to make any adjustments.

Tile follows much the same application procedure as slate (Art. 15-9): With the exception of Spanish mission tile, an undereaves course plus a cant strip are required before the first course of tile is laid.

Tile application generally starts from the bottom right-hand corner of the roof and proceeds from right to left. Tiles adjacent to chimneys, vents, and other projections are left loose so that flashing material can be inserted.

Tile joints are broken, as with other types of roofs. However, because there is an element of risk in fastening a half tile at such exposed locations as gables, tile manufacturers make special "tile-and-a-half" units. These not only save time by eliminating cutting but make the gable windtight.

These large-width tile can be used effectively at valleys and hips. Where cutting must be done, as around chimneys, the tile may be trimmed on a slater's stake—the cutting line being tapped with a hammer until the unwanted portion breaks off. Tiles that verge along the hips must be fitted tight against the hip board with mastic or cement colored to match the tile.

15-11. Metal Roofing. Metal roof coverings have suffered from ignorance of the properties of metal and of the destruction caused by galvanic action and corrosion. The harm such ignorance can produce is exemplified by the fact that, although some metal roofs have exhibited no signs of deterioration after a lapse of five centuries, other metal roofs have shown signs of disintegration after the lapse of only a few years.

The principal metals used in roofing are galvanized iron, terneplate, Monel metal, aluminum, and copper. Other metals in use are zinc, lead, cast iron, and stainless steel. To work with these metals, all of which differ in some respect, a knowledge of their characteristics is essential (Sec. 2).

Corrosion or gradual deterioration is a phenomenon met with in the use of practically all commercial metals. This disintegration is a natural function, each metal possessing a potential force tending to make it revert to the more stable state of combination in which it is frequently found in nature.

Dissimilar metals set up galvanic action, resulting in the destruction of the one lower in the electromotive-force series. Aluminum, high in the series, for example, will attack zinc, next lowest in the series.

Roofing metals in the electromotive series, listed in the order of highest potential, are: copper, lead, tin, nickel (Monel), iron, zinc, and aluminum. Since current flows rapidly from copper to iron, these metals should not be in contact.

Metals near each other in the series suffer little damage from each other's contact, but iron will damage aluminum. For this reason, a copper roof should not be applied directly over a wood roof deck without divorcing it from the deck by the introduction of an asphalt felt—to insulate it from attack by the steel nails in the roof deck. As far as possible the nails and fasteners used in securing metal roof coverings should be of the same metal or alloy as the roofing.

All building materials are in a constant if imperceptible state of motion, and metal sheets move at a much more accelerated pace than other roofing material. The following is the movement for a 150°F change in temperature of an 8-ft sheet of metal:

$$
\begin{array}{ll}
 & In. \\
\text{Iron} \ldots\ldots\ldots\ldots\ldots\ldots & \frac{6}{64} \\
\text{Monel metal} \ldots\ldots\ldots\ldots & \frac{7}{64} \\
\text{Copper} \ldots\ldots\ldots\ldots\ldots & \frac{9}{64} \\
\text{Aluminum} \ldots\ldots\ldots\ldots & 1\frac{2}{64} \\
\text{Lead} \ldots\ldots\ldots\ldots\ldots\ldots & 1\frac{5}{64} \\
\text{Zinc} \ldots\ldots\ldots\ldots\ldots\ldots & 1\frac{6}{64}
\end{array}
$$

The amount of expansion and contraction over a large area is many times that over a small area. A metal roof laid in large sheets that are permanently fastened to the deck would buckle and split at seams and joints.

To allow for expansion and contraction, four types of metal roof installations have been evolved—batten-seam, standing-seam, flat-seam, and corrugated-metal. With the exception of the last type, where corrugations take care of temperature-change movements, it is necessary to break up large roof areas into small units.

Standing-seam construction provides for expansion and contraction across narrow panels, while loose-locked seams provide for lateral motion. This is true also of batten-seam construction, a type of roofing which is disappearing in favor of the standing seam.

Flat-seam construction employs a series of small sheets soldered on all four edges. The sheets are so small that expansion and contraction are negligible and are amply provided for by a slight buckling in the center of the sheet. Because of their expense in labor and material, flat-seam metal roofs have been rapidly disappearing from the roofing field.

Except for corrugated metal, no metal roofing sheets should be fastened directly to the roof as the metal must be free to move. Recourse is taken to small metal clips in standing-seam and flat-seam roofing and a metal cap installed over the battens in batten-seam roofing. In all three cases, the clips should be locked into the folds of the roofing sheets.

15-12. Corrugated-metal Roofing. This is used primarily for roofing for factories and industrial plants. The material often combines the function of both roof covering and ceiling. It can be applied with a minimum of skill.

The sheets are manufactured in a number of gages, widths, and lengths. They are laid preferably with an end lap of $1\frac{1}{2}$ corrugations and a side lap not less than 6 in.

It is advisable to start application of the sheets at the end of the roof, in the opposite direction from prevailing winds to insure that wind and rain will blow over the laps, not into them.

Types of fasteners that are employed in securing corrugated-metal sheets include nails driven into wood sheathing, clips fastened under the toe of angle purlins, straps for fastening around channels, similar straps for around angles, clinch rivets that hook around and are clinched to angles, hook bolts that attach around channels, and studs welded to purlins. Stud welding, because of its economy in time and labor and elimination of interior staging, has become a popular method of fastening corrugated metal.

Where metal sheets are fastened directly to the roof deck, even though provisions are made for expansion and contraction, the consequent movement of the sheets makes it virtually impossible for any of the fastening devices used to remain tight. This has led to the introduction of lead and neoprene washers, which take up the slack caused by the loosening of bolts, the friction of two moving sheets and the enlargement of holes drilled for fasteners. It should be noted that interior and exterior air pressures on this type of roof are also to be reckoned with in sheet movement.

Special caps are recommended for the ridge—shaped to the angle of the roof and containing pockets on either side to house the ends of the sheets.

To guard against corrosion, aluminum sheets should not rest on steel purlins without being insulated from contact by felt strips.

15-13. Corrugated Asbestos-cement Sheets. These are applied somewhat like corrugated metal. The same type of fastener is employed. However, because asbestos cement is a more easily punctured material, the sheets are placed over welded studs on purlins and the corrugations are malleted until the studs pierce the material. Rubber mallets are used to deliver enough force without damaging the sheets or the studs.

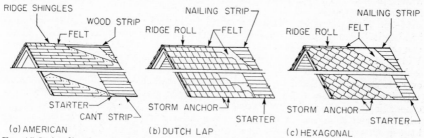

Fig. 15-3. Application of asbestos-cement shingles begins at the eaves with a cant or starter strip. Ridge shingles or ridge rolls can be used on the peak of sloping roofs.

Two methods of application are employed—the step method and the miter method. Both prevent the occurrence of four-thickness end and side laps—a feature of corrugated-metal roofing—which would be unsightly as well as difficult to waterproof with the thicker corrugated asbestos-cement roofing.

Asbestos-cement roofing differs in shape from metal roofing; the sheets are molded so that the first and last corrugations point downward, which enables the minimum side lap to be one corrugation instead of $1\frac{1}{2}$.

In the step method, alternate courses of the sheets are started with half sheets. In the miter method, no effort is made to break joints, and by mitering one corner of each sheet, end and side laps are enabled to be of uniform thickness.

15-14. Asbestos-cement Shingles. Because of their unusual durability, noncombustibility, and other desirable qualities, asbestos-cement products have won strong favor as a roofing material since their introduction early in the present century.

Composed of 15 to 25% asbestos fiber and 75 to 85% portland cement, asbestos-cement products might be described as lightweight sheets of reinforced concrete.

They are produced in a variety of shapes and sizes for numerous specific applications. Principal products are roofing shingles, flat sheets, siding shingles, and corrugated sheets.

Basically there are four standard types of asbestos-cement roofing shingles, known as American-method, multiple-unit, Dutch-lap, and hexagonal (Fig. 15-3).

American-method shingles are so called because of their shape and finish. Laid in a rectangular pattern and having a simulated wood-grain surface, they produce an appearance similar to conventional wood shingles.

Multiple-unit shingles are produced in large units, each of which covers an area equal to that of two to five standard-size shingles. Made in styles and sizes that vary with manufacturers, they retain the same general appearance when installed as the small units.

Dutch-lap shingles, sometimes called Scotch-lap, are larger than conventional shingles and are lapped at top and at one side, a method of application which effects savings in both material and labor.

The hexagonal shingle, also known as the French method, is nearly square and is laid in a diamond pattern with an overlap at top and bottom. The effect is a hexagonal pattern.

Sizes of asbestos-cement roof shingles vary from 16 × 16 in. to 14 × 30 in.

Asbestos-cement shingles are highly resistant to water—but if they are not stored under tarpaulins or under cover during inclement weather, seeping moisture may discolor them.

Special eave starters are manufactured to aid in applying the first course of shingles (Fig. 15-3). Like slate, a cant strip or furring strip is required along the eaves. Furring strips are also required at hips and ridges to enable ridge and hip shingles to cover adjacent material at the correct angle. Specially designed hip and ridge shingles and terminals are manufactured and recommended for finishing these areas.

Most asbestos-cement shingles require a minimum roof pitch of 5 in. to the foot. American-method shingles however, can be applied (because of the small exposure) on roofs with 4-in. pitch.

15-15. Wood Shingles. These are obtained in two varieties, machine-sawn and hand-split. The machine-sawn are manufactured chiefly in random widths—16, 18, and 24 in. long. Hand-splits are also in random widths—25, 31, and 37 in. long. Widths of the sawn shingles vary from 5 to 12 in. and hand-split from 5 to 18 in.

An undereaves course is required under the first course of shingles on the roof; however, no cant strip is required, since the tapered wood shingles fit closely to the roof.

Owing to the constant drip at the eaves, eaves shingles receive more abuse than the other shingles on the roof. To prevent any possibility of leakage at eaves or cornice, a triple layer of shingles is a wise and comparatively inexpensive precaution, adding little in material and labor to the average job. If a triple layer is used the joints in all three should be laid so as not to coincide.

The standard exposure of wood shingles is 5 in. But depending on the length of shingles, they may be laid at exposures ranging from $3\frac{1}{2}$ to 12 in.

As the shingles are applied in alternate courses, with joints broken in relation to courses above and below, the desired exposure is maintained, except where it is adjusted to line up with dormers or with the ridge line.

Because a sharp hatchet and saw are used for instant trimming, there is no necessity for special shingles on wood shingle roofs. At gables, joints are broken by using wide and narrow shingles in alternate courses. To prevent water dripping down the gables, it is a good plan to nail a length of beveled siding from eaves to ridge along the gable and nail shingles over it. This forces water onto the main body of the roof, and the slight elevation is imperceptible from the ground.

Though it is difficult to avoid lining up an occasional joint, applicators should avoid matching joints of shingles in any three courses. This is important because a leak is unavoidable if a shingle splits on a line between the joints in alternate courses.

To avoid such splits, nails should never be introduced in the center of a shingle—no matter how wide the shingle. There is the additional hazard that a center-nailed shingle may have a joint above it, exposing the nail to the weather, to corrosion, and to an eventual leak.

Only the widest shingles should be used on valley sides. For ridges and hips, the shingles themselves are employed, the best construction being a modified Boston hip. Hip and ridge shingles should be not less than 5 in. wide. To avoid waste, shingles of this width should be selected from the random widths available. Hip and ridge shingles should be applied horizontally and allowed to project above the ridge shingle on the other side of the roof, the projection being chipped and shaved off with the shingler's hatchet. The hip shingles should be applied so that the shingles are woven in a weathertight pattern. (A. G. H. Dietz, "Dwelling House Construction," D. Van Nostrand Company, Inc., Princeton, N.J.)

15-16. Flashings. As the result of shrinkage of material, there is a natural weakness at all intersecting surfaces. Contraction, expansion, and movement of the building all play a part in contributing to this weakness. The largest percentage of roof leaks occurs at the junction of walls, skylights, and other roof projections, in part because of faulty design or application of flashing materials. Such vulnerable points should receive special attention.

Whenever a sharp angle is introduced into roof or wall construction—in fact, at almost all intersecting planes—flashing is necessary to waterproof the angle. Since movement is to be expected at intersecting planes, flashing should be made of some fairly elastic material, or fashioned so that there is room for movement.

All flashing material is affected by the expansion and contraction of the material itself and by similar forces in the material with which it is in contact. These forces tend to pull the flashing away from the wall, leaving a gap through which water can find its way back of the flashing into the wall.

Bituminous flashings have the ability to hug tight against the wall when applied properly. Metal flashings, on the other hand, require added protection in the shape of "cap flashing" installed above and covering the top edge of the base flashing. If the flashing should pull away from the wall, there will be no gap through which water can pass to the rear.

On flat roof decks, installation of flashing is a fairly simple matter, base flashings of bituminous materials or metal being applied so that at least 6 in. of the material is secured to the roof deck and 8 in. to the wall. Counterflashing should be installed above it. Not less than $1\frac{1}{2}$ in. of the material should enter a raggle cut into a mortar line between the nearest row of bricks above the base flashing, and not less than 4 in. of the flashing should hang vertically down the wall.

On steep roofs, recourse must be had to step-flashing procedures, which entails cutting short pieces of flashing metal, bending them at right angles, and sandwiching one flange between every roofing unit adjacent to the intersecting surface, the remaining flange being in contact with the vertical plane.

In the application of the flashing units, care must be taken to see that each unit laps the unit below by at least 2 in. Thus, water traveling downward will be conducted from one metal unit to another, and should water get under the shingles or other roofing material, the sandwiched metal will conduct it safely back to the surface.

Counterflashing is installed above the base flashing in a series of steps dictated by the slope of the roof and the mortar-line raggles into which the counterflashing is inserted.

Chimneys projecting through one side of a sloping roof require the building of a cricket, or flashing saddle, behind the chimney. Ordinary methods of flashing are not suitable in a location where water propelled by a 15 mph wind can build up to a depth of 18 in. or more within minutes.

The word "saddle" is an apt description of the sheet-metal flashing designed for chimney backs. It takes the form of an equestrian saddle or a miniature roof with ridge and two valleys built to divide the streams of water traveling down the roof and conduct them away from the chimney instead of pocketing behind the chimney.

The saddle should be securely soldered to a base step flashing behind the chimney. Because of the severe punishment they take, saddles should be fabricated of heavy-gage metals, highly resistant to corrosion.

Where roofs intersect, special precautions are necessary to design a waterproof roof. It is obvious that, where the intersecting planes meet at the aptly named "valley," the area receives twice as much rain water as flows down the main roof area.

Bituminous valley materials should be laid in two plies at this vulnerable point—an 18-in.-wide base sheet followed by a 35-in. mineral-surfaced top sheet.

Valley metal should be at least 12 in. wide and preferably wider. To guard against water building up in the valley, metal should be folded back 1 in. to act both as a barrier to infiltrating water and as a device in which fastening clips can be hooked. Metal valleys, because of expansion and contraction, should be fastened not directly to the deck, but through nailing clips.

Section 16

BUILDERS' HARDWARE

RAYMOND V. MILLER

Director of Research and Development
George A. Fuller Company
New York, N.Y.

Hardware is a general term covering a wide variety of fastenings and gadgets. By builders' hardware we usually mean items made of metal or plastics ordinarily used in building construction. By common usage, the term builders' hardware generally includes rough hardware and finishing hardware.

In point of cost, the finishing hardware for a building represents a relatively small part of the finished structure. But the judicious selection of suitable items of hardware for all the many conditions encountered in construction and use of any building can mean a great deal over the years in lessened installation and maintenance costs and general satisfaction.

To make the best selection of hardware requires some knowledge of the various alternates available and the operating features afforded by each type. In this section, pertinent points relating to selecting, ordering, and installing some of the more commonly used building hardware items are discussed briefly.

16-1. Finishing and Rough Hardware. Finishing hardware consists of items that are made in attractive shapes and finishes and that are usually visible as an integral part of the completed building. Included are locks, hinges, door pulls, cabinet hardware, window fastenings, casement-sash adjusters, door closers and checks, door holders, automatic exit devices, and lock-operating trim, such as knobs and handles, escutcheon plates, strike plates, and knob rosettes. In addition, there are push plates, push bars, kick plates, door stops, and flush bolts.

Included in rough hardware are utility items not usually finished for attractive appearance, such as fastenings and hangers of many types, shapes, and sizes—nails, screws, bolts, studs secured by electric welding guns, studs secured by powder-actuated cartridge guns, inserts, anchor bolts, straps, expansion bolts and screws, toggle bolts, sash balances and pulleys, casement and special window hardware, sliding-door and folding-door supports, and fastenings for screens, storm sash, shades, venetian blinds, and awnings.

16-2. When to Select Hardware. An important point to bear in mind in connection with selection of hardware for a new building is that, in many instances, it is one of the earliest decisions that should be made, particularly when doors and windows are to be of metal. This is true despite the fact that the finished hardware may not actually be applied until near the end of the construction period.

Metal door bucks and window frames, for example, are among the first things that are needed on the job after construction gets above the first floor. These bucks and frames cannot be designed until the exact hardware to be applied to them has been decided on in detail, and precise template information has been obtained from the hardware manufacturer. Even after all the shop drawings for these items have been completely detailed, revised, and approved by the architect, it usually takes a considerable period of time to have them manufactured and delivered to the building site. Furthermore, the particular type of finishing hardware selected may also require considerable time to manufacture. Yet, if the frames are not available on the job during the early stages, work on the exterior walls and interior partitions cannot proceed. The delay would, of course, set back progress on the entire building. So it is wise to select the hardware and design the bucks and frames as soon as possible.

A good deal of time and expense can sometimes be saved on these metal frames by specifying plain, flush frames of standard design. If any fancy trim is desired, it is often advisable to have this separately made and applied later. Such trim may well be of wood; its fabrication will not delay delivery of the frames that must be built into the walls and partitions as they progress.

16-3. Function of Hardware Consultants. In view of the wide variety of types, styles, materials, and finishes found in the numerous items comprising finishing hardware, it is advisable to call in a hardware consultant or manufacturer's representative before specifications are made in too great detail. He is in the best position to streamline the requirements, to obtain the desired result in the simplest, most economical and satisfactory manner. In this way, one can often avoid unnecessary delay and complications.

It is well to remember that what was standard a short time ago may now be out of regular production. A hardware consultant should be able to advise on the selection of stock items.

Advance study with a representative of the manufacturer usually has another distinct advantage; he can often point out how definite savings can be achieved by making slight changes in the specifications. In many instances, these changes may mean little or nothing to the owner of the building and may be just as acceptable to him as what was originally specified. To the manufacturer, however, these minor changes may mean a great deal in what he can contribute to faster progress and lower ultimate cost of the completed work.

16-4. Factors Affecting Selection of Hardware. The operating characteristics of hardware items, of course, govern their selection, according to the particular requirements in each case. Then, the question of material, such as plastics, brass, bronze, aluminum, or steel can be settled, as well as the finish desired. Selection of material and finish depends on the architectural treatment and decorative scheme:

Wrought, cast, and stamped parts are available for different items. Finishes include highly polished, polished, satin, and dull; also oxidized. Plated finishes include polished and plated, and highly polished and heavily plated. When solid metal is desired rather than a surface finish that is plated on iron or steel, the order should definitely specify "solid."

United States government standards defining characteristics, sizes, dimensions, and spacings of holes, materials, and finishes for many items can assist greatly in identification and proper fit of hardware items to the parts on which they will be mounted.

16-5. Template and Nontemplate Hardware. For hardware items that are to be fastened to metal parts, such as jambs or doors, so-called template hardware is used. Template items are made to a close tolerance to agree exactly with drawings furnished by the manufacturer. The sizes, shapes, location, and size of holes in this type of hardware are made to conform so accurately to the standard drawings that the ultimate fit of all associated parts is assured. In the case of hinges or butts, holes that are template-drilled usually form a crescent-shaped pattern (Fig. 16-4a); when these holes are staggered, on the other hand, the hardware is nontemplate.

Hardware for stock is usually nontemplate; however, certain lines are all template-made, whether for stock or for a specific order. Nontemplate items may vary somewhat and may not fit into a template cutout.

For use on wood or metal-covered doors, template drilling is not necessary; nontemplate hardware of the same type and finish can be used. Nontemplate hardware has the advantage that it may be available in stock, whereas template items might take some time to obtain. Generally, there is no price difference between template and nontemplate items, except for template hinges, which cost slightly more than nontemplate.

FINISHING HARDWARE

16-6. Hinges and Butts. A hinge is a device permitting one part to turn on another. In building hardware, the two parts are metal plates known as leaves. They are joined together by a pin, which passes through the knuckle joints.

When the leaves are in the form of elongated straps, the device is usually called a hinge (Figs. 16-1 and 16-2). This type is suitable for mounting on the surface of a door.

When the device is to be mounted on the edge of a door, the length of the leaves must be shortened, because they cannot exceed the thickness of the door. The leaves

FIG. 16-1   FIG. 16-2

FIG. 16-1. Heavy strap hinge. (*C. Hager & Sons Hinge Mfg. Co.*)
FIG. 16-2. Heavy tee hinge. (*C. Hager & Sons Hinge Mfg. Co.*)

thus retain only the portion near the pin, or butt end, of the hinge (Figs. 16-3 to 16-5). Thus, hinges applied to the edge of a door have come to be known as butts, or butt hinges.

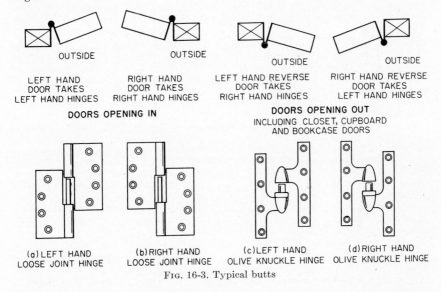

OUTSIDE   OUTSIDE   OUTSIDE   OUTSIDE

LEFT HAND   RIGHT HAND   LEFT HAND REVERSE   RIGHT HAND REVERSE
DOOR TAKES   DOOR TAKES   DOOR TAKES   DOOR TAKES
LEFT HAND HINGES   RIGHT HAND HINGES   RIGHT HAND HINGES   LEFT HAND HINGES

DOORS OPENING IN   **DOORS OPENING OUT**
                                  INCLUDING CLOSET, CUPBOARD
                                  AND BOOKCASE DOORS

(a) LEFT HAND   (b) RIGHT HAND   (c) LEFT HAND   (d) RIGHT HAND
LOOSE JOINT HINGE   LOOSE JOINT HINGE   OLIVE KNUCKLE HINGE   OLIVE KNUCKLE HINGE

FIG. 16-3. Typical butts.

Butts are usually mortised into the edge of the door. They are the type of hinge most commonly used in present-day buildings.

Sizes of butt hinges vary from about 2 to 6 in., and sometimes to 8 in. Length of hinge is usually made the same as the width; but they can be had in other widths. Sometimes, on account of projecting trim, special sizes, such as 5 × 4½ in., are used.

When soft metal such as brass or bronze is used for butts, it is customary to employ steel bushings around the pin to reduce wear. For the larger, thicker, and heavier doors receiving high-frequency service, and for doors requiring silent operation, ball-bearing butts (Fig. 16-4) or butts with Oilite bearings are generally used. It is also customary to use ball-bearing butts wherever a door closer is specified. On some butts, Oilite bronze bushings for the pin are used to take care of lateral wear, in addition to the ball bearings carrying the vertical load. In these cases the additional wearing value far exceeds the small extra cost.

Plain bearings (Fig. 16-5) are recommended for residential work. The lateral thrust of the pin should bear on hardened steel, not on soft brass.

Unusual conditions may dictate the use of extra-heavy hinges or ball bearings where normal hinges would otherwise be used. One such case occurred in a group of college dormitories where many of the doors developed an out-of-plumb condition that prevented proper closing. It was discovered that the students had been using the doors as swings. Heavier hinges with stronger fastenings eliminated the trouble.

Ball bearings usually project somewhat from the hinge barrel; but in some types they are concealed. The latter type eliminates a dust-catching surface, but it has a barrel of larger diameter.

Two-bearing and four-bearing butt hinges should be selected, as dictated by weight of doors, frequency of use, and need for maintaining continued floating, silent operation. Because most types of butt hinges may be mounted on either right-hand or left-hand doors, it should be remembered that the number of bearing units actually supporting the thrust of the vertical load is only one-half the bearing units available. With a two-bearing butt, for example, only one of the bearings carries the vertical

(a) TEMPLATE HINGE

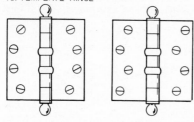

(b) NON-TEMPLATE HINGE

FIG. 16-4. Ball-bearing butts: (a) with template drilling; (b) with nontemplate drilling.

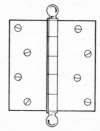

FIG. 16-5. Plain bearing butt (non-template shown).

load, and with a four-bearing butt, only two carry the load. It should be noted, however, that some hinges, particularly olive knuckle hinges (Fig. 16-3c and d), which are frequently used on high-grade work, are "handed" and must be specified for use on either a right-hand or left-hand door. The loose-joint hinge (Fig. 16-3a and b) is also "handed."

When butts are ordered for metal doors and jambs, "all machine screws" should be specified.

16-7. Location of Hinges. One rule for locating hinges is to allow 5 in. from rabbet of head jamb to top edge of top hinge and 10 in. from finished floor line to bottom of bottom hinge. If a third hinge is used it should be spaced equidistant between top and bottom hinges.

16-8. Types of Hinge Pins. A very important element in the selection of hinges is the hinge pin. It may be either a loose pin or a fast pin.

Loose pins are generally used wherever practicable, because they simplify the hanging of doors. There are four basic pin types:

1. Ordinary loose pins.
2. Nonrising loose pins.
3. Nonremovable loose pins.
4. Fast (or tight) pins.

The **ordinary loose pin** can be pulled out of the hinge barrel so that the leaves may be separated. Thus, the leaves may be installed on the door and jamb independently, with ease and "mass-production" economy. However, these pins have a tendency—with resulting difficulties—of working upward and out of the barrel of the hinge. This "climbing" is caused by the constant twisting of the pin due to opening and closing the door.   Present-day manufacture of hinges has tended to drift away from this type of pin, which is now found only in hinges in the lowest price scale.

The **nonrising loose pin** (or self-retaining pin) has all the advantages of the ordinary loose pin; but at the same time, the disadvantage of "climbing" is eliminated.   The method of accomplishing the nonrising feature varies with the type of hinge and its manufacture.

The **nonremovable loose pin** is generally used in hinges on entrance doors, or doors of locked spaces, which open out and on which the barrel of the hinge is therefore on the outside of the door.   If such a door were equipped with ordinary loose-pin hinges or nonrising loose-pin hinges, it would be possible to remove the pin from the barrel and lift the door out of the frame and in so doing overcome the security of the locking device on the door.   In a nonremovable loose-pin hinge, however, a setscrew in the barrel fits into a groove in the pin, thereby preventing its removal.   The setscrew is so placed in the barrel of the hinge that it becomes inaccessible when the door is closed. This type of hinge offers the advantage of the ordinary loose-pin type plus the feature of security on doors opening out.

The **fast (or tight) pin** is permanently set in the barrel of the hinge at the time of manufacture.   Such pins cannot be removed without damaging the hinge.   They are regularly furnished in hospital- or asylum-type hinges.   The fact that the leaves of this type of hinge cannot be separated, however, makes the installation more difficult and costly.   However, the difficulty is not too great, because with this type of hinge

Table 16-1. Hinge Sizes for Doors
Hinge Lengths

Door thickness, in.	Door width or transom height, in.	Height of butt hinges (length of joint), in.
$\frac{3}{4}$ and $\frac{7}{8}$ cupboard doors............	24 or less	$2\frac{1}{2}$
$\frac{7}{8}$ and $1\frac{1}{8}$ screen doors..............	36 or less	3
$1\frac{1}{8}$ doors..........................	36 or less	$3\frac{1}{2}$
$1\frac{1}{4}$ and $1\frac{3}{8}$ doors..................	32 or less	$3\frac{1}{2}$
	32–37	4
$1\frac{9}{16}$, $1\frac{3}{4}$, and $1\frac{7}{8}$ doors............	32 or less	$4\frac{1}{2}$
	32–37	5
	37–43	5*
	43–50	6*
2, $2\frac{1}{4}$, and $2\frac{1}{2}$ doors...............	43 or less	5*
	43–50	6*
$1\frac{1}{4}$ and $1\frac{3}{8}$ transoms...............	20 or less	$2\frac{1}{2}$
	20–36	3
$1\frac{1}{2}$, $1\frac{9}{16}$, $1\frac{3}{4}$, and $1\frac{7}{8}$ transoms.....	20 or less	3
	20–36	$3\frac{1}{2}$
2, $2\frac{1}{4}$, and $2\frac{1}{2}$ transoms............	20 or less	$3\frac{1}{2}$
	20–36	4

Hinge Widths (Full Mortise)†

Door thickness, in.	Hinge width (P = trim projection)
$1\frac{3}{8}$	$2\frac{1}{4} + P$
$1\frac{3}{4}$	$3 + P$
2	$3\frac{1}{2} + P$
$2\frac{1}{4}$	$4 + P$
$2\frac{1}{2}$	$4\frac{1}{4} + P$
$2\frac{3}{4}$	$4\frac{3}{4} + P$
3	$5\frac{1}{4} + P$

* Extra heavy.
† If table width falls between regular hinge sizes, use nearest larger size.   For doors up to $2\frac{1}{4}$ in. thick, hinges are assumed set back $\frac{1}{4}$ in. from door edge; for doors $2\frac{1}{2}$ to 3 in. thick, $\frac{3}{8}$ in.   Hinge widths of half-mortise, half-surface, and full-surface hinges are standard and depend on hinge length.

it is only necessary to hold the door in position while the screws for the jamb leaf are being inserted.

Ends of pins are finished in different ways. Shapes include flat-button, ball, oval-head, modern, cone, and steeple. They can be chosen to conform with type of archi-tecture and decoration. Flat-button tips are generally standard and are supplied unless otherwise specified.

16-9. How to Select Hinges. One hinge means one pair of leaves connected with a pin. The number of hinges required per door depends on the size and weight of the door, and sometimes on conditions of use. A general rule recommends two butt hinges on doors up to 60 in. high; three hinges on doors 60 to 90 in. high; and four hinges on doors from 90 to 120 in. high.

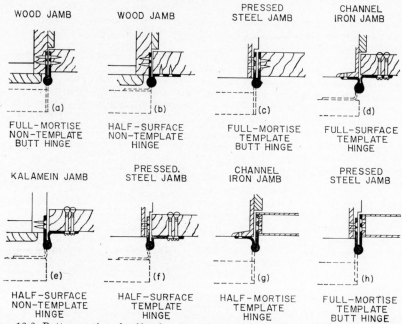

FIG. 16-6. Butt-mounting classification depends on where and how butt is fastened: (a), (c), and (h), full mortise; (d), full surface; (b), (e), and (f), half surface; and (g), half mortise.

Table 16-1 gives general recommendations covering the selection of suitable butt hinges.

For transoms, butt hinges can be either on the top or the bottom. The transom lifter or adjusting device may be any one of several types, as desired. Orders should definitely specify which location and which type.

The proper operating clearance between the hinged edge of a door and the jamb is taken care of in the manufacture of the butt hinges by "swaging" or slightly bending the leaves of the butts near the pin. Since the amount of such bending required is determined by whether one or both leaves are to be mortised or surface-mounted, it is important in ordering butt hinges to specify the type of butt needed to satisfy mount-ing conditions. If hinge leaves are to be mortised into both the edge of the door and the jamb, a full-mortise hinge is required (Fig. 16-6a, c, and h). If leaves are to be surface-applied to both the side of the door and the face of the jamb, a full-surface hinge is needed (Fig. 16-6d). If one leaf is to be surface-applied and the other mortised, the hinge is a half-surface hinge or a half-mortise hinge, depending on how the leaf for the door is to be applied—half-surface if applied to door surface (Fig. 16-6b, e, and f) and half-mortise if mortised in the door end (Fig. 16-6g).

Where door-closing devices are not installed and where quiet is demanded, as in hospitals, friction hinges or door-control hinges may be used to prevent slamming. They will cause the door to remain in any position. Only slight hand pressure is required to close it.

Exterior doors should have butts of nonferrous metal. Although chromium plating does not tarnish, it is not considered to be satisfactory on steel for exterior use. Interior doors in rooms where dampness and steam may occur should be of nonferrous metal and should also have butts of nonferrous metal. Butts for other interior work may be of ferrous metal.

Ferrous-metal butts should be of hardened cold-rolled steel. Where doors and door frames are to be painted at the job site, butts should be supplied with a prime-coat finish. For doors and trim that are to be stained and varnished, butts are usually plated.

Other types of hinges include some with a spring that keeps the door shut. They may be either single- or double-acting. The spring may be incorporated in a hinge mounted on the door in the usual manner, or it may be associated with a pivot at the bottom of the door. In the latter case, the assembly may be of the type that is mortised into the bottom of the door, or it may be entirely below the floor.

16-10. Door-closing Devices. These include overhead closers and floor-type closers (sometimes referred to as floor checks). These are some of the hardest-worked items in most buildings. To get the most satisfactory operation at low first cost and low maintenance cost, each closer should be carefully selected and installed to suit the particular requirements and conditions at each door.

Most of these devices are a combination of a spring—the closing element—and an oil-cushioned piston, which dampens the closing action, inside a cylinder (Fig. 16-7). The piston operates with a crank or a rack-and-pinion action. It displaces the fluid through ports in the cylinder wall, which are closed or open according to the position of the piston in the cylinder. Opening of the door energizes the spring, thus storing up closing power. Adjustment screws are provided to change the size of the ports, controlling flow of fluid. This arrangement makes the closer extremely responsive to the conditions of service at each individual door and permits a quiet closure, which at the same time insures positive latching of the door.

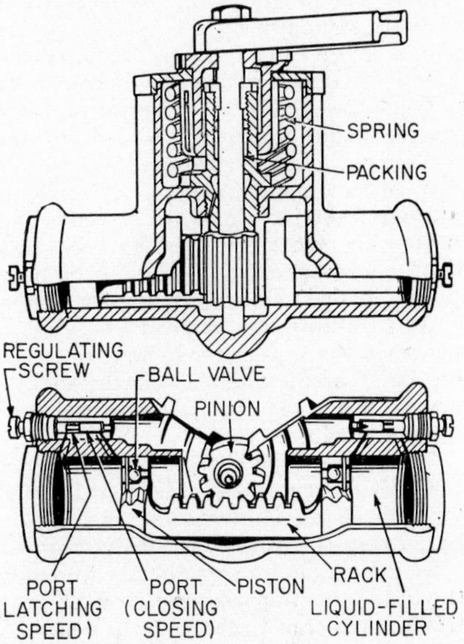

FIG. 16-7. Door closer—spring closes the door, while hydraulic mechanism (cylinder with piston) keeps the door from slamming.

While the fluid type of closer is preferred, pneumatic closers are also used, particularly for light doors, like screen doors.

Overhead door closers are installed in different ways, either on the hinge side of the door or on a bracket secured to the door frame on the stop side. Various types of brackets are available for different conditions. Also, when it is desired to install a closer between two doors hung from the same frame, or on the inside of a door that opens out, an arrangement with a parallel arm makes this possible. Other types of closers may be partly mortised into the door or housed in the head above the door.

Closers may be semiconcealed or fully concealed. Total concealment greatly enhances appearance but certain features of fine adjustment and operation are limited.

An exposed-type closer should be mounted on the door unless there is real need for a bracket mounting. Brackets are needed to keep the outside or hinge face of the door clear, for either appearance or protection; e.g., for an exterior door. When a bracket is considered, the effect on the closer's leverage, or usable power, should be carefully evaluated.

The bracket mounting that allows a closer to do the best job is a soffit bracket secured as close as possible to the face of the door and located at the precise distance from the hinge edge of the door recommended by the manufacturer. A soffit bracket, however, may obstruct the head of the opening more than is desirable. In that event, a corner bracket may be used. It places the closer nearer to the hinge edge of the door. But that type of bracket yields less power than the soffit bracket and limits the door opening to about 140°. If traffic requires a wider swing, a special type of corner bracket has to be used. However, this special bracket places the closer so near to the hinge edge of the door that operation is severely handicapped.

Whereas the use of brackets reduces headroom and may become a hazard, a parallel arm closer mounted on the door rides out with the door, leaving the opening entirely clear. The parallel arm, however, has the disadvantage of poor leverage.

When standard, surface-applied, exposed door closers are used, careful consideration should be given to the space required in order that doors may be opened at least 90° before the closers strike an adjacent wall or partition.

Semiconcealed door closers are recommended for hollow metal doors. These closers should be partly mortised into the upper door rail.

Various hold-open features also are available in different closer combinations to meet specific requirements. A fusible link closer is a type that is used to close a door automatically in case of fire. It acts like an ordinary hold-open arm closer until fire-heated air enters the doorway. At 160°F the link breaks and the closer shuts the door. Another available feature is delayed action. This allows plenty of time to push a loaded vehicle through the opening before the door closes.

A hydro-hinge is a hinge in which a door-closing device is incorporated. A spring is placed in the top hinge, a checking device in the bottom hinge. This hydro-hinge is especially useful where a conventional door closer cannot be installed or where good appearance is required; also for half doors, gates, or partition doors where closers of conventional type cannot be installed because of physical conditions.

When floor-type checking and closing devices are used, floor conditions should be carefully determined in order that there will be sufficient unobstructed depth available for their installation. Closers concealed in the floor tend to foul up faster than over-head types (because of scrub water and floor dirt) and are more expensive to install.

To get maximum performance from any door closer it must be of ample size to meet the conditions imposed on it. If abnormal conditions exist, such as drafts or severe traffic, a closer of larger than the normal capacity should be employed. Installing too small a closer is an invitation to trouble. Manufacturers' charts should be used to determine the proper sizes and types of closers to suit door sizes and job conditions.

It is very important that door closers be installed precisely as recommended by the manufacturer. Experience has shown that a large percentage of troubles with closers results from disregard of mounting instructions.

16-11. Locks and Latches. The function of locks and latches is to hold doors in a closed position. Those known as rim locks or latches are fastened on the surface of the door. The ones that are mortised into the edge of the door are known as mortise locks or latches.

When the locking bolt is beveled, the device is usually referred to as a latch; such a bolt automatically slides into position when the door is closed. A latch is usually operated by a knob or lever. Sometimes it may be opened with a key on the other side. Night latches came to be so called because they are generally used at night with other ordinary locks to give additional security.

Latches must of course take into account the hand of the door so the bevel will be right. A large percentage of latches are "reversible"—that is, they may be used on a right- or left-hand door (Art. 16-12). It is well, however, when ordering any lock to specify the hand of the door on which it is to be used.

When the locking bolt is rectangular in shape, it does not slide into position automatically when the door is closed; it must be projected or retracted by a thumb turn or key. This type of bolt is referred to as a dead bolt, and the lock as a dead lock. It may be worked with a key from one or both sides. Such a bolt is often used in conjunction with a latch. When latch bolts and dead bolts are combined into one unit, it is known as a lock.

All locks and latches have springs built into them to return the respective parts to normal position after the key or knob has been operated.

Various combinations of latches, dead bolts, knobs and keys, and locking buttons are applied to all types and kinds of doors. The exact combination most suitable for any given door is determined by a careful analysis of the use to which the door is to be put.

A point to bear in mind is that a uniform size should be selected, if practicable, for a project, no matter what the individual functions of the different locks may be. This makes possible the use of standard-size cutouts or sinkages on each installation. When this is done, not only is the cost of installation reduced, but any changes that may be made in the drawings as the job

progresses, or any changes that may have to be made later are simplified, and special hardware is avoided.

Unit locks (Fig. 16-8) are complete assemblies that eliminate most of the adjustments during installation that would otherwise be necessary. These locks have merely to be slipped into a standard notch cut into a wood door or formed in a metal door.

Bored-in locks are another type that can be installed by boring standard-size holes in wood doors or by having uniform circular holes formed in metal doors. These bored-in locks are often referred to as

Fig. 16-8. Unit lock.   (*Russwin Co.*)

tubular-lock sets or cylindrical-lock sets depending on how the holes have to be bored to accommodate them.

Tubular locks have a tubular case extending horizontally at right angles to the edge of the door. This type of case requires a horizontal hole of small diameter to be bored into the door at right angles to the vertical edge of the door; another small hole is required at right angles to the first hole to take care of the locking cylinder.

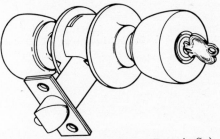

Fig. 16-9. Cylindrical lock.   (*Russwin Co.*)

Cylindrical locks (Fig. 16-9), the other type of bored-in lock, have a cylindrical case. requiring a relatively large-diameter hole in the door, bored perpendicular to the face of the door. This hole accommodates the main body of the lock. A hole of smaller diameter to take the bolt is required to be bored at right angles to the edge of the door.

When bored-in locks are used in hollow metal doors, a reinforcing unit is required in the door. This unit may be supplied by either the door or hardware manufacturer.

Locks are further classified according to the type of key required to retract the bolts. On all but the cheaper installations the principal type of key used is the cylinder key, which operates a pin-tumbler cylinder. Bit-key locks formerly were popular, but are being largely supplanted by bored-in-type locks.

In cylindrical locks, the locking cylinder, which is the assembly that supplies the security feature of the lock, is a cylindrical shell with rotatable barrel inside. The barrel has a longitudinal slot or keyway formed in it. The cross section of the keyway for every lock has a shape requiring a similarly designed key. Several holes (usually five or six) are bored through the shell and into the barrel at right angles to the axis of the barrel (Fig. 16-10). In each hole is placed a pair of pins—a driver pin in the shell

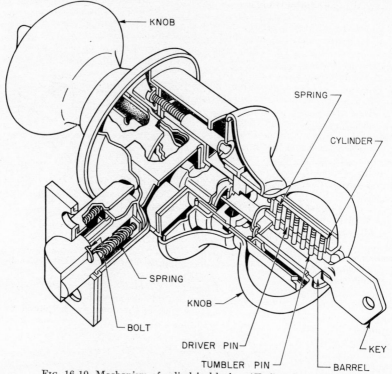

KNOB

SPRING

CYLINDER

SPRING

KNOB

BOLT

DRIVER PIN

TUMBLER PIN

KEY

BARREL

Fig. 16-10. Mechanism of cylindrical lock. (*Kwikset Locks, Inc.*)

end and a tumbler pin in the barrel end. Pins vary in length, and the combination of lengths differs from that of pins in other locks. A spring mounted in the shell end of each hole behind each driver pin forces these pins into the hole in the barrel, so that normally they are partly in the barrel portion of the hole and partly in the shell portion. Thus, the barrel is prevented from rotating in the shell to operate the bolt, and the door remains locked.

Keys have notches spaced along one side to correspond with the spacing of the pins. When a key is inserted in the slot in the barrel, each notch forces a tumbler pin back, against pressure from the spring. When the proper key is inserted in the slot, each notch pushes its corresponding pair of pins just far enough back into the shell to bring the junction point of that pair exactly at the circumference of the barrel. The barrel then can be rotated within the shell by merely turning the key.

Turning the key operates a cam attached to the end of the barrel that withdraws the bolt from its locked position.

The security feature of the cylinder lock results from the fact that only one series of notches in the key will correspond exactly to the respective lengths of the several individual pins. With as many as five or six tumblers, it is apparent that innumerable combinations are available.

By using split pins, different keyways, and various sizes and arrangements of the pins, master keying and grand master keying of cylinder locks is made possible. Thus one master key may be made to open all the separate locks on each floor of a building, while a grand master key will open any lock on any floor of that building. In case there are a number of such buildings in a group, a great-grand master key can be made that will open any door on any floor of any building in the group.

16-12. Hand of Doors. As you look at a door, the hinges can be either on your right or left, and the door can open either away from or toward you. Because of the fact that it is from the outside of a door that the lock is operated by a key, it is customary to speak of the hand of a door as viewed from the outside—the side on which protection is needed against unauthorized entry. In a series of connecting rooms, the outside of each door is considered to be the side you first approach as you proceed into the rooms from the entrance.

If when you are standing outside the door the hinges are to your right and the door opens away from you, it is a right-hand, regular-bevel door; if the door opens toward you, it is a right-hand, reverse-bevel door. Similarly, if when you are outside the door, the hinges are to your left and the door swings away from you, it is a left-hand, regular-bevel door; if the door opens toward you, it is a left-hand, reverse-bevel door (Fig. 16-11).

In ordering hardware, the hand of the door must be given; also, whether the beveled face of the latch bolt has to be regular-beveled or reverse-beveled. In some cases, the face is reversible, but it is best to state the bevel definitely anyway. For closet and cabinet doors, which never open away from you, it is sufficient to state merely whether the hand of these doors is right or left and the fact that they are closet or cabinet doors. It is then understood that reverse-beveled latch bolts are required.

For casement sash, the hand is stated a little differently; it is safest to specify

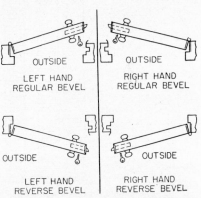

FIG. 16-11. Conventional method for determining hand of doors and bevel.

whether the hinges are on the right or on the left as viewed from the room side, and also whether the sash opens in or out.

16-13. Casement-sash Operators. There are many types of devices for operating casement sash. Some of these require that screens have openings to make the operating handle accessible. Other types, which operate independently of the screens, have an interior crank that actuates a worm gear. Various arrangements of arms actuated by the gear are used to move the sash.

16-14. Sliding Hardware. Hardware for interior and exterior sliding doors and screens ranges from light to heavy. Hangers, tracks, and wheels are of various designs to serve different requirements. Ball bearings and composition wheels are generally used. The tracks and hangers are often made of aluminum, especially for the lighter installations. Because of the wide choice, a careful examination of the features peculiar to each design is well worthwhile before a decision is made.

16-15. Folding-door Hardware. Folding doors require special supports and tracks because of their wide range of movement and their heavy weight. The piano hinges that are best for folding-door hinges are often not a stock item. These may require considerable time to fabricate; early selection and placing of the order are recommended.

16-16. Locking Bolts (Doors and Windows). Various types of bolts and rods are fastened to doors and windows for the purpose of securing them in closed position or to other doors and windows.

Top and bottom vertical bolts operated by a knob located at convenient height between them are known as **cremorne bolts.**

Fire-exit bolts, also known as **panic bolts,** are required on exit doors in public buildings. These bolts have a horizontal bar, movable up and down, on the inside of each door and running the full width of the door; they are arranged to open the doors as soon as downward pressure is applied to any part of the bar. These bolts also have various arrangements for entering with a key from the outside, and also for locking the door on the inside.

ROUGH HARDWARE

16-17. Window Hardware. Sash balances are commonly used with double-hung windows as counterweights instead of weights and pulleys. Some balances have tape or cable with clock-type springs, which coil and uncoil as the sash is raised and lowered. Another type employs torsion springs with one end fixed to the side jamb of the window and the other arranged to turn as the sash goes up or down. The turning device in this type of balance may be a slide working in a rotatable spiral tube, or it may be a slotted bushing attached to the free end of the spring and fitted around a vertical rod attached to the sash. This rod (Fig. 16-12) is a flat piece of metal twisted into a spiral shape. The up-and-down movement of the sash causes the slotted bushing to revolve on its spiral sliding rod, thus winding and unwinding the spring. Still another type utilizes a vertical tension spring of the ordinary coil variety. One end of the spring is fixed and the other is fastened to the sash; the spring stretches or compresses in a vertical direction as the sash is moved up or down.

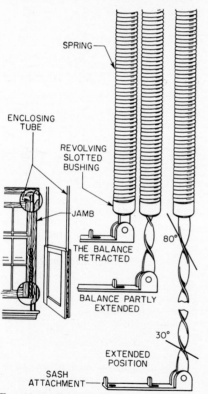

FIG. 16-12. Constant-tension sash balance. (*Unique Balance Co.*)

Some sash balances combine weather stripping with the balances. Others have friction devices to hold the sash in the desired position.

One patented type of sash balance known as the Unique sash balance incorporates a clever counterbalancing feature by making a change in the degree of pitch of the spiral rod from top to bottom, thereby controlling the increase and decrease of spring tension (Fig. 16-12). The pitch varies from 30 to 80°. As the spring turns, the changing spring tension is automatically compensated for by the variable pitch of the spiral rod sliding through the slotted bushing on the end of the spring. Thus the tension is equalized at every point of operation. This automatically prevents the sash from creeping or dropping of its own accord, without the necessity of introducing friction devices that interfere with easy operation.

Two sash balances are used per sash (one on each side) or four balances per double-hung window.

Other window hardware—locks, sash pulls, sash weights, and pulleys—are simple items, supplied as standard items with specific windows.

16-18. Inserts, Anchors, and Hangers. Metal inserts of various types are cast into concrete floor slabs to serve as hangers or connectors for other parts of the structure that will be supported from the floor system. These inserts include electric conduit and junction boxes, supports for hung ceilings, slots for pipe hangers, fastenings for door closers to be set under the floor, and circular metal shapes for vertical pipe openings.

Metal anchors of various types are used in building construction. Each type is specially shaped, according to the purpose served. These include anchors for securing stone facings to masonry walls, anchors for fastening marble slabs in place, column anchor bolts set in foundations, and anchor bolts for fastening sills to masonry.

Joist hangers are used for framing wood joists into girders and for framing headers into joists around stairwells and chimneys.

16-19. Nails. Wire nails, made of mild steel, are commonly used for most nailing purposes. Cylindrical in shape, they are stronger for driving than cut nails and are not so liable to bend when driven into hardwoods.

Cut nails, sheared from steel plate, are flat and tapered. They have holding power considerably greater than wire nails. They are usually preferred to wire nails for fastening wood battens to plaster; also in places where there is danger that the nails may be drawn out by direct pull. They are frequently used for driving into material other than wood. They are generally used for fastening flooring.

When driven with width parallel to grain of wood, they have less tendency to split wood than wire nails.

The length of cut and wire nails is designated by the unit "pennies." Both cut and wire nails come in sizes from 2-penny (2d) which are 1 in. long, to 60-penny (60d), which are 6 in. long. For each penny above 2, the length increases by $\frac{1}{4}$ in. up to and including the 12d, measuring $3\frac{1}{4}$ in. Above 12 some of the numbers are omitted, and the sizes increase by $\frac{1}{2}$ in. for each designation from 16d up. Thus, 16d is $3\frac{1}{2}$ in.; 20d, 4 in.; 30d, $4\frac{1}{2}$ in.; 40d, 5 in.; 50d, $5\frac{1}{2}$ in.; and 60 d, 6 in.

Above 6 in., the fasteners are called **spikes.** They run in 7-, 8-, 9-, 10-, and 12-in. lengths.

Various gages or thicknesses of nails, and different sizes and shapes of heads and points (Figs. 16-13 and 16-14) are

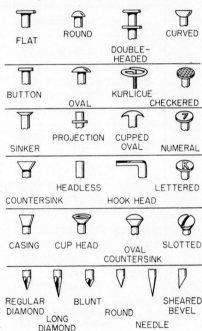

Fig. 16-13. Nail heads and points.

available in both wire and cut nails. Certain types have distinguishing names. For example, the term **brads** is applied to thin nails with small heads, suitable for small finish work.

Common brads are the same thickness as common nails but have different heads and points. **Clout nails** have broad flat heads. They are used mostly for securing gutters and metalwork.

Casing nails are about half a gage thinner than common wire nails of the same length; **finishing nails,** in turn, are about half a gage thinner than casing nails of the same length. **Shingle nails** are half a gage to a full gage thicker than common nails of the same length.

Certain manufacturers have developed nails for special purposes that hold tighter and longer. Among these are threaded nails (Fig. 16-14), which combine the ease of driving of the ordinary nail with much greater holding power.

One type is a spiral-threaded flooring nail. These nails turn as they drive, minimizing splitting of the tongues of the floor boards. These nails are said to actually grip

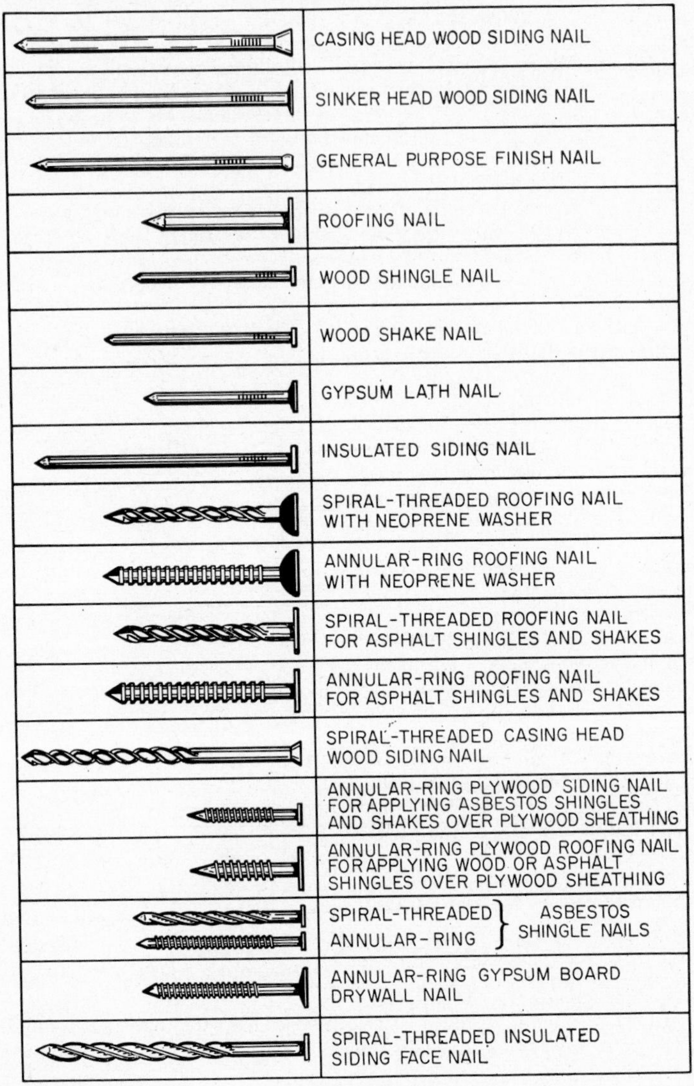

	CASING HEAD WOOD SIDING NAIL
	SINKER HEAD WOOD SIDING NAIL
	GENERAL PURPOSE FINISH NAIL
	ROOFING NAIL
	WOOD SHINGLE NAIL
	WOOD SHAKE NAIL
	GYPSUM LATH NAIL
	INSULATED SIDING NAIL
	SPIRAL-THREADED ROOFING NAIL WITH NEOPRENE WASHER
	ANNULAR-RING ROOFING NAIL WITH NEOPRENE WASHER
	SPIRAL-THREADED ROOFING NAIL FOR ASPHALT SHINGLES AND SHAKES
	ANNULAR-RING ROOFING NAIL FOR ASPHALT SHINGLES AND SHAKES
	SPIRAL-THREADED CASING HEAD WOOD SIDING NAIL
	ANNULAR-RING PLYWOOD SIDING NAIL FOR APPLYING ASBESTOS SHINGLES AND SHAKES OVER PLYWOOD SHEATHING
	ANNULAR-RING PLYWOOD ROOFING NAIL FOR APPLYING WOOD OR ASPHALT SHINGLES OVER PLYWOOD SHEATHING
	SPIRAL-THREADED ⎫ ASBESTOS ANNULAR-RING ⎬ SHINGLE NAILS
	ANNULAR-RING GYPSUM BOARD DRYWALL NAIL
	SPIRAL-THREADED INSULATED SIDING FACE NAIL

FIG. 16-14. Typical nails.

more firmly with the passage of time. A nailing machine is available for driving these nails. In one operation, it starts the nail, drives the joint between the flooring strips tight, and drives and sets the nail. With this machine, mashed tongues and marred edges of the wood are avoided.

Nails of aluminum and stainless steel are particularly useful in exposed locations where rust or corrosion of steel nails might cause unsightly stains to form on exterior finished surfaces. These nails are now made in most of the usual sizes, including special spiral-threaded nails.

Galvanized nails are used for fastening slate and shingles. These nails are sometimes used in exposed locations as protection against corrosion.

To satisfy the special requirements and varying conditions in each case, the proper nails to use for fastening various sizes and types of materials must be carefully and intelligently chosen by men experienced in this kind of work.

16-20. Screws. These are used for applying hardware of all descriptions; also for panel work, cabinet work, and all types of fine finish work. Parts of electric and

1. FLAT-HEAD WOOD SCREW
2. SHEET-METAL SCREW
3. OVAL-HEAD WOOD SCREW
4. ROUND-HEAD WOOD SCREW
5. PYRAMID-HEAD WOOD SCREW
6. PHILLIPS-HEAD WOOD SCREW
7. SPANNER-HEAD WOOD SCREW
8. FLAT-HEAD MACHINE SCREW
9 ROUND-HEAD MACHINE SCREW
10. OVAL-HEAD MACHINE SCREW
11. PHILLIPS-HEAD MACHINE SCREW
12. SPANNER-HEAD MACHINE SCREW
13. SLOTTED TWIN-HEAD MACHINE SCREW
14. OVAL-HEAD MACHINE SCREW WITH GROMMET NUT
15. LAG SCREW
16. CARRIAGE BOLT
17. FLAT-HEAD STOVE BOLT

Fig. 16-15. Typical screws.

plumbing fixtures are applied with screws. They have greater holding power than nails and permit easy removal and replacement of parts without injury to the wood or finish. Screws avoid danger of splitting the wood or marring the finish, when the screw holes are bored with a bit.

Screws are made in a large variety of sizes and shapes to suit different uses (Fig. 16-15) and they are made of different metals to match various materials. A much-used type of head, other than the ordinary single-slot type, is the **Phillips head,** which has two countersunk slots at right angles to each other. This head keeps the screw driver exactly centered during driving and also transmits greater driving power to the screw, while holding the screw driver firmly on the head. Phillips heads are smoother at the edges, because the slots in the head do not extend to the outer circumference.

Steel screws for wood vary in length from $\frac{1}{4}$ to 6 in. Each length is made in a variety of thicknesses. Heads may be ordinary flat (for countersinking), round, or oval.

Parker screws for securing objects to thin metal are self-threading when screwed into holes of exactly the correct size.

Sizes of screws are given in inches of length and in the gage of the diameter. Lengths vary by eighths of an inch up to 1 in., by quarters from there up to 3 in., and by halves from 3 to 5 in. Unlike wire gages, the smallest diameter of a screw gage is the lowest number; the larger the number, the greater is the diameter in a screw gage. Gage numbers range from 0 to 30.

Lag screws are large, heavy screws used for framing timber and ironwork. Lengths vary from 1½ to 12 in. and diameters from 5/16 to 1 in. Two holes should be bored for lag screws, one to take the unthreaded shank without binding and the other (a smaller hole) to take the threaded part. This smaller hole is usually somewhat shorter in length than the threaded portion. Lag screws usually have square heads and are tightened with a wrench.

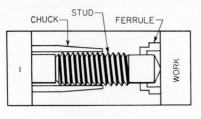
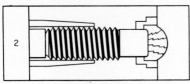
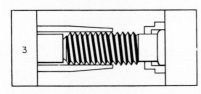
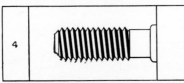

FIG. 16-16. Steps in stud welding: (1) press welding end of gun against work plate; (2) press trigger, creating an electric arc between stud and plate and melting portions of each; (3) stud is automatically plunged into molten pool; and (4) remove gun and knock off ferrule.

16-21. Welded Studs. Studs electrically welded to the steel framework of a building are often used as the primary element for securing corrugated siding and roofing, insulation, metal window frames, ornamental metal outer skins, anchorages for concrete, and other items. The welded studs thus form an integral part of the basic structure.

Many types of studs or fasteners are available, each one being designed for a particular purpose. Most of the studs have threads formed on them, either externally or internally. Some of the studs are designed to have the material impaled over them and riveted to them.

The studs are designed so as to project the exact distance desired after they have been welded. Special sealing washers and nuts are usually placed on each stud over the flat sheet of material being fastened. Tightening the nut or expanding the head of the stud with a riveting hammer then makes the fastening complete, weathertight, and secure.

Studs are usually mild steel, cadmium plated, or stainless steel. The latter is recommended for corrosive atmospheric conditions. Flux to assure a good weld is contained in the center of each stud at the welding end.

Equipment required for stud welding includes a stud-welding gun, a control unit for adjusting the amount of welding current fed to the gun, and a power source. The source of welding current may be a direct-current generator, a rectifier, or a battery unit. When a welding generator is used, the minimum National Electrical Manufacturers Association rating should be 400 amp.

The welding gun usually has a chuck for holding the stud in position for welding (Fig. 16-16), and a leg assembly holding an adjustable-length extension sleeve into which the necessary arc-shielding ferrule is inserted. Expendable ceramic arc ferrules are generally used to confine the arc and control the weld fillet. After each weld, the arc ferrule is broken and removed by a light tap with any convenient metal object. In some cases where the required finished stud is short, an extra length is provided on the stud as furnished, for proper chucking in the gun.   A groove is provided so the extra length can be easily broken off after the stud is welded.

The operation of fastening corrugated or flat asbestos-cement roofing and siding to steel girts is typical of how these stud fastenings are installed on buildings.   First, the sheet of asbestos cement is placed in the correct position on the girts or purlins.   If the sheets have not already been predrilled, a carboloy-tip drill is then used to drill a hole of proper diameter through the sheet.   Next, an end-mill drill is inserted through the hole in the material to remove any scale, rust, paint, or dirt and to provide a clean welding surface.   Then, the stud is inserted in the gun chuck, the ceramic arc shield or ferrule is put into place in the adjustable-length device, and the tubular assembly is inserted through the hole in the asbestos-cement siding.   The gun is held perpendicular to and firmly against the purlin or girt.   The stud is end-welded in a fraction of a second by pressing the gun trigger.   Finally, the ferrule is knocked off.

The sealing collar and nut are then placed on the stud and tightened sufficiently to make a positive and weathertight seal between the collar and the asbestos-cement sheet.   A similar fastening, but with corrugated-metal sheet, is shown in Fig. 16-17.

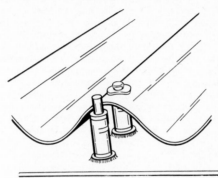

Fig. 16-17. Corrugated metal impaled on and fastened in place with welded stud.

The above method permits application of siding and roofing entirely from the outside.   A man is not required to be on the inside because there are no clips or fasteners on the interior.   The expense of an interior scaffold is thus saved.

In securing corrugated metal, it is sometimes desirable to weld the studs to the steel frame in advance of placing predrilled sheets.   In these cases, templates for quickly marking sheet and stud locations may be employed, as desired.   Stud welding is applicable to any steel frame composed of standard structural steel.   Steels of the high-carbon variety such as rerolled rail stock are not suitable for stud welding.

The manufacturer's recommendations should be followed in selecting the best type and size of stud for each specific installation.   The leading manufacturers have direct field representatives in all areas who can supply valuable advice as to the best procedures to follow.

16-22. Powder-driven Studs.   For many applications requiring the joining of steel or wood parts, or fastenings to concrete, steel, and brick surfaces, powder-actuated stud drivers are found to decrease costs because of their simplicity and speed.   These drivers use a special powder charge to drive a pin or stud into relatively hard materials.   The key to their efficiency is the proper selection of drive pins and firing charges.   Because of the high velocity, the drive pin, in effect, fuses to the materials and develops the holding power.

Pull-out tests of these driven studs prove remarkable holding power.   Average pull-out in 3,500-psi concrete exceeds 1,200 lb for 10-gage studs, and 2,400 lb for $\frac{1}{4}$-in.-diameter studs.   In steel plate the pull-out resistance is still greater.

All that is required is a stud driver, the correct stud, and the correct cartridge, as recommended by the manufacturer for each specific set of fastening conditions.

There are about a half dozen different strengths of cartridge, each identified by color, and some two dozen varieties of studs. Some studs have external threads, others internal threads. A plastic coating protects the threads from damage while driving.

The drivers will force studs into steel up to about $\frac{1}{2}$ in. thick, into concrete through steel plates up to about $\frac{1}{4}$ in. thick, into concrete through various thicknesses of woods, and into steel through steel up to $\frac{1}{4}$ in. thick.

Powder-driven studs should never be driven into soft materials or into very hard or brittle materials, such as cast iron, glazed tile, or surface-hardened steel. Neither should they be used in face brick, hollow tile, live rock, or similar materials.

In driving studs a suitable guard must be used for each operation, and the driver must be held squarely to the work. If the driver is not held perpendicular, a safety device prevents firing of the charge. There also must be sufficient backup material to absorb the full driving power of the charge. Studs cannot safely be driven closer than $\frac{1}{2}$ in. from the edge of a steel surface, or closer than 3 in. from the outside edge of concrete or brick surfaces.

16-23. Miscellaneous Anchoring Devices. Various types of expansion bolts, screw anchors, and toggle bolts are available for securing fixtures, brackets, and equipment to solid material, such as masonry, brick, concrete, and stone. Anchors also can be had for fastening to hollow walls, such as plaster on metal lath in furred spaces and hollow tile. The best device to use depends on the requirements in each case.

For use with practically any materials, including soft and brittle ones, such as composition board, glass, and tile, fiber screw anchors with a hollow metal core find a universal application. These plugs with braided metal cores possess many advantages: They can be used with wood screws and with lag screws. The flexible construction permits the plug to conform to any irregularities. Because of this elastic compression, the fibers are compressed as the screw enters. Screws can be unscrewed and replaced. Shock and vibration have no effect on gripping power. The plugs come in about 40 sizes to fit anything from a No. 6 screw to a $\frac{5}{8}$-in. lag screw. In practice, a hole is drilled first, the plug is driven into it, and then the screw is inserted, expanding the plug against the sides of the hole.

For some fastenings, one-piece drive bolts are hammered like a nail into prepared holes in masonry or concrete. Other types of expansion bolts have expansion shields or are calked into place. The expansion shield is expanded in the hole by a tapered sleeve forced against a cone-shaped nut by the tightening of a bolt threaded into the cone. These types are not recommended for soft or brittle materials.

For thin hollow walls, toggle bolts equipped with spring-actuated wings are used. The wings will pass into the hole in folded position. After entering the hollow space, the wings open out, thereby obtaining a secure hold.

For fastening lightweight materials to nailable supports, stapling machines are extensively used. In one patented system, for example, staples secure acoustic tile to wood furring strips. In this system, invisible fastenings are obtained by using a full-spline suspension for the kerfed pieces of tile and a special stapling machine adjusted to function at the proper distance below the furring strips. The machine staples the splines (at the joints of the tiles) to the supporting strips, giving a speedy, economical, and secure fastening.

16-24. Bolts. The number of sizes and varieties of this basic type of fastening found in buildings is great. One of the more significant applications is in making field connections for structural-steel framing. The bolts are known as high-tensile-strength bolts (Art. 6-52). For other types of bolts used with structural steel, see Arts. 6-47, 6-49, 6-50, and 6-51.

In timber construction, bolts generally are used with timber connectors—patented metal rings, grids, shear plates, framing anchors, and clamping plates, which increase the strength of joints (Arts. 8-13 and 8-15).

Section 17

ACOUSTICS

G. W. Handy

General Manager
Acoustical Department
The Myron Cornish Company

The first workable yardstick for prescribing corrective measures to control noise was devised about the turn of the century by Prof. Wallace C. Sabine of Harvard University. Principally by trial-and-error methods, involving the number and placement of church cushions, Prof. Sabine and his student crew of pioneers were able to improve hearing conditions in the then newly built Fogg Art Museum. Sounds had been unusually annoying because of distinct echoes and garbling of speech by continuing reverberations. With the detailed information developed from this project, together with continued study of auditoriums that were considered to be "good" and "bad," Professor Sabine was able to develop a formula for acoustical correction that is practically universal in use today [Eq. (17-1), Art. 17-7].

Studies since have developed more scientific and more accurate formulas for determining the amount of sound-absorbing material and its placement or distribution. Also more is known about the effect of pitch, noise intensity, contour, proximity to noise source, temperature, and humidity, and other variations due to site conditions or to the specific use of the auditoriums or rooms involved. However, the Sabine formula has been used continually for more than 50 years. The results accomplished when this formula has been applied by experienced acoustical engineers are outstanding.

Experience and practical interpretation of Sabine's formula are necessary not only for the best results, but also to procure the most acoustic correction for the least money expended. Optimum results are obtained when the "science of acoustics" is flavored with the "art of acoustics," which is developed by practice under varying conditions and requirements.

To master the art of acoustics, one must have a foundation of science and theory, so that experience can be fitted in this mental framework of knowledge for continued future use.

17-1. Pitch. The pitch of a sound depends on the frequency of vibrations that strike the ear. The range of sound that the average person can hear is from 20 to 20,000 cps (cycles, or vibrations, per second), although the frequency range of ordinary sounds is much more limited. High-frequency, or high-pitched, sounds are more annoying and more distracting to most people than low-pitched sounds of the same level of loudness. Nature has compensated for this, since high-frequency sound attenuates, or dies out, in the air much faster than low-pitched. Therefore, when distances from the source are substantial, one can assume that, if the low and medium frequencies are quieted, the high-frequency noise is automatically lessened.

The approximate ranges of frequency covered by a few musical instruments and the human voice are:

	Cps
Piano.................	27–4,186
Violin.................	196–2,093
Base viol..............	41– 246
Female voices..........	196–1,046
Male voices............	82– 466

Note that in sound-absorption-coefficient data as tabulated in books on acoustics the numbers 125, 250, 500, 1,000, 2,000, and 4,000 appear. These figures designate the pitch, by stating the number of cycles, or vibrations, per second at which the sound-absorption coefficients are applicable.

17-2. Sound Intensity. While the difference in frequency (cycles, or vibrations, per second) registers as a difference in pitch, the ear records the difference in sound intensity as difference in loudness. The range of intensity to which the ear responds is enormous. A particularly loud sound may develop $2\frac{1}{2}$ trillion times the intensity of a barely audible sound.

Sound intensity is measured in decibels. Table 17-1 shows the relation of decibel rating to noises usually experienced.

Table 17-1. Rating of Intensity of Various Noises

Decibels

130	Causes discomfort and pain
110	Thunder, airplane motors, pneumatic hammers
90	Noisy factory areas
70	Noisy office, rather comfortable factory area
50	Typical office with acoustical treatment
30	Typical living room (comfortable, pleasant)
10	Rustle of leaves (barely audible)

A **decibel** is the least change in sound intensity that can be distinguished by the average human ear. Empirically, it develops that the ratio between any two sound intensities with a minimum distinguishable difference in magnitude has an approximate logarithmic relation. An increase of 26% in sound intensity corresponds to a rise of 1 in the decibel scale. Thus, an intensity of 2 db (decibels) is 26% higher than 1 db; 61 db is 26% higher than 60 db. Because of this logarithmic relation, 20 db is not twice as loud as 10 db, any more than 20°F is twice as warm as 10°F. It may be helpful to think of the decibel scale as a thermometer of sound levels.

Acoustical treatment in offices, banks, schools, etc., often reduces the noise level 6 db compared with that before treatment. A 6-db reduction is equivalent to 30 to 50% noise reduction judged by the typical human ear. An 8-db reduction is equivalent to 40 to 60% reduction in noise to the average ear. The percentage of noise reduction to the same group of listeners depends on the range of noise level at which the measurements are made. Table 17-2 shows the percentage loudness reduction in relation to decibel reduction when measured by a sound-level meter at various original sound levels.

17-3. Absorption Coefficients When sound strikes a solid surface, part of it is transmitted through the barrier (wallboard, plaster, acoustical tile), part is changed into kinetic energy (transformed into heat), and part is reflected back into the room. The sound energy transmitted through the barrier or changed into motion or frictional heat is the absorption coefficient. An open window has an absorption of 100%, while a pane of glass has a coefficient of absorption of $2\frac{1}{2}$%. Acoustical materials have an absorption coefficient in between these two extremes; most of them vary between 50 and 100%. (C. M. Harris, "Handbook of Noise Control," McGraw-Hill Book Co. Inc., New York.)

17-4. Echoes. When a reflecting surface is so far away from the source that the sound is reflected back as a distinct repetition, this reflected sound is an echo. If the time interval between a sound and its reflection is too short, a true echo cannot be distinguished. No echoes will occur in small rooms.

Table 17-2. Relation of Decibel Reduction to Decrease in Loudness

Db before acoustical treatment	Db after acoustical treatment	Reduction, db	Loudness reduction, %*
40	36	4	30
	34	6	40
	32	8	55
60	56	4	25
	54	6	35
	52	8	45
80	74	6	35
	72	8	45
	70	10	55
100	74	6	40
	72	8	50
	70	10	60

* Based on material published by the Acoustical Materials Association.

Reverberation is an accumulation of echoes, one interfering with and masking the other, so that individual echoes cannot be distinguished. Thus, reverberation is the persistence of sound by reflection from surrounding surfaces after the source sound has ceased. Reverberation in a room garbles speech and distorts music.

17-5. Reverberation Time. This is the time it takes a sound to decrease from a standard intensity to below the level of hearing. Reverberation time can be checked by an experienced acoustical engineer with a calibrated organ pipe or other standard source of sound and a stop watch. Some churches, railroad stations, and other large public buildings have been found to have a reverberation time of as long as 25 sec. Reverberation times in rooms range from this maximum to less than ½ sec, depending on the volume and amount of sound-absorbing materials within the rooms.

Acoustical-correction problems may be classified into three categories: (1) control of noise transmission; (2) control of reverberation time in auditoriums, music halls, etc; and (3) noise reduction in offices, schools, and hospitals.

17-6. Control of Noise Transmission. Such control is required to mitigate annoyance of noise passing from one apartment to another through walls, partitions, and ceilings; to lessen noise caused by traffic and penetrating into homes, hospitals, and schools; to prevent clanging and banging of machinery from factory areas interfering with work in nearby offices.

Noise transmission is controlled primarily by increasing the weight of partition, ceiling, or wall. Additional reduction in noise transmission can be achieved with dual partitions that are entirely separated from each other or loosely attached with a resilient connection such as springs, felt, or cork.

Mass is necessary for a high sound-transmission loss. This loss can be substantially augmented by so-called false surfaces that are loosely attached to a massive sound barrier. A lightweight partition or ceiling, even though structurally adequate and erected on resilient mountings, would not be effective.

Since isolation of sound depends primarily on mass (weight) of partition or floor and because sound-absorption materials are usually of lightweight construction, they do not affect noise transmission significantly. For the same reason, thermal insulating materials, such as mineral wool and vermiculite granules, are relatively ineffective in stopping noise transmission, unless combined with mass and resilient mountings.

Since sound will readily pass through any openings in a room boundary, the following precaution is especially noteworthy:

When extra care and money are devoted to a partition with a high sound- or noise-transmission reduction, all openings in that partition should be sealed. Windows should be tight, possibly double-glazed, and in extreme cases, triple-glazed and mounted in rubber. Doors should be sealed with rubber or felt gaskets and should be without keyholes. In extreme cases, doors should be the multiple-jambed type.

For a more complete discussion of noise-transmission problems, together with examples of various combinations of standard building materials that will increase the sound-transmission loss over conventional construction, see *National Bureau of Standards Report BMS* 17 (Superintendent of Documents, Washington, D.C. and C. M. Harris, "Handbook of Noise Control," McGraw-Hill Book Company, Inc., New York.)

17-7. Control of Reverberation Time. In auditoriums, studios, and band rooms, reverberation time should be controlled so that everyone can hear the speaker distinctly and the soloist or the symphony orchestra without distortion.

Reverberation time in auditoriums is calculated by the use of Sabine's formula:

$$T = \frac{0.05V}{a} \tag{17-1}$$

where T = reverberation time, sec
V = volume of room, cu ft
a = absorption units

The absorption units in a room are found by summing the product of the areas of the floor, walls, and ceiling (in square feet) by the sound-absorption coefficients of the various building materials covering those areas.

Recommended reverberation time may be obtained from the chart in Fig. 17-1, which has been published by the Acoustical Materials Association and the National Bureau of Standards. It was developed by purely empirical methods and experience. Reverberation times falling within the shaded area are considered to be satisfactory. They depend on the volume of the room. Selection of the ideal reverberation time also depends on the judgment and experience of the acoustical engineer and his study of the specific use conditions of the room.

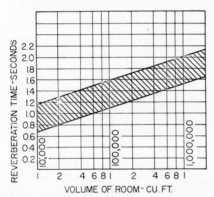

Fig. 17-1. Recommended reverberation time, indicated by shaded area, varies with size of room.

If the calculated reverberation time exceeds the recommended value, acoustic correction is desirable. Generally, covering ceiling or walls with sound-absorbing materials is all that is required; but sometimes, it may be necessary to carpet floors, cover windows and doors with drapes, cushion seats, vary the shape of walls and ceiling to change sound reflectance or install special sound-absorbing devices, depending on the purpose of the room and importance of sound control.

Following is a typical acoustical analysis of a chapel. This shows how the volume of a room and the areas of various surface materials affect sound absorption and how the addition of relatively high sound-absorbing materials reduces reverberation time to the optimum.

ACOUSTICAL ANALYSIS OF A CHAPEL

The building is 40 × 60 ft by 20 ft high to the cornice. Ridge of the roof is 16 ft above the cornice, making a total height of 36 ft from floor to ridge. The sanctuary, a small wing at the end of the building, is 10 × 20 ft by 18 ft high. Floor area of the nave is 2,400 sq ft and of the sanctuary 200 sq ft. Volume of the nave is 67,200 cu ft and of the sanctuary 3,600 cu ft. Seating calls for wood benches for 300 persons.

The nave has a wood floor; wood-panel wainscot 4 ft high all around; plaster walls and ceiling (ceiling sloped to follow pitch in ridge roof; simple trusses); 8 windows, each 5 × 12 ft; two doors, 3 × 7 ft and one door 6 × 7 ft.

The sanctuary has a platform with wood floor; wood paneling on three 8-ft-high walls, the other wall and the flat ceiling being plastered.   There are no windows or doors.

From Fig. 17-1, the recommended reverberation time for the room, which has a volume of 70,800 cu ft, is found to range from 1.05 to 1.5 sec.   Assume that the reverberation time should be in the middle of this range, or 1.3 sec.   From the Sabine formula, Eq. (17-1), with the volume V equal to 70,800 and T equal to 1.3, the number of absorption units required for the room is

$$a = \frac{0.05V}{T} = \frac{0.05 \times 70,800}{1.3} = 2,723$$

Absorption Units in Untreated Room

Material	Absorption coefficient at 512 cycles	Area, sq ft	Absorption units
Floor (wood).........................	0.03	2,600	78.0
Wall panels (wood)...................	0.06	1,076	64.5
Walls (plaster).......................	0.03	2,440	73.2
Ceiling (plaster)......................	0.03	3,260	97.8
Windows (glazed).....................	0.027	480	12.9
Audience (half capacity)...............	3.5*	150†	525.0
Total units existing in room..........	.....	......	851.4

* Per person.
† Persons.

Since 2,723 units are needed, 2,723 − 851, or 1,872, units must be added.   Assume that the ceiling will be covered with an acoustical material with an absorption coefficient at 500 cycles of 0.60.   Then, 97.8 units in the existing ceiling will be lost, making the total units to be supplied 1,872 + 97.8 = 1,969.8.   Covering the ceiling with the acoustical material will provide 3,260 × 0.60, or 1,956 units.   This is close enough to the required number to bring the reverberation time into the recommended range.

17-8. Noise Reduction.   For offices, schools, and retail stores, noise reduction may be calculated from the following formula:

$$\text{Decibel noise reduction} = 10 \log \frac{A_2}{A_1} \qquad (17\text{-}2)$$

where A_2 is the number of absorption units after the room is treated and A_1 is the number of absorption units before it is treated.   Ordinarily, noise reduction in offices and restaurants cannot be overdone.

Rooms with ceilings 12 ft high or less can be satisfactorily quieted by applying acoustical materials with a noise-reduction coefficient of 0.55 over the ceiling areas. If the ceilings are considerably higher, or if the area of a small office seriously limits available ceiling space, an acoustical material with a higher noise-reduction coefficient should be used.

In the following example, an acoustical analysis is made for a restaurant with a ceiling height of 12 ft 3 in. and a relatively high ratio of ceiling area to volume of room. An acoustical material with a noise-reduction coefficient of 0.55 is assumed for ceiling application.

ACOUSTICAL ANALYSIS OF A RESTAURANT

The room is 58 × 84 ft by 12 ft 3 in. high; volume—59,682 cu ft.   The north wall has plywood paneling and 5 windows, each 9 ft × 8 ft 6 in.   The south wall has plywood paneling, with openings 3 ft 6 in. × 4 ft 6 in. and serving areas 49 × 3 ft.   The east and west walls have a plywood finish, 4 windows, each 9 ft × 8 ft 6 in., and 2 doors, each 9 ft × 8 ft 6 in.

Ceiling area, plaster on lath, is 4,872 sq ft. Half the asphalt-tiled floor area, 2,436 sq ft, is considered in the calculations; the remainder is accounted for by the wood table tops.

Absorption Units in Untreated Room

Material	Noise-reduction coefficient at 512 cycles	Area, sq ft	Absorption units
Floor, asphalt tile.................................	0.06	2,436	146
Table tops, wood.................................	0.03	2,436	73
Walls, east side, plywood (less openings)........	0.03	567	17
Openings, east side, glazed.....................	0.027	462	13
Walls, west side, plywood (less openings)........	0.03	567	17
Openings, west side, glazed.....................	0.027	462	13
Walls, north side, plywood (less openings).......	0.03	326	10
Openings, north side, glazed....................	0.027	385	10
Walls, south side, plywood (less openings).......	0.03	548	16
Ceiling, plaster on lath (untreated).............	0.03	4,872	146
Total absorption units.....................	.....	.....	461

Since acoustical material is to be applied to the ceiling, 146 units will be lost. The acoustical material will add 4,872 × 0.55, or 2,680 units. Hence, the treated room will have a total of 461 − 146 + 2,680, or 2,995 units.

From Eq. (17-2), with $A_1 = 461$ and $A_2 = 2,995$, the reduction in decibels will be 10 log (2,995/461) = 8. If the original noise level is 60 db, the per cent noise reduction is 45% (see Table 17-2).

The **noise-reduction coefficient** used in the above example is an arithmetical average of the sound-absorption coefficients of the acoustical material at 250, 500, 1,000, and 2,000 cycles. There is no technical basis for using the average of these four sound-absorption coefficients. However, continued use has made this average the standard for evaluating acoustical materials when used primarily for quieting rooms rather than controlling reverberation. (See also C. M. Harris, "Handbook of Noise Control," McGraw-Hill Book Company, Inc., New York.)

METHODS OF INSTALLING ACOUSTIC TILES

17-9. Mounting Acoustic Tile by Cementing. About 50% of all acoustic tiles are installed by cementing them to a solid backing, such as plasterboard, plaster, or concrete. A special acoustical adhesive is used that allows the mechanic to adjust the tiles to a flat plane surface even though there are slight irregularities in the plaster or concrete base.

The best practice calls for four spots of adhesive about the size of a walnut per square foot of tile. When pressed, each spot provides an area of contact about 2½ in. in diameter and a minimum of 1/16 in. thick to a maximum of 5/16 in. thick (Fig. 17-2).

17-10. Mounting Acoustic Tile by Nailing. Some ceilings in buildings already built are not level or flat enough for good adhesive application. Under this condition, 1 × 3-in. wood furring strips can be attached to the ceiling at 12-in. centers by toggle bolts or other means. The furring strips can be made level by shimming where necessary.

Also, when wood joists are left exposed, the ceiling can be cross-furred with 1 × 3-in. wood furring strips, which should be leveled with shims before application of the tile. Building paper should be attached to furring strips under the tiles to prevent free circulation of air between the joints of the tile, which causes the edges to become dirty at a faster rate than their centers.

Each acoustical tile should be fastened to the wood furring strips with at least four nails or screws per square foot (Fig. 17-3). In perforated acoustical tiles, several shallow holes are provided in each corner of the tile to accommodate the fasteners. The nails should penetrate the wood furring a minimum of $\frac{3}{4}$ in.

The furring should be dry and well seasoned (softwood) to prevent warping or curling. A maximum span of 3 ft should be used to minimize spring action.

17-11. Mounting Acoustic Tile with Metal Suspension Systems. For suspended ceilings, acoustic tile can be attached to metal T runners with spring necks, which engage the embossed edges of perforated metal-pan-type tiles. The plenum above the hung ceiling provides a space for air-conditioning ducts, electrical conduits, plumbing, telephone wires, and other utilities. Each 12 × 24-in. metal-pan unit, which is snapped into the spring-neck T runner, becomes an access panel (Fig. 17-4).

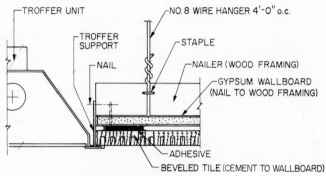

FIG. 17-2. Adhesive application of acoustic tile to wallboard.

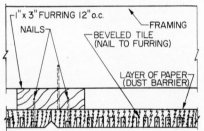

FIG. 17-3. Acoustic tile nailed to wood furring.

Several other types of metal supports are available for suspending standard 12 × 12-in. and 12 × 24-in. acoustic tile composed of mineral or cellulose fiber. One of the systems is sketched in Fig. 17-5. Basically, it involves a J section (variations are H section and Z section) formed of 22-gage galvanized sheet steel, which is attached to standard $1\frac{1}{2}$-in. channels at intervals of 4 ft or less. The edges of the tiles are kerfed and rabbeted so that the flange of the J engages and holds the tile in place. A smaller T section, at right angles to the J section, also is engaged in the kerf. Thus, support is provided on all four sides of the tile.

17-12. Special Acoustic-tile Mountings. One special type of mounting is used where the acoustical material is laid directly on a laboratory floor for testing, principally to provide research information. No conventional acoustical tile or blankets are installed on floor areas because of their innate softness.

Other special types are used in radio studios, band-practice rooms, and other special-use spaces. With this type of mounting, in which perforated asbestos-cement panels are used for the facing, low-frequency absorption can be increased by varying the thickness and density of the sound-absorbing element, which is placed in back of the perforated face. For ultra-low-frequency absorption, the air column alone (without mineral wool) is effective. This phase of acoustics is too specialized for most building designers; an acoustics specialist should be engaged.

Because the sound-absorption characteristics of acoustic materials at various frequencies are substantially affected by the depth of the air column in back of the

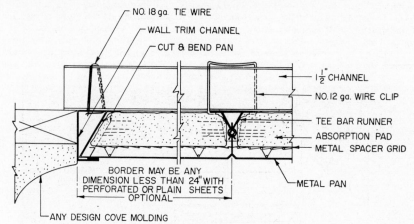

FIG. 17-4. T runner with spring neck supports metal-pan tiles.

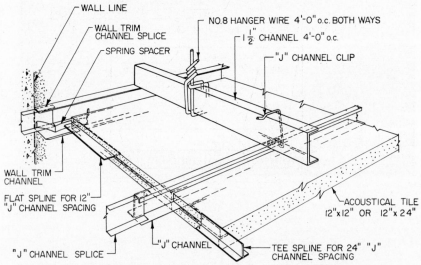

FIG. 17-5. Suspended acoustic ceiling with J sections and T splines supporting tiles.

acoustical tile, the *Acoustical Materials Association Bulletin* lists test data with the various types of mountings.

ACOUSTICAL MATERIALS

Manufacturers of acoustical products allow the designer a wide variety of features from which to select. Choice may be made not only of acoustical efficiency, but also price and various combinations of features, such as repaintability, incombustibility, light reflection, color, economy of maintenance, salvageability, texture, and appearance. For individual characteristics of acoustical tiles, including sound-absorption coefficients, noise-reduction coefficients, light-reflection values, flame resistance, trade names, and manufacturers, see *Acoustical Materials Association Bulletin* (Acoustical Materials Association, 335 E. 45th St., New York 17, N.Y.).

17-13. Felted Wood-fiber Acoustic Tiles. Acoustical units composed of felted wood fibers (Fig. 17-6) give the buyer the greatest amount of acoustical absorption for the dollar invested. The acoustical value is built into it in the felting process at the fabricating mill and does not require any subsequent mutilation with holes or slots to make it effective.

The main feature of this type of tile is its pleasing appearance and its acoustical efficiency at low cost. Its main limitation is that special care must be taken when

Fig. 17-6. Felted wood-fiber acoustic tile.

repainting it that the small surface voids are not closed. Spray painting with a good interior paint that has been thinned and applied to yield uniform color with a minimum of paint is advised.

17-14. Felted Mineral-fiber Tiles. Acoustical units composed of felted mineral fibers (Fig. 17-7), although they are in a higher price range, provide the buyer a pleasing appearance without a cribbage-board effect. The main feature of this type of tile, in addition to its smooth appearance, is its incombustibility.

The main limitation is the same as for felted wood-fiber tiles—extra care must be exercised in repainting. The same painting precautions as noted in Art. 17-13 should be taken to maintain acoustical efficiency.

17-15. Perforated Wood-fiber Tiles. Acoustical units composed of felted-wood fibers with circular perforations in the surface (Fig. 17-8) provide the buyer excellent sound-absorption value and a relatively smooth surface, which makes ceilings stay cleaner for a longer period of time. The perforations arranged in a regular pattern earmark this type of material as an acoustical tile wherever it is seen.

The main feature of this type of tile is that it can be repainted many times with both

FIG. 17.7. Felted mineral-fiber acoustic tile.

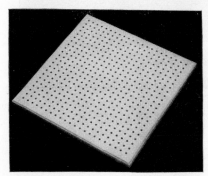

FIG. 17-8. Perforated wood-fiber acoustic tile.

FIG. 17-9. Perforated mineral-fiber acoustic tile.

brush application or spray gun—with any kind of paint—without appreciably reducing its acoustical efficiency. Perforated wood-fiber acoustical tiles are available which have been treated by the manufacturer with a flame-resistant paint, which slows the rate of flame spread significantly. The main limitation of this type of tile is the mechanical appearance of its uniform rows of holes or slots.

17-16. Perforated Mineral-fiber Tiles. Acoustical units composed of felted mineral fibers with circular perforations in the surface (Fig. 17-9) provide the buyer with the same advantages and limitations as the perforated wood-fiber tile. The additional feature of this type is that it is incombustible and has a slower rate of flame spread than the cellulose type.

17-17. Perforated Metal Tiles. Acoustical units having a perforated metal facing that acts as a decorative surface and support for the sound-absorbing material (Fig. 17-10) give the buyer the most economical acoustical construction available. This economy is achieved in spite of relatively high initial cost, since wiping it with a damp

FIG. 17-10. Perforated metal acoustic tile.

FIG. 17-11. Perforated asbestos-cement acoustic tile.

cloth, or even washing the durable surface, is cheaper than repainting or replacing other types of tile. The exposed surface is painted with baked-on white enamel to insure permanence and high light reflection.

This type of material is incombustible. It is easily removed to gain access to the plenum chamber above, and it can be moved from one room to another. The main limitation is its relatively high initial cost.

17-18. Perforated Asbestos-cement Tiles. Acoustical units having a perforated asbestos-cement board facing that acts as a decorative surface and support for the sound-absorbing material (Fig. 17-11) give the buyer the advantage of both permanence and removability when it is screwed to the furring.

The plus value of this material is that it will not corrode under abusive moisture conditions. It is incombustible. The chief limitation is that under impact, such as from balls hitting the ceiling in a gymnasium, it is more susceptible to breakage than some other types.

17-19. Fissure-surfaced Tiles. Acoustical units having a fissured surface simulating travertine stone (Fig. 17-12) give the buyer one of the most attractive finishes available for ceiling treatment. The random fissures increase sound absorption, provide surface cavities that allow repainting when necessary, and are responsible for the interesting appearance. This type of tile is made basically of rock wool and therefore is incombustible. Chief limitation is that it cannot be used in natatoriums or other areas exposed to high humidities.

FIG. 17-12. Fissured-surface acoustic tile with the appearance of travertine stone.

17-20. Sprayed-on Acoustical Materials. Monolithic acoustical material composed of mineral fibers mixed with special binder (Fig. 17-13) and applied by spraying with an air gun or blower gives the buyer high sound absorption, a high degree of thermal insulation (K factor of 0.27), and a fireproofing material (4-hr rating). It is relatively economical in cost.

The plus value of this type of acoustical treatment is that it can be used where intricate design and contours are involved—when a monolithic appearance is desired without geometric designs such as are apparent when prefabricated tiles are used. The chief limitation is that application is dusty and should not be carried out in rooms that are tenanted. Machinery and desks cannot be satisfactorily protected from the "fly."

17-21. Troweled-on Acoustical Materials. Monolithic acoustical material composed of granular aggregate mixed with a binder such as gypsum, portland cement, or lime (Fig. 17-14) and applied with a trowel gives the buyer the same monolithic appearance as sprayed-on materials without lines or geometric patterns. Acoustical plaster is used where curved ceilings and niches makes the use of tiles impractical. It is incombustible.

FIG. 17-13. Mineral fiber sprayed on lath to form a monolithic acoustical ceiling.

The main feature of troweled-on plastic acoustical material is that it has a harder surface than the spray material. The chief limitation is that sound absorption depends too much on the technique of the mechanic who is applying it.

ACOUSTICAL BAFFLES

The available data concerning acoustical baffles are fragmentary. Baffles, in contrast with conventional surface treatment for offices, schools, etc., are limited to cases where excessively high sound intensities are encountered, such as airplane-motor-test buildings; weave rooms in textile mills; and rooms with punch presses, riveting machines, etc.

Because of their diverse requirements, acoustical treatment in these factory areas cannot be designed based on regularly accepted formulas. Rather, the specific conditions for each situation must be analyzed so that maximum attenuation will result on an over-all basis and still keep within the limits of cost. The installation should offer minimum obstruction to ventilation, provide a method for cleaning and maintenance, and in some cases withstand all kinds of climatic conditions, excessive humidities, and temperature.

Baffle construction, when the baffles are spaced relatively close together, in contrast to surface treatment, substantially increases sound absorption, since it obviously exposes more sound-absorbing surface.

17-22. Acoustical Baffles in Engine-test Buildings.   Generally, acoustical cells for engine-test buildings vary in cross-sectional area from 14 × 14 ft to 45 × 45 ft, and the length of the acoustical baffles employed in them for noise control varies from 10 to 30 ft.   The acoustical cells are huge intake and exhaust ducts.   They connect to each end of a room of sufficient size to accommodate the airplane engine (jet or propeller type) and the structure that supports the engine.   Control rooms, ready rooms, and storage rooms are also part of this building.   Figure 17-15 is a simplified plan and elevation showing the location of the acoustical baffles.

Fig. 17-14. Acoustical plaster applied by trowel.

Running tests for various lengths of time and at various speeds are necessary for preflight testing and for breaking in new and reconditioned engines.   Depending on the horsepower and the speed, the intensity levels of noise generated range from 80 to 135 db.

The most important factors to consider in designing acoustical baffles for test cells are:

1. Acoustical effectiveness.
2. Minimum amount of obstruction, since the motor requires air for combustion and cooling.
3. Ability to resist stresses due to air currents and eddies at high velocity.
4. Ability to withstand climatic conditions.

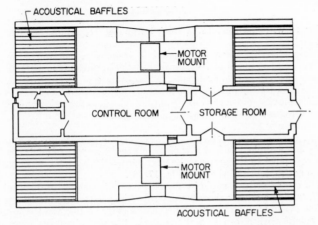

PLAN

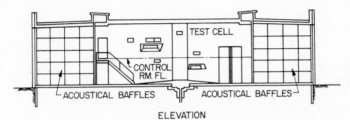

ELEVATION

FIG. 17-15. Plan and elevation of engine-test building with acoustical baffles.

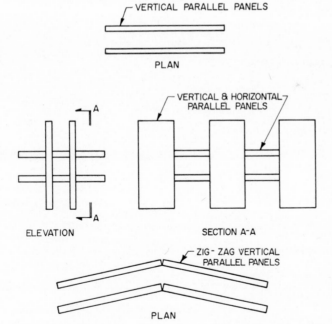

FIG. 17-16. Acoustical baffles perform better when panels are placed in a zigzag pattern or alternately vertical and horizontal.

5. Ability to withstand corrosion from burned gases, fumes, and very high temperatures.

Authorities generally agree that sound is transmitted in progressive, spherical waves. The usual practice of installing acoustical materials in parallel panels perpendicular to the ground and edgewise to the source of sound presents the sound-absorbing surfaces to the spherical waves in only one plane. That portion of the wave front which is moving downward or upward would not theoretically come in contact with the sound-absorbing material except through reflection or diffraction and variation in the intensity pattern.

This objection could be overcome by changing the direction of alternate layers of panels. As an example, the first row of panels could be perpendicular to the ground, the next row parallel to the ground, the next perpendicular. Thus, they would alternate for the entire depth of the cell (Fig. 17-16).

A series of oscillator tests made by Dariel Fitzroy, acoustical consultant, San Francisco, Calif., and the author show consistently higher attenuation with panels placed in zigzag form than with straight parallel panels (Fig. 17-16), and the tests conducted on arrangements with alternate sections at right angles give even more satisfactory results.

Section 18

THERMAL INSULATION

E. B. J. Roos

Partner, Seelye, Stevenson, Value & Knecht
New York, N.Y.

18-1. Effect of Insulation. There is a very simple way of evaluating insulation without going into details and theoretical considerations, if the following basic principles, which will be discussed later, are accepted here at their face value:

1. All materials offer some resistance to flow of heat. The resistance is directly proportional to thickness.

2. Insulations, as used in construction, are considerably more resistant to heat flow than structural materials, such as stone, brick, concrete, steel, and wood, and for the purpose of providing resistance to heat flow are considerably more economical.

The amount of heat that flows through a material is called **conductance.** Many books contain tables that give the conductance for various materials, as well as for built-up walls, roofs, slabs, etc. ("Heating, Ventilating, Air Conditioning Guide," American Society of Heating and Air-Conditioning Engineers).

Consider, for example, a wall in which we are thinking of adding, say, 1 in. of a certain insulation. From tables, we can get the heat conductance of the insulation and the over-all conductance of the wall. If, for example, the conductance of the insulation is one-third that of the wall, then the over-all conductance of the wall with the insulation added is one-fourth of what it would be without insulation. The heat flow stopped is three-fourths.

Table 18-1 will make this simple method very clear. (All terms are relative heat conductances, with the heat conductance of the uninsulated wall taken as unity.)

Table 18-1. Effect of Insulating a Wall

Insulation	Insulated wall	Decrease in heat flow
$\frac{1}{2}$	$\frac{1}{3}$	$\frac{2}{3}$
$\frac{1}{3}$	$\frac{1}{4}$	$\frac{3}{4}$
$\frac{1}{4}$	$\frac{1}{5}$	$\frac{4}{5}$
$\frac{1}{5}$	$\frac{1}{6}$	$\frac{5}{6}$
$1/n$	$1/(n+1)$	$n/(n+1)$

It can be seen that the savings in heat are considerable. Nevertheless, increasing the thickness of insulation provides diminishing returns. Considering the effect of insulation alone, if the thickness is doubled, say, from 1 in. to 2 in., the heat flow becomes 50 %, or 50 % is saved. If another 1 in. is added, the heat flow compared with the original 1-in. thickness is 33 %. With another 1-in. addition, the heat flow is reduced to 25 %. So doubling the original thickness reduces the heat flow by 50 %; tripling the thickness reduces heat flow another 17 %; and quadrupling the thickness reduces heat flow only another 8 %. So for each increase in the thickness of insulation, the effect is less, and hence an economical balance can be calculated.

In any case, once installed, insulation not subject to abuse needs no repair or maintenance. Hence, first cost is the final cost, which in a new structure is offset by a considerable reduction in the required heating or cooling plant. Furthermore, in any structure, insulation makes possible a continuous reduction in operating expense for heating or cooling. These savings can generally pay for the cost of insulation in anywhere from 3 to 10 years, depending on the structure. Any investment having a return of 10 to 30 % is attractive. Also, added comfort due to the resulting more uniform inside temperatures must be considered.

18-2. Types of Insulation. All materials have some resistance to heat flow, but modern construction and the cost and weight of structural materials do not permit or require walls of stone, brick, or other structural materials thick enough to provide sufficient resistance to heat flow for economical heating and cooling. For this reason, new and more economical insulations for structures have been and are being developed. These insulating materials generally add no strength to the structure; they are employed only for the purpose of resisting flow of heat. In every case, the cost and weight of these materials are less than those of a sufficient thickness of structural materials of the same resistance to heat flow.

Modern building insulations are made of many different materials—glass fibers, glass foam, mineral fibers, wood or other organic fibers, metal foil, foamed plastics, lightweight concrete. Proper selection depends generally first on cost and then on the physical characteristics.

Except for metal foils, these materials utilize still air, which is an excellent insulator, to resist heat flow. Some, such as cork, cellular glass, or foamed plastics, enclose small particles of air in cells. Granular materials like pumice, vermiculite, or perlite trap air in relative large enclosures. Fibrous materials employ the principle that thin films of air cling persistently to all surfaces and serve as a heat barrier.

Insulating value of these materials depends on (1) ability of each component of the material to conduct heat, (2) ability of the components to transmit heat to each other, (3) length of path of heat flow, and (4) size of cells in which air is trapped or closeness of adjacent air films on the fibers or granules.

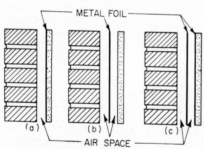

FIG. 18-1. Metal foil serving as reflective insulation is used in conjunction with an air space. (*a*) With foil placed against interior facing, only one air space is provided. (*b*) Splitting the gap with the foil improves insulation by forming two air spaces. (*c*) Adding a second foil on the warm side increases insulating value even more and prevents condensation.

Metal foils involve a different principle; they are known as reflective insulation. Just as a mirror reflects light, shiny metals, such as aluminum, reflect heat. They also have the properties of conducting heat very rapidly and emitting it very slowly from the surface away from the heat source. Thus, if heat is radiated to a bright aluminum foil, 95 % will be reflected back. If it receives heat by conduction, it will lose only 5 % by radiation from the opposite face.

To use reflective insulation properly, always provide an enclosed air space on at least one side of the material (Fig. 18-1*a*). A gap of ¾ to about 2 in. is most effective. If a foil is placed inside a gap, two air spaces are formed (Fig. 18-1*b*), thereby increasing resistance to heat flow. To prevent condensation troubles it is wise to use at least two reflective surfaces separated by an air space (Fig. 18-1*c*).

Supports for the foil should have high resistance to heat flow, so as not to carry off heat. In particular, aluminum foil should not be placed in contact with other metals, or it may be subjected to galvanic corrosion, and it should not be exposed to the alkalies in wet plaster or cement. A foil should not be placed on the cold side of a construction, unless a better vapor barrier is provided close to the warm side—to prevent condensation.

Calculation of heat transmission through a construction with reflective insulation is much more complicated than for other types of insulation. (*Federal Housing Administration Technical Circular* 7, Government Printing Office, Washington, D.C.; T. S. Rogers, "Design of Insulated Buildings for Various Climates," Owens-Corning, Toledo, Ohio.)

18-3. Heat Flow across an Air Space. The best practical heat insulation at our disposal is still air. An air space of about ¾ in. has been found to be best. Air spaces, however, have a limitation due to inability to keep the air motionless.

Surfaces of all materials exposed to air retain a film of air held fast by molecular attraction. This film also is an excellent insulation, but its thickness and effectiveness are diminished by any air motion wiping the surface.

In a vertical air space, such as may be constructed in a wall, with a higher temperature on one side than on the other, the air within the gap in contact with the warm side becomes heated. The hot air expands, becomes lighter, and tends to rise. On the cooler side, the air is cooled, contracts, becomes heaver and sinks. A circulation is set up, the warm air rising and being replaced with cooler air. The result is that the cooler air comes in contact with the warm side of the air space and absorbs heat, and the warm air comes in contact with the cooler side of the air space, giving up heat. Thus the air motion transfers heat from the warm side to the cold side. At the same time, its motion reduces the thickness of the surface air film and so decreases the film's resistance to heat.

This type of air motion is called convection. It is one of the means whereby heat flows. The amount of heat transferred is the same for the same temperature difference, regardless of which side is warm or cold.

Consider now a horizontal air space, such as may exist between a flat roof and a furred ceiling. In summer sunshine, the roof slab becomes very hot. The air in contact, in the space below, becomes heated, expands, and becomes lighter. On the other hand, the air in contact with the cooler ceiling below the air space is cooled, contracts, and becomes heavier. Since the light air is at the top of the air space it cannot rise, and the cooler, heavier air at the bottom of the air space cannot sink. Hence air motion due to temperature differences, namely, convection, is at a minimum, and so also is transfer of heat.

This condition is desirable for summer. But in winter the situation is less desirable. The roof slab is cold, and the air below is cooled, tending to fall—which it is free to do. The air above the ceiling is warmed and tends to rise—which it is free to do. So a thermal circulation is set up. This again is convection, a conveyor belt taking heat from the ceiling below and transporting it to the roof slab above.

Air spaces in pitched roofs fall somewhere in between vertical and horizontal air spaces.

Insulations that depend on air spaces for their resistance to heat flow incorporate within them a great many tiny cells. Not only do they contain a large number of air films in the path of heat flow, but the minute size of the air spaces tends to keep the air still and thus considerably reduces convection.

18-4. How Heat Flows. Heat always flows from a region of high temperature to a region of lower temperature.

Heat may be transmitted by three different methods—conduction, convection, and radiation.

When heat flows by conduction through a material, it is transmitted much like electricity through a conductor. All materials conduct heat. Some, such as metals, conduct heat very well; others, such as cork, have comparatively great resistance to heat flow. In every case, some heat will flow if a difference in temperature exists.

Convection strictly speaking is not true flow. It is a combination of flow by conduction from a warm surface to cooler air in contact with it, or from warm air to a cooler surface, the heated air tending to rise and the cooled air to fall. This rising and falling makes possible a physical transportation of heat (Art. 18-3).

The amount of heat transmitted by conduction or convection is proportional to the temperature difference. For example, take the wall of a building in winter, with an inside temperature of 70°F. When the outside temperature is 10°F, there is a temperature difference of 60°F. The heat flow out (in this case a heat loss) is twice as much as occurs when the outside temperature is 40°F, the temperature difference being 30°F.

Radiation is the flow of heat through space from a warm surface to a cooler one. This type of flow is like that of light and is of practical importance in connection with reflective insulation (Art. 18-2).

18-5. Measurement of Heat. To have practical and economical design with insulation, it is necessary to be able to measure heat. The unit of heat generally employed is the Btu (British thermal unit). For practical purposes, **1 Btu** is the amount of heat required to raise the temperature of 1 pound of water 1 degree Fahrenheit.

The basic unit used in measuring heat flow is **thermal conductivity** K, defined as the number of Btu that will flow through a material 1 ft square and 1 in. thick due to a temperature difference of 1°F, in 1 hr.

Another basic unit is **thermal conductance,** C, defined as the heat flow through a given thickness of 1-ft-square material with a 1°F temperature differential. It is useful for comparing standard structural materials, such as cinder block, hollow tile, brick, window glass, and plywood, which have standard thicknesses not equal to 1 in., as well as air spaces.

Note that these basic units do not include an allowance for air films but consider only flow from surface to surface.

Since most construction—walls, roofs, floor slabs, etc.—is built up of several different materials, possibly including air spaces, the desired end result in heat-flow measurement is the over-all heat flow through the structure including air films. This factor, U, is termed the **over-all conductance.** It is defined as the number of Btu that will flow through 1 sq ft of the structure from air to air due to a temperature difference of 1°F, in 1 hr.

The basic factors—K, C, and U—have been determined by experiment for most structural materials, as well as for most commonly used built-up walls, roofs, slabs, partitions, floors, etc., with and without insulation. These values are listed in tables for easy reference, so that little calculation is required ("Heating, Ventilating, Air Conditioning Guide," American Society of Heating and Air-Conditioning Engineers).

With these factors, it is a simple matter to calculate the heat flow (heat loss in winter, heat gain in summer) for any building.

For example, let us consider a wall. All that is required is to find in a table the over-all conductance factor U corresponding to the type of wall selected for the building. This factor is then multiplied by the wall area in square feet (less window and door area) and by the temperature difference existing between outside design conditions and desired inside conditions. The result is the number of Btu gained or lost through the wall. A similar calculation must be made for the glass area, door area, roof, floor, partition, etc., wherever temperature differences will exist.

It is of interest to note that the maximum over-all conductance U encountered is 1.5 Btu per hr per sq ft per °F. This would occur with a sheet-metal wall. The metal has, for practical purposes, no resistance to heat flow. The U value of 1.5 is due entirely to the resistance of the inside and outside air films. Most types of construction have U factors considerably less than 1.5.

The minimum U factor generally found in standard construction with 2 in. of insulation is about 0.10.

Since the U factor for single glass is 1.13, it can be seen that windows are a large source of heat gain, or heat loss, compared with the rest of the structure. For double glass, the U factor is 0.45. For further comparison, the conductivity K of most commercial insulations varies from about 0.24 to about 0.34.

18-6. Calculation of Heat Flow. It is not always possible to find in tables the U factor corresponding to the actual type of construction and choice of materials desired. In that case, it is necessary to calculate U by first finding the thermal conductivity K or thermal conductance C for each material. These are found in tables, such as those in the "Heating, Ventilating, Air Conditioning Guide" (American Society of Heating and Air-Conditioning Engineers). The thickness in inches must also be known for each material.

For example, the thermal conductivity K for brick is 9.2. The conductance of a 4-in. thickness of brick veneer is then 9.2/4, or 2.3. Note that the value 2.3 might be listed in tables as thermal conductance C for 4-in. veneer brick, in which case no calculation is needed.

Before the thermal characteristics of any wall, roof, etc., can be calculated it is necessary to know the heat conductance of the air films and possible air spaces encountered. These are generally accepted as follows:

Btu per Hr

Outside air film f_o (15-mph wind) 6.00
Inside air film f_i (still air) 1.65
Air space ¾ in. or more 1.10

In all tables, conductivities or conductances are listed, but to find the over-all conductance of, say, a built-up wall, it is necessary to compute the total resistance, which is the sum of the resistances R corresponding to the thickness of each material employed.

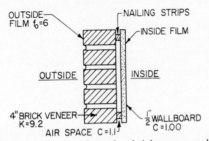

FIG. 18-2. Section through a brick-veneer wall.

Resistance is the reciprocal of conductance. If, for example, the heat conductivity of 1 in. of insulation is 0.25, then the resistance is 1/0.25 or 4.

There are formulas for calculating U, but a simpler method is as follows: Assume the hypothetical wall in Fig. 18-2.

Item	K	Thickness, in.	C	$R = 1/C$
Outside film	. . .	. . .	6	0.166
Brick	9.2	4	2.30	0.434
Air space	. . .	. . .	1.10	0.910
Wallboard	. . .	½	1.00	1.000
Inside film	. . .	. . .	1.65	0.606
Total resistance	. . .	. . .	. . . .	3.116

Over-all conductance $U = \dfrac{1}{3.116} = 0.32$

Assume we wish to find out what the over-all conductance would be for the wall in Fig. 18-2 with 1-in. insulation ($K = 0.25$).

Item	K	Thickness, in.	C	$R = 1/C$
Wall.........................	....	...	0.32	3.116
Insulation..................	0.25	1	0.25	4.000
Total resistance...........	....	...	....	7.116

$$\text{Over-all conductance } U = \frac{1}{7.116} = 0.14$$

The last calculation indicates that, if the over-all conductance of a construction is known and it is desired to add to or subtract a material from this wall, it is not necessary to recalculate completely, but as above, compute the existing resistance and add or subtract the resistance of the material to be varied. Then, the reciprocal is the conductance sought.

A simpler device for finding the over-all conductance resulting from the addition of insulation to a known wall is as follows:

Using the above example, we have 0.32 for the over-all conductance of the wall, and the conductivity of the desired 1-in. insulation is 0.25. We then multiply the two conductances together, and divide by their sum:

$$\frac{0.32 \times 0.25}{0.32 + 0.25} = \frac{0.08}{0.57} = 0.14$$

If we wish to find the over-all conductance of the above wall by the addition of 2 in. of insulation ($C = 0.25/2$) instead of 1 in., we have

$$\frac{0.32 \times 0.125}{0.32 + 0.125} = \frac{0.04}{0.445} = 0.09$$

18-7. Danger of Condensation. If reduction of heat flow were all that had to be considered in the structural application of insulation, the whole matter of design would be merely a simple matter of economics—comparing the cost of insulation with the cost saved in heating or cooling, as well as the reduction in size of heating or cooling plant in new structures.

Unfortunately for insulation, air almost always contains water vapor. When insulation is not correctly installed, this water vapor may, under certain conditions, destroy the insulating value, as well as the structure itself. This by-product nuisance of insulation is the greatest single cause of insulation failure. It is essential, therefore, to the proper installation of insulation that the behavior of water vapor be investigated, and then its effect on insulation. Here it can truthfully be stated: "It is not the heat but the humidity."

The problem involved is more easily grasped if the following two statements are kept in mind:

1. For practical purposes, water vapor is a gas and behaves exactly like air. It goes wherever air goes, penetrating voids, porous materials, etc.

2. Generally, water vapor always flows from a region of high temperature to a region of lower temperature.

When a certain volume of air contains all the water vapor it can, it is saturated, and the so-called relative humidity is 100%. The higher the temperature, the more vapor it can contain. Conversely, the lower the temperature, the less vapor it can hold.

Whatever the temperature, if the air is saturated, any drop in temperature will immediately cause some of the water to condense. Since this occurs in nature in the formation of dew, this temperature is called the **dew point.**

Fortunately, the air around us is seldom saturated. The amount of vapor actually in the air can be expressed as a percentage of the amount this air would contain if saturated at the same temperature; and this percentage is for practical purposes the **relative humidity.**

Assume air containing a certain definite amount of vapor less than saturation. As the temperature drops, it takes less and less vapor to saturate the air, until a temperature is reached at which the air is saturated with vapor. It has reached the dew point. Any further cooling will condense out moisture.

Charts are available that give the dew point for any conditions of temperature and relative humidities ("Heating, Ventilating, Air Conditioning Guide," American Society of Heating and Air-Conditioning Engineers).

Assume a room with air at 70°F and 30% relative humidity. The dew point is approximately 38°F. If the outside temperature is, say, 0°F, the temperature in the outside wall of the room will vary from 0°F at the exterior air film up to 70°F at the inside air film. Therefore, at some point within the wall the temperature will be 38°F, the dew point.

Since almost all building materials are porous, the vapor permeating the pores will tend to condense into drops of water at the point where the dew point occurs, and the higher temperature inside the room will cause more vapor to penetrate the wall, repeating the process.

The dew point often occurs within the insulation and may in time saturate it, drastically reducing its insulating value. Furthermore, the moisture may rot or rust the structure, or stain interior finishes. Under severe conditions, the moisture may freeze, and in expanding, as ice always does, it may cause cracks in the structure.

Condensation within a structure is generally a winter problem. The greater the relative humidity existing within the building, the more serious the problem becomes.

The relative humidity maintained within a structure depends on the occupancy of the building. If the conditions are intermittent, for example, as in a church, condensation that may occur for a short period will reevaporate in between such periods. On the other hand, an indoor swimming pool will maintain a continuous comparatively high inside relative humidity; so unless condensation is prevented, the process is accumulative during any cold weather.

Buildings often are maintained at lower temperatures (50 to 60°F) during the night when outside temperatures are at their minimum. The entire wall or roof is then at an even lower temperature. So condensation may occur at night, even if not during the day. On the other hand, though condensation may occur at night, it may not exceed the amount that would evaporate during daytime occupancy.

Generally, there is always danger of condensation within a wall or roof, etc., if the temperature on the cold side is below the dew point of the air on the warm side. Whenever condensation occurs on a window, it can be assumed that it is also occurring within the structure, although to a lesser degree.

18-8. Use of Vapor Barriers to Prevent Condensation. Whenever insulation is installed in a wall, roof, or slab, its resistance to the flow of heat is so much greater than that of the other elements of the construction that the dew point and resulting condensation may occur within the insulation.

Since water vapor flows from regions of high temperature to regions of low temperature, a simple solution to condensation is to stop the flow of water vapor by means of some surface material impervious to moisture—provided this surface is always maintained above the dew point. Such a surface is called a **vapor barrier.** It must always be applied on the warm side.

Because condensation is generally most severe during the heating season, all vapor barriers should be installed on the interior side of walls and roofs. From a practical standpoint, this means that the vapor barrier should be next to and part of the insulation.

One of the best and most economical vapor barriers is aluminum foil. Some insulations come equipped with this foil attached to one surface. However, unless reinforced with kraft paper or some other strong material, the foil is easily ripped, torn, or punctured, and so is of little value as a barrier.

Since vapor behaves as a gas, a vapor barrier, to be effective, must be airtight, or as nearly so as possible. But this is often an impractical requirement. For example, consider a roof with the insulation above the deck and between a vapor barrier and waterproof roofing. Unless the insulation is of a firm material, such as cellular glass, the heat of the sun will cause the air within the insulation to expand, forming bubbles under the waterproofing. During the coolness of the night, the bubbles will contract. After a series of sunny days and cool nights, the bending back and forth of the surface may destroy the roofing. One way to prevent this is to side-vent the roof insulation so the contained air can freely expand and contract. The side vents must, however, be protected from driving rain.

Vapor barriers can be made of other materials besides aluminum foil. There are aluminum paints, plastic paints, some plastic films, asphalt paints, rubber-base paints, asphalt, and foil-laminated papers. It must be remembered that water-repellent surfaces are not necessarily vapor barriers, that is, airtight.

To evaluate a vapor barrier, a unit known as the **perm** is used. It is defined as a vapor-transmission rate of 1 grain of water vapor through 1 square foot of material per hour when the vapor-pressure difference is equal to 1 inch of mercury (7,000 grains equal 1 pound). A material having a vapor-transmission rate of 1 perm or less is considered a good vapor barrier.

Resistance to vapor transmission is measured in units called rep. A **rep** is the reciprocal of a perm.

Since vapors flow from the warm side of a wall or roof to the cold side, the exterior surface should be as porous as possible or vented and yet offer protection against penetration of rain. This is particularly important with "blown-in" insulation as applied to frame houses, for which a vapor barrier generally cannot be installed. This type of insulation also involves another principle, which, if ignored, frequently is the cause of peeling of paint and leads to unnecessary repair of rain gutters that do not leak.

"Blown-in" insulation is sprayed into the spaces between the studs of frame construction. The interior surface is generally lath and plaster, or wallboard—both porous. The exterior is generally wood sheathing, with shingles, clapboards, or stucco. The heat resistance of the insulation is such that during the winter the location of the dew point falls within the insulation. Theoretically, the resulting condensation should occur within the insulation. This, however, does not occur. Condensation, when it does happen, does not form at the location of the dew point within the insulation, but on the inside surface of the sheathing.

The principle involved is this: Whenever the dew point occurs within a material, condensation will not occur until the flow of water vapor encounters the surface of another material of greater resistance to the flow of water vapor. That is, as long as the air can keep on moving, it will carry the moisture along with it and will not deposit the moisture until it reaches a surface that resists its flow and is colder than the dew point.

The problem inherent in blown-in insulation can be solved by "cold-side venting." In applying blown-in insulation, an opening usually is drilled through the exterior wall surface between each pair of studs. These holes should never be sealed, only covered with porous water-repellent material for protection against the weather. Then, whatever water vapor flows through the inside porous finish can escape to the cold air outside without condensing. With clapboard construction, "toothpick" wedges may be driven under the lower edge of each clapboard to provide the required openings for breathing.

To sum up: Vapor barriers, or as much resistance as possible to vapor flow (or air) should be provided on the warm side of walls and roofs. Openings or porous materials—as little resistance as possible to vapor flow—should be provided on the cold side.

If vapor barriers were perfect, cold-side venting would not be required. Unfortunately, vapor barriers are not perfect; therefore, cold-side venting is worthwhile insurance against failure of insulation in all cases.

18-9. Condensation during Summer Cooling. The discussions in Arts. 18-7 and 18-8 of winter condensation seem to contradict summer requirements when the warm and cold sides of a construction are the reverse of what they are in winter. In most parts of the United States, however, cooling seldom results in maintenance of inside temperatures more than 15°F below outside conditions, whereas in winter, inside temperatures are generally maintained at 60 to 75°F above outside conditions. So in winter, the prevailing maximum temperature differences are from four to five times what they are in summer. Furthermore, in summer very little cooling is required during the night. Hence, as far as insulation is concerned, summer condensation is so intermittent that it can be completely disregarded for the average structure and average occupancy.

It should be mentioned, however, that in low-temperature work, such as cold-storage rooms and low-temperature test cells, special conditions arise for which it is best to refer to a specialist.

18-10. Ventilation to Get Rid of Condensation. In addition to cold-side venting as described in Art. 18-7, ventilation is used in other circumstances to prevent damage from condensation. For example, where insulated ceilings exist below an attic, or an air space below a roof, louvers or some other provision for admission of outside air should be provided.

Under winter conditions, outside air, being very cold, has little capacity for holding moisture. Yet, outside air is the only source for inside air, and inside any structure there are many sources from which moisture is absorbed—people, shower baths, kitchens.

Hence, an occupied and heated building contains air with more moisture than in the outside air. The moisture tends to flow from the higher temperatures inside to the lower temperatures in the attic or air space under the roof. If these spaces are not ventilated with air capable of absorbing the moisture, it will condense and cause rust, rot, leaks, stains, etc.

In other words, any unheated space above heated spaces must be ventilated. Where prevailing winds are not dependable, one opening should be high, and another low, to take advantage of the tendency of heated air to rise.

As a general rule, the upward movement of heated air should be provided for in all air spaces above insulation placed over warmer spaces.

Ventilation is required because of the lack of a perfect vapor barrier and is workable only because the drier outside air is capable of absorbing more moisture. In general, vent area should total about $\frac{1}{300}$th of the horizontal projection of the roof area.

Section 19

HEATING AND AIR CONDITIONING

RALPH TOROP

Chief Engineer
Forman Air Conditioning Company, Inc.
New York, N.Y.

HEATING

In the design and installation of a heating system for a building, the first objective is to determine the size of the heating plant required and the proper distribution of the heat to the various rooms or zones of the structure.

19-1. General Procedure for Sizing a Heating Plant. The basic procedure used in sizing a heating plant is as follows: We isolate the part of the structure to be heated. To estimate the amount of heat to be supplied to that part, we must first decide on the design indoor and outdoor temperatures. For if we maintain a temperature of, say, 70°F inside the structure and the outside temperature is, say, 0°F, then heat will be conducted and radiated to the outside at a rate that can be computed from this 70° temperature difference. If we are to maintain the design inside temperature, we must add heat to the interior by some means at the same rate that it is lost to the exterior.

Recommended design inside temperatures are given in Table 19.1. Recommended design outdoor temperatures for a few cities are given in Table 19.2. (More extensive data are given in the "Heating, Ventilating, Air Conditioning Guide," American Society of Heating and Air-Conditioning Engineers.)

Note that the recommended design outdoor winter temperatures are not the lowest temperatures ever attained in each region. For example, the lowest temperature on record in New York City is −14°F, whereas the design temperature is 0°F. If the design indoor temperature is 70°F, we would be designing for $(70 − 0)/(70 + 14)$, or 83.3%, of the capacity we would need for the short period that a record cold of −14°F would last.

Once we have established for design purposes a temperature gradient (indoor design temperature minus outdoor design temperature) across the building exterior, we obtain the heat-transmission coefficients of the various building materials in the exterior construction for computation of the heat flow per square foot (Arts. 18-5 and 18-6). These coefficients may be obtained from the manufacturers of the materials or from tables, such as those in the "Heating, Ventilating, Air Conditioning Guide" (American Society of Heating and Air-Conditioning Engineers). Next, we have to take off from the plans the areas of exposed walls, windows, roof, etc., to determine the total heat flow, which is obtained by adding the sum of the products of the area, temperature gradient, and heat-transmission coefficient for each item (see Art. 19-7 for an application of these coefficients).

Table 19-1. Recommended Design Indoor Winter Temperatures

Type of Building	*Temp, °F*
Schools:	
Classrooms	72
Assembly rooms, dining rooms	72
Playrooms, gymnasiums	65
Swimming pool	75
Locker rooms	70
Hospitals:	
Private rooms	72
Operating rooms	75
Wards	70
Toilets	70
Bathrooms	75
Kitchens and laundries	66
Theaters	72
Hotels:	
Bedrooms	70
Ballrooms	68
Residences	72
Stores	68
Offices	72
Factories	65

Table 19-2. Recommended Design Outdoor Winter Temperatures

State	City	Temp, °F	State	City	Temp, °F
Ala.	Birmingham	10	Miss.	Vicksburg	10
Ariz.	Flagstaff	−10	Mo.	St. Louis	0
Ariz.	Phoenix	25	Mont.	Helena	−20
Ark.	Little Rock	5	Nebr.	Lincoln	−10
Calif.	Los Angeles	35	Nev.	Reno	−5
Calif.	San Francisco	35	N.H.	Concord	−15
Colo.	Denver	−10	N.J.	Trenton	0
Conn.	Hartford	0	N.Mex.	Albuquerque	0
D.C.	Washington	0	N.Y.	New York	0
Fla.	Jacksonville	25	N.C.	Greensboro	10
Fla.	Miami	35	N.Dak.	Bismarck	−30
Ga.	Atlanta	10	Ohio	Cincinnati	0
Idaho	Boise	−10	Okla.	Tulsa	0
Ill.	Chicago	−10	Ore.	Portland	10
Ind.	Indianapolis	−10	Pa.	Philadelphia	0
Iowa	Des Moines	−15	R.I.	Providence	0
Kans.	Topeka	−10	S.C.	Charleston	15
Ky.	Louisville	0	S.Dak.	Rapid City	−20
La.	New Orleans	20	Tenn.	Nashville	0
Maine	Portland	−5	Tex.	Dallas	0
Md.	Baltimore	0	Tex.	Houston	20
Mass.	Boston	0	Utah	Salt Lake City	−10
Mich.	Detroit	−10	Vt.	Burlington	−10
Minn.	Minneapolis	−20	Va.	Richmond	15

19-2. Heat Loss through Basement Floors and Walls. Although heat-transmission coefficients through basement floors and walls are available, it is generally not practicable to use them because ground temperatures are difficult to determine owing to the many variables involved. Instead, the rate of heat flow can be estimated, for all practical purposes, from Table 19-3. This table is based on ground-water temperatures, which range from about 40 to 60°F in the northern sections of the United States

Table 19-3

Ground water temp, °F	Basement floor loss,* Btu per hr per sq ft	Below-grade wall loss, Btu per hr per sq ft
40	3.0	6.0
50	2.0	4.0
60	1.0	2.0

* Based on basement temperature of 70°F.

and 60 to 75°F in the southern sections. (For specific areas, see "Heating, Ventilating, Air Conditioning Guide.")

19-3. Heat Loss from Floors on Grade. Attempts have been made to simplify the variables that enter into determination of heat loss through floors set directly on the ground. The most practical method breaks it down to a heat flow in Btu per hour per linear foot of edge exposed to the outside. With 2 in. of edge insulation, the rate of heat loss is about 50 in the cold northern sections of the United States, 45 in the temperate zones, 40 in the warm south. Corresponding rates for 1-in. insulation are 60, 55, and 50. With no edge insulation the rates are 75, 65, and 60.

19-4. Heat Loss from Unheated Attics. Top stories with unheated attics above require special treatment. To determine the heat loss through the ceiling, we must calculate the equilibrium attic temperature under design inside and outside temperature conditions. This is done by equating the heat gain to the attic via the ceiling to the heat loss through the roof:

$$U_c A_c (T_i - T_a) = U_r A_r (T_a - T_o) \qquad (19\text{-}1)$$

where U_c = heat-transmission coefficient for ceiling
U_r = heat-transmission coefficient for roof
A_c = ceiling area
A_r = roof area
T_i = design room temperature
T_o = design outdoor temperature
T_a = attic temperature

Thus

$$T_a = \frac{U_c A_c T_i + U_r A_r T_o}{U_c A_c + U_r A_r} \qquad (19\text{-}2)$$

The same procedure should be used to obtain the temperature of other unheated spaces, such as cellars and attached garages.

19-5. Air Infiltration. When the heating load of a building is calculated, it is advisable to figure each room separately, to ascertain the amount of heat to be supplied to each room. Then, compute the load for a complete floor or building and check it against the sum of the loads for the individual rooms.

Once we compute the heat flow through all exposed surfaces of a room, we have the heat load if the room is perfectly airtight and the doors never opened. However, this generally is not the case. In fact, windows and doors, even if weather-stripped, will allow outside air to infiltrate and inside air to exfiltrate. The amount of cold air entering a room depends on crack area, wind velocity, and number of exposures, among other things.

Attempts at calculating window- and door-crack area to determine air leakage usually yield a poor estimate. Faster and more dependable is the air-change method, which is based on the assumption that cold outside air is heated and pumped into the premises to create a static pressure large enough to prevent cold air from infiltrating.

The amount of air required to create this static pressure will depend on the volume of the room.

If the number of air changes taking place per hour N are known, the infiltration Q in cubic feet per minute can be computed from

$$Q = \frac{VN}{60} \qquad (19\text{-}3)$$

where V = volume of room, cu ft

The amount of heat q in Btu per hour required to warm up this cold air is given by

$$q = 1.08QT \qquad (19\text{-}4)$$

where Q = cfm of air to be warmed

T = temperature rise

19-6. Choosing Heating-plant Capacity. Total heat load equals the heat loss through conduction, radiation, and infiltration.

If we provide a heating plant with a capacity equal to this calculated heat load, we shall be able to maintain design room temperature when the design outside temperature prevails, if the interior is already at design room temperature. However, in most buildings the temperature is allowed to drop to as low as 55°F during the night. Thus, theoretically, it will require an infinite time to approach design room temperature. It, therefore, is considered good practice to add 20% to the heating-plant capacity for morning pickup.

The final figure obtained is the minimum heating-plant size required. Consult manufacturer's ratings and pick a unit with a capacity no lower than that calculated by the above method.

On the other hand, it is not advisable to choose a unit too large, because then operating efficiency suffers, increasing fuel consumption.

With a plant of 20% greater capacity than required for the calculated heat load, theoretically after the morning pickup, it will run only 100/120, or 83⅓%, of the time. Furthermore, since the design outdoor temperature occurs only during a small percentage of the heating season, during the rest of the heating season the plant would operate intermittently, less than 83⅓% of the time. Thus it is considered good practice to choose a heating unit no smaller than required but not much larger.

If the heating plant will be used to produce hot water for the premises, determine the added capacity required.

19-7. Heating-load-calculation Example. As an example of the method described in Arts. 19-1 to 19-6 for sizing a heating plant, let us take the building shown in Fig. 19-1.

A design outdoor temperature of 0°F and an indoor temperature of 70°F are assumed. The wall is to be constructed of 4-in. brick with 8-in. cinder-block backup. Interior finish is metal lath and plaster (wall heat-transmission coefficient $U = 0.25$).

The method of determining the heat load is shown in Table 19-4.

Losses from the cellar include 4 Btu per sq ft per hr through the walls [column (4)] and 2 Btu per sq ft per hr through the floors. Multiplied by the corresponding areas, they yield the total heat loss in column (6). In addition, some heat is lost because of infiltration of cold air. One-half an air change per hour is assumed, or 71.2 cfm [column (3)]. This causes a heat loss, according to Eq. (19-4), of

$$1.08 \times 71.2 \times 70 = 5,400 \text{ Btu per hr}$$

To the total for the cellar, 20% is added to obtain the heat load in column (7).

Similarly, heat losses are obtained for the various areas on the first and second floors. Heat-transmission coefficients [column (4)] were obtained from the "Heating, Ventilating, Air Conditioning Guide" (American Society of Heating and Air-Conditioning Engineers). These were multiplied by the temperature gradient $(70 - 0)$ to obtain the heat losses in column (6).

The total for the building, plus 20%, amounts to 144,475 Btu per hr. A heating plant with approximately this capacity should be selected.

19-8. Warm-air Heating. A warm-air heating system supplies heat to a room by bringing in a quantity of air above room temperature, the amount of heat added by the air being at least equal to that required to counteract heat losses.

The gravity system (without a blower) is going out of use, because it depends on the difference in density of the warm-air supply and the colder room air for the working pressure. It is obvious that resistance must be kept at a minimum with large ducts and very few elbows. The result usually is an unsightly duct arrangement.

A forced warm-air system can maintain higher air velocities, thus requires smaller ducts, and provides much more sensitive control. For this type of system,

$$q = 1.08Q(T_h - T_i) \tag{19-5}$$

where T_h = temperature of air leaving grille
  T_i = room temperature
  q = heat added by air, Btu per hr
  Q = cfm of air supplied to room

From Eq. (19-5), it is obvious that the higher the temperature of the discharge air T_h the less air need be handled. In cheaper installations, the discharge air may be as high as 170°F and ducts are small. In better systems, more air is handled with a discharge temperature as low as 135 to 140°F. With a room temperature of 70°F, we

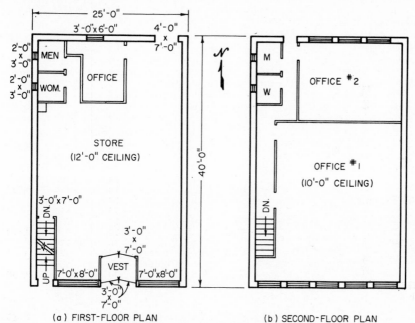

(a) FIRST-FLOOR PLAN   (b) SECOND-FLOOR PLAN

Fig. 19-1. First- and second-floor plans of a two-story building.

shall need $(170 - 70)/(135 - 70) = 1.54$ times as much air with the 135°F system as with a 170°F system.

It is not advisable to go much below 135°F with discharge air, because drafts will result. With body temperature at 98°F, air at about 100°F will hardly seem warm. If we stand a few feet away from the supply grille, 70°F room air will be entrained with the warm supply air and the mixture will be less than 98°F when it reaches us. We probably would complain about the draft.

Supply grilles should be arranged so that they blow a curtain of warm air across the cold, or exposed, walls and windows. (See Fig. 19-2 for a suggested arrangement.) These grilles should be placed near the floor, since the lower-density warm air will rise and accumulate at the ceiling.

Table 19-4. Heat-load Determination for Two-story Building

Space	Heat-loss source	Net area or cfm in-filtration	U or coeffi-cient	Temp gradi-ent, °F	Heat loss, Btu per hr	Total plus 20%
(1)	(2)	(3)	(4)	(5)	(6)	(7)
Cellar..................	Walls	1,170	4		4,680	
	Floor	1,000	2		2,000	
	½ air change	71.2	1.08	70	5,400	14,500
First-floor store..........	Walls	851	0.25	70	14,900	
	Glass	135	1.13	70	10,680	
	Doors	128	0.69	70	1,350	
	1 air change	170	1.08	70	12,850	47,600
Vestibule..............	Glass	48	1.13	70	3,800	
	2 air change	12	1.08	70	905	5,650
Office.................	Walls	99	0.25	70	1,730	
	Glass	21	1.13	70	1,660	
	½ air change	9	1.08	70	680	4,900
Men's room............	Walls	118	0.25	70	2,060	
	Glass	6	1.13	70	48	
	½ air change	3	1.08	70	226	2,800
Ladies' room...........	Walls	60	0.25	70	1,050	
	Glass	6	1.13	70	48	
	½ air change	3	1.08	70	226	1,590
Second-floor office No. 1	Walls	366	0.25	70	6,400	
	Glass	120	1.13	70	9,500	
	Roof	606	0.19	70	8,050	
	½ air change	50	1.08	70	3,780	33,300
Office No. 2.............	Walls	207	0.25	70	3,620	
	Glass	72	1.13	70	5,700	
	Roof	234	0.19	70	3,120	
	½ air change	19	1.08	70	1,435	16,650
Men's room............	Walls	79	0.25	70	1,380	
	Glass	6	1.13	70	475	
	Roof	20	0.19	70	266	
	½ air change	3	1.08	70	226	2,820
Ladies' room	Walls	44	0.25	70	770	
	Glass	6	1.13	70	475	
	Roof	20	0.19	70	266	
	½ air change	3	1.08	70	226	2,080
Hall..................	Walls	270	0.25	70	4,720	
	Door	21	0.69	70	1,015	
	Roof	75	0.19	70	1,000	
	2 air change	40	1.08	70	3,020	12,585
						144,475

Return-air grilles should be arranged in the interior near unexposed walls—in foyers, closets, etc.—and preferably at the ceiling. This is done for two reasons:

1. The warm air in all heating systems tends to rise to the ceiling. This creates a large temperature gradient between floor and ceiling, sometimes as high as 10 F. Taking the return air from the ceiling reduces this gradient.

2. Returning the warmer air to the heating plant is more economical in operation than using cold air from the floor.

19-9. Duct Design. After discharge grilles and the warm-air heater are located, it is advisable to make a single-line drawing showing the air quantities each branch and line must be able to carry (Fig. 19-2).

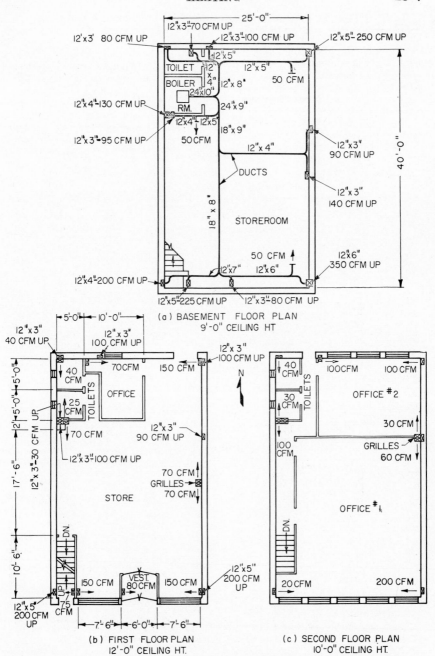

FIG. 19-2. Layout of a duct system for warm-air heating of the basement, first floor, and second floor of the building shown in Fig. 19-1.   The boiler room is in the basement.

Of the methods of duct design in use, the equal-friction method is the most practical. It is considered good practice not to exceed a pressure loss of 0.15 in. of water per 100 ft of ductwork due to friction. Higher friction will result in large power consumption for air circulation. It is also considered good practice to stay below a starting velocity in main ducts of 900 fpm in residences; 1,300 fpm in schools, theaters, and public buildings; and 1,800 fpm in industrial buildings. Velocity in branch ducts should be about two-thirds of these and in branch risers about one-half.

Too high a velocity will result in noisy and panting ductwork. Too low a velocity will require uneconomical, bulky ducts.

The shape of ducts usually installed is rectangular, because dimensions can easily be changed to maintain the required area. However, as ducts are flattened, the increase in perimeter offers additional resistance to air flow. Thus a flat duct requires an

Table 19-5. Diameters of Circular Ducts in Inches Equivalent to Rectangular Ducts

Side	4	8	12	18	24	30	36	42	48	60	72	84
3	3.8	5.2	6.2									
4	4.4	6.1	7.3									
5	4.9	6.9	8.3									
6	5.4	7.6	9.2									
7	5.7	8.2	9.9									
12	...	10.7	13.1									
18	...	12.9	16.0	19.7								
24	...	14.6	18.3	22.6	26.2							
30	...	16.1	20.2	25.2	29.3	32.8						
36	...	17.4	21.9	27.4	32.0	35.8	39.4					
42	...	18.5	23.4	29.4	34.4	38.6	42.4	45.9				
48	...	19.6	24.8	31.2	36.6	41.2	45.2	48.9	52.6			
60	...	21.4	27.3	34.5	40.4	45.8	50.4	54.6	58.5	65.7		
72	...	23.1	29.5	37.2	43.8	49.7	54.9	59.6	63.9	71.7	78.8	
84	...	....	....	39.9	46.9	53.2	58.9	64.1	68.8	77.2	84.8	91.9
96	...	....	....	....	49.5	56.3	62.4	68.2	73.2	82.6	90.5	97.9

Table 19-6. Sizes of Round Ducts for Air Flow*

Friction, in. per 100 ft	0.05		0.10		0.15		0.20		0.25		0.30	
Air flow, cfm	Diam, in.	Velocity, fpm	Diam, in.	Velocity, fpm	Diam, in.	Velocity, fpm	Diam, in.	Velocity, fpm	Diam, in.	Velocity, fpm	Diam, in.	Velocity, fpm
50	5.3	350	4.6	450	4.2	530	3.9	600	3.8	660	3.7	710
100	6.8	420	5.8	550	5.4	640	5.1	720	4.8	780	4.7	850
200	8.7	480	7.6	650	6.9	760	6.6	860	6.3	940	6.1	1,020
300	10.2	540	8.8	730	8.2	850	7.7	960	7.3	1,050	7.1	1,120
400	11.5	580	9.8	770	9.0	920	8.5	1,040	8.2	1,130	7.8	1,200
500	12.4	620	11.8	820	9.8	970	9.3	1,080	8.8	1,160	8.6	1,270
1,000	15.8	730	13.7	970	12.8	1,140	12.0	1,280	11.5	1,400	11.2	1,500
2,000	20.8	870	18.0	1,150	16.6	1,370	15.7	1,520	15.0	1,660	14.5	1,780
3,000	24.0	960	21.0	1,280	19.7	1,500	18.3	1,680	17.5	1,850		
4,000	26.8	1,050	23.4	1,360	21.6	1,600	20.2	1,800				
5,000	29.2	1,100	25.5	1,460	23.7	1,700	22.2	1,900				
10,000	37.8	1,310	33.2	1,770	30.3	2,000						

* Based on data in "Heating, Ventilating, Air Conditioning Guide," American Society of Heating and Air-Conditioning Engineers, 1957.

increase in cross section to be equivalent in air-carrying capacity to one more nearly square.

A 12 × 12-in. duct, for example, will have an area of 1 sq ft and a perimeter of 4 ft, whereas a 24 × 6-in. duct will have the same cross-sectional area but a 5-ft perimeter and thus greater friction. Therefore, a 24 × 7-in. duct is more nearly equivalent to the 12 × 12. Equivalent sizes can be determined from tables, such as those in the "Heating, Ventilating, Air Conditioning Guide" (American Society of Heating and Air-Conditioning Engineers), where rectangular ducts are rated in terms of equivalent round ducts (equal friction and capacity). Table 19-5 is a shortened version.

Charts also are available in the Guide giving the relationship between duct diameter in inches, air velocity in feet per minute, air quantity in cubic feet per minute, and friction in inches of water pressure drop per 100 ft of duct. Table 19-6 is based on data in the Guide.

In the equal-friction method, the equivalent round duct is determined for the required air flow at the predetermined friction factor.

As an example, let us compute the duct sizes for the structure for which the heat load was calculated in Art. 19-7.

Table 19-4 showed that a heating unit with 144,475 Btu per hr capacity is required. After checking manufacturers' ratings of forced warm-air heaters, we choose a unit rated at 160,000 Btu per hr and 2,010 cfm.

If we utilized the full fan capacity and supply for the rated 160,000 Btu per hr and applied Eq. (19-5), the temperature rise through the heater would be

$$\Delta T = \frac{q}{1.08Q} = \frac{160,000}{1.08 \times 2,010} = 73.6°F$$

If we adjusted the flame (oil or gas) so that the output was the capacity theoretically required, the temperature rise would be

$$\Delta T = \frac{q}{1.08Q} = \frac{144,475}{1.08 \times 2,010} = 66.5°F$$

In actual practice, we do not tamper with the flame adjustment in order to maintain the manufacturer's design balance. Instead, the amount of air supplied to each room is in proportion to its load. (See Table 19-7, which is a continuation of Table 19-4 in the design of a forced-air heating system.) Duct sizes can then be determined for the flow indicated in the table (see Fig. 19-2). In this example, minimum duct size for

Table 19-7. Air-supply Distribution in Accordance with Heat Load

Space	Load, Btu per hr	% of load	Cfm (% × 2,010)
Cellar	14,500	10.05	200
First-floor store	47,600	33.00	660
Vestibule	5,650	3.91	80
Office	4,900	3.39	70
Men's room	2,800	1.94	40
Ladies' room	1,590	1.10	25
Second-floor office No. 1	33,300	23.01	460
Office No. 2	16,650	11.51	230
Men's room	2,820	1.95	40
Ladies' room	2,080	1.44	30
Hall	12,585	8.70	175
	144,475	100.00	2,010

practical purposes is 12 × 3 in. Other duct sizes were obtained from Table 19-6, assuming a friction loss per 100 ft of 0.15, and obtaining equivalent rectangular sizes from Table 19-5.

19-10. Humidification in Warm-air Heating. A warm-air heating system lends itself readily to humidification. Most warm-air furnace manufacturers provide a humidifier that can be placed in the discharge bonnet of the heater. This usually consists of a pan with a ball float to keep the pan filled.

Theoretically, a building needs more moisture when the outside temperature drops. During these colder periods, the heater runs more often, thus vaporizing more water. During warmer periods less moisture is required and less moisture is added because the heater runs less frequently.

Some manufacturers provide a woven asbestos-cloth frame placed in the pan to materially increase the contact surface between air and water. These humidifiers have no control.

Where some humidity control is desired, a spray nozzle connected to the hot-water system with an electric solenoid valve in the line may be actuated by a humidistat.

With humidification, well-fitted storm windows must be used, for with indoor conditions of 70°F and 30% relative humidity and an outdoor temperature of 0°F, condensation will occur on the windows. Storm windows will cut down the loss of room moisture.

19-11. Control of Warm-air Heating. The sequence of operation of a warm-air heating system is usually as follows:

When the thermostat calls for heat, the heat source is started. When the air chamber in the warm-air heater reaches about 120°F, the fan is started by a sensitive element. This is done so as not to allow cold air to issue from the supply grilles and create drafts.

If the flame size and air quantity are theoretically balanced, the discharge air will climb to the design value of, say, 150°F and remain there during the operation of the heater. However, manual shutoff of grilles by residents, dirty filters, etc., will cause a reduction of air flow and a rise in air temperature above design. A sensitive safety element in the air chamber will shut off the heat source when the discharge temperature reaches a value higher than about 180°F. The heat source will again be turned on when the air temperature drops a given amount.

When the indoor temperature reaches the value for which the thermostat is set, the heat source only is shut off. The fan, controlled by the sensitive element in the air chamber, will be shut off after the air cools to below 120°F. Thus, most of the usable heat is transmitted into the living quarters instead of escaping up the chimney.

Duct systems should be sized for the design air quantity of the heater. Insufficient air will cause the heat source to cycle on and off too often. Too much air may cool the flue gases so low as to cause condensation of the water in the products of combustion. This may lead to corrosion, because of dissolved flue gases.

19-12. Warm-air Perimeter Heating. This type of heating is often used in basementless structures, where the concrete slab is laid directly on the ground. The general arrangement is as follows: The heater discharges warm air to two or more under-floor radial ducts feeding a perimeter duct. Floor grilles or baseboard grilles are located as in a conventional warm-air heating system, with collars connected to the perimeter duct.

To prevent excessive heat loss to the outside, it is advisable to provide a rigid waterproof insulation between the perimeter duct and the outside wall.

19-13. Hot-water Heating Systems. A hot-water heating system consists of a heater or furnace, radiators, piping systems, and circulator.

The gravity system without circulating pumps is going out of use. It depends on a difference in density of the hot supply water and the colder return water for working head. Obviously, resistance must be kept to a minimum, and the circulating piping system must be of large size. A forced circulation system can maintain higher water velocities, thus requires much smaller pipes and provides much more sensitive control.

Three types of piping systems are in general use for forced hot-water circulation systems:

1. One-pipe system (Fig. 19-3). This type has many disadvantages and is not usually recommended. It may be seen in Fig. 19-3 that radiator No. 1 takes hot water from the supply main and dumps the colder water back in the supply main. This causes the supply-water temperature for radiator No. 2 to be lower, requiring a corresponding increase in radiator size. (Special flow and return fittings are available to induce flow through the radiators.) The design of such a system is very difficult, and any future adjustment or balancing of the system throws the remainder of the temperatures out.

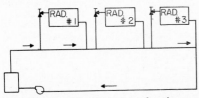

FIG. 19-3. One-pipe hot-water heating system.

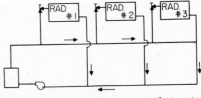

FIG. 19-4. Two-pipe direct-return hot-water heating system.

2. Two-pipe direct-return system (Fig. 19-4). Here all radiators get the same supply-water temperature, but the last radiator has more pipe resistance than the first. This can be balanced out by sizing the pump for the longest run and installing orifices in the other radiators to add an equivalent resistance for balancing.

3. Two-pipe reversed-return system (Fig. 19-5). The total pipe resistance is about the same for all radiators. Radiator No. 1 has the shortest supply pipe and the longest return pipe, while radiator No. 3 has the longest supply pipe and the shortest return pipe.

Supply design temperatures usually are 180°F, with a 20°F drop assumed through the radiators; thus the temperature of the return riser would be 160°F.

When a hot-water heating system is designed, it is best to locate the radiators, then calculate the water flow in gallons per minute required by each radiator. For a 20°F rise

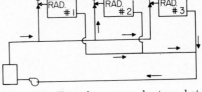

FIG. 19-5. Two-pipe reversed-return hot-water heating system.

$$q = 10,000Q \qquad (19\text{-}6)$$

where q = amount of heat required, Btu per hr
Q = flow of water, gpm

A one-line diagram showing the pipe runs should next be drawn, with gallons per minute to be carried by each pipe noted. The piping may be sized, using friction-flow charts and tables showing equivalent pipe lengths for fittings, with water velocity limited to a maximum of 4 ft per sec. (See, for example, "Heating, Ventilating, Air Conditioning Guide," American Society of Heating and Air-Conditioning Engineers.) Too high a water velocity will cause noisy flow; too low a velocity will create a sluggish system and costlier piping.

The friction should be between 250 and 600 milinches per ft (1 milinch = 0.001 in.). It should be checked against available pump head, or a pump should be picked for the design gallons per minute at the required head.

It is very important that piping systems be made flexible enough to allow for expansion and contraction. Expansion joints are very satisfactory but expensive. Swing joints as shown in Fig. 19-6 should be used where necessary. In this type of branch take-off, the runout pipe, on expansion or contraction, will cause the threads in the elbows to screw in or out slightly, instead of creating strains in the piping.

19-14. Hot-water Radiators. Radiators, whether of the old cast-iron type, finned pipe, or other, should be picked for the size required, in accordance with the manufacturer's ratings. These ratings depend on the average water temperature. For 170°F average water temperature, 1 sq ft of radiation surface is equal to 150 Btu per hr.

19-15. Expansion Tanks for Hot-water Systems. All hot-water heating systems must be provided with an expansion tank of either the open or closed type.

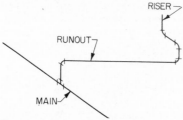

Figure 19-7 shows an open-type expansion tank. This tank should be located at least 3 ft above the highest radiator and in a location where it cannot freeze.

The size of tank depends on the amount of expansion of the water. From a low near 32°F to a high near boiling, water expands 4% of its volume. Therefore, an expansion tank should be sized for 6% of the total volume of water in radiators, heater, and all piping. That is, the volume of the tank, up to the level of its overflow pipe, should not be less than 6% of the total volume of water in the system.

FIG. 19-6. Swing joint permits expansion and contraction of piping.

Figure 19-8 is a diagram of the hookup of a closed-type expansion tank. This tank is only partly filled with water, creating an air cushion to allow for expansion and contraction. The pressure-reducing valve and relief valve are often supplied as a single combination unit.

The downstream side of the reducing valve is set at a pressure below city water-main pressure but slightly higher than required to maintain a static head in the highest

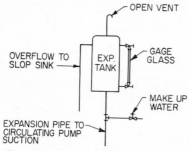

FIG. 19-7. Open-type expansion tank.

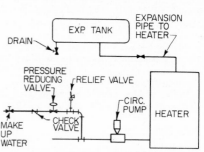

FIG. 19-8. Closed-type expansion tank.

radiator. The minimum pressure setting in pounds per square inch is equal to the *height in feet* divided by 2.31.

The relief valve is set above maximum possible pressure. Thus, the system will automatically fill and relieve as required.

19-16. Precautions in Hot-water Piping Layout. One of the most important precautions in a hot-water heating system is to avoid air pockets or loops. The pipe should be pitched so that vented air will collect at points that can be readily vented either automatically or manually. Vents should be located at all radiators.

Pipe traps should contain drains for complete drainage in case of shutdown.

Zones should be valved so that the complete system need not be shut down for repair of a zone. Multiple circulators may be used to supply the various zones at different times, for different temperature settings and different exposures.

Allow for expansion and contraction of pipe without causing undue stresses.

All supply and return piping should be insulated.

In very high buildings, the static pressure on the boiler may be too great. Heat exchangers may be installed as indicated in Fig. 19-9. The boiler temperature and lowest zone would be designed for 200°F supply water and 180°F return. The second lowest zone and heat exchanger can be designed for 170°F supply water and 150°F return, etc.

19-17. Control of Hot-water Systems. The control system is usually arranged as follows: An immersion thermostat in the heater controls the heat source, such as an oil burner or gas solenoid valve. The thermostat is set to maintain design heater water temperature (usually about 180°F). When the room thermostat calls for heat, it starts the circulator. Thus, an immediate supply of hot water is available for the radiators. A low-limit immersion stat, usually placed in the boiler and wired in series with the room stat and the pump, is arranged to shut off the circulator in the event that the water temperature drops below about 70°F. This is an economy measure; if there is a flame failure, water will not be circulated unless it is warm enough to do some good. If the boiler is used to supply domestic hot water via an instantaneous coil or storage tank, hot water will always be available for that purpose. It should be kept in mind that the boiler must be sized for the heating load plus the probable domestic hot-water demand.

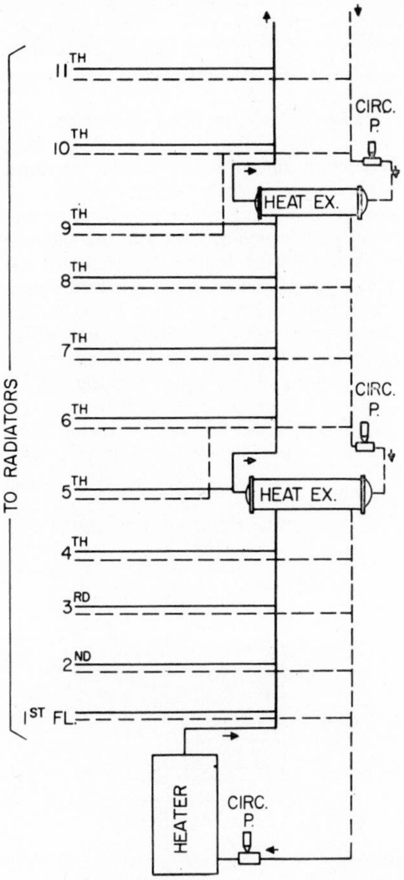

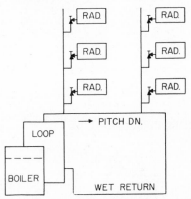

Fig. 19-9. Piping layout for tall building, including heat exchangers.

Fig. 19-10. One-pipe steam-heating system. Condensate returns through supply pipe.

19-18. Steam-heating Systems. A steam-heating system consists of a boiler or steam generator and a piping system connecting to individual radiators or convectors.

A one-pipe heating system (Fig. 19-10) is the simplest arrangement. The steam-supply pipe to the radiators is also used as a condensate return to the boiler. On start-up, as the steam is generated, the air must be pushed out of the pipe and radiators by the steam. This is done with the aid of thermostatic air valves in the radiators. When the system is cold, a small vent hole in the valve is open. After the air is pushed out and steam comes in contact with the thermostatic element, the vent hole automatically closes to prevent escape of steam.

Where pipe runouts are extensive, it is necessary to install large orifice air vents to eliminate the air quickly from the piping system; otherwise the radiators near the end of the runout may get steam much later than the radiators closest to the boiler.

Air vents are obtainable with adjustable orifice size for balancing a heating system.

The orifices of radiators near the boiler are adjusted smaller, while radiators far from the boiler will have orifices adjusted for quick venting. This helps balance the system.

The pipe must be generously sized so as to prevent gravity flow of condensate from interfering with supply steam flow. Pipe capacities for supply risers, runouts, and radiator connections are given in the "Heating, Ventilating, Air Conditioning Guide" (American Society of Heating and Air-Conditioning Engineers). Capacities are expressed in square feet of **equivalent direct radiation (EDR)**;

$$1 \text{ sq ft EDR} = 240 \text{ Btu per hr}$$

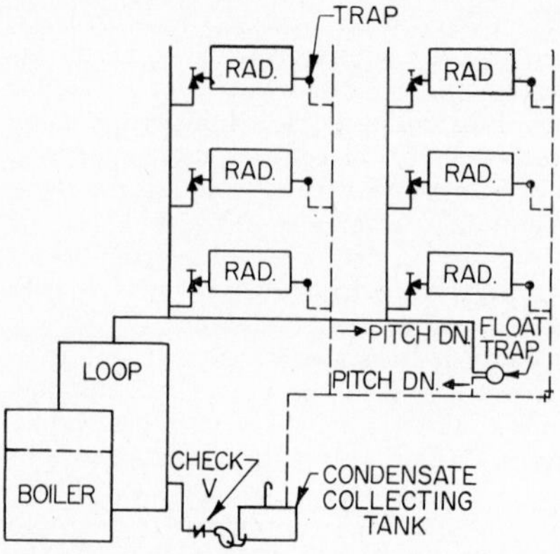

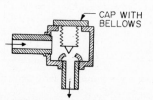

FIG. 19-11. Two-pipe steam-heating system.

Where capacities are in pounds per hour, 1 lb per hr = 970 Btu per hr.

Valves on radiators in a one-pipe system must be fully open or closed. If a valve is throttled, the condensate in the radiator will have to slug against a head of steam in the pipe to find its way back to the boiler by gravity. This will cause water hammer.

A two-pipe system is shown in Fig. 19-11. The steam supply is used to deliver steam to the supply end of all radiators. The condensate end of each radiator is connected to the return line via a thermostatic drip trap (Fig. 19-12). This trap is adjusted to open below 180°F and close above 180°F. Thus when there is enough condensate in the radiator to cool the element, it will open and allow the condensate to return to the collecting tank. A float switch in the tank starts the pump to return this condensate to the boiler against boiler steam pressure.

There are many variations in combining the two-pipe system and one-pipe system to create satisfactory systems.

In the two-pipe condensate pump return system, the pressure drop available for

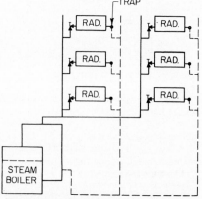

FIG. 19-12. Drip trap for condensate end of steam radiator.

FIG. 19-13. Wet-return two-pipe steam-heating system.

pipe and radiator loss is equal to boiler pressure minus atmospheric pressure, the difference being the steam gage pressure.

A wet-return system, shown in Fig. 19-13, will usually have a smaller head available for pipe loss. It is a self-adjusting system depending on the load. When steam is condensing at a given rate, the condensate will pile up in the return main above boiler level, creating a hydraulic head that forces the condensate into the boiler. The pressure above the water level on the return main will be less than the steam boiler pressure. This pressure difference—boiler pressure minus the pressure that exists above the return main water level—is available for pipe friction and radiator pressure drop.

On morning start-up when the air around the radiators is colder and the boiler is fired harder than during normal operation in an effort to pick up heat faster, the steam side of the radiators will be higher in temperature than normal.   The air-side temperature of the radiators will be lower.   This increase in temperature differential will create an increase in heat transfer causing a faster rate of condensation and a greater piling up of condensate to return the water to the boiler.

In laying out a system, the steam-supply runouts must be pitched to remove the condensate from the pipe.   They may be pitched back so as to cause the condensate to flow against the steam or pitched front to cause the condensate to flow with the steam.

Since the condensate will pile up in the return pipe to a height above boiler water level to create the required hydraulic head for condensate flow, a check of boiler-room

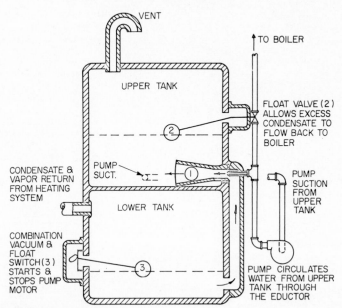

Fig. 19-14. Diagram of a vacuum pump for a vacuum steam-heating system.   The eductor (1) maintains the desired vacuum in the lower tank.

ceiling height, steam-supply header, height of lowest radiator, height of dry return pipe, etc., is necessary to determine the height the water may rise in the return pipe without flooding these components.

The pipe may have to be oversized where condensate flows against the steam (see "Heating, Ventilating, Air Conditioning Guide").   If the pitch is not steep enough, the steam may carry the condensate along in the wrong direction, causing noise and water hammer.

A vacuum heating system is basically the same as a steam system with a return condensate pump.   With such a pump the steam must always be above atmospheric pressure, because steam pressure is depended on to force out the air through the thermostatic valves.   Use of a vacuum pump allows steam pressure below atmospheric, with corresponding lower saturation temperature.   This results in an improved rate of heat transfer through the boiler tubes.   Diagrammatically, the vacuum pump is shown in Fig. 19-14.

This unit collects the condensate in a tank.   A pump circulates water through an eductor (1), pulling out the noncondensable gas to create the required vacuum.   The discharge side of the eductor nozzle is above atmospheric pressure.   Thus, an automatic control system allows the noncondensable gas to escape to atmosphere as it accumulates, and the excess condensate is returned to the boiler as the tank reaches a given level.

Vacuum systems are usually sized for a total pressure drop varying from $\frac{1}{4}$ to $\frac{1}{2}$ psi. Obviously, long equivalent-run systems (about 200 ft) will use $\frac{1}{2}$ psi total pressure drop to save pipe size.

Some systems operate without a vacuum pump by eliminating the air during morning pickup by hard firing and while the piping system is above atmospheric pressure. During the remainder of the day, when the rate of firing is reduced, a tight system will operate under vacuum.

19-19. Unit Heaters. Large open areas, such as garages, showrooms, stores, and workshops, are usually best heated by unit heaters placed at the ceiling.

Figure 19-15 shows the usual connections to a steam unit-heater installation. The thermostat is arranged to start the fan when heat is required. The surface thermostat strapped on the return pipe prevents the running of the fan when insufficient steam is available. Where hot water is used for heating, the same arrangement is used, except

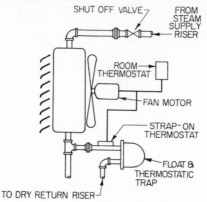

FIG. 19-15. Steam unit heater. Hot-water heater has air vent, no float and trap.

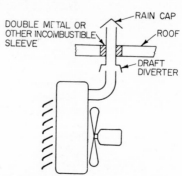

FIG. 19-16. Connections to outside for gas-fired unit heater.

that the float and thermostatic trap are eliminated and an air-vent valve is installed. Check manufacturers' ratings for capacities in choosing equipment.

Where steam or hot water is not available, direct gas-fired unit heaters may be installed. However, an outside flue is required to dispose of the products of combustion properly (Fig. 19-16). Check with local ordinances for required flues from direct gas-fired equipment. (Draft diverters are usually included with all gas-fired heaters. Check with the manufacturer when a draft diverter is not included.) For automatic control, the thermostat is arranged to start the fan and open the gas solenoid valve when heat is required. The usual safety pilot light is included by the manufacturer.

Gas-fired unit heaters are often installed in kitchens and other premises where large quantities of air may be exhausted. When a make-up air system is not provided, and the relief air must infiltrate through doors, windows, etc., a negative pressure must result in the premises. This negative pressure will cause a steady downdraft through the flue pipe from the outdoors into the space and prevent proper removal of the products of combustion. In such installations, it is advisable to place the unit heater in an adjoining space from which air is not exhausted in large quantities and deliver the warm air through ducts. Since propeller fans on most unit heaters cannot take much external duct resistance, centrifugal blower unit heaters may give better performance where ductwork is used. Sizes of gas piping and burning rates for gas can be obtained from charts and tables in the "Heating, Ventilating, Air Conditioning Guide" for various capacities and efficiencies.

The efficiency of most gas-fired heating equipment is between 70 and 80%.

19-20. Panel Heating. Panel heating, or radiant heating as it is sometimes referred to, consists of a warm pipe coil embedded in the floor, ceiling, or walls. The most common arrangement is to circulate warm water through pipe under the floor. Some installations with warm-air ducts, steam pipes, and electric-heating elements have been installed.

Warm-air ducts for panel heating are not very common. A modified system normally called the perimeter warm-air heating system circulates the warm air around the perimeter of the structure before discharging the air into the premises via grilles (Art. 19-12).

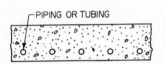

Fig. 19-17. Pipe coil embedded in a structural concrete slab for radiant heating

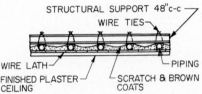

Fig. 19-18. Pipe coil embedded in a suspended plaster ceiling for radiant heating

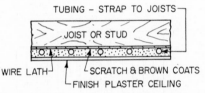

Fig. 19-19. Pipe coil attached to joists or studs and embedded in plaster for radiant heating.

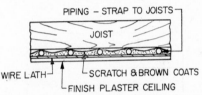

Fig. 19-20. Pipe coil embedded in plaster above lath for radiant heating.

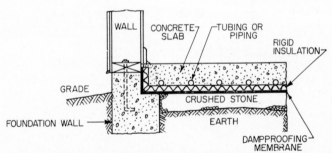

Fig. 19-21. Pipe coil embedded in a floor slab on grade for radiant heating.

Pipe coils embedded in concrete floor slabs or plaster ceilings and walls should not be threaded. Ferrous pipe should be welded, while joints in nonferrous pipe should be sweated. Return bends should be made with a pipe bender instead of fittings to avoid joints. All piping should be subjected to a hydrostatic test of at least three times the working pressure, with a minimum of 150 psig. Inasmuch as repairs are costly after construction is completed, it is advisable to adhere to the above recommendations.

Construction details for ceiling-embedded coils are shown in Figs. 19-17 to 19-20. Floor-embedded coil construction is shown in Fig. 19-21. Wall-panel coils may be installed as in ceiling panels.

Electrically heated panels are usually prefabricated and should be installed in accordance with manufacturer's recommendations and local electrical codes.

The piping and circuiting of a hot-water panel heating system are similar to hot-water heating systems with radiators or convectors, except that cooler water is used. However, a 20°F water-temperature drop is usually assumed.   Therefore, charts used for the design of hot-water piping systems may be used for panel heating, too.   (See "Heating, Ventilating, Air Conditioning Guide," American Society of Heating and Air-Conditioning Engineers.)   In panel heating, the panel coils replace radiators.   Balancing valves should be installed in each coil, as in radiators.   One wise precaution is to arrange coils in large and extensive areas so as not to have too much resistance in certain circuits.   This can be done by using high-resistance continuous coils (Fig. 19-22) or low-resistance grid (Fig. 19-23) or a combination of both (Fig. 19-24).

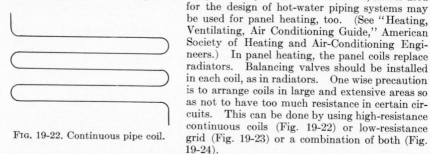

FIG. 19-22. Continuous pipe coil.

One of the advantages of this system is its flexibility; coils can be concentrated along or on exposed walls.   Also, the warmer supply water may be routed to the perimeter or exposed walls and the cooler return water brought to the interior zones.

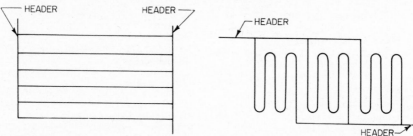

FIG. 19-23. Piping arranged in a grid for radiant heating.

FIG. 19-24. Combination of grid arrangement and continuous pipe coil.

Heat from the embedded pipes is transmitted to the panel, which in turn supplies heat to the room by two methods: (1) convection and (2) radiation.   The amount of heat supplied by convection depends on the temperature difference between the panel and the air.   The amount of heat supplied by radiation depends on the difference between the fourth powers of the absolute temperatures of panel and occupants. Thus, as panel temperature is increased, we receive a greater percentage of heat by radiation than by convection.   Inasmuch as high panel temperatures are uncomfortable, we are obliged to keep floor panel temperatures about 85°F or lower and ceiling panel temperatures 100°F or lower.   The percentage of radiant heat supplied by a panel at 85°F is about 56% and by one at 100°F about 70%.

Most advocates of panel heating claim that a lower than the usual design inside temperature may be maintained because of the large radiant surface comforting the individual; i.e., a dwelling normally maintained at 70°F may be kept at an air temperature of about 65°F.   The low air temperature makes possible a reduction in heat losses through walls, glass, etc., and thus cuts down the heating load.   However, during periods when the heating controller is satisfied and the water circulation stops, the radiant-heat source diminishes, creating an uncomfortable condition due to the below-normal room air temperature.   It is thus considered good practice to design the system for standard room temperatures (Table 19-1) and the heating plant for the total capacity required (Arts. 19-6 and 19-7).

Figure 19-25 gives the total panel output in Btu per hour per square foot for various panel surface temperatures and unheated mean radiant temperatures.

The **unheated mean radiant temperature (UMRT)** is obtained by multiplying the various areas of all unheated surfaces by their respective inside surface temperatures, adding all products, and dividing the sum by the total area.

Example. Figure 19-26 illustrates a room 10 × 10 ft with two walls exposed, two walls unexposed, ceiling exposed, floor panel heated.

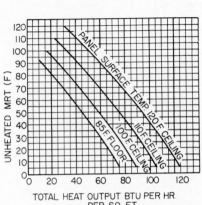

FIG. 19-25. Output of a radiant-heating panel for various panel temperatures and mean radiant temperatures of premises. (*Reprinted by permission from "Heating, Ventilating, Air Conditioning Guide," chap. 24, 1957.*)

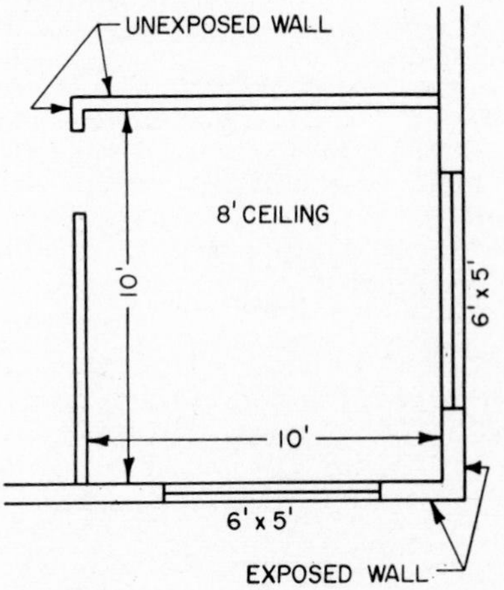

FIG. 19-26. Room to be heated by floor coils. Calculation of unheated mean radiant temperature with two exposed walls and exposed ceiling is shown in Table 19-8, and panel output required is obtained for this UMRT from Fig. 19-25.

We first obtain the panel heat output; then we can calculate from the total load the total panel area required to do the heating job. Thus, if the room heating load is 12,547 Btu per hr and the panel output per square foot from Fig. 19-25 is 40 with UMRT = 57°F (from Table 19-8), the required panel area will be

$$\frac{12,547}{40} = 313 \text{ sq ft}$$

Inasmuch as the total floor area is 100 sq ft, we shall need more than a full floor panel to do the job. Thus we must add a radiant source to either the ceiling or the walls to make up the difference.

If only one wall was exposed and insulated, the ceiling not exposed, and the windows provided with storm glass, the load would drop to 3,020 Btu per hr. The UMRT

Table 19-8. Calculation of UMRT for Fig. 19-26

	U	Area	Outside temp, F	Surface temp, °F	Area × temp
Exposed wall.........	0.3	100	0	57	5,700
Glass................	1.13	60	0	22	1,300
Unexposed wall.......	0.3	160	70	70	11,200
Exposed ceiling.......	0.3	100	0	57	5,700
Total..............	....	420	..	..	23,900

UMRT = 23,900/420 = 57°F

would be 67.8°F and the panel output per square foot (Fig. 19-25) would be 32 Btu per hr per sq ft.   Panel area required = 3,020/32 = 94 sq ft.   Thus the full floor area would be required.

Where conditions are such that only part of the floor area is required, the pipe grid should be placed near the exposed surface.

When pipe coils or grids embedded in plaster on ceilings and walls are on the finish side of the lath, the largest practical tubing is ⅝-in. OD and should be spaced 5 to 9 in. apart.   For coils nailed to the studs before the lath, 1-in. nonferrous tubing is generally used.   As a check for tube size and tube spacing, the average water temperature in the coils should be between 10 and 25°F above the desired panel surface temperature.

19-21. Snow Melting.   Design of a snow-melting system for sidewalks, roads, parking areas, etc., involves the determination of a design amount of snowfall, sizing and layout of piping, and selection of heat exchanger and circulating medium.   The pipe is placed under the wearing surface, with enough cover to protect it against damage from traffic loads, and a heated fluid is circulated through it.

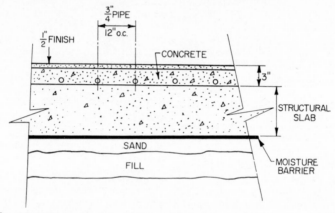

FIG. 19-27. Pipe coils embedded in outdoor concrete slab for snow melting.

If friction is too high in extensive runs, use parallel loops (Art. 19-20).   All precautions for drainage, fabrication, etc., hold for snow-melting panels as well as interior heating panels.

Table 19-9 gives a design rate of snowfall in inches of water equivalent per hour per square foot for various cities.

Table 19-10 gives the required slab output in Btu per hour per square foot at a given circulating-fluid temperature.   This temperature may be obtained once we determine the rate of snowfall and assume a design outside air temperature and wind velocity. The table assumes a snow-melting panel as shown in Fig. 19-27.

Once the Btu per hour per square foot required is obtained from Table 19-10 and we know the area over which snow is to be melted, the total Btu per hour needed for snow melting is the product of the two.   It is usual practice to add 40% for loss from back of slab.

The circulating-fluid temperature given in Table 19-10 is an average.   For a 20°F rise, the fluid temperature entering the panel will be 10°F above that found in the table, and the leaving fluid temperature will be 10°F below the average.   The freezing point of the fluid should be a few degrees below the minimum temperature ever obtained in the locality.

Check manufacturers' ratings for antifreeze solution properties to obtain the gallons per minute required and the friction loss to find the pumping head.

When ordering a heat exchanger for a given job, specify to the manufacturer the steam pressure available, fluid temperature to and from the heat exchanger, gallons per minute circulated, and physical properties of the antifreeze solution.

Table 19-9. Water Equivalent of Snowfall

City	In. per hr per sq ft	City	In. per hr per sq ft
Albany, N.Y...............	0.16	Evansville, Ind............	0.08
Asheville, N.C.............	0.08	Hartford, Conn............	0.25
Billings, Mont.............	0.08	Kansas City, Mo...........	0.16
Bismarck, N.Dak...........	0.08	Madison, Wis..............	0.08
Boise, Idaho..............	0.08	Minneapolis, Minn.........	0.08
Boston, Mass..............	0.16	New York, N.Y............	0.16
Buffalo, N.Y..............	0.16	Oklahoma City, Okla........	0.16
Burlington, Vt.............	0.08	Omaha, Nebr..............	0.16
Caribou, Maine............	0.16	Philadelphia, Pa............	0.16
Chicago, Ill................	0.06	Pittsburgh, Pa..............	0.08
Cincinnati, Ohio............	0.08	Portland, Maine............	0.16
Cleveland, Ohio............	0.08	St. Louis, Mo..............	0.08
Columbus, Ohio............	0.08	Salt Lake City, Utah........	0.08
Denver, Colo..............	0.08	Spokane, Wash.............	0.16
Detroit, Mich..............	0.08	Washington, D.C...........	0.16

Table 19-10. Heat Output and Circulating-fluid Temperatures for Snow-melting Systems

Rate of snowfall, in. per hr per sq ft of water equivalent		Air temp, 0°F			Air temp, 10°F			Air temp, 20°F			Air temp, 30°F		
		Wind, velocity, mph			Wind velocity, mph			Wind velocity, mph			Wind velocity, mph		
		5	10	15	5	10	15	5	10	15	5	10	15
0.08	Slab output, Btu per hr per sq ft	151	205	260	127	168	209	102	128	154	75	84	94
	Fluid temp, °F	108	135	162	97	117	138	85	97	110	70	75	79
0.16	Slab output, Btu per hr per sq ft	218	273	327	193	233	274	165	191	217	135	144	154
	Fluid temp, °F	142	169	198	120	149	170	117	129	142	100	105	109
0.25	Slab output, Btu per hr per sq ft	292	347	401	265	305	346	235	261	287	203	212	221
	Fluid temp, °F	179	206	234	165	186	206	151	163	176	134	139	144

NOTE: This table is based on a relative humidity of 80% for all air temperatures and construction as shown in Fig. 19-27.

19-22. Radiators and Convectors. In hot-water and steam-heating systems, heat is released to the spaces to be warmed by radiation and convection. The percentage transmitted by either method depends on the type of heat-dispersal unit used.

A common type of unit is the tubular radiator. It is composed of a series of interconnected sections, each of which consists of vertical tubes looped together. Steam-radiator sections are attached by nipples only at the base, whereas hot-water sections are connected at both top and bottom. Steam radiators should not be used for hot-water heating because of the difficulty of venting.

Pipe-coil radiators are sometimes used in industrial plants. The coils are usually placed on a wall under and between windows and are connected at the ends by branch tees or manifolds. Sometimes, finned-pipe coils are used instead of ordinary pipe. The fins increase the area of heat-transmitting surface.

Since radiators emit heat by convection as well as radiation, any enclosure should permit air to enter at the bottom and leave at the top.

Convectors, as the name implies, transmit heat mostly by convection. They usually consist of finned heating elements placed close to the floor in an enclosure that has openings at bottom and top for air circulation.

Baseboard units consist of continuous heating pipe in a thin enclosure along the base of exposed walls. They may transmit heat mostly by radiation or by convection. Convector-type units generally have finned-pipe heating elements. Chief advantage is the small temperature difference between floor and ceiling. (W. H. Severns and J. R. Fellows, "Heating, Ventilating and Air-conditioning Fundamentals," John Wiley & Sons, Inc., New York.)

19-23. Vent Connections to Chimney. Heaters in which fuel is burned must be connected in some manner to the outside so that combustion products can be removed.

A vent connection to the building chimney must be equal to the size of the boiler or heater flue. The run must be as short as possible and pitch up toward the chimney at least $\frac{1}{4}$ in. per ft. Where the vent connection must be long and there is danger that the flue gases will cool to 212°F or below before entering the chimney, be sure to insulate the vent pipe to prevent condensation of combustion products. Dissolved flue gases in the condensate could cause corrosion.

Gas-fired heaters and boilers are usually provided with an approved draft hood. This should be installed as per manufacturer's recommendations. Oil-fired heaters and boilers should be provided with an approved draft stabilizer in the vent pipe. The hoods and stabilizers are used to prevent snuffing out of the flame in extreme cases and pulling of excessive air through the combustion chamber when the chimney draft is above normal, as in extreme cold weather.

19-24. Combustion-air Requirements for Heaters. All fuel-burning heaters must have sufficient air for combustion. Every boiler room, utility room, cellar, etc., must have adequate air available from the outdoors. An area—open window or duct—equal to about twice the size of the flue connection should suffice. Too small an area will result in exhaustion of boiler-room air. The resulting lowering of the boiler-room static pressure will cause higher-pressure atmospheric air to flow through the chimney back to the boiler, causing flare-backs and smoke in the boiler room. In some cases, where boiler-room walls were constructed of light gypsum block and where the ceilings were high, complete collapse of the wall resulted because of the difference in static pressure from the outside to the inside of the wall.

AIR CONDITIONING

To determine the size of cooling plant required in a building or part of a building, we determine the heat transmitted to the conditioned space through the walls, glass, ceiling, floor, etc., and add all the heat generated in the space. This is the cooling load. The unwanted heat must be removed by supplying cool air. The total cooling load is divided into two parts—sensible and latent.

19-25. Sensible Heat. The part of the cooling load that shows up in the form of a dry-bulb temperature rise is called sensible heat. It includes heat transmitted through walls, windows, roof, floor, etc.; radiation from the sun; and heat from lights, people, electrical and gas appliances, and outside air brought into the air-conditioned space.

19-26. Latent Load. Cooling required to remove unwanted moisture from the air-conditioned space is called latent load and the heat extracted is called latent heat. Usually, the moisture is condensed out on the cooling coils in the cooling unit.

For every pound of moisture condensed from the air, the air-conditioning equipment must remove about 1050 Btu. Instead of rating items that give off moisture in pounds or grains per hour, common practice rates them in Btu per hour of latent load. These items include gas appliances, which give off moisture in products of combustion; steam baths, food, beverages, etc., which evaporate moisture; people; and humid outside air brought into the air-conditioned space.

19-27. Design Temperatures for Cooling. Before we can calculate the cooling load, we must first determine a design outside condition and the conditions we want to maintain inside.

For comfort cooling, indoor air at 80°F dry bulb and 50% relative humidity is usually acceptable.

Table 19-11 gives recommended design outdoor summer temperatures for various cities. Note that these temperatures are not the highest ever attained; for example, in New York City, the highest dry-bulb temperature ever recorded is 102°F, whereas the design outdoor dry-bulb temperature is 95°F. Similarly, the wet-bulb temperature is sometimes above the 75°F design wet-bulb for that area.

Table 19-11. Recommended Design Outdoor Summer Temperatures

State	City	Dry-bulb temp, °F	Wet-bulb temp, °F	State	City	Dry-bulb temp, °F	Wet-bulb temp, °F
Ala.........	Birmingham	95	78	Miss.......	Vicksburg	95	78
Ariz........	Flagstaff	90	65	Mo.........	St. Louis	95	78
Ariz........	Phoenix	105	75	Mont.......	Helena	95	67
Ark........	Little Rock	95	78	Nebr.......	Lincoln	95	78
Calif.......	Los Angeles	90	70	Nev........	Reno	95	65
Calif.......	San Francisco	85	65	N.H.......	Concord	90	73
Colo........	Denver	95	65	N.J........	Trenton	95	78
Conn......	Hartford	95	75	N.Mex.....	Albuquerque	95	70
D.C........	Washington	95	78	N.Y........	New York	95	75
Fla........	Jacksonville	95	78	N.C.......	Greensboro	95	78
Fla........	Miami	95	79	N.Dak.....	Bismarck	95	73
Ga........	Atlanta	95	76	Ohio......	Cincinnati	95	75
Idaho......	Boise	95	65	Okla......	Tulsa	100	77
Ill..........	Chicago	95	75	Ore........	Portland	90	68
Ind........	Indianapolis	95	75	Pa.........	Philadelphia	95	78
Iowa.......	Des Moines	95	78	R.I........	Providence	95	75
Kans......	Topeka	100	78	S.C........	Charleston	95	78
Ky........	Louisville	95	78	S.Dak.....	Rapid City	95	70
La.........	New Orleans	95	80	Tenn.......	Nashville	95	78
Maine.....	Portland	90	73	Tex.......	Dallas	100	78
Md........	Baltimore	95	78	Tex.......	Houston	95	78
Mass......	Boston	95	75	Utah......	Salt Lake City	95	65
Mich......	Detroit	95	75	Vt........	Burlington	90	73
Minn......	Minneapolis	95	75	Va.........	Richmond	95	78

19-28. Heat Gain through Enclosures. To obtain the heat gain through walls, windows, ceilings, floors, etc., when it is warmer outside than in, the heat-transfer coefficient is multiplied by the surface area and the temperature gradient (Arts. 19-1 and 19-7).

Radiation from the sun through glass is another source of heat. It can amount to about 200 Btu per hr per sq ft for a single sheet of unshaded common window glass facing east and west, about three-fourths as much for windows facing northeast and northwest, and one-half as much for windows facing south. For most practical applications, however, the sun effect on walls can be neglected, since the time lag is considerable and the peak load is no longer present by the time the radiant heat starts to work through to the inside surface. Also, if the wall exposed to the sun contains windows, the peak radiation through the glass also will be gone by the time the radiant heat on the walls gets through.

Radiation from the sun through roofs may be considerable. For most roofs, total equivalent temperature differences for calculating heat gain through sunlit roofs is about 50°F.

19-29. Roof Sprays. Many buildings have been equipped with roof sprays to reduce the sun load on the roof. Usually the life of a roof is increased by the spray system, because it prevents swelling, blistering, and vaporization of the volatile components of the roofing material. It also prevents the thermal shock of thunderstorms during hot spells. Equivalent temperature differentials for computing heat gain on sprayed roofs is about 18°F.

Water pools 2 to 6 in. deep on roofs have been used, but they create structural difficulties. Furthermore, holdover heat into the late evening after the sun has set creates a breeding ground for mosquitoes and requires algae-growth control. Equivalent temperature differential to be used for computing heat gain for water-covered roofs is about 22°F.

Spray control is effected by the use of a water solenoid valve actuated by a temperature controller whose bulb is embedded in the roofing. Tests have been carried out with controller settings of 95, 100, and 105°F. The last was found to be the most practical setting.

The spray nozzles must not be too fine, or too much water is lost by drift. For ridge roofs, a pipe with holes or slots is satisfactory. When the ridge runs north and south, two pipes with two controllers would be practical, for the east pipe would be in operation in the morning and the west pipe in the afternoon.

19-30. Heat Gains from Interior Sources. Electric lights and most other electrical appliances convert their energy into heat.

$$q = 3.42W \qquad (19\text{-}7)$$

where q = Btu per hr developed
$\qquad W$ = watts of electricity used

Where fluorescent lighting is used, add 25% of the lamp rating for the heat generated in the ballast. Where electricity is used to heat coffee, etc., some of the energy is used to vaporize water. Tables in the "Heating, Ventilating, Air Conditioning Guide" (American Society of Heating and Air-Conditioning Engineers) give an estimate of the Btu per hour given up as sensible heat and that given up as latent heat by appliances.

Heat gain from people can be obtained from Table 19-12.

19-31. Heat Gain from Outside Air. The sensible heat from outside air brought into a conditioned space can be obtained from

$$q_s = 1.08Q(T_o - T_i) \qquad (19\text{-}8)$$

where q_s = sensible load due to outside air, Btu per hr
$\qquad Q$ = cfm of outside air brought into conditioned space
$\qquad T_o$ = design dry-bulb temperature of outside air
$\qquad T_i$ = design dry-bulb temperature of conditioned space

The latent load due to outside air in Btu per hour is given by

$$q_l = 0.67Q(G_o - G_i) \qquad (19\text{-}9)$$

where Q = cfm of outside air brought into conditioned space
$\qquad G_o$ = moisture content of outside air, grains per lb of air
$\qquad G_i$ = moisture content of inside air, grains per lb of air

The moisture content of air at various conditions may be obtained from a psychrometric chart.

19-32. Miscellaneous Sources of Heat Gain. In an air-conditioning unit, the fan used to circulate the air requires a certain amount of brake horsepower depending on the air quantity and the total resistance in the ductwork, coils, filters, etc. This horsepower will dissipate itself in the conditioned air and will show up as a tempera-

Table 19-12. Rates of Heat Gain from Occupants of Conditioned Spaces*

Degree of activity	Typical application	Total heat adults, male, Btu per hr	Total heat adjusted,† Btu per hr	Sensible heat, Btu per hr	Latent heat, Btu per hr
Seated at rest................	Theater, matinee	390	330	180	150
	Theater, evening	390	350	195	155
Seated, very light work........	Offices, hotels, apartments	450	400	195	205
Moderately active office work..	Offices, hotels, apartments	475	450	200	250
Standing, light work; or walking slowly	Department store, retail store, dime store	550	450	200	250
Walking; seated.............	Drug store				
Standing; walking slowly.....	Bank	550	500	200	300
Sedentary work..............	Restaurant‡	490	550	220	330
Light bench work............	Factory	800	750	220	530
Moderate dancing............	Dance hall	900	850	245	605
Walking 3 mph; moderately heavy work...............	Factory	1000	1000	300	700
Bowling¶..................	Bowling alley				
Heavy work................	Factory	1500	1450	465	985

NOTE: Tabulated values are based on 80°F room dry-bulb temperature. For 78°F room dry-bulb, the total heat remains the same, but the sensible heat values should be increased by approximately 10%, and the latent heat values decreased accordingly.

* Published by permission from "Heating, Ventilating, Air Conditioning Guide," Chap. 13, 1957.

† *Adjusted total heat gain* is based on normal percentage of men, women, and children for the application listed, with the postulate that the gain from an adult female is 85% of that for an adult male, and that the gain from a child is 75% of that for an adult male.

‡ Adjusted total heat value for *sedentary work, restaurant*, includes 60 Btu per hr for food per individual (30 Btu sensible and 30 Btu latent).

¶ For *bowling* figure one person per alley actually bowling, and all others as sitting (400 Btu per hr) or standing (550 Btu per hr).

ture rise. Therefore, we must include the fan brake horsepower in the air-conditioning load. For most low-pressure air-distribution duct systems, the heat from this source varies from 5% of the sensible load for smaller systems to $3\frac{1}{2}$% of the sensible load in the larger systems.

Where the air-conditioning ducts pass through nonconditioned spaces, the ducts must be insulated. The amount of heat transmitted to the conditioned air through the insulation may be calculated from the duct area and the insulation heat-transfer coefficient.

19-33. Cooling Measured in Tons. Once we obtain the cooling load in Btu per hour, we convert the load to tons of refrigeration by

$$\text{Load in tons} = \frac{\text{load in Btu per hr}}{12,000} \qquad (19\text{-}10)$$

A ton of refrigeration is the amount of cooling that can be done by a ton of ice melting in 24 hr.

19-34. Example of Cooling Calculation. Consider the building shown in Fig. 19-2. The first and second floors only will be air-conditioned. The design outdoor condition is assumed to be 95°F DB (dry-bulb) and 75°F WB (wet-bulb). The design indoor condition is 80°F DB and 50% relative humidity.

The temperature gradient across an exposed wall will be 15°F (95°F − 80°F). The temperature gradient between a conditioned and an interior nonconditioned space, such as the cellar ceiling, is assumed to be 10°F.

Exterior walls are constructed of 4-in. brick with 8-in. cinder backup; interior finish is plaster on metal lath. Partitions consist of 2×4 studs, wire lath, and plaster. First floor has double flooring on top of joists; cellar ceiling is plaster on metal lath.

Lights may be assumed to average 4 watts per sq ft. Assume 50 persons will be in the store, 2 in the first-floor office, 10 in second-floor office No. 1, and 5 in second-floor office No. 2.

First-floor Store Load

Heat gain through enclosures:	Area, Sq Ft	$U(T_o - T_i)$, °F	Heat Load, Btu per Hr
North wall	92	$\times$ 0.25 $\times$ 15	344
North door	28	$\times$ 0.46 $\times$ 15	193
South wall	412	$\times$ 0.25 $\times$ 15	1,540
South glass	154	$\times$ 1.04 $\times$ 15	2,405
East wall	480	$\times$ 0.25 $\times$ 15	1,800
West wall	228	$\times$ 0.25 $\times$ 15	854
Partition	263	$\times$ 0.39 $\times$ 10	1,025
Partition door	49	$\times$ 0.46 $\times$ 10	225
Floor	841	$\times$ 0.25 $\times$ 10	2,100
Ceiling	112	$\times$ 0.25 $\times$ 10	280

Load due to conduction.. 10,766
Sun load on south glass, 154 sq ft $\times$ 98............................... 15,100
Occupants (sensible heat) from Table 19-12, 50 $\times$ 200............... 10,000
Lights [Eq. (19-7)] 841 sq ft $\times$ 4 watts per sq ft $\times$ 3.42........... 11,500
$$\overline{47,366}$$
Fan hp (4% of total)... 1,913
Total internal sensible heat load.. 49,279
Fresh air (sensible heat) at 10 cfm per person [Eq. (19-8), 500 cfm $\times$ 1.08 $\times$15]... 8,100
Total sensible load.. 57,379
Occupants (latent load) from Table 19-12, 50 $\times$ 250.................. 12,500
Fresh air (latent heat) Eq. (19-9), 500 $\times$ 0.67 (99–77).............. 7,360
Total latent load.. 19,860
Total load... 77,239

$$\text{Load in tons} = \frac{77{,}249}{12{,}000} = 6.45 \text{ tons}$$

If supply air is provided at 18°F differential, with fresh air entering the unit through an outside duct, the flow required is [from Eq. (19-8)]

$$Q = \frac{49{,}279}{1.08 \times 18} = 2{,}530 \text{ cfm}$$

If no fresh-air duct is provided and all the infiltration air enters directly into the premises, the flow required is computed as follows:

$$\text{Store volume} = 841 \times 12 = 10{,}100 \text{ cu ft}$$

$$\text{Infiltration} = \frac{10{,}100}{60} \times 1.5 = 252 \text{ cfm}$$

Sensible load from the infiltration air [Eq. (19-8)]
$$= 252 \times 1.08 \times 15 = 4{,}090 \text{ Btu per hr}$$

$$\text{Internal sensible load plus infiltration} = 49{,}279 + 4{,}090 = 53{,}369 \text{ Btu per hr}$$

$$\text{Flow with no fresh-air duct} = \frac{53{,}369}{1.08 \times 18} = 2{,}750 \text{ cfm}$$

First-floor Office Load

Btu per Hr

Heat gain through enclosures:
North wall, 102 × 0.25 × 15................................ 382
North glass, 18 × 1.04 × 15.............................. 281
Partition, 30 × 0.39 × 10................................ 117
Floor, 79 × 0.25 × 10..................................... 198
                                                        ───
                                                        978
2 occupants (sensible load) at 195.......................... 390
Lights, 79 × 4 × 3.42..................................... 1,080
                                                        ─────
                                                        2,448
Fan hp 4%... 98
Total internal sensible load..............................   2,546
Fresh air (sensible load) at 2 changes per hour, 32 × 1.08 × 15..   518
                                                              ─────
Total sensible load.......................................   3,064
Occupants (latent load), 2 at 205........................... 410
Fresh air (latent load), 32 × 0.67(99 − 77)................. 473
                                                              ───
Total latent load...   883
Total load..   3,947 Btu per h

$$\text{Load in tons} = \frac{3,947}{12,000} = 0.33 \text{ ton}$$

$$\text{Supply air required with fresh-air duct} = \frac{2,546}{1.08 \times 18} = 131 \text{ cfm}$$

$$\text{Supply air required with no fresh-air duct} = \frac{3,064}{1.08 \times .8} = 158 \text{ cfm}$$

Second-floor Office No. 1

Btu per Hr

Heat gain through enclosures:
South wall, 130 × 0.25 × 15................................. 388
South glass, 120 × 1.04 × 15............................... 1,870
East wall, 260 × 0.25 × 15................................. 975
West wall, 40 × 0.25 × 15.................................. 150
Partition, 265 × 0.39 × 10................................ 1,035
Door in partition, 35 × 0.46 × 10.......................... 161
Roof, 568 × 0.19 × 54..................................... 5,820
                                                          ──────
                                                          10,399
Sun load on south glass, 120 × 98......................... 11,750
Occupants (sensible load), 10 × 195....................... 1,950
Lights, 568 × 4 × 3.42.................................... 7,770
                                                          ──────
                                                          31,869
Fan hp 4%... 1,270
Total internal sensible load..............................   33,139
Fresh air (sensible load), 180 × 1.08 × 15................   2,910
                                                               ──────
Total sensible load.......................................   36,049
Occupants (latent load), 10 × 205......................... 2,050
Fresh air (latent load), 180 × 0.67(99 − 77).............. 2,660
                                                               ──────
Total latent load...   4,710
Total load..   40,759

$$\text{Load in tons} = \frac{40,759}{12,000} = 3.4 \text{ tons}$$

$$\text{Supply air required with fresh-air duct} = \frac{33,139}{1.08 = 18} = 1,700 \text{ cfm}$$

$$\text{Supply air required with no fresh-air duct} = \frac{36,049}{1.08 \times 18} = 1,850 \text{ cfm}$$

Second-floor Office No. 2

Heat gain through enclosures: *Btu per Hr*

North wall, 103 × 0.25 × 15	386
North glass, 72 × 1.04 × 15	1,110
East wall, 132 × 0.25 × 15	495
Partition, 114 × 0.39 × 10	445
Door in partition, 18 × 0.46 × 10	83
Roof, 231 × 0.19 × 54	2,370
	4,889
Occupants (sensible load), 5 × 195	975
Lights, 231 × 4 × 3.42	3,160
	9,024
Fan hp 4%	360

Total internal sensible load		9,384
Fresh air (sensible load), 77 × 1.08 × 15		1,250
Total sensible load		10,634
Occupants (latent load), 5 × 205	1,025	
Fresh air (latent load), 77 × 0.67(99 − 77)	1,140	
Total latent load		2,165
Total load		12,799

$$\text{Load in tons} = \frac{12,799}{12,000} = 1.07 \text{ tons}$$

$$\text{Supply air required with fresh-air duct} = \frac{9,384}{1.08 \times 18} = 483 \text{ cfm}$$

$$\text{Supply air required with no fresh-air duct} = \frac{10,634}{1.08 \times 18} = 550 \text{ cfm}$$

Cooling and supply-air requirements for the building are summarized in Table 19-13.

Table 19-13. Cooling-load Analysis for Building in Fig. 19-2

Space	Tons	Cfm with fresh-air duct	Cfm with no fresh-air duct
First-floor store	6.45	2,545	2,750
First-floor office	0.33	131	158
Second-floor office No. 1	3.40	1,700	1,850
Second-floor office No. 2	1.07	483	550
Total	11.25	4,859	5,308

19-35. Basic Cooling Cycle. In air-conditioning work, it usually takes 1 hp to produce a ton of refrigeration. Some manufacturers produce units that are able to yield a little more than 1 ton per hp, while others will yield a little less. Also, the capacity of a compressor varies with the conditions of suction pressure and head pressure.

Figure 19-28 shows the basic air-conditioning cycle of the direct-expansion type. The compressor takes refrigerant gas at a relatively low pressure and compresses it to a higher pressure. (For Freon-12, the head pressure is designed for 125 psi.) The hot gas is passed to a condenser where heat is removed and the refrigerant liquefied. The liquid is then piped to the cooling coil of the air-handling unit and allowed to expand to a lower pressure (suction pressure). The liquid vaporizes or is boiled off by the relatively warm air passing over the coil. The compressor pulls away the vaporized refrigerant to maintain the required low coil pressure with its accompanying low temperature.

In some systems, water is chilled by the refrigerant and circulated to units in or near spaces to be cooled (Fig. 19-29), where air is cooled by the water.

19-36. Air-distribution Temperature for Cooling. The air-distribution system is the most critical part of an air-conditioning system. If insufficient air is circulated,

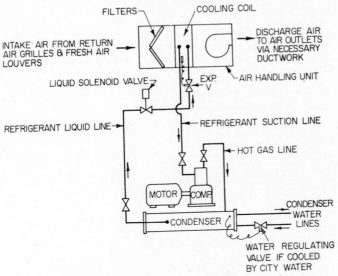

FIG. 19-28. Direct-expansion air-conditioning cycle.

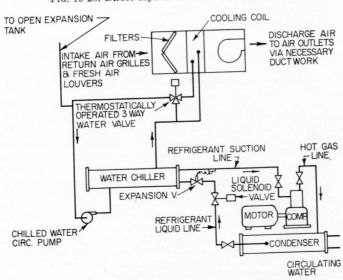

FIG. 19-29. Chilled-water air-conditioning cycle.

proper cooling cannot be done. On the other hand, handling large quantities of air is expensive in both initial cost and operation. The amount of cool air required increases rapidly the closer its temperature is brought to the desired room temperature.

If, for example, we wish to maintain 80°F DB (dry bulb) in a room and we introduce air at 60°F, the colder air when warming up to 80°F will absorb an amount of sensible heat equal to q_s. According to Eq. (19-8), $q_s = 1.08Q_1(80 - 60) = 21.6Q_1$, where Q_1 is the required air flow in cubic feet per minute. From Eq. (19-8), it can be seen also that, if we introduce air at 70°F, with a temperature rise of 10°F instead of 20°F, $q_s = 10.8Q_2$, and we shall have to handle twice as much air to do the same amount of sensible cooling.

From a psychrometric chart, the dew point of a room at 80°F DB and 50% relative humidity is found to be 59°F. If the air leaving the air-conditioning unit is 59°F or less, the duct will sweat and will require insulation. Even if we spend the money to insulate the supply duct, the supply grilles may sweat and drip. Therefore, theoretically, to be safe, the air leaving the air-conditioning unit should be 60°F or higher.

Because there are many days when outside temperatures are less than design conditions, the temperature of the air supplied to the coil will fluctuate, and the temperature of the air leaving the coil may drop a few degrees. This will result in sweating ducts.

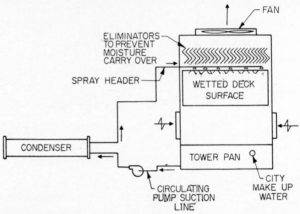

FIG. 19-30. Water-tower connection to condenser of an air-conditioning system.

It is good practice, therefore, to design the discharge-air temperature for about 3°F higher than the room dew point.

Thus, for 80°F DB, 50% RH, and dew point at 59°F, the minimum discharge air temperature would be 62°F as insurance against sweating. The amount of air to be handled may be obtained from Eq. (19-8), with a temperature difference of 18°F.

19-37. Condensers. If a water-cooled condenser is employed to remove heat from the refrigerant, it may be serviced with city water, and the warm water discharged to a sewer. Or a water tower (Fig. 19-30) may be used to cool the condenser discharge water, which can then be recirculated back to the condenser.

Where practical, the water condenser and tower can be replaced by an evaporative condenser as in Fig. 19-31.

The capacity of water savers, such as towers or evaporative condensers, depends on the wet-bulb temperature. The capacity of these units decreases as the wet-bulb temperature increases.

Such equipment should be sized for a wet-bulb temperature a few degrees above that used for sizing air-conditioning equipment.

As an example, consider an area where the design wet-bulb temperature is 75°F. If we size the air-conditioning equipment for this condition, we shall be able to maintain design inside conditions when the outside conditions happen to be 75°F WB. There will be a few days a year, however, when the outside WB may even attain 79 or 80°F WB. During the higher wet-bulb days, with the air-conditioning equipment in operation, we shall balance out at a relative humidity above design. For example, if the design relative humidity is 50%, we may balance out at 55% or higher.

However, if the water towers and evaporative condensers are designed for 75°F WB, then at a wet-bulb temperature above 75, the water-saver capacity would be decreased and the compressor head pressure would build up too high, overload the motor, and kick out on the overload relays. So we use 78°F WB for the design of water savers. Now, on a 78°F WB day, the compressor head pressure would be 125 psi, the equipment will be in operation, though maintaining room conditions a little less comfortable than desired. At 80°F WB, the compressor head pressure will build up above 125 psi and the motor will be operating above design brake horsepower, but a standard National Electrical Manufacturers Association (NEMA) motor can take prolonged operation 20 % above rated horsepower.

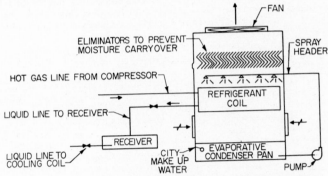

Fig. 19-31. Evaporative condenser for an air-conditioning system.

Water condensers are sized for 104°F refrigerant temperature and 95°F water leaving. When condensers are used with city water, these units should be sized for operation with the water at its warmest condition.

The amount of water in gallons per minute required for condensers is equal to

$$Q = \frac{\text{tons of cooling} \times 30}{\text{water-temperature rise}} \qquad (19\text{-}11)$$

This equation includes the heat of condensation of the compressor when used for air-conditioning service. In many cities, the water supplied is never above 75°F. Thus 75°F is used as a condenser design condition.

When high buildings have roof tanks exposed to the sun, it will be necessary to determine the maximum possible water temperature and order a condenser sized for the correct water flow and inlet-water temperature.

When choosing a condenser for water-tower use, we must determine the water temperature available from the cooling tower with 95°F water to the tower. Check the tower manufacturer for the capacity required at the design WB, with 95°F water to the sprays, and the appropriate wet-bulb approach. (Wet-bulb approach is equal to the number of degrees the temperature of the water leaving the tower is above the wet-bulb temperature. This should be for an economical arrangement about 7°F.) Thus, for 78°F, the water leaving the tower would be 85°F, and the condenser would be designed for a 10°F water-temperature rise; i.e., for water at 95°F to the tower and 85°F leaving the tower.

Evaporative condensers should be picked for the required capacity at a design wet-bulb temperature for the area in which they are to be installed. Manufacturers' ratings should be checked before the equipment is ordered.

For small cooling units, condensers can be cooled by a fan blowing air over the refrigerant coils. This type of condenser, however, generally is not so efficient as a water-cooled type, because its efficiency drops as the outside temperature rises.

19-38. Compressors for Air Conditioning. Compressor capacity decreases with the head pressure. For Freon-12, commonly used refrigerant, 125 psi head pressure is considered standard (or 104°F, which is the saturation temperature of the refrigerant at this pressure).

Capacity of the compressor also decreases with the suction pressure (or back pressure). However, it is usual practice to rate the compressors in tons or Btu per hour at various suction temperatures. For installations where the latent load is high, such as restaurants, bars, and dance halls, where a large number of people congregate, the coil temperature will have to be brought low enough to condense out large amounts of moisture. Thus, we find that a suction temperature about 40°F will be required.

In offices, homes, etc., where the latent load is low, 45°F suction will be satisfactory. Therefore, choose a compressor with capacity not less than the total cooling load and rated at 104°F head temperature and a suction temperature between 40 and 45°F, depending on the nature of the load.

Obtain the brake horsepower of the compressor at these conditions and make sure that a motor is provided with horsepower not less than that required by the compressor.

A standard NEMA motor can be loaded about 15 to 20% above normal. Do not depend on this safety factor, for it will come in handy during initial pull-down periods, excess occupancy, periods of low-voltage conditions, etc.

Compressor manufacturers have all the above data available for the asking so that one need not guess.

19-39. Air-handling Units. For an economical installation, the air-handling units should be chosen to handle the least amount of air without danger of sweating ducts and grilles. In most comfort cooling, an 18°F discharge temperature below room temperature will be satisfactory.

If a fresh-air duct is used, the required fresh air is mixed with the return air and the mix is sent through the cooling coil; i.e., the fresh-air load is taken care of in the coil and discharge air must take care of the internal load only. Then, from Eq. (19-8), the amount of air to be handled is

$$Q = \frac{q_s}{1.08 \Delta T}$$

where q_s = internal sensible load

ΔT = temperature difference between room and air leaving coil (usually 18°F) See Art. 19-36.

If a fresh-air duct is not installed and the outside air is introduced directly or by infiltration into the room, we use Eq. (19-8) with the sensible part of the fresh-air load added to q_s; for now, the fresh-air load becomes part of the internal load.

Once the amount of air to be handled is determined, choose a coil of face area such that the coil-face velocity V would be not much more than 500 fpm.

$$V = \frac{Q}{A_c} \qquad\qquad (19\text{-}12)$$

where Q = air flow, cfm

A_c = coil face area, sq ft

V = air velocity, fpm

The number of rows of coil can be determined by getting the manufacturer's capacity ratings of the coils for 3, 4, 5, 6, etc., rows deep and choosing a coil that can handle not less than the sensible and latent load at the working suction temperature.

19-40. Filters for Air-conditioning Units. All air-handling units must be provided with filter boxes. Removal of dust from the conditioned air not only lowers building maintenance costs and creates a healthier atmosphere but prevents the cooling and heating coils from becoming blocked up.

Air filters come in a number of standard sizes and thicknesses. The filter area to be chosen for a system should be such that the air velocity should not exceed 350 fpm; i.e., minimum filter area equals $Q/350$, where Q is the air flow in cubic feet per minute.

Most air filters are of either the throwaway or cleanable type. Both these types will fit a standard filter rack.

Electrostatic filters are usually employed in industrial installations, where a higher percentage of dust removal must be obtained. Check with manufacturers' ratings for particle-size removal, capacity, and static-pressure loss; also check electric service required. These units generally are used in combination with regular throwaway or cleanable air filters, which take out the large particles, while the charged electrostatic plates remove the smaller ones.

19-41. "Package" Air-conditioning Units. To meet the great demand for cheaper air-conditioning installations, manufacturers produce "package," or preassembled, units. These vary from ¼- to 1-hp window units and ¾- to 40-hp floor units. Very little labor is required to install them.

Package window units operate on the complete cycle shown in Fig. 19-28, but the equipment is very compactly arranged. The condenser is air-cooled and projects outside the window. The cooling coil extends inside. Both the cooling-coil fan and condenser fan usually are run by the same motor.

These package units require no piping, just an electric receptacle of adequate capacity. Moisture that condenses on the cooling coil runs via gutters to a small sump near the condenser fan. Many manufacturers incorporate a disk slinger to spray this water on the hot condenser coil, which vaporizes it and exhausts it to the outside. This arrangement serves a double purpose:

1. Gets rid of humidity from the room without piping.
2. Helps keep the head pressure down with some evaporative cooling.

Floor-type package units also contain the full air-conditioning cycle (Fig. 19-28). However, only small units are air-cooled. These are usually placed near a window with a duct connection for the required outside air. Larger units are water-cooled, by either city water or tower water. The same condenser can usually be arranged for either use.

A combination package unit including an evaporative condenser is also available.

Most packaged units are standardized to handle about 400 cfm of air per ton of refrigeration. This is a good average air quantity for most installations. For restaurants, bars, etc., where high latent loads are encountered, the unit handles more than enough air; also, the sensible capacity is greater than required. However, the latent capacity may be lower than desired. This will result in a somewhat higher relative humidity in the premises.

For high sensible-load jobs, such as homes, offices, etc., where occupancy is relatively low, air quantities are usually too low for the installed tonnage. Latent capacity, on the other hand, may be higher than desired. Thus, if we have a total load of 5 tons—4½ tons sensible and ½ ton latent—and we have available a 5-ton unit with a capacity of 4 tons sensible and 1 ton latent, it is obvious that during extreme weather the unit will not be able to hold the dry-bulb temperature down, but the relative humidity will be well below design value.

Under such conditions, these units may work out satisfactorily. In the cases where the latent capacity is too low and we have more than enough sensible capacity, we can set the thermostat below design indoor dry-bulb temperature and maintain a lower dry-bulb temperature and higher relative humidity to obtain satisfactory comfort conditions. Where we have insufficient sensible capacity, we have to leave the thermostat at the design setting. This will automatically yield a higher dry-bulb temperature and lower relative humidity—and the premises will be comfortable if the total installed capacity is not less than the total load.

As an example of the considerations involved in selecting package air-conditioning equipment, let us consider the structure in Fig. 19-2 and the load analysis in Table 19-13.

If this were an old building, it would be necessary to do the following:

First-floor store (load 6.45 tons). Inasmuch as a 5-ton unit is too small, we must choose the next larger size—a 7½-ton package unit. This unit has a greater capacity than needed to maintain design conditions. However, many people would like somewhat lower temperature than 80°F dry bulb, and this unit will be capable of maintaining such conditions.   Also, if there are periods when more than 50 occupants will be in the store, extra capacity will be available.

First-floor office (load 0.33 tons).   Ordinarily a ½-ton window unit would be required to do the job, because air-cooled condensing units yield less than 1 ton per hp.   But because the store unit has spare capacity, it would be advisable to arrange a duct from the store 7½-ton unit to cool the office.

Second-floor offices (No. 1, load 3.40 tons; No. 2, load 1.07 ton).   A 5-ton unit is required for the two offices.   But it will be necessary to provide a fresh-air connection to eliminate the fresh-air load from the internal load, to reduce air requirements to the rated flow of the unit.   Then, the 2,000 cfm rating of the 5-ton package unit will be close enough to the 2,183 cfm required for the two offices.

Inasmuch as the total tonnage is slightly above that required, we will balance out at a slightly lower relative humidity than 50%, if the particular package unit selected is rated at a sensible capacity equal to the total sensible load.

A remote air-conditioning system would be more efficient, because it could be designed to meet the needs of the building more closely.   A single air-handling unit for both floors can be arranged with the proper ductwork.   However, local ordinances should be checked, since some cities have laws preventing direct-expansion systems servicing more than one floor.   A chilled water system (Fig. 19-29) could be used instead.

19-42. Package Chillers.   These units consist of a compressor, water chiller, condenser, and all automatic controls.   The contractor has to provide the necessary power and condensing water, from either a cooling tower, city water, or some other source such as well or river.   The controls are arranged to cycle the refrigeration compressor to maintain a given chilled water temperature.   The contractor need only provide insulated piping to various chilled-water air-handling units.

The larger packaged chillers, 50 to 1,000 tons, are generally powered by centrifugal compressors.   When the units are so large that they have to be shipped knocked down, they are usually assembled by the manufacturer's representative on the job site, sealed, pressure-tested, evacuated, dehydrated, and charged with the proper amount of refrigerant.

19-43. Absorption Units for Cooling.   Absorption systems for commercial use are usually arranged as package chillers.   In place of electric power, these units use a source of heat to regenerate the refrigerant.   Gas, oil, or low-pressure steam is used.

In the absorption system, the compressor of the basic air-conditioning cycle (Art. 19-35) is replaced by an absorber, pump, and generator.   The refrigerant is regenerated by absorption in a weak solution of refrigerant and water, forming a strong solution, which is heated in the generator.   The refrigerant vapor is thus driven out of the solution and brought to the condenser under pressure.

Condensing water required with absorption equipment is more than that required for electric-driven compressors.   Consult the manufacturer in each case for the water quantities and temperature required for the proper operation of this equipment.

The automatic-control system with these package absorption units is usually provided by the manufacturer and generally consists of control of the amount of steam, oil, or gas used for regeneration of the refrigerant to maintain the chiller water temperature properly.

When low-cost steam is available, absorption systems may be more economical to operate than systems with compressors.

19-44. Ducts for Air Conditioning.   In designing a duct system for air conditioning, we must first determine air-outlet locations.   If wall grilles are used, they should be spaced about 10 ft apart to avoid dead spots.   Round ceiling outlets should be placed in the center of a zone.   Rectangular ceiling outlets are available that blow in either one, two, three, or four directions.

Manufacturers' catalog ratings should be checked for sizing grilles and outlets.   These catalogs give the recommended maximum amount of air to be handled by an outlet for the various ceiling heights.   They also give grille sizes for various length of blows.   It is obvious that the farther the blow, the higher must be the velocity of the air leaving the grille.   Also the higher the velocity, the higher must be the pressure behind the grille.

When grilles are placed back to back in a duct as in Fig. 19-32, be sure that grille A and grille B have the same throw; for if the pressure in the duct is large enough for the longer blow, the short-blow grille will bounce the air off the opposite wall, causing serious drafts.   But if the pressure in the duct is just enough for the short blow, the long-blow grille will never reach the opposite wall.   Figure 19-33 is recommended for unequal blows because it allows adjustment of air and build-up of a higher static pressure for the longer blow.

In some modern buildings perforated ceiling panels are used to supply conditioned air to the premises.   Supply ductwork is provided in the plenum above the suspended ceiling as with standard ceiling outlets.   However, with perforated panels, less acoustical fill is used to match the remainder of the hung ceiling.

After all discharge grilles and the air-handling unit are located, it is advisable to make a single-line drawing of the duct run.   The air quantities each line and branch must carry should be noted.   Of the few methods of duct-system design in use, the equal-friction method is most practical (Art. 19-9).   For most comfort cooling work, it is considered good practice not to exceed 0.15 in. friction per 100 ft of ductwork. It is also well to keep the air below 1,500 fpm starting velocity.

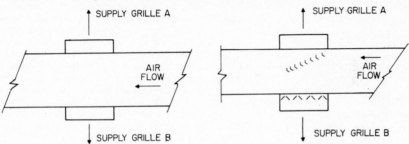

FIG. 19-32. Grilles placed back to back on an air-supply duct with no provisions for adjustment of discharge.

FIG. 19-33. Vanes placed in duct to control air flow to back-to-back grilles, useful when air throws are unequal.

If a fresh-air duct is installed, the return-air duct should be sized for a quantity of air equal to the supply air minus the fresh air.

It is advisable, where physically possible, to size the fresh-air duct for the full capacity of the air-handling unit.   For example, a 10-ton system handling 4,000 cfm of supply air—1,000 cfm fresh air and 3,000 cfm return air—should have the fresh-air duct sized for 4,000 cfm of air.   A damper in the fresh-air duct will throttle the air to 1,000 cfm during the cooling season; however, during an intermediate season, when the outside air is mild enough, cooling may be obtained by operating only the supply-air fan and opening the damper, thus saving the operation of the 10-hp compressor motor.

As an example of the method for sizing an air-conditioning duct system, let us determine the ductwork for the first floor of the building in Fig. 19-34.   Although a load analysis (see Art. 19-34 for an example) shows that the air requirement is 2,676 cfm, we must design the ducts to handle the full capacity of air of the package unit we supply.   Handling less air will unbalance the unit, causing a drop in suction temperature, and may cause freezing up of the coil.   If a $7\frac{1}{2}$-ton package unit is used, for example, the ducts should have a capacity at least equal to the 3,000 cfm at which this unit is rated.

Table 19-14 shows the steps in sizing the ducts.   The 3,000 cfm is apportioned to the various zones in the store in proportion to the load from each, and the flow for each segment of duct is indicated in the second column of the table.   Next, the size of an equivalent round duct to handle each air flow is determined from Table 19-6 with

Table 19-14. Duct Calculation for $7\frac{1}{2}$-ton Package Unit for Store (Fig. **19-34**)

Duct	Cfm	Equivalent round duct (friction = 0.15 in. per 100 ft, max velocity = 1,500 fpm), diam, in.	Rectangular duct, in.
A-B	3,000	19.7	28 × 12
B-C	2,700	18.4	24 × 12
C-D	1,900	16.1	18 × 12
D-E	1,100	13.2	12 × 12

friction equal to 0.15 in. per 100 ft.   The size of rectangular duct to be used is obtained from Table 19-5.

19-45. Control Systems for Air Conditioning.   One commonly used system has a thermostat wired in series with the compressor holding-coil circuit (Fig. 19-35).   Thus the compressor will stop and start as called for by room conditions.   The high-low pressure switch in series with the thermostat is a safety device that stops the compressor when the head pressure is too high and when the suction pressure approaches the freezing temperature of the coil.   A liquid solenoid will shut off the flow of refrigerant when the compressor stops, to prevent flooding the coil back to the compressor during the off cycle.

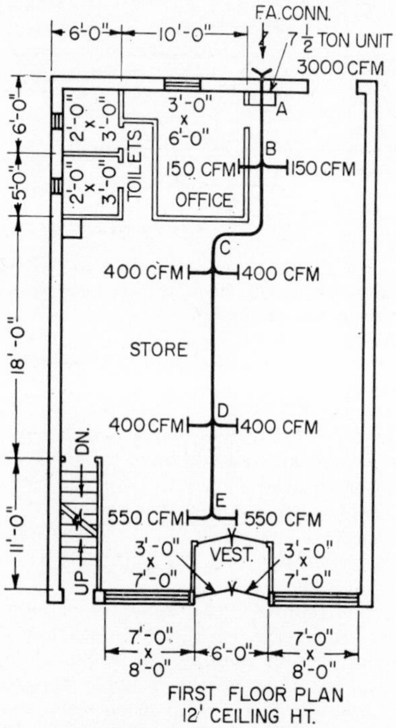

A second type of control is the pump-down system (Fig. 19-36).   The thermostat shuts off the flow of the refrigerant, but the compressor will keep running.   With the refrigerant supply cut off, the back pressure drops after all the liquid in the coil vaporizes.   Then, the high-low pressure switch cuts off the compressor.

Either of these two systems is satisfactory.   However, the remainder of this discussion will be restricted to the pump-down system.

Where city water is used for condensing purposes, an automatic water-regulator valve is supplied (usually by the manufacturer).   Figure 19-37 shows a cross section of such a valve.   The power element is attached to the hot-gas discharge of the compressor.   As the head pressure builds up, the valve is opened more, allowing a greater flow of water to the condenser, thus condensing the refrigerant at a greater rate.   When the compressor is shut off, the head pressure drops, the flow of water being cut off by the action of a power

FIG. 19-34. Ductwork for cooling a store.

spring working in opposition to the power element.   As the water temperature varies, the valve responds to the resulting head pressure and adjusts the flow automatically to maintain design head pressure.

When a water tower is used, the automatic water-regulating valve should be removed from the circuit, because it offers too much resistance to the flow of water. It is not usually necessary to regulate the flow of water in a cooling-tower system.

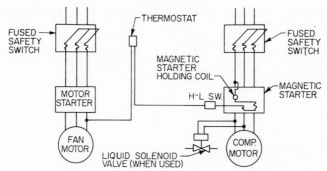

Fig. 19-35. Control circuit for an air-conditioning system in which the thermostat controls compressor operation.

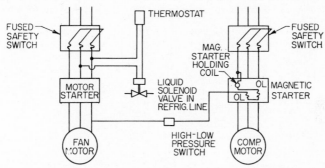

Fig. 19-36. Pump-down system for control of air conditioning.

For when the outside wet-bulb temperature is so low that the tower yields too low a water temperature, then air conditioning generally is not needed.

Figure 19-38 shows a wiring diagram for a tower system. Because of the interconnecting wiring between the magnetic starters, the tower fan cannot run unless the air-conditioning fan is in operation. Also, the circulating pump cannot run unless the tower fan is in operation, and the compressor cannot run unless the circulating pump is in operation.

When the system is started, the air-conditioning fan should be operated first, then the tower via switch No. 1, the pump via switch No. 2, and the compressor via switch No. 3. When shutting down, switch No. 3 should be snapped off, then switch No. 2, then switch No. 1, and then the air-conditioning fan.

In buildings where one tower and pump is used to provide water for many units, pressure switches may be used in series with the holding coil of each compressor motor starter. No interconnecting wiring is necessary; for the compressor will

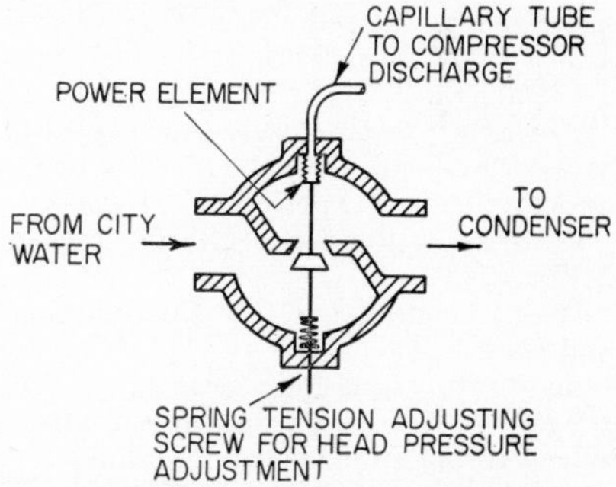

Fig. 19-37. Water-regulating valve for condensing in an air-conditioning system.

not be able to run unless the pump is in operation and provides the necessary pressure to close the contacts on the pressure switch.

Some city ordinances require that indirect-expansion, or chilled-water, systems be installed in public buildings, such as theaters, night clubs, hotels, and depots. This type of system is illustrated in Fig. 19-29. The refrigerant is used to cool water and the water is circulated through the cooling coil to cool the air. The water temperature should be between 40 and 45°F, depending on whether the occupancy is a high latent load or a low latent load. Because the cost of equipment is increased and the capacity decreased as water temperature is lowered, most designers use 45°F water as a basis for design and use a much deeper cooling coil for high-latent-load installations.

The amount of chilled water in gallons per minute to be circulated may be obtained from

$$Q = \frac{24 \times \text{tons of refrigeration}}{\Delta T} \qquad (19\text{-}13)$$

where ΔT is the temperature rise of water on passing through the cooling coil, usually 8 or 10°F. The smaller the temperature change, the more water to be circulated and the greater the pumping cost, but the better will be the heat transfer through the water chiller and cooling coil.

Coil manufacturers' catalogs usually give the procedure for picking the number of rows of coil necessary to do the required cooling with the water temperatures available.

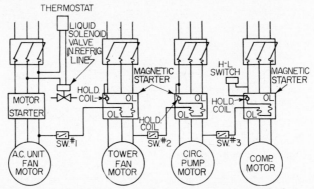

Fɪɢ. 19-38. Control circuit for a cooling-tower-type air-conditioning system.

The water chiller should be sized to cool the required flow of water from the temperature leaving the cooling coil to that required by the coil at a given suction temperature.

Assuming 45°F water supplied to the cooling coil and a temperature rise of 8°F, the water leaving the coil would be at 53°F. The chiller would then be picked to cool the required flow from 53 to 45°F at 37°F suction. The lower the suction temperature, the smaller will be the amount of heat-transfer surface required in the chiller. Also, the lower will be the compressor capacity. In no case should the suction temperature be less than 35°F, since the freezing point of water—32°F—is too close. A frozen and cracked chiller is expensive to replace.

A control system for a chilled-water system with an evaporative condenser is shown in Fig. 19-39.

19-46. Heating and Air Conditioning. Most manufacturers of air-conditioning equipment allow space in the air-handling compartment for the installation of a humidification unit and a heating coil for hot water or steam. These make it possible to humidify and heat the air in cold weather (Art. 19-10). Before a decision is reached to heat through the air-conditioning duct system, it is important to consider the many pitfalls present:

When a unit provides air conditioning in a single room, a heating coil may do the job readily, provided the Btu-per-hour rating of the coil is equal to or greater than the heating load. The fact that the supply grilles are high is usually no disadvantage; since winter heating is designed for the same amount of air as summer cooling, a small temperature rise results, and the large air-change capacity of the air-handling unit creates enough mixing to prevent serious stratification. Difficulties usually are encountered, however, in a structure with both exposed and interior zones.   In the winter, the exposed zones need heating, while the interior zones are warm.   If the heating thermostat is located in the exposed zone, the interior zones will become over-heated.   If the thermostat is located in the interior zone, the exposed zones will be too cold.   Where some heat is generated in the interior zones, the system may require cooling of the interior and heating of the exterior zones at the same time.   Thus it is impossible to do a heating and cooling job with a single system in such structures.

Where heating and cooling are to be done by the same duct system, the air-handling equipment should be arranged to service individual zones—one or more units for the exposed zones, and one or more units for the interior zones.

When a heating system is already present and an air-conditioning system is added, a heating coil may be used to temper the outside air to room temperature.   A duct-type thermostat may be placed in the discharge of the unit to control the steam or hot-water valve.   When a room thermostat is used, the spare coil capacity may be used for quick

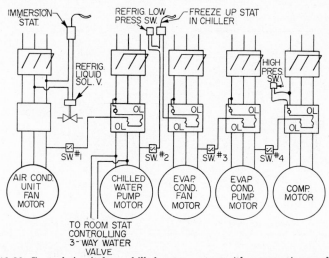

Fig. 19-39. Control circuit for a chilled-water system with evaporative condenser.

morning pickup.   Later in the day, the system may be used for cooling the premises with outside air if the building-heating system or other internal heat sources overheat the premises.

The heating-coil size should be such that its face area is about equal to the cooling-coil face area.   The number of rows deep should be checked with manufacturers' ratings.   When the unit is to be used for tempering only, the coil need be sized for the fresh-air load only [Eq. (19-8)].

When large quantities of outside air are used, it is usual practice to install a preheat coil in the fresh-air duct and a reheat coil in the air-conditioning unit.   Install the necessary filters before the preheat coil to prevent clogging.

19-47. Industrial Air Conditioning.   Certain manufacturing processes call for close control of temperature and relative humidity.   A typical control system is shown in Fig. 19-40.   The humidistat may be of the single-pole double-throw type.

On a rise in room humidity, the refrigeration compressor cuts in for the purpose of dehumidification.   Since the sensible capacity of the cooling coil usually is much higher than the sensible load, whereas the latent capacity does not too much differ from the latent load, undercooling results.   The room thermostat will then send enough steam or hot water to the reheat coil to maintain proper room temperature.

A small drop in room relative humidity will cut off the compressor.   A further drop in room relative humidity will energize the water or steam solenoid valve to add moisture to the air.   The thermostat is also arranged to cut off all steam from the reheat coil when the room temperature reaches the thermostat setting.   However, there may be periods when the humidistat will not call for the operation of the refrigeration compressor and the room temperature will climb above the thermostat setting.   An arrangement is provided for the thermostat to cut in the compressor to counteract the increase in room temperature.

When calculating the load for an industrial system, allowance must be made for the thermal capacity and moisture content of the manufactured product entering and leaving the room.   Often this part of the load is a considerable percentage of the total.

19-48. Chemical Cooling.   When the dew point of the conditions to be maintained is 45°F or less, the method of controlling temperature and humidity described in Art. 19-47 cannot be used because the coil suction temperature must be below freezing and the coil will freeze up, preventing flow of air.   For room conditions with dew point below 45°F, chemical methods of moisture removal, such as silica gel or lithium chloride, may be used.   This equipment is arranged to have the air pass through part

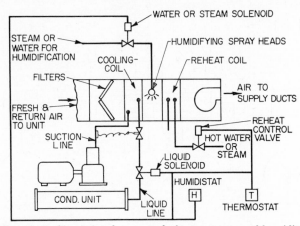

Fig. 19-40. Circuit for close control of temperature and humidity.

of the chemical and thus give up its moisture, while another part of the system regenerates the chemical by driving off the moisture previously absorbed.   The psychrometric process involved in this type of moisture removal is adiabatic or, for practical purposes, may be considered as being at constant wet-bulb temperature.   For example, if we take room air at 70°F and 30% relative humidity and pass the air through a chemical moisture absorber, the air leaving the absorber will be at a wet-bulb temperature of 53°F; i.e., the conditions leaving may be 75°F and 19% RH or 80°F and 11% RH, etc.

It may be noticed that the latent load here is converted to sensible load, and a refrigeration system will be necessary to do sensible cooling.   See Fig. 19-41 for the control of such a system.

19-49. Heat Pump.   The heat-pump cycle is an arrangement whereby the heat removed by the condenser in a refrigeration cycle is used for heating the building instead of being exhausted to the outside.   The heat absorbed by the refrigerant evaporator is taken from some colder heat source instead of the interior.

An air-to-air heat-pump cycle is shown in Fig. 19-42.   In actual practice, the equipment is arranged so that a system of dampers causes the warm air discharging from the air-cooled condenser to flow to the duct system for heating.   Outdoor air evaporates the liquid refrigerant, i.e., supplies the heat.   In summer, the dampers are arranged so that cool air from the evaporator flows to the duct system and the outdoor air is used for condensing.

This system, at present, is not so efficient as fuel-burning systems for the following reasons:

1. For winter operation, the colder the outdoor temperature (the lower the refrigerant evaporator temperature), the greater is the heating load and the lower the heat-pump capacity.

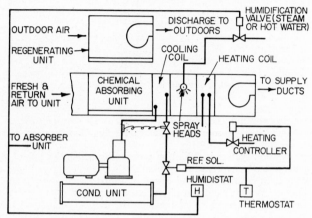

Fig. 19-41. Controls for cooling with a chemical moisture absorber.

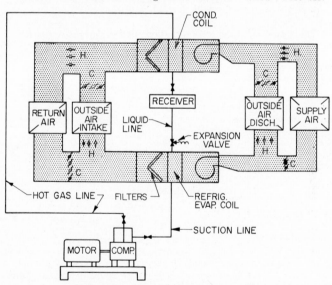

Fig. 19-42. Air-to-air heat-pump cycle.

2. For summer operation, the hotter the outdoor temperature (the higher the condensing temperature), the higher the cooling load and the lower the cooling capacity.

In spite of these shortcomings, there are some small "package," or preassembled, heat pumps on the market that are satisfactory for some areas, particularly where electrical rates are low and the cooling season is much longer than the heating season. In colder areas, where the heating load requires a larger-capacity unit than the cooling load, the heat pump usually cannot compete with conventional heating and cooling systems.

Other heat sources for heat pumps are well water or underground grid coils.   These installations usually call for a valve system permitting warm condenser water to be piped to the air-handling unit for winter heating and the cold water from the chiller to be pumped to the air-handling unit for summer cooling.   In winter, the well water or the water in the ground coil is pumped through the chiller to evaporate the liquid refrigerant, while in the summer this water is pumped through the condenser.   Obviously this system is more efficient than air-to-air but must be tailor-made for each installation and is noncompetitive except for large buildings.

19-50. Ventilation.   There are many codes and rules governing minimum standards of ventilation.   All gravity or natural-ventilation requirements involving window areas in a room as a given percentage of the floor area or volume are at best approximations.   The amount of air movement or replacement by gravity depends on prevailing winds, temperature difference between interior and exterior, height of structure, window-crack area, etc.   For controlled ventilation, a mechanical method of air change is recommended.

Where people are working, the amount of ventilation air required will vary from one air change per hour where no source of heat or offensive odors are generated to about 60 air changes per hour.

At best, a ventilation system is a dilution process, by which the rate of odor or heat removal is equal to that generated in the premises.   Occupied areas below grade or in windowless structures require mechanical ventilation to give occupants a feeling of outdoor freshness.   Without outside air, a stale or musty odor may result.   The amount of fresh air to be brought in depends on the number of persons occupying the premises, type of activity, volume of the premises, and amount of heat, moisture, and odor generation.   Table 19-15 gives the recommended minimum amount of ventilation air required for various activities.

Table 19-15. Minimum Ventilation Air for Various Activities

Type of Occupancy	*Ventilation Air, Cfm per Person*
Inactive, theaters..	5
Light activity, offices......................................	10
Light activity with some odor generation, restaurant..........	15
Light activity with moderate odor generation, bars............	20
Active work, shipping rooms..............................	30
Very active work, gymnasiums.............................	50

The amount of air to be handled obtained from the estimate of the per person method should be checked against the volume of the premises and the number of air changes per hour given in Eq. (19-14).

$$\text{Number of air changes per hr} = \frac{60Q}{V} \qquad (19\text{-}14)$$

where Q = air supplied, cfm

V = volume of ventilated space, cu ft

When the number of changes per hour is too low (below one air change per hour), the ventilation system will take too long to create a noticeable effect when first put into operation.   Five air changes per hour are generally considered a practical minimum.   Air changes above 60 per hour usually will create some discomfort because of air velocities that are too high.

Toilet ventilation and locker-room ventilation are usually covered by local codes— 50 cfm per water closet and urinal is the usual minimum for toilets and six changes per hour minimum for both toilets and locker rooms.

Removal of heat by ventilation is best carried out by locating the exhaust outlets as close as possible to the heat source.   Where concentrated sources of heat are present, canopy hoods will remove the heat more efficiently.

Figure 19-43 shows a canopy-hood installation over a kitchen range.   Grease filters reduce the frequency of required cleaning.   When no grease is vaporized, they may be eliminated.

Greasy ducts are serious fire hazards and should be cleaned periodically. There are on the market a number of automatic fire-control systems for greasy ducts. These systems usually consist of fusible-link fire dampers and a means of flame smothering—CO_2, steam, foam, etc.

Figure 19-44 shows a double hood. This type collects heat more efficiently; i.e., less exhaust air is required to collect a given amount of heat. The crack area is arranged to yield a velocity of about 1,000 fpm.

A curtain of high-velocity air around the periphery of the hood catches the hot air issuing from the range or heat source. Canopy hoods are designed to handle about 50 to 125 cfm of exhaust air per square foot of hood. The total amount of ventilation air should not yield more than 60 changes per hour in the space.

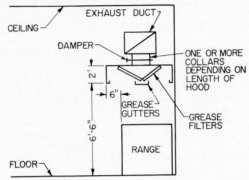

FIG. 19-43. Canopy hood for exhausting heat from a kitchen range.

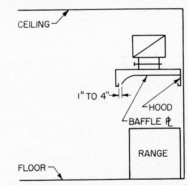

FIG. 19-44. Double hood for exhausting heat.

Where hoods are not practical to install and heat will be discharged into the room, the amount of ventilation air may be determined by the following method:

Determine the total amount of sensible heat generated in the premises—lights, people, electrical equipment, etc. (Arts. 19-30 to 19-32). This heat will cause a temperature rise and an increase in heat loss through walls, windows, etc. To maintain desired temperature conditions, ventilation air will have to be used to remove heat not lost by transmission through enclosures (Arts. 19-2 to 19-5 and 19-28).

$$q_v = 1.08Q(T_i - T_o) \qquad (19\text{-}15)$$

where q_v = heat, Btu per hr, carried away by ventilation air

Q = flow of ventilation air, cfm

T_i = indoor temperature to be maintained

T_o = outdoor temperature

With Eq. (19-15), we can calculate the amount of ventilation air required by assuming a difference between room and outdoor temperatures or we can calculate this temperature gradient for a given amount of ventilation air.

The same method may be used to calculate the air quantity required to remove any objectionable chemical generated. For example, assume that after study of a process we determine that a chemical will be evolved in vapor or gas form at the rate of X lb per min. If Y is the allowable concentration in pounds per cubic foot, then $Q = X/Y$, where Q is the ventilation air needed in cubic feet per minute.

Where moisture is the objectionable vapor, the same equation holds, but with X as the pounds per minute of moisture vaporized, Y the allowable concentration of moisture in pounds per cubic foot above outdoor moisture concentration.

Once the amount of ventilation air is determined, a duct system may be designed to handle it, if necessary.

Ventilation air may be provided by installing either an exhaust system, a supply system, or both.

In occupied areas where no unusual amounts of heat or odors are generated, such as offices and shipping rooms, a supply-air system may be provided, with grilles or ceiling outlets located for good distribution. When the building is tight, a relief system of grilles or ducts to the outside should be provided. But when the relief system is too extensive, an exhaust fan should be installed for a combination supply and exhaust system.

In spaces where concentrated heat, odor, or other objectionable vapors are generated, it is more practical to design an exhaust distribution system with hoods. The closer the hood to the source, the more efficient the system.

All air exhausted from a space must be replaced by outside air either by infiltration through doors and windows or by a fresh-air make-up system. Make-up air systems that have to operate during the winter season are often equipped with heating coils to temper the cold outside air.

Section 20

WATER SUPPLY AND PURIFICATION

ARTHUR J. FOX, JR.

Senior Editor
Engineering News-Record

For the building designer or constructor, the problem of water can range all the way from making a connection to municipal mains to the most involved development of an independent water source. Treatment necessary can vary from none to a conditioning far more thorough than that required simply to make water potable. It depends on the use to which water will be put in the building.

There are water-supply problems the building designer and constructor may meet that no handbook or text can answer. In those cases, the expert advice of a consulting sanitary engineer or competent equipment manufacturer is needed.

Also, it is recommended that the building designer or constructor, who must face and solve problems of water supply and sanitation, procure from the American Society of Civil Engineers a copy of the "Glossary—Water and Sewage Control Engineering."

The prime use of water—domestic or personal consumption—is a first consideration in locating, planning, designing, and constructing any building. There must be a sufficient potable supply to meet the personal needs of all who will reside, visit, or work within the building. In addition to this basic domestic need, there must be water for heating, air conditioning, fire protection, and flushing. And for industrial buildings, there are also a myriad of process uses plus a vast equipment-cooling job. So water supply may be the controlling factor in where and what to build.

Development of a new water supply can be the impetus for construction of buildings of many types. And conversely, the depletion or degradation of a water supply can lead to abandonment of a structure.

DEMAND FOR WATER

20-1. Domestic Uses of Water. Though it may be only a small fraction of a plant's total water needs, domestic water is the first demand to be considered.

A common basis for figuring domestic water demand is a per capita daily-consumption figure. Following are average design values for various types of buildings in gallons per capita per day:

Residential buildings (multifamily)	75–100
Institutions (except hospitals)	75–125
Hospitals	150–250
Schools	15–20
Industrial buildings	25

(Ernest W. Steel, "Water Supply and Sewerage," 3d ed., McGraw-Hill Book Company, Inc., New York; Gordon M. Fair and John C. Geyer, "Water Supply and Waste-water Disposal," John Wiley & Sons, Inc., New York.)

20–1

20-2. Water Needs in Commercial Buildings. Water demand is not as closely related to population in commercial or public buildings as in residential, hospital, and school buildings. There may be but a single potable supply, but it most likely will be used for boiler feed, cooling, air conditioning, refrigeration, and floor washing. All these are uses in addition to working-hour domestic water needs. So floor area is often used as a basis for estimating water consumption in buildings other than strictly residences.

Basic figures for such estimates were evolved by William W. Brush when he was deputy chief engineer of the Bureau of Water Supply in New York City's Department of Water Supply, Gas and Electricity. A survey of actual consumption rates in the Borough of Manhattan, New York City, was made in 1912 and the results in gallons per day per 1,000 sq ft by type of building were:

Hotels	600–1,100
Office buildings	100–500
Department stores	100–400
Apartment hotels	200–400
Average	300

While still proposed for use as a general guide for the preliminary estimate of total water demand in commercial buildings, these figures must be used with respect for their age. For one thing, the large number of public and commercial buildings with air-conditioning systems using substantial amounts of water may affect the 300 gpd per 1,000 sq ft average figure. (Ernest W. Steel, "Water Supply and Sewerage," 3d ed., McGraw-Hill Book Company, Inc., New York; Gordon M. Fair and John C. Geyer, "Water Supply and Waste-water Disposal," John Wiley & Sons, Inc., New York.)

20-3. Water for Air Conditioning and Other Cooling Needs. Rates at which air-conditioning installations use water vary with type of unit and degree of recirculation of the water used. A "Report on Planned Air Conditioning for Office Buildings," by C. R. Cheyney, to the Middle Atlantic Conference of Building Owners and Managers in 1947, gave the values in Table 20-1 for water requirements of various refrigeration plants.

Table 20-1. Water Requirements for Air Conditioning

Type of Plant	Water Required, Gpm per Refrigeration Ton
One central plant for entire building with cooling tower on roof	0.05
One central plant for each floor with cooling tower for each	0.07
With common cooling tower for all	0.05
5-hp self-contained units with cooling tower for each unit	0.10
With common cooling tower for all	0.05

Average water use has been set forth by Elwood Bean, principal assistant engineer in Philadelphia's Bureau of Water, as 0.05 gpm per ton of refrigeration with conservation and 2.5 gpm per ton without it.

Air conditioning, as a heavy seasonal use of water, can dictate installation of additional storage, pumping, or distribution facilities in any given installation (see also Arts. 19-29 and 19-37). Relatively high cost of water in some localities, and present emphasis on conservation of water resources, can dictate the provision of separate additional water sources, such as private wells, out of which air-conditioning water can be drawn and into which it can be recharged.

The basic function of water for air conditioning is to carry off heat. The colder the water, the better it can perform this function, thus the prevalent use of well water for the purpose. Where well or other water sources cannot supply a rate and temperature suitable to accomplish the required results economically, cooling towers or other means of cooling for reuse are needed (Art. 19-37).

Refrigeration—a form of cooling that is not seasonal but goes on all year—also is a water-use factor in design of buildings where food in quantity or other perishables are to be stored.

A check should be made on local restrictions pertaining to water use for air conditioning. There may be limits on amounts of water that can be drawn without provision of some cooling and recycling device. There may also be limitations on discharge of waste water after use.

Water for cooling of steam condensers, diesel plants, or other installed equipment may be another important design factor (see also Art. 20-6). Requirements generally given for steam condensation are 5 to 12 gal per lb of steam in a surface condenser; for internal-combustion-engine cooling a good range is 0.2 to 0.6 gpm per hp.

20-4. Water Quantities for Boiler Feed. Requirements for boiler-feed water may be estimated by assuming 34.5 lb of water evaporated per hour, at 212°F per boiler horsepower. In gallons per minute $Q = 0.0689$ boiler hp.

20-5. Cleaning Water. Water for flushing and cleaning in buildings—commercial, public, or industrial—will vary widely depending on the use of the building. But in no usual case should this quantity amount to more than a few per cent of the total water demand.

20-6. Water Needs in Industrial Buildings. The prime industrial use of water—cooling—is discussed in Art. 20-3, as it applies to installed heating or power units in buildings other than industrial. In industrial buildings, cooling-water demand can range up to the extreme flows needed to cool the largest new steam-power plants. (It takes roughly 100 gal of water to produce 1 kwhr of electrical energy, and 99% of this water is used for cooling.) Besides the production of power, there are countless other heat-exchange uses of water demanded by various industrial processes. And in addition to cooling water, there is also the flow needed for process requirements.

Water required per unit of product varies with the product. It has been estimated that it takes 65,000 gal of water (83% of it for cooling) to produce a single ton of steel, 750 gal to produce a ton of cement, etc. (Eskel Nordell, "Water Treatment for Industrial and Other Uses," Reinhold Publishing Corporation, New York.)

Figures for water needed per unit of product are not irreducible. Neither are these figures for use per unit of product indicative of actual consumption. Not all the water is incorporated in the product or discharged to the atmosphere. The totals include much water readily available for reuse. Thus, water demand of a product may not have to be met completely by the water source of a building, if resort is made to multiple use and recycling of the supply.

Water conservation merits consideration. As an example of what can be done, the Fontana (Calif.) steel plant of Kaiser Steel Corp. has been reported as taking from its source only 1,200 gal of water for each ton of steel it produces. The spectacular reduction from the 65,000 gal per ton figure generally cited is accomplished through multiple use of the water at hand. The plant's location, in a virtual desert, dictated the design. (Anon., "Big Steel Builds a Waterworks," *Engineering New-Record*, July 10, 1952, p. 40.) But economics, too, can be a factor. (Sheppard T. Powell, "Water Conditioning for Industry," McGraw-Hill Book Company, Inc., New York; Richard Hazen, "How Much Does Industrial Water Supply Cost?" *Engineering News-Record*, February 26, 1953, p. 30; "Manual on Industrial Water," American Society for Testing Materials; Arthur J. Fox, Jr., "Quenching Industry's Thirst," *Engineering News-Record*, May 1, 1952, p. 66.)

20-7. Water for Fire Protection. The National Board of Fire Underwriters in its standards for installation of sprinkler systems (NBFU Pamphlet 13) recommends connection to a reliable waterworks system as the preferred means of assuring adequate fire flows.

For buildings with "light-hazard occupancies," an outside hydrant should provide residual pressure at the hydrant when delivering 250 gpm, "to give at least 15 psi under the roof, allowing only for loss of pressure due to height of roof above the hydrant." Light-hazard occupancies include apartments, asylums, churches, clubs, colleges, dormitories, dwellings, hospitals, hotels, institutions, libraries, museums, office buildings, prisons, public buildings, rooming houses, schools, and tenements.

Ordinary-hazard occupancies—mercantile, warehouses, and manufacturing—should have an outside hydrant at hand to deliver 500 gpm, yet retain 15 psi under the roof.

Extra-hazard occupancies are buildings so classified by the local authority having jurisdiction. Determination of water supply for such extra-hazard occupancies may be made by consulting NBFU standards.

A secondary supply of water for fighting fire may be provided in form of a fire pump, driver, and suction supply—adequate, reliable, and properly located.

A good primary supply of water to feed sprinkler systems may be obtained from an elevated tank. For buildings of light-hazard occupancy, NBFU recommends a minimum size of 5,000 gal, with the bottom of the tank at least 35 ft above the underside of the roof. The same size tank, placed the same height above the roof, is recommended for use as sprinkler supply for buildings of ordinary-hazard occupancy; if the tank is but a secondary fire supply, it may be as low as 20 ft above the roof.

When gravity tanks are used to feed fire hoses through outside hydrants as well as feeding sprinklers, NBFU's "Standards on Outside Protection" should be consulted.

Pressure tanks for supplying sprinklers should have available at least 2,000 gal of water for buildings of light-hazard occupancy and at least 3,000 gal for ordinary-hazard occupancy.

It is important to realize that a building under construction needs water for fire protection every bit as much as does the completed structure. Local building codes should be studied for the minimum requirements during construction, and at least this much fire protection should be provided. However, minimum protection legally required may not be enough.

SOURCES OF WATER

20-8. Public Water Supply. The problem of obtaining water may be relatively simple if a project is to be located where sufficient public water supply can be had economically or at least reached within a reasonable distance. Generally, all that is necessary is to comply with local waterworks specifications for any facilities to be constructed outside the building line.

20-9. Independent Water Sources. Water to be tapped as an independent source may be on or under the earth—that is, surface water or ground water. Generally speaking, ground water is more readily and economically available, and apt to be freer of organic impurities. On the other hand, surface water can be more plentiful and available, often without cost of pumping, and it is usually freer of inorganic impurities.

Availability of water resources, their relative purity, and economics of the particular situation will dictate choice between ground water and surface water where both are available.

20-10. Ground Water. Rainfall that soaks into the earth to within the zone of saturation is called ground water and may be tapped for water supply. (The top of this zone is called the water table.) Ground water may often pierce the earth's surface as a spring, or the earth may be depressed below the water table to form a pond or lake; but most frequently, if water-bearing geologic formations are to be tapped, it must be by man-made wells or infiltration galleries.

The first problem in developing a ground-water supply is finding the aquifer and determining its yield. Existing local wells should be investigated for depth and flow; all existing reports on ground water of the state geologist, state health authorities, other local agencies with interest in wells, plus the U.S. Geological Survey, should be studied for available data.

If data are nonexistent or existing data are sparse, test wells must be sunk. For a small installation, a single test well might do; and if tests prove satisfactory, it might be that the single well will satisfy the relatively modest need. But where a well-field installation is proposed, it is advisable to sink at least three test wells from which to get data. It is equally advisable to seek advice of an expert on interpretation of such data. Not only the yield data need analysis, but quality too should be analyzed at this early stage. All physical, chemical, bacteriological, and biological determinations should be made.

To assure quality, no well for domestic water supply should be closer than 75 ft from any source of ground pollution. And this bare minimum is hardly enough in situations where soil is especially pervious or drawdown is to be unusually great. Perhaps the ground formation most vulnerable to free-flowing ground water and dangerous well pollution is eroded limestone. If wells must be installed in such ground, the check on water quality should be careful and constant.

Installation of wells is generally controlled by state regulations. When state law requires it, wells must be drilled by licensed well drillers. (Deep wells—100 ft or more—are drilled or bored; shallow wells—under 100 ft—are generally dug or driven.)

It is rarely prudent to install a single well, when water is vital to activities in the building to be supplied. Generally, at least two wells should be installed, so that 200% of the average demand is taken care of, and there is always a ready reserve in case one well should somehow fail.

If a well is to produce its rated yield dependably without being diminished by another close by, installations must be sufficiently spaced to prevent drawdown of one well from affecting another. Only tests will indicate accurately the desirable distance between installations. But as a rule, 25 to 100 ft is a safe distance for shallow wells, 400 to 1,000 ft for deep wells.

An infiltration gallery, while sometimes merely an open trench, can be, in effect, a horizontal well. A perforated or open-jointed pipe can be laid or driven horizontally through a porous stratum of earth carrying a flow of ground water (such as the bed of a stream). Such ground water can even be dammed, in effect, by the driving of sheet piling to cut off flow and thereby form underground storage.

Infiltration galleries laid parallel to rivers can be made to draw down river water through the soil, and thereby yield a naturally filtered surface water from not too far down in the ground.

Wells tapping ground water under pressure are called artesian wells. If the pressure is great enough to force water to the surface, they are flowing wells. However, in most instances, it will take pumping to extract ground water from the earth.

Pumping is most frequently accomplished with a deep-well turbine pump, centrifugal, rotary, or reciprocating pump. Air lifts and jets are sometimes used.

The commonly used turbine pump is a centrifugal type consisting of a discharge head, the pumping element, which is located down in the well under water, and the discharge column, connecting with the discharge head above. The discharge column serves the dual purpose of conducting water from the pumping element to the surface while also supporting the bearings for the revolving shaft. This type of pump is essentially a small-diameter multistage centrifugal pump. For each stage, there is a set of vanes in a bowl; water entering the impeller center of the lowest bowl is thrown outward by centrifugal force and enters the next stage under increased pressure. The pressure developed depends on rotation speed and impeller diameter (the latter being restricted by the diameter of the well). Generally the wells in which deep-well turbine pumps are installed are at least 4 in. in diameter. Care should be taken to provide a sufficient foundation for the discharge-head base plate; this supports not only the discharge head but also the pump column and the pump assembly.

The submersible electric-motor-driven pump, in which the motor is below the pump in the well and directly connected to it, is a variation of the turbine pump.

Reciprocating pumps, or displacement pumps, consist of a cylinder submerged in the well, a plunger within the cylinder, and rods connecting the plunger to a power head above ground. The single-acting type has a check valve at the bottom of the cylinder and a similar valve in the plunger. Water flows into the cylinder while the plunger is making an upstroke; the foot valve closes, and water passes through the plunger check valve on the downstroke. Double-acting types discharge water on both upstroke and downstroke and can pump about 60% more water than single-stroke units. Pump capacity depends on displacement of the cylinder and number of strokes per minute—with allowance for multiple action. Reciprocating well pumps are generally limited to small wells of moderate depth with capacities under 25 gpm.

The air lift—actually an application of the flotation principle—consists simply of an air compressor, air lines, and a discharge riser. Water filled with air in the discharge pipe will simply float on the column of water surrounding the discharge pipe. Thus, large volumes of water may be lifted simply by discharging compressed air at the lower end of the deeply submerged discharge pipe. Efficiency and capacity depend on submergence, air volume, and discharge-pipe diameter. This type of pump is useful where a group of wells can be filled by a single compressor installation. Relatively low efficiency often can be offset by inexpensive operation. It should be noted that water taken from wells by air lift should not be put directly into distribution systems; the oxygen content of this water is high, and therefore, the water tends to be highly corrosive.

Well pumps are generally powered by electricity. However, steam, gasoline, or diesel engine power can be used and in many instances should be provided as auxiliary drives to be used in case of electric-power failure.

20-11. Surface Water. That portion of rainfall that remains above ground can often be a satisfactory water source.

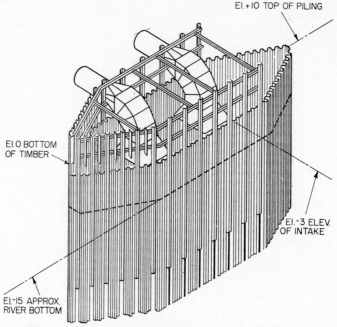

Fig. 20-1. Water supply and purification river intake, protected against damage.

Where water demand is not great, rain water can be collected as it drains from roofs and paved surfaces into catchment areas. But usually, artificial catchment areas will not collect enough water to satisfy relatively large demands.

Natural drainage areas feeding into ponds and lakes form sources that can be sufficient in both quantity and quality, depending on the size of the body of water formed. Such sources can be tapped by the screened suction end of a pipe pushed far enough out from shore to avoid pollution and deep enough to collect the coolest water possible without stirring up bottom mud. The lake intake may consist simply of an elbow pipe turned up and protected by a timber crib held down by rock. More extensive and expensive structures may be required, depending on depth of water, bottom conditions, degree of permanency, and necessary capacity.

Rivers with sufficient flow can be tapped just as readily as lakes of adequate size. But when an intake is built in a stream, the current, ice movement, and navigation are significant items affecting design.

When a stream used as a source of water supply has a flow that drops below the greatest anticipated water demand, a reservoir must be built to store water. The purpose of the reservoir is to average out flow in the stream, to hold excess flows until needed to augment subaverage runoff.

The problem in hydrology of determining whether a dam to form a reservoir is needed, and whether the reservoir will be sufficient is simplified greatly in areas where long stream-flow records are available from state or local authorities.   But if no runoff records are available, rainfall data must be collected and studied and runoff must be calculated.   The so-called **rational method** for determination of runoff involves the formula $Q = AIR$, where Q is the maximum rate of runoff in cubic feet per second; A the watershed area in acres; I the imperviousness ratio of the watershed area; and R the rate of rainfall on the area in inches per hour.

The imperviousness ratio I is the ratio of water running off the land to water precipitating on it.   It will range from 0.7 to 0.9 for built-up areas and paved surfaces; 0.05 to 0.30 for unpaved surfaces, depending on slopes.

Once the runoff has been determined, the necessary reservoir storage volume can be arrived at by use of a mass diagram, comparing cumulative runoff and cumulative consumption, with proper correction for evaporation and other losses.   A fuller analysis of the rainfall-runoff problem and an application of such a diagram may be found in L. C. Urquhart, "Civil Engineering Handbook," 4th ed., McGraw-Hill Book Company, Inc., New York.

Required reservoir size is one of the factors that determine height of dam.   But the height of a dam will also be influenced by economics of its location.   Geological conditions, which must be determined by borings, and the possibility of gravity flow to the distribution system to save pumping costs are other factors to be considered in locating the dam.   Its necessary height and the foundation conditions may also dictate type of construction.

A dam may be built of earth, masonry, or timber.   The earth type may be further divided into earth fill, hydraulic fill, and rock fill.   Urquhart's "Civil Engineering Handbook" is again recommended for information on design and construction of dams.

WATER TRANSMISSION AND DISTRIBUTION

Gravity is the ideal source of power for moving water.   Unfortunately, the source of water is not in every instance sufficiently high above all points of demand to permit complete dependence on gravity and avoidance of pumping.   A pump or pumping station is often required.

20-12. Transmission of Water by Pumping.   A low-lift station pumps water from surface supply to a point high enough for gravity flow through a treatment works; a high-lift station pumps from nonpressure storage into a pressure-treatment plant or into the distribution system.

Transmission of water is generally accomplished by centrifugal pumps, which offer the advantage of low cost and low space requirements.   Guidance of several manufacturers should be sought, and pump-characteristic curves should be studied before a particular pump is chosen.   Generally, it is sufficient to specify the type and characteristics of pump desired, permitting the manufacturer to work out details of pump construction necessary to insure the specified performance.   Heads against which the pump must operate and discharge should be specified with care; and variations in head should be noted.   Normally, centrifugal pump efficiencies fall between 40 and 85%, larger pumps generally being more efficient.

Centrifugal pumps are denoted as horizontal or vertical, depending on the plane in which their shafts lie; size of pump is the diameter in inches of its discharge pipe.

Pumping stations for groups of industrial buildings can often be as large and as intricate as those serving fair-size cities.   However, in the normal case of a pump (or pumps) supplying water to a single building, the simpler the pumping station, the better.   It is generally sufficient that the pumproom be fireproofed, ventilated, and roomy enough for equipment and operators to function properly.

Pumped water supply for buildings is usually intermittently lifted to an elevated tank.   Automatic controls may be used on the pumps to keep costs down.

For most economical pumping, permitting pumps to be operated at their maximum efficiencies, water can be pumped directly into the distribution system, with the water not immediately needed going to an elevated tank or to standpipes.   This pumped storage can then be drawn on during peak use periods, when pumping capacity is less than the rate of water consumption. This continuous pumping requires that standby units be available to replace pumps under repair.

Fire-fighting pumps are special emergency units that should be available for use during construction as well as after occupancy of a building. They should have an ample discharge rate, but it is not necessary that they have high efficiency, since they will operate only over short periods. During time of fire-pump operation, pressure in standpipes can be built up by shutting off flow to elevated storage.

A fire stream is generally 250 gpm. Flow required for various densities of occupancy will dictate how many hose connections will be required. These flows are sometimes used for estimating purposes: 500 gpm for open residential areas, 1,500 to 3,000 gpm for dense commercial areas, and up to 6,000 gpm for dense residential areas with multistory buildings. Hydrants must be close enough to concentrate a sufficient number of streams on the fire; a safe distance between hydrants is 500 ft or less.

Pressure in municipal mains will generally range up to 60 psi in open residential areas and 75 psi in commercial areas. Such pressures in the mains are usually sufficient for sprinkler service up to four stories without booster pumping.

It is up to the building designer to investigate not only the pressure of the local public supply (if such supply is to be used) but also capabilities of the local fire fighters. Such investigations will serve as a guide as to what special pumping capacity might be needed to fight fires.

20-13. Water Pipelines, Aqueducts, and Open Channels. Transmission of water, for the purpose of this discussion, will be considered as its conveyance over relatively long distances from source to point of consumption. Pipelines, aqueducts, or open channels may be necessary.

If the ideal condition of gravity flow over not-too-rugged terrain prevails, an open channel may be a possible and economical means of transmission. Its disadvantages are water loss due to seepage and evaporation and dangers of pollution. But a well-built open channel, constructed as nearly as possible to the hydraulic gradient, perhaps paved to prevent seepage losses, and well maintained to lessen pollution hazards, can be used advantageously. Pavement thickness can be as little as 2 in. in trapezoidal sections with flat side slopes. Steep side walls or special foundation problems, such as uplift or poor bearing capacity, will require heavier, reinforced structures.

The gravity flow also lends itself to use of an aqueduct at the hydraulic gradient—a covered masonry structure generally constructed by cut-and-cover methods. When the aqueduct gets below the hydraulic gradient, it usually is a tunnel in rock—deep and under considerable pressure. The aqueduct because of its permanent nature and costly on-site construction is an expensive, though permanent, means of transmission for water.

A pipeline is an on-the-job assembly of manufactured units. The units can be bought to meet a wide range of carrying capacity and pressure requirements. And capacities can always be increased in the future by laying other, parallel lines. Lines of cast-iron, steel, reinforced or prestressed concrete, asbestos cement, or wood staves may all be used under pressures normally encountered in transmission mains. Pressures that develop are due either to drops below the hydraulic gradient, as the line generally follows the ground level, or pumping pressures, in cases where gravity flow is impossible or impractical. Since the pipe normally follows the profile of the ground, it is wise to put relief valves at high points and blowoff valves at the low points for flushing or draining the line. A 2 to 2.5 fps velocity in the line ought to prevent too much settling out of solids in the water.

When velocity is suddenly affected by a shutoff in the line, the danger of water hammer exists; a surge tank or standpipe at the discharge end can take care of this effect. Often, a transmission line is not direct-connected to the water-distribution system of a building or group of buildings but leads to an elevated distributing reservoir or tank instead. Such a reservoir can be made to "float on the line" or otherwise absorb the shock of flow surges.

Size of pipe is a hydraulic problem. (C. V. Davis, "Handbook of Applied Hydraulics," 2d ed., McGraw-Hill Book Company, Inc., New York.) The line should be made large enough in diameter for peak loads and for a reasonable amount of future growth.

Type of pipe and the material to be used are questions of economics. Carrying capacity, estimated life, and maintenance are involved, along with first cost of purchasing plus installation. Because a pipeline must often carry raw water—except possibly for a dose of chlorine to prevent biological growth—the water's quality also should be considered, since it might affect the pipe by corrosion, scaling, or erosion. For corrosive waters, cast-iron pipe ought generally to be cement-lined; steel pipe should be bituminous-enamel-lined.

Cast-iron water pipe may be assumed to have a useful life of 100 years or more. Class B cast-iron pipe, used mostly for water mains, is good for a 200 ft head or 86 psi. Mechanical joints (bolted flanges and gaskets) or bell-and-spigot pipe and lead joints may be used. Other materials, such as sulfur and sand mixtures, make good joints and have the advantages of being lighter than lead and requiring no calking. Cement too, is used in cast-iron pipe joints. For stream crossings or other conditions where settlement is probable, and for lines subject to vibration, such as those on bridges, flexible joints of some type, such as ball-and-socket joints or Dresser couplings, are necessary.

Steel pipe, welded or riveted, is commonly used in diameters 30 in. or greater. It is especially suitable for high-pressure lines and is generally less expensive than cast iron. Dresser-type couplings are useful on steel pipelines as well as riveted and welded joints. Air valves are important in steel pipelines; vacuum might collapse the pipe. Corrosion is more a factor with steel than with cast iron, but if the metal is protected with a $\frac{1}{16}$-in. thickness of bituminous coating it should last 50 years under good conditions.

Corrosive soil is as damaging to the outside of steel pipe as corrosive water is to the inside. Steel pipe should not be buried in cinder fill; if it must go through corrosive soils, it can be wrapped in asphalt-impregnated cloth or building paper. Portland-cement mortar as a lining and coating of steel pipe is an effective protection against corrosion. Naturally, it is a cost factor to be considered.

Concrete pipe may be reinforced or prestressed (or even unreinforced in diameters under 2 ft on lines under no pressure). It has a life expectancy probably somewhere between that of cast iron and steel. It is commonly cast in sizes up to 69 in. in diameter and larger. Flow characteristics are good and are not adversely affected with age. Pressure pipe, available for static heads in the 100- to 600-ft range, is generally reinforced with a welded steel cylinder and prestressed. Reinforced pipe with neither steel cylinder nor prestressing is available for up to 120 ft head. Patented joints with rubber or other gaskets are somewhat flexible, make installation relatively simple, and provide good watertightness.

Asbestos cement, also corrosionproof and with excellent flow characteristics, is a material now made into pipe capable of withstanding 100, 150, and 200 psi. Patented couplings make installation fast. Relatively few joints (because of long sections made practical by light weight) also figure into the economy of installation of this pipe. The nature of the material necessitates normal care in handling, placing, and backfilling.

Wood-stave pipe is still used in new pipelines—notably in the West. Life of this pipe is generally expected to be about the same as steel, and carrying capacity—good to begin with—is not affected by age. It is capable of withstanding 150 psi.

For all pipe commonly used in transmission of water, the American Water Works Association has set up specifications. These can be procured from AWWA, 2 Park Ave., New York, N.Y.

20-14. Water-distribution Systems. When water has been brought to the general area of use (or if it was there to begin with), the remaining supply problem is distributing it to the individual points of use. The transmission line, or the city main, must be made to feed its flow into various lines inside and outside the building. (Of course, treatment, when required, will have to fit into the line of flow somewhere before delivery).

If water is delivered from an independent source through a transmission line by gravity, it is possible that it might be distributed with enough head to meet all needs, with the probable exception of high-pressure flow for fire fighting.   Water delivered through a transmission main from a remote pumping station may also satisfy all the pressure and quantity requirements of distribution—except for fire flows.   And the water directly from city mains may likewise meet requirements.

But, more often, when water demand is large and height of building or other factors demand increased pressures, a distribution reservoir is needed.   This may be an elevated tank, a surface tank (at grade but on high ground), or a roof tank.   Its purpose is to equalize flow and pressure and store water for emergency use, such as fire or temporary interruption of supply.   The distribution reservoir can be an economic factor by diminishing size of pumps or pipes needed in a distribution system.

Size of the distribution reservoir may possibly be determined entirely by the storage required for emergency; fire demand may rule.   If, on the other hand, fire demand can be satisfied from a separate supply, it is desirable to design storage so as to level off the rate of supply.   Rate of demand, of course, is also involved, and the problem resolves itself to one of balancing an ideally constant rate of supply, plus storage, against the vagaries of demand.

For a graphical determination of this problem and a discussion of how to use it, see Babbitt and Doland's "Water Supply Engineering," 5th ed., McGraw-Hill Book Company, Inc., New York.

Type of reservoir will be determined by economic factors, including its size and its location.   If topography permits, a surface reservoir on nearby high ground may be the economic solution.   It may be a lined or unlined earth basin; a masonry, reinforced, or prestressed concrete tank.   Or it may be a steel tank set on or in the earth. Roofs or covers become necessary when the supply is to be potable.

Earth reservoirs must be built with all the care and technique of earth dams, if they are to be watertight.   Concrete lining on floor and side slopes will improve watertightness, of course.   Lining thickness ought to be at least 4 in., and reinforcing equal in area to about 0.25% of the cross-sectional area of concrete is advisable.

Reinforced and prestressed concrete tanks, as ground-level distribution reservoirs, should be designed for fluid pressures from within and earth pressures from without, if the structure is even partly buried.   An L or T cantilevered wall or a counterforted wall may be used for rectangular tanks.   Tanks circular in plan involve cylinder design and generally require prestressed concrete.

For elevated tanks, lighter materials, such as steel and wood, are usually preferable.   Concrete, however, should be considered where it might possibly compete economically.

Size of a tower-supported tank for a low building or a roof-supported tank for a tall building will often be determined by demand for fire flows.   Where city water is not available and the independent supply must feed outside hydrants as well as sprinklers, capacity and height of the tank must be sufficient to do the job.   It is desirable in this case to have an elevated tank, kept full always, just for the purpose of meeting fire demand.

Standard tank sizes for steel are in 5,000-gal increments from 5,000 to 30,000 gal; 10,000-gal increments from 30,000 to 60,000 gal; then 75,000, 100,000, 150,000, 200,000, and 500,000 gal.   Standard wood water tanks come in the same sizes, but only up to 100,000 gal.   Standard tower heights for tanks over 40,000 gal are 50, 75, 100, 125, and 150 ft.

Where possible, the water tank should be an independent structure, well founded and stable.   It should be fairly isolated from the buildings—or else the tank itself must be fire-protected with a sufficient sprinkler system.

If the tank must go on a building, the structure must be designed for the maximum tank load.   A preferred location is over elevator or stair tower walls.   Bracing of roof tanks with structural members inside the building introduces problems of protecting the bracing from fire (local building codes should be consulted).

Wood tanks require lightning protection.   A $\frac{3}{4}$-in. solid copper rod, extending 30 in. above the tank's highest point and connected by copper conductor (weighing at least 6 oz per ft) to a ground clamp on the tank's discharge pipe, generally will suffice.

For complete and detailed standards and details of design of steel gravity and suction tanks, steel towers, wood water tanks, pipe connections and fittings, tank-heating equipment, frost protection for valves, and pressure tanks, see Pamphlet 22, National Board of Fire Underwriters, New York, N.Y., and *Journal of the American Waterworks Association*, December, 1940, "Tentative Standards and Specifications for Elevated Steel Water Tanks, Standpipes and Reservoirs."

Distribution of water from the distribution reservoir to the buildings is simply a determination of pipe size and pipe material. (C. V. Davis, "Handbook of Applied Hydraulics," 2d ed., McGraw-Hill Book Company, Inc., New York.) Size can be determined from rate of flow with an assumed velocity of 3 or 4 fps. Six-inch lines should serve all fire hydrants. Other mains should be sized according to prospective flows; in general, mains feeding into many service lines will be not less than 4 in. in diameter.

Material for distribution lines is determined on the basis of economics as discussed for transmission pipelines in Art. 20-13. Smaller-diameter lines, such as $\frac{3}{4}$-in., can be made of materials not included in the foregoing discussion of transmission pipe. These materials include copper, lead, iron, wrought iron, red brass, and plastics.

Copper tubing has the advantages of flexibility and easy installation along with corrosion resistance and good flow characteristics. Lead pipe has the same advantages but is unpopular for potable supplies because of fear of lead poisoning.

Galvanized iron (or steel) pipes are subject to corrosion but have low first cost. Wrought iron can be expected to last longer than galvanized iron or steel. Brass pipe will last still longer, red brass being high in copper content.

Plastic pipe and tubing are corrosionproof and easily installed. They are in wide use in and around industrial buildings, where they have also been used for carrying off corrosive and acid wastes. Flexible polyethylene, butyrate, saran, styrene polymers, and rigid vinyl are some of the plastics in use, and polyester resin pipe, reinforced with glass fibers, is claimed to be suitable for working pressures of 200 and 400 psi in $3\frac{1}{2}$ and $4\frac{1}{2}$-in. diameters.

20-15. Valves for Pipelines. Valves in either transmission or large distribution-line piping are most often gate valves of cast iron with brass mountings. Such valves, when buried underground, can be operated from a box at the surface without need for gearing.

In the smaller distribution lines—4 in. and under—globe valves are used most. Angle valves are a less expensive type of globe valve.

Check valves, for prevention of flow reversal, may be swing, ball, or vertical type. They are important in preventing pollution of potable water due to backflow or cross connection.

Pressure-control valves are required in the delivery of water under high pressure to a low-pressure system. Pressure-relief valves and air-relief valves are used in transmission pipelines (Art. 20-13). Altitude valves on lines to elevated tanks or standpipes are operated generally by pressure in the lines (Pamphlet 22, National Board of Fire Underwriters, New York, N.Y.).

20-16. Water Meters. Meters for gaging flow through water lines measure either quantity of flow (displacement type) or velocity. They should be selected for accuracy, durability, and availability of replacements and spare parts. (*Journal of the American Water Works Association*, February, 1947, "Tentative Standard Specifications for Cold Water Meters, Fire Service Type.")

WATER QUALITY AND TREATMENT

"Pure" water is a laboratory curiosity. In practice, it is the necessary "degree of purity" which is of concern.

20-17. Physical Characteristics of Water. Physical factors to be considered in raw water are temperature, turbidity, color, taste, and odor. All but temperature are characteristics to be determined in the laboratory by qualified technicians working on carefully procured samples. A sample of about 2 qt, taken at enough points and at different times to be representative, should be brought to the laboratory in clean glass bottles and tested within 72 hr. Polluted water should be tested within 12 hr.

Turbidity, a condition due to fine, visible material in suspension, is usually due to presence of colloidal soils. It is expressed in parts per million (ppm) of suspended solids. It may vary widely with discharge of relatively small streams of water. Larger streams or rivers tending to be muddy are generally muddy all the time. The objection to turbidity in potable supplies is its ready detection by the drinker; 10-ppm turbidity shows up as cloudiness in a glass of water. Therefore, the usual limit is 5 ppm.

Color, also objectionable to the drinker, is preferably kept down to 10 ppm or less. It is measured, after all suspended matter (turbidity) has been centrifuged out, by comparison with standard hues.

Tastes and odors due to organic matter or volatile chemical compounds in the water should of course be removed completely from drinking water. But slight, or threshold, odors due to very low concentrations of these compounds are not harmful— just objectionable. Perhaps the most common source of taste and odor is due to decomposition of algae.

20-18. Chemical Analysis of Water. Chemical constituents commonly found in raw waters and measured by laboratory technicians if the water is to be considered for potable use include hardness, pH, iron, and manganese, as well as total solids. Total solids should not exceed 1,000 ppm and in some places are kept below 500 ppm. Other limits on individual chemical constituents generally are:

	Ppm
Lead	0.1
Arsenic	0.05
Copper	0.2
Zinc	5.0
Magnesium	125
Iron	0.3
Chlorides	250
Sulfates	250
Phenol (in compounds)	0.001
Fluorine	1.0 (optimum concentration for prevention of tooth decay)

Hardness, measured as calcium carbonate, may be objectionable as a soap waster with as little as 150 ppm of $CaCo_3$ present. But the growing use of synthetic detergents decreases its significance and makes even much harder waters acceptable for domestic uses. Hardness is of concern, however, in waters to be used for boiler feed, where boiler scale must be avoided. Here, 150 ppm would be too much hardness; the water would require softening.

Hydrogen-ion concentration of water, commonly called pH, can be a real factor in corrosion and encrustation of pipe and in destruction of cooling towers. A pH under 7 indicates acidity; over 7 indicates alkalinity; 7 is neutral. Color indicators commonly used can measure pH to the nearest tenth, which is near enough.

Iron and manganese when present in more than 0.3-ppm concentrations may discolor laundry and plumbing. Their presence and concentration should be determined. More than 0.2 ppm is objectionable for most industrial uses.

20-19. Biological Analysis of Water. Bacteriological tests of water must be made on carefully taken and transported samples. A standard sample is five portions of 10 cu cm, each sample a different dilution of the water tested. A competent laboratory will use standard methods for analyses.

Organisms other than bacteria, such as plankton (free-floating) and algae can in extreme cases be real factors in the design of water treatment; therefore, biological analyses are significant. Microscopic life, animal and vegetable, is readily tracked down under a high-powered microscope.

20-20. Water-treatment Works. All the quality factors of water (Arts. 20-17 to 20-19), when viewed in the light of required degree of purity for ultimate use, influence the design of treatment facilities. Since no two raw-water sources are likely to yield identical products, and since the uses to which the water can be put can vary over a wide range of quantity and quality demands, water treatment cannot easily be simplified, and must not be oversimplified. This article will merely outline some basic principles, purposes, and effects of major treatment processes; there are numerous volumes devoted to the subject. (Eskell Nordell, "Water Treatment for Industrial and Other Uses," Reinhold Publishing Corporation, New York; "Water Quality and Treatment," American Water Works Association; M. N. Baker, "The Quest for Pure Water," American Water Works Association; W. A. Hardenburg, "Water Supply and Purification," International Textbook Company, Scranton, Pa.; Sheppard T. Powell, "Water Conditioning for Industry," McGraw-Hill Book Company, Inc., New York—to mention a few.)

Obviously, treatment must precede use, but whether treatment should be at the source or after transmission to the point of consumption is usually a question of economics, involving hydraulic features, pumping energies and costs, and possible effects of raw water on transmission mains.

In general, treatment, in addition to disinfection, should be provided for water averaging over 20 coliform group organisms per 100 ml, if the water is to be used for domestic purposes. Treatment methods include screening, plain settling, coagulation and sedimentation, filtration, disinfection, softening, and aeration. It is the designer's problem to choose the method that will take the objectionable elements out of the raw water in the simplest, least expensive manner.

Screening is a means of removing floating or heavy suspended matter. The place for the heavy (about 1-in.-mesh) screen is at the water intake; a finer mesh—down to about $\frac{1}{4}$ in.—may be useful at the treatment works if rustproof and provided with means of cleaning. Moving screens with cleaning mechanisms are commercially available.

Plain settling is a process that might be considered achieved to a degree in the storage reservoir and in the distribution reservoir. However, if the water is especially muddy, a basin solely for the purpose of removing settleable solids may be a desirable means of saving chemicals in the coagulation and sedimentation to follow.

Settling basins can be constructed of earth or masonry, with or without sludge-removal devices. They should be equipped, however, with baffles to prevent short-circuiting. A rectangular basin with length twice its width and depth of 10 to 14 ft is effective; circular tanks may be as effective in smaller installations. Entrance velocity should be kept down to $\frac{1}{2}$ to 1 fps, and the detention period should be 5 to 6 hr.

Coagulation and sedimentation are achieved in settling basins provided with means for adding the chemical coagulants. Means must be provided for mixing thoroughly with the water to be treated the proper proportion of chemicals to effect the coagulation. Chemicals for pH control are also generally added here.

In the coagulation process, suspended solids form into particles heavy enough to settle out as a precipitate. Detention time of 2 hr is generally enough, where mixing and flocculating equipment are working efficiently.

Chemical control is important. Water and chemicals must be brought together intimately, revolving paddle arms generally being used to afford the necessary mixing. Turbulent, flash mixing can be followed by slower, more gentle mixing. The idea is to build up a floc, but then handle it gently enough to keep it growing rather than breaking it up. Precision is required for best results.

After flash mixing and slow mixing, the formed floc should begin sedimentation, which should take about 60 min as water moves through the basin at about $\frac{1}{2}$ fps. The floc that settles to the bottom of the sedimentation tank is a sludge, which can be removed continuously or periodically. If it is to be removed periodically, enough storage space in the bottom of the sedimentation basin must be provided. There is no fixed formula for figuring the required storage space, but after a convenient depth for the basin has been determined, a generous measure of it should be considered reserve for sludge storage. A sloped bottom to a valve outlet will facilitate periodic sludge removal.

Most modern water-treatment plants using coagulation have sedimentation tanks provided with means for continuous sludge removal. Wood or metal scrapers drag across the bottom, moving sludge to a hopper or gutter, from which is can be drained off to disposal. The scrapers should move at about 15 fpm, not fast enough to cause turbulence.

Among the many chemicals used for coagulation of suspended solids in water are aluminum sulfate (alum), ferrous sulfate, calcium oxide, hydrated calcium oxide, sodium carbonate, ferric chloride, ferric sulfate, and Bentonite.

Filtration is the process by which suspended and colloidal matter getting by the sedimentation basin is removed. Filtration will also reduce the bacteria count and can actually change chemical characteristics of water treated.

Here is how filtration works: Solids too large to pass through the spaces between sand grains are mechanically filtered out. Colloids or bacteria too small to be filtered out by mechanical straining are caught by adsorption or sedimentation. The spaces between sand grains actually act as tiny sedimentation basins; fine particles settle within them to the grains of sand and adhere. The process is helped by a gelatinous coating on the sand grains formed by previous adsorption. It is the living organism caught in the filter that can cause actual chemical change in the water passing through. Filters in use for some time develop what is called a "schautzdecke" on their surface, a layer of biological substance active in affecting chemical make-up of the water.

Most sand filters in use today are rapid sand filters, as opposed to the slow sand filters, more popular in the past. Rapid sand filters are generally built with at least 24 to 30 in. of sand of 0.0 to 0.5 mm effective size and with uniformity coefficient of 1.5 to 2.0. The designed rate of flow through the filter is usually 2 gpm per sq ft—although there are filters designed today for higher rates. The standard rate can be doubled in periods of emergency.

Filters should be in fireproof structures safe from infiltration and leakage. Troughs above the sand surface should be provided to carry off dirty water, since filters are cleaned by backwashing.

Filtered water goes to basins effectively sealed off and is distributed through sealed piping to prevent unfiltered water mixing with the filtered product.

Slow sand filters are generally 3 to 5 ft of sand on 6 to 12 in. of gravel. An open-joint system of underdrain carries off the filtered water at a rate of from 2.5 to 7.5 mgd per acre of sand surface. Cleaning, although necessary perhaps only at 2-month intervals, is a relatively difficult operation. The filter must be put out of service while an inch of sand is removed from the surface, or the whole bed must be backwashed and harrowed simultaneously.

Rapid sand filters can be placed in watertight compartments and used as pressure filters. The advantage of pressure filters is the maintenance of head under which water is delivered; this may permit delivery of filtered water to points of water demand under pressure without use of additional pumps.

Diatomite filters are those in which water flows through a thickness of diatomaceous earth built up on permeable surfaces in a pressure tank. This type of filter has had limited use on waters to be delivered for human consumption.

Softening of water is a process that must be justified by its need, depending upon the use to which the water will be put. It has been stated that, with a hardness in excess of about 150 ppm, cost of softening will be offset partly by the saving in soap. When synthetic detergents are used instead of soap, this figure may be stretched considerably. But when some industrial use of water requires it, the allowable figure for hardness must be diminished appreciably.

Among processes available for softening, the lime-soda method is commonly used. It generally precedes sedimentation and filtration. Lime and soda are mixed with the raw water, the softening reaction following during the flocculation. Calcium and magnesium settle out.

The zeolite process is applicable whether or not the water supply requires filtration. Natural zeolites form a granular bed. When water is passed through it, calcium and magnesium are taken up by the zeolites, and sodium is given in exchange for them. The process is a sodium cation exchange. The zeolite bed must be regenerated periodically; common salt is the regenerant most commonly used. (Sea water is especially useful and economical for the purpose, where it is available.)

Treatment of water for tastes and odors involves the destruction or removal of organic matter, minerals, or gases. Organic matter is the most prevalent cause of tastes and odors in surface water; minerals or gases, or both, can be the cause most prevalent in ground water.

Aeration has the effect of releasing gases and supplying oxygen to prevent formation of some foul-smelling compounds. The idea is simply to bring oxygen in contact with as much water as possible. The water can be sprayed into the air, spilled over steps or trays, or dropped through slats or perforated structures. (It should be noted that aeration of water tends to increase its corrosiveness.)

Activated carbon, commercially available under several trade names, is effective in adsorbing solids, liquids, and gases in water. The powder or granular material can be mixed into a slurry and inserted for treatment by chemical-feed devices. A dose of 3 ppm removes most tastes and odors from water. In extreme cases, the dosage may have to be boosted to 8 or 10 ppm. The additive may be introduced by spraying on the reservoir or in the mixing basin, just before filtration, or the dosage can be split and applied in a combination of these places.

The chemical most commonly used in the reservoir to control tastes and odors by killing algae is copper sulfate. Most algae can be killed by 1 ppm of copper sulfate, if the water is soft. In hard water, larger doses are needed, perhaps up to $4\frac{1}{2}$ ppm. The upper limit on copper sulfate is determined by the need to preserve fish life in the reservoir. Here are the concentrations that kill common varieties of fish in soft water, given in pounds of copper sulfate per million gallons of soft water:

Trout...............	1.2
Catfish.............	2.5
Suckers.............	2.5
Carp...............	2.1
Pickerel............	3.5
Black bass..........	16.6
Goldfish............	4.0
Perch..............	6.0

It is possible to use copper sulfate in a limited concentration so as to preserve the fish, but with chlorine added in an amount sufficient to finish destruction of the undesirable algae. The volume of water to be treated is generally taken as that within a depth of 5 ft; sunlight will not penetrate deeper to promote algae growth. Application of copper sulfate in solution to the surface of a reservoir can be effected either by addition to water as it enters the reservoir, spraying on the surface, or dragging a bag of copper sulfate behind a boat zigzagging back and forth over the entire surface.

Iron and manganese removal to prevent red water or black stain is generally effected by aeration, sedimentation, and filtration. Small amounts of lime introduced in a closed system of sedimentation tanks may remove iron without aeration. The same lime or lime-soda treatment used for softening may be used. Special zeolites are sometimes used, although to a limited extent.

Since corrosion can be costly, corrosive water must often be treated in the interest of economics. In some cases, it may be enough to provide threshold treatment that will coat distribution lines with a light but protective film of scale. But in other cases—boiler-feed water for high-pressure boilers is one—it is important to have no corrosion or scaling. Then, deaeration and pH control may be necessary. (The real danger here is failure of boiler-tube surfaces because of overheating due to scale formation.)

In either hot- or cold-water lines—but *never* in boiler-feed water—a generally effective corrosion inhibitor is a caustic silicate solution.

Waters having less than 25 ppm of calcium, high carbon dioxide, and low pH are corrosive in the presence of dissolved oxygen. Langlier's index, or $CaCO_3$ saturation index, will indicate whether corrosive tendencies exist. The CO_2 can be neutralized with lime. Addition of sodium silicate as well will precipitate a protective scale. If calcium is in concentrations of 25 to 50 ppm, it will not cause a heavy scale; neither can it be depended on to form a protective layer. This water would be corrosive in presence of oxygen. Alkali other than lime should be used to control pH.

Waters having over 50 ppm of calcium are generally scale-producing, according to Langlier's index.

In the case of boiler-feed water, corrosion must be prevented, even if it means removal of all dissolved oxygen and CO_2, plus pH control.   Aeration will rid the water of its CO_2.   Deaeration will take out the oxygen—and any other gases remaining. Deaeration is accomplished by boiling; either by adding heat to the water or by extracting the air by vacuum.   There are deaerating heaters of various types as well as different methods of creating vacuum for cold-water deaeration.   (Eskell Nordell, "Water Treatment for Industrial and Other Uses," Reinhold Publishing Corporation, New York.)

Akin to boiler-feed waters are the cooling waters so important for condensing, plus a myriad of other industrial heat-exchange uses.   Cooling waters are perhaps ideally given once-through use.   That is, they are pulled from the ground, a surface source, or the sea; they perhaps get some inexpensive treatment; they flow through a heat exchanger of some sort; and finally, they are discharged back to the ground, the surface, or the sea.   But there are many places where such one-time use of water is not possible.   It must be used for other purposes in addition to cooling, or in many cases used and reused in its cooling capacity.   The water must be run to a spray pond or cooling tower after use—through a timber-slatted structure with natural or forced draft to be aerated and evaporated, and thus cooled.

Aeration of the coolant in the tower increases its corrosiveness; evaporation of it tends to concentrate its mineral impurities.   Therefore, treatment of reused cooling water is an important factor.   It must be rendered as near neutral as possible (on the Langlier scale) to prevent both corrosion and scaling.   Information needed for using this handy indicator of scale problems includes methyl orange alkalinity, calcium hardness, total solids, pH, and temperature to which the water is to be raised.   The cooling water must also be "blown off" for disposal of undesirable solids, the loss to be made up by treated make-up water.   Cooling-water treatment, depending on specific needs, may be necessarily as strenuous as that for boiler feed.

20-21. Disinfection of Water.   This means the killing of infectious bacteria to render the water safe for domestic use.   Disinfection can be accomplished by heat and ultraviolet light, but it is generally effected chemically.   Liquid chlorine, conveniently and accurately measured out in gaseous form by chlorine-feed devices, is most widely used.   Hypochlorites are used quite widely; chloramine formed by combining ammonia and chlorine is an effective disinfectant.   Ozone has had limited use because of high first cost of installation, but it is an effective taste and odor destroyer.

No domestic water system should begin supplying water until all its facilities (pipes, tanks, filters, etc.) are disinfected.   Whenever repairs or additions are made on an existing system, disinfection must be carried out before water is delivered for domestic use.   This disinfection will be effected by 100 ppm available chlorine; not less than 50 ppm should be used.   The solution should remain in facilities to be disinfected for 12 hr.

Continued chlorination, once the water supply is in use, should be maintained with dependable equipment and chemical supplies.   Liquid chlorine comes under pressure in metal containers of 100-, 150-, and 2,000-lb capacity.   It must be remembered that the gas fed from the container is a poison.   Thus, chlorine-feed rooms must be carefully ventilated.   Direct-feed, solution-feed, pressure-feed, or vacuum-feed equipment should all be installed in duplicate to insure uninterrupted service.   Automatic proportioning devices should be provided.

Chlorine in relatively pure water reacts to form hypochlorous acid, and the remaining free Cl_2 in solution is called the free available chlorine.

When ammonia and nitrogenous organic matter are present, the free available chlorine forms chloramics, termed combined available chlorine.

The amount of free or combined available chlorine needed to react with impurities in the water and disinfect them in a given period (10 min) is the chlorine demand.   Chlorine in excess of the total demand is the chlorine residual, and this is readily measured by orthotolodine test.   The point at which all oxidizable material is oxidized is the break point.

For effective chlorination, pH of water must be over 9.0; effectiveness decreases with water temperature; contact period should be not less than 20 min. General practice calls for 0.1 to 0.2 ppm chlorine residual for 10 to 20 min.

Ammonia is commonly used with chlorine to prevent chlorine odors and to foster a persistent chlorine residual. A ratio of 1 part ammonia to 3 parts chlorine is commonly used.

Superchlorination is the application of more chlorine than needed to produce the desired residual—followed by dechlorination with activated carbon or aeration; the method is effective in burning out color of some waters.

Chlorine as an algaecide can control growths of slimes in pipelines and on cooling towers. Chlorine is also used as a filter aid, applied directly during backwashing.

Section 21

PLUMBING AND SPRINKLER SYSTEMS

TYLER G. HICKS

Mechanical Engineer

WASTE PIPING

Human, natural, and industrial wastes resulting from building occupancy and use must be disposed of in a safe, quick manner if occupant health and comfort are to be safeguarded. So design of an adequate plumbing system requires careful planning and adherence to state or municipal regulations governing these systems.

The National Plumbing Code, American Standard A40.8, gives basic goals in environmental sanitation and is a useful aid in designing plumbing systems for all classes of buildings. It is also helpful for areas having antiquated codes or none at all. Much of the material in the present chapter is based on this code.*

21-1. Plumbing-system Design. The usual steps in planning a plumbing system are: (1) secure a sewer or waste-disposal plan of the site; (2) obtain preliminary architectural and structural plans and elevations of the building; (3) tabulate known and estimated occupancy data, including the number of persons, sex, work schedules, and pertinent details of any manufacturing process to be performed in the building; (4) obtain copies of the latest edition of the applicable code; (5) design the system in accordance with code recommendations; and (6) have the design approved by local authorities before construction is begun.

21-2. Plumbing-system Elements. The typical plumbing layout in Fig. 21-1 shows the major elements necessary in the usual plumbing system. *Fixtures* (lavatories, water closets, bathtubs, showers, etc.) are located as needed on each floor of the structure. Table 21-1 lists the minimum facilities required by the National Plumbing Code for various classes of buildings. In industrial and commercial buildings, the number of fixtures on a given floor may be extensive because, besides including the above sanitary fixtures, there may be other units, such as central locker and washrooms, process-machine drains, and water coolers.

Each fixture is served by a *soil* or *waste stack*, a *vent* or *vent stack*, and a *trap*, Fig. 21-1. Vertical soil stacks conduct waste solids and liquids from one or more fixtures to a sloped *house* or *building drain* in the building cellar, crawl space, or wall. Each vent stack extends to a point above the building roof and may or may not have *branch vents* connected to it. Vents and vent stacks permit the entrance of fresh air to the plumbing system, diluting any gases present and balancing the air pressure in various branches.

Traps on each fixture provide a water seal, which prevents sewer gases from entering the working and living areas. The house drain delivers the discharge from the various

* Extracted with permission of the publisher, The American Society of Mechanical Engineers, 29 West 39th St., New York 18, N.Y.

Table 21-1. Minimum Facilities Recommended by National Plumbing Code, ASA A40.8-1955[a]

Type of building or occupancy[b]	Water closets		Urinals	Lavatories		Bathtubs or showers	Drinking fountains[c]
Dwelling or apartment houses[d]	1 for each dwelling or apartment unit		. . . .	1 for each apartment or dwelling unit		1 for each apartment or dwelling unit	
	Male	Female					
Schools:[e] Elementary	1 per 100	1 per 35	1 per 30 male	1 per 60 persons			1 per 75 persons
Secondary	1 per 100	1 per 45	1 per 30 male	1 per 100 persons			1 per 75 persons
Office or public buildings	No. of persons 1–15 16–35 36–55 56–80 81–110 111–150 1 fixture for each 40 additional persons	No. of fixtures 1 2 3 4 5 6	Wherever urinals are provided for men, one water closet less than the number specified may be provided for each urinal installed[b] except that the number of water closets in such cases shall not be reduced to less than ⅔ of the minimum specified	No. of persons 1–15 16–35 36–60 61–90 91–125 1 fixture for each 45 additional persons	No. of fixtures 1 2 3 4 5		1 for each 75 persons
Manufacturing, warehouses, workshops, loft buildings, foundries and similar establishments[f]	No. of persons 1–9 10–24 25–49 50–74 75–100 1 fixture for each additional 30 employees	No. of fixtures 1 2 3 4 5	Same substitution as above	1–100 persons, 1 fixture for each 10 persons Over 100, 1 for each 15 persons[g,h]		1 shower for each 15 persons exposed to excessive heat or to skin contamination with poisonous, infectious, or irritating material	1 for each 75 persons
Dormitories[i]	Male: 1 for each 10 persons Female: 1 for each 8 persons Over 10 persons, add 1 fixture for each 25 additional males and 1 for each 20 additional females		1 for each 25 men Over 150 persons, add 1 fixture for each additional 50 men	1 for each 12 persons. (Separate dental lavatories should be provided in community toilet rooms. Ratio of dental lavatories for each 50 persons is recommended.) Add 1 lavatory for each 20 males, 1 for each 15 females		1 for each 8 persons. In the case of women's dormitories, additional bathtubs should be installed at the ratio of 1 for each 30 females. Over 150 persons, add 1 fixture for each 20 persons	1 for each 75 persons

Table 21-1. Minimum Facilities Recommended by National Plumbing
Code, ASA A40.8-1955[a] (Continued)

Type of building or occupancy[b]	Water closets		Urinals		Lavatories		Bathtubs or showers	Drinking fountains[c]
	No. of persons	No. of fixtures	No. of persons	No. of fixtures	No. of persons	No. of fixtures		
	Male	Fe-male	(Male)		1–200	1		
Theaters, auditoriums			1–200	1	201–400	2		1 for each 100 persons
			201–400	2	401–750	3		
	1–100	1	1	401–600	3	Over 750, 1 for	
	101–200	2	2	Over 600; 1 for		each addition-	
	201–400	3	3	each addition-		al 500 persons	
	Over 400, add 1 fixture for each additional 500 males and 1 for each 300 females		al 300 males					

[a] The figures shown are based upon one fixture being the minimum required for the number of persons indicated or any fraction thereof.

[b] Building category nots hown on this table will be considered separately by the administrative authority.

[c] Drinking fountains shall not be installed in toilet rooms.

[d] Laundry trays—one single compartment tray for each dwelling unit or 2 compartment trays for each 10 apartments. Kitchen sinks—1 for each dwelling or apartment unit.

[e] This schedule has been adopted (1945) by the National Council on Schoolhouse Construction.

[f] As required by the American Standard Safety Code for Industrial Sanitation in Manufacturing Establishments (ASA Z4.1-1935).

[g] Where there is exposure to skin contamination with poisonous, infectious, or irritating materials, provide 1 lavatory for each 5 persons.

[h] 24 lin in. of wash sink or 18 in. of a circular basin, when provided with water outlets for such space, shall be considered equivalent to 1 lavatory.

[i] Laundry trays, 1 for each 50 persons. Slop sinks, 1 for each 100 persons.

General. In applying this schedule of facilities, consideration must be given to the accessibility of the fixtures. Conformity purely on a numerical basis may not result in an installation suited to the need of the individual establishment. For example, schools should be provided with toilet facilities on each floor having classrooms.

Temporary workingmen facilities:
1 water closet and 1 urinal for each 30 workmen
24-in. urinal trough = 1 urinal.   48-in. urinal trough = 2 urinals.
36-in. urinal trough = 2 urinals.   60-in. urinal trough = 3 urinals.   72-in. urinal trough = 4 urinals.

stacks to the *house* or *building trap* (Fig. 21-1), which is generally provided with a separate vent. Between the house trap and *public sewer*, or other main sewer pipe, is the *house sewer*. The house sewer is outside the building structure, while the house trap is just inside the building foundation wall. (V. T. Manas, "National Plumbing Code Handbook," McGraw-Hill Book Company, Inc., New York.)

21-3. Plumbing Piping. Cast iron is the most common piping material for systems in which extremely corrosive wastes are not expected. In recent years, copper has become increasingly popular because it is lightweight and easy to install. Vitrified-clay, steel, brass, wrought-iron, and lead pipe are also used in plumbing systems.

No matter what material is used for plumbing-system piping, it should conform to one or more of the accepted standards approved by the National Plumbing Code, or the code used in the area in which the building is located. Figure 21-2 shows a number of different traps used in plumbing piping systems.

In cast-iron pipe, the fitting joints are calked with oakum or hemp and filled with molten lead not less than 1 in. deep. This provides some flexibility without the danger of leaks. Clay pipe is calked with oakum, cement grout, and mortar. Copper pipe is commonly brazed, while screwed and wrought-iron pipe have screwed or flanged connections.

When planning a plumbing system, check with the applicable code before specifying the type of joint to be used in the piping.   Joints acceptable in some areas may not be allowed in others.

21-4. Sump Pits.   Where the house drain is below the level of the public sewer line, some arrangement for lifting the sewage to the proper level must be provided.   This can be done by allowing the house drain to empty into a suitably sized *sump pit*.   The sewage is discharged from the sump pit to the public sewer by a pneumatic ejector or motor-driven pump.

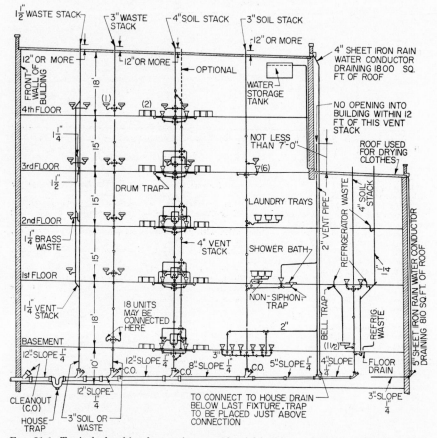

Fig. 21-1. Typical plumbing layout for a residential building.   (*Babbitt, "Plumbing," 2d ed., McGraw-Hill Book Company, Inc., New York.*)

21-5. Rain-water Drainage.   Exterior sheet-metal *leaders* for rain-water drainage are not normally included in the plumbing contract.   Interior leaders or storm-water drains, however, are considered part of the plumbing work.   Depending on the size of the building and the code used in the locality, rain water from various roof areas may or may not be led into the house drains.   Where separate rain-water leaders or storm drains are used, the house drains are then called *sanitary drains* because they convey only the wastes from the various plumbing fixtures in the building.

Interior storm-water drain pipes may be made of cast iron, steel, or wrought iron. All joints must be tight enough to prevent gas and water leakage.   It is common practice to insert a cast-iron running trap between the storm drain and the house drain to

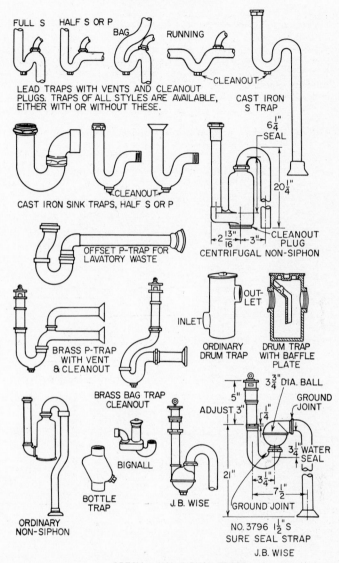

FIG. 21-2. Types of traps used on plumbing fixtures. (*Babbitt, "Plumbing," 2d ed., McGraw-Hill Book Company, Inc., New York.*)

maintain a seal on the storm drain at all times. However, not every code requires this type of protection. Use of storm drains does not eliminate the need for separate drains and vents for sewage. All codes prohibit use of storm drains for any type of sewage.

Water falling on the roof may be led either to a gutter, from where it flows to a leader, or it may be directed to a leader inlet by means of a slope in the roof surface. Many different designs of leader inlets are available for different roof constructions and storm-water conditions.   When vertical leaders are extremely long, it is common practice to install an expansion joint between the leader inlet and the leader itself.

Drains for building yards, areaways, and floors may be connected to the inlet side of an interior rain-leader trap.   Where this is not possible, these drains may be run to a municipal sewer, or to a dry well.   When a dry well is used, only the drains may discharge to it, other sewage being prohibited by most codes.

21-6. Plumbing-pipe Sizes.   There are two ways of specifying the pipe size required for a particular class of plumbing service: (1) directly in terms of area served, as in roof-drainage service (Table 21-2) and (2) in terms of "fixture units" (Table 21-3).

Table 21-2. Sizes of Vertical Leaders and Horizontal Storm Drains*

Vertical Leaders

Size of leader or conductor,† in.	Max projected roof area, sq ft
2	720
2½	1,300
3	2,200
4	4,600
5	8,650
6	13,500
8	29,000

Horizontal Storm Drains

Diam of drain, in.	Max projected roof area for drains of various slopes, sq ft		
	⅛-in. slope	¼-in. slope	½-in. slope
3	822	1,160	1,644
4	1,880	2,650	3,760
5	3,340	4,720	6,680
6	5,350	7,550	10,700
8	11,500	16,300	23,000
10	20,700	29,200	41,400
12	33,300	47,000	66,600
15	59,500	84,000	119,000

* From National Plumbing Code, ASA A40.8-1955.
† The equivalent diameter of square or rectangular leader may be taken as the diameter of that circle which may be inscribed within the cross-sectional area of the leader.

As can be seen from these tables, the capacity of a leader or drain varies with the pitch of the installed pipe.   The greater the pitch per running foot of pipe, the larger the capacity allowed, in terms of either the area served or the number of fixture units. This is because a steeper pitch increases the static head available to produce flow through the pipe.   As static head increases, so does the amount of liquid which the pipe can handle.

21-7. Fixture Unit.   This is the average discharge, during use, of an arbitrarily selected fixture, such as a lavatory or toilet.   Once this value is established, the discharge rates of other types of fixtures are stated in terms of the basic fixture.   For example, when the basic fixture is a lavatory served by a 1¼-in. trap, the average flow during discharge is 7.5 gpm.   So a bathtub that discharges 15 gpm is rated as two fixture units (2 × 7.5).   Thus, a tabulation of fixture units can be set up, based on an assumed basic unit.

Table 21-3. Sizes of Building Drains and Sewers*

| Diam of pipe, in. | Max number of fixture units that may be connected to any portion† of the building drain or the building sewer | | | |
| | Fall per ft | | | |
	$\frac{1}{16}$ in.	$\frac{1}{8}$ in.	$\frac{1}{4}$ in.	$\frac{1}{2}$ in.
2	.....	.....	21	26
2½	.....	.....	24	31
3	.....	20‡	27‡	36‡
4	.....	180	216	250
5	.....	390	480	575
6	.....	700	840	1,000
8	1,400	1,600	1,920	2,300
10	2,500	2,900	3,500	4,200
12	3,900	4,600	5,600	6,700
15	7,000	8,300	10,000	12,000

* From National Plumbing Code, ASA A40.8-1955.
† Includes branches of the building drain.
‡ Not over two water closets.

Table 21-4 gives fixture-unit values recommended by the National Plumbing Code. These values designate the relative load weight to be used in estimating the total load carried by a soil waste pipe. They are to be used in connection with Tables 21-2 and 21-3 and similar tabulations for soil, waste, and drain pipes for which the permissible load is given in terms of fixture units.

Fixtures not listed in Table 21-4 should be estimated in accordance with Table 21-5. For a continuous or semicontinuous flow into a drainage system, such as from a pump, pump ejector, air-conditioning system, or similar device, two fixture units should be used for each gallon per minute of flow. When additional fixtures are to be installed in the future, the drain size should be based on the ultimate load, not on the present load. Provide plugged fittings at the stack for connection of future fixtures.

21-8. Branches and Vents. The fixture unit (Art. 21-7) is also used for sizing vents and vent stacks (Table 21-6). In general, the diameter of a branch vent or vent stack is one-half or more of the branch or stack it serves, but not less than $1\frac{1}{4}$ in. Smaller diameters are prohibited, because they might restrict the venting action.

Fixture branches connecting one or more fixtures with the soil or waste stack are usually sized on the basis of the maximum number of fixture units for a given size of pipe or trap (Table 21-7). Where a large volume of water or other liquid may be contained in a fixture, such as in bathtubs, slop sinks, etc., an oversize branch drain may be provided to secure more rapid emptying.

21-9. Gutters. Semicircular gutters are sized on the basis of the maximum projected roof area served. Table 21-8 shows how gutter capacity varies with diameter and pitch. Where maximum rainfall is either more than, or less than, 4 in. per hr, refer to the National Plumbing Code for suitable correction factors.

21-10. How to Use Fixture Units. The steps in determining pipe sizes by means of fixture units (Art. 21-7) are: (1) list all fixtures served by one stack or branch; (2) alongside each fixture, list its fixture unit; (3) take the sum of the fixture units and enter the proper table (Tables 21-3, 21-6, 21-7) to determine the pipe size required for the stack or the branch.

21-11. Traps. Separate traps are required by almost every code on most fixtures not fitted with an integral trap. The trap should be installed as close as possible to the unit served. More than one fixture may be connected to a trap if certain code regulations are observed. For specific requirements, refer to the governing code.

Table 21-4. Fixture Units per Fixture or Group*

Fixture type	Fixture-unit value as load factors	Min size of trap, in.
1 bathroom group consisting of water closet, lavatory and bathtub or shower stall	Tank water closet, 6 Flush-valve water closet, 8	
Bathtub† (with or without overhead shower)	2	$1\frac{1}{2}$
Bathtub†	3	2
Bidet	3	$1\frac{1}{2}$
Combination sink and tray	3	Nominal $1\frac{1}{2}$
Combination sink and tray with food-disposal unit	4	Separate traps $1\frac{1}{2}$
Dental unit or cuspidor	1	$1\frac{1}{4}$
Dental lavatory	1	$1\frac{1}{4}$
Drinking fountain	$\frac{1}{2}$	1
Dishwasher, domestic	2	$1\frac{1}{2}$
Floor drains‡	1	2
Kitchen sink, domestic	2	$1\frac{1}{2}$
Kitchen sink, domestic, with food-waste grinder	3	$1\frac{1}{2}$
Lavatory¶	1	Small P.O. $1\frac{1}{4}$
Lavatory¶	2	Large P.O. $1\frac{1}{2}$
Lavatory, barber, beauty parlor	2	$1\frac{1}{2}$
Lavatory, surgeon's	2	$1\frac{1}{2}$
Laundry tray (1 or 2 compartments)	2	$1\frac{1}{2}$
Shower stall, domestic	2	2
Showers (group) per head	3	
Sinks:		
Surgeon's	3	$1\frac{1}{2}$
Flushing rim (with valve)	8	3
Service (trap standard)	3	3
Service (P trap)	2	2
Pot, scullery, etc.	4	$1\frac{1}{2}$
Urinal, pedestal, siphon jet, blowout	8	Nominal 3
Urinal, wall lip	4	$1\frac{1}{2}$
Urinal stall, washout	4	2
Urinal trough (each 2-ft section)	2	$1\frac{1}{2}$
Wash sink (circular or multiple) each set of faucets	2	Nominal $1\frac{1}{2}$
Water closet, tank-operated	4	Nominal 3
Water closet, valve-operated	8	3

* From National Plumbing Code, ASA A40.8-1955.
† A shower head over a bathtub does not increase the fixture value.
‡ Size of floor drain shall be determined by the area of surface water to be drained.
¶ Lavatories with $1\frac{1}{4}$- or $1\frac{1}{2}$-in. trap have the same load value; larger P.O. (plumbing orifice) plugs have greater flow rate.

Table 21-5. Other Fixture-unit Values*

Fixture Drain or Trap Size, In.	Fixture-unit Value
$1\frac{1}{4}$ in. and smaller	1
$1\frac{1}{2}$	2
2	3
$2\frac{1}{2}$	4
3	5
4	6

* From National Plumbing Code, ASA A40.8-1955.

Table 21-6. Size and Length of Vents*

Size of soil or waste stack, in.	Fixture units connected	Diam of vent required, in.								
		1¼	1½	2	2½	3	4	5	6	8
		Max length of vent, ft								
1¼	2	30								
1½	8	50	150							
1½	10	30	100							
2	12	30	75	200						
2	20	26	50	150						
2½	42		30	100	300					
3	10		30	100	200	600				
3	30			60	200	500				
3	60			50	80	400				
4	100			35	100	260	1,000			
4	200			30	90	250	900			
4	500			20	70	180	700			
5	200				35	80	350	1,000		
5	500				30	70	300	900		
5	1,100				20	50	200	700		
6	350				25	50	200	400	1,300	
6	620				15	30	125	300	1,100	
6	960					24	100	250	1,000	
6	1,900					20	70	200	700	
8	600						50	150	500	130
8	1,400						40	100	400	120
8	2,200						30	80	350	110
8	3,600						25	60	250	80
10	1,000							75	125	100
10	2,500							50	100	50
10	3,800							30	80	35
10	5,600							25	60	25

* From National Plumbing Code, ASA A40.8-1955.

Table 21-4 lists the minimum trap size recommended by the National Plumbing Code for various fixtures.

A water seal of at least 2 in., and not more than 4 in., is generally required in most traps. Traps exposed to freezing should be suitably protected to prevent ice formation in the trap body. Cleanouts of suitable size are required on all traps except those made integral with the fixture or those having a portion which is easily removed for cleaning of the interior body. Most codes prohibit use of traps in which a moving part is needed to form the seal. Double trapping is also usually prohibited.

21-12. Cleanouts. In horizontal drainage lines, at least one cleanout is required per 50 ft of 4-in. or smaller pipe. For larger sizes, a cleanout is required for each 100 ft of pipe. In underground drainage lines, the cleanout must be extended to the floor or grade level to allow easier cleaning. Cleanouts should open in a direction opposite to that of the flow in the pipe, or at right angles to it.

In pipes up to 4 in., the cleanout should be the same size as the pipe itself. For pipes larger than 4 in., the cleanout should be at least 4 in. in diameter but may be larger, if desired. When underground piping over 10 in. in diameter is used, a manhole is required at each 90° bend and at intervals not exceeding 150 ft.

21-13. Interceptors. These are devices installed to separate and retain grease, oil, sand, and other undesirable matter from the sewage, while permitting normal liquid wastes to discharge to the sewer or sewage-treatment plant.

Table 21-7. Horizontal Fixture Branches and Stacks*

Diam of pipe, in.	Max number of fixture units that may be connected to			
	Any horizontal† fixture branch	One stack of 3 stories in height or 3 intervals	More than 3 stories in height	
			Total for stack	Total at one story or branch interval
$1\frac{1}{4}$	1	2	2	1
$1\frac{1}{2}$	3	4	8	2
2	6	10	24	6
$2\frac{1}{2}$	12	20	42	9
3	20‡	30¶	60¶	16‡
4	160	240	500	90
5	360	540	1,100	200
6	620	960	1,900	350
8	1,400	2,200	3,600	600
10	2,500	3,800	5,600	1,000
12	3,900	6,000	8,400	1,500
15	7,000			

* From National Plumbing Code, ASA A40.8-1955.
† Does not include branches of the building drain.
‡ Not over two water closets.
¶ Not over six water closets.

Table 21-8. Size of Gutters*

Diam of gutter,† in.	Max projected roof area for gutters of various slopes, sq ft			
	$\frac{1}{16}$-in. slope	$\frac{1}{8}$-in. slope	$\frac{1}{4}$-in. slope	$\frac{1}{2}$-in. slope
3	170	240	340	480
4	360	510	720	1,020
5	625	880	1,250	1,770
6	960	1,360	1,920	2,770
7	1,380	1,950	2,760	3,900
8	1,990	2,800	3,980	5,600
10	3,600	5,100	7,200	10,000

* From National Plumbing Code, ASA A40.8-1955.
† Gutters other than semicircular may be used provided they have an equivalent cross-sectional area.

Grease interceptors are used for kitchens, cafeterias, restaurants, and similar establishments where the amount of grease discharged might obstruct the pipe or interfere with disposal of the sewage. Oil separators are used where flammable liquids or oils might be discharged to the sewer. Sand interceptors are used to remove sand or other solids from the liquid sewage before it enters the building sewer. They are provided with large cleanouts for easy removal of accumulated solids.

Other types of plants in which interceptors are usually required include laundries, beverage-bottling firms, slaughterhouses, and food-manufacturing establishments.

21-14. Plumbing Fixtures. To insure maximum sanitation and health protection, most codes have rigid requirements regarding fixtures used in plumbing systems. These usually include items like materials of construction, connections, overflows,

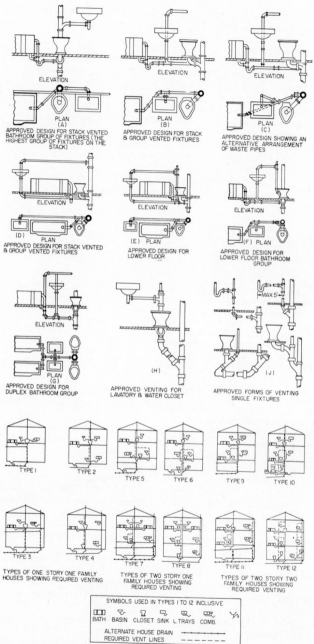

FIG. 21-3. Typical plumbing installations. (*Babbitt, "Plumbing," 2d ed., McGraw-Hill Book Company, Inc., New York.*)

installation, prevention of backflow, flushing methods, types of fixtures allowed, and inlet and outlet sizes. So before specifying or purchasing a given fixture, check the governing code carefully to see that the proposed units are acceptable. Figure 21-3 shows a typical connection diagram for a group of fixtures.

21-15. Pipe Hangers. To insure adequate support of piping used in plumbing systems, the National Plumbing Code allows the following *maximum* distance between supports in vertical pipes: cast-iron soil pipe, one story; screwed pipe, every other story; copper tubing $1\frac{1}{2}$ in. and over, each story; copper tubing $1\frac{1}{4}$ in. and under, 4-ft. intervals; lead pipe, 4-ft intervals.

For horizontal pipes, the following maximum distances are allowed: cast-iron soil pipe, 5-ft intervals; screwed pipe, 12-ft intervals; copper tubing $1\frac{1}{2}$ in. and smaller, 6-ft intervals; copper tubing 2 in. and larger, 10-ft intervals; lead pipe is to be supported by strips or other means for its entire length. Pipes run in the ground should have firm support for their complete length.

Note that the above allowances are for the *maximum* distances between supports. Where possible, supports that are closer together than the allowable maximum distance should be used.

    (a)   (b)   (c)   (d)   (e)

FIG. 21-4. Typical water closets. (*a*) Siphon-vortex—water from rim washes bowl, creates vortex, becomes a jet, and discharges by siphon action. (*b*) Siphon-jet—water from rim becomes jet in the upleg of discharge, then is siphoned out in downleg. (*c*) Reverse trap— similar to siphon-jet, but the water closet is smaller. (*d*) Washdown—pressure buildup causes upleg to overflow, creating discharge siphon. (*e*) Blowout—used with direct-flush valve, strong jet into upleg causes discharge. (See also C. G. Ramsey and H. R. Sleeper, "Architectural Graphic Standards," and C. M. Gay, C. de Van Fawcett, and W. J. McGuinness, "Mechanical and Electrical Equipment for Buildings," John Wiley & Sons, Inc., New York.)

The hangers and anchors used for plumbing piping should be metal, and strong enough to prevent vibration. Each should be designed and installed to carry its share of the total weight of the pipe.

21-16. Piping for Indirect Wastes. Certain wastes like those from food-handling, dishwashing (commercial), and sterile-materials machines should be discharged through an indirect waste pipe; i.e., one that is not directly connected with the building drainage pipes but handles waste liquids by discharging them into a plumbing fixture or receptacle from where they flow directly to the building drainage pipes. Indirect-waste piping is generally required for the discharge from rinse sinks, laundry washers, steam tables, refrigerators, egg boilers, iceboxes, coffee urns, dishwashers, stills, sterilizers, etc. It is also required for units that must be fitted with drip or drainage connections but are not ordinarily regarded as plumbing fixtures.

An air gap is generally required between the indirect-waste piping and the regular drainage system. The gap should have at least twice the effective diameter of the drain it serves. A common way of providing the required air gap is by leading the indirect-waste line to a floor drain, slop sink, or similar fixture that is open to the air and is vented or trapped in accordance with the governing *code*. To provide the necessary air gap, the indirect-waste pipe is terminated above the flood level of the fixture.

Where a device discharges only clear water, such as engine-cooling jackets, water lifts, sprinkler systems, or overflows, an indirect-waste system must be used. Or, if desired, devices discharging only clear water may be emptied by leading their waste lines to the building roof. The roof provides the air gap and the waste flows off it into the building storm drains.

Hot water above 140°F and steam pipes usually must be arranged for indirect connection into the building drainage system or into an approved interceptor.

To prevent corrosion of plumbing piping and fittings, any chemicals, acids, or corrosive liquids are generally required to be automatically diluted or neutralized before being discharged into the plumbing piping. Sufficient fresh water for satisfactory dilution, or a neutralizing agent, should be available at all times. A similar requirement is contained in most codes for liquids that might form or give off toxic or noxious fumes.

21-17. Plumbing-system Inspection and Tests. Plans for plumbing systems must usually be approved before construction is started. After installation of the piping and fixtures is completed, both the new work and any existing work affected by the new work must be inspected and tested. The plumber or plumbing contractor is then informed of any violations. These must be corrected before the governing body will approve the system.

Either air or water may be used for preliminary testing of drainage, vent, and plumbing pipes. After the fixtures are in place, their traps should be filled with water and a final test made of the complete drainage system.

When testing a system with water, all pipe openings are tightly sealed, except the highest one. The pipes are then filled with water until overflow occurs from the top opening. Using this method, either the entire system or sections of it can be tested. In no case, however, should the head of water on a portion being tested be less than 10 ft, except for the top 10 ft of the system. Water should be kept in the system for at least 15 min before the inspection starts. During the inspection, the piping and fixtures must be tight at all points; otherwise approval cannot be granted.

An air test is made by sealing all pipe outlets and subjecting the piping to an air pressure of 5 psi throughout the system. The system should be tight enough to permit maintaining this pressure for at least 15 min without the addition of any air.

The final test required of plumbing systems uses either smoke or peppermint. In the smoke test, all traps are sealed with water and a thick, strong-smelling smoke is injected into the pipes by means of a suitable number of smoke machines. As soon as smoke appears at the roof stack outlets, they should be closed and a pressure equivalent to 1 in. of water should be maintained throughout the system for 15 min before inspection begins. For the peppermint test, 2 oz of oil of peppermint are introduced into each line or stack.

GAS PIPING

As with piping and fixtures for plumbing systems, gas piping and fixtures are subject to code regulations in most cities and towns. Natural and manufactured gases are widely used in stoves, water heaters, and space heaters of many designs. Since gas can form explosive mixtures when mixed with air, gas piping must be absolutely tight and free of leaks at all times. Usual codes cover every phase of gas-piping size, installation, and testing. The local code governing a particular building should be carefully followed during design and installation.

21-18. Gas Supply. The usual practice is for the public-service gas company to run its pipes into the building cellar, terminating with a brass shutoff valve and gas meter inside the cellar wall. From this point the plumbing contractor or gas-pipe fitter runs lines through the building to the various fixture outlets. When the pressure of the gas supplied by the public-service company is too high for the devices in the building, a pressure-reducing valve can be installed near the point where the line enters the building. This valve is usually supplied by the gas company.

Besides municipal codes governing the design and installation of gas piping and devices, the gas company serving the area will usually have a number of regulations that must be followed. In general, gas piping should be run in such a manner that it is unnecessary to locate the meter near a boiler, under a window or steps, or in any other area where it may be easily damaged. Where multiple meter installations are used, the piping must be plainly marked by means of a metal tag showing which part of the building is served by the particular pipe. When two or more meters are used in a building to supply separate consumers, there should be no interconnection on the outlet side of the meters.

Table 21-9. Heat Input to Common Appliances

Unit	Approx Input, Btu per Hr
Water heater, side-arm or circulating type..........	25,000
Water heater, automatic instantaneous:	
4 gpm.....................................	150,000
6 gpm.....................................	225,000
8 gpm.....................................	300,000
Refrigerator....................................	2,500
Ranges, domestic:	
4 top burners, 1 oven burner....................	62,500
4 top burners, 2 oven burners....................	82,500

Table 21-10. Typical Heating Values of Commercial Gases

Gas	Net Heating Value, Btu per Cu Ft
Natural gas (Los Angeles).........	971
Natural gas (Pittsburgh)..........	1,021
Coke-oven gas...................	514
Carbureted water gas.............	508
Commercial propane..............	2,371
Commercial butane..............	2,977

21-19. Gas-pipe Sizes. Gas piping must be designed to provide enough gas to appliances without excessive pressure loss between them and the meter. It is customary to size gas piping so the pressure loss between the meter and any appliance does not exceed 0.3 in. of water during periods of maximum gas demand. Other factors influencing the pipe size include maximum gas consumption anticipated, length of pipe and number of fittings, specific gravity of the gas, and the diversity factor.

21-20. Estimating Gas Consumption. Use the manufacturer's Btu rating of the appliances and the heating value of the gas to determine the flow required in cubic feet per hour. When Btu ratings are not immediately available, the values in Table 21-9 may be used for preliminary estimates. The average heating value of gas in the area can be obtained from the local gas company, but when this is not immediately available, the values in Table 21-10 can be used for preliminary estimates.

Example. A building has two 8 gpm hot-water heaters and 10 domestic ranges, each of which has four top burners and one oven burner. What is the maximum gas consumption that must be provided for if gas with a net heating value of 500 Btu per cu ft is used?

Solution: Heat input, using values from Table 21-9, is

$$2(300,000) + 10(62,500)$$
$$= 1,225,000 \text{ Btu per hr}$$

Maximum gas consumption is therefore

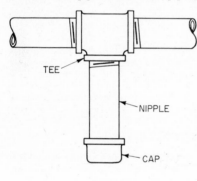
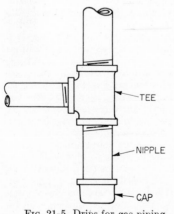

TEE

NIPPLE

CAP

TEE

NIPPLE

CAP

Fig. 21-5. Drips for gas piping.

1,225,000/500 = 2,450 cu ft per hr. The supply piping would be sized for this flow, even though all appliances would rarely operate at the same time.

21-21. Gas-pipe Materials. Materials recommended for gas piping in buildings are wrought iron or steel complying with American Standard B36.10. Malleable-iron or steel fittings should be used, except for stopcocks and valves. Above 4-in. nominal size, cast-iron fittings may be used.

Some local codes permit the use of brass or copper pipe of the same sizes as iron pipe if the gas handled is not corrosive to the brass or copper. Threaded fittings are generally required with these two materials.

Since the usual gas supplied for heating and domestic cooking generally contains some moisture, all piping should be installed so it pitches back to the supply main, or

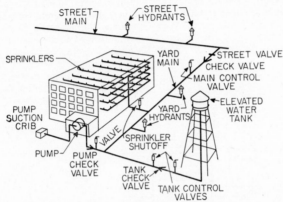

Fig. 21-6. Water-supply piping for sprinklers.

drips should be installed at suitable intervals. Neither unions nor bushings are permitted in gas pipes because of the danger of leakage and moisture trapping. To permit moisture removal, drips are installed at the lowest point in the piping, at the bottom of vertical risers, and at any other places where moisture might accumulate. Figure 21-5 shows typical drips for gas piping.

21-22. Testing Gas Piping. Once installation of the gas piping in a building is complete, it must be tested for leaks. Portions of the piping that will be enclosed in walls or behind other permanent structures should be tested before the enclosure is completed.

The usual code requirement for gas-pipe testing stipulates a test pressure of about 10 psig for 15 min, using air, city gas, or some inert gas. Use of oxygen in pressure tests is strictly prohibited. Prior to connecting any appliances, the piping should be purged, using the regular gas supply.

SPRINKLER SYSTEMS

Well-proved as effective in preventing the spread of fires in buildings of all types, sprinkler systems for fire protection are in wide use. Essentially (Fig. 21-6), they consist of a series of horizontal parallel pipes placed near the building ceiling. Vertical risers (Fig. 21-7) supply the liquid—usually water—used for extinguishing fires. The horizontal pipes contain sprinklers (Fig. 21-8) preset to open automatically and discharge liquid when the temperature of the air in the room reaches a certain predetermined level—usually 135 to 160°F. No manual control of the sprinklers is required; so they provide continuous protection day and night.

21-23. Types of Sprinkler Systems. Four common types of automatic sprinkler systems are in use today: (1) wet-pipe, (2) dry-pipe, (3) preaction, and (4) deluge (see also Art. 21-25). The type of system to be used depends on a number of factors, including occupancy classification, local code requirements, and the requirements of the building fire underwriters. Since the requirements vary from one area to another, no attempt will be made here to list those of each locality or underwriter. The Standards of the National Board of Fire Underwriters, as recommended by the National Fire Protection Association, are excerpted instead because they are so widely used as to be applicable for the majority of buildings.

21-24. Occupancy Classifications. The classifications of occupancy used by the National Board of Fire Underwriters (NBFU) are: (1) light-hazard, (2) ordinary-hazard, and (3) extra-hazard occupancy. Light hazards are those met in apartment houses, asylums, clubhouses, colleges, churches, dormitories, hospitals, hotels, libraries, museums, office buildings, and schools. Ordinary hazards include mercantiles, warehouses, manufacturing, and occupancies not classed as light or extra-hazardous. Extra-hazard occupancies include only those buildings or portions of buildings where the inspection agency having jurisdiction determines the hazard is severe.

21-25. Sprinkler-system Details. Pipes in a wet-pipe system contain water at all times. They are connected to the water supply so that water is discharged immediately when a fire causes the sprinklers to open. In a dry-pipe system, the sprinkler pipes contain air under pressure. When the sprinklers open because of a fire or other reason, the air flows from the pipes, permitting the water pressure to open the dry-pipe valve. Water then enters the pipes and is discharged by the sprinklers. Dry-pipe systems find greatest use in unheated buildings, like warehouses, and in unheated portions of heated buildings.

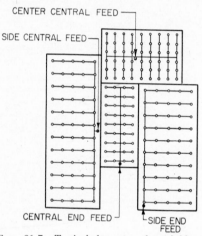

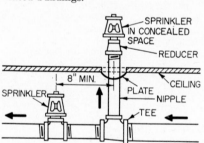

FIG. 21-7. Typical layouts of sprinkler piping.

FIG. 21-8. Sprinklers below and above ceiling.

Preaction systems have pipes containing air, which may or may not be under pressure. Heat-responsive devices, in the same area as the sprinklers, open a valve to permit water to flow into the piping system and the sprinklers when a fire occurs.

The deluge system has sprinklers attached to a piping system. Heat-responsive devices, in the same area as the sprinklers, open a valve permitting water to discharge from all sprinklers, when a fire occurs in the area served.

Prior to installing or remodeling any sprinkler system, the applicable drawings should be submitted to the local municipal agency and the underwriter of the building. Since beneficial reductions in insurance rates may be obtained by suitable installation of sprinkler systems, it is important that the underwriter have sufficient time for a full review of the plans before construction begins. Likewise, municipal approval of the sprinkler-system plans is usually necessary before the structure can be occupied. In actual construction, the piping contractor installing the sprinkler system generally secures the necessary municipal approval. However, existence of the approval should always be checked before construction is begun.

21-26. Water Supply for Sprinklers. At least one automatic water supply having sufficient capacity and pressure is required for every sprinkler system. Factors influencing the type of supply include the area, height, and value of the structure protected, occupancy, type of construction, type and availability of public fire protection, and in some instances, the exposures of the structure. A secondary supply may be required, depending on a number of factors, including those mentioned above. For a single, or a primary supply, a connection from a reliable waterworks system having adequate pressure and capacity is preferred.

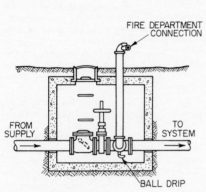

FIG. 21-9. Fire-department tie-in pit for tapping a water supply.

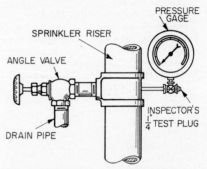

FIG. 21-10. Drain connection for sprinkler riser.

A good secondary supply can be obtained by use of one or more fire pumps, provided they have suitable drivers, sufficient capacity and reliability, and an adequate suction supply and are properly located in the premises. Underwriters may accept a motor-driven automatically controlled fire pump supplied from a water main or taking its suction under pressure from a storage system having sufficient capacity to meet the requirements of the structure protected.

Table 21-11. Pipe-size Schedule for Typical Sprinkler Installations

Occupancy and Pipe Size, In.	No. of Sprinklers
Light Hazard	
1	2
$1\frac{1}{4}$	3
$1\frac{1}{2}$	5
2	10
$2\frac{1}{2}$	40
3	No limit
Ordinary Hazard	
1	2
$1\frac{1}{4}$	3
$1\frac{1}{2}$	5
2	10
$2\frac{1}{2}$	20
3	40
$3\frac{1}{2}$	65
4	100
5	160
6	250
Extra Hazard	
1	1
$1\frac{1}{4}$	2
$1\frac{1}{2}$	5
2	8
$2\frac{1}{2}$	15
3	27
$3\frac{1}{2}$	40
4	55
5	90
6	150

For light-hazard occupancy, the pump should have a capacity of at least 250 gpm; when supplying sprinklers and hydrants, the capacity of the pump should be at least 500 gpm. Where the occupancy is classed as an ordinary hazard, the capacity should be at least 500 gpm, or 750 gpm, depending on whether or not hydrants are supplied in addition to sprinklers. For extra-hazard occupancy, consult the underwriter and local fire-protection authorities.

Other sources of water supply include gravity tanks, pressure tanks, penstocks, flumes, and fire-department connections suitable for pumping from the outside. In

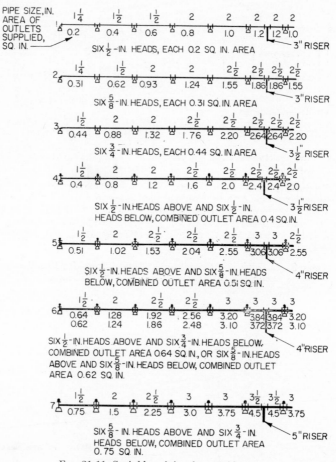

Fig. 21-11. Sprinkler piping for outside areas.

general, gravity tanks must have a capacity of at least 5,000 gal with the tank bottom not less than 35 ft above the underside of the roof for light- and ordinary-hazard occupancies. Pressure tanks must have at least 2,000 and 3,000 gal of water available, respectively, for these occupancies. Where penstocks, flumes, rivers, or lakes supply the water, approved strainers or screens must be provided to prevent solids from entering the piping. Figure 21-9 shows a fire-department tie-in pit.

21-27. Sprinkler Piping. The local fire-prevention authorities and the fire underwriters usually have specific requirements regarding the type, material, and size of pipe used in sprinkler systems. They should be consulted prior to the design of any system.

Table 21-11 lists pipe-size schedules for the three occupancy classifications met in various structures. Figure 21-10 shows a typical drain connection for a sprinkler riser pipe.

21-28. Area Protected by Sprinklers. In structures of fire-resistive construction and light-hazard occupancy, the area protected by one sprinkler should not exceed 196 sq ft; the distance between the center lines of the sprinkler pipes and between the sprinklers themselves should not exceed 14 ft. In this type of construction with ordinary-hazard occupancy, the area protected per sprinkler should not ordinarily exceed 100 sq ft; the distance between pipes and between sprinklers should not be more than 12 ft. For extra-hazard occupancy, the area protected by each sprinkler should not exceed 90 sq ft; distance between pipes and between sprinklers should not be more than 10 ft. Local fire-protection codes and underwriters' requirements cover other types of construction, including mill, semimill, open-joist, and joist type with a sheathed or plastered ceiling.

21-29. Sprinkler Position. In all usual applications, the sprinklers should be installed in the upright position, where they are protected from damage by vehicles and other objects passing beneath them. When it is necessary to install sprinklers in a pendent position, they must be of a design approved for that position.

Sprinkler deflectors should be parallel to the building ceilings and roof, or the incline of stairs when installed in a stairwell. Deflectors for sprinklers in the peak of a pitched roof should be horizontal. The distance between the deflectors and ceiling should not exceed 14 in. in fire-resistive structures; in mill and other smooth construction, the distance should not be more than 10 in.

21-30. Sprinkler Alarms. These are often required, depending on what other types of alarms or fire-notification devices are installed in the structure. The usual sprinkler alarm is designed to sound automatically when the flow from the system is equal to or greater than that from a single automatic sprinkler. Dry-pipe systems use a water-actuated alarm; preaction and deluge systems use electric alarm attachments actuated independently of the water flow in the system.

21-31. Outside Sprinklers. For protection of structures against exposure fires, outside sprinklers may be used. They can be arranged to protect cornices, windows, side walls, ridge poles, mansard roofs, etc. They are also governed by underwriters' requirements. Figure 21-11 shows the pipe sizes used for sprinklers protecting outside areas of a building, including cornices, windows, side walls, etc.

HOT- AND COLD-WATER SUPPLY

Most plumbing codes contain sections dealing with hot- and cold-water distribution within buildings. Table 21-12 lists the minimum fixture-supply pipe sizes recommended by the National Plumbing Code for various types of plumbing fixtures requiring a water supply. These sizes apply to both hot- and cold-water fixtures.

Table 21-12. Minimum Sizes for Fixture-supply Pipes*

Type of Fixture or Device	Pipe Size, In.	Type of Fixture or Device	Pipe Size, In.
Bath tubs	$\frac{1}{2}$	Shower (single head)	$\frac{1}{2}$
Combination sink and tray	$\frac{1}{2}$	Sinks (service, slop)	$\frac{1}{2}$
Drinking fountain	$\frac{3}{8}$	Sinks, flushing rim	$\frac{3}{4}$
Dishwasher (domestic)	$\frac{1}{2}$	Urinal (flush tank)	$\frac{1}{2}$
Kitchen sink, residential	$\frac{1}{2}$	Urinal (direct flush valve)	$\frac{3}{4}$
Kitchen sink, commercial	$\frac{3}{4}$	Water closet (tank type)	$\frac{3}{8}$
Lavatory	$\frac{3}{8}$	Water closet (flush valve type)	1
Laundry tray, 1, 2 or 3 compartments	$\frac{1}{2}$	Hose bibs	$\frac{1}{2}$
		Wall hydrant	$\frac{1}{2}$

* From National Plumbing Code, ASA A40.8-1955.

21-32. Water Pressure at Fixtures. No fixture should have a water-supply pressure less than 8 psi, except for flushometer-type water closets. There, a minimum pressure of 15 psi is required. There also are units for which the manufacturer requires a higher pressure.

The minimum required pressure should be available at the fixture, with sufficient allowance for pressure loss in the piping and fittings between the supply source and the fixture. Where there is a possibility that the minimum pressure in the system will fall below that required by the local plumbing code, some means must be provided to raise the pressure to the desired level. Devices used for this purpose include gravity and pressure tanks, and booster pumps. Where there is danger of excessive pressure causing water hammer, an air chamber or approved device must be installed to protect the piping from pressure surges and to reduce noise.

21-33. Hot- and Cold-water Piping. All water-supply and distribution piping must be designed so there is no possibility of backflow at any time. The minimum required air gap—distance between the fixture outlet and the flood-level rim of the receptacle—should be maintained at all times. Table 21-13 shows minimum air gaps generally used. Before any potable-water piping is put into use it must be disinfected with chlorine, using a procedure approved by the local code.

Table 21-13. Minimum Air Gaps for Generally Used Plumbing Fixtures*

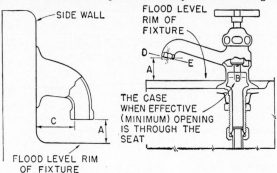

Fixture	Minimum air gap	
	When not affected by near wall†	When affected by near wall‡
Lavatories with effective openings not greater than ½-in. diameter...................................	1.0	1.50
Sink, laundry trays, and goose neck bath faucets with effective openings not greater than ¾-in. diameter	1.5	2.25
Overrim bath fillers with effective openings not greater than 1-in. diameter............................	2.0	3.00
Effective openings greater than 1-in................	¶	§

* From National Plumbing Code, ASA A40.8-1955.

† Side walls, ribs, or similar obstructions do not affect the air gaps when spaced from inside edge of spout opening a distance greater than three times the diameter of the effective opening for a single wall, or a distance greater than four times the diameter of the effective opening for two intersecting walls (see figure).

‡ Vertical walls, ribs, or similar obstructions extending from the water surface to or above the horizontal plane of the spout opening require a greater air gap when spaced closer to the nearest inside edge of spout opening than specified in note † above. The effect of three or more such vertical walls or ribs has not been determined. In such cases, the air gap shall be measured from the top of the wall.

¶ 2 × effective opening.

§ 3 × effective opening.

Pipes and tubing for water distribution may be made of copper, brass, lead, cast iron, wrought iron, or steel, provided they are approved by the local code. Threaded fittings are usually required to be galvanized or cement-coated. When choosing materials for potable-water piping, care should be taken to see there is no possibility of chemical action, or any other action that might cause a toxic condition. Figure 21-12 shows a typical piping arrangement for hot- and cold-water supply to plumbing fixtures.

21-34. Water-pipe Sizing. Since hot- and cold-water demand and usage vary considerably from one type of building to another, much care is necessary in pipe sizing.

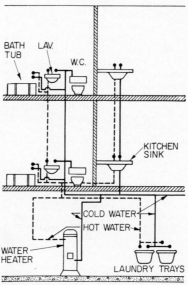

Fig. 21-12. Domestic piping arrangement. (*Babbitt, "Plumbing," 2d ed., McGraw-Hill Book Company, Inc., New York.*)

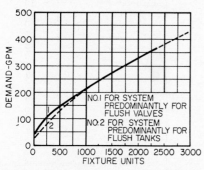

Fig. 21-13. Estimate curves for domestic water-demand load. (*National Plumbing Code.*)

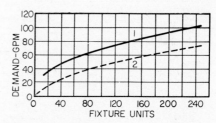

Fig. 21-14. Enlargement of low-demand portion of Fig. 21-13. (*National Plumbing Code.*)

In domestic installations, each person will use a total of 20 to 80 gal per day, depending on family size, garden requirements, etc. For apartment houses, a consumption of 50 gal per person per day is generally assumed in system design, while 40 gal per person per day is often used for housing projects.

Table 21-14 shows the water pressure and flow required for various plumbing fixtures of usual design. In some instances, where special designs are used, a higher pressure or flow rate may be required.

PLUMBING AND SPRINKLER SYSTEMS

Table 21-14. Rate of Flow and Required Pressure During Flow for Different Fixtures*

Fixture	Flow pressure,† psi	Flow rate, gpm
Ordinary basin faucet	8	3.0
Self-closing basin faucet	12	2.5
Sink faucet, ⅜ in	10	4.5
Sink faucet, ½ in	5	4.5
Bathtub faucet	5	6.0
Laundry-tub cock, ½ in	5	5.0
Shower	12	5.0
Ball cock for closet	15	3.0
Flush valve for closet	10–20	15–40‡
Flush valve for urinal	15	15.0
Garden hose, 50 ft and sill cock	30	5.0

* From National Plumbing Code, ASA A40.8-1955.
† Flow pressure is the pressure in the pipe at the entrance to the particular fixture considered.
‡ Wide range due to variation in design and type of flush-valve closets.

Table 21-15. Demand Weight of Fixtures in Fixture Units*·†

Fixture or group‡	Occupancy	Type of supply control	Weight in fixture units¶
Water closet	Public	Flush valve	10
Water closet	Public	Flush tank	5
Pedestal urinal	Public	Flush valve	10
Stall or wall urinal	Public	Flush valve	5
Stall or wall urinal	Public	Flush tank	3
Lavatory	Public	Faucet	2
Bathtub	Public	Faucet	4
Shower head	Public	Mixing valve	4
Service sink	Office, etc.	Faucet	3
Kitchen sink	Hotel or restaurant	Faucet	4
Water closet	Private	Flush valve	6
Water closet	Private	Flush tank	3
Lavatory	Private	Faucet	1
Bathtub	Private	Faucet	2
Shower head	Private	Mixing valve	2
Bathroom group	Private	Flush valve for closet	8
Bathroom group	Private	Flush tank for closet	6
Separate shower	Private	Mixing valve	2
Kitchen sink	Private	Faucet	2
Laundry trays (1-3)	Private	Faucet	3
Combination fixture	Private	Faucet	3

* From National Plumbing Code, ASA A40.8-1955.
† For supply outlets likely to impose continuous demands, estimate continuous supply separately and add to total demand for fixtures.
‡ For fixtures not listed, weights may be assumed by comparing the fixture to a listed one using water in similar quantities and at similar rates.
¶ The given weights are for total demand. For fixtures with both hot and cold water supplies, the weights for maximum separate demands may be taken as three-fourths the listed demand for supply.

As with drain and vent piping, the required flow for cold-water fixtures is usually computed in terms of fixture units. Table 21-15 lists the demand weight of fixtures in fixture units. Once the number of fixtures of various types is known, the load for a given type is determined by multiplying the number in the building or on a particular

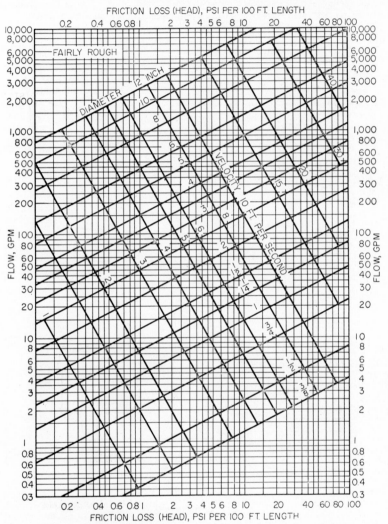

FIG. 21-15. Chart for selecting water-pipe size for various flows.

riser by the demand weight for this type. Figure 21-13 gives the demand of any group of fixtures in terms of gallons of water per minute. Figure 21-14 is an enlargement of Fig. 21-13 in the range of 0 to 250 fixture units. Where fixtures other than those listed in Table 21-15 must also be supplied, such as air-conditioning units, garden hoses, process devices, etc., the required flow in gallons per minute must be computed and added to the fixture demand of the riser supplying the unit or units.

The National Plumbing Code recommends the following steps in sizing cold-water distribution piping systems: (1) Sketch all the proposed risers, horizontal mains, and branch lines, indicating the number and type of fixtures served, together with the required water flow. (2) Compute the demand weights of the fixtures, in fixture units, using Table 21-15. (3) Using Fig. 21-13 or 21-14, and the total number of fixture units, determine the water demand in gallons per minute. (4) Compute the equivalent length of pipe for each stack in the system, starting from the street main. (5) Obtain by test or from the water company the average minimum pressure in the

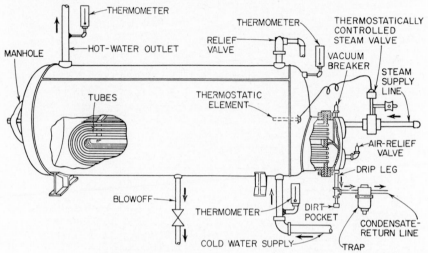

Fig. 21-16. Storage heater for domestic hot water.

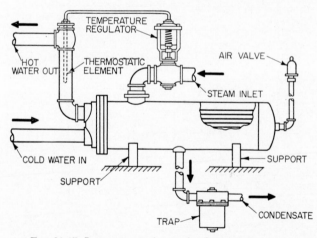

Fig. 21-17. Instantaneous heater for domestic hot water.

street main. Determine the minimum pressure needed for the highest fixture in the system. (6) Compute the pressure loss in the piping, using the equivalent length found in item 4. (7) Choose the pipe sizes from a chart like that in Fig. 21-15, or from the charts given in the National Plumbing Code. (See also V. T. Manas "National Plumbing Code Handbook," McGraw-Hill Book Company, Inc. New York.)

21-35. Hot-water Heaters. Two types of heaters are in common use. *Storage heaters* (Fig. 21-16) generally use steam as the heating medium, though hot water, gas,

Table 21-16. Hot-water Demand per Fixture for Various Building Types
(Based on average conditions for types of buildings listed, gallons of water per hour per fixture at 140°F)

Type of fixture	Apartment house	Hospital	Hotel	Industrial plant	Office building
Basins, private lavatories......	2	2	2	2	2
Basins, public lavatories.......	4	6	8	12	6
Showers.....................	75	75	75	225	
Slop sinks...................	20	20	30	20	15
Dishwashers (per 500 people)...	250	250	250	250	250
Pantry sinks.................	5	10	10		
Demand factor...............	0.30	0.25	0.25	0.40	0.30
Storage factor...............	1.25	0.60	0.80	1.00	2.00

Table 21-17. Hot-water Temperatures for Various Services, °F

Cafeterias (serving areas)...........	130
Lavatories and showers............	130
Slop sinks (floor cleaning)..........	150
Slop sinks (other cleaning).........	130
Cafeteria kitchens................	130 + steam

or electricity also find some use. The tank used with this type of heater stores hot water for future use. In general, the less uniform the demand for hot water, the greater the storage capacity needed in the tank. When the water demand is fairly uniform, a smaller storage capacity is allowable, but the capacity of the heating coil must be greater. However, a large storage capacity is used whenever possible, because this reduces the load on the boiler and allows use of a smaller heating coil. Industrial, office, and school-building hot-water demands are usually nonuniform with peak loads occurring during very short periods. Loads in hotels, apartment houses, and hospitals are usually more uniform.

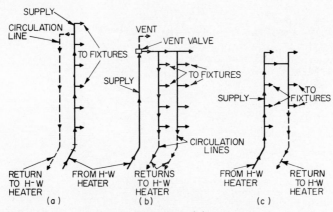

FIG. 21-18. Hot-water piping systems.

Instantaneous heaters (Fig. 21-17) have V-shaped or straight tubes to heat the water. Steam or hot water is the usual heating medium. The water for the building is heated as needed; there is no storage section in the heater. The heater coils may be installed in a boiler instead of a tank.

The hot-water load for a given building is computed in a manner similar to that described above, using Table 21-16 and the tabulated demand factor for the particular building type. The heating-coil capacity of the heater must at least equal the maximum probable demand for hot water.

For storage-type heaters, the storage capacity is obtained by multiplying the maximum probable demand by a suitable factor, which usually varies from 1.25 for apartment houses to 0.60 for hospitals. Table 21-17 lists hot-water temperatures for various services.

Example. An industrial plant has 9 showers, 200 private lavatories, 20 slop sinks, 20 public lavatories, and 1 dishwasher. What is the hourly water consumption and what storage and heating capacities are required for this load?

Using Table 21-16:

$$
\begin{array}{lcl}
\text{9 showers at 225 gph} & = & \text{2,025 gph} \\
\text{200 private lavatories at 2 gph} & = & \text{400} \\
\text{20 slop sinks at 20 gph} & = & \text{400} \\
\text{20 public lavatories at 12 gph} & = & \text{240} \\
\text{1 dishwasher at 250 gph} & = & \underline{\text{250}} \\
\text{Total hourly demand} & = & \text{3,315 gph}
\end{array}
$$

Using the demand factor from Table 21-16, maximum probable demand is

$$0.40 \times 3{,}315 = 1{,}326 \text{ gph}$$

Heating-coil capacity must at least equal this maximum probable demand. Storage capacity should be $1.00 \times 3{,}315 = 3{,}315$ gal.

21-36. Hot-water Piping System. Upfeed or downfeed systems (Fig. 21-18) can be used to supply hot water to the building fixtures. To supply hot water continuously, circulating piping is often employed. Unused water is returned through this piping to the heater. Here, its temperature is raised to the desired level and the water is returned to the risers.

Section 22

WASTE-WATER DISPOSAL

ARTHUR J. FOX, JR.

Senior Editor
Engineering News-Record

Disposing of water after use can be a greater problem than initially supplying it for use.

As with water supply and treatment (Sec. 20), problems of domestic-sewage and industrial-waste disposal often can be very complex, requiring for solution the knowledge of a specialist in the field of sanitary engineering.

Whether or not the liquid-waste-disposal problem is of sufficient magnitude or complexity to call for services of a consultant, it will in many cases call for contact with the local and state departments of health. Whatever disposal facilities are to be provided may depend on local requirements; whatever facilities are designed may depend on state health-department approval before construction.

Just as water supply is often a deciding factor in the location of a building, disposal of waste water is a significant item in early planning of any building project.

Even if the project is only a small private house with the normal small flow of domestic sewage, questions must be answered as to whether sewers are available for easy connection, or whether local regulations or physical conditions permit use of cesspools or septic tanks. Price of the finished building may depend on it.

If the project is a large industrial installation, expected to use great quantities of water for cooling and processes, available and allowable means of waste-water disposal may decide its location. Many a big process industry settled on a large stream is finding that the cost of bringing water into its plant is small compared with the cost it faces in getting it back out in a condition acceptable to those responsible for regulating sanitation of the receiving water body.

The problem of industrial wastes has grown to the point where industries are being kept off certain streams; they are being compelled by law or by public sentiment to close down or spend considerable sums for building and operating treatment facilities. Existing conditions of gross pollution of some streams may have to await, for correction, the obsolescence of some of the buildings on their banks. But there is every evidence that those concerned with conserving water quality (as well as quantity) will prevent everywhere possible the construction of any new industrial building not incorporating acceptable facilities for disposal of industrial wastes. It therefore rests with building owners and designers to consider provisions for disposing of liquid wastes as an integral part of functional design.

Treatment methods for industrial wastes are nearly as numerous as the wastes themselves, for each new waste is a new problem (E. B. Besselievre, "Industrial Waste Treatment," McGraw-Hill Book Company, Inc., New York). And we have not seen the end of new types of wastes.

22-1

Treatment methods for domestic sewage, on the other hand, are fairly well established (Karl Imhoff and Gordon M. Fair, "Sewage Treatment," John Wiley & Sons, Inc., New York).

SEWERS

A sewer is a conduit for water carriage of wastes. For the purpose of this section any piping for waste water inside a building will be considered plumbing or process piping; outside the building, waste-water lines are called sewers.

Sewers carry **sewage**. And a system of sewers and appurtenances is **sewerage**. (See "Glossary—Water and Sewage Control Engineering," American Society of Civil Engineers.)

22-1. Types of Sewers. Sanitary sewers carry domestic wastes or industrial wastes. Where buildings are located on large sites or structures with large roof areas are involved, a storm sewer is used for fast disposal of rain and is laid out to drain inlets located for best collection of runoff.

For figuring rates of runoff to determine storm-sewer requirements, the rational method (Art. 20-11) may be used. In storm-sewer design, however, it is necessary to know not only rate of runoff and total runoff, but also at what point in time after the start of a storm the rate of runoff reaches its peak. It is this peak runoff for which pipe must be sized and sloped. It should be noted that the water necessary to fill the drainage system—storm sewers and manholes—is, in effect, storage. Such storage is a sort of buffer tending to decrease slightly the magnitude of theoretical maximum flow. Its effect can be approximated by figuring about how much flow it would take to fill the system before it can begin to flow as designed (Fig. 22-1).

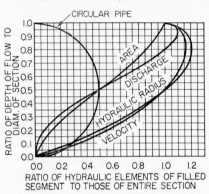

FIG. 22-1. Hydraulic properties of circular pipe for various depths of flow.

22-2. Determining Sewer Size. Sanitary sewers or lines carrying exclusively industrial wastes from a building to disposal must be sized and sloped according to best hydraulic design. The problem is generally one of flow in a circular pipe. (C. V. Davis, "Handbook of Applied Hydraulics," 2d ed., McGraw-Hill Book Company, Inc., New York.) Gravity flow is to be desired; but pumping is sometimes required.

Pipe should be straight and of constant slope between manholes, and manholes should be used at each necessary change in direction, slope, elevation, or size of pipe. Manholes should be no farther apart than 500 ft, and preferably as close as 200 ft where pipe used is of a diameter too small to enter.

The sewer from a building must be sized to carry out all the water carried in by supply mains or other means. Exceptions to this are the obvious cases where losses might be appreciable, such as an industrial building where considerable water is consumed in a process or evaporated to the atmosphere. But, in general, water out about equals water in, plus all the liquid and water-borne solid wastes produced in the building.

Another factor to consider in sizing a sewer is infiltration. Sewers, unlike water mains, often flow at less pressure than that exerted by ground water around them. Thus they are more likely to take in ground water than to leak out sewage. An infiltration rate of 2,000 to 200,000 gal per day per mile might be expected. It all depends on diameter of pipe (which fixes length of joints), type of soil, ground-water pressure—and, of course, workmanship.

In an effort to keep infiltration down, sewer-construction contracts are written with a specified infiltration rate. Weir tests in a completed sewer can be used to check the contractor's success in meeting the specification; but unless the sewer is large enough to go into, prevention of excessive infiltration is easier than correction.   In addition to groundwater infiltration through sewer-pipe joints, the entry of surface runoff through manhole covers and thus into sewers is often a factor.   Observers have gaged as much as 150 gpm leaking into a covered manhole.

Size and slope of a sanitary sewer depend lastly—and vitally—on a requirement that velocity when flowing full be kept to at least 2 fps to keep solids moving and prevent clogging.   In general, no drain pipe should be less than 6 in. in diameter; an 8-in. minimum is safer.

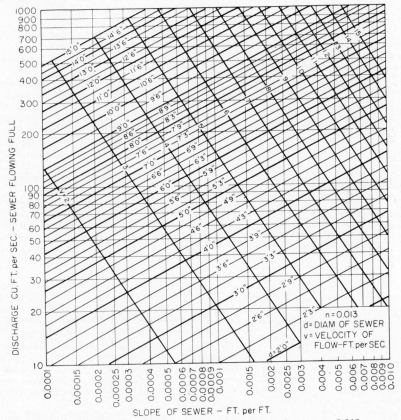

FIG 22-2. Flow in circular sewers for a roughness factor $n = 0.013$.

Among sewer-line appurtenances—such as manholes for access, lampholes for dropping a light for inspections as well as for extra ventilation, catch basins for holding grit and debris out of a sewer, and siphons for passing flow over or under obstacles—a measuring device should be considered important.   The building owner may find valuable use for a weir, venturi meter, or flume for gaging flow; it may help in treatment-plant operation or pollution analyses.

Siphons are used more commonly when a pipe must go below the hydraulic gradient —as in dipping under a stream or river—called an **inverted siphon**.   This device generally consists of two or more parallel pipes, arranged so that the smallest will carry low flows and the others will come into service on higher flows, so that in no case will velocity drop below 3 fps.   The danger to be designed against is, of course, clogging. Pressures inside and outside an inverted siphon, plus weight required to keep it from floating, dictate that the pipe be cast iron or reinforced concrete. Manholes should be provided at siphon ends for access and cleaning. (H. E. Babbitt, "Sewerage and Sewage Treatment," John Wiley & Sons, Inc., New York; E. W. Steel, "Water Supply and Sewerage," 3d ed., McGraw-Hill Book Company, Inc., New York.)

22-3. Sewer-pipe Materials. Vitrified clay, concrete, asbestos cement, cast iron, bituminized fiber, and steel may be used for pipe to carry sewage and industrial wastes. Vitrified clay up to about 36 in. diameter and concrete in larger sizes are used most generally; asbestos cement is growing in use for the smaller diameters.

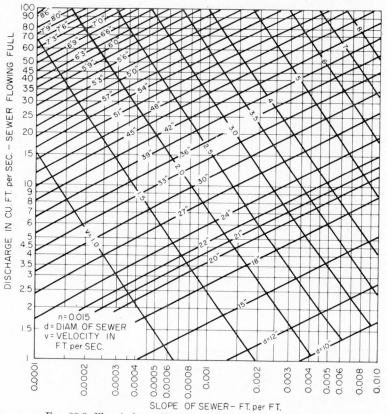

FIG. 22-3. Flow in large-diameter circular sewers for $n = 0.015$.

Choice of pipe material depends on required strength to resist load or internal pressure; corrosion resistance, which is especially vital in carrying certain industrial wastes; erosion resistance in sewers carrying coarse solids; roughness factor where flat slopes are desirable; and cost in place.

Vitrified-clay pipe requires some care in handling to minimize breakage. Concrete pipe must be made well enough or protected to withstand effects of damaging sewer gas (hydrogen sulfide) or industrial wastes. Asbestos-cement pipe comes in greater lengths, therefore has fewer joints. It is smooth, noncorrosive, and easily jointed. Cast-iron sewer pipe is good under heavy loads, exposed as on bridges, in inverted siphons, or in lines under pressure. Bituminized-fiber pipe in smaller diameters (to 8 in.) for drains is lighter than but about as strong as clay or concrete. It may deteriorate in sunlight and must be handled with reasonable care. Steel is used chiefly for its strength or flexibility. Corrugated-steel pipe with protective coatings is made especially for sewer use; its long lengths and light weight ease handling and jointing.

22-4. Joints in Sewer Pipe.   As indicated in Art. 22-2, the usual sewer-pipe joint is designed to keep something out, rather than in.   It must keep out infiltration as much as possible, and it must keep out roots, for obvious reasons.   Only for siphons, force mains, or exposed lines is the problem of leakage much of a factor; flow is generally in the other direction.

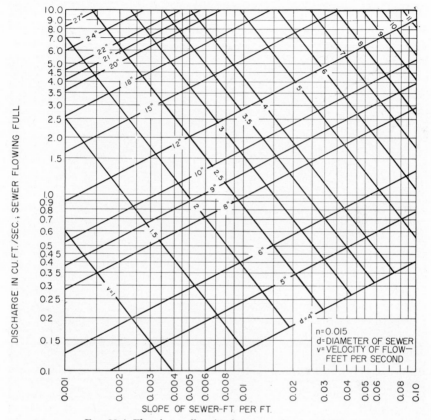

Fig. 22-4. Flow in smaller circular sewers for $n = 0.015$.

The usual sewer joint is bell-and-spigot (Fig. 22-5); but tongue-and-groove pipe ends are also used.   With bell-and-spigot pipe, joint space is filled with cement or mortar, sulfur components, rubber rings, or bituminous compounds.

A rubber ring, which gives a tight joint, is widely used for both concrete and asbestos-cement pipe.   It is coming into greater use for clay and cast-iron pipe. Where infiltration is a serious factor and a tight joint is necessary, the greater lengths of pipe can about offset expense of joints for many makes of pipe.   And flexibility is an added advantage of the rubber joint.

22-5. Allowable Loads on Sewer Pipe.   Most present-day design of sewers to carry external loads is based on work begun at Iowa Engineering Experiment Station in the 1920s.   All the data evolved by actual-scale tests by Anson Marston and others are still good.   But there is danger that sewer designers may apply Marston's principles without full consideration of the changes in construction methods that have been made since they were evolved.

Marston's work took into consideration the types of soil, methods of bedding, and types of cradles. Also, it considered moving loads from vehicles, and stationary and more-or-less uniform loads, such as from piles of building materials on a street surface. Marston's general formula for vertical load on a buried conduit due to weight of backfill is $W = CwB^2$, where W is in pounds per foot; C is a coefficient; w is density of superimposed load in pounds per cubic foot; B is the width of ditch in feet at the top of the conduit. (See *Bulletins* 96 and 108, Iowa State College Engineering Experiment Station for sewer-pipe design charts and tables.) However, present-day construction methods—of digging trenches, handling pipe, and backfilling—require conservative use of Marston's data, care in construction of cradles, and use of a factor of

Fɪɢ. 22-5. Clay pipe with bell-and-spigot joints laid in a trench with straight walls with clearance on each side providing room for a man to work.

Fɪɢ. 22-6. Neat trenching and well-braced sheeting make for safe and sound pipe laying. (*Courtesy of National Clay Pipe Manufacturers, Inc.*)

safety. Added cost of building a sewer sure of carrying the load to be imposed on it is small indeed compared with cost of opening and repairing an inadequate sewer that collapses.

22-6. Construction and Maintenance of Sewer Pipe. Inspection is perhaps the most important part of sewer construction. Pipe is generally tested under inspection and marked as approved before delivery to the job. Then it is up to the inspector and the engineer on the job to see that the pipe goes into the ground the way the designer intended—and to stop the work where discrepancies are noted. Sewers, unlike much building construction, often cannot be thoroughly inspected when they are completed. It is too late then; they are buried. Sewer inspection, insuring exact application in construction of what was envisioned in design, must keep very close to each step in the construction operation. Too many faulty sewers have been laid where inspection has been lax.

Aside from quality of the finished product, there is another important reason for close inspection during construction of a sewer. And that is safety. Trench work and tunnel work encountered in sewer construction can be dangerous if improperly executed.

Whether to dig a trench by hand tools or by machine, whether to trench or to tunnel are questions of economics. It all depends on the amount and type of excavation and unit price. Trenches should be dug no wider than necessary to place and joint the pipe. Continuous-bucket excavators, power shovels, and draglines all have their place in trench excavation—about in that order with increasing trench widths.

Trench walls above the top of sewer may slope for reasons of safety or economy in digging, but the pipe itself should be between vertical walls (Fig. 22-6). This often means sheeting and bracing to prevent caving. Sheeting is also a help in holding out water in wet ground, if a tight fit is obtained.

Most sheeting and bracing methods have been in use for a long time. They range from stay bracing placed at random in trenches already excavated to tight vertical sheeting driven and braced or horizontal sheeting spanning driven soldier piles. Relatively recent innovations include use of strong, easily handled, and salvageable plywood panels behind braced vertical boards; and use of prefabricated steel-braced sheeting units, which can be dug inside of like a caisson and moved along as excavation and pipe laying progress, with backfilling close behind. In deep trenches or subaqueous work, steel sheet piling may be used—braced as necessary.

Ground-water control can be a vital part of sewer construction. It is often best to work upgrade and count on some ground water being drained off by the new sewer as it is completed. A subdrain—open-joint pipe leading to a sump—can be used and left in place along the line of the sewer and below its invert level. But where ground water is a problem at all, it most likely will require pumping. Pumps must be capable of passing soils along with water; so centrifugal and diaphragm types generally are used. Air lifts are also useful.

Well points are commonly used in dewatering the ground around a sewer excavation. They generally include a 2-in. point leading into a 6-in. header. Points are spaced and pumps are sized according to the amount of water to be removed.

Actual sewer construction in a prepared and dried trench varies as widely as do the types and diameters of pipe and the methods of jointing. Small-diameter lightweight pipe is largely man-handled. Larger sizes (meaning heavier loads) are placed by rope slings, or mechanically powered derricks or cranes. Often, it is advantageous to assemble a few lengths of pipe on the bank, reinforcing them, if necessary, with timber strong-backs for hoisting and handling. This means fewer joints to be made in the ditch, where jointing is more difficult, and thus makes for a speedier, cheaper job.

The bed on which the sewer pipe is laid is as important as the joints that hold it together. For if the foundation is poor, the joints will not last. It is simply a problem of distributing the load of the pipeline over a reasonably firm support. Rock is too firm and too likely to mean uneven distribution of load; thus, rock should be cushioned with a mat of sand. Some soils, extra-wet soils, are not firm enough; foundation structures must be built in or on them to carry the sewer. In extreme cases, such as on a marsh, the sewer pipe may have to be carried on pile bents spaced as closely as pipe lengths and loads dictate.

A concrete cradle is the surest support for sewer pipe where no good natural foundation exists and is worth its cost for the insurance it gives against the dangers of uneven support or washout of bedding material. The method often specified for molding trench bottoms to fit the bottom quarter or third of the pipe, with recesses to fit the bell at every joint, is more easily said than done. A cradle of concrete takes the doubt out of the support problem.

What goes around and over the sewer pipe is as important as the support under it. Backfilling is a vital operation. Fill should be placed and tamped equally and carefully on each side of the pipe and to at least 2 ft above the top of the sewer. From there up, the method of placement and importance of tamping backfill depends on what loads are to be imposed on the ground surface above. Trench sheeting to be pulled can be withdrawn as the backfilling progresses.

Sewer maintenance, like sewer construction, is largely dependent on inspection. Close and frequent inspection can mean the difference between easy maintenance and costly repair—if possible causes of clogging, breaking, deterioration, or danger of explosion are located soon enough. Sewers large enough should be entered with full appreciation of possible dangers of explosive or toxic gases. Sewers too small to enter must be inspected with lights and mirrors and cleaned with rods or jets or by flushing. Many special devices for clearing and cleaning sewer pipes are available. (E. W. Steel, "Water Supply and Sewerage," 3d ed., McGraw-Hill Book Company, Inc., New York; H. E. Babbitt, "Sewerage and Sewage Treatment," John Wiley & Sons, Inc., New York.)

SEWAGE DISPOSAL

Sewage disposal has come to be almost synonymous with sewage treatment. But there still remain instances where waste waters of buildings might be disposed of without treatment. Buildings discharging sewage to municipal sewers can do so without pretreating them under usual conditions. And there are many isolated buildings yet to be built whose wastes will be of not too great a volume or strength to be received untreated by nearby surface waters or used for irrigation on or under a nearby surface of the ground. The state health department involved will quickly determine whether surface or subsurface disposal without treatment is permissible in any given instance.

22-7. Sewage Pumping. Low or level land may make necessary pumping of sewage or industrial wastes. If the building site is large and level, it may pay to lift the flow by pumping, rather than excavate extremely deep to provide slopes required for minimum allowable velocities of flow. Often, the only lift required in a small disposal system is at the treatment plant, to give sewage flow sufficient head to carry it through the process by gravity.

Where practical, sewage pumps should be preceded and protected by screens. But centrifugal pumps with bladeless impellers can easily pass solids normally carried in sewage, and centrifugal pumps with impellers having only two vanes can pass solids only slightly less than the pump size. Ruggedness and automatic control are important; efficiency is less important for a sewage pump.

Sewage ejectors, operating on compressed air, have been used in large installations. They are worth considering for basements where compressed air is available.

Pumping plants should have stand-by capacity as well as an auxiliary power source. In addition, there should be, where possible, an emergency bypass for extreme and rare occurrences that might shut the plant down entirely. Pump installations ought to be roomy, airy, reasonably dry, and well lighted. Piping should be laid out with the man who must check and maintain the plant in mind. Joints and fittings should be readily accessible.

A properly designed pumping station wet well can help smooth out variations in inflow and thus effect economies by permitting use of constant-speed pumps.

22-8. Septic Tanks. With **cesspools** (underground storage chambers) widely disapproved as means of sewage disposal by subsoil irrigation, even for household-sewage disposal, one of the simpler sewage-disposal installations for buildings not served by municipal sewers is a septic tank, with seepage pit or tile drainage field.

Table 22-1 gives required capacities and dimensions of septic tanks to serve various numbers of people. These figures have been developed for day schools; they may therefore be taken as generally applicable to the type of building in which people would work the normal 8-hr day, producing domestic wastes only.

Septic tanks to serve more people can be designed, but generally, when the sewage load goes beyond that from the 480 daytime inhabitants of Table 22-1, a more complete means of treatment than the septic tank should be used.

The septic tank is a means of retaining settleable solids; thus, it requires cleaning normally about every 4 years (this will vary).

The septic tank does not work alone; it depends for proper functioning on an adequate tile field or seepage pit to carry its effluent into a receptive soil. The tank effluent is generally taken off into the soil through open-joint drain tiles, laid out with separate lines spaced preferably at least 6 ft apart from one another. Length of tile required will vary from 100 ft upward, by various state requirements, depending on type of soil and quantity of flow.   Most soil-absorption capacity figuring is based on a percolation test.   Recent U.S. Public Health Service studies have evolved a 4-in. auger-hole method in place of the previously standard square test hole used since 1927.

Table 22-1. Capacity and Size of Septic Tanks*

People served	Nominal capacity of tank, gal	Recommended dimensions			
		Width	Length	Liquid depth	Total depth
60	1,000	4'0''	8'6''	4'0''	5'0''
120	2,000	5'0''	11'0''	5'0''	6'3''
180	3,000	6'0''	13'6''	5'0''	6'3''
240	4,000	6'0''	18'0''	5'0''	6'3''
300	5,000	7'6''	18'0''	5'0''	6'6''
360	6,000	8'0''	20'0''	5'0''	6'6''
420	7,000	8'6''	20'0''	5'6''	7'0''
480	8,000	8'6''	23'0''	5'6''	7'0''

* From E. W. Steel, "Water Supply and Sewerage," 3d ed., McGraw-Hill Book Company, Inc., New York.

The test hole, dug on the site to the depth of proposed drainage trenches, is first thoroughly saturated, then filled with water to a 6-in. depth.   The average time per inch it takes the water level to drop is a measure of the soil's relative absorptive capacity.   In the past, empirical figures have been used to determine length of 4-in. drain needed to handle 50 gal per capita per day for various percolation rates.   Where water in the test hole drops 1 in. in 1 min, 12 ft of drain have been specified; 5 min, 20 ft; 10 min, 30 ft; 30 min, 60 ft; 60 min, 80 ft.   Where the time required for water in the hole to drop 1 in. has exceeded 60 min, the soil has been judged unsuitable for use of a disposal field.   PHS studies have concluded that the effluent load applied to an absorption field may have to decrease, because the absorption rate of a given soil may decrease some 20% over a 16-month period.   This means that the designer should reduce the percolation rate indicated by test to 80% to approximate the conditions that will exist after 16 months.

Generally, the septic-tank disposal-field system does a complete job of disposing of relatively small flows of domestic sewage.   ("Designing and Operating Septic Tanks for Homes," *Engineering News-Record*, April 20, 1950, p. 32.)

22-9. Sewage Lagoons.   Small cities may find a sewage lagoon advantageous for complete treatment of municipal wastes.   This has been done, for example, with approval of the state health departments in the Dakotas and Montana.   Even in more highly industrialized Ohio, the state health department has given approval to cities to try out lagooning.

The method is so simple it is almost primitive.   Raw sewage is discharged into an open earth basin where sunshine and wind can effect natural and complete treatment. Obvious advantages are low first cost and almost insignificant operating costs.   A clear well-stabilized effluent is produced and no nuisance caused, according to reports from the North Dakota Department of Health.

The recommended lagoon size is 10 acres per 1,000 population.   The entire facility should be fenced in.   In municipal practice, it has been recommended that this natural treatment facility be constructed about ½ mile out of town, preferably to leeward from the prevailing wind.   This same precaution could be taken in the case of many building projects where space is available.

Water depth is specified at no less than 3 ft, and no more than 5 ft, lest sunlight be kept from penetrating to the bottom and wave action be prevented from mixing the entire body of fluid.　Banks of impervious soil around the basin require normal maintenance.

A simple spillway can discharge effluent.　Ordinarily, there would not be much discharge from a lagoon, since evaporation and percolation would about balance inflow. However, in winter months with ice covering the facilities, evaporation would be curtailed and overflow might be experienced.

In a lagoon of 5-ft depth and the specified 10 acres per 1,000 population, retention time is somewhere near 200 days.　Build-up of a sludge deposit is so slow as to be negligible; so no sludge-removal apparatus is required.　(W. J. Wenzel, "Sewage Lagoons—Low-cost Treatment and Disposal Method," *Engineering News-Record*, August 20, 1953, p. 48.)

The sewage lagoon is not to be confused with the **oxidation pond**.　The latter is a means of secondary treatment for the effluent of a primary-treatment (sedimentation) process.

22-10. Imhoff Tanks.　Whereas in septic tanks sewage is settled and sludge is decomposed in a single chamber (Art. 22-8), the time-honored Imhoff tank separates the two processes in a two-story tank.

In the Imhoff tank, sewage flow enters into an upper chamber.　Solids settling out form a sludge, which slides down inclined walls through a slot, into a lower digestion chamber.　Digestion must be accomplished without benefit of an external source of heat; thus, use of the process in cold climates is questionable.

Design of Imhoff tanks has had many variations.　Generally, depth of flow in the upper chamber should not exceed 9 ft; overflow rate should not exceed 600 gal per sq ft per day.

Vents are important to the Imhoff tank.　Excess gases of digestion not allowed to escape can cause serious foaming difficulties.　The digestion-chamber size has been set by state health departments at from 3 to 4 cu ft per capita.　State health department requirements for Imhoff tank design should be consulted whenever the process is considered for sewage treatment.　(Karl Imhoff and G. M. Fair, "Sewage Treatment," John Wiley & Sons, Inc., New York.)

22-11. Primary Treatment of Sewage.　Degree of treatment necessary generally is decided by the assimilation potential of the water body to receive the sewage.　Sometimes, receiving waters can take full strength the quantity of sewage to be produced. For other conditions of assimilation potential, treatment required may be primary, intermediate, or secondary (complete).

By primary treatment is generally meant treatment through sedimentation (see also Art. 22-13).　Sewage may be screened and grit may be settled out in a chamber or enlarged portion of channel; then sewage is detained for 1 to 2 hr in a sedimentation basin where something in the order of 30% of its **BOD (biochemical oxygen demand—** a measure of amount of pollution) may be removed.

Fine screens can be used in place of sedimentation tanks for removal of suspended solids; the screens have the practical advantage of shorter detention time and are particularly valuable where a large part of the flow is wastes that would become increasingly offensive and hard to handle, the longer it takes them to get through the treatment plant.

Coarse screens or bar racks generally used are sloped back in the direction of flow for easy cleaning—mechanically or by hand.　Sewage must flow through the screen chamber at a speed (1 to 2 fps) fast enough to prevent sedimentation there.　Screenings may be disposed of directly by burying or burning, but more frequently they are ground by some method of comminution and put back into the sewage flow for further treatment.　A type of comminutor widely used rotates right in the sewage channel, grinding up solids as it passes them.

Next, a grit chamber removes sand and other heavy settleable solids before the flow even gets to the settling tank.　As flow passes through the grit chamber, its velocity is cut down just enough for grit and sand to be deposited.　Recent improvements on this simple process have added aeration, which gives the flow a rolling, corkscrew path through the chamber, with greater effectiveness at depositing out grit.　Horizontal flow through the grit chamber is kept about 1/2 to 1 fps—any slower would permit settling of offensive organic matter.　Nearly constant velocity desired is attained by using a Parshall flume or specially shaped grit chamber. Grit settled can be cleaned out with hand tools or with continuous cleaning mechanisms produced by a number of manufacturers. Unless mechanically cleaned, the grit chamber must have more than one parallel channel, so that one can be shut down long enough for manual cleaning.

After grit removal in primary treatment comes sedimentation of the suspended solids by retention of the flow for 2 to 3 hr in a baffled rectangular tank or a radial-flow circular tank. In the sedimentation tank, sewage flows at 1 to 5 fpm at depths to 10 ft. The loading is generally expressed as gallons per day per square foot of settling-tank area. Imhoff and Fair ("Sewage Treatment," John Wiley & Sons, Inc., New York) state that this loading rate should be 180 times the tank depth in feet divided by retention time in hours. For example:

$$\frac{180 \times 10 \text{ ft}}{2} = 900 \text{ gal per day per sq ft}$$

In the primary-treatment plant, the plant effluent flows over a weir, across the end or around the outside of the sedimentation tank. It is ready to be chlorinated and discharged. However, the sludge settled at the bottom of the tank remains a problem for final disposal (see Art. 22-15).

Continuous mechanical cleaning of settling tanks is advantageous, leaving the settled sludge no time to begin going septic on the bottom of the tank. Cleaning mechanisms are available for tanks of almost any practical shape and size. The same mechanism that scrapes bottom sludge into a sump for pump removal also can skim top scum (often greases and oils) into an overflow for removal. (H. E. Babbitt, "Sewage and Sewage Treatment," John Wiley & Sons, Inc., New York.)

22-12. Intermediate Treatment. When better-than-primary treatment is desired but installation of secondary-treatment facilities is not justified, the intermediate step of chemical flocculation to improve sedimentation is often advisable. BOD reductions (Art. 22-11) between 35 and 60% can be realized. A large-scale example of the worth of intermediate treatment is the Little Miami sewage-treatment plant in Cincinnati, Ohio. Primary treatment is deemed perfectly good enough there when the Ohio River flow is normal, but in times of unusually low flows in the receiving river, better-than-primary treatment is needed. Chemical feed, mixing, and flocculation facilities were put in ahead of settling basins to effect intermediate treatment, whenever it is called for.

An outstanding recent installation of intermediate treatment is in Daytona Beach, Fla., where waste sludge from the city's water-softening plant is used as the chemical to achieve precipitation. This indicates like possibilities for use of the process at industrial plants where chemical processes and chemicals are at hand. Generally, the chemicals used in sewage treatment are alum, copperas, ferric chloride, ferric sulfate, ferrous chloride, and lime—among others.

Chemical feed is best accomplished in sewage treatment (as in water purification) by manufactured equipment with close controls, automatic or manual. Mixing and flocculation can be accomplished with or without mechanical aids, depending on conditions of flow and requirements of the process. Retention time in flocculation has been given as 30 to 40 min, with flow-through velocity at least 3 fpm to prevent floc settling before it goes into the sedimentation tank beyond.

Flocculated sewage goes to sedimentation. Settling-tank effluent, chlorinated for disinfection, is again the plant effluent—as it is for primary treatment. (H. E. Babbitt, "Sewage and Sewage Treatment," John Wiley & Sons, Inc., New York.)

22-13. Secondary Treatment. Whereas primary treatment (Art. 22-11) generally may be thought of as mechanical handling of sewage, and intermediate treatment goes into a chemical process (Art. 22-12), secondary treatment is largely a biological oxidation. Secondary treatment follows primary treatment and consists usually of either filtration or aeration, followed by secondary sedimentation. Whether by filtration or aeration, aerobic bacteria are made to act upon suspended and dissolved organic matter, with BOD removals (Art. 22-11) up to and above 95%.

Filtration has come to mean predominantly use of a trickling filter. Settled sewage is sprinkled onto a bed of crushed stone on which has been developed a zoogloeal coating of bacteria that adsorbs suspended solids and biologically breaks them down. Low-rate or standard trickling filters employ a once-through process with recirculation of but a small part, if any, of the filter effluent.

High-rate trickling filters employ four or five times the standard dosing rate, plus continuous recirculation.

Often, two filters in series with various arrangements of recirculation are used in what is called two-stage filtration. Loadings up to 5,000 lb of BOD per acre-ft per day are acceptable on high-rate filters; 3,000 lb is a common loading. Measured by volume of sewage flow, loadings of 10 to 30 mgd per acre (or mgad, as it is generally expressed) are acceptable for high-rate filters. Standard filter loadings are acceptable around 400 lb of BOD per acre-ft per day, or 2.5 mgad.

Removal of BOD by trickling-filter treatment will depend on how the filter is operated. In fact, high-rate filtration is often used as an intermediate treatment (60 to 65% BOD removal). It can be made, however, to effect reductions of 85% and better.

In construction, the high-rate filter is basically a rotary distributing mechanism over a 3- to 5-ft depth of $2\frac{1}{2}$- to $3\frac{1}{2}$-in. stone (some types have depths to 8 ft) in a circular tank with an underdrain system built of specially made filter-bottom blocks.

A necessary adjunct to the trickling filter is final sedimentation. This is important as a means of removing the dead organic matter that sloughs off or unloads from the filter media as sewage flow passes through. Final settling should be a detention period of 2 to $2\frac{1}{2}$ hr; maximum overflow rate has been given as 900 gal per sq ft per day. This final sedimentation is the last chance of removing BOD and suspended solids that pass the filters. Sludge collected in the secondary-sedimentation basins goes to disposal with that from the primary tanks.

Aeration of sewage has come to mean predominantly the activated-sludge process—though it must be recognized that variations of this process are now about as numerous as are methods of filtration. (Plain aeration, where practiced today, is generally called preaeration and is used ahead of settling for coagulation of colloidals and greases.)

The **activated-sludge process** is the aeration of sewage after primary treatment in a mixture of 10 to 25% previously aerated (activated) sludge. The activated sludge is the vehicle for aerobic bacteria, which oxidize suspended and dissolved organic matter in the sewage. Aeration of the mixed liquor of sewage and activated sludge is carried out for 4 to 8 hr; then final settling tanks remove sludge from the liquor to discharge a completely treated effluent (95% or more BOD removed). What sludge is not needed for return to the aeration tanks goes to disposal.

The activated-sludge plant first gained acceptance for large municipal plants. But now it has been improved, refined, and often scaled down to the point where there is no practical lower limit on its size. It is used for industrial as well as municipal wastes.

Compressed air for aeration is a factor of cost and operation for activated sludge. Air demand varies roughly from $\frac{1}{2}$ to $1\frac{1}{2}$ cu ft per gal of sewage—or from 750 to 1,100 cu ft per lb of BOD to be removed. Air is diffused into mixed liquor in the aeration tanks by any one of a number of patented devices.

(Generally, so much of the activated-sludge process is wrapped up in patents that the building designer considering the method for his disposal problem might well consult early with representatives of manufacturers with equipment for doing the job.)

Modifications of the activated-sludge process further complicate the picture. High-rate activated-sludge treatment uses 3-hr aeration with 60 to 85% BOD reductions attributed to the complete process. Step aeration, activated aeration, and almost as many trade-name processes as there are major manufacturers concerned are all attempts to increase the speed, economy, efficiency, or shock resistance of the basic activated-sludge process.

Contact aeration—a kind of cross between the trickling filter and activated sludge—passes sewage through a contact medium while blowing air through it. A few patented methods have been effectively used, especially in small installations. It is relatively inexpensive and easily operated. (Karl Imhoff and G. M. Fair, "Sewage Treatment," John Wiley & Sons, Inc., New York.)

22-14. Chlorination of Sewage. Chief purpose of chlorination in sewage works is to disinfect plant effluent to protect public health and minimize pollution of the receiving body of water. For this purpose, most states require a chlorine contact period of 30 min and a residual of 0.5 ppm. Chlorination of sewage is accomplished generally the same as chlorination of a water supply.

Prechlorination is practical at many sewage works to control odors or growths, to improve clarification and thereby help reduce BOD (10 to 35%, depending on sewage strength), to kill Psychoda flies around trickling filters, and for other purposes.

22-15. Sludge Disposal. Settled solids cleaned from bottoms of primary- and secondary-sedimentation tanks form the sludge of sewage disposal. And sludge, where it is produced in volume, forms one of the knotty, costly problems of disposal.

Sludge is generally 95% or more water. The water content must be reduced to decrease the volume of sludge to be handled. Many methods of volume reduction are used; and many final disposal methods follow volume reduction.

Digestion is one method of volume reduction (to about double the solids concentration), which serves the corollary purposes of rendering the sludge inoffensive and more ready to give up its remaining water. Digestion is anaerobic and takes place in a closed tank with temperature controlled to 85 to 95°F for a detention time of about 30 days. Digester capacity is generally prescribed in terms of cubic feet per capita by state health authorities. For heated tanks, 2 to 3 cu ft per capita may be taken as the generally acceptable range for primary sludge; 3 to 5 cu ft for trickling-filter sludge; 4 to 6 for activated sludge. But individual local requirements should be ascertained.

Two-stage digestion, using two digesters in series (the first one heated), is claimed to afford equal result in less total tank volume than for single-tank operation.

It has been found that recirculation of the gases of digestion will not only overcome any prevalent scum problem but will also speed up digestion considerably in the more homogeneous mass developed by the gas movement. It has also been found that concentration of sludge by thickening before digestion can cut well into the formerly accepted digestion period, as well as reducing space required. Also, a method of concentration of raw sludge by flotation has been evolved for direct incineration; it holds promise of affording a readily digested product of up to 20% solids.

All the above are patented processes. Some are in early stages of development and use. But all rate consideration by designers of future digesters, wherever the digester is a significant item of plant cost.

Some plants digest sludge solely to reduce its volume—as in New York City where millions of gallons must be transported for ultimate dumping at sea. But most digestion is for the purpose of making the sludge inoffensive for further handling and other means of ultimate disposal.

These methods include drying on underdrained 6- to 12-in. beds of sand, either in the open or under a "greenhouse." Area required for open beds by state authorities is ½ to 2 sq ft per capita, varying inversely with outdoor temperature. Covered beds, protected from rain, can be as much as 50% smaller. Sludge goes on in depths to 1 ft and dries to a thickness of about 4 in. It can be scraped off the sand beds and removed for use as a soil conditioner.

Sludge filtration is practiced where volumes produced would require too large an area of drying beds or where dried sludge is to be packaged for sale or incinerated. Vacuum filters are large revolving drums with cloth or spring covering. Vacuum applied in the drum causes a mat or cake of sludge to form on the drum. This is peeled off as the drum rotates, partly immersed in a tank of conditioned or elutriated sludge. The cake (about 70% moisture) is conveyed to flash drying for disposal as soil conditioner or final disposal by incineration. Even undigested sludges can be filtered and burned.

22-16. Packaged Sewage-treatment Plants. Sewage-disposal problems may often lend themselves to treatment that need not be tailor-made. Many manufacturers produce process equipment that can be combined to form packaged plants capable of flexible yet thorough treatment. But in any individual case, sound engineering judgment based on knowledge of the facts must determine the relative ultimate economies of custom-built vs. packaged units.

INDUSTRIAL WASTES

Volumes have already been written, and many more volumes are to be written on the as-yet young problem of industrial wastes. It is an interesting problem, for an industrial waste may be anything from sawdust to radioisotopes. And the methods of disposal vary accordingly.

Industrial-waste output indicated for a proposed building project might well determine its location. More and more, industries are finding themselves not wanted on rivers and streams where waste-assimilation potential is already used up by existing industrial plants. Industries are finding themselves choosing one site over an otherwise equal site because of a better receiving body of water for wastes, yielding more economical disposal. Once located, the industrial building is quite apt to have its process affected or its over-all cost determined by waste-treatment requirements imposed.

22-17. Industrial-waste Treatment. Prevention of wastes is preferable to cure. It is wise to prevent the formation of any liquid industrial waste—in so far as this is possible—by proper process design, plant layout, and plant housekeeping. Recycling and reuse of water is an example of this. There are many good-sized industries today that take in a fair amount of water and let out as waste hardly more than that evaporated to the atmosphere.

When industrial-waste disposal will definitely require a treatment plant and equipment, disposal facilities should be incorporated as a vital and significant part of the industrial-plant design and the cost estimate.

The important thing is first to determine what the industrial waste to be discharged from the given building will be—in quantity and in strength.

Next, determine whether it is possible, practical, and economical to tie the building into a municipal sewer and discharge its industrial wastes in this way. This possibility will be decided by the municipality on the basis of the quantity and strength of wastes to be produced. No sewage-works superintendent will knowingly accept wastes into his plant that will disrupt his process in any serious way.

Practicality will depend in many instances on proximity to a receiving sewer of adequate size; grades may also be a factor. But economy will often decide. Though the municipal sewage works may accept the wastes, but only after expensive pretreatment, it might be cheaper to treat them fully in an industrial-waste works. If extensive sewer lines or pumping facilities were to be required for getting wastes to the sewer system, it might not pay. If sewage-service charges by the municipality were to be especially high (based perhaps on volume, suspended solids, BOD, and chlorine demand) because of some special characteristic of the wastes, it might pay to treat them at home. Also, in many instances, it has paid groups of neighboring industries to pool their resources and combine their wastes for treatment.

As with sewage works, the industrial-waste works is a facility requiring approval of local health authorities for its construction. Plans for industrial-waste treatment must in most cases (should, in all cases) be presented for approval of the responsible state agency.

BOD (Art. 22-11) is both an aid and a curse to the industrial waste specialist. It is sometimes convenient to consider BOD and population equivalents of industrial wastes. But too often this perfectly logical measure of domestic-sewage pollution is applied as a sole measure of industrial-wastes strength. It is no indication at all of the temperature, pH, toxicity, inflammability, oils, greases, or other substances that may be the true measure of the industrial-waste strength.

All these characteristics must be learned from the process engineers or from consulting sanitary engineers for the owner before any determination can be made of whether treatment is necessary, what treatment should be used, and type of treatment plant. (E. B. Besselievre, "Industrial Waste Treatment," McGraw-Hill Book Company, Inc., New York; Willem Rudolfs, "Industrial Wastes—Their Disposal and Treatment," Reinhold Publishing Corporation, New York; G. M. Fair and J. C. Geyer, "Water Supply and Waste-water Disposal," John Wiley & Sons, Inc., New York.)

Section 23

ELECTRIC POWER AND LIGHTING

Consulting Electrical Engineer
Brooklyn, N.Y.

23-1. Definitions. Electrical energy can be generated by forcing electrons to move in certain paths or circuits. By convention, electric current is assumed to flow from a positive $(+)$ terminal to a negative $(-)$. The force that makes electrons move is called an **electromotive force, potential difference or voltage,** E. It is measured in volts.

$$E = IR \qquad \text{(Ohm's law)} \qquad (23\text{-}1)$$

where I = current, amp
R = resistance, ohms, of portion of circuit for which voltage drop is to be computed

Electric currents are classified as:
1. Direct current, dc, which always flows in the same direction.
2. Alternating current, ac, whose direction is reversed at regular intervals.

Electric power, P, is the rate of doing electrical work. The unit is the **watt or kilowatt** (1,000 watts). 746 watts = 0.746 kw = 1 hp. Power in watts in a dc circuit can be computed from

$$P = EI = I^2R \qquad (23\text{-}2)$$

where E = voltage drop
I = current, amp
R = resistance, ohms

Power in ac circuits is very seldom equal to direct product of volts and amperes alone. For instance, in single-phase ac circuits, power generally is the product of volts times amperes multiplied by a power factor, which is a measure of the effect of a phase difference between current and voltage.

Electric current, I, is the rate at which electricity flows through a conductor or circuit. The practical unit is the ampere, which is a current of one coulomb per second. A coulomb is a basic quantity of electricity.

Resistance, R, is the opposition offered by a material to the flow of an electric current in it. The unit of electrical resistance is expressed in ohms. It determines, for a given current, the average rate at which electrical energy is converted into heat.

Kilowatthour (kwhr) is the energy expended if work is done for 1 hr at the rate of 1 kw.

Efficiency is the ratio of output to input. Output is the useful energy delivered by a machine. Input is the energy supplied to the machine.

A **cycle** is a complete set of positive and negative values through which an alternating current repeatedly passes.

23-1

The **frequency** of ac is the number of cycles completed in 1 sec.

Two currents or a voltage and current with the same frequency are said to be in **phase** if the zero, maximum, minimum, and intermediate values occur at the same time. If the magnitudes of an ac current or voltage are assumed to be represented by a sine curve with zero values at 0, 180, and 360°, a maximum at 90°, and a minimum at 270°, then the phase difference can be as much as 360°. If, for example, the maximum of a current occurs 90° from the maximum of the voltage, the current may be considered either to lag the voltage by 90° or to lead by 270°.

A **three-phase current** consists of three different alternating currents 120° out of phase with each other. A **two-phase current** consists of two different alternating currents 90° out of phase with each other.

A three-phase system is preferable to and more economical than two-phase for both transmission and distribution. Two-phase equipment is seldom purchased except for addition or replacements of existing two-phase installations.

Power factor is the ratio of the true power to apparent power and is expressed as a percentage. The real and apparent power are identical only when current and voltage are in phase. Apparent power is composed of two components—an energy component and a wattless (inductance or capacitance) component.

Much larger equipment and conductors are required to deliver a certain amount of power at a low power factor than at a power factor closer to unity. Wattless components of current heat the line conductors, just as energy components do, and cause losses in them. Also losses due to the extra current manifest themselves in heat and the capacity of electric machines is reduced.

Excessively low power factor is usually due to underloaded induction motors, because the power factor of motors is much less at partial loads than at full loads. Power factor can be corrected by installing synchronous motors, which, when overexcited, have the property of neutralizing the wattless components of currents, or by connecting static condensers across the line.

Inductance, L, occurring in a circuit carrying alternating current (ac), produces opposition to the flow of the current that makes the current lag behind the voltage in time or phase. It is measured in a unit called henry. **Inductive reactance**, X_L, is the opposition to the flow of changing current due to inductance. It is measured in ohms.

Capacitance, C, is a measure of the ability of a circuit to store electrical energy. When two conducting materials are separated by an insulating material, they have the ability to store electrical energy when the circuit carries ac. Such an arrangement of materials is called a condenser or capacitor. The unit of capacity is the farad. **Capacitive reactance**, X_C, is the opposition to the flow of ac due to capacity. Measured in ohms, it makes the voltage lag behind the current in phase.

Impedance, Z, is the total combined opposition to the flow of alternating current. It consists of resistance, R, and inductive and capacitive reactance (X_L and X_C). The **impedance** of an ac circuit or path is the vector sum of the resistance and reactance of the path. The practical unit is the vector ohm.

$$Z^2 = R^2 + (X_L - X_C)^2 \tag{23-3}$$

A **series circuit** is one in which all components are connected in tandem. The current at every point of a series circuit is the same and the generator electromotive force varies with the load. The most important commercial application of series circuit is in street lighting. This type of circuit has the disadvantage that a break any place in the circuit disrupts the current. Thus, if one lamp in a group connected in series goes out, all go out.

Multiple, parallel, or shunt circuits are those in which the components are so arranged that the current divides among them. In multiple circuits, the current through the generator varies with the load and the generator electromotive force is maintained practically constant.

Multiple circuits generally are employed for the distribution of electrical energy for all lighting and power in buildings.

Circular mil is the area of a circle 0.001 in. in diameter.

Square mil is the area of a square having sides 0.001 in. long.

(C. L. Dawes, "A Course in Electrical Engineering"; A. Gray and G. A. Wallace, "Principles and Practice of Electrical Engineering," 7th ed., McGraw-Hill Book Company, Inc., New York.)

23-2. Standard Frequencies. Alternating current at 60 cycles is most commonly used in this country. Higher frequencies sometimes are used for fluorescent lighting.

Lower frequencies, such as 25 cycles, are not particularly well adapted for electric lighting because of flickering due to the filament cooling down every half cycle while the current is at a low value. At 60 cycles, the time of low current values is so short that no flickering is noticeable. However, a lower frequency is necessary for satisfactory operation of rotary converters used in dc electric traction systems. Furthermore, 25-cycle series motors have higher power factor and better commutation; hence they are used for dc railroad electrification. It is not economical to build large slow-speed motors for main drives in steel mills and cement plants at 60 cycles; so these plants use 25 cycles.

On the other hand, transformers and most other apparatus are cheaper at 60 cycles and delivery is better. About 90% of the equipment sold in the United States is for 60 cycles.

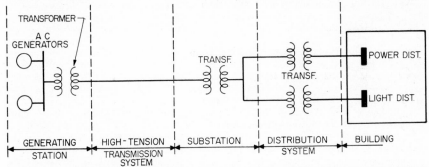

FIG. 23-1. Electric power is transmitted from a power plant (*left*) through a high-voltage line to a substation, where the voltage is lowered. Then, the power is distributed to nearby users (*right*).

23-3. Electric Wiring Systems. The purpose of an electric wiring system is to transmit energy from the source of power to the point of utilization.

In designing a wiring system, the electrical load of the project has to be determined first. Provision should be made for probable future loads; ample space should be provided for additional switchgear, transformers, and feeders. Structural supports should also be provided for the installation of future wiring and equipment.

Since, in many instances, a complete layout of the power and lighting requirements is not available in advance or in the early stages of the design, certain assumptions must be made. Power loads may range up to 25 watts per sq ft and lighting loads from 1 to 10 watts per sq ft of floor area. (A. E. Knowlton, "Standard Handbook for Electrical Engineers," 9th ed., McGraw-Hill Book Company, Inc., New York.)

The voltage supplied to a project will be determined by the utility company, based on the approximate maximum power demand. The electrical engineer should design the building's distribution system for that supply voltage or change it to a more suitable voltage by means of transformers.

A complete electric wiring system (Fig. 23-1) consists of the following:

1. Transmission system.
2. Distribution system.
3. Interior wiring systems.

The transmission system consists of a high-tension primary transmission from the generating station to substation transformers. The distribution system includes the light and power distribution from the secondary side of the substation transformers to

Table 23-1. Electrical Symbols*

Wall	Ceiling	
⊢○	○	Outlet
–Ⓑ	Ⓑ	Blanked outlet
	Ⓓ	Drop cord
–Ⓔ	Ⓔ	Electrical outlet—for use only when circle used alone might be confused with columns, plumbing symbols, etc.
–Ⓕ	Ⓕ	Fan outlet
–Ⓙ	Ⓙ	Junction box
–Ⓛ	Ⓛ	Lamp holder
–Ⓛ$_{PS}$	Ⓛ$_{PS}$	Lamp holder with pull switch
–Ⓢ	Ⓢ	Pull switch
Ⓥ	–Ⓥ	Outlet for vapor-discharge lamp
–Ⓧ	Ⓧ	Exit-light outlet
–Ⓒ	–Ⓒ	Clock outlet (specify voltage)
⊖		Duplex convenience outlet
⊖$_{1,3}$		Convenience outlet other than duplex. 1 = single, 3 = triplex, etc.
⊖$_{WP}$		Weatherproof convenience outlet
⊖$_R$		Range outlet
⊖$_S$		Switch and convenience outlet
⊖Ⓡ		Radio and convenience outlet
⊘		Special-purpose outlet (designated in specifications)
⊙		Floor outlet
S		Single-pole switch
S$_2$		Double-pole switch
S$_3$		Three-way switch
S$_4$		Four-way switch
S$_D$		Automatic door switch
S$_E$		Electrolier switch
S$_K$		Key-operated switch

Table 23-1. Electrical Symbols (*Continued*)

Wall   *Ceiling*

S_P Switch and pilot lamp

S_{CB} Circuit breaker

S_{WCB} Weatherproof circuit breaker

S_{MC} Momentary-contact switch

S_{RC} Remote-control switch

S_{WP} Weatherproof switch

S_F Fused switch

S_{WF} Weatherproof fused switch

a,b,c etc.
a,b,c etc.
$S_{a,b,c}$ etc.   Any standard symbol as given above with the addition of a lower-case subscript letter may be used to designate some special variation of standard equipment of particular interest in a specific set of architectural plans. When used they must be listed in the key of symbols on each drawing and if necessary further described in the specifications

Lighting panel

Power panel

Branch circuit; concealed in ceiling or wall

Branch circuit; concealed in floor

Branch circuit; exposed

Home run to panel board. Indicate number of circuits by number of arrows. NOTE: Any circuit without further designation indicates a two-wire circuit. For a greater number of wires indicate as follows: —///— (3 wires), —////— (4 wires), etc.

Feeders. NOTE: Use heavy lines and designate by number corresponding to listing in feeder schedule

Underfloor duct and junction box. Triple system. NOTE: For double or single systems eliminate one or two lines. This symbol is equally adaptable to auxiliary-system layouts

(G)   Generator

(M)   Motor

(I)   Instrument

(T)   Power transformer (or draw to scale)

Controller

Isolating switch

Table 23-1. Electrical Symbols (*Continued*)

Wall	Ceiling	
⊡		Push button
		Buzzer
		Bell
		Annunciator
		Outside telephone
		Interconnecting telephone
		Telephone switchboard
Ⓣ		Bell-ringing transformer
D		Electric door opener
F		Fire-alarm bell
F		Fire-alarm station
		City fire-alarm station
FA		Fire-alarm central station
FS		Automatic fire-alarm device
W		Watchman's station
W		Watchman's central station
H		Horn
N		Nurse's signal plug
M		Maid's signal plug
R		Radio outlet
SC		Signal central station
		Interconnection box
		Battery

— · — · — Auxiliary-system circuits. NOTE: Any line without further designation indicates a 2-wire system. For a greater number of wires designate with numerals in manner similar to 12—No. 18W-¾″-C., or designate by number corresponding to listing in schedule.

□a,b,c Special auxiliary outlets. Subscript letters refer to notes on plans or detailed description in specifications

* National Electrical Code, National Fire Protection Association, Boston, Mass.

the light- and power-distribution centers. The interior wiring systems include the wiring from the light- and power-distribution centers to all light and power outlets and services in the building.

23-4. Interior Wiring Installations. Interior wiring may be installed in the following ways as indicated in the National Electrical Code and local codes:

• Rigid conduit. Wiring is installed in rigid steel conduit concealed or exposed. Outlet boxes are inserted in the conduit runs at points as required.

• Electrical metallic tubing or thin-wall conduit. Wiring is installed in thin-wall conduit with outlet boxes provided in the conduit system at points as required. Thin-wall conduit is similar to rigid steel conduit but is of thinner material and lighter in weight.

• Flexible conduit (Greenfield). Wiring is installed in flexible steel armor with outlets provided in the conduit system. Installation is similar to rigid conduit except that this conduit is flexible. It is used concealed or for short, flexible extensions of rigid conduit to vibrating equipment.

• Metal wireway and raceway. Wiring is installed in sheet-steel raceways exposed on walls or ceiling. Outlet boxes are installed in the runs at points as required.

• Armored cable (BX). Rubber-insulated wires are protected by a flexible steel armor, the combination being furnished as a unit. Outlet boxes are inserted in the runs at points as required. Armored cable is used in concealed locations.

• Underfloor raceway. Wiring is installed in sheet-metal or fiber duct, which is embedded in the concrete or cement fill of the floor.

• Cellular-metal floor raceway. Wiring is installed in a floor constructed of metal deck containing hollow spaces that are used as raceways for the wiring.

• Busway and bus duct. Power is transmitted through bare rods or bars insulated from each other, supported and protected by a sheet-metal housing. Bus duct provides a flexible system for distributing power up to 600 volts and for lighting in industrial buildings. Bus ducts are made in the plug-in type, no-plug in, and movable-trolley contact type.

• Nonmetallic sheathed cable. Rubber-insulated wires are bound together and covered with a cotton-bound paper sheath, which is protected with an outer cotton braid treated with a heat-resisting and moistureproof compound. Cable is installed exposed or concealed in hollow spaces in partitions, floors, or ceiling.

• Nonmetallic waterproof cable. Rubber-insulated wires are covered with a rubber sheath mounted on surface of walls and ceilings in such buildings as ice plants, cold storage, breweries, and wet locations.

(A. L. Abbott and C. L. Smith, "National Electrical Code Handbook," 9th ed., McGraw-Hill Book Company, Inc., New York.)

23-5. Types of Circuits. A circuit is a complete path of an electric current. It permits electric current to flow from a wire connected with a generating source through energy-consuming units and return through another wire to the source. The positive wire is known as such because of its potential or voltage above or below zero. The negative wire may be a neutral maintained at a potential of zero voltage.

The neutral wire is ordinarily grounded to the earth at the point of service entrance. The ground is carried through the electric system as a third wire or through the enclosing metallic raceway of the conductors.

A **service feeder** is a set of entrance conductors from the utility company's network to main building switches or switchboard.

A **feeder** is a set of conductors in a distribution system that extends from the building switches or switchboard to distribution centers or panel boards In calculating the size of a feeder, the carrying capacity needed is determined by the total connected load multiplied by the demand factor. (Demand factor is the ratio of the maximum demand to the total connected load. For example, if the heaviest load ever carried is only half the total connected load, the demand factor is 50 per cent.) Provision should be made for increasing the capacity of the initial system for future growth or expansion by installation of feeders of excess size, installation of oversize raceways to permit replacing of initial conductors at a later date, or installing spare raceways for future feeders.

A **subfeeder** is an extension of a feeder from one distribution center to another.

A **main** is a supply circuit to which branch or service circuits are connected through circuit breakers, switches, or fuses at different points along its length. The wire size of the main is the same for its entire length.

A **branch circuit** consists of a set of conductors that is fed from a distribution center through a fused cutout to one or more electrical outlets or devices. It is that portion of a wiring system extending beyond the final overcurrent device protecting the circuit.

A **multiwire branch circuit** is a circuit consisting of two or more ungrounded conductors having a potential difference between them and an identified grounded conductor having equal potential difference between it and each ungrounded conductor of the circuit. The grounded conductor is connected to the neutral conductor of the system (Fig. 23-2).

The three-wire circuit in Fig. 23-2 is a multiwire circuit. Its advantages over the two-wire circuit also shown are that only three wires are required to supply a load that would require four wires when two-wire circuits are used; and that, when other conditions are the same, the percent voltage drop is only half as great as in a two-wire

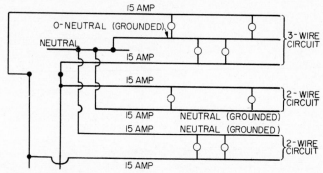

FIG. 23-2. A three-wire circuit consists of two ungrounded wires and a neutral, whereas a two-wire circuit has only one ungrounded wire and a neutral.

circuit. (See National Electrical Code for color code for identifying conductors in a multiwire circuit.)

There is no code limit on the electrical capacity of subfeeders, feeders or service feeders. Lighting branch circuits are usually limited to 15 amp but may carry heavy-duty loads up to 50 amp in commercial and industrial areas. Branch circuits for convenience receptacles for general use are usually limited to 20 amp. Receptacles for heavy-duty circuits (above 20 amp) are provided with special connection plugs.

Motor branch circuits except for very small sizes are subject to special requirements in the National Electrical Code and are designed accordingly. (A. L. Abbott and C. L. Smith, "National Electrical Code Handbook," 9th ed., McGraw-Hill Book Company, Inc., New York.)

23-6. Selection of Current for Distribution. Direct current is more satisfactory and economical than alternating current:

1. Where many adjustable-speed motors are to be served by a distribution system. Adjustable-speed ac motors are more expensive than dc shunt motors with field control, and the results are not so satisfactory.

2. Where a small amount of current is to be distributed only for lighting, at a distance not greater than 1 mile from the generating plant.

Alternating current is more satisfactory and economical:

1. When electricity is distributed to points more than 1 mile from the generating station. It may be generated and transmitted at a high voltage and stepped down at the point of use with transformers to the voltage required. Transmitting at high voltage makes possible the use of small transmission conductors.

2. When many constant-speed motors will be used, polyphase ac is always preferable for long and short distances, because polyphase constant-speed motors are cheaper, simpler, and more reliable than dc motors. Motors can be operated on higher voltages with ac than with dc.

3. Alternating current is always used where it is necessary to transform from one voltage to another without the use of moving apparatus. When the main system is alternating current, conversion by means of motor-generator sets, rectifiers, and in special cases, converters may be justified where the load requires extra-wide speed range or severe accelerating or reversing duty. (C. L. Dawes, "A Course in Electrical Engineering," 4th ed., McGraw-Hill Book Company, Inc., New York.)

23-7. Selection of Voltage for Distribution Systems. High distribution voltage is desirable from the standpoint of cost of line conductors because power lost varies inversely as the square of the voltage.

Most power equipment may be operated at a voltage within 10% above to 10% below the nominal.

For incandescent lighting or small motors (for distribution distances not exceeding about 1,000 ft), a two-wire dc system with a voltage of 110 is advantageous. However, a three-wire system with 220 volts across the power wires will cost less to install and is economical for distances up to about 1 mile.

For a constant-speed motor load with a lighting load, a 120/208-volt three-phase four-wire ac system can be used. The motors can be operated three-phase at 208 volts and the lighting load at 120 volts, single-phase. Incandescent lamps operating at 240 volts cost more and are less efficient than those operating at 120 volts.

For large-sized motors or larger total motor load, a 440- or 550-volt three-phase distribution system is more economical; it saves about three-fourths the copper needed for a 220-volt system. Use transformers to provide 110/220-volt three-wire ac for lighting circuits.

For central stations or industrial plants distributing to distances up to a few miles from the station, 2,400/4,160-volt distribution is economical.

Table **23-2.** Standard Direct-current Voltages

Voltages	Applications
110	Multiple-circuit incandescent lighting
115–230, 550	Direct-current motors

Table **23-3.** Standard Alternating-current Voltages

Voltages	Applications
110–120	One-phase used for lighting, small motors, and appliances, obtained from a 120/208-volt three-phase four-wire system or a 120/240-volt three-wire one-phase system
240, 480, 550	Three-phase three-wire system used for distribution of power for polyphase motors up to about 50 to 60 hp
480/277	Three-phase four-wire distribution for light and power in commercial and industrial buildings
2,400	One-phase primary distribution in residential areas; three-phase three-wire polyphase motors above 60 or 100 hp for feeders for large industrial plants
2,400/4,160	Three-phase four-wire distribution in moderately heavily loaded districts
7,200, 11,000, 13,200	Distribution systems for large cities, power transmission over distances of a few miles, highest voltages for which motors can ordinarily be effectively designed
Over 13,200	Power transmission for up to about 125 miles

Most modern buildings are illuminated with fluorescent lighting and are air-conditioned. Air conditioning is a large power load consisting of integral motors. So office buildings and industrial plants are being designed for combined light and power on 480-Y/277-volt three-phase four-wire network (Fig. 23-3). The motors are connected line-to-line at 480 volts, and the fluorescent lighting line-to-neutral at 277 volts. The cost of the power system is therefore considerably reduced by using a combined light- and power-distribution system in lieu of separate light- and power-distribution systems. A major factor effecting lower cost compared with lower-voltage distribution is that the carrying capacities of the feeders and switchboard equipment are reduced in size.

A small control relay can be mounted in the high-voltage fluorescent lighting fixtures for controlling the 277-volt distribution circuit to the fixtures. The control relay is operated by coils whose nominal voltage is 24 volts, thereby permitting 24-volt wiring to the wall switches controlling the lighting. The high-voltage fluorescent lighting fixtures may also be controlled by 20-amp 277-volt ac switches, which are now standard equipment. (A. E. Knowlton, "Standard Handbook for Electrical Engineers," 9th ed., McGraw-Hill Book Company, Inc., New York; T. Croft, "American Electricians' Handbook," 7th ed., McGraw-Hill Book Company, Inc., New York.)

23-8. Batteries. An electric battery is a device for transforming chemical energy into electrical energy.

Batteries are classified as primary type, which requires renewal of the parts that react chemically; and storage type, in which the original chemical conditions may be restored, after complete or partial discharge by charging the battery electrically. A storage battery is alternately discharged and charged.

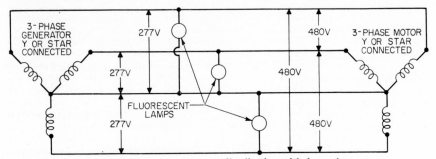

Fig. 23-3. Three-phase power distribution with four wires.

Primary batteries are classified as wet-cell and dry-cell types.

The only wet primary cells now used commercially to any extent are the types that employ a caustic-soda solution as the electrolyte and zinc as the negative electrode. These cells are used for open- as well as closed-circuit work for telephone, telegraph, and fire-alarm systems, program and self-winding clocks, etc.

The dry cell usually consists of a cylindrical zinc container, which acts as the negative electrode, and a carbon rod placed in the center, which acts as the positive electrode. The positive electrode is separated from the negative electrode by a depolarizer, which is a mixture of crushed coke, graphite, and manganese dioxide. The sides and bottom of the zinc cylinder are lined with a layer of absorbent material. The depolarizer and absorbent material are impregnated with a solution of zinc chloride and sal ammoniac.

A small dry cell is used for flashlights and a heavy-duty type for industrial and telephone service.

A storage battery consists of positive plates connected together electrically, negative plates connected together electrically, separators, sulfuric acid electrolyte for lead-acid battery, connecting straps and terminals, and a suitable container.

Storage batteries are rated in ampere-hour capacity. Their principal applications are for emergency lighting and power, stand-by service, telephone and fire-alarm service, farm lighting, railway signaling, starting and lighting of automobiles, airplanes, etc., train lighting and air conditioning, marine and submarine service, etc.

23-9. Electric Power Plants. Generating plants are divided into the following types:

• Steam-engine plant. Suitable only in small sizes, particularly for small private plants. The steam engine is well adapted to industries that require process steam.

• Steam-turbine plant. No definite limit to the size of the steam unit. Has low first cost, low maintenance and attendance. It is free from vibration, has uniform angular velocity and high efficiencies with large variations in load. There is no oil in condensed steam.

• Hydraulic plant. Classified according to the type of water wheels used, such as propeller, impulse, and reaction.

• Diesel-engine plant. Available in small and large sizes. In small sizes, the initial cost is not in large excess over steam plants and economy is greater. The investment and maintenance costs of larger sizes are high but are offset by the saving in fuel with steady load and high load factor.

Diesel plants are used for hydraulic auxiliaries, emergency stand-by or reserve, and to carry normal peaks, allowing steam equipment to be operated with high efficiency at the most favorable constant loads.

• Gas-engine plant. Economical and suitable for any industrial plant which has by-product gas, such as that obtained from blast furnaces in steel mills.

The type of plant, as well as the best location, should be selected after carefully analyzing and studying the particular requirements and conditions of each individual project. Standard engineering handbooks should be consulted for guiding factors in making the selection. (A. E. Knowlton, "Standard Handbook for Electrical Engineers," 9th ed., McGraw-Hill Book Company, Inc., New York; C. L. Dawes, "A Course in Electrical Engineering," 4th ed., McGraw-Hill Book Company, Inc., New York.)

23-10. Engine-driven Generators. These are especially designed for direct connection to gas, oil, or steam engines. They are used for power generation in industrial and municipal power plants, buildings, construction projects, ships, dredges, etc., or wherever it is desirable to use low-speed engines to generate electrical energy.

In selecting generator capacities, continuity of service, as well as load requirements, should be considered. An isolated generating station should be designed for a minimum of three generators of such size that any two generators will carry the total load at about 75% of rated capacity. Where continuity of service is not important, two generators may be selected of such size that either machine will easily carry the total load.

Generators are usually available in sizes ranging from 25 to 8,000 kw at all voltages from 240 to 13,800, single-, two-, or three-phase, 25 to 50 or 60 cycles, and at speeds ranging from 100 rpm and up.

23-11. Emergency Standby Units. Emergency standby electric plants are installed for the purpose of taking over critical loads when storms, floods, fires, or accidents cut off central-station service. When the normal source of power fails, the emergency lighting circuits are usually transferred to the standby unit through an automatic transfer switch. Light and power are furnished as long as regular service is off. The standby equipment stops automatically when regular current is restored.

Hospitals should have standby electricity and emergency lights in operating rooms and current for X rays, iron lungs, sterilizers, etc.; schools, stores, theaters, and other places of public assembly should enjoy the protection and convenience of adequate lighting; homes should have power for automatic heating; farms, manufacturing plants, etc., should have power for essential operations.

Standby plants can be operated on butane, propane, or natural gas, gasoline, or oil. They are available in standard voltages. Battery-type plants are available in 32- and 115-volt systems. Sizes of plants range from 500 watts to 30 kw.

23-12. Substations. A distributing substation is an assembly of equipment designed to receive electric energy at a high supply voltage and convert it to a form desirable for local distribution.

The electric energy may be received as alternating current and distributed as direct current, or as alternating current at one frequency and distributed at another frequency.

A transformer substation is also used as a reserve for feeders in adjacent areas in emergencies and to regulate the voltage delivered to feeders.

Master-unit substations are metal-enclosed factory-assembled units, with switchgear matched to transformer ratings, for handling incoming supply voltages ranging from 11 to 132 kv.   They supply load-center unit substations with voltages ranging from 2,400 to 13,200.   The capacities of the units range from 750 to 25,000 kva.

Load-center unit substations are metal-enclosed factory-built substations for serving 120/208-, 240-, 480-, and 600-volt loads from supply voltages ranging from 2,400 to 15,000.   They are furnished in flexible combinations of incoming-line and secondary circuit arrangements ranging from 100 to 2,000 kva.

Small industrial plants usually require only one unit substation (Fig. 23-4a). Large industrial plants usually require several unit substations each located near the center of its load area (Fig. 23-4b).

Unit substations and feeders may be arranged in different ways to meet power needs:

In the simple radial arrangement (Fig. 23-5a) the unit substation is supplied through one incoming high-voltage circuit and the unit can have one or more low-voltage feeders, each serving an individual load center.   This system is used in small

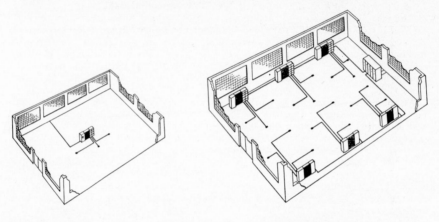

(a) FOR SMALL PLANT   (b) FOR LARGE PLANT

Fig. 23-4. Unit substation requirements vary with the size of the building, from one unit substation for a small industrial plant (a) to a large number for a big plant (b), each located close to the loads served.

plants with loads ranging from 100 to 1,500 kva and medium-sized plants with loads ranging from 1,000 to 2,000 kva with one incoming line.

In the high-voltage selective arrangement (Fig. 23-5b), the unit substation is connected to either of two incoming lines, thereby providing a spare incoming high-voltage line which permits switching over to the spare circuit in case of failure of the used circuit.   It is used in medium or large plants having loads of 1,000 kva and up with two or more incoming lines.

In the low-voltage selective arrangement (Fig. 23-5c), provision is made for emergency interconnections between the low-voltage sides of two or more unit substations. This arrangement permits restoration of service after an outage of either a high-voltage circuit or a transformer.   It is used in medium or large plants having loads of 1,000 kva and up with two or more incoming lines.

In a spot network (Fig. 23-5d), the system consists of a double-ended unit substation having two transformers, one connected to each end of its low-voltage bus.   Each transformer is supplied through a separate high-voltage line.   The failure of either transformer or incoming line will not interrupt the load.   This system is used in medium or large plants having loads of 1,000 kva and up with two or more incoming lines.

23-13. Transformers.   A transformer is used primarily to convert electrical power in an ac system from one voltage and current to some other voltage and current.   It permits transmission of large amounts of power over long distances at high voltages and its economic utilization in small quantities at low voltages at its destination. A transformer is also used to change phase relation or number of phases and for other special purposes.

A constant-potential transformer (Fig. 23-6) consists essentially of three parts—a primary coil, core (usually iron), and secondary coil. The primary winding of the

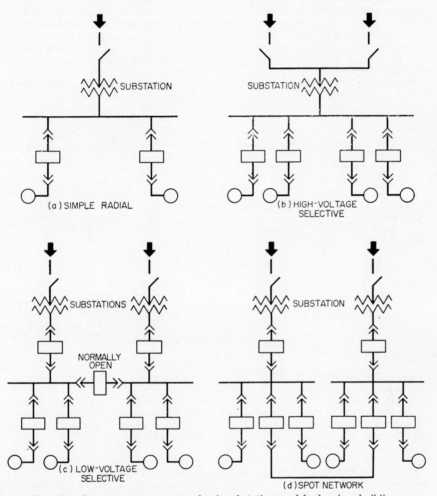

FIG. 23-5. Common arrangements of unit substations and feeders in a building.

transformer is connected to the power source. The secondary winding delivers the power to the load.

A step-up transformer is a transformer so connected that the delivered voltage is higher than the supplied voltage.

A step-down transformer is so connected that the delivered voltage is lower than the supplied voltage.

A potential transformer is used to change the voltage of a system.

A current transformer is used to change the current of a system.

Transformers are classified into the following general types:
1. Dry, self-cooled.
2. Oil- or liquid-immersed.
 a. Self-cooled.
 b. Water-cooled.
 c. Forced-oil-cooled.
 d. Forced-air-cooled.
3. Air blast.

Dry self-cooled transformers are used mainly for taking lighting loads in power circuits. They are also used for stepping down voltages for electrical appliances and for stepping up voltages for special applications. Dry-type transformers are usually confined to about 50 kva or less and not over 600 volts, although units have been built up to 200 kva.

In an oil-immersed self-cooled unit, the transformer is immersed in oil contained in a smooth case or tank. However, it is not economical to provide smooth tanks with large enough cooling surface for dissipating heat for transformers rated above about 25 kva.

Oil-immersed water-cooled transformers are used when the cost of water is not prohibitive, especially when self-cooled transformers are so large that it is costly to provide sufficient cooling surface with radiators or other means.

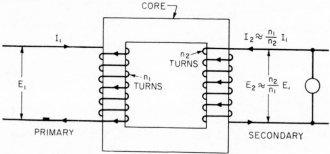

FIG. 23-6. Simplified transformer, with voltages symbolized by E, current by I, and number of turns on the core by n.

Oil-immersed forced-oil-cooled transformers are used when a high rate of cooling is desired but impurities in the water available make it difficult to maintain circulation in the cooling coils because of incrustation.

In oil-immersed forced-air-cooled transformers, air is forced over the surface of radiators of self-cooled oil-immersed types of power transformers. With this method, the kva capacity of the transformer is increased from 25 to 33% above the self-cooled rating.

Air-blast transformers are used for electric locomotives where use of inflammable oil may be dangerous and where fire underwriters' rules prohibit use of inflammable oil in stations located in large cities. Air-blast transformers have been built as large as 18,500 kva and voltages as high as 34,500. Air-blast transformers are more expensive than self-cooled or water-cooled types. (A. E. Knowlton, "Standard Handbook for Electrical Engineers," 9th ed., McGraw-Hill Book Company, Inc., New York.)

The efficiency of a transformer equals

$$\frac{\text{Output}}{\text{Input}} = \frac{\text{output}}{\text{output} + \text{copper loss} + \text{iron loss}}$$

The output in kw (kilowatts) will be the same as the kva (kilovolt-amperes) output if the load supplied by a transformer is at 100% power factor. With a lower power factor, the kw output will be less than the kva output in the same ratio as the power factor to 100%. For example, at 90% power factor the output of a 100-kva transformer will be 90 kw.

A tap in a transformer is a connection brought out of a winding at some point between its extremities, usually to permit changing the voltage ratio.

Transformers are built in single and polyphase units. A polyphase transformer consists of separate insulated electric windings for the different phases, wound on a single core, certain portions of which are common to the different phases.

Three-phase distribution transformers are widely used in underground city network service because of the smaller space required, higher efficiency, and lower initial cost.

Three single-phase transformers are commonly used for overhead service because of ease of handling and mounting smaller-sized units on a pole or platform. A three-phase transformer costs less to install and has simpler connections than three single-phase transformers but has no flexibility. It is usually purchased for a particular size and type of load and calls for a large investment. If the type of load should be changed, the transformer becomes inapplicable, whereas a single-phase transformer of one-third the size could be adapted for some other service. Another important consideration is that failure of a three-phase transformer will interrupt service more than failure of one single-phase transformer.

Use of power transformers in stepping down from a transmission voltage to the distribution voltage required for a building may permit purchase of power at the high-voltage rate, thereby making possible a saving in operating cost.

Transformers are constructed with different types of metal enclosing structures to meet the requirements of different conditions of installation, such as outdoor pole or platform mounting, subway, or vault.

Transformer vaults are located at or near the point of entrance of the service conductors into the building. Vaults are located so they can be ventilated to the outside air without ducts wherever possible. Ventilating openings should be proportioned to kva capacity of the transformer and should be not less than 3 sq in. per kva capacity of the transformers.

23-14. Service-entrance Switch and Metering Equipment. Near the point of entrance of service supply cables to a building, fused switches or circuit breakers must be provided for disconnecting all the service cables from the incoming source of supply.

The National Electric Code provides that in a multiple-occupancy building each incoming service must be controlled near the point of entrance by not more than six switches or breakers.

Service-entrance switches are manufactured in many types so as to meet the requirements of utility companies. Generally service switches may be classified into: fuse pull switch, externally operated safety switch, bolted pressure contact-type switch, and circuit breaker.

Metering equipment, also placed near the point of entrance, consists of a meter pan, meter cabinet, current transformer cabinet, or a combination of these cabinets, depending on the load requirements and other characteristics of the specific project. The meters and metering transformers for recording current consumed are furnished by the utility company.

The service switch and metering equipment may be combined in one unit or the switch may be connected with conduit to a separate meter trough. The detachable-socket-type meter which is provided with prongs that fit into the jaws of the meter mounting trough is the most used type for single-phase individual metering.

Service-entrance equipment may be located outside of a building as well as inside.

A service that supplies more than one building under a single management is called a master service. The supply to each building should be separately controlled by an externally operated safety switch or circuit breaker. The service switch or breaker may be located in the building supplied or in any other building that is accessible to the person operating the installation.

(A. L. Abbott and C. L. Smith, "National Electrical Code Handbook," 9th ed., McGraw-Hill Book Company, Inc., New York; T. Croft, "American Electrician's Handbook," 7th ed., McGraw-Hill Book Company, Inc., New York.)

23-15. Switchboards. A switchboard is defined in the National Electrical Code as a large single panel, frame, or assembly of panels, on which are mounted, on the face or back or both, switches, overcurrent and other protective devices, buses, and usually instruments. Switchboards are generally accessible from the rear as well as from the front and are not intended to be installed in cabinets (see also Art. 23-16).

Switchboards are commonly divided into the following types:
1. Live-front vertical panel.
2. Dead-front switchboards.
   a. Vertical panel.
   b. Bench or desk.
   c. Pedestal and post.
   d. Combustion.
3. Safety enclosed switchboards.
   a. Unit or sectional.
   b. Draw-out.

Live-front switchboards have the current-carrying parts of the switch equipment mounted on the exposed front of the vertical panels and are usually limited to systems not exceeding 600 volts. They generally are installed in restricted areas.

Dead-front switchboards have no live parts mounted on the front of the board and are used in systems limited to a maximum of 600 volts for dc and 2,500 volts for ac.

Bench, desk, pedestal and post, and combustion dead-front boards are used for the support of control and metering equipment for remote-controlled electrically operated circuit breakers in central stations.

Unit safety-type switchboard is a metal-enclosed switchgear consisting of a completely enclosed self-supporting metal structure, containing one or more circuit breakers or switches.

Draw-out-type switchboard is a metal-clad switchgear consisting of a stationary housing mounted on an angle-iron framework and a horizontal draw-out circuit-breaker structure. The equipment for each circuit is assembled on a frame forming a self-contained and self-supporting mobile unit.

A metal-clad switchgear consists of a metal structure completely enclosing a circuit breaker and associated equipment such as current and potential transformers, interlocks, controlling devices, buses and connections. (A. L. Abbott and C. L. Smith, "National Electrical Code Handbook," 9th ed., McGraw-Hill Book Company, Inc., New York; T. Croft, "American Electrician's Handbook," The McGraw-Hill Book Company, Inc., New York; Gay, Fawcett, and McGuinness, "Mechanical and Electrical Equipment for Buildings," John Wiley & Sons, Inc., New York.)

23-16. Panelboards. A panelboard is a single panel or a group of panel units designed for assembly in the form of a single panel in which are included buses and perhaps switches and automatic overcurrent protective devices for control of light, heat, or power circuits of small capacity. It is designed to be placed in a cabinet or cutout box placed in or against a wall or partition and accessible only from the front. In general, panelboards are similar to but smaller than switchboards (see Art. 23-15).

A panelboard consists of a set of copper mains from which the individual circuits are tapped through overload protective devices or switching units.

Panelboards are designed for dead-front or live-front construction. In dead-front construction, no live parts are exposed when the door of the panelboard is opened. In the live-front type, the current-carrying parts of the fuses or switches are exposed when the door of the panelboard is opened. Panelboards preferably should be dead-front construction.

Panelboards are designed for flush, semiflush, or surface mounting. They fall into two general classifications, those designed for medium loads, usually required for lighting systems, and those for heavy-duty industrial-power-distribution loads.

Lighting panelboards are generally used for distribution of branch lighting circuits and fall into the following types: plug-fuse branches; single-pole tumbler switch, with one-fuse branches, plug or cartridge type; double-pole tumbler switch, with two-fuse branches, plug or cartridge type; single-pole quick-lag circuit-breaker branches; single-pole quick-make and quick-break circuit-breaker branches.

Panelboards are designed with mains for distribution systems consisting of:

1. Three-wire, single-phase, 120/240-volt, solid-neutral, alternating current.
2. Three-wire, 120/240-volt, solid-neutral, direct current.
3. 120/208-volt, three-phase, four-wire, solid-neutral, alternating current.

Distribution panelboards are designed to distribute current to lighting panelboards and power loads and panelboards.

The mains in the panelboard may be provided with lugs only, fuses, switch and fuses, or circuit breakers.

When several tenants occupy one floor, such as in office buildings, panels should be removable-strap metering type, with branch circuits in separate sections, each provided with a fuse gap for metering.

Power panelboards fall into the following types:

1. Live-front, fused cutouts in branches.
2. Live-front, fused knife switches in branches.
3. Safety dead-front, pull switch in branches.
4. Safety dead-front, circuit breaker in branches.

Since motors fed from power panelboards vary in sizes, switches and breakers in a power panelboard are made of several different sizes corresponding to the rating of the equipment.

The following items should be taken into consideration in determining the number and location of panelboards:

1. No lighting panelboard should exceed 42 protective devices.
2. Panelboard should be located as near as possible to the center of the load it supplies.
3. Panelboard should always be accessible.
4. Length of run from panelboard to the first outlet should not exceed 100 ft.
5. Panelboard should be located so that the feeder is as short as possible and have a minimum number of bends and offsets.
6. Spare circuit capacity should be provided at the approximate rate of one spare to every five circuits originally installed.
7. At least one lighting panelboard should be provided for each floor of a building.

(A. L. Abbott and C. L. Smith, "National Electrical Code Handbook," 9th ed., McGraw-Hill Book Company, Inc., New York; T. Croft, "American Electrician's Handbook," 7th ed., McGraw-Hill Book Company, Inc., New York; Gay, Fawcett, and McGuinness, "Mechanical and Electrical Equipment for Buildings," John Wiley & Sons, Inc., New York.)

23-17. Switches, Circuit Breakers, and Fuses.   A switch is a mechanism designed for making, breaking, or changing connections in an electric circuit.

Switches are generally divided into classifications based on:

1. Type of contact, such as knife-blade, mercury, or butt-contact.
2. Number of poles, such as single-pole, double-pole.
3. Number of closed positions and breaks, such as single- or double-throw and single- or double-break.
4. Method and speed of operation, such as manual, magnetic, or motor and ordinary or quick-make and break.
5. Whether open or enclosed.
6. Protection provided to circuits or equipment.
7. Type of service, such as power switches, wiring switches, control switches, instrument switches.

A pole of a switch is the part that makes or breaks one connection.   A single-pole switch makes and breaks the connection in one leg of a circuit, two-pole makes and breaks connections in two legs, etc.

A single-throw switch makes and breaks a circuit when the switch is thrown in one position only.   A double-throw switch makes and breaks a circuit when the switch is thrown in either of two positions.

A knife-blade switch makes contact when movable copper blades are inserted into forked contact jaws.

In a butt-contact switch, the two contacts are butted together when the switch is closed.

A mercury-contact switch consists of a mercury tube with a stationary contact located in its opposite ends.   When the tube is tilted by the switch handle, the mercury moves from one contact to the other, thereby making and breaking the circuit.

Switches are operated manually; by electromagnets (magnetic switches for motor controllers and remote control of circuits); by motors, particularly for oil circuit breakers; and by solenoids.

In a safety-type switch, the switch mechanism is mounted inside a metal box and is operated by a handle outside the box.

A disconnecting switch is used for disconnecting a light or power circuit from its source of supply.

Wiring switches are used for controlling branch circuits and individual lights or appliances in interior wiring systems.   They are manufactured with push-button, rotary, toggle, locking, quiet or mercury types of operating mechanism, arranged for flush or surface mounting.

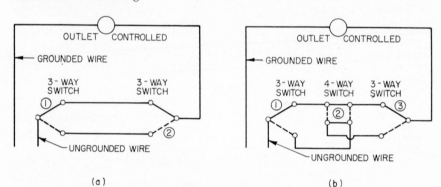

(a)   (b)

FIG. 23-7. Switches arranged to put lights on and off from more than one point: (a) control from two locations; (b) control from three locations.

A three-way switch controls lights from two different locations (Fig. 23-7a).   A four-way switch is used with three-way switches for controlling lights from three or more different locations (Fig. 23-7b).

A momentary-contact switch opens or closes a circuit for only a short period.   The switch returns to its normal position when a handle or button is released.

An Electrolier switch is a multiple-circuit switch.   One lamp or group of lamps may be turned on alone or in combination with other lamps.

A **circuit breaker** is a mechanical device used to close or open an electric circuit under normal or abnormal conditions.   Under heavy overloads, a circuit breaker opens automatically without damage to itself.

A **fuse** consists of a housing in which is a wire or strip material that will melt when carrying abnormal current and thus break the circuit.

An Amp-Trap or Hi-Cap is a high-interrupting-capacity, current-limiting, fusible device that anticipates dangerous short-circuit currents and breaks the circuit.

A circuit breaker or fuse is used as a protective device against overloading of circuits and equipment.   It is also used to protect smaller conductors where the size of conductors is changed.

Circuit breakers as well as fuses possess a time element of operation.   They operate instantaneously on short circuits and with time lag on overload.

Circuit breakers have an advantage over fuses in that they can be reset in less time than required for replacing blown fuses.   Circuit breakers are desirable where service is an important factor and where fuse replacement is inconvenient.   The initial cost of equipment provided with circuit breakers is higher than similar equipment provided with fuses.

Plug fuses are available in sizes up to 30 amp for installation in circuits not exceeding 150 volts. Plug fuses are low in cost, compact, and easy to inspect.

Cartridge fuses are manufactured in ferrule type for capacities not exceeding 60 amp and knife-blade type from 61 to 600 amp capacity in voltages not to exceed 600. They are manufactured for one-time operation or as a renewable type. In the renewable type, the blown fuse links in the casing are replaceable. In the one-time operation, the entire fuse has to be replaced. (A. L. Abbott and C. L. Smith, "National Electrical Code Handbook," 9th ed., McGraw-Hill Book Company, Inc., New York; A. E. Knowlton, "Standard Handbook for Electrical Engineers," 9th ed., McGraw-Hill Book Company, Inc., New York; T. Croft, "American Electrician's Handbook," 7th ed., McGraw-Hill Book Company, Inc., New York.)

23-18. Receptacles. A convenience receptacle is a device used as a safe means of connecting a portable electrical appliance to an electric circuit. The receptacle, which is provided with openings for insertion of the blades of an attachment plug, is mounted in an insulated enclosure of porcelain or composition arranged for flush or surface mounting.

An attachment plug consists of projecting blades enclosed in an insulated enclosure. It is connected to the electrical wiring cord leading to an electrical appliance.

Receptacles are classified as flush mounting, surface mounting, and for mounting in special enclosures. They are specified according to current rating and the number and arrangement of blades, such as two-pole parallel blades, two-pole tandem blades, two-pole polarized, three-pole, and four-pole.

23-19. Electric Motors. The problem of motor application consists essentially in finding and satisfying the requirements of the load, variation of speed, torque, starting torque, acceleration characteristics, duty cycle, and operating conditions.

In selecting a motor, the important factors to be considered are power supply, requirements of the driven machine, the surrounding conditions, and codes, standards, and ordinances applicable to the specific project.

The type of power supply available will generally determine whether ac or dc motors should be used. If ac is available, the conditions of the supply voltage and frequency with respect to value and regulation must be known. With ac power, the voltage can be changed with transformers when necessary.

In selecting motors that will deliver sufficient torque to start and carry a load, it is necessary to know the voltage regulation of the supply. Synchronous-motor starting torque and pull-in torque and induction-motor torques vary as the square of the voltage.

When speed adjustment is required, the charge in the power rates should be considered in the selection of the type of motor. Since rates are usually based on the maximum demand, motors that will keep the power demand down should be selected.

The effect of motor starting currents on the supply and the allowable limits for starting currents also will influence selection of the proper type of motor. With fluctuating loads the allowable limits for starting current should not be exceeded in order to avoid light flicker.

The mechanical arrangement, such as horizontal, vertical, or tilted shaft, plus the actual operating speed and number of speeds required, are additional factors that must be considered.

The horsepower and torque requirements of the driven machine are the main factors that will determine the type of motor, motor rating, and motor-control equipment. The motor selected for a specific project must have sufficient horsepower and torque capacity under running conditions and must be capable of developing sufficient torque to start the load satisfactorily under the most severe conditions.

Special conditions of operation and surrounding conditions of temperature, atmosphere, and water must also be considered.

Motors and control equipment must meet all national and local standards, such as those of the National Electrical Manufacturers Association, National Electrical Code, state laws, and city ordinances.

Motors are generally divided into three groups—direct current, single-phase alternating current, and polyphase alternating current   They may be further classified as:

1. *General-purpose.* Any motor having a continuous rating and designed for use without restriction to a particular application.

2. *Special-purpose.* A motor specifically designed and listed for a particular power application.

3. *Universal.* A series-wound motor that may be operated on dc or single-phase ac at about the same speed and output.

4. *Squirrel-cage Induction.* A motor in which the secondary circuit consists of a squirrel-cage winding suitably disposed in slots in the secondary core. Squirrel-cage induction motors are further classified according to the torque and starting-current characteristics.

5. *Shunt-wound.* A dc motor in which the field and armature circuits are connected in parallel.

6. *Compound-wound.* A dc motor that has two separate field windings, one connected in parallel with the armature circuit and the other connected in series with the armature circuit.

7. *Constant-speed.* A motor that has a constant or practically constant speed at normal operation, such as an ordinary dc shunt-wound motor, a synchronous motor, or an induction motor with small slip.

8. *Variable-speed.* A motor in which the speed varies with the load. The speed generally decreases as the load increases, as in a series motor or an induction motor with large slip.

9. *Adjustable-speed.* A motor in which the speed varies gradually over a considerable range but once adjusted remains unaffected by the load, such as shunt motor with field-resistance control.

10. *Adjustable Variable-speed.* A motor in which the speed can be adjusted gradually but once adjusted for a given load will vary with change in load, such as a compound-wound dc motor with field control or slip-ring induction motor with rheostat speed control.

11. *Multispeed.* A motor that can be operated at different speeds, independent of the load, such as a dc motor with two armature windings or an induction motor with windings capable of various pole groupings.

A resistor is an electrical device that introduces resistance into an electrical circuit. A **rheostat** is a resistor with varying resistance. Rheostats have a variety of applications, such as:

1. Theater dimmers which consist of a varying number of rheostats mounted in a bank and which are controlled by interlocking levers, used for dimming the auditorium and stage lighting to various desired levels of illumination.

2. Field rheostats, which are used to regulate the voltage of a generator and the speed or power factor of a motor.

3. DC motor-starting rheostats, which are used to start motors in steps.

4. DC speed-regulating rheostats, which are used for motors requiring varying conditions.

5. DC battery-charging rheostats, which are used for charging storage batteries.

A **capacitor** is a condenser used for improving the power factor of inductive loads. Capacitors are designed for indoor and outdoor use and are made in single-, two- and three-phase types.

Since many utility companies base their rates on power factor, penalizing a customer with low power factor, it is advantageous to an industrial consumer to improve the power factor by installing capacitors in the electrical distribution system.

Capacitors are usually classified by the dielectric medium used in their construction, such as air, gas or vacuum-type capacitor; mica capacitor; ceramic or glass capacitor; oil, oil-paper or paper capacitor; and wax capacitor.

(A. E. Knowlton, "Standard Handbook for Electrical Engineers," 9th ed., McGraw-Hill Book Company, Inc., New York; and C. L. Dawes, "A Course in Electrical Engineering," 4th ed., McGraw-Hill Book Company, Inc., New York.

Table **23-4**. Characteristics and Applications of Various Types of Motors

Type	Hp rating	Speed control	Application
DC shunt constant speed	Up to 200	Speed may be increased 25% above normal by field control, reduced any amount below normal by armature control	Constant-speed applications. May be used for slightly adjustable speeds. Light or medium starting duty
DC shunt adjustable speed	Up to 200	Speed range of 4 to 1, by field control, for all loads	Same as above for applications requiring adjustable speed control
DC compound......	Up to 200	Not usually used but may be increased 25% by field control	Heavy starting duty or intermittent peak load service or both
DC series..........	Up to 200	By series rheostat	Adjustable, varying-speed service. Heavy intermittent starting duty or heavy running loads for short periods of time
Polyphase squirrel-cage, normal torque and starting current	$\frac{1}{2}$–200	None	Constant speed load, no speed control, where high starting torque is not needed
Polyphase squirrel-cage, normal torque and low starting current	$7\frac{1}{2}$–200	None	Same as polyphase squirrel-cage motor, normal starting current. Has lower starting current but slightly lower power factor
Polyphase squirrel-cage, high torque and low starting current	$1\frac{1}{2}$–150	None	Constant speed loads requiring fairly high starting torque and lower starting current
Polyphase squirrel-cage, high torque, medium and high slip	$\frac{1}{2}$–150	None	Intermittent peak loads, heavy starting duty
Polyphase squirrel-cage, normal starting torque and starting current	40–200	None	Constant-speed loads, medium starting duty
Polyphase squirrel-cage, low starting torque and low starting current	40–100	None	Constant-speed loads, light starting duty
Polyphase wound rotor	$\frac{1}{2}$–1,000	Speed can be reduced 50% below normal at full load	Constant-speed service for very heavy or frequent starting duty or where starting period is of long duration; adjustable varying-speed loads; service with peak loads for short periods
Polyphase synchronous, high speed (above 500 rpm)	25 to several thousand	None	Constant (exacting) speed service. Frequency changers. For power-factor correction

Table 23-4. Characteristics and Applications of Various Types of Motors (*Continued*)

Type	Hp rating	Speed control	Application
Polyphase synchronous, low speed (below 500 rpm)	25 to several thousand	None	Exacting-speed, direct-connected loads, such as reciprocating compressors, when started unloaded, rolling mills, ball mills, pumps, dc generators. Constant speed. Useful for power-factor correction
Single-phase repulsion-start induction-run	Up to 15	None	Constant-speed service with no speed control. Light or heavy starting duty. Repulsion induction motors require twice as much current for starting
Single-phase capacitor-start induction-run	$\frac{1}{8}$–$\frac{3}{4}$	None	Constant-speed service with no speed control—high starting torque. Heavy starting duty
Single-phase capacitor-start capacitor-run	$\frac{1}{3}$–10	None	Constant-speed service with no speed control for heavy starting duty; high power factor
Single-phase, split-phase, general-purpose	Up to $\frac{1}{2}$	None	Constant-speed service with no speed control. Continuous operation loads. Light starting duty
Single-phase, split-phase, high-torque	$\frac{1}{6}$–$\frac{1}{3}$	None	Constant-speed service with no speed control. Heavy starting duty

23-20. Electric Lighting. Illuminating engineering is the art of integrating lighting with the architectural and other features of a particular environment. Lighting design should include a study of the quantity and quality of the illumination to be provided.

Quantity of illumination is determined by the visual seeing tasks performed. When intensity (foot-candle) values have been established, the engineer proceeds to select the type of lamp and luminaire to be utilized. Spacing of luminaires should be determined by their light-distribution characteristics and the number of units required to produce the recommended foot-candle levels, always being mindful of the architectural and esthetic purpose of the interior.

Quality of illumination prescribes luminaire brightness to prevent glare at normal viewing angles and the brightness of all surfaces within the environment to minimize brightness contrasts. Luminaire brightness is a function of the light-distribution characteristics and the type of control medium used—louvers, lenses, diffusing glass, baffles, or open bottoms.

Glare results from excessive brightness contrast. It can be caused by the light source itself or by reflections from shiny objects or surfaces in the field of view.

Brightness of all surfaces, such as ceilings, walls, floors, and furniture, can be controlled by selection of reflection factors of paints, coatings or finishes used. Matte paint finishes are preferable for most interiors, because they reflect light in a diffuse manner.

Following are definitions of basic illuminating-engineering terminology:

Light is radiant energy of those wavelengths to which the human eye is sensitive.

Luminous flux is the time rate of flow of light.

Lumen is the unit of luminous flux, a basic unit of light measurement used to express the total output of a light source. It is equal to the luminous flux on a unit surface area all points of which are a unit distance from a uniform point source of 1 candle.

Illumination is the density of the luminous flux incident on a surface; therefore, it is flux divided by the area over which the flux is distributed.

Foot-candle is the unit of illumination when the foot is taken as the unit of length. It is the illumination produced by distributing 1 lumen uniformly over an area 1 ft square.

$$\text{Ft-c} = \frac{\text{lumens on a surface}}{\text{area of surface in sq ft}} \qquad (23\text{-}4)$$

Brightness is the luminous intensity of any surface in a given direction per unit of projected area of the surface as viewed from that direction. It is the property of a surface.

Foot-lambert is the unit of brightness of a perfectly diffusing surface emitting or reflecting light at the rate of 1 lumen per sq ft.

Reflectance is the ratio of the light reflected by a body to the incident light.

Candlepower is the luminous intensity expressed in candles. Mean horizontal candlepower is the average candlepower in the horizontal plane passing through the luminous center of the light source. Mean spherical candlepower is the average candlepower of a light source in all directions in space.

Lamp is a man-made source of light.

Reflector is a device for redirecting the light of a lamp by reflection in a desired direction.

Globe is an enclosing device of clear or diffusing glass, which is used to protect the lamp, diffuse or redirect its light, or modify its color.

Luminaire is a complete lighting unit consisting of a light source, globe, reflector, refractor, housing, and such support as is integral with the housing.

A candlepower-distribution curve is a graphic presentation of the distribution of light intensity from a lamp or luminaire in a vertical plane. As shown in Fig. 23-8, the curve is plotted on polar coordinates, which indicate the light intensity in any direction.

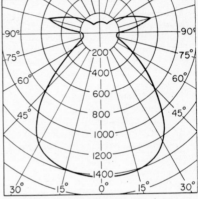

FIG. 23-8. Candlepower-distribution curve.

Electric-light sources may be classified as follows:

1. Incandescent (tungsten filament).
2. Gaseous discharge.
   a. Mercury vapor.
   b. Neon.
   c. Sodium.
   d. Fluorescent.

Tungsten-filament lamps have the following favorable characteristics:

1. Unity power factor.
2. Operate directly from standard distribution circuits.
3. Wide range of filament shapes.
4. Wide range of interchangeability in standard sockets.
5. Not affected by surrounding air temperature.
6. Favorable radiation characteristics within the luminous range.

Gaseous-discharge lamps have the following characteristics:

1. Production of radiation is by electronic activity within the gas.
2. Electrodes are necessary to initiate and maintain electronic flow.
3. The arc column has a negative resistance characteristic and hence requires ballasting to maintain a steady flow of current.
4. Starting voltage and operating voltage are not the same, thus requiring high-leakage type of transformers.

5. On alternating current, the electron flow is interrupted at each cycle change, thus producing rapid flicker or stroboscopic effect.

6. High lumen output, good efficiency.

One form of gaseous discharge is found in neon tubing. Its efficiency of light production is not high; its principal use is for advertising.

Lamps using sodium vapor produce monochromatic light that is orange-yellow. Objects whose color is not the same as this light appear in it in different shades of gray. The principal use of sodium-vapor light is for highway lighting.

Mercury-vapor lamps produce large amounts of ultraviolet radiation. If special glass is used, mercury lamps become efficient producers of ultraviolet for therapeutic purposes, skin tanning, and special fluorescent effects. Mercury lamps cannot be dimmed. Correct voltage and ballasting are obtained by autotransformers; two lamps may be operated from one transformer.

Fluorescent lamps are a means of converting the ultraviolet radiation of the mercury arc, which is invisible, to visible radiation. This is accomplished with chemical phosphors, which are distributed over the inside of the tube. These phosphors produce certain basic fixed colors, but an infinite range of colors is obtained by mixing them.

Fluorescent lamps can be used advantageously in buildings where high-voltage distribution systems are employed because the ballast primary can be designed for various voltage operations. This permits savings in cost of copper and transformers.

Lamp manufacturers have developed systems for high-frequency operation of fluorescent lamps. At the higher frequencies, the transformers for ballasting can be replaced by properly designed capacitors, which reduce fixture size and cost. High-frequency operation is economical only in large installations.

In a high-frequency high-voltage fluorescent-lighting system, lighting is distributed at 400 cycles and 600 volts. The conventional 60 cycles is changed to a higher frequency by means of:

1. Static system (magnetic frequency multiplier—360 cycles).

2. Rotary converters (motor-generator sets—400 cycles or higher).

The magnetic frequency multiplier has no moving parts and can be treated as a transformer.

A rotary converter, in effect, is a motor generator in a single machine. (A. Gray and G. A. Wallace, "Principles and Practice of Electrical Engineering," 7th ed., McGraw-Hill Book Company, Inc., New York.)

The advantages of the high-frequency high-voltage fluorescent system over the conventional 60-cycle system are:

1. Low-loss ballasts used are lighter in weight than 60-cycle ballasts, making fixtures lighter.

2. Flexibility in fixture design is greater.

3. Fewer branch circuits are required.

4. Lamp efficiency increases with higher frequencies.

5. Operating costs are lower.

6. Lumen output per lamp is higher.

7. Heat loss at fixture is less.

At 400 cycles, a choke-coil ballast weighing about 2 lb will operate a 96-in. T-12 slimline lamp instead of the 8-lb ballast required at 60 cycles.

Since a high voltage (600 volts) is distributed to the load, wire sizes of branch circuit feeders are at a minimum. A No. 12 wire feeder will take care of 42 lamps at a current of about 7 amp.

Fluorescent lamps can be operated on direct current by substituting a resistance for the autotransformer.

Direct-current operation of fluorescent lamps is not satisfactory for the following reasons:

1. Lamp life is shorter.

2. Lumen maintenance is poorer.

3. One end of lamp will show excessive blackening due to one-way flow of current, unless line-reversing switches are used to reverse the flow of current once a day.

There are several distinct types of fluorescent lamps, namely:

1. Preheat hot-cathode lamps, which have filament-type electrodes and require a starting device.

2. Instant-start hot-cathode lamps, which have filament electrodes, start without auxiliary starters. This type is referred to as a slimline lamp.

3. Rapid-start lamps, which are similar to preheat, but require no starters.

4. Cold-cathode lamps, which have iron-shell electrodes, start instantly, and operate at a lower temperature.

The characteristics of the different types of fluorescent lamps are as follows:

In the hot-cathode preheat lamp, a small coated filament produces the electrons required to sustain the mercury-arc discharge. The life of the lamp depends on this filament coating, and each time the lamp is started, some part of the filament coating is used up; consequently, the life of the lamp is reduced by the number of starts. A starter permits current to flow through the lamp filaments before the full lamp voltage is applied across the ends of the lamp, thus heating the electrodes and initiating the arc at a relatively low voltage.

In the hot-cathode rapid-start lamp, an auxiliary coil heats the filament by passing a small quantity of current continuously through it. It takes about 1 sec for the lamp to start and the filament is continuously heated thereafter with a reduced current.

The hot-cathode instant-start (slimline) lamp is started, without a separate starting device, by applying an increased voltage across the ends of the lamp to draw off electrons required to start the arc discharge. The life of this lamp, which also depends on the number of lamp starts, is the same as the life of the hot-cathode preheat type.

The cold-cathode lamp uses a rugged iron thimble-type electrode at each end of the lamp and is not affected by the number of lamp starts. The lamp is started instantly by voltage across the ends of the lamp, which draws off enough electrons to establish the arc.

The following advantages are derived from cold-cathode lighting:

1. The cold-cathode lamp is adapted for use in a series-type circuit. One transformer operates a number of lamps. In a series lighting circuit, it is not necessary to provide any wiring between lamps, since these lamp connections are accomplished through the sockets.

2. The life of a cold-cathode lamp ranges from 15,000 hr for the low-pressure type to 25,000 hr for the high-pressure type.

3. Cold-cathode lamps can be economically fabricated into special shapes, contours, etc.

4. The rate of light loss with time is extremely low because of the relatively low current operation and higher internal gas pressures.

5. Cold-cathode lamps can be operated over a wide range of temperature conditions.

6. Some cold-cathode ballasts operate on a constant-wattage principle. Ballasts deliver to the lamp a constant design wattage for a wide range of inputs.

7. Cold-cathode lamps are well adapted for use on dc. Standard lamps can be used. The estimated life of a standard cold-cathode lamp on dc is about 70% of the ac rating.

8. Cold-cathode lamps can be operated over a wide frequency range.

9. Cold-cathode lamps can be dimmed by regular dimming devices.

10. Cold-cathode lamps have low brightness.

The average illumination on a horizontal working plane is usually calculated by the lumen method, which is based on Eq. 23-5.

$$\text{Ft-c} = \frac{\text{lamp lumens} \times \text{coefficient of utilization} \times \text{maintenance factor}}{\text{area of surface in sq ft per lamp}} \quad (23\text{-}5)$$

This equation contains two empirical terms—maintenance factor and coefficient of utilization.

Maintained illumination is the average performance of a lighting system under actual conditions and is always lower than the initial illumination because of:

1. Depreciation from dust and dirt on lamps and fixtures.
2. Depreciation of lamps due to aging.

The effect of these is expressed as a maintenance factor.

Since all the light from the lamp will not reach the working plane, the lamp lumens must be multiplied by a coefficient of utilization, which represents the percentage of the generated lumens that reaches the working plane. It includes losses due to the effect of room proportions, and absorption of light in the luminaire and by various room surfaces.

The effect of room proportions on the coefficient of utilization is accounted for by a proportionality factor called the room index. It is determined by the room dimensions and either the mounting or ceiling height, depending upon the distribution classification.

Handbooks and textbooks on lighting and manufacturers' publications contain extensive tables giving values of room index and coefficient of utilization. (See, for example, "Lighting Handbook," Illuminating Engineering Society, New York.)

Selection of luminaires should be analyzed from the mechanical, electrical, illuminating, and esthetic points of view.

Proper spacing of luminaires results in uniform illumination. When luminaires are spaced too far apart, the resulting illumination is nonuniform. Spacing limitations are related to the mounting height above the floor of direct, semidirect, and general-diffuse luminaires and to ceiling height for indirect and semi-indirect luminaires.

Greater uniformity of illumination will be generally achieved with greater mounting height and closer spacing. Uniformity of illumination is normally considered satisfactory if the minimum value between luminaires is two-thirds or more of the maximum value under the luminaires. Noticeable differences in illumination will exist if the minimum value is one-half or less of the maximum.

Distance between luminaires and walls should not exceed one-half the distance between luminaires. The distance between luminaires and walls should not exceed one-third the distance between luminaires where working surfaces are along the walls.

Closer spacings are desirable to retain symmetry with the arrangement of bays, columns, partitions, and other architectural designs. This will reduce shadows at any point, thereby improving uniformity of illumination.

The form and disposition of the lighting facilities in a building interior are generally determined by the physical structure in which the light is to be used. Lighting is often used by the architect to dramatize other features of his plan and design. No lighting system is, therefore, completely satisfactory if it fulfills merely primary utilitarian requirements. With the exception perhaps of factories and workshops, most lighting layouts in all types of building structures require a certain degree of decorative design.

The major purpose of a lighting system, however, is to improve conditions under which people live and work. Since light is a highly versatile and expressive medium and is so integrated with a building's use and appearance, lighting should always be designed with the coordination and cooperation of the architect and decorator, keeping the function of the building in mind.

Lighting systems may be grouped into five classifications: (1) direct, (2) semidirect, (3) general-diffuse, (4) semi-indirect, and (5) indirect.

Direct lighting distributes 90 to 100% of the lighting downward; semidirect lighting 60 to 90% downward; general diffusing about half above and half below horizontal; semi-indirect 60 to 90% upward, with a downward component to improve utilization or reduce contrast with ceiling; indirect 90 to 100% upward, with a small downward component to illuminate the enclosure of the luminaire to reduce its contrast with the ceiling.

Lighting design in structures such as theaters, churches, museums, and public buildings cannot be classified simply as direct or indirect. Since the architectural design of these structures involves complex and special planning, the lighting system should be designed with full consideration of all factors.

Where special lighting effects are required in a room, it may be accomplished with the following lighting schemes:

1. General lighting from direct or indirect luminaires.
2. Accent lighting at fixed locations for artistic purpose.
3. Cove lighting for indirect effects, consisting of lighting sources concealed by a cove, ledge, or horizontal recess, from which light is distributed over wide areas of ceiling space to be redirected downward.
4. Wall lighting behind valances for mural illumination, etc.
5. Lighting behind windows or skylights.
6. Color added to any of above schemes.

Design of a general lighting system consists of the following principal items:
1. Selection of foot-candle level required.
2. Arrangement of luminaires to provide uniform lighting throughout the room.
3. Convenient switching and control of luminaires.
4. Selection of efficient, flexible, and properly designed luminaires for easy maintenance.
5. Computation of size of lamps to provide the foot-candles required [see Eq. (23-5)].
6. Minimizing direct and reflected glare.
7. Provision of adequate wiring for future requirements.

Maintenance is a primary factor in the effectiveness of a lighting installation. Dirt depreciation of lighting varies with the room occupancy, luminaire design, air movements in the room, and the nature of the dirt in the area. So provision should be made for regular maintenance of lighting.

A light source adds 3.413 Btu per hr per watt of power consumed to the total heat in a room in which it is operated. The power consumed for lighting in an air-conditioned interior, therefore, is an important factor. It affects the decision as to type of lamps to use, because for a desired illumination level, a lower total wattage is required with fluorescent lamps than with incandescent.

In deciding which lighting system is best suited for a particular application, it is necessary to make a cost analysis for the several types of lighting applicable for the particular installation. Such an analysis depends upon two fundamental factors:

1. *Initial cost*, which includes cost of installation, depreciation, interest, taxes, and insurance on capital investment.
2. *Operating cost*, which includes repairs, replacements, relamping, cleaning, added cooling costs, and electric power.

A system with a low first cost is not necessarily the cheapest. Operating costs play an important part in selecting one system over another. Often, the savings in operating costs of a more expensive system will make up for the additional initial cost.

The common denominator for comparing systems in a cost analysis should be the cost per foot-candle to own and operate a lighting system per year for the predicted life of the installation. ("Lighting Handbook," Illuminating Engineering Society, New York; H. M. Sharp, "Introduction to Lighting," Prentice-Hall, Inc., Englewood Cliffs, N.J.; Kraehenbuehl, "Electric Illumination," John Wiley & Sons, Inc., New York; E. W. Commery and C. E. Stephenson, "How to Decorate and Light Your Home," Coward-McCann, Inc., New York; W. B. Boast, "Illumination Engineering," 2d ed., McGraw-Hill Book Company, Inc., New York; W. E. Barrows, "Light, Photometry and Illuminating Engineering," 3d ed., McGraw-Hill Book Company, Inc., New York.)

23-21. Underfloor Distribution Systems. Modern commercial, industrial, and institutional buildings are designed for flexibility in use of the enclosed space. Many of these buildings consist essentially of outside shells, floor and roof slabs, and interior columns. Movable partitions are used to subdivide the floor areas to meet constantly changing requirements of departments and tenants.

An underfloor duct system provides electrical distribution with the flexibility and capacity required to meet the increasing use of telephones, intercommunicating systems, electrically operated business machines, etc.

Some of the advantages in distributing electrical wiring under the floor are:
1. The appearance of the building is improved and the danger of power failure through accidental injury to wires is removed.

2. Overhead conduit and wires are eliminated, thereby providing freer movement of materials to and from machines, and interference with proper and efficient layout of the lighting system is avoided.

3. Underfloor duct has greater wire-carrying capacity than conduit.

4. Flexibility for installation of new machines or the rearrangement of existing equipment is assured by provision of inserts at regular (2-ft) intervals in the under-floor duct (Fig. 23-9).

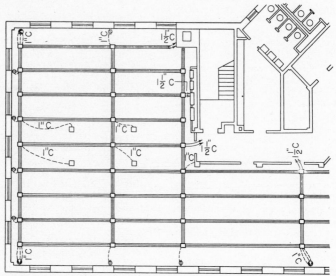

Fig. 23-9. Underfloor distribution of electric power through ducts.

5. The expense and inconvenience of tearing up floors to install conduit and boxes are eliminated.

6. Underfloor duct permits an electrical distribution system to be laid out and installed for an entire building without waiting for partitions, equipment, and furniture plans.

7. It provides a system of distribution that will efficiently serve the building's needs for a long period no matter how often electrical requirements may change.

8. Underfloor duct can be readily installed in almost all types of floors (Figs. 23-10 and 23-11).

Cellular-steel deck construction offers unique advantages in construction, over-all economy, and electrical availability, because the cells can be used as under-floor ducts (Fig. 23-11). It provides unlimited electrical-raceway capacity and can never become electrically obsolete. Outlets can be installed on the floor surface where and when needed without digging trenches.

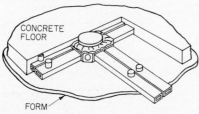

Fig. 23-10. Electric ducts in a concrete floor.

23-22. Lightning Protection. Lightning is the electrical phenomenon that accompanies the discharge of atmospheric charges from cloud to cloud or from cloud to earth. Since lightning seeks the path of least resistance, it tends to follow the shortest course between cloud and earth, taking advantage of buildings, masts, and trees.

An electrical charge accumulates in the clouds, and an equal and opposite charge forms simultaneously in the earth below. A pilot streamer starts toward earth when the cloud charge builds up to sufficient intensity; and when it comes close to the earth, a short streamer rises to meet it.   When the streamers meet, contact is established between cloud and earth or some object connected with the earth—like closing a switch in an electric circuit.   Electricity is discharged at high voltage in the form of lightning—a brilliant flash of light following a zigzag path.

Struck by lightning, an object of high impedance, such as masonry, transmission line, or tree, may be ruptured by the high voltage; fire or flashover sometimes results. In conductors of low impedance, the voltage between electrically adjacent points will be much lower and no damage may result.

Lightning can be prevented from striking structures by shielding with rods, masts, or overhead wires electrically grounded.   In industrial plants, protection of motor and control equipment connected to the electric circuits is the main problem, and the lightning voltages must therefore be kept out of the supply circuit.

Circuits completely contained within well-grounded metal buildings do not generally require protection from lightning. Circuits completely contained within buildings that are adequately shielded by rods or masts will not require lightning protection if the circuits are of grounded metal-sheathed cable or conduit.

Open-wire circuits in wood or masonry buildings without any shielding require lightning protection.   Circuits that pass outside buildings and then are not grounded

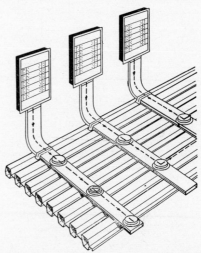

Fig. 23-11. Cellular-steel decking serving as underfloor electric ducts, with wires in headers distributing power to the wires in the cells.

in metal-sheathed cable should be protected regardless of the type of building, because lightning can strike the outside sections and enter the structure.

Outdoor circuits should be protected by overhead ground wires or other shields. Arresters and capacitors should be installed wherever circuits leave the building.

The main purpose of a lightning-protection system is to dissipate the charges with the least possible disturbance.   It is essential, therefore, that the lightning-protection system should be designed to intercept direct hits, prevent accumulation of charges on insulated metallic objects, and permit the discharge to pass safely to the ground. Metal provides the greatest conductivity; consequently, copper, aluminum, and galvanized iron are used as the conductor.   The conductor must be in good contact with permanently moist earth to provide a ground connection having low electrical resistance.   The number of ground connections will vary with the nature of the structure and the composition of the earth.

Insulated metallic objects should be bonded to the lightning-protection system or grounded directly to prevent accumulation of electrical charges.   By using metal points or air terminals that are electrically and mechanically connected to the ground, interception of direct charges may be effected.   The number, height, and location must be determined by the nature of the structure.

Terminals generally are located on high points such as chimneys, towers, and gables.   The routing of roof and down conductors and proper methods of joining and splicing and fastening of connections should be carefully detailed by lightning-protection experts.

Design and specifications of lightning-protection systems should follow the requirements of the National Board of Fire Underwriters and should be done by experts in the field.

Section 24

VERTICAL TRANSPORTATION

FREDERICK S. MERRITT

Senior Editor
Engineering News-Record

Vertical circulation of traffic in a multistory building is the key to successful functioning of the design, both in normal use and in emergencies. In fact, location of elevators or stairs may determine the floor plan. So in the design of a building, much thought should be given to the type of vertical circulation to be provided, number of units needed, and their location, arrangement, and design.

Traffic may pass from level to level in a multistory building by ramps, stairs, elevators, or moving stairs. The powered equipment is always supplemented by stairs for use when power is shut off, or there is a mechanical failure, or maintenance work is in process, or in emergencies. In addition to conventional elevators, other types of man lifts are occasionally installed in residences, factories, and garages. For moving small packages or correspondence between floors, dumb-waiters or vertical conveyors also are installed in certain types of buildings.

24-1. Ramps. When space permits, a sloping surface, or ramp, can be used to provide an easy connection between floors. In some garages, to save space, every floor serves as a ramp; each one is split longitudinally, each section sloping gradually in opposite directions to meet the next level above and below.

Ramps are especially useful when large numbers of people or vehicles have to be moved from floor to floor. Therefore, they are frequently adopted for public buildings, such as railroad stations, stadiums, and exhibition halls. They are often used in garages. And they are sometimes incorporated in special-purpose buildings, such as schools for crippled children. (Talbot Hamlin, "Forms and Functions of 20th Century Architecture," Vol. I, Columbia University Press, New York.) In all cases, ramps should be constructed with a nonslip surface.

Ramps generally have been built with slopes up to 15% (15 ft in 100 ft), but 10% is a preferred maximum. Some idea of the space required for a ramp may be obtained from the following: With the 10% maximum slope and a story height of, say, 12 ft, a ramp connecting two floors would have to be 120 ft long. The ramp need not be straight for the whole distance, however. It can be curved, zigzagged, or spiraled. (Building Exits Code, National Fire Protection Association, Boston, Mass.)

24-2. Stairs. Less space is required for stairs than for ramps, because steeper slopes can be used. Maximum slope of stairs for comfort is estimated to be about 1 on 2 (27°), but this angle frequently is exceeded for practical reasons. Exterior stairs generally range in slope from 20 to 30°, interior stairs from 30 to 35°.

Among the principal components of a stairway are:

Flight. A series of steps extending from floor to floor, or from a floor to an intermediate landing or platform. Landings are used where turns are necessary or to break up long climbs.

Rise.   Distance from floor to floor.

Run.   Total length of stairs in a horizontal plane, including landings.

Riser.   Vertical face of a step.   Its height is generally taken as the vertical distance between treads.

Tread.   Horizontal face of a step.   Its width is usually taken as the horizontal distance between risers.

Nosing.   Projection of a tread beyond the riser below.

Carriage.   Rough timber supporting the steps of wood stairs.

Strings.   Inclined members along the sides of a stairway.   The string along a wall is called a wall string.   Open strings are those cut to follow the lines of risers and treads.   Closed strings have parallel top and bottom, and treads and risers are supported along their sides or mortised into them.   In wood stairs, strings are placed outside the carriage to provide a finish.

Railing.   Protective bar placed at a convenient distance above the stairs for a handhold.

Baluster.   Vertical member supporting the railing.

Newel Post.   Post at which the railing terminates at each floor level.

Angle Post.   Railing support at landings or other breaks in the stairs.   If an angle post projects beyond the bottom of the strings, the ornamental detail formed at the bottom of the post is called the **drop.**

Winders.   Steps with tapered treads in sharply curved stairs.

Headroom.   Minimum clear height from a tread to overhead construction, such as the ceiling of the next floor, ductwork, or piping.

Ample headroom should be provided not only to prevent tall people from injuring their heads but to give a feeling of spaciousness.   A person of average height should be able to extend his hand forward and upward without touching the ceiling above the stair.   Minimum vertical distance from the nosing of a tread to overhead construction should never be less than 6 ft 6 in.

Width of a stair depends on its purpose and the number of people to be accommodated in peak hours or emergencies.   Generally, the minimum width that can be used is specified in the local building code.   For example, theater stairs may be required to be 4 ft wide for the first 50 persons of capacity in the upper floors, plus 6 in. for each additional 50 persons.   (Building Exits Code, National Fire Protection Association, Boston, Mass., contains recommendations for various building types.)

The number of stairs required in a building also is usually controlled by local building codes.   This control may be achieved through a restriction on the maximum horizontal distance from any point on a floor to a stairway or on the maximum floor area contributory to a stairway.   In addition, codes usually have special provisions for public buildings, such as theaters and exhibition halls.   Restrictions might also be placed on the maximum capacity of a stairway.

Risers and treads generally are proportioned for comfort, though sometimes space considerations control, or the desire to achieve a monumental effect, particularly for outside stairs of public buildings.   The most comfortable height of riser is 7 to $7\frac{1}{2}$ in. Risers less than 6 in. and more than 8 in. should not be used.   Also, the steeper the slope of the stairs, the greater the ratio of riser to tread.   Among the more common, simple formulas generally used to proportion risers and treads are:

1. Product of riser and tread must be between 70 and 75.

2. Riser plus tread must equal 17 to 17.5.

3. Sum of the tread and twice the riser must lie between 24 and 25.

In designing stairs, account should be taken of the fact that there is always one less tread than riser per flight of stairs.

Winders should be avoided when possible, because the narrow width of tread at the inside of the curve may cause accidents.   Sometimes, instead, **balanced steps** can be used.   Instead of radiating from the center of the curve, like winders, balanced steps, though tapered, have the same width of tread along the line of travel as the straight portion of the stairs.   (Line of travel in this case is assumed to be about 20 in. from the rail on the inside of the curve.)   With balanced steps, the change in angle is spread over a large portion of the stairs.

Railings generally are set 2 ft 6 in. to 2 ft 8 in. above the intersections of tread and risers at the front of the steps. At landings, railings usually are from 2 ft 10 in. to 3 ft high, though lower railings can be used safely if the parapet is very wide. Low, wide railings usually are used for monumental stairways. (Talbot Hamlin, "Forms and Functions of 20th Century Architecture," Vol. I, Columbia University Press, New York.)

24-3. Fire Exits. In many types of buildings, stairs must be enclosed with walls having a high resistance to fire and with self-closing fire-resistant doors, to prevent spread of smoke and flame. If the doors are glazed, wire glass should be used. It also is wise to incorporate some means of opening the top of the shaft, either with a thermally operated device or with a skylight, to let escape any heat that might get into the stairway.

In public buildings, there should be more than one fire tower, and these should be as far apart as possible. Some building codes require that access to at least one fire tower be from an outside balcony, for greater protection against spread of smoke and flame. Exits at the bottom of fire towers should be directly to the outdoors where

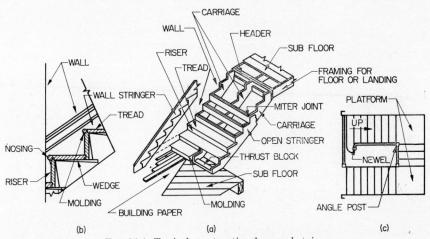

FIG. 24-1. Typical construction for wood stairs.

people can remove themselves quickly to a safe distance from the building. (Building Exits Code, National Fire Protection Association, Boston, Mass.)

For some types of buildings, building codes require fire escapes on the exterior. These may be of four general types: (1) For industrial buildings of low height, fire escapes may consist merely of vertical metal ladders with platforms at exit doors and windows. (2) For most other types of buildings, however, fire escapes are open metalwork stairways supported on brackets attached to the building walls, with platforms at exits. At the bottom, a ladder or counterbalanced stair is lowered when needed. (3) When the fire escape cannot be attached to the building wall, a free-standing stair, supported independently on steel columns, may be used, with platforms connecting to building exits. (4) For hospitals, old-age homes, and other buildings where people are under institutional care, chutes are sometimes used. (Ramsey and Sleeper, "Architectural Graphic Standards," John Wiley & Sons, Inc., New York.)

24-4. Wood Stairs. In wood-frame buildings, low nonfireproof buildings, and one- and two-family houses, stairs may be constructed of wood. They may be built in place or shop-fabricated.

Construction of a built-in-place stair starts with cutting of carriages to the right size and shape to receive the risers and treads. Next, the lower portion of the wall string should be cut out at least $\frac{1}{2}$ in. deep to house the steps (Fig. 24-1). The string should be set in place against the wall with the housed-out profile fitted to the stepped profile of the top of the carriage. Then, treads and risers should be firmly nailed to the carriages, tongues at the bottom of the risers fitting into grooves at the rear of the treads. Nosings are generally finished on the underside with molding.

If the outer string is an open string, it should be carefully cut to the same profile as the steps, mitered to fit corresponding miters in the ends of risers, and nailed against the outside carriage. Ends of the treads project beyond the open string.

If the outer string is a curb or closed string, it should be plowed out in the same way as the wall string to house the steps. Ends of the treads and risers should be wedged and glued into the wall string. (A. G. H. Dietz, "Dwelling House Construction," D. Van Nostrand Company, Princeton, N.J.; Ramsey and Sleeper, "Architectural Graphic Standards," John Wiley & Sons, Inc., New York; Gay and Parker, "Materials and Methods of Architectural Construction," John Wiley & Sons, Inc., New York.)

24-5. Steel Stairs. Pressed-sheet steel stairs generally are used in fire-resistant buildings. They may be purchased from various manufacturers in stock patterns.

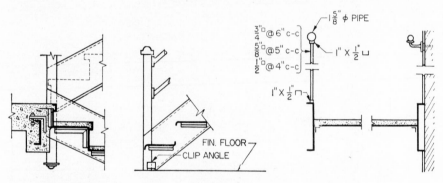

(a) PAN TYPE   (b) FLOOR PLATE TREADS   (c) SECTION THROUGH METAL STAIRS

Fig. 24-2. Metal-stair details.

The steel sheets are formed into risers and subtreads or pans, into which one of several types of treads may be inserted (Fig. 24-2). Strings usually are channel-shaped. Treads may be made of stone, concrete, composition, or metal. Most types are given a nonslip surface. (Ramsey and Sleeper, "Architectural Graphic Standards," John Wiley & Sons, Inc., New York; Gay and Parker, "Materials and Methods of Architectural Construction," John Wiley & Sons, Inc., New York.)

24-6. Concrete Stairs. Depending on the method of support provided, concrete stairs may be designed as cantilevered or inclined beams and slabs. The entire stairway may be cast in place as a single unit, or slabs or T beams formed first and the steps built up later. Soffits formed with plywood or hardboard forms may have a smooth enough finish to make plastering unnecessary. Concrete treads should have metal nosings to protect the edges.

To cut costs, a pair of concrete stairs are often enclosed in the same fire tower. Known as scissor stairs, they slope in opposite directions on either side of a reinforced-concrete wall (Fig. 24-3). For additional economy, the following technique may be used: Leave a hole in the wall where the stair slabs on opposite sides of the wall cross. (These slabs are cast after the floors above and below.) A beam is cast, continuous through the hole in the wall and cantilevering on either side of the wall. The stair slabs are supported on these cantilevers and on the floors above and below. Hence, the stair slabs have only half the span of that required when they have to extend unsupported from floor to floor. There is also an additional saving because the slabs can be constructed without the necessity of recessing the wall. (Abel and Severud, "Apartment Houses," Reinhold Publishing Corporation, New York.)

24-7. Moving Stairs. Escalators, or electric stairs, are used when it is necessary to move large numbers of people from floor to floor   They have the advantage of continuous operation without the need for operators.   They have large capacity with low power consumption.   Large department stores provide vertical-transportation facilities for one person per hour for every 20 to 25 sq ft of sales area above the entrance floor, and moving stairs generally carry 75 to 90% of the traffic, elevators the remainder.

In effect, a moving stairway is an inclined bridge spanning between floors.   It includes a steel trussed framework, handrails, and an endless belt with steps (Fig. 24-4).   At the upper end are a pair of motor-driven sprocket wheels and a worm-gear

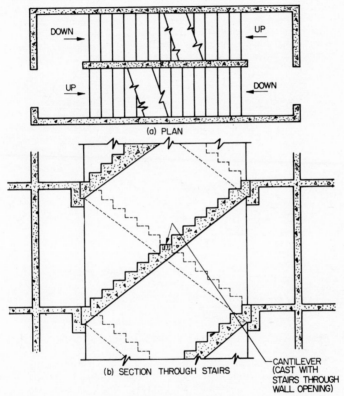

FIG. 24-3. Concrete scissor stairs.

driving machine.   At the lower end is a matching pair of sprocket wheels.   Two precision-made roller chains travel over the sprockets pulling the endless belt of steps around.   The steps move on an accurately made set of tracks attached to the trusses, with each step supported on four resilient rollers.

Generally accepted speed for moving stairs is 90 fpm.   Slope of the stairs is standardized at 30°.

For a given speed of travel, width of step determines the capacity of the moving stairs.   Standard widths range from 2 to 4 ft between balustrade panels, with corresponding capacities of 4,000 to 8,000 persons per hour.   Floor area required varies from about 90 sq ft for the 2-ft width to about 120 sq ft for the 4-ft.

Location of moving stairs should be selected only after a careful study of traffic flow in the building.   They should be installed where traffic is heaviest and where convenient for passengers, and their location should be obvious to people approaching them. In stores, moving stairs should lead to strategic sales areas.

In the design of a new building, adequate space should be allotted for moving stairs. Structural framing should be made adequate to support them.

For a moving-stair installation in an existing building, careful study should be made to determine the necessary alterations to assure adequate space and supports. When the driving machine cannot be housed inside the trussed framework, building beams must be cut to permit passage of the drive chain; these beams must be reinforced.

Floor-to-floor height should be taken into account in determining loads on supporting members. If the total rise is within certain limits, the stairs need be supported only at top and bottom; otherwise, they may have to be supported at intermediate points also. A structural frame should be installed around the stair well to carry the floor and wellway railing. The stairway should be independent of this frame.

Moving stairs are "tailor-made" for the building in which they are to be installed. At the site, each part must fit perfectly into the over-all assembly to assure smooth quiet operation, and the assembly must fit exactly into the allotted space.

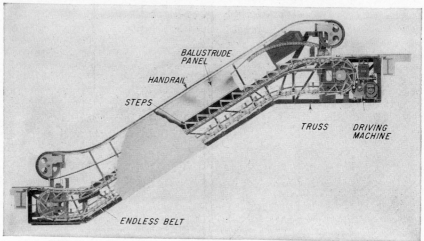

FIG. 24-4. Moving-stair details. (*Courtesy of Otis Elevator Co.*)

Design of the moving stairs permits a vertical variation of $\frac{1}{2}$ in. in the level of the supporting beams from the specified floor-to-floor height. The stairway is shimmed to bring it level. If variations in elevation exceed $\frac{1}{2}$ in., installation is difficult and much time may be lost. Also, when upper and lower beams are too far apart horizontally, there will be delay, because an extension must be added to the trussed framework.

Trusses generally are brought to the job in three sections. There, they are assembled and raised into position with chain hoists, either through an elevator shaft or on the outside of the building.

Either the owner or the manufacturer may furnish the exterior treatment of the balustrade and wellway railings. Often, plaster is specified, and the owner's forces apply it.

Moving stairs usually are installed in pairs—one for carrying traffic up and the other for moving traffic down. The units may be placed parallel to each other in each story (Fig. 24-5) or crisscrossed (Fig. 24-6). Crisscrossed stairs generally are preferred because they are more compact, reducing walking distance between stairs at various floors to a minimum.

Fire-protection devices may be incorporated with the stairway installation when desired. These may take the form of rolling steel shutters, which are electrically or manually operated to close a stair well, or a combination exhaust system and sprinkler system may be used.

24-8. Elevators. Two major types of elevators are in general use—electrically operated and hydraulic. Electric elevators are used exclusively in tall buildings and in most low buildings. Hydraulic elevators are usually used for low-rise freight, with lifts up to about 50 ft, where they cost less to operate.

Major components of an electric-elevator installation include the car or cab, cables, elevator machine, control equipment, counterweights, shaft, rails, penthouse, and pit (Fig. 24-7). The cab is a cage of light metal supported on a structural frame, to the top of which the cables are attached. The cables raise and lower the cab in the shaft. They pass over a grooved motor-driven sheave and are fastened to the counterweights. The elevator machine that drives the sheave consists of an electric motor, brakes, and auxiliary equipment, which are mounted, with the sheave, on a heavy structural frame. The counterweights, consisting of blocks of cast iron in a frame, are needed to reduce power requirements.

The path of both the counterweights and the cab is controlled by separate sets of T-shaped guide rails. The operating machinery may be located in a penthouse above

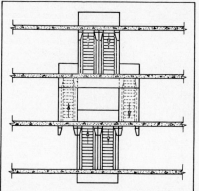

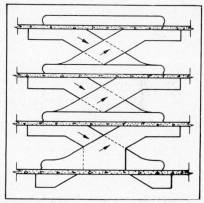

Fig. 24-5. Parallel arrangement of moving stairs.

Fig. 24-6. Crisscross arrangement of moving stairs.

the shaft or in the basement. Safety springs or buffers are placed in the pit, to break the fall of the cab and counterweights if an accident should occur. Shafts must be enclosed with noncombustible materials of high fire resistance. (F. A. Annett, "Electric Elevators," 2d ed., McGraw-Hill Book Company, Inc., New York; Safety Code for Elevators, American Standard A17.1, American Standards Association, New York.)

Elevators and related equipment, such as machinery, signal systems, cables, and guide rails, are generally supplied and installed by the manufacturer. The general contractor has to guarantee the dimensions of the shaft and its freedom from encroachments. The owner's architect or engineer is responsible for the design and construction of components needed for supporting the plant, including buffer supports, machine-room floors, trolley beams, and guide-rail bracket supports. Magnitudes of loads generally are supplied by the manufacturer with a 100% allowance for impact.

For the design of the supports, an allowable steel unit stress of 12,000 psi and a ratio less than 10 for span to depth of beams are recommended, to limit deformations. Hoistway dimensions must be within 1 in. of plumb with respect to dimensions given on the manufacturer's drawings.

24-9. Roping for Elevators. For a given weight of cab and load, the method of "roping up" the elevator has a considerable effect on the loading of the cables, machine bearings, and building members.

Elevator machines may be winding-drum or traction type, depending on whether the cables are wound on drums on the drive shaft or are powered by a drive sheave.

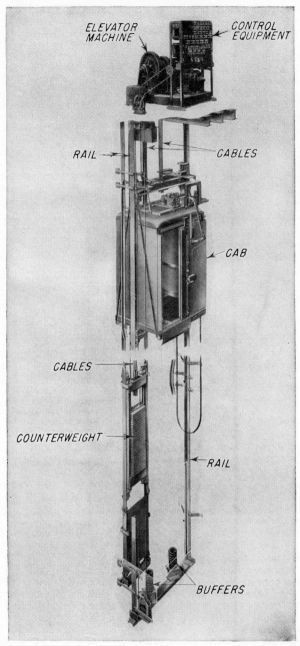

FIG. 24-7. Typical passenger-elevator installation. (*Courtesy of Otis Elevator Co.*)

(For types of controls, see Art. 24-20.)   The traction type is usually used.   It may
be classified as double wrap or single wrap.

For the double wrap—to obtain sufficient traction between the cables and the
driving sheave, which has U-shaped or round-seat grooves—a secondary or idler
sheave is used (Fig. 24-8a).

In the single-wrap type, the cables pass over the traction or driving sheave only
once; so there is a single wrap, or less, of the ropes on the sheave (Fig. 24-8d).   The
traction sheave has wedge-shaped or undercut grooves that grip the cables by virtue
of the wedging action between the sides of the grooves and the ropes.   With this type
of installation, the sheave has one-half the loading obtained with the double-wrap

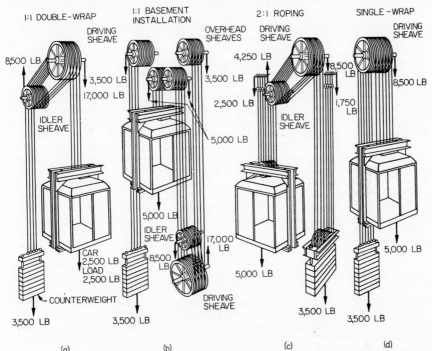

Fig. 24-8. Types of roping for elevators driven by traction machines.

machine for the same weight of car and counterweight.   As a result, the single-wrap
design is lighter than the double-wrap.   Also, cable life usually is a little longer
because there are fewer bends in the ropes.

In most buildings, elevator machines are located in a penthouse.   When a machine
must be installed in the basement (Fig. 24-8b), the load on the overhead supports is
increased, cable length is tripled, and additional sheaves are needed, adding substantially to the cost.   Other disadvantages include higher friction losses and larger
number of rope bends, requiring greater traction between cables and driving sheaves
for the same elevator loads and speeds; higher power consumption; more cable wear;
and consequently, greater operating expenses.

When heavy loads are to be handled and speed is not important, a 2-to-1 roping
may be used (Fig. 24-8c), in which case the car speed is only one-half that of the
cable.   Ends of the rope are dead-ended to the overhead beams, instead of being
attached to car and counterweights, as for 1-to-1 roping.   With this setup, the
anchorages carry one-half the weight of car and counterweights.   So the loading on
the traction and secondary sheaves is only about one-half that for the 1-to-1 machine,

and therefore, a lighter machine can be used.   (F. A. Annett, "Electric Elevators," 2d ed., McGraw-Hill Book Company, Inc., New York.)

24-10. Passenger Elevators.   The number of passenger elevators needed to serve a building adequately depends on their capacity, the volume of traffic, and the interval between cars.

Traffic is measured by the number of persons handled in 5-min periods.   For proposed buildings, peak traffic generally can be estimated from comparisons with existing buildings of the same class and occupancy located in the same or a similar neighborhood.   Or the peak traffic may be estimated in terms of the probable population. The maximum 5-min traffic flow can be counted (in existing buildings) or estimated from the population of the building, which in turn may be computed from the net rentable area (see Arts. 24-12 to 24-19).

Dividing the peak 5-min traffic flow by the 5-min handling capacity of an elevator gives the minimum number of elevators required.   The 5-min handling capacity of an elevator is determined from the round-trip time.

In addition to handling capacity, there is another factor to be considered in determining the number of elevators for adequate service—**interval,** the average time between elevators leaving the ground floor.   As an indication of the length of time passengers must wait for an elevator, it is a significant measure of good service.

After the number of elevators has been computed on the basis of traffic flow, the interval should be checked (see also Arts. 24-12 and 24-15).   It is obtained by dividing the round-trip time by the number of elevators.

Round-trip time is composed principally of the time for a full-speed round-trip run without stops, time for accelerating and decelerating per stop, time for leveling at each stop, time for opening and closing gates and doors, time for passengers to move in and out, reaction time of operator, lost time due to false stops, and standing time at top and bottom floors.

Opening and closing of doors may contribute materially to lost time unless the doors are properly designed.   A 3-ft 6-in. opening is good, because two passengers may conveniently enter and leave a car abreast.   A slightly wider door would be of little advantage.   Department stores, hospitals, and other structures served by large passenger elevators (4,000 lb and over) usually require much bigger openings.

Center-opening doors, preferred for power operation, are faster than either the single or two-speed type of the same width.   The impact on closing is smaller with the center-opening door; hence, there is less chance of injuring a passenger.   Also, transfer time is less since passengers can move out as the door starts to open.

Another factor affecting passenger-transfer time is the shape of the car.   The narrower and deeper a car, the greater is the time required for passengers to leave likely to be.   Platform sizes should conform to the standards of the National Elevator Manufacturing Industry.

24-11. Automatic Elevators.   Elevator operation may be either car-switch (operator-controlled) or automatic (see also Art. 24-20).   With dual operation, the car may be operated by a car switch or by push buttons under the control of an operator, the buttons at each floor signaling but not operating the car.   Several types of automatic elevator are available.

The simplest type is the **single automatic.**   The cab responds to the first button pressed, ignoring all future calls until it arrives at the destination.   Used principally in apartment houses and hospitals, these elevators have the disadvantage of not being able to store calls.

With collective controls, calls can be stored.   When the **selective-collective type** is used, calls are answered in the direction of the car's travel; when an "up" button is pressed at a landing, for example, the elevator will stop there only if it is on the way up.   The controls can be extended to groups of cars, so that the call is answered by the first car to pass in the proper direction.

In addition, the elevators may also be dispatched automatically.   A timer signals the cars to leave the terminal at predetermined intervals.   Since automatic dispatching reduces the round-trip time, it actually results in an increase in the carrying capacity of the elevators.

Fully automatic systems (operatorless) are available for tall office buildings. These systems are capable of adjusting to varying traffic conditions.

When office employees report for work in the morning and traffic is predominantly up, the supervisory control sets itself for the up peak. Cars leave either at the end of a fixed interval or when loaded to 80% of capacity, as indicated by a load-weighing device in the floor of the cab. As soon as the highest call is answered, each car returns to the lower terminal.

For very heavy up traffic, the building is divided into a high and low zone, and elevators are automatically assigned to each zone. This results in a decrease in the round-trip time, which improves the carrying capacity of the elevators.

At the close of business in the evening, the system adjusts to a down peak. The building again is divided into two zones. Waiting time at the bottom terminal is eliminated. Cars start down as soon as they reach the highest call, and when fully loaded, automatically bypass remaining floor calls. High-zone cars meanwhile answer all up calls. For very heavy down traffic, each zone is again divided in two.

Between peak periods, when traffic up and down are nearly balanced, cars operate at uniform intervals. As traffic grows heavier—for example, around lunch hour—cars leave top and bottom terminals at more rapid intervals, as they become available. If a car arrives at its lower terminal after the time scheduled for departure, it is dispatched up immediately. If there is no car at the upper terminal when the start-down signal is given, the highest car starts down as soon as it has made its highest call.

During off hours—nights, Sundays, holidays—cars park at the bottom terminal with motor generators shut off. When a call is registered, the motor-generator set powering one car starts up automatically.

Since the elevators are operatorless, several safety devices are incorporated in these automatic elevators in addition to those commonly carried by manually operated cars—automatic load weigher to prevent overcrowding, buttons in car and starter station to stop the doors from closing and to hold them open, lights to indicate floor stops pressed, two-way loudspeaker system for communication with the starter station, and auxiliary power systems if the primary power and supervisory systems should fail. Safety devices also prevent the doors from closing when a passenger is standing in the doorway, and of course, the elevators cannot move when the doors are open. (Safety Code for Elevators, American Standard A17.1, American Standards Association, New York.)

24-12. Elevators in General-purpose Buildings. For a proposed diversified-tenancy, or general-purpose, office building, peak traffic may be estimated from the probable population computed from the net rentable area (usually 65 to 70% of the gross area). Net rentable area per person may range from 90 to 135 sq ft. However, when several floors are occupied by a single organization with a large clerical staff, the population density may be much higher.

Diversified-tenancy office buildings usually have important traffic peaks in the morning, at noon, and in the evening, and very little interfloor traffic. The 5-min morning peak generally is the controlling factor, because if the elevators can handle that peak satisfactorily, they can also deal with the others. In a well-diversified office building, the 5-min peak will be about one-ninth of the population; but it can rise to one-eighth if the tenancy is not sufficiently diversified.

For busy, high-class office buildings in large cities, time intervals between elevators may be classified as follows: 20 sec, excellent; between 20 and 25 sec, good; between 25 and 30 sec, fair; between 30 and 35 sec, poor; and over 35 sec, unsatisfactory. In small cities, however, intervals of 30 sec and longer may be satisfactory.

When elevators are divided into local and express service, it is desirable to equalize the intervals. Often, this cannot be done because the necessary number of express elevators would not be economically justified. Intervals for high-use elevators of 30 to 35 sec, therefore, may be considered acceptable.

Car speeds used vary with height of building: 4 to 10 stores, 200 to 500 fpm; 10 to 15 stories, 600 to 700 fpm; 15 to 20 stories, 700 to 800 fpm; 20 to 50 stories, 900 to 1,200 fpm; and over 50 stories, 1,200 to 1,500 fpm.

Elevators should be easily accessible from all entrances to a building. For maximum efficiency, they should be grouped near the center. Except in extremely large buildings, two banks of elevators located in different parts of the structure should not serve the same floors. Generally, traffic cannot be equalized on the two banks, and the bank near the principal exit or street will handle most of the traffic.

Elevators should not serve two lower terminal floors. The extra stop increases the round-trip time and decreases the handling capacity. If there is sufficient traffic between the two lower floors, moving stairs should be installed.

In laying out an elevator group, not more than six elevators should be placed in a straight line. Elevators placed in alcoves off the main corridor make a good arrangement. Such a layout eliminates interference between elevator and other traffic, makes possible narrow corridors, saves space in the upper floors, decreases passenger-transfer time, and reduces walking distances to the individual elevators. Width of alcove need not be more than 8 to 10 ft, except for large elevators, where the width may be 14 ft.

It is necessary to divide elevator groups into local and express banks in tall buildings, especially those with setbacks and towers, and in low buildings with large rental areas. In general, when more than eight elevators are needed, consideration should be given to such an arrangement. One or two of the elevators of the high-use express bank should be provided with openings at all floors for Sunday and holiday service. In addition to improving service, the division into local and express banks has the advantage that corridor space on the floors where there are no doors can be used for toilets, closets, and stairs.

Unless the building is very large (500,000 sq ft of net rentable area), separate service elevators are not needed for a diversified-tenancy office building. One of the passenger elevators can be detached from the bank for freight work when passenger traffic is light.

24-13. Elevators in Single-purpose Buildings. Elevator requirements and layouts are similar in general for both single-purpose and diversified-tenancy office buildings, but several different factors should be taken into consideration: Single-purpose buildings are occupied by one large organization. Generally, the floors that are occupied by the clerical staff are not subdivided into many offices; the net rentable area is about 80% of the gross area. Population densities are higher than for general-purpose buildings. Depending on the kind of business to be carried on, population density varies from 40 sq ft per person for some life-insurance companies to about 100 for some telephone companies.

While traffic peaks occur at the same periods as in the diversified-tenancy type, the morning peak is very high, unless working hours are staggered. The maximum 5-min period may be one-eighth to one-half the population, depending on the type of occupancy. Because of this volume of traffic, elevators should have a capacity of 3,000 lb or more, to keep the number required to a minimum. Furthermore, interfloor traffic is large in this type of building and must be considered in designing the elevator system. Usually, so many elevators are required for handling traffic that the interval is satisfactory.

24-14. Professional-building Elevators. Population cannot be used as the sole basis for determining the number of elevators needed for buildings occupied by doctors, dentists, and other professional men, because of the volume of patient and visitor traffic. Peaks may occur in the forenoon and mid-afternoon, with the maximum taking place when reception hours coincide. Traffic studies indicate that the maximum peak varies from two to six persons per doctor per hour up and down.

Since crowding of incapacitated patients is inadvisable, elevators should be of at least 3,000 lb capacity. If the building has a private hospital, then one or two of the elevators should have stretcher-size platforms, 5 ft 8 in. by 8 ft 4 in.

24-15. Hotel Elevators. Hotels with transient guests average 1.3 to 1.5 persons per sleeping room. They have pronounced traffic peaks in morning and early evening. The 5-min maximum occurs at the check-out hour in the evening and is about 10% of the estimated population, with traffic moving in both directions.

Ballrooms and banquet rooms should be located on lower floors and served by separate elevators. Sometimes it is advisable to provide an express elevator to serve heavy roof-garden traffic. Passenger elevators should be of 3,000 lb capacity or more to allow room for bellboys with baggage. Intervals for passenger elevators should not exceed 50 sec.

Service elevators are very important in hotels. They should have a capacity of at least 3,000 lb, with platforms about 6 ft 4 in. by 6 ft 2 in. The number required usually is determined by comparison with existing hotels.

24-16. Hospital Elevators. Traffic in a hospital is of two types: (1) medical staff and equipment and (2) transient traffic, such as patients and visitors. Greatest peaks occur when visitor traffic is combined with regular hospital traffic. Waiting rooms should be provided at the main floor and only a limited number of visitors should be permitted to leave them at one time, so that the traffic peaks can be handled in a reasonable period and to keep corridors from getting congested.

For flexibility of service, hospital elevators should be of stretcher size—5 ft 4 in. wide by 8 ft or 8 ft 4 in. deep, with a capacity of 3,500 or 4,000 lb, respectively. Speeds vary from 50 to 700 fpm, depending on height of building and load. The elevators should be self-leveling, to avoid bumping patients on and off.

Elevators should be centrally located and readily accessible from the main entrance. Service elevators can be provided with front and rear doors and so located that they can assist the passenger elevators during traffic peaks.

24-17. Apartment-house Elevators. Multistory residential buildings do not have peaks so pronounced as other types of buildings. Generally, the evening peak is the largest. Traffic flow at that time may be 6 to 8% of the building population in a 5-min period. Building population may be estimated at 2.6 persons per apartment.

One elevator rated at 2,000 lb and 200 fpm usually is sufficient for a six-story apartment house with 50 to 75 units. For taller buildings, two elevators operating at 400 to 500 fpm are generally adequate. One of these elevators can be used for service work at times.

24-18. Elevators in Government Buildings. Municipal buildings, city halls, state office buildings, and other government office buildings may be treated the same as single-purpose office buildings. Population density for large structures may be assumed as one person per 100 sq ft of net area. The 5-min maximum peak occurs in the morning and may be as large as one-third the population.

24-19. Department-store Elevators. Department stores should be served by a coordinated system of moving stairs and elevators. The required capacity of the vertical-transportation system should be based on the transportation or merchandising area and the maximum density to which it is expected to be occupied by shoppers.

The **transportation area** is all the floor space above or below the first floor to which shoppers and employees must be moved. Totaling about 80 to 85% of the gross area, it includes the space taken up by counters, showcases, aisles, fitting rooms, public rooms, restaurants, credit offices, and cashiers' counters but does not include kitchens, general offices, accounting departments, stockrooms, stairways, elevator shafts, or other areas for utilities.

The **transportation capacity** is the number of persons per hour that the vertical-transportation system can distribute from the main floor to the other merchandising floors. The ratio of the peak transportation capacity to the transportation area is called the density ratio. This ratio is about 1 to 20 for a busy department store. So the required hourly handling capacity of a combined moving stairs and elevator system is numerically equal to one-twentieth, or 5%, of the transportation area. The elevator system generally is designed to handle about 10% of the total.

The maximum peak hour usually occurs from 12 to 1 P.M. on weekdays and between 2 and 3 P.M. on Saturdays.

The type of elevator preferred for use with moving stairs is one with 3,500 lb capacity or more. It should have a center-opening, solid-panel, power-operated car and hoistway doors, with a 4-ft 6-in. opening and a platform 8 ft by 5 ft 6 in.

24-20. Freight Elevators. In low-rise buildings, freight elevators may be of the hydraulic type, but in taller buildings (higher than about 50 ft) electric elevators (Fig. 24-9) generally will be found more economical. In selecting freight elevators, the following should be considered:

1. Building characteristics, including the travel, number of floors, floor heights, and openings required on two sides of a car. Also, structural conditions that may influence the size, shape, or location of the elevator should be studied.

2. Units to be carried on the elevator—weight, size, type, and method of loading.

3. Number of units to be handled per hour.

4. Probable cycle of operation and principal floors served during the peak of the cycle.

5. Will the elevator handle passengers during periods of peak passenger traffic?

Two types of control equipment are generally used for electric freight elevators— variable voltage and ac rheostatic.

With **variable voltage,** the hoisting motor is dc operated. A motor-generator set is provided for each elevator, and the speed and direction of motion of the car are controlled by varying the generator field. This type of elevator permits the most accurate stops, the most rapid acceleration and deceleration, and minimum power consumption and maintenance for an active elevator. Automatic leveling to compensate for cable stretch or other variations from floor level is an inherent part of variable-voltage equipment. Variable voltage is generally used for passenger elevators.

Standard speeds with variable-voltage geared freight elevators are 75, 100, 150, and 200 fpm, with 75 fpm a popular standard for 10,000-lb cars. Generally recommended are 100 fpm for 2 or 3 floors, 150 fpm for 4 or 5 floors, and 200 fpm for 6 to 10 floors. If one of the stories exceeds 20 ft, however, the next higher speed should be used.

The **ac rheostatic type** is often chosen to keep initial cost down when the elevator is to be used infrequently (less than five trips per hour on a normal business day). If the ordinary landing accuracy of this type will not be acceptable for the loading methods expected, either of two leveling devices may be installed:

1. Inching, which may be added to the controller for a single-speed ac motor at nominal cost. It permits moving the car to floor level within a limited zone (about 9 in.) with the doors open.

2. Automatic leveling, which is achieved with a two-speed motor and control apparatus. It is available only with selective-collective or single-automatic operation (Art. 24-11) at speeds up to 100 fpm, for capacities up to 8,000 lb, and at 75 fpm, for 10,000-lb elevators.

Standard speeds for ac rheostatic-type geared freight elevators are 50, 75, and 100 fpm. Generally recommended are 50 fpm for two floors, 75 fpm for three or four floors, and 100 fpm for five to eight floors. If one of the stories is more than 20 ft high, the next higher speed should be used.

The size of cab to be used for a freight elevator is generally dependent on the dimensions of the freight package to be carried per trip and the weight of the package and loading equipment. Power trucks, for example, impose severer strains on the entire car structure and the guide rails than do hand trucks. As a power truck with palletized load enters an elevator, most of the weight of the truck and its load are concentrated at the edge of the platform, producing heavy eccentric loading. Maximum load on an elevator should include most of the truck weight as well as the load to be lifted, since the truck wheels are on the elevator as the last unit of load is deposited.

The carrying capacity per hour of freight elevators is determined by the capacity or normal load of the elevator and the time required for a round trip. Round-trip time is composed of the following elements:

1. Running time, which may be readily calculated from the rated speed, with due allowance for accelerating and decelerating time (about $2\frac{1}{4}$ sec for ac rheostatic with inching, $1\frac{3}{4}$ sec for variable voltage), and the distance traveled.

2. Time for operation of the car gate and hoistway doors (manual 16 sec, power 8 sec).

3. Loading and unloading time (hand truck 25 sec, power truck 15 sec). Wherever practical, a study should be made of the loading and unloading operations for a similar elevator in the same type of plant.

The most useful and flexible type of operation for both variable-voltage and ac rheostatic freight elevators is selective-collective with an annunciator. When operated without an attendant, the car automatically answers the down calls as approached

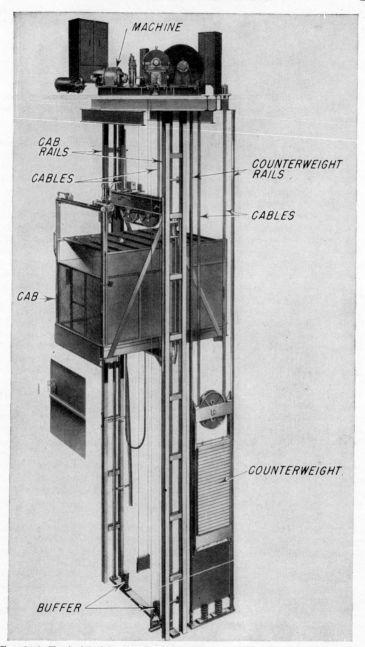

FIG. 24-9. Typical freight-elevator installation. (*Courtesy of Otis Elevator Co.*)

when moving down and similarly answers up calls when moving up. The elevator attendant, when present, has complete control of the car and can answer calls indicated in the annunciator by pressing the corresponding car button.

The single-automatic type, available for both variable-voltage and ac rheostatic controls, is a somewhat simpler, less expensive type for operation without an attendant. But it has the disadvantage that corridor calls cannot be registered when the car is in motion, nor can the car respond to more than one call at a time.

If an attendant will always operate the elevator, use may be made of car-switch releveling, which is a simple, inexpensive means of operating with variable-voltage control. The car will travel in either direction, or stop, in response to the movement of a switch, leveling automatically at each floor.

Also, a car-switch type of operation with ac rheostatic control may be used for freight elevators. The car is leveled to a mark on the hoistway door by the attendant using the normal car switch.

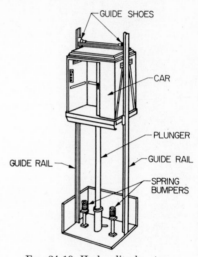

Fig. 24-10. Hydraulic elevator.

The least expensive type of operation is the continuous-pressure type. It is available for light-service ac rheostatic elevators. Buttons are installed in the corridor and car and, when pressed, will cause the car to move in a selected direction. The car will stop when the button is released. This control is not recommended for travel of more than 70 ft.

The standard hoistway door is the vertical bi-parting metal-clad wood type. For active elevators and openings wider than 8 ft, doors should be power-operated.

When passengers are carried on a freight elevator, the most important safeguards are: (1) a capacity rating equal to that of a passenger elevator with the same net area; (2) interlocks on hoistway doors, instead of locks and contacts; (3) interlocking of the car gate and the counterbalanced hoistway door, so that the hoistway door opens first and the car gate closes first to eliminate the tripping hazard. This third requirement is met preferably by use of power-operated doors and gates with sequence operation. The door time with sequence operation is about the same as for manual doors. (F. A. Annett, "Electric Elevators," 2d ed., McGraw-Hill Book Company, Inc., New York; Safety Code for Elevators, American Standard A17.1, American Standards Association, New York.

24-21. Electrohydraulic Elevators. For low-rise elevators, hydraulic equipment may be used to supply the lift. The cab sits atop a plunger, or ram, which operates in a pressure cylinder (Fig. 24-10). Oil serves as the pressure fluid and is supplied through a motor-driven positive-displacement pump, actuated by an electric-hydraulic control system.

To raise the car, the pump is started, discharging oil into the pressure cylinder and forcing the ram up. When the car reaches the desired level, the pump is stopped. To lower the car, oil is released from the pressure cylinder, returning to a storage tank.

Single-bearing cylinders (Fig. 24-11a) are a simple type that operate like a hydraulic jack. They are suitable for elevator and sidewalk lifts where the car is guided at top and bottom, preventing eccentric loading from exerting side thrust on the cylinder bearing. A cylinder of heavy steel usually is sunk in the ground as far as the load rises. The ram, of thick-walled steel tubing polished to a mirror finish, is sealed at the top of the cylinder with compression packing. Oil is admitted under pressure near the top of the cylinder, while air is removed through a bleeder.

A different cylinder design should be used where the car or platform does not operate in guides. One type capable of taking off-balance loads employs a two-bearing plunger (Fig. 24-11b). The bearings are kept immersed in oil.

Another type, suitable for general industrial applications, has a movable bearing at the lower end of the ram to give support against heavy eccentric loads (Fig. 24-11c). At the top of the cylinder, the plunger is supported by another bearing.

For long-stroke service, a cage-bearing type can be used (Fig. 24-11d). The cage bearing is supported by a secondary cylinder about 3 ft below the main cylinder head. Oil enters under pressure just below the main cylinder head, passes down through holes in the bearing, and lifts the plunger.

When the car or platform is not heavy enough to insure gravity lowering, a double-acting cylinder may be used (Fig. 24-11e). To raise the plunger, oil is admitted under pressure below the piston; to lower it, oil is forced into the cylinder near the top, above the piston, and flows out below. Jack plunger sizes for the various types range from $2\frac{1}{2}$ in. in diameter for small low-capacity lifts to 18 in. for large lifts, operating at 150 to 300 psi.

Electrohydraulic elevators have several advantages over electric elevators: They are simpler. The car and its sling rest on the hydraulic ram that raises and lower them. There are no wire ropes, no overhead equipment, no penthouse. Without heavy overhead loads, hoistway columns and footings can be smaller. Car safeties or speed governors are not needed, because the car and its load cannot fall faster than normal speed. Speed of the elevators is low; so the bumpers need be only heavy springs.

Capacity of electrohydraulic passenger elevators ranges from 1,000 to 4,000 lb at speeds from 40 to 125 fpm. With gravity lowering, down speed may be 1.5 to 2 times up speed. So the average speed for a round trip can be considerably higher than the up speed.

Capacity of standard freight elevators ranges from 2,000 to 20,000 lb at 20 to 85 fpm, but they can be designed for much greater loads. (F. A. Annett, "Electric Elevators," 2d ed., McGraw-Hill Book Company, Inc., New York.)

24-22. Dumb-waiters. For small loads, dumb-waiters may be used in multistory buildings to transport items between levels. These are cars, generally too small for an operator or passenger, which are raised or lowered like elevators. They may be powered—controlled by push buttons—or manually operated by pulling on ropes.

24-23. Vertical Conveyors. When there is a continuous flow of materials to be distributed throughout a multistory building, vertical conveyors may be the most economical means. In some installations, 200 lb or more of paper work and light supplies are circulated per minute.

A typical conveyor installation is similar to moving stairs (Art. 24-7). A continuous roller chain is driven by an electric motor. Engaging sprockets at top and bottom, the chain extends the height of the building, or to the uppermost floor to be served. Carriers spaced at 9-ft intervals along it transport trays from floor to floor at a speed of about 72 fpm.

Like elevators, however, vertical conveyors are enclosed in fire-resistant shafts. Generally, the only visual evidence of the existence of a machine is the 18-in. wall cutouts for receiving and dispatching trays at each floor. Short gravity-control conveyor sections may lead from the conveyor receiving station into the work area.

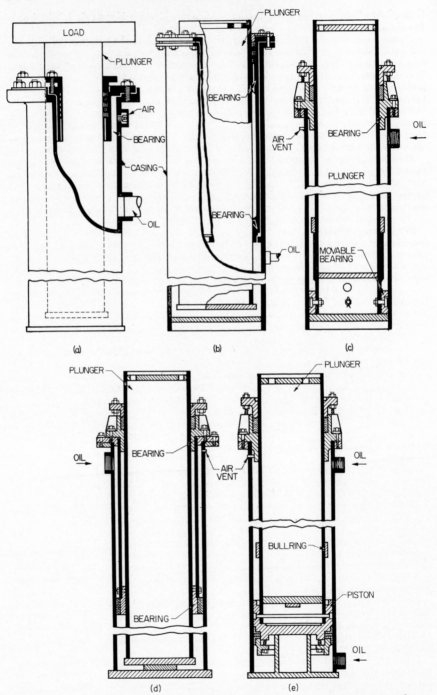

FIG. 24-11. Jacks commonly used for electrohydraulic elevators: (*a*) single-bearing plunger for guided loads; (*b*) two-bearing plunger for off-balance loads; (*c*) movable-bearing plunger for heavy service; (*d*) cage bearing for long-stroke service; (*e*) double-acting plunger.

In event of fire, vertical sliding doors, released by fusible links, will snap down over the openings, sealing off the conveyor shaft at each floor.

Operation of vertical conveyors is simple. When the trays are ready for dispatch, the attendant sets the floor-selector dial or presses a button alongside the dispatch cutout. As the trays are placed on the loading station, they are automatically moved into the path of the traveling carriers. Each tray rides up and around the top sprocket and is automatically discharged on the downward trip at the preselected floor. It takes only $4\frac{1}{2}$ min for a 26-story delivery of interoffice correspondence.

The best place to install a vertical conveyor is in a central location, next to other vertical shafts, to minimize horizontal runs in collecting and distributing correspondence at each level. An installation alongside a stairway is advantageous in providing access to the rear maintenance platform of the conveyor, for servicing equipment.

Vertical conveyors are fabricated and shipped in sections 10 ft long, which are assembled in the shaft. Principal components include the head sprocket and drive unit, the foot sprocket and take-up units, and intermediate sections consisting of braced steel shapes and tubular track guides. Generally, one or more walls of the shaft are left open until the conveyor is installed. A removable floor plate is provided in the top floor above the shaft for access to the drive machinery.

In choosing between vertical conveyors and pneumatic tubes, the designer's first consideration should be the number of floors to be served. An arterial system of pneumatic tubes would satisfy the requirements of a predominantly horizontal building, whereas a vertical conveyor generally would be more advantageous in a tall building. The amount of paper work to be distributed is a second consideration.

Section 25

SURVEYING FOR BUILDING CONSTRUCTION

REGINALD S. BRACKETT

Architectural Superintendent
Voorhees, Walker, Smith & Smith
New York, N.Y.

Surveying for building construction can be divided into three classifications:

1. *Preliminary.* So the architect can prepare plans for the building, information should be obtained on:

    a. Boundary lines and general topography (Art. 25-2).
    b. Streets, curbs, and pavements.
    c. Utilities—sewers, water mains, gas lines, electric and steam service.
    d. Buildings on and adjacent to the site.
    e. Subsurface conditions—from test holes and borings.
    f. Soil tests.
    g. Quantity survey (engineers' estimate).

2. *Construction.* Condition survey of adjacent structures and establishing lines and grades. Needed are:

    a. Survey of conditions of adjacent structures that are subject to damage from new construction (Art. 25-3).
    b. Elevation readings on existing structures, including utility appurtenances and street pavements (Art. 25-4).
    c. General layout for construction—base lines, offsets, and bench marks (Art. 25-5).

3. *Possession Survey.* Made after the building is completed.

25-1. Units of Measurement. In land surveying, both horizontal and vertical distances are measured in feet and decimals of a foot. In building construction, however, horizontal distances are given in feet and inches, while as a rule, elevations are noted in feet and decimals of a foot. Conversion is easily made by remembering that there are 96 eighth inches in 1 ft, or ⅛ in. equals 0.01 ft (more accurately 0.0104) and 1 in. equals 0.0833 ft.

25-2. Survey of General Topography. For a preliminary survey, property lines can be established by any competent person, provided the locality is properly monumented. In many cities and towns where monuments are not established, the local surveyor is the only one who has the knowledge of landmarks referred to in deeds for land in the vicinity. In such cases, it is always advisable to have the main corners of property staked out by a local licensed surveyor.

One or two bench marks are also required to establish the datum, or reference point for elevation.   It is a good policy when the excavation goes below ground-water level to call water level +100, so as to eliminate minus elevations.

The new survey should show any difference between the present standard and that used in the original survey.   Surveys will differ when a city has been monumented

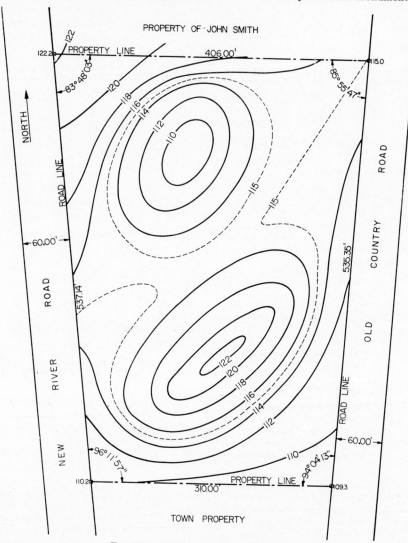

Fig. 25-1. Building site in open country.

long after the buildings are in place.   The differences should be noted so that the architect can make corrections before the new plans are started.   It is confusing to find too late that 100 ft in the deed is only 99.85 ft.

After property lines have been staked out, record with practical accuracy all pertinent information required to make detail drawings, such as slope of ground and location of any existing buildings or excavated areas.

In general, there are two types of site—open country and built-up city plots.   A map for the first would be similar to Fig. 25-1, showing contours, and a map for the second would be like Fig. 25-2 showing existing buildings. The contours can be drawn using either a cross-section grid system (Fig. 25-3) or the stadia method, laying off angles and distances (Fig. 25-4). The latter is perhaps a little quicker but probably

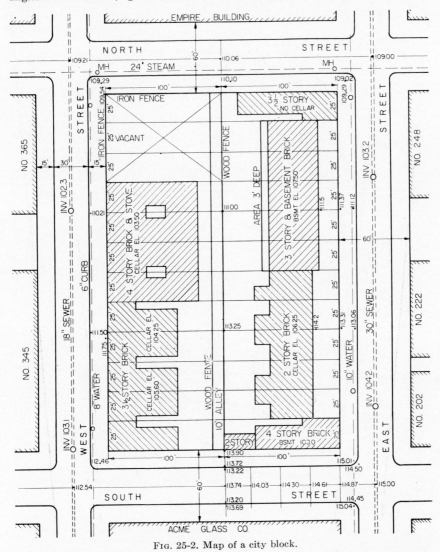

FIG. 25-2. Map of a city block.

less accurate. (Davis and Foote, "Surveying," 4th ed., McGraw-Hill Book Company, Inc., New York.)

The type of building to be constructed and its details will determine the frequency with which elevations and dimensions are required. Walls of existing buildings should be plumbed when on the property line.

For street curbs and pavements in this preliminary work, only the location, elevation, and condition are required.

Record sizes and condition of sewers, giving invert elevations at manholes. Other utilities can be arrived at from hydrants and other manhole covers.

Existing buildings on the site should be shown. The number of stories, kind of material, and whether there is a cellar or basement should be noted as in Fig. 25-2.

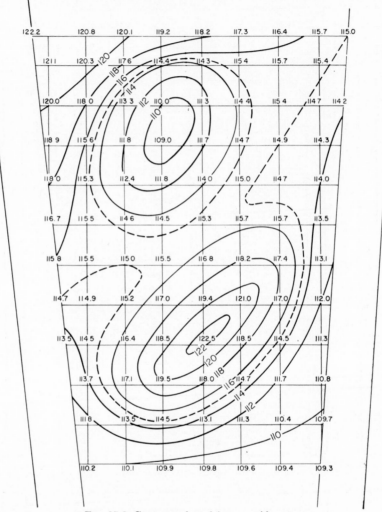

FIG. 25-3. Contours plotted from a grid system.

Unless the character of the soil on which the foundation is to rest is known, test holes or borings should be made (Sec. 4).

An estimate should be made of excavation quantities. This involves plotting cross sections from elevations obtained from a survey and grading for the new building. Volumes can be figured by either the end-area formula [Eq. (25-1)] or the prismoidal formula [Eq. (25-2)].

$$V = \tfrac{1}{2}L(A_1 + A_2) \tag{25-1}$$
$$V = \tfrac{1}{6}L(A_1 + 4A_m + A_2) \tag{25-2}$$

where V is the volume in cubic feet of a prismoid with end bases or cross sections having areas in square feet A_1 and A_2 and a mid-section of A_m and with a length in feet of L.

25-3. Survey of Nearby Buildings. It is always possible that adjacent buildings might be damaged by construction operations for a new building. So an examination,

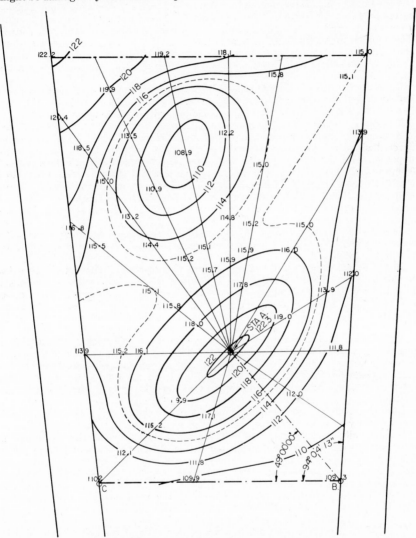

FIG. 25-4. Stadia method of plotting contours.

both inside and out, of all buildings close enough to the new construction to be affected should be made. The survey should be carried out, prior to start of construction, by a party representing the architect, contractor, and owners of the building to be inspected.

The record of this survey should be made accurately and in detail, to be available for comparison, if needed, to prove or disprove any change in appearance. The exterior can be examined, where beyond range of unaided vision, with high-powered field glasses. Record all defects or irregularities of masonry, which if noted later could be contributed to construction of the new building. It is a good policy to mention all sides where exposed, whether defective or not. If various elements of existing structures are in good condition, just state no comment.

For example, the record of an examination could read as follows: "Empire Building on the north side of North St.—South elevation, granite watertable requires pointing, no cracks in stone, a few spalls at corners; limestone above to 3rd floor, no comment. The entablature at 3rd floor has a large crack, starting at the top of the 5th column from the west corner of the building and extending diagonally upward through the architrave and frieze to the cornice; open at the top about the thickness of a mortar joint. Above the 3rd floor . . . "

The interior inspection should cover all rooms from the lowest floor to the roof. Cracks developing from settlement will generally carry from floor to floor. If a crack in a wall does not appear in rooms above and below it, it is safe to say that it did not come from settlement of the foundation.

In describing rooms, describe floor, walls, and ceiling. Thus: "Room 203—Floor covered with asphalt tile. South wall has a diagonal crack in plaster, starting in the upper left hand corner and running down to a point one foot above the floor and 3 ft from the right corner. Starts as $\frac{1}{32}$ in. closing to zero. East wall has one vertical crack in center, extending from floor to ceiling, open $\frac{1}{16}$ in. for full height. North wall—no comment. West wall has some hairline crazing near ceiling. Ceiling is acoustical gypsum tile, two pieces missing. Door to room binds at top on the lock side. Door trim split at top on the hinge side . . . "

Sewers and pavement should be examined by the architect, contractor, and a city representative. As with the building survey, photographs contribute an important part of the record.

25-4. Establishment of Elevations Before Construction. The examination described in Art. 25-3 must be supported by readings of elevations at the foundations of the various buildings to determine any settlement or lateral movement. The number and type of such reference marks will be controlled by the kind of new foundation. In general, reference points should be located and recorded in such a way that settlement or horizontal motion can be detected.

A reference grid can be laid out on street pavements and sidewalks. (Spikes driven into the pavement will aid in making future readings.) The water table, window sills, or mortar joints on existing buildings can be used as reference points to observe settlement. These have an advantage over marks placed on walls at some convenient arbitrary elevation, inasmuch as readings on them will show up any irregular previous settlement.

Establish levels inside the buildings too, if they are close to the excavation. Readings on utility castings, hydrants, valve boxes, etc., will tie in subsurface pipelines.

It is generally accepted that most buildings settle during construction as the loading increases; but it also must be remembered that settlement continues for many years. If any of the adjacent buildings are comparatively new, then differential settlement would have to be watched for. After work starts, keep a record of readings taken at regular intervals. Let the readings give warning; do not wait for cracks to appear.

25-5. General Layout for Construction. This differs, in general, for private dwellings, low industrial buildings, and large commercial buildings. However, they all require building lines at the start.

Since it is not practical to work to a mason line without the risk of disturbing it, offset lines are used. Distances to control points—building corners, wall faces, footings, etc.—are measured from these lines. The simplest layout (Fig. 25-5) requires principally setting batter or corner boards nailed to posts or other supports. They should be long enough to enable the building and offset lines to be marked, and the top should be set to a known elevation, such as level of the first floor. The posts should be driven first and grade nails set so as to determine the elevation of the boards before the lines are marked. A piece of shiplap, laid with the tongue projecting up, is generally used for the board. The step in the shiplap top is set at the desired elevation, and a saw cut the depth of the tongue allows a string to rest on the step at the correct level.

Layouts for low industrial buildings follow the same pattern, except that the corner boards are farther apart, and additional intermediate batter boards are needed. The position of the batter boards will vary with the depth and method used in excavation.

The layout for large commercial buildings, although basically the same, has to be expanded. Offset lines have to be established with the accuracy of a base line and will be called base lines for identification in the following discussion.

Temperature correction for tape measurements is very important for layouts of large buildings; so it is necessary to have a standardized tape, which is kept in the field office and is used for this kind of work only. (The temperature at which any tape is standard can be found by comparison with a standard tape. For this purpose, the tape may be sent to the National Bureau of Standards, Washington, D.C.) A 100-ft steel tape will change $\frac{3}{4}$ in. when the temperature changes 100°F.

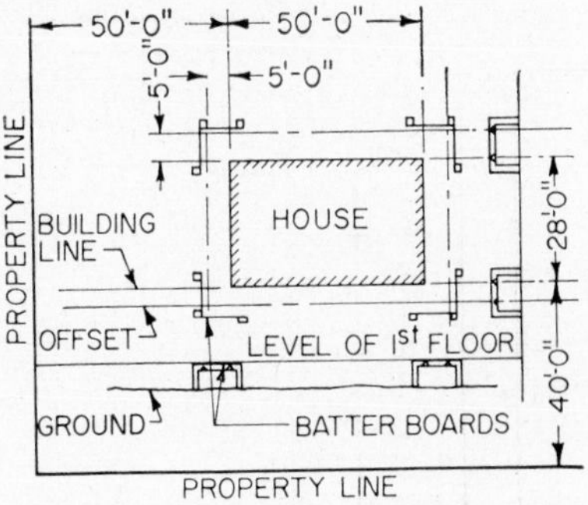

Work that requires extreme accuracy should be done on a cloudy day, in the early morning or evening. It is very difficult to determine the temperature of a steel tape in the sun. One expedient is to measure two lines, each 100 ft long—one that will remain in the sun and the other in the shade all day,

Fig. 25-5. Offset line for building layout determined with batter boards.

where they will be readily accessible for checking a tape at any time. This will automatically give the correction to be applied to tape measurements.

Figure 25-6 shows a typical layout of main reference lines. The offset traverse or base line, which is wholly outside the building site, can vary in distance from the building line, but 6 ft is good because the line will clear the conventional swing scaffold. The sidewalk bridge, which is necessary for protection, prevents sighting above it, unless the transit is set up outside the curb line at either end. The base line, therefore, must be produced well beyond the limits of the sidewalk bridge so as to be of use above it.

After the base line is finished and checked, all points of use in layout should be projected to a permanent location on nearby existing buildings. Control points for base lines can in many cases be obtained by sighting on some architectural ornamentation a short distance away. Those for the inside building-line offset and column offset lines should be located as high as possible, so as to be seen from the bottom of the excavation. The roof cornice in Fig. 25-7 is ideal. Targets at such locations can be used to establish column lines by "bucking in" or double centering between control points on opposite sides.

The inside building line is useful in aligning foundation walls after the general excavation is completed. Placing removable windows in the sidewalk fence, which is part of the sidewalk bridge, permits transit lines to be dropped into the excavation.

The center lines of columns can be marked on batter boards set with the top a given number of feet above subgrade, footings, or pile caps. If piles are used, they can be staked out with a tape by measuring from the center lines. Before columns are set, transit lines can be run on the center lines, but after they are in place, the offset lines have to be used.

There is a certain satisfaction in being able to sight directly on the line to be used. As soon as some concrete is placed, get a permanent bench mark set in it. In a steel-frame building, an anchor bolt may be used; if not, set a special rod for this purpose.

When all the walls and columns are in place to ground level, set at least two bench marks some distance apart, preferably at each end of the building where they can be used to make vertical measurements as the building rises. Stair wells or elevator shafts are good locations for these control points.

Most mechanics work from a level mark 4 ft above each finished floor.   Therefore, such marks should be placed on each column, or about 25 ft apart, in every story. They must be tied in accurately between floors, which is the reason for the vertical base lines.   Two marks must be seen from the same level setup before the 4-ft marks

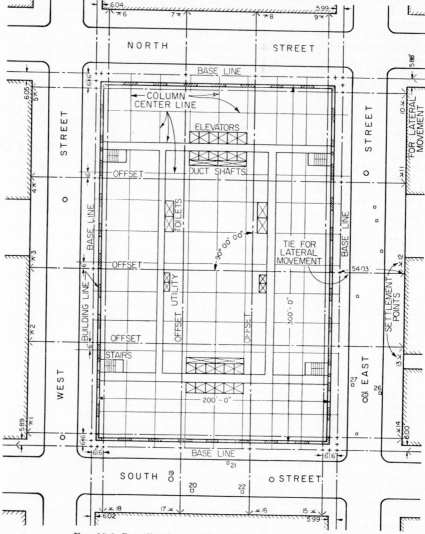

FIG. 25-6. Base-line layout for a large commercial building.

are established on the columns.   With an extension-leg tripod, set the horizontal hair of the level directly on the taped 4-ft marks.   On the original run do not set above or below the mark and read a rule.   Between setting the rule and reading the backsight, and reading the rule to set the foresight, errors can be made, especially when about ½ in. from it.   If the rule is turned the wrong way, the error will be twice the amount of the reading.

Since the building starts to settle shortly after loading, do not try to check with an outside bench mark. Hold and watch the original vertical base lines, and from time to time take a quick check on the preestablished 4-ft marks on the lower floors to spot a differential settlement. If there is any, set the 4-ft marks on the upper floors so that, when a particular column that is slow or fast in settling catches up, all the marks will be level. In some factory buildings, settlement effects are unimportant, but when the interior finish is marble, trouble may be encountered if settlement is not taken care of in advance.

Extreme care must be used in setting columns around elevator shafts. Check independently with a heavy plumb bob. (It can consist merely of a 4-in. pipe, 8 in. long, filled with lead and suspended by piano wire.) Swinging can be reduced by suspending the bob in a pail of oil. If the columns are not plumb, it may be necessary to decrease the size of the elevator cab so as to be able to install the guide rails plumb.

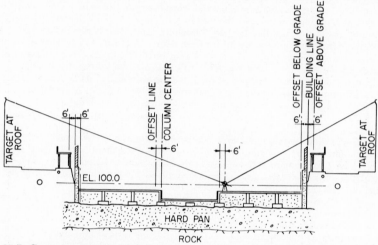

Fig. 25-7. Control points for base line are set high upon an existing building to permit sighting by an instrument in the excavation.

As the building rises above ground level, the exterior base line is the most important control line. The interior column offset lines, when used, must always be checked with the building line.

Accuracy of alignment of a steel-framed building stems from the anchor bolts and billets. It is important to have all horizontal measurements correct so that the lower section will go together without difficulty. Each tier of framing above depends on the accuracy of shop fabrication.

The elevation of the column base plates controls for the full height of the building; so it is obvious that extreme care must be used in setting them. If this is done, column splices, as a rule, will be as close to the true elevation as if established with a tape. This is very important so that the beams and girders will be in the correct vertical location. Clearances for mechanical work also could be affected by variation from the true location.

As columns are loaded, a shortening takes place. So vertical measurements must be made and tied in before this happens. Any total over-all measuring done after loading will have to be corrected by calculated deformations based on the modulus of elasticity of the column material.

Fireproofing and the rough floor are located with respect to the steel. This is done because it is not practical to use an instrument on the frame until it is braced by some kind of deck, whether concrete or steel.

The frame is plumbed by the steel erector with a heavy bob and checked by the engineer using the base line produced beyond the sidewalk bridge. When the temperature in the field differs from that of the fabrication shop, the frame will be longer or shorter, an effect to be considered when checking.   (Shop temperature is always a little above tape standard.)

After the structural floors are in place, the center line is marked on each exterior column in each story for the mason and other trades to work from.   This also is done from the base-line extension.

A straight piece of 1 × 1-in. white pine, about 8 ft long, should be used for an offset rod, with a 6-in. piece fastened to the end, forming a tee.   Two nails are driven into the head of the tee to sight on.   The transit man will know the rod is at right angles to his line when the nails line up.

The column marks should be set accurately, but the mechanic building the walls should be instructed to set his masonry line ¼ in. inside the finish line.   This is advisable to compensate for the slight variations usually found in masonry work.

The column offset lines can be plumbed from the opposite side of the street to the floor edge at both ends or sides of the building.   The lines can be carried through the building by setting up on the floor and "bucking in" between the end marks.

A concrete frame requires a layout for each floor.   A temporary level mark to work from is put on a column splice rod 1 ft above the finish floor.   Exterior column centers are set from the base line.   Intermediate columns may be located by taping.

After column forms are stripped, 4-ft marks are established as is done with a steel frame.   Column centers for masonry also are established as for a steel frame.   The mason uses the 4-ft marks to determine window head and sill heights.

A competent mason foreman checks to the level mark on the floor above before he gets there.

25-6. Surveying Instruments and Their Adjustments.   For construction work, the instruments with the minimum number of parts will generally hold their accuracy longer.   The transit should have standards high enough to permit a 360° vertical swing of the telescope with a prism eyepiece in place.   A dumpy level has proved itself throughout the years.

It is only necessary to check adjustments of the parts that affect the kind of work the instrument is to be used for.   (Davis and Foote, "Surveying," 4th ed., McGraw-Hill Book Company, Inc., New York.)

25-7. Transit Adjustments.   Prime parts requiring adjustment include:

Plate level.   Important for all work.

Cross hairs.   Horizontal, for leveling and reading vertical angles.   Vertical, useful in plunging telescope to extend a line.

Standards.   For plumbing and horizontal angles between points of different elevations.

Telescope bubble.   Need when using transit as a level.

Vertical circle.   For measuring vertical angles.

To make each bubble perpendicular to the plate spindle: Position plate bubbles parallel to two diagonally opposite leveling screws and level both.   Turn the plate on the spindle 180° until bubbles are reversed end for end.   Bring bubbles halfway back with capstan screws at end of bubble tubes.   Repeat for check.

Cross hairs.   Horizontal.   Set two stakes in line about 200 ft apart.   Set the transit in line and behind one as close as possible and yet be able to focus on it.   Sight the telescope about parallel with the ground and clamp.   Read the rod when set on both stakes.   Turn the plate 180°, plunge, and with the telescope inverted, set it to the reading on the far rod.   Check the reading on the near rod.   If different, move the cross-hair ring to one-half the difference.   Repeat for check.

Cross hairs.   Vertical.   Set up the transit and take a backsight on a point about 200 ft away.   Plunge the telescope and establish point No. 1 about 200 ft away in the opposite direction.   With telescope inverted, turn the plate 180° and sight again on the backsight point.   Plunge the telescope and establish point No. 2.   If it is different from No. 1, correct the vertical hair by bringing the cross-hair ring back one quarter of the distance between No. 2 and No. 1.   Repeat for check.

Standards.   Set up and level the transit.   Sight at a high point so that the telescope is over 60° with the horizontal.   Depress the telescope and mark point No. 1 on the ground 15 ft away. Plunge the telescope and turn the plate 180°. Sight again on the high point with the telescope inverted. Then, depress the telescope again and mark point No. 2. If different from No. 1, sight on a point halfway between No. 2 and No. 1. Raise the telescope. The sight will not strike the original high point. Make it strike the point by raising or lowering the adjustment screw on the standard.

Telescope bubble. Use peg adjustment, description of which follows adjustment of the dumpy level (Art. 25-9).

Vertical circle. After the telescope bubble has been adjusted, shift the vernier to zero.

25-8. Wye-level Adjustments. Important parts requiring adjustment include:

Cross hairs. Important for all work.

Bubble tube. Important for all work.

Wyes. Required only to save leveling for each sight.

Cross hairs. Set up the level and sight the cross hairs on a point about 200 ft away. Loosen the telescope clips and rotate the telescope on the horizontal axis 180°. If the hairs now are off the point, move the cross-hair ring back one-half the distance from the start of rotation.

Bubble tube. Level up and clamp the horizontal rotation with the bubble over two diagonally opposite leveling screws. Loosen the telescope clips, remove the telescope from the wyes, and replace it end for end. If the bubble is off center, bring it halfway back with the adjusting screws at the end of the bubble tube. If the axis of the bubble tube is not in the same plane as the axis of the wyes, it can be checked by rotating the telescope in the wyes about 15° each way from the vertical. If required, correct with the screws on each side of the level holder.

Wyes. Level the instrument. Turn 180° from either set of diagonally opposite screws. If required, bring the bubble halfway back with the adjusting nuts at the ends of the level bar.

25-9. Dumpy-level Adjustments. Major parts requiring adjustment include:

Bubble tube. Important for all work.

Cross hairs. Important for all work.

Bubble tube. Level the instrument. Turn 180° from either set of diagonally opposite screws. If required, bring the bubble halfway back with the adjusting screws at the end of the level tube.

Cross hairs. Use the peg adjustment:

Peg adjustment. This is the simplest system without calculations. With either transit or level, establish two level marks about 300 ft apart by setting up exactly halfway between them on a fairly level street. Next, set the instrument close to one mark so that the cross hair is exactly on it.

For a transit—Sight the telescope on the second mark, and if necessary correct the bubble tube.

For a dumpy level—With the instrument level, move the cross hairs to hit second mark, if required.

For a wye level—If adjustments for cross hairs, bubble tube, and wyes have been made, this direct adjustment is only used as a check against wear of the telescope collars. If necessary, adjust the bubble as with a transit.

(Davis and Foote, "Surveying," 4th ed., McGraw-Hill Book Company, Inc., New York.)

Section 26

ESTIMATING BUILDING CONSTRUCTION COSTS

M. DE LA TORRE

Consulting Engineer
Miami, Fla.

In recent years, estimating is being given its proper place in the over-all structure of construction companies. Management has realized that the construction-cost estimate is not merely a tabulation of figures, but a complex structure into which a great deal of engineering analysis has been applied. It is common practice for the cost-accounting structure to parallel the estimate, the reason being that only in this way can any advantages be gained for future estimating. Cost distribution for each project points out those unit costs that were used in the estimate that could not be met during construction.

The modern type of estimate is a coordinated structure capable of answering pertinent questions concerning the prosecution of the work. For example, from the estimate, you should be able to obtain:

1. List of equipment required to do the work.
2. Number of units required at any specific time during the life of the project.
3. List of crafts needed.
4. Number and classification of men required at any specific time during the project.
5. List of total requirements, by kind, of material needed for the execution of the project.
6. Detail of the manpower, equipment, and materials needed for the execution of any unit of work, plus the scheduled time required for the completion of each item of work, including the proposed starting and completion dates.

This is not confusing job analysis with estimating. These two functions are integral parts of a whole that cannot and should not be separated.

26-1. Rough Estimate with Unit Costs. For very rough estimating, cost of constructing a building can be approximated by multiplying a unit cost by the number of units in the proposed building. While only by chance will this method yield accurate costs, some types of units may yield truer costs than other units for a particular type of building. For example, for a school, the unit may well be number of pupils or classrooms; for a hotel, number of rooms; for a hospital, number of beds. In general, the square feet of floor area is an appropriate unit.

For example, a school with 30 classrooms, to be constructed in a community where schools are averaging $20,000 per classroom, may be expected to cost 30 × $20,000, or $600,000. A factory with 100,000 sq ft of floor area, similar to a type that averages $12 per square foot, may be estimated at $1,200,000. And a church with 100,000 cu ft of space, of a type of construction that may average $1.50 per cu ft, may cost $150,000. Table 26-1 gives unit costs reported in 1957 for various types of buildings.

Such costs should never be used as a basis for a bid or a proposal, but they can be used to determine the approximate requirements for financing, and for answering the requests of clients who require a figure for study of the economic advisability of a project.   Generally, these figures are sufficiently accurate for discussions within the board of directors of a company for the purpose of determining, in general, whether the company should consider making an investment.

Table 26-1. Building Costs, April, 1957*

Type of building	Cost, dollars per sq ft			Cost, dollars per cu ft		
	Low	Avg	High	Low	Avg	High
Lofts......................	7	8	13	0.65	0.70	1.05
Warehouses.................	7	11	18	0.30	0.70	1.35
Factories..................	6	13	22	0.30	0.75	1.55
Garages....................	7	12	18	0.75	0.85	1.85
Publishing.................	8	14	17	0.65	0.95	1.15
Apartments.................	8	11	13	0.85	1.10	1.50
Public Schools.............	14	21	27	1.05	1.15	1.20
Private Schools............	13	23	33	0.90	1.90	3.10
Retail Stores..............	12	17	31	0.70	1.25	2.20
Breweries and distilleries.......	17	24	28	1.05	1.40	1.75
Packing Houses.............	12	17	22	0.85	1.50	2.10
Athletic buildings.............	22	25	28	1.15	1.60	1.95
Laboratories...............	17	24	33	1.40	1.65	2.75
Office Buildings............	14	27	43	1.25	2.10	2.95
Hotels and Clubs...........	17	26	37	1.50	2.10	2.70
Hospitals..................	21	26	34	1.70	2.10	2.90
Boiler Houses..............	43	67	89	2.05	2.70	2.80
Banks.....................	27	44	58	2.00	3.10	3.65

*Compiled from costs developed by Turner Construction Co. and reported in *Engineering News-Record*, October 24, 1957, p. 79.

When only outdated unit costs are available, as is sometimes the case they can be modified to approximate current costs by multiplying by a factor obtained from a reliable cost index, such as the *Engineering News-Record* Building Cost Index.   The updating factors are derived by dividing the current value of the cost index by those values of the index corresponding to the dates of the available unit costs.   For example, if the average cost of a factory was $10 per sq ft in 1957, when the ENR Building Cost Index was 500, the unit cost of the factory at a time when the index registers 600 would approximate $\frac{600}{500} \times 10 = \$12.00$ per sq ft.

To apply the square-foot and cubic-foot costs in Table 26-1, it is necessary to arrive first at a net floor area or volume of the proposed structure.   Usually, when a rough estimate is to be made, only the general layout will be available.   In that case, it will be sufficiently accurate to compute the approximate net area or volume of the structure by taking the inside dimensions of the layout.   If no layout is available, it should be possible to determine the estimated area requirements for the proposed project, and from this figure, the approximate net area or volume can be obtained.

26-2. Preliminary Estimates.   The description of the work, furnished to the engineer who is to make a preliminary estimate, can vary between a general description of what is required and a set of final plans.   It might seem incongruous, at this point, that when final plans are available only a preliminary estimate is desired.   Nevertheless, there are times when this is true, and therefore, the estimate must be prepared in accordance with the request.

Preliminary estimates generally are based on unit costs obtained from past experience.   Following the principle of consistent accuracy, and if only approximate unit costs are to be used, the take-off should be on an area or volume basis (Art. 26-1).   For this purpose, the use of outside dimensions of the structures contemplated are sufficiently accurate.   The result of this take-off should be tabulated so that it can be entered into a form such as shown in Table 26-2.

After the form has been completed, the total arrived at will be the estimated direct cost. A percentage of the direct cost must be added to the total to make provision for indirect costs, such as administrative and management overhead and profit. The factors that determine the percentage to be used depend on the types and location of the structures, the basic company overhead, and the company policy on profit.

Table 26-2. Form for Preliminary Estimate

Item description	Unit	Quantity		Unit cost	Direct cost
		Gross	Net		

In using preliminary estimates, it should be remembered that the cost figures on which they are based are the result of cost-accounting procedures by which capital investment has been depreciated in accordance with the length of time equipment is used on a particular job.   Therefore, these costs do not reflect the total capital investment required for the construction plant needed for the execution of the work.

26-3. Intermediate Estimates.   These are prepared to obtain more accurate costs than with the methods in Arts. 26-1 and 26-2.   Nevertheless, intermediate estimates should not be used for commitment purposes, since they are only a refinement of preliminary estimates.   Generally, they are made prior to the detailing of the working drawings and specifications for a project.

The take-off for an intermediate estimate should be consistent with the amount of engineering design completed and details available.   The approximate take-off should be by type of work, such as preparation of site, excavation, foundations, drainage structures, masonry, structural steel, concrete, rough carpentry, finished carpentry, plumbing, electrical, roofing, and air conditioning.   A final estimate goes into greater detail; it would include items of work such as clearing and grubbing, stumping and stripping under "preparation of site"; common, hardpan, and rock excavation and trenching under "excavation"; etc.

For intermediate estimates, the form in Table 26-3 should be used.

Table 26-3. Form for Intermediate Estimates

Type of work	Unit	Quantity	Unit cost	Direct cost	Estimated cost	
					Labor	Materials

The sum of the direct-cost column will give the total estimated direct cost.   A percentage of this cost must be added for office supervision, administrative and management overhead, and profit.   This percentage is determined as described in Art. 26-2.

The advantage of an intermediate estimate is that, within a consistent accuracy, the approximate breakdown of the direct costs into labor and materials can be made by percentages derived from averages computed from previous work.

This breakdown makes it possible to estimate payroll requirements and volume of procurement.

Intermediate estimates also serve as an excellent general check when the details of the final estimate are worked out.

26-4. Final Estimates.   Final direct-cost estimates can be made only when the scope of the work is determined by firm design, final working plans, and complete specifications.   Usually, at this point, it is necessary to arrive at an accurate estimated cost for the proposed work, on which a commitment for its execution can be made.

The estimate should be prepared in such form that it will be easy to determine from it facts that are necessary for proper administration and management of construction. A final estimate prepared by this method gives the required cost analysis and determines the structure of the cost-accounting procedure to be used.   It can also serve as a very efficient tool for proper construction management.   The method of estimating presented in this article eliminates the inherent shortcomings of estimating by the unit-cost method.   In preparing the final estimate, the scope of the work is broken down into labor, materials, and equipment requirements, and to these factors, the costs for labor, materials, and equipment operation are applied.   These costs can be obtained and can be considered as constant for a given locality and period of time.

The quantity take-off for the final estimate may be considered the most important part of estimating.   It must be done with the greatest of care.   To make sure that no item of work, or part of any item of work, has been forgotten, it is good practice to establish a rigid control of the take-off.   Check marks should be placed on each sheet of the final plans as the take-off is made, and the results should be tabulated on a form where the items of work have already been printed.   This list of items of work should be carefully checked periodically, to insure that it contains all the possible items that may be encountered in the type of project being estimated.   In order for this list not to be too cumbersome, separate forms should be available for various kinds of work.

The mechanics of the take-off should follow a procedure in which all dimensions that determine the items of work are taken off each drawing and tabulated on work sheets (where all the computations should be shown) so that the quantity of each item of work that is shown in each drawing can be computed.   These work sheets should show, in their upper part, the estimate number, the drawing number, the date of the last revision, description of the project, and the signature of the man who is making the take-off.

The advantage of this method is that, if a take-off is required in a short period of time, a number of men can be assigned, the various drawings being distributed among them.   Under this system, each man can check the completeness of his take-off by inspection of the check marks made on the drawings.

The result of the computations on the work sheets should be assembled into the printed form detailing the items of work.   The result of this tabulation should be a complete take-off.   Provisions should be made at the head of the printed form for the estimate number, date, description of the project, date bid is due, and the signature of the man doing the work.

At this point, a second check should be made on the completeness of the work by referring back to the drawings to make sure that those listed items of work for which no quantities are shown are actually not detailed in the drawings or are not required.

The results of the analysis should be recorded on a printed form similar to the one in Table 26-4.   The analysis is carried out in five steps: (1) derivation of working-unit criteria, (2) determination of time required for each item of work, (3) calculation of labor requirements, (4) computation of equipment requirements, and (5) determination of materials required.

It can be clearly seen that, if the actual execution of the work parallels the criteria developed under "Job Analysis" (Table 26-4), the estimate will be a true forecast of the actual cost.   In contrast, use of unit costs for pricing proposed work can be misleading because a composite or derived unit cost never reflects the actual conditions that will be encountered on a new job.   Also, the breakdown of an estimate, made by the use of derived unit costs into labor, materials and equipment operation costs, by the use of percentages, is dangerous because a small mistake in the determination of the percentage factor will be multiplied many times in the final figures.

The first step of the analysis—determination of "working units"—is probably the most important phase of estimating.   The working-unit criteria determine for each item the amount of work under job conditions that it is possible to do with a given

Table 26-4. Job-analysis Form

Form E-4

John Doe & Co.

Page _____ of _____

Project _____

Computed by _____ Checked by _____

Date _____

Estimate No. _____

Step 1.   Working-unit criteria:

Item of work—Clearing and grubbing.   A group of three D-8 Cat. tractors or equal with bulldozer, treedozers, and Hyster winches complimented by a 5-man gang will clear and grub 7 acres per 8-hr day.

Step 2.   Derivation of time required:

Subitem	Total quantity	Production of working unit	Total No. days	Total No. hr
(1)	(2)	(3)	(4)	(5)
Clearing and grubbing..........	2,000 acres	7	285	2,280

Step 3.   Labor required:

Classification	No. of men in working unit	Total No. days	Total No. man-days	Unit cost, Col. (15), Table 26-7	Total cost, Col. (4) × Col. (5)
(1)	(2)	(3)	(4)	(5)	(6)
Foreman.................	1	285	285	$33.84	$9,644.40
Labor....................	5	285	1,425		
Heavy-equipment operators.	3	285	755		

Step 4.   Equipment required:

Equipment list	No. of units per working unit	Total No. hr	Total No. equipment hr	Unit cost, Col. (15), Table 26-8	Total cost, Col. (4) × Col. (5)
(1)	(2)	(3)	(4)	(5)	(6)
Cat. D-8 track tractors.....	3	2,280	6,840	$15.433	$105,561.72
Bulldozer and treedozer attachments..............	3	2,280	6,840		
Hyster winches...........	3	2,280	6,840		
Singledrum P. control units	3	2,280	6,840		

Step. 5.   Materials required:

Material list	Required by working unit	Factor	Total quantity required	Unit cost, Col (11), Table 26-9	Total cost, Col. (4) × Col. (5)
(1)	(2)	(3)	(4)	(5)	(6)
Axes, units.................	3	3	9		
1-in. steel wire rope, ft........	300	3	900		
Gloves, pairs.................	5	9	45		

group of men, materials, and equipment. They should be derived from extensive experience and should be modified, after the completion of each project, to take advantage of the refinements in construction methods that might have been developed during the execution of the work.

There is an optimum grouping of a specific number of men, units of equipment, and quantities of material that will efficiently and economically produce a certain amount of work. Working units should be based on such groupings. Let us take, for example, the clearing and grubbing of a site for a large industrial plant. An efficient and economical working unit might be a group of three track-type 120-hp tractors, with bulldozer, treedozer, and winch attachments, plus 5 men with hand tools. This working unit will clear and grub in an 8-hr day 7 acres of flat dry terrain covered with heavy underbrush and medium-sized trees.

Because of the importance of determining the working units, the thinking of the most experienced and qualified man in the organization should be used. It is well to remember that the job analysis on the basis of "working units" is the core of the estimating structure, and that any deficiency or error will be multiplied many times in its application to the full scope of the work.

The job analysis should be the result of intensive research and should be made only after careful study of the proposed site of the work and all the features of the project. After the "working unit" analysis has been made by the most competent men available, the completion of the estimate is a matter of extensions and therefore can be performed by clerical help.

The working-unit determination defines the production per unit of time that can be obtained with an ideal grouping of manpower, equipment, and materials for each item of work. In the second step of the job analysis, the production of this ideal grouping is divided into the total quantities of each item to obtain the number of work periods required to complete each item. If production, for example, is based on a 8-hr day, the resulting number of periods will be in 8-hr days, while if working unit output is based on hourly production, then the answer will be in hours required for completion. Both periods of time, hours and days, are required for the extension of the final estimate.

The last step in the job analysis is the determination of labor, equipment, and materials required for the execution of each item of work.

To determine labor requirements (step 3) list the actual number of men required to operate the group setup established under "working unit" criteria by number and classification. Multiply the number of men by the number of days arrived at previously. The result will be the total number of man-days required to do the item of work.

To compute equipment requirements (step 4), itemize the number and types of equipment required, in accordance with the "working unit" criteria. Multiply the number of equipment units by the number of hours derived previously.

To obtain materials requirements (step 5), list the quantity and class of materials required for the operation of the "working unit" and by analysis of the nature of the material and its end use (permanent installation or use only during construction) determine the factor to be used in arriving at the total quantity required for the execution of the item of work.

Columns (5) and (6) of Table 26-4 cannot be completed at this stage until the detailed analysis indicated in Tables 26-7 to 26-9 has been executed.

It is general practice for the owner to specify the approximate date of completion of the work. The contractor, therefore, establishes general project time schedules and determines the number of working periods to arrive at the rate at which construction must be executed to meet the requested completion date. Table 26-5 shows the form to be used for this purpose.

Column (1) of this form lists the items of work. Columns (2) and (3) give approximate starting and completion dates for each item as visualized by the builder and in accordance with total time limit. This determination, although important, does not require too great accuracy because minor changes in this scheduling will not affect the estimate. Column (4) is used to determine the number of calendar periods within the scheduled period.   Column (5) indicates calendar periods in relation to inclement weather and holidays.   The result of this analysis is the estimated number of productive calendar periods that are available for construction within the scheduled time limit.   Column (6) is derived from the calendar periods in column (5) by multiplying by the number of days in the work week.   Column (7) is obtained by multiplying the number of working days in column (6) by the daily production of one working unit as shown in the "job analysis" (Table 26-4).   Column (8) is a tabulation of the total quantities for each item of work.   Column (9) is the result of dividing the quantities in column (8) by the quantities in column (7) and gives the number of working units required to do all of the work during the scheduled period.

The second part of the project-schedules form is a bar chart (Fig. 26-1) detailing the coordinated item-of-work time schedules in relation to the over-all calendar period required for completion of the project.   In preparing this chart, great care must be taken in coordinating the sequence of construction operations for maximum use of manpower and equipment.

This bar chart can be used in conjunction with column (9), Table 26-5, and the detail in step 3 of the job analysis (Table 26-4) to determine the number of men required to perform the work.   These figures can be used to draw a manpower curve for the project.

The equipment list in column (1), Table 26-6, is a listing of the various types of equipment that appear in the first column, step 4, of the job analysis (Table 26-4). The number of units of equipment shown under "job analysis" should be multiplied by the number of groups needed as indicated in column (9), Table 26-5.   The product should be entered in the corresponding "Item-of-work" column.

The tabulations in this form indicate the number of units of equipment of each kind needed for each item of work.   A study of the schedule bar chart (Fig. 26-1), which shows which items of work are going to be done simultaneously and which will be completed prior to the starting date of other items, will determine the last column of Table 26-6.   This column represents the number of units of each type of equipment required for the execution of the project.

The labor list should be compiled by using a procedure similar to that used for arriving at the equipment list.   The second part of Table 26-6 is the form to be used for this purpose.

Determination of the unit costs of labor is effected by tabulation of all the pertinent costs of labor, as detailed in the form in Table 26-7.

Column (1), Table 26-7, is a list of the labor requirements by classification as derived in the job analysis [column (1), step 3, Table 26-4].   In column (2) are the base salaries or hourly wages.   Columns (3), (4), (5), etc., detail other payments to labor expressed in the same units as the base salaries.   The last column is the summation of items on each line for each classification and gives the total cost of labor per unit of time. These costs should be entered also in the job-analysis form in column (5), step 3 (Table 26-4).

Table 26-8 shows a form that can be used to derive hourly cost rates for equipment operation.   Column (1) is the equipment list by type of equipment as derived in the job analysis [column (1), step 4, Table 26-4].   Column (2) gives the cost of ownership, which includes the purchase price, insurance, taxes, and interest on the investment. This column must be divided by the life expectancy of the type of equipment, in hours, to arrive at the hourly cost of ownership, which is tabulated in column (3).   Columns (4), (5), (6), and (7) detail the lump-sum costs required to deliver a piece of equipment to the job site and to return it to the point of origin.

Line summation of columns (4), (5), (6), and (7) is tabulated in column (8), which represents the total cost of delivery and return of each item of equipment.   These costs divided by the estimated life of the project in hours, result in a rate per hour for these expenditures, which is tabulated in column (9).

Column (10) is the summation of columns (3) and (9) and represents the fixed charges, on an hourly basis, for each piece of equipment.

Columns (11), (12), (13), and (14) are the cost of operating services, expressed in dollars per hour of operation.   Line summation of column (10), (11), (12), (13), and

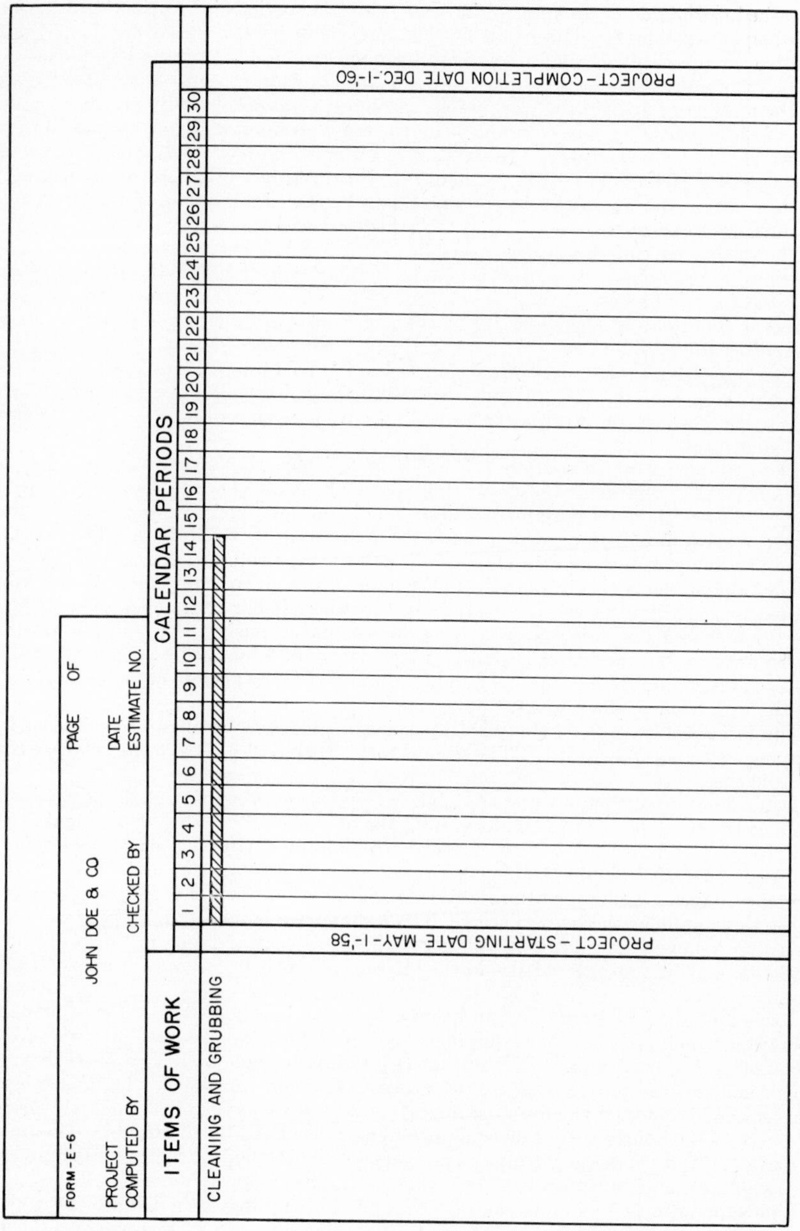

FIG. 26-1. Project time schedule.

Table 26-5. Project-schedules Form

Form E-5   Determination of working period

John Doe & Co.

Project _____   Date _____

Computed by _____ Checked by _____ Estimate No. _____

Items of work	Starting date	Completion date	No. of calendar periods	No. of productive calendar periods	No. of working days	Production of one working unit during No. of working days	Total quantity of work to be performed	No. of working units required
(1)	(2)	(3)	(4)	(5)	(6)	(7)	(8)	(9)
Clearing and grubbing....	May 1	Aug. 1	14 weeks	12, 2 lost due to rain and holidays	72	504	2,000	4

Table 26-6. Form for Determination of Equipment and Labor Requirements

Form E-7

John Doe & Co.

Project _____ Date _____

Computed by _____ Checked by _____ Estimate No. _____

Equipment list by type	Clearing and grubbing	Excavating										Total No. of units	Adjusted total No. of units required
(1)	(2)	(3)	(4)	(5)	(6)	(7)	(8)	(9)	(10)	(11)	(12)	(13)	(14)
No. of working units required from Col. (9), Table 26-5	4												
Tractors, Cat. D-8	12												
Bulldozer attachments	8												
Treedozer attachments	4												
Hyster winches	12												
Single-drum power-control units	12												

Items of work	Clearing and grubbing	Excavating											
Number of working units required from Col. (9), Table 26-5	4												
Labor list by classification	No. of men											Total No. of men	Adjusted total No. of men
Operators, tractor	12												
Labor foreman	4												
Common labor	20												

Table 26-7. Labor-cost Analysis

Form E-8

John Doe & Co.

Project ——————— Date ———————

Computed by ——————— Checked by ——————— Estimate No. ———————

Classification	Base salary or rate	Severance pay	Vacation pay	Social Security	Workman's compensation	Insurance	Profit sharing	Overtime	Portal pay	Holiday pay	Living allowance	Total salary or rate	No. work days included in salary or rate	Man-day unit cost
	(2)	(3)	(4)	(5)	(6)	(7)	(8)	(9)	(10)	(11)	(12)	(13)	(14)	(15)
(1)								1 hr per day	15 min each way	6 days per year				
Labor foreman...........	2.35	....	....	0.06	0.12	0.02	....	0.44	1.18	0.06	....	4.23	Hr, 8	33.84
Heavy-equipment operator...	2.65	....	....	0.07	0.13	0.02	....	0.66	1.33	0.07	....	4.93	Hr, 8	39.44
Common labor............	2.10	....	....	0.05	0.12	0.02	....	0.43	1.05	0.05	....	3.82	Hr, 8	30.56

Form E-9

John Doe & Co.

Project ——————————————————   Dave ——————————————————

Computed by ———————— Checked by ————————   Estimate No. ————————

Table 26-8. Equipment-operation-cost Analysis

Equipment list	Purchase price or book value	Hourly cost of ownership	Crating and shipping	Duty, wharfage, and loading	Delivery to job site	Return from job site to company yard	Total cost of delivery and return	Hourly cost for delivery and return	Fixed charge per hr	Fuel, oil, and greases per hr	Spare parts cost per hr	Shop operation charges per hr	Lubrication and refueling per hr	Total cost of operation per hr
(1)	(2)	(3)	(4)	(5)	(6)	(7)	(8)	(9)	(10)	(11)	(12)	(13)	(14)	(15)
D-8 Cat. tractors.........	$16,000	4.23	180.0	22.0	30.0	210.0	442.0	0.088	4.318	0.850	0.175	4.870	5.220	15.433
Bulldozer attachment.....														
Treedozer attachment.....														
Hyster winches...........														
Power-control units.......														

(14) is tabulated in column (15), which represents total cost of operating per hour. The values in column (15) also should be entered in the job-analysis form in column (5), step 4 (Table 26-4).

Table 26-9 shows a form that can be used for determination of the total cost of materials. Column (1) lists each class of material. Column (2) gives the unit of measure, and column (3) the total quantity required, as derived in step 5 of the job analysis (Table 26-4). Columns (4), (5), (6), (7), (8), and (9) detail costs that are required to deliver the total quantity of material needed to the site. Column (10) is the summation of line items and represents the total cost of materials required for the execution of the work. The unit costs in column (11) are obtained by dividing the costs in column (10) by the quantities in column (3). These values should also be entered in column (5), step 5, Table 26-4, to complete the job analysis.

The reason that total cost of materials was derived is that, in analyzing a job, total material requirements and costs are needed for setting up purchasing schedules and bulk procurement. Scheduling of material deliveries is made in accordance with the schedule bar chart (Fig. 26-1).

Table 26-10 shows a form that can be used for recapitulation of total direct costs.

Summation of columns (2), (3), and (4) gives the estimated total number of men required. This information is used to set up timekeeping and payroll functions.

Summation of columns (6), (7), and (8) gives the estimated total number of units of equipment required. This information is used to set up the equipment yard, spare parts warehouse, shop facilities, and maintenance requirements.

Summation of columns (10) and (11) gives the estimated tons of materials that are to be handled, inside or outside storage, and is used to set up the warehousing requirements.

Summation of columns (5), (9), and (12), shown in column (13), gives total estimated direct costs for the project. Figures given in those columns can also be used for determining unit costs for each item of work in case a unit-cost bid or proposal is required.

The total estimate for a project consists of direct and indirect costs. Direct costs are those that can be distributed into items of work by established cost-accounting methods based on the proper use and distribution of costs derived from time cards, daily equipment operation reports, shop orders, and warehouse issue slips. Indirect costs are those that cannot be distributed to items of work and are accumulated into lump sums that are added as one quantity to the direct cost, to obtain the total cost of the work.

Table 26-11 shows a form that can be used in arriving at overhead costs.

Column (1) details, items of overhead. On a large project, generally overhead items consist of engineering costs, including engineering and drafting, requisitioning, cost-accounting reports, field engineering, progress reports and charts, inspection of construction, scheduling and materials inspection for procurement; supply costs, consisting of purchasing, expediting, off-site transportation, central receiving, warehousing and inventory control; personnel costs, consisting of recruiting and hiring, safety program, hospital and first aid, housing and feeding (if required), and off-site personnel transportation; costs of labor relations, including arranging union agreements, handling of grievances and jurisdictional disputes, hearings, mediation and arbitration and dispute settlement; costs of accounting, including general accounting, subcontract accounting, equipment and property accounting, and finance reports; and costs of construction supervision, including planning and scheduling, construction control and assignment of work, operation of temporary facilities, and construction plant maintenance.

Expenses for management, supervisory, and administrative personnel are the greatest part of the cost of the overhead items, and therefore, personnel requirements must be thoroughly analyzed prior to posting costs in columns (2), (3), (4), and (5) of Table 26-11. A form similar to the one shown in Table 26-7 should be used in arriving at the unit and total cost for overhead personnel.

The other overhead costs detailed in Table 26-11 are generally derived from the records of past work and depend on methods to be used, type of management, and company policy.

Table 26-9. Materials-cost Analysis

Form E-10

John Doe & Co.

Project _____ Date _____

Computed by _____ Checked by _____ Estimate No. _____

Material list	Unit	Total re-quirements	Purchase price	Insurance, freight	Unloading	Delivery to yard or warehouse	Warehouse and yard charges	Delivery to work	Total cost	Unit cost
(1)	(2)	(3)	(4)	(5)	(6)	(7)	(8)	(9)	(10)	(11)
Axes............	doz									
Gloves..........	doz									
1-in. cable......	ft									

Table 26-10. Form for Determination of Total Labor and Equipment Costs

Form E-11

John Doe & Co.

Project _____ Date _____

Computed by _____ Checked by _____ Estimate No. _____

Items of work	Labor				Equipment operation				Materials			Total direct cost
	No. of men, supervision	No. of men, skilled	No. of men, common	Total cost	No. units, heavy	No. units, light	No. units, automotive	Total cost	Tons, outside storage	Tons, warehouse	Total cost	
(1)	(2)	(3)	(4)	(5)	(6)	(7)	(8)	(9)	(10)	(11)	(12)	(13)
Clearing and grubbing.......	4	12	20		12							

Table 26-11. Form for Determination of Overhead Cost

Form E-12

John Doe & Co.

Project _____ Date _____

Computed by _____ Checked by _____ Estimate No. _____

Items of overhead	Labor				Cost of equipment				Cost of supplies and services				Total overhead cost
	No. of men, management	No. of men, administration	No. of men, supervision	Total cost	Office	Shop	Field	Total cost	Office	Shop	Field	Total cost	
(1)	(2)	(3)	(4)	(5)	(6)	(7)	(8)	(9)	(10)	(11)	(12)	(13)	(14)
Engineering:													
Requisitioning........													
Cost accounting......													
Field layout.........													
Inspection..........													
Etc................													
Supply:													
Purchasing.........													
Warehousing.......													
Inventory control...													
Etc..............													

Section 27

CONSTRUCTION MANAGEMENT

Robert McLean

Executive Vice-president
Hegeman-Harris Company, Inc.
New York, N.Y.

27-1. General Contracting. A general contractor is an organized group of engineers and technicians with executive and supporting personnel who, by training and experience, are capable of interpreting building plans and specifications and of constructing buildings in accordance with the information contained in them.

Usually, contractors operate on a competitive basis. However, there are many instances when a contractor, through the years, has completely satisfied an owner and consequently is awarded repeat contracts without competition. This situation is not at all unusual in cost-plus-fixed-fee work, where an owner and his architect are convinced that the budget reflects an honest estimate of cost and they are satisfied with the services rendered by the contractor.

A general contractor usually does not erect a building only with his own forces. Most firms subcontract part of the work to specialty trades, such as plumbing, heating, electrical, etc.

27-2. Common Types of Bid Proposals. Bid proposals generally can be classified under four categories: (1) lump sum; (2) guaranteed upset price; (3) cost plus fixed fee; and (4) management contract. There are two or three other forms of submitting proposals, but by far the great bulk of construction comes under these categories.

27-3. Lump-sum Contracts. Under this form of contract, the plans and specifications are expected to be as complete as possible. Invitations to bid are sent to a list of contractors determined between the owner and architect.

The contractors then distribute copies of the plans and specifications to their own estimating departments and to subcontractors. A bid card requests each subcontractor to submit a bid and advises them of a due date, which generally allows 10 to 20 days for preparation of the bid, depending on the complexity of the work involved. It is customary to request bids from 5 to 7 subcontractors for each trade. Such sections of the work as may be executed by the general contractor himself are, of course, taken off and priced in his own office.

The various estimates or bids are then compiled and analyzed. Due consideration is given to the low bid in each case, and everything being equal, the low bid for each trade is used for the preparation of the contractor's final estimate and proposal. (A general contractor may sometimes modify a subcontractor's price in preparing his estimate if his past experience or special circumstances indicate this to be advisable. Such adjustments can subsequently be resolved in a meeting between the two parties.)

When all estimates have been thoroughly analyzed and specific bids chosen for the contractor's proposal, he then adds to this total amount his estimated costs for general conditions, an amount for contingencies, and his profit. This constitutes the contractor's bid proposal for the project and is customarily submitted to the architect by a specified date.

Under this form of contract, the owner, with the approval of the architect, pays to the successful general contractor the total amount of the bid proposal for the work rendered, assuming, of course, that the work has been properly executed. Payments for such projects are generally made on submission of a requisition to the architect at the end of each month. The architect must approve such requisitions before submission to the owner. These requisitions include that portion of the general contractor's own work and profit plus such portions of any subcontractor's work that would have been executed during that month. It is customary to withhold 10% of the payment each month from the total requisition. Payment is generally expected by the contractor by the fifteenth of the following month.

Additional work or extras beyond the scope of the drawings and specifications require additional estimates and corresponding increases in the original bid proposal.

27–4. Guaranteed-maximum-price Contracts. The same procedure is followed by a general contractor as outlined in Art. 27-3 for lump-sum contracts except that the contractor agrees to perform the contract for a fixed fee and guarantees that the work will not cost more than the prescribed budget, unless extras are required.

Under this type of proposal, the owner gains the benefit of savings if costs are less than the prescribed budget. However, in return for having guaranteed the total cost under a prearranged fixed fee, it is customary for the general contractor to participate in the savings at a percentage agreed between the parties at the time of negotiating the contract. Such participation may be 50-50, 40-60, 25-75, etc. Inasmuch as the fixed fee cannot be changed, this arrangement constitutes an inducement to the contractor to confine the ultimate cost, and the owner benefits accordingly.

27–5. Cost-plus-fixed-fee Contracts. This form of contract, if executed by a reputable contractor, is by far the most economical and most satisfactory procedure. In most cases, time is of the essence, and if an owner requires space quickly, a cost-plus-fixed-fee contract makes it possible to start a building with preliminary plans and thus save many months in time of completion.

General contractors who have made it their practice to operate under this form of contract can take a set of preliminary drawings and outline specifications and develop a working budget in close collaboration with the architect. This budget not only will represent the outside cost of a project but will also compete favorably with a lump-sum figure for the same project that could only be arrived at 6 to 8 months later when final drawings become available.

The services required for this type of budget are highly specialized. Therefore, cost-plus-fixed-fee contracts should be awarded only to contractors who understand them and have operated continuously under them. Under this form of contract, as under the guaranteed-upset-price contract (Art. 27-4), the fee is fixed so that the only incentive for the contractor is to confine the ultimate cost and gain a new client for the future.

Highly specialized personnel are required to service cost-plus-fixed-fee contracts. The responsibility of spending an owner's money efficiently and economically and recording the savings involved demands a greater degree of accuracy in purchasing and accounting. The books, of course, are always open to the inspection of the architect and owner, and all services on cost-plus-fixed-fee contracts are rendered with the close cooperation and approval of the architect and owner.

27–6. Management Contracts. Often, an owner wishing to have an important project constructed prefers to award the general contract to a local contractor but also wants the direct supervision of a nationally known contractor with a greater amount of experience in the particular type of work contemplated. This owner will consider, with a certain amount of justification, that the purchasing power of the larger contractor, together with greater influence in various manufacturing shops, would reflect favorably on the ultimate cost and time elements. Yet, for reasons of policy, he is desirous of engaging the local contractor.

The solution is to award a management contract to the more experienced firm. This form of contract has a lot of merit because it affords an owner the services of a well-establish concern at a nominal cost and, at the same time, permits him to advance the interests of local industry. Management and general supervision of the project are obtained under this contract for a lower fee than would be normal. Between the owner and consulting, or management, contractor, and with the collaboration of the architect, the actual construction work would be awarded to a local contractor, either under competitive bidding or for a negotiated fee.

The personnel and services supplied by the supervising contractor include a competent superintendent with adequate knowledge of inside and outside phases of a construction contract; preparation of budget with the local contractor; checking and approval of all subcontracts; preparation of monthly financial statements; approval of extras and changes; approval of requisitions for payment; inspection of work in the field; assistance in expediting and general liaison with owner and architect.

27-7. Co-venture Contracts. Co-venturing of general contractors permits an owner, whether a corporation or government agency, to award contracts covering work of unusually large scope instead of several smaller contracts. Not only are those co-ventured contracts backed up by the assets of two or more outstanding contractors, but they permit melding of contractors who specialize in different departments of the construction industry into one large organization for the project.

Generally, an executive committee is formed to direct the activities of the co-venture. This committee is composed of an officer of each of the companies involved, and they in turn determine the project personnel and procedures.

27-8. Contractor's Organization for a Project. A well-rounded construction company under a board of directors and executive officers consists of several departments: sales; estimating and purchasing; mechanical; construction; accounting and auditing; and special services and assignments.

The sales department has no active part in the execution of a contract. But the individual who is primarily responsible for obtaining a specific contract maintains frequent contacts with the owner and architect while the work is in progress.

Efficient estimating and purchasing are fundamental to the success of a general contractor. This department is generally under the administration of a company officer who has had long years of experience and has the aptitude of watching and checking labor and material markets.

Some of the well-established general contractors employ within their organizations a mechanical department, headed by competent mechanical engineers. This department is a must for those contractors who specialize in cost-plus-fixed-fee work (Art. 27-5) and are required to develop accurate budgets on preliminary information. Even with completed drawings, the value of an experienced mechanical department has been proved time and again. Careful studies of mechanical designs have produced variations or equal substitutions yielding large savings to an owner.

The construction department covers a wide field involving inside superintendents or project managers with their assistants and outside or field superintendents with their staff.

The project manager is a vital cog in the organization machinery. He is responsible for general liaison between the field and the architect and owner, preparation of monthly statements for comparison with the budget (see Art. 27-12), final check on monthly subcontractor requisitions, change orders and office correspondence pertaining to his projects. He must be available for all meetings. On occasion, and depending on the size and complexity of the work involved, a competent project manager, with an assistant, can efficiently service two contracts concurrently.

Many contractors locate the inside superintendent or project manager in the field office. This makes for a more unified control of the project and permits closer cooperation between the "inside" and the "outside" when the work is of sufficient proportions to require the full-time services of an "inside man."

The field superintendent is responsible for all activities on the site, starting with demolition, site engineering, etc., and continuing until the building is completed. Size of his staff depends on the size of the project, but generally, he will be aided by an assistant superintendent, one or more field engineers, one or more accountants and paymaster, foremen, watchmen, etc.

Among the more important functions of a field superintendent are checking field engineering, keeping close watch on time schedules, supervising all trades, checking quantity and quality of production, attending meetings with architect and owner, collaboration with architect's field representative, establishing sequence and coordination of operations, and manning the project.   He also must resolve disputes, supervise job meetings, keep daily job diaries, make insurance reports, check and approve subcontractors' requisitions, order material and equipment, and check equipment rentals. In addition, he must maintain contact with the expediting department, keep a constant check on requirements of plans and specifications, check cost records, and check and approve payrolls.   He is responsible for guarding against construction accidents. It can be seen that the field superintendent plays an extremely important part in the successful execution of any project, and therefore he deserve all the support that the organization can give him.

General accounting, auditing, billing of requisitions, etc., are done in the main office under the direction of the treasurer and controller of the company, who maintains close contact with both the inside and field superintendents on all company projects.

The field payroll and accounts are under the control of an accountant chosen by the company controller, and the procedure for job accounting is precisely the same on all jobs.   This establishes a pattern that readily facilitates the monthly recapitulation in the main office.

It is paramount that the job accountant be sufficiently experienced in accounting. He should be prepared to check invoices, make discounts, and handle many other details comprising normal book routine.   The bulk of the paper work is done at the field office and payrolls are handled in the most expedient way—sometimes by establishing a fund and sometimes by remittance from the main office.   Distance and convenience determine this factor.

All work must be handled promptly and with vigilance.   When paper work lags, cost statements by the inside superintendent fall behind, and without proper servicing and checking, requisitions pile up at the end of the month.   Constant liaison between the controller in the main office and the field personnel is recommended to prevent any lagging in the book work.

Forms have been developed to simplify servicing of various contracts, orders, reports, payrolls, etc.

The special services and assignments department takes care of commitments often given to general contractors having the necessary qualifications to supply services somewhat beyond the scope of normal construction work.   In such instances, these commitments can sometimes be serviced within the company organization.   However, often it is deemed advisable to call in expert technicians to collaborate on the problem at hand.   In following this procedure, the company would assume guidance for the various aspects of the investigation and funnel the findings of the experts, together with their own data, into a general report.   The company's own knowledge and experience constitute a sound basis, which can readily be augmented as needed by specialists, to execute assignments efficiently and in one complete package.

27-9. Construction Scheduling.   Scheduling means a carefully planned and developed system designed to produce the desired results on a construction project.   This involves availability of plans and specifications, access to site, securing necessary permits, setting up the time schedule, purchase of materials and subcontracts, and execution of field operations.

The hub of these items is the time schedule, which is prepared as soon as sufficient data are available.   A comprehensive time schedule will show each trade, starting with demolition and ending with the final decorative or special feature, as may be required (Fig. 27-1).   A structure of medium height can readily be scheduled in a horizontal pattern, but anticipated progress on a tall building can best be developed by a vertical pattern.

To prepare a time schedule, it is recommended that a meeting be held with the architect to determine the completion date of working drawings in sequence, such as

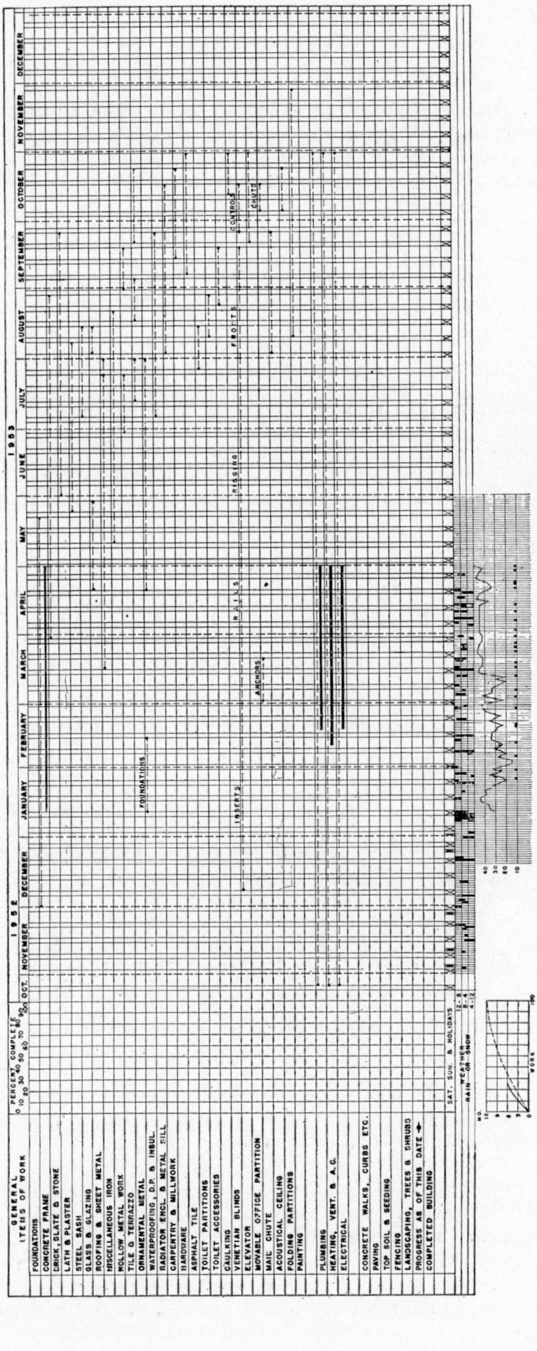

FIG. 27-1. Time schedule for an office building.

foundations, steel, walls below grade, arches, masonry, interiors, etc. Receipt of these drawings will determine the date on which quantity estimates and subcontractors' bids can be taken for each trade. This in turn develops the commencement date for each trade on the site.

The length of time to allow for the work of the various trades, often as many as 35 or 40, is a matter of experience and judgment on the part of the general contractor, as well as his knowledge of material and manpower procurement in a particular area. Certainly, the only efficient method of construction is to plan ahead and schedule the

---

SHEET......1......OF......1

HEGEMAN-HARRIS COMPANY, INC.

TEMP. A. M. ......48......
P. M. ......60......

DAY ......Wednesday......

WEATHER: ......Clear...... **DAILY JOB DIARY** DATE ......April 8, 1953.......

JOB No. ......885......NAME ......Esso Standard Oil Company......

CONTRACTOR	CLASS OF LABOR	NO. OF MEN	DESCRIPTION OF WORK
John W. Harris Assoc., Inc.	Genl Supt	1	General field and office work.
	Asst Supt	1	Hand excavation for trenches on South and East sides
	Mech Eng	1	of Bldg for temporary light and power lines.
	Field Acct	1	
	Laborer	2	Lowering tile drain as requested by Mr. Mangelsdorf.
Poirier & McLane Corp.	Supt	1	Foundations:
	Field Engrs	2	Grading for and laying Poroswall Drain pipe, North Wall.
	Timekeeper	1	Superstructure:
	Carp Fore	3	Forms:
	Carpenters	39	Erecting for the 4th floor and columns (from East end

Remarks: Representative of Pittsburgh Plate Glass Co. on job today to review Plans and Specs for Glass and Glazing Work.

Representative of Wm Isherwood Co. on job today to review Plans and Specs for Lath and Plaster Work.

	TOTAL	132	SUPT......(SGD) R. S. Brackett......

FIG. 27-2. Daily job diary form is filled out daily by the general superintendent in a sufficient number of copies to supply the local office, the owner, and the main office.

---

project trade by trade, allowing for systematic sequence of operation. Each trade should have sufficient warning so as to be ready when required. Also, a constant check on the progress of the work should be maintained to insure that it is in line with the schedule.

It is useful to record along the bottom of the time schedule a flow diagram of daily weather conditions and the time lost because of inclement weather.

27-10. Coordinating Trades on Building Construction. Coordination of the various trades is fundamental for maintenance of the time schedule and successful execution of the work. A competent construction superintendent knows, when starting a job and having prepared a time schedule, exactly when each trade is supposed to commence work.

Several trades are expected on the site within a short time of each other, and the number of trades concurrently required increases as the project advances. This requires the field superintendent to have the foresight to give each trade sufficient warning so that it, in turn, will be ready with men and material in order not to hold up other trades. It is the careful planning of the work and coordination of the many trades that result not only in adherence to time schedules but the good will of sub-contractors.

The most proficient way to insure coordination of trades is to discuss their progress openly at weekly job meetings.

HEGEMAN-HARRIS COMPANY, INC.
30 ROCKEFELLER PLAZA
NEW YORK 20, N. Y.

PURCHASE ORDER

JOB No_____   [ORIGINAL]   ORDER Nº 2500

DATE_____

KINDLY FURNISH TO US AT_____

_____ MATERIALS LISTED BELOW:

QUANTITY	ITEMS	PRICE	

PRICES_____   CHARGE TO_____ JOB
PROMISED DELIVERY_____   ENTERED_____
DISTRIBUTION   ACCTG. DEPT.

INVOICES TO BE HONORED MUST BE RENDERED IN TRIPLICATE

HEGEMAN-HARRIS COMPANY, INC.

FIG. 27-3. Purchase order for materials and labor where the total does not exceed $500 or there is not a covering contract. This form originates in the main or inside superintendent's office of the builder in the number of copies required. When the invoice and the material-received report arrive, they are checked against the purchase order, and if the order is complete, the invoice is passed for payment. The purchase order is marked complete and is removed to the completed purchase-order file. Usually, the original is sent to the vendor, three copies to the owner, one to the main office, and one to the job office for pending file.

This same spirit of coordination can be just as valuable in the purchasing department of a contracting firm. Purchase of material and letting of subcontracts should be scheduled in a sequence that will conform to the job requirements.

27-11. Expediting Material Deliveries for Construction. No matter how efficient a superintendent might be, he cannot be expected to produce results if material is held up in transit or is being delayed in manufacture or is not delivered in time for a dozen other reasons. Consequently, contractors generally employ one or more expediters.

The duty of an expediter requires him to obtain from the inside superintendent or project manager immediate advice on the purchase of material or the letting of a sub-contract, plus a bill of materials. He then discusses the required delivery dates of such materials with the field superintendent, sets up a card index for each trade, and proceeds to obtain listings of the sources of the materials from each dealer and sub-contractor.

From that time on, the expediter is constantly on the telephone or goes to the manu-facturing plant, when necessary, to follow through the manufacture and delivery of materials or equipment needed. He makes a weekly report for all trades on each job, with copies going to all interested parties, including the architect or owner.

When an expediter can handle more than one project simultaneously, he is best located in the main office. On a large job requiring his full time, it is far more practical for him to be stationed on the site, where he would be in close contact with the field superintendent. Experience has proved, however, that a competent expediter who knows his way around can readily and efficiently service two or three sizable projects.

Location of a project has a marked influence on delivery of material. In an open and uncongested area, it is quite simple for a superintendent to order material well

CHANGE ORDER

HEGEMAN-HARRIS COMPANY
INC.
BUILDING CONSTRUCTION

Job No.________

Date________ Change No.________

Archt's No.________

Sub. No.________

You are hereby authorized to make the following change in your work at the ________ Building ________ Architects it being understood that the above change is to be executed under the terms of and conditions embodied in your contract for________

This work will alter the price mentioned in your contract by the________ of________dollars.

HEGEMAN-HARRIS COMPANY, INC.

BY________

Fig. 27-4. Change order authorizes changes from original plans. This form originates with the builder in the number of copies required and is prepared by the inside superintendent. One copy is sent to the subcontractor, one to the main office, four to the owner, and one to the job office.

ahead of time and store it on the property adjacent to the building. However, in congested areas, where a building is to be erected on busy streets and all material must be confined within the building, the superintendent and expediter must arrange with suppliers and subcontractors for delivery at specified times—not only to avoid traffic congestion but to accommodate job requirements efficiently.

It is under these latter circumstances that a field superintendent is really put on his mettle, and it is here that an efficient expediter can be of the greatest service. A successful operation depends on the maximum manpower being continually supplied with material without having it arrive in such proportions at any one time as to impede progress elsewhere in the building.

27-12. Construction Records and Reports. Success in future operations depends to a large extent on knowledge obtained on previous work (see, for example, Sec. 26).

ORDER

Job No.................

Extra Order No..........................

HEGEMAN-HARRIS COMPANY, INC.

BUILDING CONSTRUCTION
30 ROCKEFELLER PLAZA
NEW YORK 20, N. Y.

Date..........................

M..

Please furnish to...

QUANTITY			PRICE	CHARGE TO SUBDIVISION

HEGEMAN-HARRIS COMPANY, INC.

Per..........................

Material to be delivered or work to be done on or before..........................

If not complete on this date, we reserve the right to cancel this order.

If this order is for work to be done on a time and material basis, the amount of labor and material furnished must be certified daily by our superintendent.

FIG. 27-5. Work order authorizes a subcontractor to proceed with work not covered in the original plans and specifications or prior work or change orders. A change order is always written confirming the work order. This form originates in the job office with the general superintendent in sets of six. One copy is sent to the party doing the work, one to the job office, and four to the owner.

ARCHITECT'S EMERGENCY ORDER

No................   Date..........................

To Hegeman-Harris Company, Inc.

Job. No................   ....Building

Please proceed at once with the following extra work, which is not shown on original plans or specifications, it being understood that bill for same is to be rendered promptly on its completion, and that you will be paid not less than cost, plus................%, for its execution.

....
Architect.

Send original to Main Office.
This order is to be used only when there is not time for the work involved to be first taken up with Main Office.
Number orders consecutively as received, starting with No. 1.
Charge ALL work done on each of these orders to its emergency order number only.

FIG. 27-6. Architect's emergency order authorizes the builder to proceed with changes as indicated prior to receiving the change order. The owner or his architect originates this form in six copies when changes are considered necessary and there is insufficient time to negotiate a change order with the builder. It is followed up by a change order. The original is kept by the builder, a duplicate stays in the book, and four copies are sent to the owner.

Consequently, it behooves a contractor to keep accurate costs and records of each contract. The actual compilation is usually carried out by a cost engineer, whose duty is to record all material and labor costs for each classification of work. Every item of work that may be performed by the general contractor, such as concrete, masonry, and carpentry, has numerous headings or subitems, and the more detailed these headings are the more accurate will be the cost accounting. A good superintendent recognizes the importance of job costs and will insist on continuous and accurate reports, not only as a gage for his present work, but as an official record for the future.

TIME CHECKERS REPORT

DATE:

NAME OR NUMBER	CHECK IN	A.M.CHECK	P.M.CHECK	CHECK OUT

FIG. 27-7. Time checker's report serves four purposes: (1) to check men in on the job; (2) to see that men are on the job; (3) to check men out at quitting time; and (4) to serve as the basis for making up the time (payroll) sheet. It is used as a check on the foreman's daily report. A timekeeper originates this form—one each day—in single copy only and turns it in to the payroll clerk.

HEGEMAN-HARRIS COMPANY, INC.
FOREMAN'S DAILY REPORT

JOB_____   DATE_____

DESCRIPTION	QUANTITY		NO. MEN	TOTAL HOURS	RATE	AMOUNT

FOREMAN_____

H. H. CO. F. R. No. 1

C-10-5M-

FIG. 27-8. Foreman's daily report serves as a daily report to the payroll office and as a distribution of charges to the respective accounts.

Field superintendents are also required to prepare and record a daily job diary (Fig. 27-2). This diary is a form of log. It summarizes, in brief, the number of each trade on the job each day, the scope of the work executed by each trade, visitors to the job, decisions rendered or instructions received; also any unusual or outstanding event that may have occurred during the day. The diary also records weather, overtime, information that may be lacking, etc. It is an official document and must not be slighted.

General records of a project are kept in the main office. It is customary to keep these records for about 7 years, at which time they are put in dead storage or destroyed.

Other records and reports that are kept in the field cover accidents, insurance, social security, etc. These reports are generally kept by the job accountant who maintains close contact with the main office and insurance inspector.

Mention has previously been made of the monthly financial report by the project manager (Art. 27-8). He records for each trade the cost to date, plus extras, and the

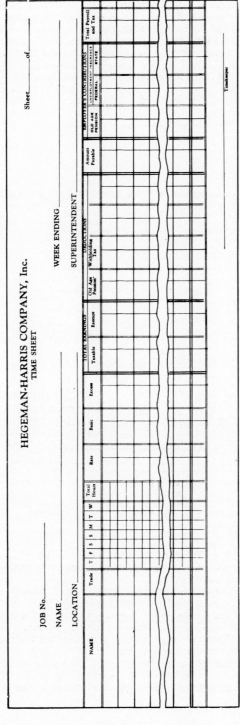

FIG. 27-9. Time (payroll) sheet summarizes the weekly time put in by each employee and serves as the basis for computation of payroll taxes and issuance of pay checks or pay envelopes. The payroll office at the job site prepares this form in four copies from information shown on the daily time checker's report and the foreman's daily report. The original and two copies are sent to the main office, while one copy is kept for the job office files.

cost to complete, as compared with the budget.   The final column shows the antici-pated plus or minus for each trade and readily gives the contractor, architect, and owner a constant picture of the financial status of the project.

Some typical forms used by a general contractor are shown in Figs. 27-3 to 27-15. Standard forms are available for contracts with owners and agreements with sub-contractors and vendors.

Other commonly needed forms not reproduced include subcontractor's guarantee to the owner against defective workmanship, payroll reports to state and Federal govern-ments, invoice for billing subcontractors for services or materials, invoice register for

HEGEMAN-HARRIS COMPANY, INC.

S. S. NO._____NO._____

NAME_____

PAY ROLL EARNINGS
FOR WEEK ENDING_____

TIME WORKED		RATE	AMOUNT
REGULAR HRS. @			
OVERTIME HRS. @			
TOTAL WAGES			
DEDUCTIONS			
FEDERAL WITHHOLDING TAX			
FEDERAL OLD AGE INS.			
STATE UNEMPLOYMENT INS.			
BONDS			
TOTAL DEDUCTED			
NET AMOUNT DUE ENCLOSED			

RECEIVED WAGES AS PER ABOVE STATEMENT

(SIGN HERE)_____

FIG. 27-10. Pay envelope and receipt are used as a container for payrolls paid in cash and to advise the employee of amount earned and deductions made.   It originates in the pay-roll office from information shown on the time (payroll) sheet.   Duplicate information is provided on the receipt and face of the envelope.   The receipt is signed by the recipient, detached, and filed chronologically.

keeping a running record of invoices received and handled, accounting code for coding charges for the owner's accounting purposes and for budget comparisons, and work-men's compensation accident reports.

27-13. Insuring Safety on Construction Projects.   Good progress has been made during the last generation by general contractors in improving safety to labor and the public during construction.   Those efforts have been aided by periodic visits to each building site by insurance inspectors and state safety inspectors.   These companies and agencies have formulated a list of rules in pamphlet and placard form for field distribution to insure safe working conditions.

Safety of the men working on the project must be a superintendent's foremost thought.   Not only are insurance rates kept to a minimum by lack of accidents, but an aura of satisfaction and willingness develops among the men when an evident effort

EMPLOYEE'S COMPENSATION RECORD

FF9. S/S NO._____

NAME_____ADDRESS_____

TYPE OF WORK _____RATE OF WAGE_____

DATE BEGAN   DATE ENDED   REASON FOR
EMPLOYMENT_____   __EMPLOYMENT_____   TERMINATING
                                        EMPLOYMENT_____

REMARKS_____

YEAR 19

WEEK ENDING	TOTAL WAGES	DEDUCTIONS			NET PAYMENT	WEEK ENDING	TOTAL WAGES	DEDUCTIONS			NET PAYMENT
		STATE UNEMP INS TAX	F. I. C. T.	WITHHOLDING TAX				STATE UNEMP INS. TAX	F. I. C. T.	WITHHOLDING TAX	
1/7						7/1					
1/14						7/8					
TOTAL 1ST QUARTER						TOTAL 3RD QUARTER					
4/1						10/7					
4/8						10/14					
TOTAL 2ND QUARTER						TOTAL 4TH QUARTER					
TOTAL 1ST HALF						TOTAL 2ND HALF					
						TOTAL FOR YEAR					

Fig. 27-11. Employee's compensation record notes the earnings of each employee, his deductions, and his net pay. It serves also as the basis for preparation of the social security reports at the end of each quarter. This form originates in the field payroll office—one being kept for each employee. It is prepared in original copy only and remains in the job office until completion of the job, when it is forwarded to the main office.

CHARGE MEMO.

HEGEMAN-HARRIS COMPANY, INC.

DATE_____

TO_____

_____

The following has been done by us at the_____
Building and is chargeable to your account, for which you will receive a bill from our Main Office; if you have any objection to this charge, please make it within *Five Days*, before the charge is entered upon our books.

_____
Superintendent

DATE	QUANTITY OF HOURS	KIND OF MATERIAL OR LABOR, AND FOR WHAT FURNISHED

Use this form for labor, material and expenses, furnished on account of Subcontractors   The above work was done
Render these memos, promptly at least once a week; send both copies to Main Office.
Have this memo. O. K. by the subcontractor's Foreman if possible.
Do not give rates on original but only on yellow copy.   _____
                                                                          Foreman

Fig. 27-12. Charge memo advises a subcontractor of charges made to his account and is the basis for preparation of a covering invoice. This form originates in the builder's job office in three copies. It is used to charge the subcontractor for any work the builder does for him, including use of hoisting facilities. The charge memo should be signed by the subcontractor as an acceptance of the work to be done. The original is given to the subcontractor, a duplicate is sent to the main office, together with an invoice in three copies, and the third copy is filed.

HEGEMAN-HARRIS COMPANY, INC.

APPLICATION FOR PAYMENT

Applications for payment must be submitted on this form on
or before the 27th day of the month. Fill out and return all
but one of the enclosed forms.

Sub-Contractor   Date............................

    Name...

    Address...

Project..

Class of Work...

    We hereby make application for payment in the sum of $.............................on account of work performed by us

on our Contract at the above project to...19.........

Extra or Credit Orders on which Change Order has been issued. H.-H. Change Order No.	$	Amount	
			Value of Work Performed on Contract to Date......... $.........
			Value of Work Performed on Extras to Date ....
			Total Value to Date.........
			Less reserve of.......% as per Contract ....
			Previously Requisitioned.........
			Amount of this application $.........
			By .... (Signature)
			(Applicants will please not write in space below)
Other Extra or Credit Orders, on which Change Order has not been issued. (List in detail and state authority)	$		Voucher No.........
			Job No.........
			On Req. No.........
			Amt. This Invoice $.........
Total Extras to Date.........			Contracts and Extras Checked.........
Total Credits to Date.........			Payments Checked.........
Net Extras to Date.........			"Total Value to Date" approved for $.........
Original Contract.........			By.........
Total Contract and Extras.........			Job. Supt.

FIG. 27-13. Subcontractor's application for payment is used as an invoice to the builder covering work done as provided by the contract, and as detail for billing the owner. The subcontractor originates this form in six copies. Five copies are delivered to the builder on or before the second day of each month. The job office sends four copies to the main office, for disposition as follows: two copies are attached to the requisition to the owner, one copy is receipted and placed in the subcontractor's contract file, and one is receipted by the subcontractor when he receives payment and sent to the owner.

has been made by the contractor to protect properly stair and elevator wells, temporary openings, railings, lighting, temporary steps, scaffolding, fencing, etc.

Modern building practice includes the installation of partial elevator service immediately after the structural steel, so that it is unnecessary and actually unlawful to ride material hoists. This rule has been consistently broken in years gone by, but the present trend to separate lifts for personnel and materials is definitely in the right direction.

27-14. Mass-housing Construction. Mass-housing developments include every kind of construction—masonry, fieldstone, concrete, metal, etc.—but the majority of the houses are one- or two-story, wood-frame, with exterior walls of wood or brick, and are constructed by so-called conventional methods or by prefabricating sections, or a combination of both. It is an unsettled argument as to which method is the cheapest and more practical. However, experience to date indicates the costs are about

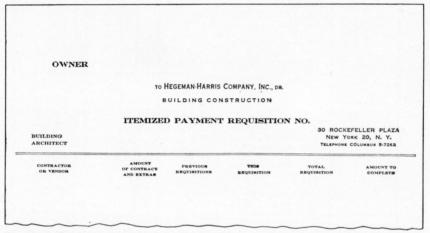

Fig. 27-14. Payment requisition is used as an invoice to the owner covering work done in accordance with the contract. It also serves as the basis of a journal entry recording billings to the owner. It originates in the main office of the builder in six copies and is coded on the basis of the owner's requirements. Two copies, together with complete supporting data, are delivered to the owner, another extra copy also is sent to the owner, one copy is filed in the main office, one in the journal file, and one in the job office.

equal for any of these methods. The really important feature in housing is, after the buying, the organization of staff and work in the field, regardless of the type of house structure.

A successful housing-development contractor organizes his forces somewhat along the idea of a mass-production line in an automobile factory. Gangs of men move from one house site to the next in sequence, each of them doing one specific job—one gang on foundations, one on framing, one on flooring and sheathing, and one on interiors, etc. The mechanical trades work along in unison. And the field engineers keep ahead with lines and grades.

With these sequences in mind, it is mandatory that the superintendent arrange in advance for site delivery of material, that cutting lists be prepared, and that complete requirements for each house are bundled, tagged, and delivered to the house site before the mechanics move over from the last site.

To accomplish the above and maintain a prearranged schedule, it is vital that proper access to the individual sites be a primary consideration. Many house builders start off by erecting houses without preparing access roads. Presumably they do this to invite sales and facilitate promotion. However, they are not adopting the most advantageous procedure. First of all, the cost of delivering materials and operating

GENERAL CONDITIONS & ADMINISTRATION

HEGEMAN-HARRIS COMPANY, Inc.
BUILDING CONSTRUCTION

BUILDING..

LOCATION...

ARCHITECT..

DATE

SHEET 1 OF 1
BUILDING CUBE.................................
BUILDING AREA................................

CODE		UNIT	MATERIAL	UNIT	LABOR
800	**PERMITS**				
A	Building				
B	Bridge & Fence				
C	Curb				
D	Street repair				
E	Crossing sidewalk				
F	Sidewalk Vault				
G	Street Storage				
810	**GENERAL CONDITIONS**				
A	Blueprints & Photographs				
B	Surveys, Batterboards & Benchmarks				
C	Tests, Inspection & Samples				
D	Field Office, Sheds Equipment & Supplies				
E	Telephones & Telegraph				
F	Traveling Expenses				
820	**ADMINISTRATION**				
A	Field Superintendent				
B	" " Assistant				
C	Field Engineer				
D	Transitman				
E	Rodman				
F	Mechanical Engineer				
G	" " Assistant				
H	Watchmen				
I	Project Manager				
J	" " Assistant				
K	Chief Clerk				
L	Cost Engineer & Extra work checker				
M	Time Checker				
N	Plan Clerk & Office boys				
O	Stenographers				
P	Payroll Distribution (Armored Car Service)				
Q	Expediters				
R	Field draftsmen				
S	Inspectors Piles				
T	" Steel				
U	" Masonry				
	CARRY FORWARD				

FIG. 27-15. General conditions summarize the overhead charges of the general contractor and are used for analysis in the local office.

TEMPORARY CONSTRUCTION & SERVICES

HEGEMAN-HARRIS COMPANY, Inc.

BUILDING CONSTRUCTION

BUILDING..

LOCATION...

ARCHITECT...

DATE

SHEET 1 OF 2

BUILDING CUBE..

BUILDING AREA..

CODE		UNIT	MATERIAL	UNIT	LABOR
830	**TEMPORARY CONSTRUCTION**				
A	Sidewalk Bridge & Fence				
B	Outrigger Protection				
C	Safety Barricades & Enclosures				
D	Temporary Stair protection				
E	Temporary Partitions				
F	Temporary Driveways and Planking				
G	Protection to Grounds & Property				
H	Protection of Finished Work				
I	Repairs to Streets & Pavements				
840	**Hoisting, Scaffolds, Plant & Equipment**				
A	Hod hoist Towers				
B	Temporary Runways from Hoist & Doors				
C	Hoisting Equipment				
D	Hoisting Engineer				
E	Temporary Elevators & Maintenance				
F	" " Operation				
G	Temporary Elevator Doors & Enclosures				
H	Swing Scaffolding				
I	Pole "				
J	Special "				
K	Plant & Equipment				
850	**TEMPORARY SERVICES**				
A	Temporary Toilets & Enclosures				
B	Temporary Water & Service				
C	Temporary Light & Power Installation				
D	" " " Maintenance				
E	" " " Current				
F	Temporary Heat — Installation				
G	" " Maintenance				
H	" " Fuel				
I	Temporary Fire protection				
860	**WINTER CONDITIONS**				
A	Snow removal				
B	Tarpaulins				
C	Heat (Salamanders & Fuel & Labor)				
		CARRY FORWARD				

FIG. 27-15 (*Continued*)

TEMPORARY CONSTRUCTION & SERVICES

HEGEMAN-HARRIS COMPANY, Inc. ,

BUILDING CONSTRUCTION

BUILDING..

LOCATION..

ARCHITECT..

DATE

SHEET 2 OF 2

BUILDING CUBE...

BUILDING AREA...

CODE		UNIT	MATERIAL	UNIT	LABOR
880	Cleaning Building and Remove Rubbish				
A	Rubbish Chutes and Hoppers				
B	Cleaning & Removal of Rubbish				
C	Cleaning at Completion				
D	Cleaning Windows & Replace Broken Glass				
870	INSURANCE & TAXES				
A	Fire				
B	Compensation				
C	Public Liability				
D	Property Damage				
E	Social Security & Unemployment				
F	Protective Liability (Subcontractors)				
G	Automobile Insurance				
	CARRY FORWARD				

FIG. 27-15 (*Continued*)

equipment is greatly increased by moving them through heavy mud. The mechanics lose time by being unable to park their cars anywhere near the area in which they are working, and potential purchasers are not interested in wading through a sea of mud to inspect a house. It is far better to put in the access roads so they can be used by construction forces.

The cost of installing utilities—water, gas, electric, and sewerage—is just as much at the end of the house construction as at the beginning. Consequently, it doesn't make sense to delay those all-important installations and be penalized financially in the bargain.

A well-organized housing project under competent supervision should be an outstanding success if a contractor adheres approximately to the following sequence: surveying, clearing, site engineering, installation of utilities, rough grading of sites, roads (top finish later), foundations, house construction, drives and walks, decorations, finished grading, planting and seeding, road surfacing, if any.

27-15. Labor Relations. It is axiomatic that all contractors are reliant upon labor for the execution of their contracts to the same extent that labor is reliant upon contractors for employment. A contractor and his labor force constitute a team, which in the normal course of events works to everyone's advantage.

In the construction industry, committees have been established both by the labor unions and by the various employers' associations to resolve any claims or disputes that may arise. This procedure has proved very satisfactory.

Once in a while, disputes or discussions of minor importance arise between an individual contractor and some labor union. In these cases, it is customary for the union delegate and a representative of the contractor to arrive at an amicable solution.

As a general rule, a contractor delegates one particular officer of the company to maintain liaison with employer's committees and the union delegates. By doing this, the company is not only kept abreast of new developments but its representative is more readily accepted when his role is on a permanent basis.

Too much emphasis cannot be placed on the wisdom of mutual respect in negotiations between labor and management. The expression of a difference in opinion is the inherent right of everyone, and much more can be gained by both sides from a frank discussion of each opinion before arriving at a solution or decision.

Practically all unions delegate one of their members as shop steward on the job. The purpose of this steward is to see that there are no infractions of the agreement by the contractor and to protect the interests of all members on that job. A smart superintendent always has access to the steward through the foreman. Consequently, it is rare that any local dispute should go any farther.

Pleasant relations between labor and management can be readily maintained with a minimum amount of judicious effort.

Section 28

SPECIFICATIONS

BEN JOHN SMALL

Architect
LaPierre, Litchfield & Partners
New York, N.Y.

Specifications are written by architects and engineers as instructions to contractors. The contractors use them as instruments for purchasing materials, as a basis for agreements with their subcontractors, and as installation data governing erection.

Specifications form one of the four elements that constitute the **contract documents.** The others are the contract drawings, general conditions of the contract, and the agreement between the owner and the contractor.

28-1. Interpretation of Contract Documents. Article 2 of the American Institute of Architects' general conditions of the contract explains that the contract documents are complementary and that what is called for by any one shall be as binding as if called for by all. It is often a problem for the specifier to adjust equitably a conflict that may exist between the contract drawings and the specifications. To inform the contractor of the sequence to be used when such a conflict occurs, many specifiers add the following clause to the general conditions:

"Interpretation of the Contract Drawings and the Specifications shall be given preference in the following order:

(a) Addenda (later dates to take precedence over earlier dates).

(b) Specifications.

(c) Drawings."

A good set of drawings will indicate only that which has greater clarity when drawn rather than described in words. The reverse is true of specifications. One must never lose sight of the fact that drawings and specifications are a combination of graphic and word instructions to the many concerned with the erection of a project.

The designer and specifier must join in an effort to tell their story with comprehensiveness, clarity, and conciseness if the owner's interest is to be safeguarded properly.

28-2. Streamlined Specifications. In recent years, specifications have grown in importance and in volume in proportion to the refinements of trade practices. Architects spend 10% of their production time in the preparation of specifications. All this has brought about a greater need for specifications standards to help the specifier produce a better document without wasted effort.

To combat the problem of increasing volume, which has a bad psychological effect on bidders, a technique of specification writing known as the abbreviated or streamlined form is often used. This form utilizes sentences such as: "Glaze interior sash with type A glass" instead of "The Contractor shall furnish and install all the interior sash type A glass as specified hereinbefore." The words, "The Contractor shall," "furnish and install," "all," "The," "as specified hereinbefore," are inferred by incorporation of the following paragraphs, which appear either in the general conditions of the contract or at the beginning of each trade section of the contract:

"These Specifications are of the abbreviated or 'streamlined' type and include incomplete sentences. Omissions of words or phrases, such as 'the Contractor shall,' 'in conformity therewith,' 'shall be,' 'as noted on the Drawings,' 'according to the plans,' 'a,' 'an,' 'the,' and 'all' are intentional. Omitted words or phrases shall be supplied by inference in the same manner as they are when a 'note' occurs on the Drawings. Words 'shall be' or 'shall,' shall be supplied by inference where a colon (:) is used within sentences or phrases.

"Contractor shall provide all items, articles, materials, operations or methods listed, mentioned or scheduled on the Drawings or herein, including all labor, materials, equipment and incidentals necessary and required for their completion."

Another application of the streamlining technique is most useful in connection with descriptions of materials, such as: "Portland Cement: ASTM, C150, Type I" instead of "Portland cement shall meet the requirements of the Standard Specification of the American Society for Testing Materials, Designation C150, Type I, latest edition thereof." The omission of "latest edition thereof" is covered under another article of the General Conditions, which requires all such technical references to be the latest editions.

The streamlining technique can reduce the bulk of traditionally written specifications by about 33% without injuring comprehensiveness, clarity, conciseness, or legality. (Ben John Small, "Streamlined Specifications Standards," Reinhold Publishing Corporation, New York.)

28-3. Standard Specifications. These are extremely useful instruments designed to save the specifier time and money. They do much to reduce errors and tend to produce superior specifications because the standards are reviewed generally by trade associations and other authorities. The advantages ascribed to the use of standards can be summarized as follows:

1. They definitely save time and resultant expense.
2. They reduce research to a minimum. (Research usually consumes the most time in specification writing.)
3. Because of time saved, they permit delaying of specification writing until working drawings are practically completed and most of the decisions on materials and details are settled. Thereby, they prevent many disagreements between drawings and specifications due to last-minute drawing changes.
4. By always working from the same basic document instead of from old specifications, the specifier prevents reference to peculiar conditions of one job from getting into specifications of another.
5. They may be used in the drafting room as a check list for determining what shall be indicated on drawings and what to describe by specifications.
6. They eliminate the need for retyping prior to final reproduction.
7. They can be used by students in practice specification writing. Several standard specifications are in current use.

(H. R. Sleeper, "Architectural Specifications," John Wiley & Sons, Inc., New York; Ben H. Dyer, "Specification Work Sheets," American Institute of Architects, Washington, D.C.; and Ben John Small, "Streamlined Specifications Standards," Reinhold Publishing Corporation, New York.)

28-4. Subdivision of Work in Standard Specifications. Ben John Small's "Streamlined Specifications Standards," first published in 1952 (Reinhold Publishing Corporation, New York) groups specifications into 63 alphabetically arranged sections, numbered both for quick reference and for separate filing, by either individual sections or entire categories. Its contents indicate subdivision of work as follows:

CONTRACTUAL:
Proposal Invitation, Bidder's Instructions. Proposal. Form of Agreement. General Conditions.
SITE WORK:
Demolition. Excavating, Filling, Grading. Test Borings, Lawns and Planting.

STRUCTURAL:

Carpentry. Cast-in-place Metal-shell Concrete Piling. Cellular-steel Floor and Roof. Composite Piling. Concrete and Glass-block Roof Lights. H-section Steel Piling. Precast Concrete Joists. Precast Concrete Piling. Precast Lightweight-concrete Slabs. Structural Steel. Wood Piling.

MASONRY:

Exterior Architectural Terra Cotta. Exterior Stone Work. Interior Architectural Terra Cotta. Masonry Mortars. Masonry Work.

WEATHER PROTECTION:

Asbestos-cement Roofing and Siding. Calking. Cement Stucco. Copper Roofing and Sheet-metal Work. Dampproofing. Glass and Glazing. Metal Roofing and Siding. Roofing and Insulation. Tempered Glass Doors. Waterproofing.

METALWORK:

Aluminum Work, Hollow Metalwork. Kalamein and Tin-clad Work. Miscellaneous Metalwork. Miscellaneous Specialties. Metals. Metal Toilet Partitions (Flush Pilaster Type, without Headrail). Metal Toilet Partitions (Flush Type, with Headrail and Posts). Metal Windows (Except Aluminum). Movable Metal Partitions. Ornamental Metalwork (Except Aluminum).

FINISHING:

Acoustical Work. Asphalt Tile. Cork Flooring. Elevator Work. Hardware. Hardware Allowance. Interior Marble Work. Lathing and Plastering. Linoleum Flooring. Painting. Refrigerator Work. Rubber Tile. Rubber Wall Covering. Structural Glass. Terrazzo. Tile. Toilet-room Accessories. Vinyl-plastic Roll Flooring, Tile, Wall Covering. Wall Covering Materials. X-ray and Radium Protective Work.

28-5. Coordination of Specifications. Coordination is a very important word in the specifier's vocabulary. Just as the mechanical and electrical work have to coordinate thoroughly with the construction features of a building, so do the various sections or divisions of the specifications have to coordinate with each other.

It is customary to include in the general conditions of the contract a statement to the effect that, for convenience of reference and to facilitate letting of subcontracts, the specifications are separated into sections and that such separations shall not operate to make the architect or engineer an arbiter to establish subcontract limits between the contractor and subcontractors. It is nevertheless imperative to avoid duplication and errors resulting from lack of coordination. If the same item of work appears in two trade sections, it may be long after the award of subcontracts that the error becomes apparent. The owner may be penalized by paying twice for the same item.

Coordination is more difficult for multicontract projects. A specifier should develop a "score card" similar to the following example, as a guide to keep him from duplications and contradictions.

Contract No. 1.   General Construction Work

Nature of work	Furnished by	Installed by
1. Toilet room and other accessories	Contractor for general construction	Contractor for general construction
2. Masonry flue and flue lining for incinerator (incinerator by contractor for work)	Contractor for general construction	Contractor for general construction
3. Access panels	Other contractors	Contractor for general construction
4. Sleeves	Other contractors	Furnishing and setting by others; building in of sleeves by contractor for general construction
5. Water-closet safes	Contractor for general construction	Contractor for general construction
6. Hose cabinets and doors	Contractor for general construction	Contractor for general construction
7. Built-in refrigerators and incubators, excluding mechanical and electrical services	Contractor for general construction	Contractor for general construction
8. Finished painting of mechanical and electrical services excluding machinery and stenciling of piping	Contractor for general construction	Contractor for general construction
9. Conduits and wiring required for operation of electrically operated equipment	Contractor for electrical work	Contractor for electrical work
10. Starters, controllers, transformers, signal boards, relays, and the like	Contractor for general construction delivers to contractor for electrical work at building site	Contractor for electrical work unloads, handles, erects, connects up such equipment
11. Monorails for laundry equipment	Contractor for laundry equipment	Contractor for general construction
12. Monorails for kitchen services	Contractor for general construction	Contractor for general construction
13. Wiring and grounding of floor grids in terrazzo or tile work	Contractor for electrical work	Contractor for electrical work

Contract No. 2. Plumbing Work

Nature of work	Furnished by	Installed by
1. Excavation work inside (in otherwise unexcavated spaces) and outside of building, for plumbing installations	Contractor for plumbing work	Contractor for plumbing work
2. Roof flashings for piping and roof drains	Contractor for general construction	Contractor for general construction
3. Kitchen equipment	Contractor for kitchen equipment	Plumbing work, including trimmings for this equipment, by contractor for plumbing work
4. Sterilizing equipment	Contractor for sterilizing equipment delivers to contractor for plumbing work at building site	Contractor for plumbing work receives, sets, and installs sterilizing equipment, with required plumbing connections; also protects and is responsible therefor until completion of building
5. Metal equipment without piping and fittings	Contractor for metal equipment	Contractor for plumbing work furnishes and installs all plumbing lines and fittings to and within equipment
6. Laundry equipment	Contractor for laundry equipment	Contractor for plumbing work furnishes and installs waste, vent, water, gas, and air connections, shut-off valves on branches from mains to equipment
7. Sleeves	Contractor for plumbing work	Contractor for plumbing work (furnishing and setting)
8. Conduit and wiring required for operation of electrically operated equipment	Contractor for electrical work	Contractor for electrical work
9. Starters, controllers, transformers, signal boards, relays, and the like	Contractor for plumbing work delivers to contractor for electrical work at building site	Contractor for electrical work unloads, handles, erects, connects up such equipment
10. Painting of all exposed piping and pipe covering, excluding machinery and stenciling of piping	Contractor for general construction	Contractor for general construction
11. Stenciling of piping	Contractor for plumbing work	Contractor for plumbing work

Contract No. 3. Heating and Ventilating Work

Nature of work	Furnished by	Installed by
1. Concrete steam trenches..........	Contractor for general construction	Contractor for general construction
2. Roof flashings for ductwork..........	Contractor for general construction	Contractor for general construction
3. Kitchen equipment..........	Contractor for kitchen equipment	Heating and ventilating work for this equipment by contractor for heating and ventilating work
4. Sterilizing equipment..........	Contractor for sterilizing equipment	Contractor for heating and ventilating work hooks up sterilizing equipment with steam supply and return lines and other required steam fixtures
5. Metal equipment without piping and fittings......	Contractor for metal equipment	Contractor for heating and ventilating work furnishes and installs all heating lines and fittings to and within equipment
6. Laundry equipment..........	Contractor for laundry equipment	Contractor for heating and ventilating work furnishes and installs steam supply, returns, and the like to valved outlets on equipment
7. Sleeves..........	Contractor for heating and ventilating work	Contractor for heating and ventilating work (furnishing and setting)
8. Refrigeration for built-in refrigerators..........	Contractor for heating and ventilating work	Contractor for heating and ventilating work
9. Portable refrigerators, ice makers, and ice-cap freezers	Contractor for heating and ventilating work	Contractor for heating and ventilating work
10. Conduit and wiring required for operation of electrically operated equipment	Contractor for heating and ventilating work delivers to contractor for electrical work at building site	Contractor for electrical work unloads, handles, erects, connects up such equipment
11. Starters, controllers, and the like..........	Contractor for general construction	Contractor for general construction
12. Finished painting of all exposed work, excluding machinery and stenciling of piping	Contractor for heating and ventilating work	Contractor for heating and ventilating work
13. All concealed piping and ironwork, interior of all ductwork and radiator enclosures	Contractor for heating and ventilating work	Contractor for heating and ventilating work
14. Stenciling of piping..........	Contractor for heating and ventilating work	Contractor for heating and ventilating work
15. Refrigeration for air conditioning..........	Contractor for heating and ventilating work	Contractor for heating and ventilating work
16. Compressed-air systems..........	Contractor for heating and ventilating work	Contractor for heating and ventilating work

Contract No. 4. Electrical Work

Nature of work	Furnished by	Installed by
1. Lighting fixtures..........	Contractor for lighting fixtures	Contractor for lighting fixtures
2. Kitchen equipment..........	Contractor for kitchen equipment	Electrical work for this equipment by contractor for electrical work
3. Sterilizing equipment..........	Contractor for sterilizing equipment	Electrical work for this equipment by contractor for electrical work
4. Metal equipment without wiring and fittings......	Contractor for metal equipment	Contractor for electrical work furnishes and installs electric-wiring work and fixtures to and within equipment
5. Laundry equipment..........	Contractor for laundry equipment	Contractor for electrical work furnishes and installs conduit and wiring to and from controls needed for operation of equipment, including connecting up of motors on such equipment
6. Sleeves..........	Contractor for electrical work	Contractor for electrical work (furnishing and setting)
7. Elevators and dumb-waiters..........	Contractor for elevator and dumb-waiter work	Contractor for elevator and dumb-waiter work
8. Underground conduits, ducts, and the like including excavating, concrete work, backfilling, and restoration work and the like..........	Contractor for electrical work	Contractor for electrical work
9. All finished painting excepting machinery..........	Contractor for general construction	Contractor for general construction

Contract No. 5. Elevator and Dumb-waiter Work

Nature of Work   *Furnished and Installed by*

1. Elevators and dumb-waiters............. Contractor for elevator and dumb-waiter
2. Hoistway enclosures.................... Contractor for general construction
3. Elevator pits......................... Contractor for general construction
4. Permanent feeders and the like.......... Contractor for electrical work
5. Machine room........................ Contractor for general construction
   a. Trolley beam
   b. Frames and grating for smoke hole and other gratings in machine room or sheave spaces
6. Fill and finish under controllers.......... Contractor for general construction
7. Concrete slab in machine room or sheave spaces............................... Contractor for general construction
8. Pit-access ladders..................... Contractor for general construction
9. Hoistway door and bucks............... Contractor for elevator and dumb-waiter

Contract No. 6. Metal Equipment

Nature of Work   *Furnished and Installed by*

1. Laboratory furniture and all metal equipment throughout building, including shelving, wall-hung cabinets, bookcases, and the like, but not including plumbing, heating, and ventilating work, electrical work and fittings therefor within and without equipment................................ Contractor for metal equipment
2. Holes and cutouts in equipment, necessary for mechanical and electrical services...... Contractor for metal equipment
3. Shop drawings........................ Contractor for metal equipment furnishes shop drawings to contractors for plumbing work, heating and ventilating work, and electrical work, for verification of holes, cutouts, and the like

Contract No. 7. Sterilizing Equipment

Nature of work	Furnished by	
Sterilizers........	Contractor for sterilizing equipment delivers to contractor for plumbing work at building site	No installation required under this contract. Contractor for sterilizing equipment furnishes roughing drawings for his equipment and all other necessary information to contractors for general construction, plumbing work, heating and ventilating work, electrical work

Contract No. 8. Kitchen Equipment

Nature of Work   *Furnished and Installed by*

1. Kitchen equipment without connections... Contractor for kitchen equipment
2. Holes and cutouts in equipment, necessary for mechanical and electrical services...... Contractor for kitchen equipment
3. Shop drawings........................ Contractor for kitchen equipment furnishes shop drawings to contractors for plumbing work, heating and ventilating work, and electrical work, for verification of holes, cutouts, and the like
4. Refrigeration for cold plates of serving counters............................... Contractor for kitchen equipment

Contract No. 9. Laundry Equipment

Nature of work	Furnished by	Installed by
1. Laundry equipment without connections.........	Contractor for laundry equipment	Contractor for laundry equipment
2. Foundations, gutters, and insulation for washers, extractors, and tumblers.........	Contractor for general construction	Contractor for general construction
3. Isolation pads under washers and over concrete floor	Contractor for laundry equipment	Contractor for laundry equipment
4. Monorails.........	Contractor for laundry equipment	Contractor for general construction
5. Anchors and inserts for monorails.........	Contractor for laundry equipment	Contractor for general construction
6. Washers, vents, water, gas and air connections, shut-off valves on branches from mains to equipment...	Contractor for plumbing work	Contractor for plumbing work
7. Steam supply, returns, and condensation drips to valved or control outlets on equipment	Contractor for heating and ventilating work	Contractor for heating and ventilating work
8. Conduit and wiring on equipment to and from controls needed for operation of equipment, including connecting up of motors on such equipment......	Contractor for electrical work	Contractor for electrical work

Contract No. 10.   Lighting Fixtures

Nature of Work	*Furnished and Installed by*
1. Lighting fixtures, completely wired...............	Contractor for lighting fixtures
2. Lighting branch circuit wiring work..............	Contractor for electrical work

Contract No. 11.   Curtain Cubicles

Nature of Work	*Furnished and Installed by*
Cubicle curtains and rods.........................	Contractor for curtain cubicles

Contract No. 12.   Landscaping Work

Nature of Work	*Furnished and Installed by*
Topsoiling, seeding, and planting...................	Contractor for landscaping work

Contract No. 13.   Animal Cages

Nature of Work	*Furnished and Installed by*
Animal cages and racks...........................	Contractor for animal cages

A good specification writer will never write by "remote control." He will comb the drawings with great care, making notes as he goes along. It is useful to set up a pad of paper bearing trade-section titles similar to those in any standard specification. Each blank sheet of paper is titled with a different trade. As drawings are studied, materials and other notes are jotted down on the pad on the appropriate sheets. Eventually, these sheets become the "scope guides" for the trade sections of the final specifications.

28-6. Trade-association Specifications.   These constitute a very important source of authoritative information for the specification writer. No library of those who take a conscientious view toward specification writing is complete without standard specifications as well as related literature prepared by the trade associations. With few exceptions, trade-association specifications are available without charge.

There is no need for specifications for a building project to repeat in full any trade-association specification since they are for the most part well known and certainly easily available to contractors and subcontractors.

The proper way to employ trade-association specifications is first to study them carefully and then specify them with only such modifications as found necessary to meet the project requirements. This approach serves a twofold purpose, in that it is conducive to greater specification accuracy and at the same time utilizes the most effective streamlining device.

Use of trade-association specifications entails considerable care in making the necessary modifications for project applicability. Experience and judgment are the only guides in determining for a project whether or not a trade-association specification is worth the necessary time investment in its modification. Where modifications are so extensive as to approach the trade-association specification in length, then it is obviously best not to attempt the modification approach; edit the trade-association specification and retype it for direct use as the contract specifications.

The typical wording used in contract specifications to include by reference a trade-association specification is as follows:

"1.   REQUIREMENTS FOR ALUMINUM WINDOWS:

(a) Install aluminum windows to meet requirements for 'Quality-approved' aluminum windows as specified in Aluminum Window Manufacturers Association Master Specifications for—
DH-A3 'Double-hung Windows for Monumental-type Buildings.'
A-A2 'Awning Windows for Commercial and Monumental-type Buildings'
except as follows:

(b) Double-hung Type Windows.
1. Hardware.   Provide upper sash with one pull-down handle; position at underside of lower rail; provide inner side of top rail with pull-down socket for pole operation.

2. Window Cleaners Bolts. Provide windows with window cleaners bolts to comply with requirements of N.Y. State Labor Law. Reinforce windows to receive approved bolts and anchors. Use stainless steel or other approved metal; match finish of aluminum windows.
3. Sills: $\frac{3}{16}$-in. thick extruded aluminum.
4. Stools: 12-gage aluminum.
5. Aprons and casings: 14-gage aluminum.
6. Anchors: perforated steel, $\frac{3}{16}$ in. thick; except as otherwise indicated, provide at least three anchors for each jamb.
7. Mullions. Form mullions by abutting interlocking window sections; set joints in mastic.
8. Window Cleaner's Belts. Provide two window cleaner's belts; meet requirements of N.Y. State Labor Department.
9. Shop Drawings. Submit shop drawings; indicate materials, thicknesses, sizes, shapes, other pertinent information.

(c) Awning Type Windows.
   1. Hardware. Provide roto-type operator for crank-type operation. Control sash operation with one mechanism to insure operating sash working in unison. Enclose sash operator completely; provide removable casings, where required, for access to window operator parts.
   2. Awning type windows shall consist of multiplicity of top-hinged ventilators arranged in vertical series and operated by control device that swings bottom edges of ventilators outward.
   3. Ventilators shall operate simultaneously; provide fixed units as indicated.
   4. Main frame and sash members, including sills: 0.062 in. thick.
   5. Provide windows with metal weatherstripping of approved material compatible with aluminum.
   6. Sills: $\frac{3}{16}$-in. thick extruded aluminum.
   7. Stools: 12-gage aluminum.
   8. Aprons and casings: 14-gage aluminum.
   9. Anchors: perforated steel, $\frac{3}{16}$ in. thick; except as otherwise indicated, provide at least three anchors for each jamb.
  10. Mullions: sizes and shapes indicated.
  11. Shop Drawings. Submit shop drawings; indicate materials, thicknesses, sizes, shapes, other pertinent information."

The following is a reference list of principal trade associations:

Acoustical Materials Association, 57 E. 55th St., New York 22, N.Y.
Aluminum Window Manufacturers Association, 75 West St., New York 6, N.Y.
American Concrete Institute, P. O. Box 4754, Redford Station, Detroit 199, Mich.
American Gas Association, 420 Lexington Ave., New York 17, N.Y.
American Hot Dip Galvanizers Association, Inc., First National Building, Pittsburgh 22, Pa.
American Institute of Steel Construction, Inc., 101 Park Ave., New York 17, N.Y.
American Iron and Steel Institute, 150 E. 42d St., New York 17, N.Y.
American Standards Association, Inc., 70 E. 45th St., New York 17, N.Y.
American Walnut Manufacturers Association, 666 N. Lake Shore Dr., Chicago 11, Ill.
Appalachian Hardwood Manufacturers, Inc., 414 Walnut St., Cincinnati 2, Ohio.
Architectural Terra Cotta Institute, 1520 18th St., N.W., Washington 6, D.C.
Asphalt Tile Institute, 101 Park Ave., New York 17, N.Y.
California Redwood Association, 576 Sacramento St., San Francisco 11, Calif.
Cast Iron Soil Pipe Institute, 1627 K St., N.W., Washington 6, D.C.
Concrete Reinforcing Steel Institute, 38 S. Dearborn St., Chicago 3, Ill.
Copper and Brass Research Association, 420 Lexington Ave., New York 17, N.Y.
Cork Institute of America, 342 Madison Ave., New York 17, N.Y.
Douglas Fir Plywood Association, Tacoma 2, Wash.

Facing Tile Institute, 1520 18th St., N.W., Washington 6, D.C.

Fir Door Institute, Tacoma 2, Wash.

Gypsum Association, 20 N. Wacker Drive, Chicago 6, Ill.

Hardwood Dimension Manufacturers' Association, Broadway National Bank Building, Nashville 3, Tenn.

Hardwood Plywood Institute, 600 S. Michigan Ave., Chicago 5, Ill.

Indiana Limestone Institute, Bedford, Ind.

Lead Industries Association, 420 Lexington Ave., New York 17, N.Y.

Mahogany Association, Inc., 666 Lake Shore Dr., Chicago 11, Ill.

Maple Flooring Manufacturers Association, 35 E. Wacker Drive, Chicago 1, Ill.

Marble Institute of America, Inc., 108 Forster Ave., Mount Vernon, N.Y.

Metal Lath Manufacturers Association, 636 Engineers Building, Cleveland 14, Ohio.

Metal Roof Deck Technical Institute 2250 E. Grand Blvd., Detroit 11, Mich.

National Association of Architectural Metal Manufacturers, 228 N. LaSalle St., Chicago 1, Ill.

National Builders Hardware Association, 515 Madison Ave., New York 22, N.Y.

National Building Granite Quarries Association, Inc., 1028 Connecticut Ave., N.W., Washington 6, D.C.

National Concrete Masonry Association, 38 S. Dearborn St., Chicago 3, Ill.

National Electrical Manufacturers Association, 155 E. 44th St., New York 17, N.Y.

National Fire Protection Association, 60 Batterymarch St., Boston 10, Mass.

National Hardwood Lumber Association, 59 E. Van Buren St., Chicago 5, Ill.

National Lumber Manufacturers Association, 1319 18th St., N.W., Washington 6, D.C.

National Metalclad Door Association, 266 Bryant St., Buffalo, N.Y.

National Mineral Wool Association, 1270 Avenue of the Americas, New York 20, N.Y.

National Oak Flooring Manufacturers Association, 814 Sterick Building, Memphis 3, Tenn.

National Paint Varnish & Lacquer Association, Inc., 1500 Rhode Island Ave., N.W., Washington 5, D.C.

National Terrazzo and Mosaic Association, Inc., 711 14th St., N.W., Washington 5, D.C.

National Warm Air Heating & Air Conditioning Association, Engineers Building, Cleveland 14, Ohio.

National Woodwork Manufacturers Association, Inc., 332 S. Michigan Ave., Chicago 4, Ill.

Northern Hemlock and Hardwood Manufacturers Association, 46 Washington Blvd., Oshkosh, Wis.

Oxychloride Cement Association, Inc., 29-28 41st Ave., Long Island City, N.Y.

Painting & Decorating Contractors of America, 540 N. Michigan Ave., Chicago 11, Ill.

Perlite Institute, 45 W. 45th St., New York 36, N.Y.

Philippine Mahogany Association, 111 W. Seventh St., Los Angeles 14, Calif.

Plumbing Fixture Manufacturers Association, 1145 19th St., N.W., Washington 6, D.C.

Portland Cement Association, 33 W. Grand Ave., Chicago 10, Ill.

Red Cedar Shingle Bureau, 5508 White Building, Seattle 1, Wash.

Rubber Manufacturers Association, Inc., 444 Madison Ave., New York 22, N.Y.

Scientific Apparatus Makers Association, 20 N. Wacker Drive, Chicago 6, Ill.

Sheet Metal Contractors National Association, 170 Division St., Elgin, Ill.

Southern Cypress Manufacturers Association, 2133 Kings Ave., Jacksonville 7, Fla.

Southern Hardwood Producers, Inc., 805 Sterick Building, Memphis 3, Tenn.

Southern Pine Association, National Bank of Commerce Bldg., New Orleans 4, La.

Stained Glass Association of America, 822 Wilmington Ave., St. Louis 11, Mo.

Steel Joist Institute, Dupont Circle Building, Washington 6, D.C.

Structural Clay Products Institute, 1520 18th St., N.W., Washington 6, D.C.

Tile Council of America, 10 E. 40th St., New York 16, N.Y.
Tile Manufacturers Association, Inc., 50 E. 42d St., New York 17, N.Y.
Vermiculite Institute, 1720 Madison St., N.E., Minneapolis 13, Minn.
West Coast Lumberman's Association, 1410 S.W. Morrison St., Portland 5, Ore.
Western Pine Association, 510 Yeon Building, Portland 4, Ore.
Wire Reinforcement Institute, National Press Building, Washington 4, D.C.

28-7. Other Sources of Information for Specifiers. Architectural, engineering, and trade magazines constitute an important source of information for the specifier principally through news of new products. It is well to peruse advertisements with great care. Much effort is expended by manufacturers in the preparation and dissemination of technical information for the benefit of those who specify. An alert specification writer will write frequently for data to implement his technical library and thereby better serve his client.

A product manufacturer who recognizes the needs of the specifier by providing lucid technical information, prepared without bias and emotion, serves the specifier well. It is wise for a product manufacturer to sell the specifier by employing teaching techniques in preference to the traditional consumer-goods approach.

"Sweet's File" (F. W. Dodge Corporation, New York) contains information, catalogs, and related data prepared by material manufacturers, contracting organizations, and trade associations. The files constitute an invaluable aid to the specifier in that he can be assured that the information therein is up to date.

28-8. Bibliography for Specification Writers. A well-read specification writer should possess a library stocked at least with the following:

Magazine Articles

Brostrom, E. O.: "Arrangement of Specifications," *Architectural Forum*, November, 1929.
Sleeper, H. R.: "Assembly of Specification Data," *Architectural Forum*, May, 1931.
Small, Ben John: "Case for the Streamlined Specification," in "The Construction Specifier," Construction Specifications Institute, Washington, D.C., 1949.
Small, Ben John: "Cavity Wall Construction," *Progressive Architecture*, August, 1947.
Emerson, David B.: "Growth of the Specification," *Pencil Points*, February, 1930.
Fruauff, H. H.: "Master Specifications and How They Can Be Adapted to Small Jobs," *American Architect*, May, 1933.
Emerson, D. B.: "Pitfalls for the Specifications Writer," *Pencil Points*, July, 1929.
Krahmer, C. E.: "Specifications for Quality," *Architectural Record*, August, 1932.
Small, Ben John: "Specification Surgery," *Progressive Architecture*, July, 1946.
Sleeper, H. R.: "Standard Specifications," *Architectural Forum*, February, 1931.
Peaslee, Horace: "Streamlined Specifications," *Pencil Points*, August, 1939.
Small, Ben John: "Streamlined Specifications for Metal Casework for Hospitals," *Progressive Architecture*, November, December, 1947.
Small, Ben John: "Waterproofing and Dampproofing," *Progressive Architecture*, August, September, 1946.
Goldsmith, G.: "Why Scope of the Work?" *Pencil Points*, March, 1932.

Books

Kidder, F. E., and H. Parker: "Architects' and Builders' Handbook," John Wiley & Sons, Inc., New York.
Goldsmith, Goldwin: "Architects' Specifications," John Wiley & Sons, Inc., New York.
Tomson, Bernard: "Architectural and Engineering Law," Reinhold Publishing Corporation, New York.
"Architectural Metal Handbook," National Association of Architectural Metal Manufacturers, Washington, D.C.
Cowgill, Clinton H., and Ben John Small: "Architectural Practice," Reinhold Publishing Corporation, New York.
Sleeper, H. R.: "Architectural Specifications," John Wiley & Sons, Inc., New York.
Hayward, Morris L.: "Contractors' Legal Problems," McGraw-Hill Book Company, Inc., New York.
Abbett, Robert W.: "Engineering Contracts and Specifications," John Wiley & Sons, Inc., New York.

"Handbook of Fire Protection," National Fire Protection Association, 60 Batterymarch St., Boston, Mass.

Werbin, I. Vernon: "Legal Phases of Construction Contracts," McGraw-Hill Book Company, Inc., New York.

"National Directory of Commodity Specifications," National Bureau of Standards, Washington, D.C.

"Reference Manual of American Architect," American Architect, New York.

Seelye, Elwyn E.: "Specifications and Costs," John Wiley & Sons, Inc., New York.

Dyer, Ben H.: "Specification Work Sheets," American Institute of Architects, Washington, D.C.

"Steel Construction," American Institute of Steel Construction, New York.

"Stevens Master Specifications," Stevens Master Specifications, Inc., 165 W. Wacker Drive, Chicago, Ill.

Small, Ben John: "Streamlined Specifications Standards," Reinhold Publishing Corporation, New York.

Beach, W. W.: "Supervision of Construction Operations," Charles Scribner's Sons, New York.

"Sweet's File," F. W. Dodge Corporation, New York.

"Wood Handbook," Forest Products Laboratory, U.S. Department of Agriculture, Superintendent of Documents, Washington 25, D.C.

28-9. Check Lists for Specifications. These are guideposts designed to insure the comprehensiveness of specifications. Such lists are composed usually on an individual basis, their scope being determined by the predominant nature of building types handled.

A good way to prepare a check list is to utilize the titles employed throughout the sections or divisions, as the case may be, indicated in a standard specification. (H. R. Sleeper, "Architectural Specifications," John Wiley & Sons, Inc., New York; Ben H. Dyer, "Specification Work Sheets," American Institute of Architects, Washington, D.C.; Ben John Small, "Streamlined Specification Standards," Reinhold Publishing Corporation, New York; see Art. 28-4.)

If the size of an architect's or engineer's office warrants the development of an office manual, it is well to include a check list augmented by a schedule of "do's" and "don't's" prepared with a view toward reflecting office policy.

The following schedules are intended only as examples of such listings and do not necessarily represent the policy of any one individual or office. These lists are not organized in terms of logical trades but are deliberately haphazard in arrangement to force constant rereading and review.

DO'S

1. Be sure large metal surfaces are grounded to soil and that copper roofs, steeples, or domes have lightning arresters.

2. Provide access to statues for cleaning.

3. Protect areaways by gratings or high fences.

4. Use revolving doors to conserve heat and avoid drafts; provide an emergency door for use when the revolving door is inoperative.

5. Use a nonslip material near sidewalks at entrances.

6. Call for a ramp at approaches to freight elevators instead of steps.

7. Provide protective fencing on parapets where the roof adjoins the roof of another building.

8. Use simple window grille design and material.

9. Expose plumbing lines where feasible—otherwise, specify access doors for chases.

10. Provide ample space for cleaning personnel to store cleaning implements.

11. Call for low slop sinks for janitor's closet to discharge mop truck; provide nozzle of long-swing type to fill water in mop pail and trucks directly; provide hooks for brooms, pails, ladders, mops, vacuum-cleaner hose, etc.

12. Specify doors for a large room in pairs, both operating.

13. Insulate all pipes outside the building where freezing is a possibility.

14. Slope stone chimney caps inward to avoid staining on the exterior.

15. Study the properties of stone proposed for facades for durability and easy maintenance.

16. Consider use of light-colored brick for inside courts or yards—light reflection is important for rooms depending solely on these courts for natural light.

17. Consider expansion joints for large concrete buildings from roof to ground; also for large concrete surfaces, such as sidewalks and driveways, exposed to weather.

18. Make stair and balcony railing high enough and of well-anchored sturdy construction to prevent accidents and to avoid repairs.

19. Use roofing material for flat roofs of such nature that defects may be detected easily.

20. On promenade tile roofs, use expansion joints for each 100 sq ft; flash them with copper and elastic calking.

21. Anchor windows and doors in walls adequately.

22. Locate leaders in accessible places where they are repaired easily. Use shafts for this purpose.

23. Use stock size and design of doors and windows wherever possible.

24. For built-in construction, such as concealed flashing, use good materials—to repair a cheap material would involve much demolishing and rebuilding.

25. For corridor floors exposed to hard usage, use terrazzo with strips for each 16 sq ft. Borders and bases should also have strips to prevent cracks.

26. For toilet floors, give preference to nonslip ceramic tile. Terrazzo is not advisable near urinals and slop sinks because it is more absorbent than tile.

27. Use smooth plaster of light color for ceilings—sand finish or textures are not recommended.

28. Select acoustical materials for ceilings with careful consideration of light reflection, durability, cleanliness, repair, and effectiveness.

29. Design wood paneling so that damaged parts can be replaced easily. Shrinkage can be concealed by using slip joints or cover moldings. Miter joints should be given careful thought because they are the main source of trouble.

30. Call for back painting of wood wainscot with white lead. The wainscot should not be in contact with plaster.

31. In public buildings with variable occupancy, use dividing partitions that permit easy alteration; use hollow metal, asbestos cement, etc. Panels in partitions should be small, for economy in glass breakage. Anchor long partitions to floor and ceiling.

32. Consider toilet or shower partitions in the following order—structural glass, hard domestic marble, slate, metal.

33. See that marble or glass partitions are well protected against distortion and door slamming.

34. Give preference to double-hung sash in public buildings over steel casements or projected windows, and to noncorrosive metal over wood or steel.

35. In nonfireproof buildings, consider white pine for double-hung sash.

36. For hardware material, use heavy solid cast bronze.

37. Use round doorknobs in lieu of oval knobs or lever handles.

38. Equip doors with heavy butts, 5 in. high.

39. Have ash-pull sockets on double-hung windows fastened to the top rail of the upper sash so that the pole hole hangs below the rail and is easily discernible.

40. For door holders, use heavy foot action, push-down type with rubber tip for interiors. Exterior doors should have overhead bronze holders.

41. Call for doorstops of the rubber-tipped type, selected for strength and secure setting.

42. Consider doorknob bumpers for most doors; toilet-door bumpers should be incorporated with a removable nut into the coat hook. Spring action in this combination coat hook and bumper is desirable.

43. Use a checking hinge on dwarf doors for toilet vestibules.

44. Install nonslip nosings and strips on stair treads.

45. See that the brackets supporting wall handrails in stairs are well anchored in the wall.

46. Specify saddles at the main entrance of nonslip nonferrous metal.

47. Paint plastered walls exposed to dirt and smudges to wainscot height with high-gloss neutral color for easy cleaning.

48. Paint radiators with lead and oil flat finish—light color increases efficiency.

49. In membrane waterproofing, see that felt is not in contact with felt.

50. Have main doors glazed with polished glass reinforced with wire.

51. Glaze large sash with ¼-in. polished plate glass.

52. Glaze other window sash with A quality, double-strength glass.

53. In corridors to offices and toilets, use heavy translucent figured or ground plate glass.

54. For interior partitions, specify ⅛-in. translucent glass.

55. Glaze skylights with ¼-in.-thick rough wire glass, except over elevators, where ribbed glass is preferable, with a screen below and above.

56. For underground work, call for leaders of extra-heavy cast iron or corporation pipes.

57. Interior soil and waste pipes to be extra-heavy wrought iron except in laboratories where duriron or other acid-resisting pipe shall be used.

58. For vent lines, consider standard-weight steel pipe.

59. Give special consideration to support of lighting fixtures, such as candelabras and ornamental ceiling lights. Be sure that revolving of fixtures while cleaning will not loosen them.

60. Study vent-hood exhaust fans and motor as to location in chemical laboratories.

61. Provide outlets for vacuum-cleaning systems not more than 40 ft apart to avoid use of long hoses.

62. See that radiator grilles are easily removable; provide access doors to valves.

63. Locate vent chambers for air-conditioning systems at places of easy accessibility for cleaning and upkeep.

64. Extend footing drains to create an outlet at grade into which poisons may be poured to destroy roots that might clog the drains.

65. Show construction joints in the form of a key for cast-in-place concrete walls. V-type joints are preferred for vertical joints, while tongue shape is useful for horizontal ones.

66. Leave vertical chases, preferably 4 in. deep, in concrete walls for adjoining brickwork.

67. Consider natural seasoning of woods in lieu of kiln drying to check shrinkage.

68. Have wood sheathing laid diagonally; rough flooring should not be laid in the same direction as the finish floor.

69. Insist on a full bed of mortar for every horizontal and vertical joint in brickwork.

70. Limit corbeling in brickwork to 1-in. projection.

71. Give brick arches a minimum of 1-in. rise per foot of span. (For a well-proportioned arch, the rise should be at least one-eighth the span.)

72. In brick buildings with wood-frame floors, call for joist strap anchors built into the brickwork; bevel joist ends.

73. For ends of steel beams on masonry, specify bearing plates and government anchors.

74. Call for thin mortar joints in brickwork—they offer less chance for leakage.

75. Specify that mortar joints should be rubbed to obtain hardness and imperviousness against leakage.

76. Call for wetting of all porous bricks before they are laid.

77. Specify that frames for doors and window openings should be hemp (oakum) filled and calked with plastic calking cement. Rowlock brick window sills are especially susceptible to leakage—they should be backed up with copper flashing.

78. Call for joints in flashing similar to the locked-seam type, to permit free expansion or contraction.

79. Use copper gravel stops along the eaves of an inclined built-up roof where no parapets exist.

80. Specify gypsum plaster in lieu of lime plaster; the latter is obsolete—it requires several months to harden, gives off moisture, and stays damp for a long period.

81. Specify that metal lath sheets should be applied with the rolls running horizontally, so that the holes in the mesh should point down to clinch the plaster. Laps should not be greater than 1 in.; otherwise, mesh movement will develop.

82. For inside work on metal, plaster, or cement surface, use boiled linseed oil as the paint vehicle.

83. For woodwork inside or outside, use boiled linseed oil or raw oil with dryer as a paint vehicle.

84. For a steel priming coat, consider iron-oxide pigment. For an elastic superior finishing coat, use carbon-black pigment.

85. To minimize efflorescence, use a water-repelling mortar and provide drips and washes for all projections.

86. Use limestones of dolomitic nature where exposed to acid action.

87. Remember that fire resistance of stones is not high. They may be arranged in order of fire resistance as follows: (1) fine-grained sandstone with silica binder; (2) fine-grained granite or oölitic limestone; (3) ordinary limestone; (4) coarse-grained granite and (5) marble.

88. Specify that all stones should be laid on their natural bed.

89. See that heavy stone sections have load pad bedding.

90. Require that bond stones occupy at least 20% of the wall surface.

91. Use nonstaining, waterproof, white portland cement for stone-setting mortar.

92. Specify that pure white-lead pigment should be mixed with zinc white for exterior work; otherwise, the paint becomes chalky, and rain will wash it off.

93. Give careful consideration to the selection of sandstones for any building purpose. They are not readily dressable; some of them are worked easily but are not durable.

DON'T'S

1. Don't use soft stones for treads on heavily traveled stairs.

2. Don't use overhanging cornice members.

3. Don't use ornamental rustication, belt courses, etc., having no surface slope or wash.

4. Don't use large-sized doors; they are difficult to open.

5. Avoid stucco-covered penthouses; they deteriorate easily in northern climates.

6. Don't use borrowed lights from one office to another.

7. Don't use ornamental grillework around elevators, cages, etc.; maintenance is costly.

8. Don't use soft stone for a building base; it will deteriorate easily.

9. Don't use light-colored material for a facade; it soils easily, especially in metropolitan areas.

10. Don't specify a marble facade on public buildings in areas where they may not last long and are hard to repair, match, or point up.

11. Don't use architectural terra cotta for building facades with large projecting cornices; they craze readily and require pointing often.

12. Don't use composition roll roofing; it buckles and becomes brittle, needing mopping with asphalt often.

13. Don't nail copper roofing directly to the roof; allow for expansion and contraction.

14. Don't use tin roofs; they need repainting often.

15. Don't use clogging-type roof drains.

16. Don't use wood revolving doors; use a durable metal. Revolving doors receive harder usage than ordinary doors.

17. Don't use marble flooring in entrances and vestibules, since it usually wears easily and becomes a slipping hazard.

18. Don't use travertine wainscots; they soil easily.

19. Don't use wood partitions in public buildings.

20. Don't specify casement sash for windows unless they have been considered carefully, in view of the difficulty in screening them. They require special devices to prevent damage from wind; cleaning is not easy.

21. Don't use special-finish hardware; use simple stock design wherever possible.

22. Use floor-type check hinges sparingly.　To repair them, the door may have to be dismantled.

23. Don't use hinges with a cast-iron malleable pin; use steel pins.

24. Don't use dissimilar metals in contact; electrolytic action may develop.

25. Don't set bars of mesh grilles close to window glass; they make window cleaning difficult.

26. Avoid lacquer-paint finish; it is inflammable.

27. Don't specify waterproofing compounds and other materials to facilitate early setting of concrete without taking into account possible strength reductions.

28. Don't use special plumbing fixtures, such as drinking fountains made of marble, stone, or tile.

29. Don't use standard-weight black pipes for steam returns in trenches; extra-heavy cast iron will not corrode so quickly.

30. Don't skimp in pipe sizing of risers for heating lines; proper heat supply takes precedence over economy in this respect.

31. Don't use timber piles where they are likely to be exposed to alternate dryness and wetness.

32. Don't allow wood piles to be driven without bark, destroying skin friction.

33. Shrinkage and consequent cracks developing in concrete wall masses are the result of too rich a mix and sections that are too large to be poured at one time.

34. Don't add more than 10% coloring material per bag of cement to any concrete finishes; it weakens the mixture.

35. For weathering qualities, don't use oak doors if white pine might be satisfactory However, where strength is required, oak is preferred.

36. Don't use hemlock except for cheap boards and in unimportant places.

37. Don't use southern yellow pine in spaces without ventilation; use cypress in contact with soil or damp places.

38. If lime mortar is specified, do not use joints larger than $\frac{3}{8}$ in. in brickwork. Pure lime mortar for brickwork is obsolete.

39. Don't use pure cement mortar for bricklaying, because it is not plastic, is hard to work with, and loses its moisture too quickly.

40. Don't overlook the anchorage of windows in exterior walls or leakproofing around the perimeter of window and door casings.

41. Don't have less than 4-in. bearing for wood joists or iron lintels.

42. Don't specify a strong acid solution for washing masonry surfaces; it may leave burn marks.　Use about 5% solution, such as 1 pt of acid to 3 gal of water.

43. Don't forget that leaks in brick walls are apt to occur more often in vertical than in horizontal joints; consequently, brick laid in header courses are exposed to leakage more than stretchers.

44. Don't use tarred roofing material on roofs having a slope of more than 2 in. per ft.　Tar melts in warm weather and flows.　Use four-ply over concrete and five-ply over other materials.　Felt should not touch felt directly.

45. Don't use copper flashing over limestone because of copper corrosion; use lead sheet flashing.

46. Don't use gypsum or lime plaster for outside work; use cement plaster.

47. Don't call for wood-lath base for plaster work to be jointed continuously on one support, if cracks due to wood shrinkage are to be avoided.

48. Don't break joints in wood lath along the line of the sides of openings.　This is a precaution to avoid cracks at such locations.

49. Don't fail to specify that wood lath should be wetted before plaster is applied.

50. Don't use gypsum or plaster of paris for outside work; it is soluble in water and will wash away.

51. In the design of ornamental plaster ceilings, avoid large protruding cornices with deep-cut members; they collect dust and constitute a menace if they break down.

52. Don't use carbon or graphite pigments for priming steel, because they tend to increase the action of corrosion.

53. Don't use red-lead paint as a finishing coat; it fades rapidly when exposed to sunlight.

54. Asphalt paint does not weather well when exposed to sunlight; it is serviceable, however, for underground work.

55. Don't use as much turpentine in a metal-preservative paint as would be used for wood paint.

56. Don't use dryers in a larger-than-necessary quantity; they destroy the elasticity of paints. Don't add dryers to red lead.

57. Don't apply paint to new masonry surfaces before applying a zinc sulfate solution.

58. Don't call for chases in brick piers or 8-in. brick walls. Horizontal chases should not exceed 4 ft in length. The aggregate area of recesses and chases in any wall should not exceed one-fourth the area of the face of the wall.

59. Avoid use of foreign marbles; most of them deteriorate faster than domestic marble.

60. Don't pitch coping stones on parapets to the face of the building; discoloration will develop.

61. Don't use costly stone finishes. Above a certain height, they cannot be discerned; four-cut finish above the second story looks the same as six.

62. Hammered finishes are not suitable for soft limestones and sandstones; use tooled finishes on these stones, such as sawed-smooth or rubbed-face.

63. Don't use materials for waterproofing that contain resinous substances.

64. Don't use gypsum tile or block in the presence of any moisture.

65. Don't use other than gypsum plaster on gypsum block. Most materials other than gypsum plaster will not adhere.

66. Don't cut chases or recesses in hollow-tile partitions or tile backing; build them in place.

67. Don't swing doors against the flow of traffic; don't obstruct stair exits with doors.

68. Don't specify wood-sash putty for steel sash; the steel will not absorb linseed oil.

69. Don't require lockers, filing, cabinets, and shelving to be built-in type—easy transfer to other locations should be considered.

70. For plastering, don't use expanded-metal lath lighter than No. 27 U.S. gage or woven wire lath lighter than No. 20 U.S. gage. The lath should be galvanized.

71. Don't require concrete ceilings to be plastered directly. Use of bonding plaster is advised.

28-10. Arrangement of Specifications. The framework of a book of specifications should be arranged somewhat as follows:

Title Page

Invitation to Submit a Proposal and Instructions to Bidders.
Proposal Form.
Agreement.
General Conditions.
Specifications.

For furnishing all labor and materials necessary and required for:

Prepared By:
PETER LAWRENCE, A.I.A.
ARCHITECT
415 Lexington Ave.
New York 17, N.Y.
Job No: Issued:

PETER LAWRENCE, A.I.A.
ARCHITECT
415 Lexington Ave.
New York 17, N.Y.

INVITATION TO SUBMIT A PROPOSAL AND INSTRUCTIONS TO BIDDERS

Job No: Date:
Name of contractor _____
Address _____

1. INVITATION TO BID:

Gentlemen: You are invited to submit a (stipulated sum proposal) (cost-plus-fee-proposal) (cost-plus-fee-proposal with stipulated sum) for furnishing of all labor and material, as called for in the contract documents for the (construction) (alteration) (extension) of _____

for _____
at _____

2. TOTAL CONTRACT PRICE:

(To be used when independent bids are received for certain sections of the work that are later to become part of the general contract.)

(a) This stipulated sum shall include your fee for the inclusion under the (general construction work) of the management and administration of the following subcontracts in addition to those included in the specifications: (Plumbing) (Heating and Ventilating) (Electric Wiring Work) (Lighting Fixtures) (Elevators) _____

(b) The subcontractors for these trades will be selected by the architect, and the aggregate of their contract price will be added to the stipulated sum proposal of the successful general contractor to form the total contract price.

(c) The subcontractors so included in the general contractor's work are to be satisfactory to the general contractor.

3. DRAWINGS AND SPECIFICATIONS:

(a) One (1) set of contract drawings and specifications will be (held for you at this office) or (delivered to you at your office) or to be called for on (date) _____ _____ at (time) _____, or will be mailed to you, if so requested.

(b) Extra sets may be secured at your expense directly from Blank Blue Print Co., 416 Lexington Ave., New York 17, N.Y.

(c) All documents must be returned to this office not later than _____ (or) with the Proposal.

4. EXAMINATION OF SITE (PREMISES):

(a) All bidders submitting proposals for this work shall first examine the site (premises) and all conditions thereon (therein). All proposals shall take into consideration all such conditions as may affect the work under this contract.

(b) (For Alterations). The bidder shall measure all existing work at the building and verify all dimensions.

(c) (For Alterations). The bidder shall obtain all necessary measurements at the building as required.

5. PROPOSAL FORMS:

(a) Proposals must be submitted on the enclosed "Proposal Form," delivered to the office of Peter Lawrence, A.I.A., Architect, 415 Lexington Ave., New York 17, N.Y., on or before noon of _____ 195–. The proposal must be enclosed in a sealed opaque envelope plainly marked "BID" and shall bear the title of the work and the name of the bidder. This envelope shall be enclosed in a mailing envelope. Oral, telegraphic, or telephonic proposals or modifications will not be considered.

(b) All blank spaces on the "Proposal Form" must be fully filled in, and all amounts must be in words as well as in figures.

(c) The signatures must be in longhand and executed by a principal duly authorized to make contracts. The bidder's legal name must be fully stated. The completed "Proposal Form" shall be without interlineation, alteration or erasure.

6. DISCREPANCIES:
   (a) Should a bidder find, during the examination of the contract drawings and specifications, or after his visit to the site (premises) any discrepancies, omissions, ambiguities, or conflicts in or among the contract documents, or should he be in doubt as to their meaning, he shall at once bring the question to the attention of the architect for answer and interpretation. The architect will review the question and, where the information sought is not clearly shown on the contract drawings or specified, will issue a bulletin to all bidders in which the interpretation will be made.
   (b) The architect will make no interpretations orally and only instructions in writing will be deemed valid. Neither the owner nor the architect will be responsible for any oral instructions. To receive consideration, requests for interpretation must be made not later than three (3) days prior to the date set for the receipt of bids.

7. BULLETINS:
   (a) All bulletins to bidders are to be incorporated in the proposal and will become part of the contract documents.

8. QUALIFICATION OF BIDDERS:
   (a) In selecting the (general) (or) _____ contractor, type of work completed, experience and financial status of bidders (and their proposed subcontractors) will be considered, as well as the proposal submitted.
   (b) Data in regard to your qualifications as a contractor shall be submitted independently of the proposals.

9. OPENING OF BIDS:
   (a) The right is reserved to open the proposals privately and unannounced and to reject any and all bids without explanation.
   (b) Bids will be opened publicly at _____

   _____

   on _____

SPECIFICATIONS

PROPOSAL FORM

To:_____   Date:

c/o Peter Lawrence, A.I.A.

415 Lexington Ave., New York 17, N.Y.

Gentlemen: We hereby submit our proposal for the (general) or _____ contract for

_____

1. STIPULATED SUM (OR) COST-PLUS-FEE (OR) COST-PLUS-FEE WITH STIPULATED SUM BASIS:
   (a) Having carefully examined "The General Conditions of the Contract for the Construction of Buildings" and Specifications entitled:

   dated _____ 195–, including bulletins numbered _____
   _____ inclusive, and the contract drawings, similarly entitled,
   numbered:

   and having visited the site (premises) and examined all conditions affecting the work, the undersigned proposes to furnish all labor, materials, equipment and appliances necessary and required by the said documents for the (entire work) or the _____ work.
   (b) For the stipulated sum of _____
   _____ dollars ($_____).
                                    (or)
   (c) On a cost-plus-fee basis, for the fee of _____ per cent of the cost of the work
   (or) _____ dollars
   ($_____).
                                    (or)
   (d) On a cost-plus-fee with a stipulated sum basis. Such stipulated upset maximum sum, which shall include the aforesaid fee, to be _____
   _____ dollars ($_____).
   The undersigned guarantees that the total cost of the work plus fee will not exceed this stipulated sum.
   (e) (To be used when independent bids are received for certain sections of the specifications that are later to become part of the general contract.) This stipulated sum shall include all commissions, overhead, and fees for the inclusion under the general contract of the (number) _____ subcontractors listed in the "Invitation to Submit a Proposal and Instruction to Bidders." The undersigned agrees, therefore, to assume the management and responsibility of these trades and will make no claim beyond the amount stated above, and agrees that the status of these contractors shall be identical with that of such subcontractors as the general contractor uses for other trades.
   (f) Where changes in the work are ordered involving extra cost over and above the contract sum, and when such work is ordered to proceed on the basis of cost-plus-fee, such fee shall be _____ (Contractor to fill in) per cent of the cost of such extra work.

2. COMPLETION OF WORK:
   (a) If the undersigned be notified of the acceptance of this proposal within fourteen (14) days after the above date, he agrees to execute a contract for the above work for the above-stated compensation, in the form of the Standard Agreement of the

American Institute of Architects (and to guarantee the completion of this work (on or before (date) _____) if he is awarded the contract before (date) _____ (or) in _____ working days after the award of the contract).

(or)

(b) The undersigned agrees, if awarded the contract, to complete it within _____ days. Sundays and whole holidays not included.

3. LIQUIDATED DAMAGES:

(a) The undersigned agrees that the owner may retain the sum of _____ _____ dollars ($_____) from the amount of the compensation to be paid the undersigned (for each day after the above mentioned completion date, Sundays and holidays included), (or) (for each working day in excess of the above number of working days) that the work remains incompleted. This amount is agreed upon as the proper measure of liquidated damages that the owner will sustain by the day by the failure of the undersigned to complete the work at the stipulated time, and is not to be construed in any sense as a penalty.

4. GUARANTY BOND:

(a) The undersigned agrees, if awarded the contract, to furnish and deliver to the architect within _____ days after the signing of the contract, a satisfactory guaranty bond in the form currently issued by the American Institute of Architects, in an amount equal to _____ per cent of the contract sum.

5. CERTIFIED CHECK:

(a) The undersigned agrees to the following:

If the undersigned defaults in executing and delivering the above named "Agreement" and "Guaranty Bond," the owner would sustain liquidated damages for _____ dollars ($_____), the measure of which is the amount of the accompanying certified check, payable to _____, Owner. This check is left in escrow with the architect.

(b) If the undersigned defaults in executing that Agreement within five (5) days of written notification of the award of the contract to him, or in furnishing the guaranty bond within thirty (30) days thereafter, the check will become the property of the owner, and will be delivered to him by the architect.

(c) If the undersigned executes and delivers the Agreement and guaranty bond within the time specified, or if this proposal is not accepted within fourteen (14) days of the time set for submission of bids, the check shall be returned to the undersigned upon delivery of receipt therefor.

6. UNIT PRICES:

(a) Should the undersigned be required to perform work over that required by the contract documents, or should he be ordered to omit work required by the contract documents, he will be paid an extra, or shall credit the owner, as the case may be, on the basis of unit prices he quotes herein, the prices quoted being the sum-total compensation payable or creditable for such items of work.

Nature of Work	Unit of Measure	Extra	Credit

7. ALTERNATES:

    (a) The undersigned proposes to perform the substitutions called for in the following alternates for the work as called for in the specifications, for the following resulting additions or deductions from the stipulated sum:

	Add	Deduct
Alternate No. 1 _____		
_____	$	$
Alternate No. 2 _____		
_____	$	$
Alternate No. 3 _____		
_____	$	$
Alternate No. 4 _____		
_____	$	$
Alternate No. 5 _____		
_____	$	$

    (b) The additions and/or deductions as listed shall include any modifications of work or additional work that the undersigned may be required to perform by reason of the acceptance of the alternate.

8. SUBCONTRACTORS:

    (a) The undersigned proposes to employ the following subcontractors for the work of: (List sections of specifications for which names shall be submitted)

        Section No.-   Name _____

                                          Address _____

        Section No.-   Name _____

                                          Address _____

        Section No.-   Name _____

                                          Address _____

        Section No.-   Name _____

                                          Address _____

9. WORK TO BE DONE DIRECTLY:

    (a) The undersigned proposes to perform the work of the following sections of the specifications directly without subcontractors:

        Section No.-

        Section No.-

        Section No.-

        Section No.-

                       Witness: _____

                       Date: _____

                       Signed: _____

AGREEMENT

BETWEEN CONTRACTOR AND OWNER, Standard Form of the American Institute of Architects, latest edition, is hereby made a part of the contract documents, to the same extent as if herein written out in full. This form may be purchased from the American Institute of Architects, Washington, D.C., or may be examined at the architect's office.

GENERAL CONDITIONS

"THE GENERAL CONDITIONS OF THE CONTRACT FOR THE CONSTRUCTION OF BUILDINGS," Standard Form of The American Institute of Architects, latest edition, are hereby, except as the same may be inconsistent herewith, made a part of the contract documents, to the same extent as if herein written out in full. These "General Conditions" may be purchased from the American Institute of Architects, Washington, D.C. or may be examined at the architect's office. Where any article of the "A.I.A. General Conditions" is supplemented hereby, the A.I.A. provisions of such article shall remain in effect. All the supplemental provisions shall be considered as added thereto. Where any such article is amended, voided, or superseded thereby, the provisions of such article not so specifically amended, voided or superseded shall remain in effect.

(These printed General Conditions should be included in full for all sets which require the Owner's and Contractor's signatures.)

Amendments to A.I.A. General Conditions.

These amendments are written specifically to suit project requirements.

SPECIFICATIONS

Various trade sections or divisions.

28-11. American Society for Testing Materials Specifications. The standard specifications of the American Society for Testing Materials describe materials and tests useful for purchasing, design, and production. Except for Federal projects, their use is extensive, particularly where proprietary names for basic products are omitted deliberately. The ASTM standards are described in six volumes:

Part 1, Ferrous Metals (steels, both carbon and alloy, irons, ferroalloys); Part 2, Nonferrous Metals (copper, lead, aluminum and magnesium, metal powders); Part 3, Cementitious, Soils, Road and Waterproofing Materials (cement and concrete, refractories, soils, bituminous materials and other nonmetallic materials widely used in construction); Part 4, Paint, Wood, Adhesives, Shipping Containers, Paper; Part 5, Fuels, Petroleum, Aromatic Hydrocarbons, Soap, Water, Textiles; and Part 6, Electrical Insulation, Plastics, Rubber.

28-12. Federal Specifications. The specification symbol used to designate a Federal specification has three component parts:

1. Group for procurement to which the specification relates.
2. The initial letter of the title of the specification.
3. A serial number determined by the alphabetical location of the title.

Minor changes in a Federal specification are printed in the form of an amendment. Amendment sheets are printed on green paper and bear the specification symbol, the amendment number, and the date in the upper right-hand corner. Only one amendment is in effect for an individual specification; subsequent changes in the specification are made in a superseding amendment that includes all changes up to the date of issue. Second or third amendments are indicated by the figure "2," "3," etc. Example:

QQ-S-624
AMENDMENT-2
27 September 1951
SUPERSEDING
AMENDMENT-1
6 March 1951

Every effective amendment sheet should be filed with, and issued with, the Federal specification to which it pertains.

To show certain types of changes in Federal specifications, addenda or errata were formerly issued. These are superseded now by amendments whenever additional changes in the individual specification are necessary.

A revision of a Federal specification supersedes entirely the previous edition, including any amendments. A revision is indicated by the addition of a letter to the symbol in the upper right-hand corner of the first page. Example:

> GG-H-216a
> 23 November 1951
> SUPERSEDING
> Fed. Spec. GG-H-216
> 17 June 1946

When the content and title of a specification are greatly changed by a revision, a new symbol is frequently assigned because of the change in alphabetical sequence of the title. In certain instances it is desirable to supersede a specification by two or more Federal specifications; or two or more specifications may be superseded by one Federal specification with a new title and symbol. In such instances the original specifications, when entirely superseded, are canceled. Example:

> NN-C-121
> CANCELLATION
> 21 June, 1951

List of Groups for Procurement

A. Aircraft, Boats, and Ships*
B. Animals*
C. Animal Products
D. Arms (Small)*
E. Artillery*
F. Boilers, Engines, and Tanks
G. Books and Printed Matter
H. Brooms and Brushes
J. Cable and Wire (Insulated)
K. Canvas Articles
L. Cellulose Products and Synthetic Resins
M. Ceramics
N. Cereals and Products
O. Chemicals
P. Cleaning and Polishing Materials
Q. Coal and Products
R. Coal Tar and Products
S. Cooking and Heating Apparatus, Furnaces and Ovens (Nonelectric)
T. Cordage, Twine, and Products
U. Drugs and Medicines
V. Dry Goods and Notions
W. Electric Apparatus
X. Explosives
Y. Fruits
Z. Fruit Products
AA. Furniture
BB. Gases
CC. Generators and Motors
DD. Glass and Glassware
EE. Groceries
FF. Hardware
GG. Instruments

HH. Insulating Materials
JJ. Knit Goods, Netting and Webbing
KK. Leather and Leather Goods
LL. Livestock, Poultry, and Marine Products†
MM. Lumber and Timber
NN. Lumber Products
OO. Machinery
PP. Meats and Sea Foods
QQ. Metals
RR. Metal Products
SS. Minerals and Products (Nonmetallic)
TT. Paints, Pigments, Varnishes, and Products
UU. Paper and Products
VV. Petroleum and Products
WW. Pipe, Pipe Fittings, Plumbing Fixtures, Tubes and Tubing (Metallic)
XX. Pumps
YY. Recreational Articles*
ZZ. Rubber and Rubber Goods
AAA. Scales
BBB. Suits and Uniforms
CCC. Textiles (Yardage)
DDD. Textile Products
EEE. Tobacco and Products*
FFF. Toilet Articles
GGG. Tools
HHH. Vegetables
JJJ. Vegetable Products
KKK. Vehicles
LLL. Wood Products
MMM. Adhesives

* No Federal specification has been prepared for this group.
† No Federal specification is available for this group.

28-13. National Fire Codes. The National Fire Codes are comprehensive volumes bringing together for convenient reference all the National Fire Protection Association official standards in the respective fields. Vol. I covers flammable liquids, gases, chemicals, and explosives; Vol. II prevention of dust explosions. Vols. III, IV, and V are especially useful to those concerned with construction.

Vol. III contains 37 standards on various phases of building construction and equipment; it is not a building code. Vol. IV contains 48 standards on fire extinguishing and alarm equipment and is purely advisory as far as the NFPA is concerned, but widely used for legal and insurance purposes. Vol. V is the well-known National Electrical Code. The codes are available through the National Fire Protection Association, 60 Batterymarch St., Boston 10, Mass.

28-14. American Standards Association, Inc. This is a federation of over one hundred national technical and trade organizations, maintained by industry to promote the development and use of standards and to serve as a national clearinghouse for material standards. The standards represent general agreement on the part of maker, seller, and user groups as to the best current industrial practice. Manufacturers, consumers, technical and governmental agencies are represented on the committees that set standards.

In addition to covering materials employed in construction work, these standards include a large variety of other materials, as well as safety codes, symbols, definitions, and other data.

Section 29

INSURANCE AND BONDS

C. S. Cooper

Manager, Eastern Bond and Burglary Department
Fireman's Fund Insurance Group
New York, N.Y.

Insurance policies are contracts under which an insurance company agrees to pay the insured, or a third party on behalf of the insured, should certain contingencies arise.

The importance of insurance protection cannot be overemphasized. No business is immune to loss resulting from ever-present risks. It is imperative, therefore, that a sound insurance program be designed and that it be kept up to date.

Because few businesses can afford the services of a full-time insurance executive, it is important that a competent agent or broker be selected to: (1) prepare a program that will provide complete coverage against the hazards peculiar to the construction business, as well as against the more common perils; (2) secure insurance contracts from qualified insurance companies; (3) advise about limits of protection; and (4) maintain records necessary to make continuity of protection certain. While a responsible executive of the business should interest himself in the subject of insurance, much of the detail can be eliminated by utilizing the services of a competent agent or broker.

There are three kinds of insurance carriers—stock, mutual, and reciprocal. Nevertheless, policy forms are rather well standardized. Rates are established by the rating organizations that serve the member companies of different groups of carriers, but generally, basic rates are very nearly the same.

It is necessary, of course, that the responsibility for providing protection be placed upon an insurance company whose financial strength is beyond doubt.

Another important point for the buyer of insurance is the service that the company selected may be in a position to render. Frequently, construction operations are conducted at a considerable distance from city facilities. It is necessary that the company charged with the responsibility of protecting the construction operations be in a position to render "on-the-job" service from both a claim and an engineering standpoint.

The interests of contractors and building owners are very closely allied. Particular attention should be given to the definition of these respective interests in all insurance policies. Where the insurable interest lies may depend upon the terms of the contract. Competent advice is frequently needed in order that all policies protect all interests as required.

The forms of protection purchased and the adequacy of limits are of great importance to a prime or general contractor. It is also of great importance to him to see that the insurance carried by subcontractors is written at adequate limits and is broad enough to protect against conditions that might arise as a result of their acts. Also, the policies should include the interests of the prime or general contractor in so far as such interests should be protected.

This section merely outlines those forms of insurance that may be considered fundamental. It includes brief, but not complete, descriptions of coverages without which a contractor should not operate. It is not intended to take the place of the advice of experienced insurance personnel.

29-1. Fire Insurance. Fire-insurance policies are now very well standardized. They insure buildings, contents, and materials on job sites against direct loss or damage by fire or lightning. They also include destruction that may be ordered by civil authorities to prevent advance of fire from neighboring property. Under a policy, the fire-insurance company agrees to pay for the direct loss or damage caused by fire or lightning and also to pay for the removal of property from premises that may be damaged by fire.

Careful attention should be given to the selection of the amount of insurance to be applied to property exposed to loss. The question of valuation is frequently troublesome; but it is extremely important that a careful analysis be made to arrive at adequate values in order that sufficient amounts of insurance may be purchased. It is important to bear in mind that under no circumstances will the amount paid ever exceed the amount stated in the policy. Should the fire policy carry a co-insurance clause the problem of valuation and adequate amount of insurance becomes even more important.

A form of fire insurance particularly applicable in the construction industry is that known as builder's risk insurance. The purpose of this form is to insure an owner or contractor, as their interests may appear, against loss by fire while buildings are under construction. Such buildings may be insured under the builder's risk form by several methods, three of which are:

1. The form that describes the property covered, but does not provide automatic coverage as values increase during construction. The amount of insurance must be increased by endorsement to keep the insurance in line with increasing values. This form is available in most states.

2. The reporting form, under which values are reported monthly. Reports must be made regularly and accurately. If so made, the form automatically covers increases in value.

3. The completed-value form under which insurance is written for the actual value of the building when completed. This is written at a reduced rate, because it is recognized that the full amount of insurance is not at risk during the entire term of the policy. No reports are necessary in connection with this form.

There are certain hazards that, while not quite so common as fire and lightning, are nevertheless real. These should be covered by endorsement. A few of the endorsements available provide:

1. Extended-coverage endorsement, which covers property for the same amount as the basic fire policy, against loss or damage caused by windstorm and hail, explosion, riot and civil commotion, aircraft, vehicles, and smoke.

2. Vandalism and malicious mischief endorsement, which extends protection to include loss caused by vandalism or malicious mischief.

3. Removal-of-debris endorsement, which extends the policy to include the cost of removal of debris following loss by hazards insured under the policy.

Other forms that broaden and make fire-insurance protection more complete are also available. Special conditions and specific exposures should be studied to determine the advisability of the purchase of certain of these additional protections.

29-2. Insurance Necessitated by Contractor's Equipment. The "Inland Marine" insurance market is the place to look for many coverages needed by contractors. From the insurance point of view, each contractor's problem is considered separately. The type of operation, the nature of equipment, the area in which the contractor works, and other pertinent factors are all points considered by an Inland Marine underwriter in arriving at a final form and rate.

Obvious contractors' equipment—mechanical shovels, hoists, bulldozers, ditchers, and all other mobile equipment not designed for highway use—is the primary subject of the "Contractors Equipment Floater." Such protection is necessary because of the size of the investment in such equipment and of the multiplicity of perils to which the equipment is exposed.

Some companies will write the Contractors Equipment Floater Policy only on a named-perils basis, which ordinarily includes fire, collision, or overturning of a transporting conveyance, and sometimes theft of an entire piece of equipment. Other companies will write certain kinds of contractors' equipment on the so-called "all-risk" basis. Certain perils, such as collision during use, are subject to a deductible fixed amount. The rate for this broader insurance generally is higher than that for the named-perils form. In the "all-risk" form, the customary exclusions, such as wear and tear, the electrical exemption clause, strikes, riots, and other similar exclusions, are present.

In addition to the equipment, there is a need to provide protection for the materials and supplies en route to or from the site. If these materials and supplies are transported at the risk of a contractor and are in the custody of a common carrier, a Transportation Floater should be obtained. If, on the other hand, these materials and supplies are moved on the contractor's own trucks, a "Motor Truck Cargo-owners Form" should be obtained. The premium for the transportation form is usually based on the value of shipments coming under the protection of the policy. The coverage is usually on an "all-risk" basis. The Motor Truck Cargo-owners Form is generally on a named-perils basis at a flat rate applied against the limit of liability required by the insured's needs.

Occasionally, a contractor may be responsible for machinery, tanks, and other property of that nature until such time as they are completely installed, tested, and accepted. Exposures of this kind are usually covered under an "Installation Floater," which would provide insurance to and from the site as well.

The Installation Floater Form is generally on a named-perils basis, including perils of loading and unloading, at a rate for the exposure deemed adequate by the underwriter. This is nearly always written on a reporting basis to reflect the increasing values as installation progresses.

There is also a form of policy known as a "Riggers Floater" that is designed for contractors doing that type of work. This policy is usually a named-perils form at rates based on the nature of the rigging operation.

Neither the forms nor rates in any of these classes are standard among the companies writing them, although in general they are all similar.

Some contractors building bridges might be required to take a Bridge Builders Risk Form. This is an exception to most of the insurance provided to contractors, in that it is required to be rated in accordance with forms and rates filed in most of the states and administered by a licensed rating bureau.

29-3. Motor-vehicle Insurance. Loss and damage caused by or to motor vehicles should be separately insured under specific policies designed to cover hazards resulting from the existence and operation of such equipment. Bodily injury or property damage sustained by the public as a result of the operation of contractor's motor vehicles, which include automobiles, tractors, and trucks, are insured under a standard policy of automobile liability and property-damage insurance.

It is important that all vehicles be covered, and it is also extremely important that high limits be carried.

Protection furnished by automobile liability and property damage insurance serves in two ways: (1) the insurance company agrees to pay any sum for bodily injury and property damage for which the insured is legally liable; (2) the policy agrees to defend the insured. It is important, therefore, that the limits be adequate to guarantee that the insured obtain full advantage of the services available. For example, suppose $25,000 and $50,000 limits are carried, and action is brought against the contractor in the amount of $100,000. It may be necessary that he employ an attorney to safeguard his interests for the amount of the action that exceeds the limits of the policy.

It is presumed that no contractor would operate any type of motor vehicle without insurance. It is important, therefore, that automatic coverage be provided to include all motor vehicles owned or acquired. Too great emphasis cannot be placed on adequacy of limits since the cost for highest available limits is reasonable.

Damage to owned motor vehicles may be insured under a fire, theft, and collision policy. Comprehensive motor-vehicle protection covers physical damage sustained by motor vehicles caused by fires, theft, and other perils, including glass breakage. Collision insurance insures against loss from collision or upset. While the latter is available on a full-coverage basis, it is generally written on a deductible basis (loss less a fixed sum).

To cover a contractor for liability arising from the use by employees of their own automobiles while on his business, nonownership or contingent liability coverage is necessary. This may be included in the policy by endorsement.

Frequently, contractors have occasion to hire trucks or other vehicles. Liability and property damage insurance to cover the contractor's liability when using hired vehicles should be included at the time automobile insurance is arranged.

While few contractors have occasion to operate horse-drawn vehicles, the occasional necessary use should be covered under a team's liability policy. It is usually provided under a general liability policy covering the contractor's operations (Art. 29-4).

Maintenance and use of boilers and other types of pressure vessels and machinery require the protection provided by boiler and machinery insurance. These policies cover loss resulting from accidents to boilers or machinery, and in addition, cover contractor's liability for damage to the property of others. Policies may also include liability arising from bodily injuries sustained by persons other than employees. This may be of importance because of the exposure that many contractors have as a result of the interest of the public in construction work.

The service rendered by boiler and machinery companies is of great importance and cannot be overemphasized. Nearly all insurance companies that write this form have staffs of competent and experienced inspectors whose job it is to see that boilers, pressure vessels, and other machinery are adequately maintained.

29-4. Liability Policies Covering Contractor's Operations. Anyone who suffers bodily injury or whose property is damaged as a result of the negligence of another person can recover from that person, if the latter is legally liable. Every business should protect itself against claims and suits that may be brought against it because of bodily injuries or property damage suffered by third parties.

Maintenance of an office or yard, as well as the conduct of a construction job, presents exposures to the public. There may be no negligence, and consequently no legal liability on the part of the contractor, but should claim be brought or suit instituted for an injury, the contractor will require trained personnel to investigate the claim and negotiate a settlement or defend a lawsuit if the claim goes to court.

Public-liability insurance is expressly designed to serve contractors by providing insurance that will pay for bodily injuries and property damage suffered by third parties if the contractor is legally liable, but the policy will also serve by defending the interests of the contractor in court. Sometimes the problem in court is one of amount of damage; but frequently, it is one in which the contractor being sued is not legally liable for the injuries or damage. It is fundamental, therefore, that a policy be obtained at substantial limits for both bodily injuries and property damage, that the policy cover all existing exposures and also provide for protection against exposures that may not exist or be contemplated on the inception date of the policy. The scope of operations conducted by most contractors is such that it is frequently difficult to visualize all the hazards that may exist or come about simply by being in the construction business.

The changes that have taken place in public-liability protection have been very rapid and in the best interests of the insurance-buying public. While at one time it was necessary to obtain several policies to cover the numerous public-liability hazards, it is possible now to obtain a comprehensive policy that will include the legal liability resulting from known operations and hazards, as well as those from operations and hazards not contemplated at the time the policy is written. The comprehensive general-liability policy that covers all liability of the insured, except that resulting from the use of automobiles, is a standard form available in all states at rates regulated by law.

The comprehensive general-liability policy protects the contractor under one insuring clause and with one limit against claims that formerly had to be covered specifically under a schedule liability policy or by a number of different policies and endorsements.

Blanket coverage is provided by this policy at a premium based upon actual exposures disclosed by an audit at the end of the policy term.   Because of the value of this policy, every contractor should make provisions for maintaining accurate records of payrolls, value of sublet work, dollar amount of sales, and other factors that will be important at the time an audit is made.

Under the bodily injury liability clause of this policy the insurance company agrees "to pay on behalf of the insured all sums that the insured shall become legally obligated to pay as damages because of bodily injury, sickness or disease, including death at any time resulting therefrom, sustained by any person and caused by accident." This is a very broad insuring clause.   It obviously includes the entire business operations of the insured.

Property-damage liability is an optional coverage.   If it is written, and no contractor should be without property-damage insurance, the coverage will apply to the entire risk with one or two exceptions.

There are certain exclusions in the policy that should be noted.   The policy does not include:

1. Ownership, maintenance, or use (including loading or unloading) of water craft away from premises owned, rented, or controlled by the insured; automobiles while away from the premises or the ways immediately adjoining; and aircraft under any condition.   However, this exclusion does not apply to operations performed by independent contractors or to liability assumed by any contract covered by the policy.

2. Bodily injury sustained by employees while engaged in the employment of the insured.

3. Liability for damage to property occupied, owned, or rented to the insured or in his care, custody, or control.

Of particular importance to contractors is the provision of the comprehensive policy pertaining to contractual liability.   The policy restricts coverage for liability assumed under contract, and there is an exclusion that makes the restriction more definite.   A "contract" is defined as "a warranty of goods or products, or if in writing, a lease of premises, easement agreement, agreement required by municipal ordinance, side-track agreement or elevator or escalator maintenance agreement."   A premium is charged for such agreements as may be disclosed by audit.

There is no protection for the liability assumed in some very common types of agreements that include service, delivery, and work contracts.   Many of these contracts are signed without full realization of the liability assumed.   Each such agreement should be submitted to the insurance company at the time the policy is written in order that a premium charge may be computed and the agreement covered under the policy.

Another very important coverage, from the standpoint of contractors, is provided by products-liability coverage.   The comprehensive general liability policy includes complete and automatic products-liability insurance, including completed-operations protection.   The one exception to this complete coverage is that the policy does not include liability for damage to the work or to the goods themselves, such as the obligation of the contractor to repair or replace if there are defects.   While the policy provides coverage, it is in fact an optional protection, which may be deleted.   However, it should be stressed that, because of the completed-operations protection provided under products-liability insurance, every contractor should take advantage of this coverage.

Most building contractors use elevators or hoists during construction.   The comprehensive policy automatically covers elevators, hoists, and other such hazards at the appropriate premium for the exposure.

The breadth of public-liability protection available, the numerous hazards to which a contractor may be exposed, both known and unknown, and the necessity for having complete coverage at all times further emphasize the need for the advice of trained insurance representatives.

29-5. Workmen's Compensation.   Every state requires an employer to secure a policy of workmen's compensation to provide for an injured employee the benefits of the workmen's compensation law of that state.   It is not necessary to emphasize the need for this insurance.   It is, however, necessary to point out that an insurance company that has had extensive experience in the workmen's compensation field is best suited to meet the requirements of most contractors.

The problem of acquiring and keeping labor may be troublesome. It is in the employer's, as well as the employee's, best interests to see that the company entrusted to provide workmen's compensation insurance is equipped to provide loss-prevention service, prompt first aid, and to settle compensation claims fairly and speedily.

Contractors should note that the workmen's compensation laws in 37 states impose on principals or contractors liability for compensation payments to employees of contractors or subcontractors, if the primary employer is not in a position to pay or has not secured insurance. In the following states, contractors are liable to the employees of subcontractors for injuries arising during the course of their employment: Arizona, Arkansas, Colorado, Connecticut, Florida, Georgia, Idaho, Illinois, Indiana, Kansas, Kentucky, Louisiana, Maryland, Massachusetts, Michigan, Minnesota, Missouri, Mississippi, Montana, Nebraska, New Jersey, New Mexico, New York, North Carolina, Oklahoma, Pennsylvania, South Carolina, South Dakota, Tennessee, Utah, Vermont, Virginia, and Wisconsin.

The law of the state in which the work is done is the one that will control.

Subcontractors' insurance should be carefully examined and made complete where it is deficient. Certificates of insurance should be required. Because many complex situations arise, it is important that the advice of a qualified agent or broker be obtained.

29-6. Construction Contract Bonds. The United States government, state, county, and municipal governments generally obtain competitive bids on all construction. Awards are made to the lowest responsible bidder, who is required to furnish bond provided by qualified corporate surety. Also, more and more private owners are requiring bonds of contractors to whom they award construction contracts.

Generally, bidders are required to post a certified check or furnish a bid bond. A bid bond assures that, if a contract is awarded to the contractor, he will, within a specified time, sign the contract and furnish bond for its performance. If the contractor fails to furnish the performance bond, the measure of damage is the smaller of the following: the penalty of the bid bond or the amount by which the bid of the lowest bidder found to be responsible and to whom the contract is awarded exceeds the bid of the principal.

It should be noted that most surety companies follow the practice of authorizing a bid bond only after the performance bond on a particular contract has been underwritten and approved. For this reason, contractors are well advised against depositing a certified check with a bid unless there are assurances that the performance bond on that particular contract has been underwritten and approved.

There is no standard form of construction contract bond. The Federal government and each state, county, or municipal government has its own form. Private owners generally use the bond form recommended and copyrighted by the American Institute of Architects. Within the last few years, surety companies have developed a very broad form of bond, which is available to owners of private construction. Whatever form is used, the surety generally has a twofold obligation:

1. To idemnify the owner against loss resulting from the failure of the contractor to complete the work in accordance with the contract.

2. To guarantee payment of all bills incurred by the contractor for labor and materials.

Sometimes two bonds are furnished, one for the protection of the owner, and another to protect exclusively those who perform labor or furnish materials. If one bond is furnished, the owner has prior rights.

Sureties underwrite construction contract bonds carefully. They are interested in determining whether a contractor has the capital to meet all financial obligations, the equipment to handle the physical aspects of the particular undertaking, and the construction experience to fulfill the terms of the contract.

It is essential that contractors understand all the information that a surety will require and that is necessary to the underwriting of a contract bond. It is also important that a contractor take advantage of the services of a competent agent or broker who has close affiliations with a surety company that has the capacity to meet all the contractor's needs. Handling of construction contract bonds is rather highly specialized; consequently, agents and brokers must be experienced in the insurance requirements of contractors and they can be of valuable assistance in many ways to principal and obligee.

The importance of maintaining books and records was pointed out in Art. 29-4. Here again, the importance of complete records cannot be stressed too highly. Accurate information about the amount of work on hand, value of equipment, value of materials, and records of past performances will prove necessary.

To be more specific, there are outlined below several items of information that will be required by the surety:

1. A complete balanced financial statement with schedules of the principal items. This is a condition precedent to the approval of any contract bond. Sureties have forms on which contractors may furnish financial information. However, when such forms are used, they should be completed by the individual responsible for the financial operations of the company and the data taken directly from the company's books. It is preferable to have the financial statement prepared and certified by a public accountant. Contractors will find that they will save time and money if the services of qualified accountants are obtained.

2. A report regarding the contractor's organization. The surety is interested in knowing the length of time the contractor has been in business, whether he operates as an individual, a partnership, or a corporation, and certain specific details depending upon the form of organization.

3. A report of the technical qualifications and experience of the individuals who will be in charge of work to be performed.

4. A report of the type of work undertaken in the past, together with information regarding jobs successfully completed.

5. An inventory of equipment, together with the age of each piece and any existing encumbrance. An inventory of materials will also be helpful.

Contractors should be fully acquainted with the penalties of liquidated damages that attach in the event any difficulties arise to prevent completion of a contract. Sometimes things occur over which the contractor has no control—sometimes mistakes are made that prevent completion—whatever the contingency it is far better to have qualified with a corporate surety bond than to have undertaken a job without the protection of a bond.

No contractor should feel that the requirement of a surety bond is a reflection upon him. Rather, a contractor should feel that a sound financial condition, a successful past, and the ability to carry out a contract are something of which to be proud. Furthermore, the cost factor is an item included in the gross contract price. To be qualified by a corporate surety is a stamp of approval.

29-7. Money and Securities Protection. Nearly every contractor has cash, securities, and a checking account that are vulnerable to attack by dishonest people, both on and off the payroll. The same hazards present in every business are present also in the construction business. And no contractor is immune to dishonesty, robbery of payroll, burglary of materials, or forgery of his signature on a check.

Employee dishonesty may be covered on a blanket basis, either under a Primary Commercial or Blanket Position Form of Bond. The fact that contractors generally entrust the maintenance of payroll records and the payment of employees to subordinates demonstrates the necessity for blanket dishonesty protection.

While many contractors maintain an organization on a year-round basis, some may not. For those contractors who do have a permanent staff, the bond may be written on a 3-year basis at a saving. It is important that adequate limits be purchased. A blanket bond in an amount equal to 5% of the gross sales is desirable.

General funds, securities, and payroll funds should be covered on the broadest basis now available that protects against burglary, robbery, mysterious disappearance, and destruction, on and away from any premises. The general funds may be covered in an amount sufficient to protect against the maximum single exposure. Payroll funds may be insured specifically and in a different amount.

Contractors who maintain inventories of materials should insure them against burglary and theft. It should be noted, however, that insurance companies are not willing to insure against loss by burglary or theft unless materials are under adequate protection. Insurance is not available to cover property on open sites or in yards, but only while within buildings that are completely secured when not open for business.

Forgery and alteration of checks is a very common crime. Forgeries are cleverly committed by "gentlemen" who have devoted their lives to acquiring the ability to duplicate the signature of another. Every business that maintains a checking account, however small the balance may be, should insure against loss caused by the forgery of the maker's name or by the forgery of an endorsement of checks issued.

The modern policy to cover all these hazards is the comprehensive dishonesty, disappearance, and destruction policy. Its several insuring agreements include employee-dishonesty coverage, broad-form money and securities protection, on and off the premises, and forgery. Other coverages to provide burglary and theft protection for merchandise and materials may be added by endorsement. Optional coverages available are numerous, and the contract may be designed specifically for all a contractor's exposures.

29-8. Employee Group Benefits. Interest in group benefits for employees has grown appreciably in recent years. There are many forms of group insurance, some of which are very new. Included in the following is a brief description of those forms of "group insurance benefits" that are of greatest current interest.

Group Life Insurance. A form of term life insurance written to cover in a specified amount a group of employees of a single employer. Frequently, the amount of insurance is related to an employee's earnings and increases as the earnings increase. However, the amount of insurance may be a flat sum. Usually, a specified number of employees must participate.

Group Disability Insurance. If an employee is away from work as a result of a nonoccupational disability, this insurance provides a continuing income during his period of absence. The following states have adopted compulsory disability laws: Rhode Island, California, New Jersey, and New York. Other states are studying this insurance.

The amount of benefit is usually a percentage of earnings. Compulsory laws generally provide a benefit of 50% of the weekly earnings, subject to a maximum of $30. Under other plans, the benefit may range from 50 to 70%, with a maximum weekly benefit of from $40 to $60.

The period during which benefits will be paid may vary from 13 to 26 weeks, but in plans that are administered by employers the term during which benefits will be payable may be related to the length of service.

Group Hospitalization and Surgical Benefits. These forms of group protection are designed to protect an employee from the results of high hospital expense or the expense of a surgical operation. The protection may be written to cover an employee solely or it may be written to cover an employee and dependents.

The allowance for hospital room and board charges may be set at a figure intended to provide semiprivate care. Certain extras, such as the use of operating room, drugs, X rays, and electrocardiograms, may be included either on a service basis or on a basis that provides a maximum amount that will be paid for such service.

The period during which benefits are payable will vary depending on the contract and may run as long as 70 days. Some plans provide for payment of full charges for a comparatively short period and half charges for a longer specified period.

Surgical benefits are usually based on a schedule of amounts set forth in the policy. The maximum provided will, of course, depend upon the premium.

Group Coverage for Major Medical Expenses. Increased medical expense has brought about a demand for protection against catastrophic medical costs. This is one of the newest forms of group insurance. Rates vary greatly, as do forms of policy. The coverage is usually provided on a deductible basis (medical expense less a fixed sum). Frequently, a co-insurance feature is included so that the individual protected by such insurance bears part of the cost.

INDEX

1